# ActivStats Elements in *Intro Stats*, Third Edition

The following is a list of pages containing ActivStats pointers for each chapter. Use this  ActivStats multimedia resources that complement these discussions in the text.

| Topics | Animated Activities | Teaching Applets | Videos |
|---|---|---|---|
| Data | pp. 8, 9, 10 | pp. 11, 12, 13, 16 | |
| Displaying Categorical Data | p. 21 | pp. 23, 24 | p. 20 |
| Displaying and Summarizing Quantitative Data | pp. 50, 54, 63, 64 | pp. 52, 65, 66, 75 | |
| Understanding and Comparing Distributions | pp. 89, 91 | p. 97 | p. 92 |
| The Standard Deviation as a Ruler and the Normal Model | p. 135 | pp. 125, 126, 127, 130, 135, 142 | |
| Scatterplots, Association, and Correlation | pp. 167, 170, 173 | pp. 167, 172, 173, 176, 182 | |
| Linear Regression | p. 195 | pp. 195, 196, 200, 214 | p. 194 |
| Regression Wisdom | | pp. 227, 230, 234 | |
| Re-expressing Data: Get It Straight! | p. 252 | pp. 255, 258 | |
| Understanding Randomness | p. 290 | pp. 293, 296, 298 | |
| Sample Surveys | pp. 303, 306, 307, 318, 321 | p. 305 | pp. 305, 307, 320 |
| Experiments and Observational Studies | pp. 333, 339, 340 | pp. 333, 337 | p. 332 |
| From Randomness to Probability | p. 366 | pp. 368, 371, 373 | |
| Probability Rules! | pp. 389, 391, 393 | pp. 390, 391 | p. 393 |
| Random Variables | p. 410 | p. 420 | |
| Probability Models | p. 433 | pp. 436, 439 | |
| Sampling Distribution Models | pp. 459, 470 | pp. 460, 461, 462, 468, 469, 470, 475 | |
| Confidence Intervals for Proportions | p. 493 | pp. 487, 488, 489, 491 | p. 494 |
| Testing Hypotheses About Proportions | pp. 509, 513, 519 | pp. 508, 515, 523 | |
| More About Tests | p. 543 | pp. 536, 538, 544, 546, 548 | p. 536 |
| Comparing Two Proportions | | pp. 558, 566 | |
| Inferences About Means | pp. 590, 593 | pp. 588, 590, 595, 600, 607 | p. 597 |
| Comparing Means | | pp. 620, 624, 625, 631 | p. 617 |
| Paired Samples and Blocks | | p. 652 | |
| Comparing Counts | pp. 687, 693 | pp. 693, 694, 701, 702, 708 | p. 695 |
| Inferences for Regression | pp. 722, 734 | pp. 728, 730, 743 | |

Instructor's Edition

# Intro Stats

## THIRD EDITION

Instructor's Edition

EDITION
**3**

# Intro Stats

**Richard D. De Veaux**
Williams College

**Paul F. Velleman**
Cornell University

**David E. Bock**

PEARSON
Addison
Wesley

Boston  San Francisco  New York
London  Toronto  Sydney  Tokyo  Singapore  Madrid
Mexico City  Munich  Paris  Cape Town  Hong Kong  Montreal

| | |
|---|---|
| President | Greg Tobin |
| Editor in Chief | Deirdre Lynch |
| Associate Editor | Sara Oliver Gordus |
| Editorial Assistant | Christina Lepre |
| Senior Managing Editor | Karen Wernholm |
| Senior Production Supervisor | Peggy McMahon |
| Cover Design | Barbara T. Atkinson |
| Interior Design | The Davis Group, Inc. |
| Cover Photo | Pete McArthur |
| Marketing Manager | Wayne Parkins |
| Marketing Assistant | Kathleen DeChavez |
| Photo Researcher | Beth Anderson |
| Media Producer | Christine Stavrou |
| Software Development | Edward Chappell and Marty Wright |
| Senior Author Support/ Technology Specialist | Joe Vetere |
| Rights and Permissions Advisor | Dana Weightman |
| Manufacturing Manager | Evelyn Beaton |
| Senior Manufacturing Buyer | Ginny Michaud |
| Production Coordination, Illustrations, and Composition | Pre-Press PMG |

For permission to use copyrighted material, grateful acknowledgment has been made to the copyright holders listed in Appendix B, which is hereby made part of this copyright page.

Many of the designations used by manufacturers and sellers to distinguish their products are claimed as trademarks. Where those designations appear in this book, and Pearson Education was aware of a trademark claim, the designations have been printed in initial caps or all caps.

**The Library of Congress Control Number is 2008270256.**

ISBN-13: 978-0-321-50381-7     ISBN-10: 0-321-50381-3
2 3 4 5 6 7 8 9 10—DOW—11 10 09

*To Sylvia, who has helped me in more ways than she'll ever know,*
*and to Nicholas, Scyrine, Frederick, and Alexandra,*
*who make me so proud in everything that they are and do*
*—Dick*

*To my sons, David and Zev, from whom I've learned so much,*
*and to my wife, Sue, for taking a chance on me*
*—Paul*

*To Greg and Becca, great fun as kids and great friends as adults,*
*and especially to my wife and best friend, Joanna, for her*
*understanding, encouragement, and love*
*—Dave*

# Meet the Authors

**Richard D. De Veaux** is an internationally known educator and consultant. He has taught at the Wharton School and the Princeton University School of Engineering, where he won a "Lifetime Award for Dedication and Excellence in Teaching." Since 1994, he has been Professor of Statistics at Williams College. Dick has won both the Wilcoxon and Shewell awards from the American Society for Quality. He is a fellow of the American Statistical Association. Dick is also well known in industry, where for the past 20 years he has consulted for such companies as Hewlett-Packard, Alcoa, DuPont, Pillsbury, General Electric, and Chemical Bank. He has also sometimes been called the "Official Statistician for the Grateful Dead." His real-world experiences and anecdotes illustrate many of this book's chapters.

Dick holds degrees from Princeton University in Civil Engineering (B.S.E.) and Mathematics (A.B.) and from Stanford University in Dance Education (M.A.) and Statistics (Ph.D.), where he studied with Persi Diaconis. His research focuses on the analysis of large data sets and data mining in science and industry.

In his spare time he is an avid cyclist and swimmer. He also is the founder and bass for the "Diminished Faculty," an a cappella Doo-Wop quartet at Williams College. Dick is the father of four children.

**Paul F. Velleman** has an international reputation for innovative Statistics education. He is the author and designer of the multimedia statistics CD-ROM *ActivStats*, for which he was awarded the EDUCOM Medal for innovative uses of computers in teaching statistics, and the ICTCM Award for Innovation in Using Technology in College Mathematics. He also developed the award-winning statistics program, Data Desk, and the Internet site Data And Story Library (DASL) (http://dasl.datadesk.com), which provides data sets for teaching Statistics. Paul's understanding of using and teaching with technology informs much of this book's approach.

Paul has taught Statistics at Cornell University since 1975. He holds an A.B. from Dartmouth College in Mathematics and Social Science, and M.S. and Ph.D. degrees in Statistics from Princeton University, where he studied with John Tukey. His research often deals with statistical graphics and data analysis methods. Paul co-authored (with David Hoaglin) *ABCs of Exploratory Data Analysis.* Paul is a Fellow of the American Statistical Association and of the American Association for the Advancement of Science.

Out of class, Paul sings baritone in a barbershop quartet. He is the father of two boys.

**David E. Bock** taught mathematics at Ithaca High School for 35 years. He has taught Statistics at Ithaca High School, Tompkins-Cortland Community College, Ithaca College, and Cornell University. Dave has won numerous teaching awards, including the MAA's Edyth May Sliffe Award for Distinguished High School Mathematics Teaching (twice), Cornell University's Outstanding Educator Award (three times), and has been a finalist for New York State Teacher of the Year.

Dave holds degrees from the University at Albany in Mathematics (B.A.) and Statistics/Education (M.S.). Dave has been a reader and table leader for the AP Statistics exam, serves as a Statistics consultant to the College Board, and leads workshops and institutes for AP Statistics teachers. He has recently served as K–12 Education and Outreach Coordinator and a senior lecturer for the Mathematics Department at Cornell University. His understanding of how students learn informs much of this book's approach.

Dave relaxes by biking and hiking. He and his wife have enjoyed many days camping across Canada and through the Rockies. They have a son, a daughter, and three grandchildren.

# Contents

*Indicates an optional chapter.

# From the Data at Hand to the World at Large    457

# Learning About the World    585

# Inference When Variables Are Related    685

## Appendixes    A-1

*Indicates an optional chapter.

# Preface

## About the Book

We've been thrilled with the feedback we've received from instructors and students using *Intro Stats*. If there is a single hallmark of this book it is that students actually read it. We have reports from every level—from high school to graduate school—that students find our books easy and even enjoyable to read. We strive for a conversational, approachable style, and introduce anecdotes to maintain students' interest. And it works. Instructors report their amazement that students are voluntarily reading ahead of their assignments. Students write to tell us (to their amazement) that they actually enjoyed the book.

Unlike any other introductory book in the market, *Intro Stats* is written from the ground up with the understanding that Statistics is practiced with technology. This insight informs everything from our choice of forms for equations (favoring intuitive forms over calculation forms) to our extensive use of real data. Most important, it allows us to focus on teaching Statistical Thinking rather than calculation. The questions that motivate each of our hundreds of examples are not "how do you find the answer?" but "how do you think about the answer?"

## Our Goal: Read This Book!

The best text in the world is of little value if students don't read it. Here are some of the ways we have made *Intro Stats,* Third Edition even more approachable:

- *Readability.* You'll see immediately that this book doesn't read like other Statistics texts. The style is both colloquial and informative, engaging students to actually read the book to see what it says.
- *Humor.* We know that humor is the best way to promote learning. You will find quips and wry comments throughout the narrative, in margin notes, and in footnotes. If we sometimes cross the line and seem to trivialize something important, we apologize.
- *Informality.* Our informal diction doesn't mean that the subject matter is covered lightly or informally. We have tried to be precise and, wherever possible, to offer deeper explanations and justifications than those found in most introductory texts.
- *Focused lessons.* The chapters are shorter than in most other texts, to make it easier to focus on one topic at a time.
- *Consistency.* We've worked hard to avoid the "do what we say, not what we do" trap. Having taught the importance of plotting data and checking assumptions and conditions, we have been careful to model that behavior right through the rest of the book. (Check the exercises in Chapter 27 and you'll see us still requiring and demonstrating the plots and checks that were introduced in the early chapters.) This consistency helps to reinforce these fundamental principles.

- *The need to read.* Students who plan just to skim the book may find our presentation a bit frustrating. The important concepts, definitions, and sample solutions don't sit in little boxes. This is a book that needs to be read, so we've tried to make the reading experience enjoyable.

# New to the Third Edition

The third edition of *Intro Stats* continues and extends the successful innovations pioneered in our books, teaching Statistics and statistical thinking as it is practiced today. We've rewritten sections throughout the book to make them clearer and more interesting. We've introduced new up-to-the-minute motivating examples throughout. Many chapters lead with new examples—and we follow through with analyses of the data from those examples. And, we've added a number of new features, each with the goal of making it even easier for students to put the concepts of Statistics together into a coherent whole.

▶ *Where Are We Going?* Each chapter now starts with an introduction that points out the kinds of questions students will learn how to answer in the chapter. Each chapter ends with a *What Have We Learned?* summary to help students review what they should understand from the chapter.

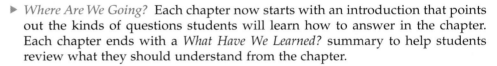

▶ *For Example.* In every chapter, you'll now find new worked examples that illustrate how to apply the concepts and methods discussed up to that point. We've added approximately 4 of these examples, called *For Example*, to each chapter for further illustration. (With 27 chapters, that's **more than 100 new illustrative examples**.) As we introduce each important, new concept, we provide a focused example applying it—usually with real up-to-the-minute data. But these aren't isolated examples. We carry the discussion through the chapter with each *For Example*, picking up the story and moving it forward as students learn more about the topic of the chapter. Providing these examples in sequences enhances and illustrates the story of each chapter.

▶ *Step-by-Step Worked Examples.* We've brought our innovative *Think/Show/Tell Step-by-Step* examples up-to-date with new examples and data, and restructured them so that each example begins with a clear question to address and ends with a conclusion that answers that question.

▶ *Just Checking.* This edition contains even more *Just Checking* exercises within chapters to help students ensure they understand the key ideas.

▶ *ActivStats Pointers.* Each chapter includes pointers to *ActivStats* activities (animations, simulations, activities, videos) that parallel the book's discussions to enhance learning. In the third edition, the *ActivStats* pointers have been revised for clarity and now indicate exactly what they are pointing to—activity, video, simulation, etc.

▶ *Exercises.* We've added **hundreds of new exercises,** including more single-concept exercises at the beginning of each set so students can be sure they have a clear understanding of each important topic before they're asked to tie them all together in more comprehensive exercises. Exercises have been **updated with the most recent data.** Many come from news stories; some from recent research articles. Whenever possible, the data are on the DVD so students can explore them further.

▶ *Data Sources.* Most of the data used in examples and exercises are from real-world sources, and we've listed more sources in this edition. Whenever we could, we've included references to the Internet data sources used, often in the form of URLs. As Internet users (and thus, our students) know well, URLs can "break" as Web sites evolve. To minimize the impact of such changes, we've pointed as high in the address tree as we thought practical. Moreover, the data themselves will often change as more recent values become available. The data we use are usually on the DVD. If you seek the data—or an updated version of the data—on the Internet, we try to direct you to a good starting point.

▶ *Chapters 4 and 5* have been entirely rewritten and reorganized. We think you'll agree with our reviewers that the new organization—discussing displays and summaries for quantitative data in Chapter 4 and then expanding on those ideas to discuss comparisons across groups, outliers, and other more sophisticated topics in Chapter 5—provides a more exciting and interesting way to approach these fundamental topics.

▶ *Simulation.* We've improved the discussion of simulation in Chapter 11 so it could relate more easily to discussions of experimental design and probability. The simulations included in the *ActivStats* multimedia software on the book's DVD carry those ideas forward in a student-friendly fashion.

▶ *Integrated Instructor's Guide.* The Instructor's Edition of the book has the *Instructor's Resource Guide* bound with each of the six parts of the book. You'll find chapter-by-chapter comments on the major concepts, tips on presenting topics (and what to avoid), extra teaching examples, and a list of resources.

▶ *Instructor's Podcasts* (10 points in 10 minutes). Created and presented by the authors, these podcasts focus on key points in each chapter to help you with class preparation. They can be easily downloaded from MyStatLab and the Adjunct and Instructor Support Site.

▶ *Video Lectures* featuring the textbook authors will help students review the high points of each chapter. Video presenters also work through examples from the text. The presentations feature the same student-friendly style and emphasis on critical thinking as the text. The DVD format makes it easy and convenient to watch the videos from a computer at home or on campus. Videos are available with captioning upon request. They also can be downloaded from within MyStatLab.

# Continuing Features

▶ *Think, Show, Tell.* The worked examples repeat the mantra of *Think, Show,* and *Tell* in every chapter. They emphasize the importance of thinking about a Statistics question (What do we know? What do we hope to learn? Are the assumptions and conditions satisfied?) and reporting our findings (the *Tell* step). The *Show* step contains the mechanics of calculating results, and conveys our belief that it is only one part of the process. This rubric is highlighted in the *Step-by-Step* examples that guide the students through the process of analyzing the problem with the general explanation on the left and the worked-out problem on the right. The result is a better understanding of the concept, not just number crunching.

▶ *Just Checking.* Within each chapter, we ask students to pause and think about what they've just read. To help them check their understanding, we ask some questions to ensure that they understand the material. These questions are designed to be a quick check; most involve very little calculation. We've put the answers at the end of the exercise sets in each chapter so students can easily check themselves. This edition contains even more *Just Checking* questions to help students ensure they understand the key ideas.

▶ *What Can Go Wrong?* Each chapter still contains our innovative *What Can Go Wrong?* sections that highlight the most common errors that people make and the misconceptions they have about Statistics. The most common mistakes for the new user of statistical methods usually involve misusing a method, not miscalculating a statistic. One of our goals is to arm students with the tools to detect statistical errors and to offer practice in debunking misuses of statistics, whether intentional or not. In this spirit, our exercises include some that probe the understanding of such failures.

**WHAT HAVE WE LEARNED?**

▶ *What Have We Learned?* These chapter-ending summaries provide a complete overview that highlight the new concepts, define the new terms introduced in the chapter, and list the skills that the student should have acquired. Students can think of these as study guides. If they understand the concepts in the summary, know the terms, and have the skills, they're probably ready for the exam.

**A  S**

▶ *ActivStats Pointers.* The DVD bound into new copies of the book includes the *ActivStats* multimedia materials. *ActivStats* matches the book chapter by chapter, so we've included occasional pointers to *ActivStats* activities that parallel discussions in the book. (To find a complete list of activities organized by topic, just open the front cover.) In the third edition, these pointers have been revised for clarity and now indicate exactly what they are pointing to—activity, video, simulation, etc. Many students choose to look at these first, before reading the chapter or attending a class on each subject.

▶ *Exercises.* Throughout, we've maintained the pairing of examples so that each odd-numbered exercise (with answer in the back of the book) is followed by an even-numbered exercise on the same statistics topic. Exercises are still ordered by level of difficulty.

▶ *By Hand.* Even though we encourage the use of technology to calculate statistical quantities, we realize the pedagogical benefits of occasionally doing a calculation by hand. The *By Hand* boxes break apart the calculation of many simpler formulas to help the student through the calculation of a worked example.

**REALITY CHECK**

▶ *Reality Check.* We regularly remind students that Statistics is about understanding the world with data. Results that make no sense are probably wrong, no matter how carefully we think we did the calculations. Mistakes are often easy to spot with a little thought, so we ask students to stop for a reality check before interpreting their result.

**NOTATION ALERT:**

▶ *Notation Alert.* Throughout this book we emphasize the importance of clear communication, and proper notation is part of the vocabulary of Statistics. Students who know that in Algebra $n$ can stand for any variable may be surprised to learn that in Statistics $n$ is always and only the sample size. We've found that it helps students when we are clear about the letters and symbols statisticians use to mean very specific things, so we've included notation alerts whenever we introduce a special notation that students will see again.

▶ *Connections.* The book presents material in 27 short, focused chapters, but they tell one overall story. Each chapter has a *Connections* section to link key terms and concepts with previous discussions and to point out the continuing themes. The *Connections* help to fit newly learned concepts into a growing understanding of Statistics. The best way to retain new learning is to connect it with old understanding.

ON THE COMPUTER

▶ *On the Computer.* In the real world, Statistics is practiced with computers. We prefer not to choose a particular Statistics program. Instead, at the end of each chapter, we summarize what students can find in the most common packages, often with annotated output. We then offer specific guidance for several of the most common packages (Data Desk, Excel, JMP, Minitab, SPSS, TI-83/84 Plus,[1] and TI-89) to help students get started with the software of their choice. We've updated these summaries for Excel 2007 and recent versions of the other software packages.

# Coverage

Textbooks are often defined more by what they choose not to cover than by what they do cover. We've been guided in the choice and order of topics by several fundamental principles. First, we have tried to ensure that each new topic fits into the growing structure of understanding that we hope students will build. Several topic orders can support this goal. We explain our reasons for the topic order of the chapters in the Instructor's Resource Guide materials bound before each Part in the Instructor's Edition. We also describe some alternative orders that also work comfortably with these materials.

*GAISE Guidelines.* We have worked to provide materials to help each class, in its own way, follow the guidelines of the GAISE (Guidelines for Assessment and Instruction in Statistics Education) project sponsored by the American Statistical Association. That report urges (among other detailed suggestions) that Statistics education should

1. emphasize Statistical literacy and develop Statistical thinking,
2. use real data,
3. stress conceptual understanding rather than mere knowledge of procedures,
4. foster active learning,
5. use technology for developing concepts and analyzing data, and
6. make assessment a part of the learning process.

# Mathematics

Mathematics traditionally appears in Statistics texts in several roles:

1. It can provide a concise, clear statement of important concepts.
2. It can describe calculations to be performed with data.
3. It can embody proofs of fundamental results.

Of these, we emphasize the first. Mathematics can make discussions of Statistics concepts, probability, and inference clear and concise. We have not shied away from using math where we felt that it helped to clarify without intimidating. We have tried to be sensitive to those who are discouraged by equations by also providing verbal descriptions and numerical examples.

This book is not concerned with proving theorems about statistics. Some of these theorems are quite interesting, and many are important. Often, though, their proofs are not enlightening to introductory Statistics students, and can distract the audience from the concepts we want them to understand.

Nor do we concentrate on calculations. Although statistics calculations are generally straightforward, they are also usually tedious. And, more to the point,

---

[1] For brevity, we will write TI-83/84 Plus for the TI-83 Plus and/or TI-84 Plus. Keystrokes and output remain the same for the TI-83 Plus and the TI-84 Plus, so instructions and examples serve for both calculators.

they are often unnecessary. Today, virtually all statistics are calculated with technology, so there is little need for students to spend time summing squared deviations by hand. The equations we use have been selected for their focus on understanding concepts and methods. Often these equations are unsuited to hand calculation. When that happens, we've provided more calculation-friendly versions, often in a marginal note that lays out the calculation for those who find following the process a better way to learn about the result.

# Technology and Data

To experience the real world of Statistics, it's best to explore real data sets using modern technology.

▶ *Technology.* We assume that you are using some form of technology in your Statistics course. That could be a calculator, a spreadsheet, a statistics package, or some combination of these. We also assume that you'll put little emphasis on calculating answers by hand, even though we often show how. However, this is not a technology-heavy book. Rather than adopt any particular software, we discuss generic computer output. We also offer guidance to help students get started on seven common software platforms: Excel, Minitab, Data Desk, JMP, SPSS, TI-83/84 Plus, and TI-89 graphing calculators. This guidance is found at the end of each chapter, specific to the methods learned in that chapter. The book's DVD includes *ActivStats*, the statistics package *Data Desk,* and the DDXL add-in for Excel.

▶ *Data.* Because we use technology for computing, we don't limit ourselves to small, artificial data sets. In addition to including some small data sets, we have built examples and exercises on real data with a moderate number of cases—usually more than you would want to enter by hand into a program or calculator. Machine-readable versions of the data are included on the DVD as well as on the book's Web site, **http://www.aw-bc.com/dvb**. Once the data set is located, you can copy the data in the format appropriate for the software of your choice.

## ON THE DVD

A new DVD replaces the old CD bound with the book. The DVD holds a number of supporting materials, including *ActivStats,* the *Data Desk* statistics package, an Excel add-in (DDXL), all large data sets from the text formatted for the most popular technologies, and two additional chapters.

*ActivStats (for Data Desk).* The award-winning *ActivStats* multimedia program supports learning chapter by chapter with the book. It complements the book with videos of real-word stories, worked examples, animated expositions of each of the major Statistics topics, and tools for performing simulations, visualizing inference, and learning to use statistics software. The new version of *ActivStats* includes

- improved navigation and a cleaner design that makes it easier to find and use tools such as the Index and Glossary
- over **1000 homework exercises,** including many new exercises plus answers to the "odd numbered" exercises. Many are from the text, providing the data already set up for calculations, and some are unique to *ActivStats*. Many exercises link to data files for each statistics package.
- **17** short **video clips,** many new and updated
- **70 animated activities**
- **over 300 data sets**

- a new feature just for instructors provides direct access to the materials on the disk most useful in teaching, including simulations, demonstrations, and videos
- activities to learn how to use Data Desk. Versions that teach Excel, JMP, Minitab, or SPSS are available on the all-in-one version of the DVD (see page xvii).
- plus interactive graphs, simulations, dynamic statistics tables, and visualization tools

*Data Desk,* a student version of the professional statistics package gives students the ability to perform any analysis in the textbook. Its interactive dynamic displays help students visualize relationships and models.

*DDXL,* an Excel add-in, adds sound statistics and statistical graphics capabilities to Excel. DDXL adds, among other capabilities, boxplots, histograms, statistical scatterplots, normal probability plots, and statistical inference procedures not available in Excel's Data Analysis pack.

*Data.* Data for exercises marked **T** are available on the DVD and Web site formatted for Data Desk, Excel, JMP, Minitab, SPSS, and the TI calculators, and as text files suitable for these and virtually any other statistics software.

*Additional Chapters.* Two additional chapters cover **Analysis of Variance** (Chapter 28) and **Multiple Regression** (Chapter 29). These topics point the way to further study in Statistics.

# Supplements

## STUDENT SUPPLEMENTS

*Intro Stats* Third Edition for-sale student edition. (ISBN-13: 978-0-321-50045-8; ISBN-10: 0-321-50045-8)

Student's Solutions Manual, by William Craine, provides detailed, worked-out solutions to odd-numbered exercises. (ISBN-13: 978-0-321-49941-7; ISBN-10: 0-321-49941-7)

TI-83/84 Plus and TI-89 Manual, by Patricia Humphrey (Georgia Southern University), is organized to follow the sequence of topics in the text, and is an easy-to-follow, step-by-step guide on how to use the TI-83/84 Plus and TI-89 graphing calculators. It provides worked-out examples to help students fully understand and use the graphing calculator. (ISBN-13: 978-0-321-49943-1; ISBN-10: 0-321-49943-3)

Statistics Study Card is a resource for students containing important formulas, definitions, and tables that correspond precisely to the DeVeaux/Velleman/Bock Statistics series. This card can work as a reference for completing homework assignments or as an aid in studying. (ISBN-13: 978-0-321-46370-8; ISBN-10: 0-321-46370-6)

Graphing Calculator Tutorial for Statistics will guide students through the keystrokes needed to most efficiently use their graphing calculator. Although based on the TI-84 Plus Silver Edition, operating system 2.30, the keystrokes for this calculator are identical to those on the TI-84 Plus, and very similar to the TI-83 and TI-83 Plus. This tutorial should be helpful to students using any of these calculators, though there may be differences in some lessons. The tutorial is organized by topic. (ISBN-13: 978-0-321-41382-6; ISBN-10: 0-321-41382-2)

## INSTRUCTOR SUPPLEMENTS

Instructor's Edition contains answers to all exercises as well as a chapter-by-chapter Instructor's Guide which includes extra examples, teaching suggestions, and commentary. (ISBN-13: 978-0-321-50381-7; ISBN-10: 0-321-50381-3)

Printed Test Bank and Resource Guide, by John Diehl, complements and expands on the commentary and teaching suggestions included in the Instructor's Edition. It includes solutions to the extra examples in the Instructor's Edition, as well as chapter quizzes, part-level tests, and suggestions for projects. (ISBN-13: 978-0-321-50382-4; ISBN-10: 0-321-50382-1)

Instructor's Solutions Manual, by William Craine, contains detailed solutions to all of the exercises. (ISBN-13: 978-0-321-49944-8; ISBN-10: 0-321-49944-1)

TestGen® TestGen enables instructors to build, edit, print, and administer tests using a computerized bank of questions developed to cover all the objectives of the text. TestGen is algorithmically based, allowing instructors to create multiple but equivalent versions of the same question or test with the click of a button. Instructors can also modify test bank questions or add new questions. Tests can be printed or administered online. The software and testbank are available for download from the Instructor Resource Center at www.aw-bc.com/irc.

Adjunct and Instructor Support Site (www.aw-bc.com/dvb_support) is a one-stop resource to help instructors plan and prepare for their course. Features include downloadable Lesson Podcasts that expand on the Printed Test Bank and Resource Guide, WebEX workshops on key topics and technology, and all teaching tools (such as sample syllabi, extra data sets, class examples, and supplements) in one place.

PowerPoint Lecture Slides provide an outline to use in a lecture setting, presenting definitions, key concepts, and figures from the text. These slides are available within MyStatLab or at www.aw-bc.com/irc.

# Technology Resources

**Companion DVD** is bound in new copies of this text and replaces the CD bound in previous editions. The DVD holds a number of supporting materials, including:

- *ActivStats® for Data Desk* The award-winning *ActivStats* multimedia program supports learning chapter by chapter with the book. It complements the book with videos of real-word stories, worked examples, animated expositions of each of the major Statistics topics, and tools for performing simulations, visualizing inference, and learning to use statistics software. The new version of *ActivStats* includes 17 short video clips; 170 animated activities and teaching applets; 300 data sets; 1,000 homework exercises, many with links to Data Desk® files; interactive graphs, simulations, visualization tools, and much more.

- *Data Desk,* student version, is a subset of the full-featured professional statistics and graphics system that has won awards both for design and for education support. It features interactive graphs for visualizing relationships and a full range of statistics calculations in a point-and-click interface that is easy for students to learn and use.

- *DDXL,* an Excel add-in, adds sound statistics and statistical graphics capabilities to Excel. DDXL adds, among other capabilities, boxplots, histograms, statistical scatterplots, normal probability plots, and statistical inference procedures not available in Excel's Data Analysis pack.

- *Data.* Data for exercises marked 🅣 are available on the DVD and Web site formatted for Data Desk, Excel, JMP, Minitab, SPSS, and the TI calculators, and as text files suitable for these and virtually any other statistics software.

- *Additional Chapters.* Two additional chapters cover **Analysis of Variance** (Chapter 28) and **Multiple Regression** (Chapter 29). These topics point the way to further study in Statistics.

**ActivStats** (all-in-one version) is a DVD containing all of the materials on the Companion DVD plus versions of ActivStats that teach and directly link to each of the statistics packages supported by the text: Data Desk, Excel, JMP, Minitab, and SPSS. For each, ActivStats has lessons to introduce students to using the package and datasets formatted for the package. Lessons and exercises are the same for all packages, so this version works well in a class in which students are free to use their choice of software. ActivStats runs on both Mac and PC, and supports each package on the appropriate platforms. (ISBN-13: 978-0-321-50014-4; ISBN-10: 0-321-50014-8)

**MathXL® for Statistics** is a powerful online homework, tutorial, and assessment system that accompanies Pearson textbooks in statistics. With MathXL for Statistics, instructors can create, edit, and assign online homework and tests using algorithmically generated exercises correlated at the objective level to the textbook. They can also create and assign their own online exercises and import TestGen tests for added flexibility. All student work is tracked in MathXL's online gradebook. Students can take chapter tests in MathXL and receive personalized study plans based on their test results. The study plan diagnoses weaknesses and links students directly to tutorial exercises for the objectives they need to study and retest. Students can also access supplemental animations and video clips directly from selected exercises. MathXL for Statistics is available to qualified adopters. For more information, visit our Web site at www.mathxl.com, or contact your sales representative.

**MyStatLab™** (part of the MyMathLab® and MathXL® product family) is a text-specific, easily customizable online course that integrates interactive multimedia instruction with textbook content. Powered by CourseCompass™ (Pearson Education's online teaching and learning environment) and MathXL (our online homework, tutorial, and assessment system), MyStatLab gives you the tools you need to deliver all or a portion of your course online, whether your students are in a lab setting or working from home. MyStatLab provides a rich and flexible set of course materials, featuring free-response tutorial exercises for unlimited practice and mastery. Students can also use online tools, such as video lectures, animations, and a multimedia textbook, to independently improve their understanding and performance. Instructors can use MyStatLab's homework and test managers to select and assign online exercises correlated directly to the textbook, and they can also create and assign their own online exercises and import TestGen tests for added flexibility. MyStatLab's online gradebook—designed specifically for mathematics and statistics—automatically tracks students' homework and test results and gives the instructor control over how to calculate final grades. Instructors can also add offline (paper-and-pencil) grades to the gradebook. MyStatLab also includes access to the **Pearson Tutor Center** (www.pearsontutorservices.com). The Tutor Center is staffed by qualified mathematics instructors who provide textbook-specific tutoring for students via toll-free phone, fax, email, and interactive Web sessions. MyStatLab is available to qualified adopters. For more information, visit out websites at www.mystatlab.com or contact your sales representative.

**StatCrunch** (available within MyStatLab) is a powerful online tool that provides an interactive environment for doing statistics. StatCrunch can be used for both numerical and graphical data analysis, and uses interactive graphics to illustrate the connection between objects selected in a graph and the underlying data. In MyStatLab, all of the data sets from the textbook are preloaded in StatCrunch, and StatCrunch is also available as a tool from all of the online homework and practice exercises.

**Video Lectures on DVD with Optional Captioning** feature the textbook authors reviewing the high points of each chapter. Video presenters also work through examples from the text. The presentations continue the same student-friendly style and emphasis on critical thinking as the text. The DVD format makes it easy and convenient to watch the videos from a computer at home or on campus. Videos are available with captioning upon request. They can also be downloaded as video podcasts from within MyStatLab. Contact your Pearson representative for details. (ISBN 13: 978-0-321-50160-8; ISBN-10: 0-321-50160-8)

**Companion Web Site** (www.aw-bc.com/dvb) provides additional resources for instructors and students.

**Active Learning Questions** for use with classroom response systems ("clickers") include Multiple Choice questions to review lecture material. Available within MyStatLab or from the Instructor Resource Center at www.aw-bc.com/irc.

**The Student Edition of Minitab** is a condensed edition of the Professional release of Minitab statistical software that offers the full range of statistical methods and graphical capabilities, along with worksheets that can include up to 10,000 data points. Individual copies of the software can be bundled with the text. (ISBN 13: 978-0-321-11313-9; ISBN-10: 0-321-11313-6)

**JMP** Student Edition is an easy-to-use, streamlined version of JMP desktop statistical discovery software from SAS, Institute, Inc. and is available for bundling with the text. (ISBN 13: 978-0-321-51738-8; ISBN-10: 0-321-51738-5)

**SPSS**, a statistical and data management software package, is also available for bundling with the text. (ISBN 13: 978-0-205-56941-0; ISBN-10: 0-205-56941-2)

# Acknowledgments

Many people have contributed to this book in both of its editions. This edition would have never seen the light of day without the assistance of the incredible team at Addison-Wesley. Our Editor in Chief, Deirdre Lynch, was central to the genesis, development, and realization of the book from day one. Sara Oliver Gordus, Associate Editor, kept us on task as much as humanly possible with much needed humor and grace. Peggy McMahon, Senior Production Supervisor, kept the cogs from getting into the wheels where they often wanted to wander. Christina Lepre, Editorial Assistant, and Caroline Celano and Kathleen DeChavez, Marketing Assistants, were essential in managing all of the behind-the-scenes work that needed to be done. Christine Stavrou, Media Producer, put together a top-notch media package for this book. Barbara Atkinson, Senior Designer, and Geri Davis are responsible for the wonderful way the book looks. Evelyn Beaton, Manufacturing Manager, and Ginny Michaud, Senior Manufacturing Buyer, worked miracles to get this book and DVD in your hands, and Greg Tobin, VP/Publisher, was supportive and good-humored throughout all aspects of the project.

Special thanks go out to Pre-Press PMG, the compositor, for the wonderful work they did on this book, and in particular to Laura Houston, the project manager, for her close attention to detail.

We'd also like to thank our accuracy checkers whose monumental task was to make sure we said what we thought we were saying. They are Nazanin Azarnia, Santa Fe Community College; Phyllis Curtiss, Grand Valley State University; and Helen Noble, San Diego State University.

We extend our sincere thanks for the suggestions and contributions made by the following reviewers and Forum attendees:

Mary Kay Abbey
*Montgomery College*

Froozan Pourboghnaf Afiat
*Community College of Southern Nevada*

Mehdi Afiat
*Community College of Southern Nevada*

Nazanin Azarnia
*Santa Fe Community College*

Carl D. Bodenschatz
*University of Pittsburgh*

Robert L. Carson
*Hagerstown Community College*

Jerry Chen
*Suffolk County Community College*

Kim (Robinson) Gilbert
*Clayton College & State University*

Ken Grace
*Anoka-Ramsey Community College*

Jonathan Graham
*University of Montana*

Mary R. Hudachek-Buswell
*Clayton State University*

Becky Hurley
*Rockingham Community College*

Kelly Jackson
*Camden County College*

Martin Jones
*College of Charleston*

Michael Kinter
*Cuesta College*

Kathleen Kone
*Community College of Allegheny County*

Susan Loch
*University of Minnesota*

Elaine McDonald
*Sonoma State University*

Hari Mukerjee
*Witchita State University*

Helen Noble
*San Diego State University*

Monica Oabos
*Santa Barbara City College*

Linda Obeid
*Reedley College*

Charles C. Okeke
*Community College of Southern Nevada*

Pamela Omer
*Western New England College*

Mavis Pararai
*Indiana University of Pennsylvania*

Juana Sanchez
*UCLA*

Gerald Schoultz
*Grand Valley State University*

Jim Smart
*Tallahassee Community College*

Heydar Zahedani
*California State University, San Marcos*

We also extend our sincere thanks for the suggestions and contributions made
by the following reviewers of the previous edition:

Sanjib Basu
*Northern Illinois University*

Steven Bogart
*Shoreline Community College*

Ann Cannon
*Cornell College*

Rick Denman
*Southwestern University*

Jeffrey Eldridge
*Edmonds Community College*

Karen Estes
*St. Petersburg Junior College*

Richard Friary

Nancy Heckman
*University of British Columbia*

James Helreich
*Marist College*

Susan Herring
*Sonoma State University*

Patricia Humphrey
*Georgia Southern University*

Debra Ingram
*Arkansas State University*

Rebecka Jornsten
*Rutgers University*

Michael Lichter
*State University of New York–Buffalo*

Pamela Lockwood
*Western Texas A & M University*

Wei-Yin Loh
*University of Wisconsin–Madison*

Catherine Matos
*Clayton College & State University*

Gina Reed
*Gainesville College*

Chamont Wang
*The College of New Jersey*

Edward Welsh
*Westfield State College*

# Index of Applications

*Note:* IE = In-Text Example, FE = For Example, JC = Just Checking, SBS = Step-By-Step and E = Exercise

## ILLUSTRATIVE (MADE UP) EXAMPLES

## LAW

# Exploring and Understanding Data

# About This Guide

Whether you are teaching Statistics for the first time, or just adapting to the new approach we take in this book, we hope this Instructor's Guide will help you optimize your students' experience. You'll find pages like this preceding each of the book's seven Parts in this Instructor's Edition. Here we explain the reasoning behind our approach. We summarize each chapter, highlighting the important concepts and pointing out where they'll show up later in the course. We offer some pedagogical suggestions—do's and don'ts—and include examples and activities you might use in teaching your class. And we provide references to *ActivStats* and other resources that you may find helpful.

The discussion for each chapter in this Instructor's Guide contains some or all of the following features.

## What's It About?

This section summarizes the major topics included in the chapter. More important, we tell the *story* of the chapter. Each chapter introduces new concepts and methods, and each one fits with what students have learned in previous chapters and will learn in subsequent ones. We give you the overview to help you show your students how it all fits together.

## Comments

The Comments section explains the statistical and pedagogical reasons for the choices we've made in what to teach, in how to present it, and in what order to discuss it. Some of these choices may differ from those made by other textbooks. We try to point out these differences and explain our approach.

## Looking Ahead

The Looking Ahead sections point out ways that many of the ideas we introduce in early chapters foreshadow or pave the way for important features of later chapters. These are often good points to make in class to motivate students and to help them fit all these new concepts together into a coherent whole.

## Class Do's

We offer pedagogical advice about approaches that have worked for us, ideas to stress, and other ways to highlight important concepts or take advantage of important features of this text.

## The Importance of What You Don't Say

One of the challenges of teaching Intro Stats is that there's so much to say. But too much information at the wrong time can be confusing to the beginning student. Because deciding how much to say and when to say it can be tricky, we offer some suggestions about what *not* to say and what not to say *quite yet*.

## Class Examples

It's always good to have another example for class. Students seem to always want one more example. So we provide new examples different from those in the book or on the *ActivStats* DVD. These can include actual classroom materials in the form of worksheets or guided explorations.

## Resources

We offer a list of resources for background information, data sets, and classroom activities. These may include other books, videos, software, or Web sites.

## Just a Few More Words About the Text . . .

We think this text is different.[1] We hope to entice students to read the book with our easy-to-understand conversational style—and to entertain them with occasional humor. We have created several features that provide consistent themes and resources for doing Statistics. Take advantage of them!

The 27 chapters of this book are grouped into seven parts. The end of each part includes a one-page **Quick Review** of the major concepts, followed by a large set of **Exercises**. These exercises are comprehensive, often integrate several concepts, and appear in random order. You should find everything you need to prepare your students for tests.

### SOME IMPORTANT RESOURCES

We offer advice on books, videos, Web sites, software, and other resources we think you'll find helpful.

### *ActivStats* **and** *Data Desk*

These award-winning programs are on the DVD bound in the book. You can also obtain versions from Addison Wesley for a student lab. *ActivStats* provides a complete set of multimedia activities to support the course, arranged by chapters that match the book. Activities include narrated and animated expositions, video stories of real-world applications, simulations that support discovery learning, interactive tools, online quizzes, and more. *ActivStats* is also a source of hundreds of additional exercises, most with data sets provided on the DVD

---

[1] But what authors wouldn't say this?

and prepared for use by statistics software. Versions of *ActivStats* are available to support *Data Desk* (on the DVD provided with the book), *Excel, JMP, Minitab,* and *SPSS*. Versions for packages other than *Data Desk* can optionally be bundled with student versions of the software. (Contact Addison Wesley for price information.)

*ActivStats* can support student learning in several ways. We have found it helpful to have students prepare for class by working through the appropriate *ActivStats* activities. Students often are more willing to encounter new material with interactive materials than in a textbook. Students can also treat *ActivStats* as a "TA on a DVD" who has infinite patience. And you can encourage students to use the index in *ActivStats* to find quick explanations of specific concepts and methods as they find that they need them.

If you have elected to use the online materials that come with the book, these can also be used either for class preparation or review. Many of the *ActivStats* activities are available in this way as well, imbedded in the multimedia textbook found on the *MyMathLab* Web site that goes with the book.

### Printed Test Bank and Resource Guide

This resource complements and expands on the commentary and teaching suggestions found in the Instructor's Guide sections of this Instructor's Edition. It includes chapter quizzes, unit tests, and suggestions for projects, as well as Web links and lists of other resources. (ISBN: 978-0-321-50382-4)

### Adjunct and Instructor Support Site (www.aw-bc.com/dvb-support)

This is a one-stop resource to help you plan and prepare for your course. Features include (1) downloadable lesson podcasts designed to help you prepare for class, (2) WebEx Workshops on key topics and technology, and (3) all teaching tools (such as sample syllabi, extra data sets, class examples, and supplements) in one place.

### Videos

- *ActivStats* presents video and animated presentations of real-world applications of Statistics. Some are condensed from the *Decisions Through Data* stories (see below). Others are unique to *ActivStats*.

- *Video lectures,* presented by the authors, to support the book's content. Contact your Pearson Sales Rep for more information.

- *Decisions Through Data;* COMAP (1-800-77COMAP), 1992. This set of 5 VHS tapes contains 21 lessons to show in class. Each looks at real-life situations and demonstrates the use of statistics to answer important questions. The units are typically 10 to 15 minutes in length, allowing you to show the video segment and have time to discuss the statistical concepts and techniques introduced.

### Other Books and Magazines

- *Chance,* Springer-Verlag (1-800-SPRINGER). This magazine, published quarterly, provides articles about statistics as well as excellent examples and data sets to use in class.

- *Stats,* American Statistical Association. This is a magazine for students that provides articles about statistics and examples that you might find useful for class preparation.

### Net Links

The Internet is a valuable source of data sets, examples, tables, random numbers, and current events. The good news is that you can probably find almost everything you need or want to know there. The bad news is that the materials will not be consistent or integrated. Be especially wary of introducing students to a variety of online applets, each with its own interface, notation, terminology, and assumptions.

Many of the data sets and examples in the book are sourced from Internet sites. Where appropriate, we provide URL references to the top level, and key search terms to help locate the particular data or discussion. These references may, of course, lead to even more up-to-date data than were available when we found them for the book. The data used in the book are available on the DVD, but you may prefer to discuss the most recent versions in class.

We provide below some useful jumping-off points, with the obvious caveat that many of them may move, change, or disappear altogether between the time we compile this list and the time you try to use it. With our apologies in advance when a link fails, we hope you find this effort of value. You'll find information on many other useful links at our Web site, www.aw-bc.com/dvb.

- Software–calculators, commercial software, and some free Web software
www.ti.com
www.activstats.com
www.datadesk.com
www.minitab.com
www.jmp.com
www.spss.com
www.statcrunch.com

- Sources of Data
dasl.datadesk.com (data sets indexed by topic)
www.fedstats.gov
www.madd.org/stats/0,1056,1845,00.html (DWI statistics)
www.fbi.gov/ucr/01cius.htm (crime statistics)
www.amstat.org/publications/jse (*Journal of Statistics Education*)

- Statistics Background
www.dartmouth.edu/~chance/index.html
http://courses.ncssm.edu/math/Stat_Inst/Notes.htm

This Part of the book covers data displays and summaries. Many students will recognize some of the material from middle and high school, so our emphasis is on statistical thinking. Of course, we define terms and provide examples. But we also discuss *why* methods presented are used and what we hope to learn from them. These are concepts that appear throughout the course. Even more important than what to look for in a histogram or how to summarize the spread of a distribution is the underlying lesson that there are *reasons* for displaying and summarizing data. These reasons inform and motivate the entire course.

## Instructor's Guide

# Stats Starts Here

## What's It About?

Chapter 1 describes the important features of the text. We've given the chapter an unusual title and tried to grab students' attention with a humorous footnote. (Some have e-mailed us to assure us that they *do* read the footnotes.) If we can get them to read three words and the footnote, maybe we can get them to read on.

## Comments

This is the students' first look at the style of the book, and we do lay it on more heavily here than we will when discussing, say, confidence intervals. We want to shake things up. We want them to notice that this is not the same old math or science textbook they've seen before. And we'd like to get them on our side. That's the reason for the humor and self-deprecating remarks.

Every Statistics text starts with a definition of *Statistics*. We do too, but ours is different. And the difference matters. We say that Statistics is *a way of reasoning* and that the goal is *to help us understand the world*. We've found it helpful to reinforce this idea throughout the semester, especially when we get into the methods sections of the course. This book is first and primarily about statistical thinking. Methods, definitions, and skills are all here, but each is presented with the purpose of understanding the world. That's why every example follows the *Think, Show, Tell* pattern, starting with careful reasoning and concluding with a sentence or two telling what we've learned about the world.

It is easy to be drawn into a focus on definitions, on algorithms, and on getting the "right answer." Those are easier to teach and certainly easier to grade. Please resist the temptation. If you can help your students to stay focused on statistical thinking and understanding, this course can change the way they view the world.

## A Note on Teaching

We don't spend an entire class period on this chapter; in fact, sometimes we just start right in on Chapter 2. Chapter 1 is meant to be read *by* students, not *to* them. Discuss the important definitions, collect some data, and move on as fast as you can. We've got a lot to cover and can't afford a full class just to get moving.

## Looking Ahead

Technology plays an important role in this book. We expect students to use a calculator or statistics package (such as the Student *Data Desk* program supplied on the DVD) for finding the numerical "answers." So we won't spend much time worrying about the calculation details, although we do expect them to understand what's happening. Instead, we focus on understanding and meaning. But the book is "technology neutral." The "computer output" in the book is designed to look a lot like many packaged results, but exactly match none of them. Students should feel comfortable using almost any statistics program or graphing calculator.

The DVD in the back of the book also provides the *ActivStats* multimedia package. Each chapter of *ActivStats* matches a chapter of *Intro Stats*. Most offer a video story from the real world and then go on to look at the data. Many offer simulations and interactive animations to help students discover and grasp the sometimes surprising concepts in this course. Some students will find the multimedia materials to be the best introduction to these ideas.

## Class Do's

One of our favorite definitions says, "Statistics is the art of distilling meaning from data." Data have a story to tell. Our objective is to uncover that story. Collect some data in class, and ask students to look for interesting facts hiding there.

Encourage students to think about the concepts and definitions in this chapter. For example, why do we talk about "a statistic" when we don't discuss "a mathematic" or "a physic"? Statistics is a whole that is made up of many parts, and each of those parts has its own meaning and its own story to tell.

## The Importance of What You Don't Say

One of the reasons Statistics can be difficult to teach is that we often deal with vague concepts. Students and teachers both like clear definitions; they're easier to teach, learn, and grade. But reasonable people can disagree about whether a histogram is symmetric or skewed, whether a straggling point is really an outlier or just the largest value, or whether the spread really is the same in two groups we want to compare. It is important to allow students their own opinions and insights into data.[1]

This raises the issue of ethical practice in Statistics. We are engaged in an honest search for truth and understanding, and that's what should guide our (and our students') judgments. Emphasize this point now to alert students that this isn't a course about calculating the right answer, but about understanding the world.

Avoid the temptation to lead students in any particular direction or give them hints about how to examine the data you collected. They know some things to do—they'll find percents and averages, maybe draw some simple graphs, and write a few sentences about what they see. Just let it happen. You'll have plenty of chances to suggest, lead, and modify later on.

The motivation of hoping to understand the world is quite sufficient to justify thinking beyond the numbers at hand. This is not the time to introduce technical concepts such as *population* and *sample*. We'd rather not even see these terms yet (and you won't find them this early in the text). We all know that we'll be heading that way eventually, but if we make reasoning about patterns in the data too formal too soon, we'll stifle students' interest and enthusiasm and burden them with a lot of terms they don't have a context for just yet.

## Class Examples

You might take a quick class survey. We suggest asking for things like gender, political leaning (Liberal, Moderate, Conservative), number of siblings, number of countries ever visited, whether they play varsity sports, GPA, height, handedness (left or right), and shoe size. Be sure to include both categorical and quantitative values.[2] Try this question, after getting everyone's attention: Ask your students to pick a number at random between 1 and 10 and write it down quickly. (Later you can look to see how "random" these numbers really are.) Have the data collected and duplicated, or put it up on a Web site before the next class. Ask the students what story the data tell about their class. If you wish, you can make a stem-and-leaf display or scatterplot of some of the data immediately.

*Hints:* Data are rarely as simple as they seem. Suggest these variables, then pause for some discussion. Does touching down at an airport qualify as "visiting" a country? Does an only child count herself when counting siblings? Should shoe sizes be adjusted because men's and women's size 7 are different sizes? If you write with your left hand but throw

with your right, are you left handed? Give them a chance, and they'll find other issues—and they'll be developing a healthy skepticism toward data. That's just what we want, so they'll value the tools that help them look at data more carefully.

If you don't specify units for height, you may get some values in centimeters. Alternatively, if you specify inches, you may get a "55" from someone who meant 5'5". Those outliers make for good class discussion.

If you teach a large section, consider collecting data online. There are a number of services that will let you design an online survey and will host it for a modest price, letting students respond online at their convenience and providing you with anonymous and machine-readable responses. One we have used successfully is at http://www.surveymonkey.com. They reference others.

## RESOURCES

### ActivStats

Have your students work through the initial chapter in *ActivStats* now to be sure there are no glitches. Most students are computer savvy enough to pop a disk into the computer and run, and that's all the *ActivStats* disk requires.

### Printed Test Bank and Resource Guide

The *Printed Test Bank and Resource Guide* includes chapter quizzes, unit tests, and suggestions for projects, as well as Web links and lists of other resources. (ISBN: 978-0-321-50382-4)

### Net Links

We like the use of course Web sites. The course resources offered by Addison Wesley to accompany the book are a good place to start. They include the service of hosting your course Web site, starting with a template that is already richly populated. (http://www.mymathlab.com).

### Adjunct and Instructor Support Site (www.aw-bc.com/dvb-support)

This one-stop site is designed to help you plan and prepare for your course. Features include downloadable lesson podcasts that highlight the important points to cover, WebEx Workshops on key topics and technology, and all teaching tools (such as sample syllabi, extra data sets, class examples, and supplements) in one place.

And don't overlook the book's Web site, www.aw-bc .com/dvb.

---

[1] There was a time, not long ago, when our students' first question, "Why am I taking this course?" was typically answered by "It's required. Sit down and be quiet." We propose that a better answer is "So you can learn how data can tell us about the world. Stand up and tell us what you see."

[2] Recall what you were really interested in at that age and try some carefully worded questions on those subjects.

## What's It About?

Chapter 2 introduces students to data. We talk about the importance of context (the W's), about variables, and we make the distinction between categorical and quantitative data. We begin to introduce the vocabulary of Statistics.

## Comments

It is valuable to get students involved with data from the start. We don't take a "big picture" approach at this time. There will be plenty of time to build models and draw inferences later. For now, let's just get our hands dirty playing with the data. When students have a good sense of what kinds of things data can say to us, they learn to expect to listen to the data. Throughout the course, we insist that no analysis of data is complete without telling what it means. This is where that understanding starts.

Rather than head directly for the "real purpose" of the course in the inference chapters, we prefer to emphasize the connection between our work with data and what they tell us about the world. No analysis is complete without a connection back to the real-world circumstances. Setting that stage is the underlying motivation for this chapter. We'll spend the next 10 chapters or so looking at and exploring data without making formal inferences.

## Looking Ahead

You might have the students thumb through the book and read the opening of some chapters. Each one starts with a story and data, and all have additional stories and more data inside. Statistics is about the real world. Among other topics, we'll be discussing how well we can predict hurricane tracks, whether generic batteries perform as well as their brand-name competitors, the debate over the safety of a widely used drug, and whether or not people over 30 snore more. We need to get students thinking about the context of data and able to make the distinction between categorical and quantitative data. These are fundamental skills for everything that follows, and they'll be used throughout the course.

This is also a good time to introduce whatever technology your students will be using. Have them summarize the results of the survey you did on day 1 using the software package or calculator they will be using for the course. Point them to the computer grid found near the end of most chapters. It offers instructions on several common statistics packages and calculators. The *ActivStats* DVD is available in versions that teach *Data Desk, JMP, Minitab, SPSS,* and *Excel* (with an add-in provided on the disk). You may want to give students a customized handout to get them started in your school's particular computing environment.

## Class Do's

Get the class thinking about what the term "data" means. Students need to understand that data are not just numbers and

that they must have a context (the W's). When data are quantitative, they should also have units. There are two ways we treat data: **categorical** and **quantitative.** Don't get distracted by worrying about ratio, interval, and other distinctions. These are problematic and don't matter for the concepts and methods discussed in this book. Emphasize that the distinction between treating data as categorical or quantitative may be more about how *we* display and analyze data than it is about the variable itself. The variable "sex" is data, but just because we might label the males as 1 and the females as 0 doesn't mean that it's quantitative. On the other hand, taking the average of those 0's and 1's does give us the percentage of males. How about *age*? It is often quantitative, but could be categorical if broken down only into *child, adult,* and *senior.* Zip code is usually categorical, but if one business had an "average" zip code for their customers of 10000 while another had 90000, we'd know the latter had more customers in the western United States. Emphasize the importance of the context and the W's in summarizing these data.

Students should recognize that every discipline has its own vocabulary, and Statistics is no exception. They'll need to understand and use that vocabulary properly. Unfortunately, many Statistics words have a common everyday usage that's not quite the same. We'll be pointing those out as we go along.

Write vocabulary words on the board as they come up. One of the first should be *variable.* Make the point that it does not mean exactly the same thing as it did in Algebra. There, we call "*x*" a variable, but often that means that we just don't currently know its value. In Statistics a variable is an attribute or characteristic of an individual or object whose value varies from case to case.

A *statistic* is a numerical summary of data; one of the first you'll likely hear is that the class is *x*% male. Point out the difference between statistics and data. The book wisecracks that, contrary to an advertised saying, you can't be a statistic, only a datum.

Some students will suggest pie charts or histograms. It's sufficient for now to point out that graphical displays are useful visual summaries of data.

Point out that summaries of data can be verbal, visual, and numerical. All are important. In fact, any complete analysis of data almost always includes all three of these.

After looking at the data from your class survey, some students may say things like, "The males are more conservative." Point out the difference between *univariate* and *bivariate* analysis. Note that bivariate is a lot more interesting.

Hope that someone objects to finding an overall average shoe size or to comparing men's and women's sizes—shoe sizes are inconsistent in terms of units. This adds emphasis to the importance of units and the W's.

## The Importance of What You Don't Say

We are laying a foundation here. Stretching up to the attic at this point just makes everyone feel unsafe. Many fundamental Statistics terms are left unmentioned in this chapter. You'll find it best to leave it that way. We'll get to them when the students have a safe place to file them along with their other knowledge. So we have an unusually long list of terms we recommend leaving for later in the course. In particular, avoid saying the following:

***Population, Sample, Hypothesis, Inference.*** These are certainly important in this course, but we have no background for discussing them honestly now, so they would just be confusing and intimidating.

***Nominal, Ordinal, Interval, Ratio.*** "Nominal" is used by some software packages as a synonym for "categorical" as "continuous" is used for "quantitative." These distinctions arise from studies of measurement scales. But it isn't correct to claim that each variable falls into one of these categories. It is the use to which the data are put that determines what properties the variable must have. Ordinal categorical data may come up, but there are no special techniques for dealing with ordered categories in this course. And any differences between interval- and ratio-scaled data are commonly ignored in statistical analyses. If any of these terms were mentioned now, they'd never come up again anyway.

***Random, Probability, Correlation.*** Everyone has some intuitive sense of these terms, and we'll deal with them formally—but not for a while. Students may want to use these terms, but at this early stage in the course, we don't need them. Without background and careful definition, they are likely to be misused and can simply be frightening.

## Class Examples

1. Ask students to tell some things they learned about the class from inspecting the data collected in the opening-day's survey. You can use that discussion to develop several of the important points of the chapter.
2. Consider 17, 21, 44, and 76. Are those data? Context is critical—they could be test scores, ages in a golf foursome, or uniform numbers of the starting backfield on the football team. In each case, our reaction changes.

3. Run through some other examples of data, asking about the W's, the variables (what are they, what type is each used as, and what are the units), and so on.
   - A *Consumer Reports* article on energy bars gave the brand name, flavor, price, number of calories, and grams of protein and fat.
   - A report on the Boston Marathon listed each runner's gender, country, age, and time.

## RESOURCES
### ActivStats
▸ Start with Chapter 1 to let students familiarize themselves with the features of the software. Chapter 2 examines types of data and context.

### Printed Test Bank and Resource Guide
▸ The *Printed Test Bank and Resource Guide* has three chapter quizzes, activities, and specific teaching suggestions.

### Web Links
▸ Data and Story Library (DASL) is a source of data for student projects and classroom examples.
▸ The U.S. Census Bureau, www.census.gov

### Other
▸ Read polls, studies, or other reports in newspaper and magazine articles. It's always interesting to see how well (or poorly) they provide information about the W's.

If you have a computer and projection capabilities in class, you can find daily surveys at Gallup (www.gallup.com) and other polling organizations (e.g. http://pewresearch.org/). Current data are often particularly interesting to students. But don't use results of voluntary-response online surveys. We'll be making the point that these are fatally flawed—but we can't say that clearly without concepts and terms that we haven't developed yet.

## Instructor's Guide

**CHAPTER 3**

# Displaying Categorical Data

## What's It About?
We introduce students to distributions of categorical variables. The mathematics is easy (summaries are just percentages), and the graphs are straightforward (pie charts and bar graphs). We

challenge students to uncover the story the data tell, and to write about it in complete sentences in context.

Then we up the ante, asking them to compare distributions in two-way tables. Constructing comparative graphs, discussing conditional distributions, and considering (informally) the issue of independence give students a look at issues that require deeper thought, careful analysis, and clear writing.

## Comments

By Chapter 3 it will begin to dawn on your students that this isn't a math class. At the very least, they are going to be expected to write often and clearly. For those who have not yet developed the skill of writing clearly, this may be one of the most valuable things learned in this course.

1. Continue to emphasize precision of vocabulary (and notation). These are an important part of clear communication, critical to success.
2. We find it helpful to emphasize *Think-Show-Tell* right from the start. The key to doing well in Statistics is to think carefully about what each question is asking and what statistical techniques can address those issues before starting to write an answer. And then, after showing some calculations or other work, to write clear and concise explanations of what it all means. Your students may rebel at first at having to write sentences, much less paragraphs, in a course they may have thought was a math class. They are used to just doing the *Show. Tell* is at least 50% of each solution. If you make that point consistently, right from the start of the course, it soon becomes second nature. Continually remind them: *Answers are sentences, not numbers.*
3. This is the first substantial chapter, and it gets pretty involved right away. We deal with conditional distributions, independence, and confounding (Simpson's paradox). It may seem early to bring up such sophisticated concepts, but our experience is that students can get lulled into a false sense of security in the early part of this course if all they see are things like means and histograms that many have dealt with since middle school. They think the course is going to be pretty easy, and they may not see the level of sophistication that is required until it's too late. The ideas in Chapter 3 are not hard, and are introduced only informally, but they do require some thought and present difficulties making clear explanations. We want these ideas to be interesting, to engage imaginations, and to challenge students. We hope the level of thought required will get their attention and arouse their interest.

## Looking Ahead

There are many important skills and ideas here that prepare students for later topics. They need to think about what comparisons will answer questions posed, and write clear explanations in context. They begin to think about independence, one of the most important issues in Statistics. And, in Simpson's paradox, they see the need to think more deeply to avoid being misled by lurking or confounding variables.

## Class Do's

Discuss categorical data and appropriate summaries: numerical (counts/percentages), graphical (pie charts, bar graphs). Discuss *distribution, frequency, relative frequency.*

It gets more interesting when we make comparisons (using bivariate data): e.g., political leanings by gender?

Discuss two-way tables, *marginal* and *conditional* distributions.

Make sure students can correctly sort out (*Think-Show-Tell*) answers to similar-sounding questions:

1. What percent of the class are women with liberal political views?
2. What percent of the liberals are women?
3. What percent of the women are liberals?

Raise the issue of independence. It's not formal independence yet, just the general idea that if gender and political view were independent the percentages for either gender would mirror the class as a whole, or the percentages of Liberal, Moderate, and Conservative would be the same for both genders.

Pay attention in each chapter to the What Can Go Wrong? (WCGW) sections.

Simpson's paradox is fun, but don't overemphasize it. It's not a critical issue, but it's a good discussion point about making valid comparisons and not overlooking lurking or confounding variables.

## The Importance of What You Don't Say

You can see that we are patrolling the perimeter of probability. Concepts like relative frequency, conditional relative frequency, and independence cry out for a formal discussion in probabilistic terms.

Don't heed the cry.

You and we know that we are setting up the habits of thought that students will need for learning about probability. But this isn't the time to discuss the formalities, or even to say the word "probability" out loud. (Notice that the book doesn't use the term in this chapter at all—it'll still be a while before we get to it.) Talk about "relative frequency" instead. In this class probability is a relative frequency, so we are encouraging students to think about the concepts correctly. By the time we introduce formal probability, they will have a sound intuitive foundation.

## Class Examples

1. 200 adults shopping at a supermarket were asked about the highest level of education they had completed and whether or not they smoke cigarettes. Results are summarized in the table. Is there an association between education level and smoking?

| | | Smoker | Nonsmoker | Total |
|---|---|---|---|---|
| Education | High school | 32 | 61 | 93 |
| | 2-yr college | 5 | 17 | 22 |
| | 4+-yr college | 13 | 72 | 85 |
| | Total | 50 | 150 | 200 |

**THINK**   The individuals are 200 shoppers surveyed while they were at a grocery store. We don't know where or when the survey was done, or who did it.

It appears that smokers tend to have lower education levels than nonsmokers. 64% of the smokers had only a high-school education, compared to 40% of nonsmokers. And nonsmokers were almost twice as likely as smokers (48% to 26%) to have completed at least 4 years of college.

2. Is the color distribution of M&Ms independent of type of candy? Break open bags of plain and peanut M&Ms and count the colors. (Then eat the data. . . .)

3. Simpson's paradox example:

It's the last inning of an important game. Your team is a run down, with the bases loaded and two outs. The pitcher is due up, so you'll be sending in a pinch hitter. There are two batters available on the bench. Whom should you send in to bat? First show the students the overall success history of the two players.

| | | Batting Average | | |
|---|---|---|---|---|
| | | **Overall** | **vs. LHP** | **vs. RHP** |
| Player | **A** | 33 for 103 (.320) | 28 for 81 (.346) | 5 for 22 (.227) |
| | **B** | 45 for 151 (.298) | 12 for 32 (.375) | 33 for 119 (.277) |

A's batting average is higher than B's (.320 vs. .298), so he looks like the better choice. Someone, though, will raise the issue that it matters whether the pitcher throws right or left handed. Now add the rest of the table. It turns out that B has a higher batting average against both right- and left-handed pitching, even though his overall average is lower. Students are stunned.

Here's an explanation: B hits better against both right- and left-handed pitchers. So no matter the pitcher, B is a better choice. So why is his batting "average" lower? Because B sees a lot more right-handed pitchers than A, and (at least for these guys) right-handed pitchers are harder to hit. For some reason, A is used mostly against left-handed pitchers, so A has a higher average.

Suppose all you know is that A bats .227 against righties and .346 against lefties. Ask the students to guess his overall batting average. It could be anywhere between .227 and .346, depending on how many righties and lefties he sees. And B's batting average may slide between .277 and .375. These intervals overlap, so it's quite possible that A's batting average is either higher or lower than B's, depending on the mix of pitchers they see.

Pooling (nice word to use . . .) the data together loses important information and leads to the wrong conclusion. We always should take into account any factor that might matter.

4. Refer to Simpson, again. Here's a nice thought problem to pose to the class; give them a few minutes to work it out: Two companies have labor and management classifications of employees. Company A's laborers have a higher average salary than Company B's, as do Company A's managers. But overall Company B pays a higher average salary. How can that be? And which is the better way to compare earning potential at the two companies?

### *Printed Test Bank and Resource Guide*

The *Printed Test Bank and Resource Guide* offers an Investigative Task on Race and the Death Penalty. The Test Bank provides three chapter quizzes.

## CHAPTER 4

### Instructor's Guide

# Displaying and Summarizing Quantitative Data

### What's It About?

In Chapter 4, we turn our attention to quantitative variables. First, we examine visual displays: histograms, stem-and-leaf plots, and dotplots. We want students to learn to describe the important features of a distribution: shape, center, spread, and any unusual features such as outliers, gaps, or clusters. Next, we learn how to summarize the center and spread of a distribution. We start with median and interquartile range because it's always appropriate to describe distributions with these

two statistics. Then we look at mean and standard deviation as special statistics for use with symmetric distributions. We discuss the problems that arise when these statistics are used for skewed data or in the presence of outliers.

### Comments

We continue to focus on understanding and interpretation. Many of the concepts in this chapter are vague—something students might not expect if they were taking a math class. For example, there's no fixed criterion for declaring a distribution to be "skewed" or even "bimodal." How far away must a point get before it is an outlier? Is a gap real if it disappears when we rescale the histogram?

It's a good idea to point out to students that these are deliberately vague concepts. That insight can help students who might otherwise think that they aren't understanding them. Don't underestimate the importance of these vague concepts. Although methods we deal with later for inference require precise distributional assumptions for their *theoretical* background, in *practice* the best we can do is look at the *shape* of histograms to judge whether they are roughly unimodal and symmetric. And we will insist that students do just that before using these advanced methods.

*A Word About Precision.*   Some math-oriented students may show signs of frustration with what they see as lack of precision here. The fact that Statistics has a lot of gray areas may frustrate them.

It may help to point out to your students that Statistics deals with the real world, not *MathWorld*. In *MathWorld*, the bicyclist rides in a straight line along a level road at a constant speed without encountering any air resistance past a tree that stands perpendicular to the ground. For this scenario, there is a "right answer." In Statistics, we liberate ourselves from these unrealistic constraints, but that liberty comes at a price. Uncertainty, caution, and approximation will accompany everything we do. The real world is more complicated—and more interesting—than *MathWorld*.

It is the demands of dealing with the real world that generate the ambiguities in Statistics. We deal with them honestly by maintaining our connection to the real world and by facing the ambiguities head on. The answer is almost never just a number. Instead, it must come with interpretation in terms of context of the data and the questions we asked of the data— the things we considered at the *Think* step and now must report in the *Tell* step.

Even the numbers that are part of the answer may not— indeed, usually cannot—be known with perfect precision. Sometimes the problem is translating an ideal, model-based concept to the reality of a finite sample. We point out in the chapter that many alternative calculations match the ideal definition of a quartile well enough that several are actively in use.[1] They generally converge to the same values for large samples, but the differences for small samples can be striking.

Sometimes the challenge is the reality of computing with real-world numbers. Digital devices such as computers and calculators cannot represent most numbers without some rounding error. Students who round intermediate results (perhaps as part of dutifully showing their work) exacerbate the problem. Statistics calculations are notorious for magnifying the errors introduced by rounding and truncation. For example, rounding the mean to, say, three decimal places and then using it to find the standard deviation can introduce a substantial change in the calculated standard deviation value.

We advise the following:

▸ Don't round or truncate intermediate results. Keep the full precision your technology can carry.

▸ Report statistics to one decimal place more than the precision of the data.

▸ Focus on the meaning in the Tell section and not on minor differences in the numeric results. Don't sweat the small differences.

You may need to reassure your students that their answers need not match those in the back of the book to the last digit and that their interpretation is more important than their calculation.

## Center and Spread

We introduce *center* as the first thing we want to know about a variable. *Spread* is the second thing we want to know. These two numbers, center and spread, should always be reported together.

Emphasize the importance of spread to your students by showing them several histograms with the same center but very different spreads. This gets the point across that you can't describe a variable by using only its center.

In Chapter 6, we'll make it clear that the central concept in all of Statistics is that distances and differences are measured with a ruler based on *spread*. The practical approach we take in this book makes the vague concepts of this chapter central to even the most advanced methods found in the concluding chapters. That may not be what you've seen in older texts where one could fly by these ideas and never look back, but it is the way that practicing statisticians think and work.

*Why y?*   This is the first chapter in which it becomes clear that we use the letter $y$ to denote the variable we are summarizing, about which we would like to know something, or that we are modeling. This won't bother your students, who are not likely to have any preconceived ideas about what letter to use. But it might take you by surprise if you studied Statistics from a text that used $x$ by default or are reading other texts for background. We made this choice with much thought. Most Statistics methods model the world with equations. Once we get beyond one-variable summaries, the Statistics convention is to denote the variable that is being modeled, described, or predicted as $y$ and to plot it on the vertical axis of graphs. We consistently use $x$ (and even $x_1, x_2, \ldots$) to denote the variables that describe, predict, or model $y$. Why should we do otherwise when we consider only one variable? We want to emphasize that we are modeling the world through Statistics. The consistency of naming the variable that we model $y$ whenever we need a generic letter helps to convey that message.

As a purely practical matter, if we had used $x$ in early chapters, we'd have had to switch to modeling $y$ for Chapters 7, 8, and 9, then back to $x$ for the early chapters on inference, and back again to $y$ for regression inference and beyond. That seemed unnecessarily confusing.

Nevertheless, it may be worth pointing out the choice to your students. Other textbooks do use $x$, as do some statistics packages and some functions on the TI calculator.

## Looking Ahead

Almost everything we do in Statistics starts by making a picture of the data. We'll be making histograms and other displays to check out our data in almost every chapter of the book. Visual displays can reveal things that the data itself and

---

[1] At least *six* different definitions are in use by different programs.

numerical summaries may miss or hide. You may want to invite your students to thumb through the book to see how often we show displays of data even in the later chapters, and even in the exercises. They should be encouraged to understand that these skills and concepts are fundamental and will be used throughout the course.

The notion that we need to look at the data—a histogram, for example—before deciding which descriptive statistics are appropriate is important in a broader sense. Every statistical method we encounter will require some underlying assumptions. We should not forge ahead blindly until we *Think* about whether those assumptions are reasonable in our situation. Often we need to check some conditions before proceeding. Making a histogram of the data to rule out skewness, multiple modes, and outliers before finding the mean and standard deviation sets the stage for other such checks that we'll require later on.

Concepts introduced here will be covered in more depth soon. We'll look at a rule for identifying outliers in Chapter 5, and we'll explore more deeply the importance of one measure of spread, the standard deviation, in Chapter 6.

We'll also use re-expressions of data to accomplish a variety of objectives in several chapters, most notably in constructing regression models. Chapter 5 offers the first glimpse of what lies ahead. We'll return to the idea in subsequent chapters, pull the concepts together in Chapter 10, and then use these methods as needed later in the course.

## Class Do's

Continue to build students' vocabularies. There are many terms that are critical to sound understanding and clear communication. We can't *Think, Show,* or *Tell* without understanding and using the proper terminology. Write vocabulary words on the board as they come up: *uniform, unimodal, bimodal, symmetric, skewed, cluster, gap, outlier.*

Many students will think that skewness is backwards—that the body rather than the tail should determine whether we say a distribution is skewed left or right. If you liken "skewed" to "strewn," it can help. The bulk of people's incomes are low, but a histogram looks as though a few have been strewn further to the right of the main body—hence "skewed to the right." (Think Bill Gates and Oprah Winfrey.) It might be a good time to talk about the difference between skewed and biased (although bias won't come back until Chapter 12). News media and others sometimes use "skewed" to mean "biased."

Students have better intuition about distributions than they may realize. Exercises 5 and 6 in this chapter demonstrate that fact. Exercises in which students see that they can indeed picture what a distribution ought to look like just from knowing what has been measured and how (and something about the world) help them realize that they can understand and work with these vague concepts.

Ask students when to use a bar graph and when to use a histogram. They have to *Think* about the type of variable before getting on with the *Show*. And be sure they understand that bars represent piles of data. We often see ill-conceived displays in which a bar is used for each datum.

Get students to *Think* about why one might prefer one type of graph to another. In what ways are stem-and-leaf displays, dotplots, and histograms all similar? What information is apparent in some but not others? What are the advantages and disadvantages of using each type of graph?

Be sure that students learn to look for all the important aspects of a distribution. The shape, center, and spread describe different features. No description is complete without talking about all three, and adding comments about any unusual features such as outliers, gaps, or clusters.

Present the summary statistics as ways of describing center and spread. Group them that way: first median and IQR, then mean and standard deviation. Median and IQR are appropriate for any data. Mean and standard deviation are a bit more powerful, as they have some important mathematical properties we can exploit. But we cannot use mean and standard deviation effectively when the data are strongly skewed or outliers are present.

When reporting measures of center and spread, use statistics that "go together." Median and IQR are the same type of measurement, based on positions in the data. Likewise, mean and standard deviation are based on the size of the data, so they should be paired. We would not talk about, say, median and standard deviation together.

Focus on the meaning of the quartiles rather than on the details of calculation. There are alternative methods for finding the quartiles. Some sources advise including the median in each half of the data; others leave it out entirely. In large data sets, this is rarely an issue. Tell students that they should clearly state their choice of method if there can be any doubt about the answer.

Students often misuse the terms "range" and "interquartile range," mistakenly thinking these are intervals rather than numbers. They will say things like "His test score was in the IQR" when they mean the score was between the first and third quartiles (or within the middle 50% of all scores). As always, clear and correct use of the vocabulary is critical.

Be sure students understand the effect of outliers on summary statistics. When there is an outlier in the data, the mean, range, and standard deviation can change a lot. The median and IQR are more stable, and therefore better descriptors in the presence of outliers.

More generally, be sure students understand the relationship between the median and the mean in skewed distributions. Once they see that a high outlier can raise the mean without having much impact on the median, it's easy to talk about skewed distributions; maybe there's no outlier, but there are several unusually large values. When they see that the median divides the area in half, but does not provide a balance point for the distribution, it becomes clearer why we use different summaries for skewed distributions.

Students who check assumptions and conditions before proceeding are more likely to deal properly with outliers, skewness, and other issues. Keep requiring this key step.

It may help some students to calculate a few standard deviations by hand—but don't do many. This is not an essential skill. It's more important that they know how to have a calculator or statistics package find SDs, and even more important that they grasp what is being measured.

Remind students that summarizing distributions, or comparing them, still requires discussion of shape, center, spread, and unusual features. As always, answers are sentences, not numbers.

Emphasize and practice verbal descriptions of distributions that observe the four C's: clear, complete, concise, and in context.

## The Importance of What You Don't Say

***Don't teach "measures of center," then "measures of spread."*** Students should think of these statistics in pairs that describe center and spread: median and IQR, or mean and standard deviation.

***Don't say "Measure of central tendency."***   At this point, without a Law of Large Numbers, there's no "tending" involved. The mean and median are measures of center; the IQR and standard deviation are measures of spread. Simpler, shorter phrases encourage correct use.

Many students will have heard about three centers: mean, median, and mode. *Don't make a big deal out of trying to attach a number to the mode.* Especially in a small data set, this can be problematic. A single data value that is repeated can be declared the "mode" even when it is nowhere near the middle hump of a unimodal distribution. Also, the value of the mode can be changed simply by how much the data are rounded. We care more about the overall shape of a histogram, and especially if it tells us there are two commonly occurring clusters of data rather than just one. It's the *number* of modes that matters, not the numerical value of a mode.

***Don't fret over the different ways to find quartiles.***   There are many different ways to find quartiles. Some include the median in both halves (as we recommend in the text); some exclude it (the TI, for example). Still others use various methods of interpolation. This means two things: (1) Different methods don't always agree with each other about the precise values of the quartiles, and (2) it really doesn't matter. The values will usually differ very little, especially for large data sets. Our goal is to get a feel for the story the data tell. Knowing (say) that the upper quartile of incomes is around $45,000 paints the picture we want. It's really irrelevant that the book's method finds Q3 to be $45,103 and the calculator says it's $45,104.50. Close enough.

***Don't get hung up over the divisor of (n − 1) in the formula for standard deviation.***   It's an issue we'll discuss in more detail later in the course. Some students accept it willingly, others grudgingly. You can appeal to the fact that if the mean is used in the calculation, then only $n - 1$ of the $n$ scores are actually free to vary. Or you can discuss the fact that using $n$ in finding standard deviations of small groups would underestimate the variability actually present in the larger groups they represent—and this is perfectly compensated for by dividing by $n - 1$.

***Don't get hung up on calculating the standard deviation by hand.***   That's what the technology is for. It's far more important that students understand what the standard deviation says about the distribution.

***Don't worry about always reporting answers to a fixed number of decimal places.***   This is the real world, not *MathWorld*. We simply can't find an average height to the nearest thousandth of an inch. Just keep a reasonable number of significant digits when rounding off, and be careful about using rounded values in future calculations.

***Don't offer rules for deciding when a point is an outlier, when a distribution is bimodal, or what constitutes skewness.*** We'll talk about a rule for deciding about outliers in Chapter 5. Until then, encourage students to describe unusual values in a histogram as "possible" outliers. Consider quiz questions for which the "correct" answer isn't clear and alternative interpre-

tations can be considered if they are explained and defended appropriately.

## Class Examples and Activities

1. Use the data you collected the first day. There are many distributions you can compare:
   - Make a dotplot of the number of siblings. It will be skewed to the right.
   - Make a histogram of the number of states visited.
   - Compare heights for males and females. (Or use shoe sizes.) Point out the importance of having the same scale for both graphs.
   - Describe the center, spread, and any unusual features in each of these variables.

2. Spend a while discussing stem-and-leaf displays, especially how to create stems and leaves for data with various orders of magnitude and ranges. For example:
   - A stem-and-leaf display of quiz scores (out of 100) is probably okay if done in the obvious way, tens digit for the stems and units digits as leaves.
   - A stem-and-leaf display of states visited might benefit from splitting the stems: 0–4, 5–9, etc. You can compare the distribution for males and females with back-to-back stem-and-leaf displays.
   - A stem-and-leaf display of students' weights (in pounds) should split 145 as 14 (stem) and 5 (leaf), but a stem-and-leaf display of SAT scores should split 520 as 5 (stem) and 2 (leaf). We might want to split the stems as well (into lower 500s and upper 500s). A stem-and-leaf display of heights may split the "4," "5," and "6" stems into two or even five lines each.
   - A stem-and-leaf display of weights of cattle (1000–2000 pounds) should probably split 1368 pounds as 13 (stem) and 6 (leaf), ignoring the 8. It's quicker to truncate than to round off, and it makes little difference in the shape.

3. Compare two histograms or two dotplots, asking which has a larger SD.
   - Compare the distributions of heights for right-handed and left-handed students. For which group do we have a better idea of the center? Why?

4. Collect some data and plot them.
   - (Yet another way to use M&Ms!) Buy a bunch of the little bags and count the number of candies and their colors. (Save these data for analysis in later chapters.)
   - Get a good scale from your Science faculty and weigh the bags. If you get a really sensitive scale, weigh individual candies.
   - Weigh pennies. The mint changed from copper to zinc in the early 1980s, so the distribution of weights is bimodal—a surprise. You could use these weights (in grams), but the lesson is much more compelling if your class does it themselves.

2.57 2.56 3.14 3.03 3.13 2.47 2.43 3.11 3.06 2.48
2.51 2.50 3.07 3.08 3.01 2.45 2.50 3.13 2.51 3.12
3.10 3.08 2.46 2.44 2.47 2.54 3.09 3.13 2.56 2.49

## Solution

**THINK** We are assuming that these pennies are a representative sample of all pennies minted.

| Group | Light | Heavy |
|-------|-------|-------|
| Count | 16 | 14 |
| Min | 2.43 | 3.01 |
| Max | 2.57 | 3.14 |
| Mean | 2.496 | 3.091 |
| SD | 0.044 | 0.039 |
| Median | 2.495 | 3.095 |
| Q1 | 2.465 | 3.07 |
| Q3 | 2.525 | 3.13 |
| IQR | 0.06 | 0.06 |

**TELL** The distribution of weights of pennies is bimodal. About half of the pennies are in the lighter cluster, which is roughly symmetric with a median weight of 2.495g. Half of the lighter pennies weigh between 2.465g and 2.525g. The rest of the pennies are in the heavier cluster, which is slightly skewed to the left with a median weight of 3.095g. Half of the heavier pennies weigh between 3.07g and 3.13g. Each group has an interquartile range of 0.06g. A little research tells us that the mint stopped using copper and started using zinc in the early 1980s. What we thought was one population of pennies was actually two: those minted before the switch and those minted after the switch. (Note that we used the median and IQR to describe the lighter cluster, even though it was symmetric. That's because we were comparing it to the heavier cluster, in which we had to use the median and IQR.)

▸ A look at home sales records at your city or county clerk's office, or a scan of the real-estate ads, can give you data about home values in your area. These data will almost certainly be skewed, with many low and moderately priced homes and fewer very expensive homes. Such data can often be made more symmetric with a logarithmic re-expression.

5. To help establish the concept of what the standard deviation measures, have students calculate a few by hand. Consider this scenario: A class has been divided into groups of five students each. The groups have completed an independent study project, and at the end they take an individual 20-point quiz. Here are the scores, by group:

| | Group | | | | | |
|---|---|---|---|---|---|---|
| | **1** | **2** | **3** | **4** | **5** | **6** |
| **Quiz Scores (out of 20)** | 10 | 8 | 0 | 0 | 0 | 4 |
| | 10 | 10 | 10 | 8 | 2 | 6 |
| | 10 | 10 | 10 | 10 | 10 | 8 |
| | 10 | 10 | 10 | 12 | 18 | 14 |
| | 10 | 12 | 20 | 20 | 20 | 18 |

Note that all the means are 10. Center alone cannot describe the differences we see among these groups. Note also that three of the groups have ranges of 20, yet we see clear differences in how far the scores are spread from the mean. The SD for group 1 is certainly 0. Hand-calculate the SD for group 2. Note that it's only slightly larger, indicating a little more spread. Have the class calculate the other SDs and talk about how the SD reflects the spread in the scores.

## Solution

| Summary of For categories in No Selector | **Quiz Score Group** | | |
|---|---|---|---|
| Group | Mean | StdDev | Range |
| **Group1** | 10 | 0 | 0 |
| **Group2** | 10 | 1.41421 | 4 |
| **Group3** | 10 | 7.07107 | 20 |
| **Group4** | 10 | 7.21110 | 20 |
| **Group5** | 10 | 9.05539 | 20 |
| **Group6** | 10 | 5.83095 | 14 |

The standard deviation measures spread. Generally, distributions that are more spread out have higher standard deviations. For example, Group 4 is more spread out than Group 3 and therefore has a higher standard deviation. Standard deviation is a good measure of spread when distributions are roughly symmetric with no outliers. Standard deviation probably isn't a good summary of spread for Group 6.

## RESOURCES

### Activity-Based Statistics

▸ "Matching Plots to Variables" defines a variable and asks students to guess what kind of shape the distribution might take.

### *ActivStats*

▸ Chapter 4 activities teach students to construct stem-and-leaf displays, dotplots, and histograms, and to describe distributions.

▸ The activity on standard deviations is a nice introduction, explaining the process and saving you from having to explain the formula. Both the activities on centers and those on spreads let students drag points to see the influence of outliers and individual points on alternative measures of center and spread. A few minutes with these activities can be much more effective than any abstract discussion of the effects of outliers on these statistics.

### *Printed Test Bank and Resource Guide*

The *Printed Test Bank and Resource Guide* offers a worksheet for an Investigative Task on the average amount spent per

student by public schools in each state. Students are guided in writing a report on their analysis. The Test Bank provides three chapter quizzes.

### Web Links

▸ At the U.S. Census Bureau's International Data Base (CIDB), you can create population pyramids for any country and any year (and even animate the changes).

▸ http://www.stat.tamu.edu/~west/ has an applet for playing with histogram bin widths.

▸ You can find an applet to explore the relationship between mean and median at http://www.stat.tamu.edu/~west/

▸ A nice collection of good and bad statistical graphs can be found at the Gallery of Data Visualization. (www.math.yorku.ca/SCS/Gallery/)

▸ For still more data sets, try the Data and Story Library. (http://lib.stat.cmu/DASL/)

## Instructor's Guide

CHAPTER

# 5

# Understanding and Comparing Distributions

## What's It About?

In Chapter 4, students summarized the distribution of a single variable by displaying and describing its shape and by finding numerical summaries of center and spread. In Chapter 5 they get to compare distributions and look for trends and patterns in centers and spreads. Throughout the book we'll follow this habit, presenting fundamental ideas for describing a single variable and then generalizing them to talk about relationships, differences, and trends.

Here we want to whet students' appetites. There's a lot to be learned just from comparing groups. The story in this chapter is made even more intriguing because we look at the same data at different levels of aggregation, seeing something new each time. So behind the new methods is the lesson that how you structure your data can matter a great deal.

We examine the average daily wind speed and other weather data recorded in a single year in the Hopkins Forest of western Massachusetts. We start with the overall distribution, noting its shape, center, and spread as we learned to do in Chapter 4. The chapter introduces 5-number summaries (extremes, quartiles, and median) and uses them to construct boxplots. We define a rule of thumb for nominating possible

outliers. The rule is based on the quartiles, which have the advantage of not being influenced by outliers. They also allow the nomination rule to be asymmetric around the median, stretching out farther on one side of the center if the data are skewed and the quartile on that side is farther from the center.

This is a very useful rule, which has been validated in simulation studies. Nevertheless, it is a rule of thumb and not a *definition* of "outlier." "Outlierhood" is one of those judgments that we are called on to make, take responsibility for, and defend if necessary.

We split the year into two halves and compare the distributions within the two groups. Then we split things still further into months to see annual patterns in both center and spread. This aggregation level reveals outliers, one of which we can identify as a major blizzard. Finally, we get down to the individual observations and consider patterns and trends over time. Timeplots, of course, set up the use of scatterplots in Chapter 7, but for now we just talk about trends over time.

The chapter ends with an optional introduction to data re-expression. At this point, we mostly want to show that it works, without discussing how or why.

## Looking Ahead

Whenever we compare groups, it is natural to use the spread as a background measure of how big a difference is "real." Encourage that line of thinking; it will be fundamental throughout the course (and indeed, throughout all of Statistics).

When we compare boxpots, students should discuss several aspects. The first one they'll see is how the centers compare. Perhaps more important is how the spreads change. And, of course, they should note and discuss any outliers. Later in the course we'll use boxplots when we test independent groups for differences between means, and these will be precisely the aspects we'll care about. Students who go on to learn about analysis of variance (for example, using the chapter on the DVD), will *always* make boxplots before computing the ANOVA.

## Class Do's

Insist that when students compare groups with boxplots, they discuss the centers, the spreads, any outliers, and the overall shapes in their *Tell* step.

This is the place to discuss the *concept* of an outlier. Point out that whether a point appears to be an outlier can depend on how we define the group to which we compare it. Outliers seem to come and go in these data as we aggregate differently. Does this mean they weren't "really" outliers? Or is the concept of "outlier" sensible only relative to some base group?

When we re-express a skewed variable, points that seemed at first to be outliers may, in the re-expressed form, be simply part of the tail of the distribution. Were they not "really" outliers?

Generally, an outlier is a point that genuinely doesn't belong with the rest of the data. Of course, that means we must define "rest of the data" appropriately. If the data stretch out in a consistent (but thinning) pattern from the third quartile to the maximum, and the maximum is just barely beyond the fences but not otherwise unusual, then you'll probably elect not to call it an outlier. On the other hand, if the maximum is widely separated from the other data values, yet just inside the fence, by all means, it's an outlier. An outlier that is no longer extraordinary after the data are re-expressed to be more nearly symmetric is often not really different. When we can identify a point as truly different—as we do with the blizzard days in the wind speed data—then we can be reasonably sure it should not be analyzed along with the other data values.

## The Importance of What You Don't Say

***Don't ignore or "throw away" outliers.*** Outliers can affect data summaries, but we can't just toss them aside. If they are errors, we should correct them (if possible) or set them aside. Outliers are often the most interesting values in a data set because they don't follow the same pattern as the other values. We should call attention to them, not conceal them. The best policy when we identify an outlier is to make note of it and gather more information about it if possible. If you can't identify a reason for that point to be different, then do the calculations with and without the outlier to see how much effect it has on your results.

***Don't use the word "trend" if time is not a variable.*** It can help to keep in mind the difference between "trend" and

"tend." There is a clear trend of increasing numbers of girls involved in sports since the passage of Title IX—it is changing over time. Nonetheless, in general, men tend to be stronger physically than women. That's a tendency, not a trend, since there's no time element involved.

## Class Examples

1. If you ever need an example of skewed data, just take a look at baseball salaries. The mean salary for players in 2003 was $2.5 million, but the median was $800,000. Also, Alex Rodriguez made more money ($22 million) than the entire Tampa Bay Devil Rays team ($19.5 million).
2. Use the data you collected at the start of the year—states visited or number of siblings. Find 5-number summaries, make boxplots, check for outliers, and compare the mean and median.
3. You can also use your data on the count and weight of M&Ms.
4. Here are the weekly payrolls for two imaginary restaurants, Mooseburgers and McTofu. Ask students to draw parallel boxplots and write sentences comparing the distributions. Ask them to decide where they would rather work, and explain why.

| Mooseburgers | | McTofu | |
|---|---|---|---|
| Al | $123 | Ken | $110 |
| Boris | $136 | Latisha | $115 |
| Connie | $144 | Maria | $130 |
| Dwight | $150 | Nate | $100 |
| Ernie | $110 | Otto | $120 |
| François | $131 | Pablo | $146 |
| Gloria | $140 | Quentin | $117 |
| Horace | $160 | Rosa | $129 |
| Isaac | $120 | Sally | $360 |
| Juan | $130 | Ted | $132 |
| | | Uta | $107 |

5. Spend some time matching histograms or dotplots to boxplots; it's a good way to help students see what these displays say.
6. If you haven't done so yet, it's time to get students working with statistical software. By now they can create pie charts, histograms, and boxplots, and they can calculate summary statistics. We offer a *Data Desk* lab activity that uses the Students datafile on your *ActivStats* CD and some of the class data. Some aspects of our instructions may be system-specific and hence require modification for your computers—or for different software or a different data set, of course. Our lab can at least provide you with some ideas, we hope. We also offer some *Data Desk* tips on the back of the lab, to help students use the software with their own data. They won't need all of the tips now, but the rest will be useful later on.

*ActivStats*

▸ Watch how boxplots are constructed.

**Activity-Based Statistics**

▸ "Matching Statistics to Plots" asks students to match histograms to boxplots and also asks them to match summary statistics to histograms. The latter is a challenge best used after students have had lots of experience with summary statistics, especially the standard deviation.

*Printed Test Bank and Resource Guide*

▸ The *Printed Test Bank and Resource Guide* offers a worksheet for an in-class activity; reproduce it and hand it around. To help students become more comfortable on the computer, there's a step-by-step worksheet that leads them through an analysis on *Data Desk* and a page of *Data Desk* tips. Then

you'll find an Investigative Task on auto safety (and a grading key). And, of course, the Test Bank provides three chapter quizzes.

**Web Links**

▸ You can get more weather data from the Williams College Center for Environmental Studies at http://oit.williams.edu/weather/archives.cfm.

▸ The *Chance* Data Sets provide data for the number of births on each day of the year. Plotted as a histogram, the distribution is bimodal. As a timeplot, another pattern emerges. (You'll find many other data sets there, too. www.dartmouth.edu/~chance/teaching_aids/data.html)

▸ The Data and Story Library (http://dasl.datadesk.com) has a large number of complex data sets suitable for comparing several groups.

**Instructor's Guide**

**CHAPTER 6**

# The Standard Deviation as a Ruler and the Normal Model

## What's It About?

Chapter 6 looks at the effects of shifting and scaling on summary statistics. We explore further the importance of standard deviation as a measure of spread, showing that it serves as a universal yardstick for measuring variables. And we introduce the Normal curve as a useful model for some variables whose distributions are unimodal and symmetric.

This chapter concludes Part I of the text. We provide a Quick Review of the concepts encountered so far, and a large collection of review exercises.

## Comments

Although students need to develop some mechanical skills, the underlying concepts in this chapter should be your main focus. They'll show up repeatedly throughout the rest of the course.

The first concept involves changing numerical data by adding (or subtracting) a constant and/or by multiplying (or dividing) by one. We do this often, changing units or re-expressing our data. We need to know how these changes will affect the summary statistics, and recognize that location and spread are not affected the same way.

The second concept, standardizing, allows us—literally—to compare apples to oranges. In Chapter 4, students learned how to calculate a standard deviation and to recognize that it describes the spread of the data. In Chapter 5, we compared spreads of different groups. We now show how using the standard deviation as a unit of measurement provides us with a universal yardstick. This yardstick enables comparisons of widely different measurements. More important later on, it

allows us to decide if the results of a study are unusually different from what we might have expected—the very essence of statistical inference.

At its heart, inference involves looking at sample data and trying to guess what's actually going on in a population. It is vitally important that students be able to see that such comparisons involve known, observed data on the one hand and unknown—indeed, unknowable—facts about the world on the other. To help make that distinction we have adopted the term "model" to represent these images of theoretical perfection, as distinguished from what we observe. In class, begin now to draw the lines of distinction between these two worlds. The difference between what we see in actual data and conjectures we make about the world is a central issue throughout this course, and something students often confuse. It will appear again when we build linear models to fit scatterplots, when we do simulations, when we formally discuss probability, and throughout inference.

You can start now to establish the idea that statisticians talk about models, and that these models differ from real data. We will build on this understanding over and over. It is one of the central unifying themes of the book.

We don't spend much time on the Normal tables. There is a table (Table Z[1]) at the back of the book, but there is little need

---

[1] We've never understood why statistics tables should be numbered or lettered arbitrarily rather than mnemonically. Our Normal table is table Z, our Chi-square table, table X, and our t-table . . . , well, you get the idea. You won't have to look in the back of the book to name a table.

to drill students extensively in its use. Most calculators serve the purpose more conveniently, as does any major statistics package and the *ActivStats* program on the DVD. The book calls the Normal table a "desert island" method—something we might do if we were stranded far from technology and desperately needed a Normal percentile. In fact, the people who still use Normal tables fall into two categories:

1. Students in introductory Statistics classes, and
2. Teachers writing homework exercises for (1)

Emphasize instead the 68–95–99.7 Rule and encourage them to use technology otherwise.

## Looking Ahead

We hardly have to promise to get back to $z$-scores and the Normal model. But the really important concept here is the standard deviation as a ruler. That idea is central to all of Statistics, whether in this course or in a course in multivariate statistical methods. Be sure to let students know that they'll see it again and again. And, if they understand it now, they'll find many things that come up later look just like something they already have under their belts.

It's important to require students to justify the use of a Normal model. The assumption that a Normal model is appropriate should be specified in the exercise or verified by checking the corresponding Nearly Normal Condition that the distribution of the data is roughly unimodal and symmetric. We'll encounter many situations where we must check some conditions to verify underlying assumptions before going forward with some statistical procedure.

## Class Do's

With a little thought, students will see how changes in scale affect summary statistics. It boils down to whether we are merely shifting the data (a translation) or rescaling it (a dilation). Don't be afraid to use geometric or algebraic intuition. Translating any geometric shape or a function to the left or right leaves an object the same size but just positioned elsewhere. The same is true of a distribution of data (think histogram). Sliding it a few units left or right relocates the center, max, min, and quartiles but leaves the size (spread) the same. A dilation of a triangle or a function from the origin both relocates it and changes its size. A rescaling of a histogram therefore resizes everything about it, now including its spread.

Emphasize the usefulness of standard deviations as units of measurement. It's commonly said that one can't compare apples to oranges. But actually we can, and all it takes is a standard deviation. An apple and an orange might each weigh 12 ounces, but if that makes the apple 2 standard deviations above the mean weight for apples while the orange is only 1 standard deviation above the mean weight for oranges, then the apple is comparatively bigger. Most students know this intuitively. The idea that we can standardize deviations from mean values is very powerful, and essential to the rest of Statistics. You'll want to spend enough time working on this idea to be sure students grasp the concept—not just the mechanics! Just finding a $z$-score of $-1.5$ is not enough; have students *Tell* you that such-and-such is $1\frac{1}{2}$ standard deviations below the mean.

Do use the "model" terminology. We carry the models theme throughout the text. Emphasize the difference between a distribution and a model.

| Distribution | Model |
|---|---|
| real data | theoretical values |
| observed | imagined |
| histogram | mathematical curve |
| statistics | parameters |
| center $\bar{y}$ | center $\mu$ |
| spread $s$ | spread $\sigma$ |

To quote George Box, "All models are wrong, but some are useful." One very useful model is the Normal. No data are ever Normally distributed, but when data are roughly unimodal and symmetric, a Normal model may provide some useful insights. Make students justify their use of a Normal model (with a histogram that is unimodal and symmetric, or a reasonably straight Normal probability plot) before they apply it.

Spend time with the 68–95–99.7 Rule. Having students draw and label models can help them develop a feel for what standard deviations tell them about distributions for which Normal models are appropriate. Don't be in a great rush to get to tables or technology.

Have students work with $z$-scores. Understanding what a $z$-score is and developing a feel for how $z$-scores relate to probabilities are skills that provide valuable insights into much of what we do later in the course (including correlation and regression, confidence intervals, and hypothesis testing).

Remember our "make a picture" rule. Every problem students do that involves a Normal model—including all the exercises that ask them to use $z$-scores to determine probabilities, means, standard deviations, or cutoffs—needs an accompanying picture. Students will understand what they are doing sooner and spot errors more easily if you insist on this. And we will insist on it later in the book when we work with models that require Normally distributed data or errors. (Glance ahead at the Step-by-Steps in Chapter 23, for example.)

Again, expect students to read the chapter. We hope by now that they are engaged in reading the book and have seen how helpful it can be. This chapter has many new ideas and important skills. The narrative, the Step-By-Step worked examples, and the What Can Go Wrong? sections are all intended to be part of the process of building understanding.

## The Importance of What You Don't Say

This chapter touches on a number of topics that you will probably recognize as central to Statistics. But it isn't time to discuss them yet. Please don't distract students with advanced concepts that they are not yet ready for. We have important principles to establish now. We'll get to the more advanced application of these principles in due time.

***Density.*** We have in fact introduced a Normal density, but that formal concept isn't actually needed in this course. By contrast, the concept of a model is fundamental. Push that term instead. Discussing the Normal model reminds students of its function in this course as an idealized model.

***Empirical Rule.*** The name "68–95–99.7 Rule" is more useful because it carries the important numbers. The rule is "empirical" only for historical reasons; that name carries no useful information or mnemonic.

***Probability.*** We are still talking about relative frequencies or areas under a curve. We'll get to probability, but not for a number of chapters yet. We don't yet have a good place for students to "hang" the concepts they'll need.

***Critical Value.*** That's an idea that shows up in inference, but it doesn't belong here.

***Normal Data.*** No data are ever or can ever be Normal. The Normal model can serve as a useful way of thinking about data, but the model is not the data. Always make this distinction clear.

Finally, as we explained earlier, try not to get hung up making students learn to use the Normal table. It's a nice backup when the calculator fails, but it's unlikely they'll ever use one otherwise.

## Class Examples

1. Suppose the class took a 40-point quiz. Results show a mean score of 30, median 32, IQR 8, SD 6, min 12, and Q1 27. (Suppose YOU got a 35.) What happens to each of the statistics if . . .
   - I decide to weight the quiz as 50 points, and will add 10 points to every score. Your score is now 45.
   - I decide to weight the quiz as 80 points, and double each score. Your score is now 70.
   - I decide to count the quiz as 100 points; I'll double each score and add 20 points. Your score is now 90.

2. Let's talk about scoring the decathlon. Silly example, but suppose two competitors tie in each of the first eight events. In the ninth event, the high jump, one clears the bar 1 in. higher. Then in the 1500-meter run the other one runs 5 seconds faster. Who wins? It boils down to knowing whether it is harder to jump an inch higher or run 5 seconds faster. We have to be able to compare two fundamentally different activities involving different units. Standard deviations to the rescue! If we knew the mean performance (by world-class athletes) in each event, and the standard deviation, we could compute how far each performance was from the mean in SD units (called z-scores). So consider the three athletes' performances shown below in a three-event competition. Note that each placed first, second, and third in an event. Who gets the gold medal? Who turned in the most remarkable performance of the competition?

| Competitor | Event | | |
|---|---|---|---|
| | 100-m dash | Shot put | Long jump |
| A | 10.1 sec | 66' | 26' |
| B | 9.9 sec | 60' | 27' |
| C | 10.3 sec | 63' | 27'3" |
| Mean | 10.0 sec | 60' | 26' |
| SD | 0.2 sec | 3' | 6" |

3. Sketch Normal models using the 68–95–99.7 Rule:
   - Birth weights of babies, $N(7.6 \text{ lb}, 1.3 \text{ lb})$
   - ACT scores at a certain college, $N(21.2, 4.4)$

4. Use knowledge of Normal models to guess plausible standard deviations for common variables: height of 16-year-old girls, weight of high-school boys, current price of gasoline. You can base such estimates on a general knowledge that the distributions are likely to be unimodal and symmetric, then estimate that the range (excepting *very* extreme cases) is probably about ±3 standard deviations wide. Why can't we do this for the data we collected about number of states visited?

5. Examine your M&Ms data. Are the number of candies or the weights plausibly Normal?

6. Suppose a Normal model describes the fuel efficiency of cars currently registered in your state. The mean is 24 mpg, with a standard deviation of 6 mpg.
   - Sketch the Normal model.
   - What percent of all cars get less than 15 mpg?
   - What percent of all cars get between 20 and 30 mpg?
   - What percent of cars get more than 40 mpg?
   - Describe the fuel efficiency of the worst 20% of all cars.
   - What gas mileage represents the third quartile?
   - Describe the gas mileage of the most efficient 5% of all cars.
   - What gas mileage would you consider unusual? Why?

7. Consider the fuel economy model again: N(24,6). Sketch pictures as you answer these questions.
   - What percent of cars get under 20 mpg?
   - An ecology group is lobbying for a national goal calling for no more than 10% of all cars to have a fuel efficiency of less than 20 mpg. If the SD does not change, what average fuel efficiency must be attained?
   - Car manufacturers argue that they cannot raise the average that much—they can only reach 26 mpg. What standard deviation would allow them to meet the "only 10% under 20 mpg" goal?
   - What change in the fuel economy of cars would that standard deviation bring about? What are the advantages and disadvantages?

## RESOURCES

### Web Links

▸ If you want some math background on the derivation of the Normal model, look at the math talks on the NCSSM courses Web site. (http://courses.ncssm.edu/math/talks/index.htm)

### *ActivStats*

▸ Chapter 6 explores Normal models. It introduces a tool that allows students to drag cut points on a Normal curve and see the resulting areas under the curve. It also introduces an interactive Normal table in which the illustration at the top of the table adjusts to correspond to the selected $z$-score to help students understand how to read and use Table Z in the book. This can be a good tool for in-class demonstrations if you have projection equipment.

## Printed Test Bank and Resource Guide

The *Printed Test Bank and Resource Guide* has worksheets for an Investigative Task about Normal models. This is the end of Part I, so the Test Bank has three Part Tests covering Chapters 1–6.

# Stats Starts Here[1]

Statistics gets no respect. People say things like "You can prove anything with Statistics." People will write off a claim based on data as "just a statistical trick." And Statistics courses don't have the reputation of being students' first choice for a fun elective.

But Statistics *is* fun. That's probably not what you heard on the street, but it's true. Statistics is about how to think clearly with data. A little practice thinking statistically is all it takes to start seeing the world more clearly and accurately.

## So, What Is (Are?) Statistics?

Q: What is Statistics?
A: Statistics is a way of reasoning, along with a collection of tools and methods, designed to help us understand the world.
Q: What are statistics?
A: Statistics (plural) are particular calculations made from data.
Q: So what is data?
A: You mean, "what *are* data?" Data is the plural form. The singular is datum.
Q: OK, OK, so what are data?
A: Data are values along with their context.

*"But where shall I begin?" asked Alice. "Begin at the beginning," the King said gravely, "and go on till you come to the end: then stop."*

—Lewis Carroll,
*Alice's Adventures
in Wonderland*

It seems every time we turn around, someone is collecting data on us, from every purchase we make in the grocery store, to every click of our mouse as we surf the Web. The United Parcel Service (UPS) tracks every package it ships from one place to another around the world and stores these records in a giant database. You can access part of it if you send or receive a UPS package. The database is about 17 terabytes big—about the same size as a database that contained every book in the Library of Congress would be. (But, we suspect, not *quite* as interesting.) What can anyone hope to do with all these data?

Statistics plays a role in making sense of the complex world in which we live today. Statisticians assess the risk of genetically engineered foods or of a new drug being considered by the Food and Drug Administration (FDA). They predict the number of new cases of AIDS by

---

[1] This chapter might have been called "Introduction," but nobody reads the introduction, and we wanted you to read this. We feel safe admitting this here, in the footnote, because nobody reads footnotes either.

> The ads say, "Don't drink and drive; you don't want to be a statistic." But you can't be a statistic.
> We say: "Don't be a datum."

regions of the country or the number of customers likely to respond to a sale at the mall. And statisticians help scientists and social scientists understand how unemployment is related to environmental controls, whether enriched early education affects later performance of school children, and whether vitamin C really prevents illness. Whenever there are data and a need for understanding the world, you need Statistics.

So our objectives in this book are to help you develop the insights to think clearly about the questions, use the tools to show what the data are saying, and acquire the skills to tell clearly what it all means.

*FRAZZ reprinted by permission of United Feature Syndicate, Inc.*

## Statistics in a Word

> Statistics is about variation.
> Data vary because we don't see everything and because even what we do see and measure, we measure imperfectly.
> So, in a very basic way, Statistics is about the real, imperfect world in which we live.

It can be fun, and sometimes useful, to summarize a discipline in only a few words. So,

Economics is about . . . *Money (and why it is good)*.

Psychology: *Why we think what we think (we think)*.

Biology: *Life.*

Anthropology: *Who?*

History: *What, where, and when?*

Philosophy: *Why?*

Engineering: *How?*

Accounting: *How much?*

In such a caricature, Statistics is about . . . **Variation.**

Data vary. People are different. We can't see everything, let alone measure it all. And even what we do measure, we measure imperfectly. So the data we wind up looking at and basing our decisions on provide, at best, an imperfect picture of the world. This fact lies at the heart of what Statistics is all about. How to make sense of it is a central challenge of Statistics.

## So, How Will This Book Help?

A fair question. Most likely, this book will not turn out to be quite what you expected. What's different?

*Close your eyes and open the book to a page at random. Is there a graph or table on that page? Do that again, say, 10 times. We'll bet you saw data displayed in many ways, even near the back of the book and in the exercises.*

We can better understand everything we do with data by making pictures. This book leads you through the entire process of thinking about a problem, finding and showing results, and telling others about what you have discovered. At each of these steps, we display data for better understanding and insight.

You looked at only a few randomly selected pages to get an impression of the entire book. We'll see soon that doing so was sound Statistics practice and reasoning.

*Next, pick a chapter and read the first two sentences. (Go ahead; we'll wait.)*

We'll bet you didn't see anything about Statistics. Why? Because the best way to understand Statistics is to see it at work. In this book, chapters usually start by presenting a story and posing questions. That's when Statistics really gets down to work.

There are three simple steps to doing Statistics right: *think, show,* and *tell:*

**Think** first. Know where you're headed and why. It will save you a lot of work.

**Show** is what most folks think Statistics is about. The *mechanics* of calculating statistics and making displays is important, but not the most important part of Statistics.

**Tell** what you've learned. Until you've explained your results so that someone else can understand your conclusions, the job is not done.

You'll see a **Where Are We Going?** section at the beginning of every chapter. In it, you'll see the kinds of questions about the real world that you'll be able to tackle by the end of the chapter. The best way to learn new skills is to take them out for a spin. In **For Example** boxes you'll see brief ways to apply new ideas and methods as you learn them. You'll also find more comprehensive worked examples called **Step-by-Steps**. These show you fully worked solutions side by side with commentary and discussion, modeling the way statisticians attack and solve problems. They illustrate how to think about the problem, what to show, and how to tell what it all means. These step-by-step examples will show you how to produce the kind of solutions instructors hope to see.

Sometimes, in the middle of the chapter, we've put a section called **Just Checking . . . .** There you'll find a few short questions you can answer without much calculation—a quick way to check to see if you've understood the basic ideas in the chapter. You'll find the answers at the end of the chapter's exercises.

From time to time, you'll see an icon like this in the margin to signal that the *ActivStats* multimedia materials on the DVD in the back of the book have an activity that you might find helpful at this point. Typically, we've flagged simulations and interactive activities because they're the most fun and will probably help you see how things work best. The chapters in *ActivStats* are the same as those in the text—just look for the named activity in the corresponding chapter.

**A S**   ActivStats parallels the chapters in this book, and includes expanded lessons and activities to increase your understanding of the material covered in the text.

One of the interesting challenges of Statistics is that, unlike in some math and science courses, there can be more than one right answer. This is why two statisticians can testify honestly on opposite sides of a court case. And it's why some people think that you can prove anything with statistics. But that's not true. People make mistakes using statistics, sometimes on purpose in order to mislead others. Most of the unintentional mistakes people make, though, are avoidable. We're not talking about arithmetic. More often the mistakes come from using a method in the wrong situation or misinterpreting the results. Each chapter has a section called **What Can Go Wrong?** to help you avoid some of the most common mistakes.

*"Get your facts first, and then you can distort them as much as you please. (Facts are stubborn, but statistics are more pliable.)"*
—Mark Twain

**BY HAND**

**ON THE COMPUTER**

**A S** Introduction to (Your Statistics Package). *ActivStats* launches your statistics package (such as Data Desk) automatically. Try it now.

You'll find all sorts of stuff in margin notes, such as stories and quotations. For example,

*"Computers are useless. They can only give you answers."*

—Pablo Picasso

While Picasso underestimated the value of good statistics software, he did know that creating a solution requires more than just *Showing* an answer—it means you have to *Think* and *Tell,* too!

*"Far too many scientists have only a shaky grasp of the statistical techniques they are using. They employ them as an amateur chef employs a cookbook, believing the recipes will work without understanding why. A more* cordon bleu *attitude . . . might lead to fewer statistical soufflés failing to rise."*

—The Economist, June 3, 2004, **"Sloppy stats shame science."**

Some exercises are marked with an orange ⓣ. You'll find the data for these exercises on the DVD in the back of the book, or on the book's Web site, www. aw.com/dvb. You may want to use technology as you work these exercises.

Although we'll show you all the formulas you need to understand the calculations, you will most often use a calculator or computer to perform the mechanics of a statistics problem. But there are times when you may want to see how it's done **by hand**, too. So we'll show you how.

There are a number of statistics packages available for computers, and they differ widely in the details of how to use them and in how they present their results. But they all work from the same basic information and find the same results. Rather than adopt one package for this book, we present generic output and point out common features that you should look for. The **. . . on the Computer** section of most chapters (just before the exercises) holds this information. We also give a table of instructions to get you started on any of several commonly used packages.

> **Time out.** From time to time, we'll take time out to discuss an interesting or important side issue. We indicate these by setting them apart like this.[2]

At the end of each chapter, you'll see a brief summary of the important concepts you've covered in a section called **What Have We Learned?** That section includes a list of the **Terms** and a summary of the important **Skills** you've acquired in the chapter. You won't be able to learn the material from these summaries, but you can use them to check your knowledge of the important ideas in the chapter. If you have the skills, know the terms, and understand the concepts, you should be well prepared for the exam—and ready to use Statistics!

Beware: No one can learn Statistics just by reading or listening. The only way to learn it is to do it. So, of course, at the end of each chapter (except this one) you'll find **Exercises** designed to help you learn to use the Statistics you've just read about.

We've paired up the exercises, putting similar ones together. So, if you're having trouble doing an exercise, you will find a similar one either just before or just after it. You'll find answers to the odd-numbered exercises at the back of the book. But these are only "answers" and not complete "solutions." Huh? What's the difference? The answers are sketches of the complete solutions. For most problems, your solution should follow the model of the Step-By-Step Examples. If your calculations match the numerical parts of the "answer," and your argument contains the elements shown in the answer, you're on the right track. Your complete solution should explain the context, show your reasoning and calculations, and state your conclusions. Don't fret too much if your numbers don't match the printed answers to every decimal place. Statistics is more about getting the reasoning correct—pay more attention to how you interpret a result than what the digit in the third decimal place was.

In the real world, problems don't come with chapters attached. So, in addition to the exercises at the ends of chapters, we've also collected a variety of problems at the end of each part of the text to make it more like the real world. This should help you to see whether you can sort out which methods to use when. If you can do that successfully, then you'll know you understand Statistics.

---

[2] Or in a footnote.

# *Optional Sections and Chapters

Some sections and chapters of this book are marked with an asterisk(*). These are optional in the sense that subsequent material does not depend on them directly. We hope you'll read them anyway, as you did this section.

# Onward!

It's only fair to warn you: You can't get there by just picking out the highlighted sentences and the summaries. This book is different. It's not about memorizing definitions and learning equations. It's deeper than that. And much more fun. But . . .

**_You have to read the book!_**[3]

---

[3] So, turn the page.

# Data

## Where are we going?

This is a book about understanding the world by using data. So we'd better start by understanding data. There's more to that than you might have thought.

Many years ago, most stores in small towns knew their customers personally. If you walked into the hobby shop, the owner might tell you about a new bridge that had come in for your Lionel train set. The tailor knew your dad's size, and the hairdresser knew how your mom liked her hair. There are still some stores like that around today, but we're increasingly likely to shop at large stores, by phone, or on the Internet. Even so, when you phone an 800 number to buy new running shoes, customer service representatives may call you by your first name or ask about the socks you bought 6 weeks ago. Or the company may send an e-mail in October offering new head warmers for winter running. This company has millions of customers, and you called without identifying yourself. How did the sales rep know who you are, where you live, and what you had bought?

The answer is data. Collecting data on their customers, transactions, and sales lets companies track their inventory and helps them predict what their customers prefer. These data can help them predict what their customers may buy in the future so they know how much of each item to stock. The store can use the data and what it learns from the data to improve customer service, mimicking the kind of personal attention a shopper had 50 years ago.

Amazon.com opened for business in July 1995, billing itself as "Earth's Biggest Bookstore." By 1997, Amazon had a catalog of more than 2.5 million book titles and had sold books to more than 1.5 million customers in 150 countries. In 2006, the company's revenue reached $10.7 billion. Amazon has expanded into selling a wide selection of merchandise, from $400,000 necklaces[1] to yak cheese from Tibet to the largest book in the world.

---

[1] Please get credit card approval before purchasing online.

Amazon is constantly monitoring and evolving its Web site to serve its customers better and maximize sales performance. To decide which changes to make to the site, the company experiments, collecting data and analyzing what works best. When you visit the Amazon Web site, you may encounter a different look or different suggestions and offers. Amazon statisticians want to know whether you'll follow the links offered, purchase the items suggested, or even spend a longer time browsing the site. As Ronny Kohavi, director of Data Mining and Personalization, says, "Data trumps intuition. Instead of using our intuition, we experiment on the live site and let our customers tell us what works for them."

# But What *Are* Data?

We bet you thought you knew this instinctively. Think about it for a minute. What exactly *do* we mean by "data"?

Do data have to be numbers? The amount of your last purchase in dollars is numerical data, but some data record names or other labels. The names in Amazon.com's database are data, but not numerical.

Sometimes, data can have values that look like numerical values but are just numerals serving as labels. This can be confusing. For example, the ASIN (Amazon Standard Item Number) of a book, like 0321286715, may have a numerical value, but it's really just another name for *Intro Stats*.

Data values, no matter what kind, are useless without their context. Newspaper journalists know that the lead paragraph of a good story should establish the "Five W's": *Who, What, When, Where,* and (if possible) *Why.* Often, we add *How* to the list as well. Answering these questions can provide the **context** for data values. The answers to the first two questions are essential. If you can't answer *Who* and *What,* you don't have **data,** and you don't have any useful information.

---

**THE W'S:**
**WHO**
**WHAT**
   and in what units
**WHEN**
**WHERE**
**WHY**
**HOW**

---

# Data Tables

Here are some data Amazon might collect:

| | | | | | | | | |
|---|---|---|---|---|---|---|---|---|
| B000001OAA | 10.99 | Chris G. | 902 | 15783947 | 15.98 | Kansas | Illinois | Boston |
| Canada | Samuel P. | Orange County | N | B000068ZVQ | Bad Blood | Nashville | Katherine H. | N |
| Mammals | 10783489 | Ohio | N | Chicago | 12837593 | 11.99 | Massachusetts | 16.99 |
| 312 | Monique D. | 10675489 | 413 | B00000I5Y6 | 440 | B000002BK9 | Let Go | Y |

---

**A S**   *Activity:* **What Is (Are) Data?** Do you really know what's data and what's just numbers?

Try to guess what they represent. Why is that hard? Because these data have no *context.* If we don't know *Who* they're about or *What* they measure, these values are meaningless. We can make the meaning clear if we organize the values into a **data table** such as this one:

| Purchase Order | Name | Ship to State/Country | Price | Area Code | Previous CD Purchase | Gift? | ASIN | Artist |
|---|---|---|---|---|---|---|---|---|
| 10675489 | Katharine H. | Ohio | 10.99 | 440 | Nashville | N | B00000I5Y6 | Kansas |
| 10783489 | Samuel P. | Illinois | 16.99 | 312 | Orange County | Y | B000002BK9 | Boston |
| 12837593 | Chris G. | Massachusetts | 15.98 | 413 | Bad Blood | N | B000068ZVQ | Chicago |
| 15783947 | Monique D. | Canada | 11.99 | 902 | Let Go | N | B000001OAA | Mammals |

Now we can see that these are four purchase records, relating to CD orders from Amazon. The column titles tell *What* has been recorded. The rows tell us *Who*. But be careful. Look at all the variables to see *Who* the variables are about. Even if people are involved, they may not be the *Who* of the data. For example, the *Who* here are the purchase orders (not the people who made the purchases). A common place to find the *Who* of the table is the leftmost column. The other W's might have to come from the company's database administrator.[2]

## Who

In general, the rows of a data table correspond to individual **cases** about *Whom* (or about which—if they're not people) we record some characteristics. These cases go by different names, depending on the situation. Individuals who answer a survey are referred to as *respondents*. People on whom we experiment are *subjects* or (in an attempt to acknowledge the importance of their role in the experiment) *participants,* but animals, plants, Web sites, and other inanimate subjects are often just called *experimental units*. In a database, rows are called *records*—in this example, purchase records. Perhaps the most generic term is **cases.** In the table, the cases are the individual CD orders.

Sometimes people just refer to data values as *observations*, without being clear about the *Who*. Be sure you know the *Who* of the data, or you may not know what the data say.

Often, the cases are a **sample** of cases selected from some larger **population** that we'd like to understand. Amazon certainly cares about its customers, but also wants to know how to attract all those other Internet users who may never have made a purchase from Amazon's site. To be able to generalize from the sample of cases to the larger population, we'll want the sample to be *representative* of that population—a kind of snapshot image of the larger world.

**A S**   *Activity:* **Consider the Context . . .** Can you tell who's *Who* and what's *What*? And *Why?* This activity offers real-world examples to help you practice identifying the context.

> ### FOR EXAMPLE     Identifying the "Who"
>
> **Question:** In March 2007, *Consumer Reports* published an evaluation of large-screen, high-definition television sets (HDTVs). The magazine purchased and tested 98 different models from a variety of manufacturers. Describe the population of interest, the sample, and the *Who* of this study.
>
> The magazine is interested in the performance of all HDTVs currently being offered for sale. It tested a sample of 98 sets, the "Who" for these data. Each HDTV set is a sample of all similar sets offered by that manufacturer.

## What and Why

The characteristics recorded about each individual are called **variables.** These are usually shown as the columns of a data table, and they should have a name that identifies *What* has been measured. Variables may seem simple, but to really understand your variables, you must *Think* about what you want to know.

Although area codes are numbers, do we use them that way? Is 610 twice 305? Of course it is, but is that the question? Why would we want to know whether

---

[2] In database management, this kind of information is called "metadata."

It is wise to be careful. The *What* and *Why* of area codes are not as simple as they may first seem. When area codes were first introduced, AT&T was still the source of all telephone equipment, and phones had dials.

To reduce wear and tear on the dials, the area codes with the lowest digits (for which the dial would have to spin least) were assigned to the most populous regions—those with the most phone numbers and thus the area codes most likely to be dialed. New York City was assigned 212, Chicago 312, and Los Angeles 213, but rural upstate New York was given 607, Joliet was 815, and San Diego 619. For that reason, at one time the numerical value of an area code could be used to guess something about the population of its region. Since the advent of push-button phones, area codes have finally become just categories.

---

By international agreement, the International System of Units links together all systems of weights and measures. There are seven base units from which all other physical units are derived:

- Distance            Meter
- Mass                Kilogram
- Time                Second
- Electric current    Ampere
- Temperature         Kelvin
- Amount of substance Mole
- Intensity of light  Candela

---

**A S**   *Activity:* **Recognize variables measured in a variety of ways.** This activity shows examples of the many ways to measure data.

---

Allentown, PA (area code 610), is twice Key West, FL (305)? Variables play different roles, and you can't tell a variable's role just by looking at it.

Some variables just tell us what group or category each individual belongs to. Are you male or female? Pierced or not? . . . What kinds of things can we learn about variables like these? A natural start is to *count* how many cases belong in each category. (Are you listening to music while reading this? We could count the number of students in the class who were and the number who weren't.) We'll look for ways to compare and contrast the sizes of such categories.

Some variables have measurement **units.** Units tell how each value has been measured. But, more importantly, units such as yen, cubits, carats, angstroms, nanoseconds, miles per hour, or degrees Celsius tell us the *scale* of measurement. The units tell us how much of something we have or how far apart two values are. Without units, the values of a measured variable have no meaning. It does little good to be promised a raise of 5000 a year if you don't know whether it will be paid in euros, dollars, yen, or Estonian krooni.

What kinds of things can we learn about measured variables? We can do a lot more than just counting categories. We can look for patterns and trends. (How much did you pay for your last movie ticket? What is the range of ticket prices available in your town? How has the price of a ticket changed over the past 20 years?)

When a variable names categories and answers questions about how cases fall into those categories, we call it a **categorical variable.**[3] When a measured variable with units answers questions about the quantity of what is measured, we call it a **quantitative variable.** These types can help us decide what to do with a variable, but they are really more about what we hope to learn from a variable than about the variable itself. It's the questions we ask a variable (the *Why* of our analysis) that shape how we think about it and how we treat it.

Some variables can answer questions only about categories. If the values of a variable are words rather than numbers, it's a good bet that it is categorical. But some variables can answer both kinds of questions. Amazon could ask for your *Age* in years. That seems quantitative, and would be if the company wanted to know the average age of those customers who visit their site after 3 a.m. But suppose Amazon wants to decide which CD to offer you in a special deal—one by Raffi, Blink182, Carly Simon, or Mantovani—and needs to be sure to have adequate supplies on hand to meet the demand. Then thinking of your age in one of the categories child, teen, adult, or senior might be more useful. If it isn't clear whether a variable is categorical or quantitative, think about *Why* you are looking at it and what you want it to tell you.

---

[3] You may also see it called a *qualitative variable.*

One tradition that hangs on in some quarters is to name variables with cryptic abbreviations written in uppercase letters. This can be traced back to the 1960s, when the very first statistics computer programs were controlled with instructions punched on cards. The earliest punch card equipment used only uppercase letters, and the earliest statistics programs limited variable names to six or eight characters, so variables were called things like PRSRF3. Modern programs do not have such restrictive limits, so there is no reason for variable names that you wouldn't use in an ordinary sentence.

A typical course evaluation survey asks, "How valuable do you think this course will be to you?" 1 = Worthless; 2 = Slightly; 3 = Middling; 4 = Reasonably; 5 = Invaluable. Is *Educational Value* categorical or quantitative? Once again, we'll look to the *Why*. A teacher might just count the number of students who gave each response for her course, treating *Educational Value* as a categorical variable. When she wants to see whether the course is improving, she might treat the responses as the *amount* of perceived value—in effect, treating the variable as quantitative. But what are the units? There is certainly an *order* of perceived worth: Higher numbers indicate higher perceived worth. A course that averages 4.5 seems more valuable than one that averages 2, but we should be careful about treating *Educational Value* as purely quantitative. To treat it as quantitative, she'll have to imagine that it has "educational value units" or some similar arbitrary construction. Because there are no natural units, she should be cautious. Variables like this that report order without natural units are often called "ordinal" variables. But saying "that's an ordinal variable" doesn't get you off the hook. You still must look to the *Why* of your study to decide whether to treat it as categorical or quantitative.

 **A S**   *Activities:* Variables. Several activities show you how to begin working with data in your statistics package.

**FOR EXAMPLE**   Identifying "What" and "Why" of HDTV's.

**Recap:** A *Consumer Reports* article about 98 HDTVs lists each set's manufacturer, cost, screen size, type (LCD, plasma, or rear projection), and overall performance score (0–100).

**Question:** Are these variables categorical or quantitative? Include units where appropriate, and describe the "Why" of this investigation.

The "what" of this article includes the following variables:
- manufacturer (categorical);
- cost (in dollars, quantitative);
- screen size (in inches, quantitative);
- type (categorical);
- performance score (quantitative).

The magazine hopes to help consumers pick a good HDTV set.

# Counts Count

In Statistics, we often count things. When Amazon considers a special offer of free shipping to customers, it might first analyze how purchases are shipped. They'd probably start by counting the number of purchases shipped by ground transportation, by second-day air, and by overnight air. Counting is a natural way to summarize the categorical variable *Shipping Method*. So every time we see counts, does that mean the variable is categorical? Actually, no.

We also use counts to measure the amounts of things. How many songs are on your digital music player? How many classes are you taking this semester? To measure these quantities, we'd naturally count. The variables (*Songs*, *Classes*) would be quantitative, and we'd consider the units to be "number of . . . ," or generically, just "counts" for short.

So we use counts in two different ways. When we count the cases in each category of a categorical variable, the category labels are the *What* and the individuals counted are the *Who* of our data. The counts themselves are not the data, but are something we summarize about the data. Amazon counts the number of purchases in each category of the categorical variable *Shipping Method.* For this purpose (the *Why*), the *What* is shipping method and the *Who* is purchases.

| Shipping Method | Number of Purchases |
|---|---|
| Ground | 20,345 |
| Second-day | 7,890 |
| Overnight | 5,432 |

Other times our focus is on the amount of something, which we measure by counting. Amazon might record the number of teenage customers visiting their site each month to track customer growth and forecast CD sales (the *Why*). Now the *What* is *Teens,* the *Who* is *Months,* and the units are *Number of Teenage Customers. Teen* was a category when we looked at the categorical variable *Age.* But now it is a quantitative variable in its own right whose amount is measured by counting the number of customers.

| Month | Number of Teenage Customers |
|---|---|
| January | 123,456 |
| February | 234,567 |
| March | 345,678 |
| April | 456,789 |
| May | . . . |
| . . . | . . . |

# Identifying Identifiers

What's your student ID number? It is numerical, but is it a quantitative variable? No, it doesn't have units. Is it categorical? Yes, but it is a special kind. Look at how many categories there are and at how many individuals are in each. There are as many categories as individuals and only one individual in each category. While it's easy to count the totals for each category, it's not very interesting. Amazon wants to know who you are when you sign in again and doesn't want to confuse you with some other customer. So it assigns you a unique identifier.

Identifier variables themselves don't tell us anything useful about the categories because we know there is exactly one individual in each. However, they are crucial in this age of large data sets. They make it possible to combine data from different sources, to protect confidentiality, and to provide unique labels. It is easy to see that identifier variables are just categorical variables with exactly one individual in each category. The variables *UPS Tracking Number, Social Security Number,* and Amazon's *ASIN* are all examples of identifier variables.

You'll want to recognize when a variable is playing the role of an identifier so you won't be tempted to analyze it. There's probably a list of unique ID numbers for students in a class (so they'll each get their own grade confidentially), but you might worry about the professor who keeps track of the average of these numbers from class to class. Even though this year's average ID number happens to be higher than last's, it doesn't mean that the students are better.

Just because a variable has one case per category doesn't limit it to being an identifier. Even these variables can play different roles, depending on the questions we ask of them. For its annual reports, Amazon refers to its database and looks at the variables *Sales* and *Year*. When analysts ask how many books Amazon sold in 1995, what role does *Year* play? There's only one row for 1995, and *Year* identifies it, so it is an identifier. But analysts also track sales growth over time. In this role, *Year* measures time. Now it's a quantitative variable with units of . . . years. Again, the difference is in the *Why*.

## Where, When, and How

**A S**    *Self-Test:* **Review concepts about data.** Like the Just Checking sections of this textbook, but interactive. (Usually, we won't reference the *ActivStats* self-tests here, but look for one whenever you'd like to check your understanding or review material.)

We must know *Who, What,* and *Why* to analyze data. Without knowing these three, we don't have enough to start. Of course, we'd always like to know more. The more we know about the data, the more we'll understand about the world.

If possible, we'd like to know the **When** and **Where** of data as well. Values recorded in 1803 may mean something different than similar values recorded last year. Values measured in Tanzania may differ in meaning from similar measurements made in Mexico.

**How** the data are collected can make the difference between insight and nonsense. As we'll see later, data that come from a voluntary survey on the Internet are almost always worthless. One primary concern of Statistics, discussed in Part III, is the design of sound methods for collecting data.

Throughout this book, whenever we introduce data, we will provide a margin note listing the W's (and H) of the data. It's a habit we recommend. The first step of any data analysis is to know why you are examining the data (what you want to know), whom each row of your data table refers to, and what the variables (the columns of the table) record. These are the *Why,* the *Who,* and the *What.* Identifying them is a key part of the *Think* step of any analysis. Make sure you know all three before you proceed to *Show* or *Tell* anything about the data.

> **There's a world of data on the Internet.**    These days, one of the richest sources of data is the Internet. With a bit of practice, you can learn to find data on almost any subject. Many of the data sets we use in this book were found in this way. The Internet has both advantages and disadvantages as a source of data. Among the advantages are the fact that often you'll be able to find even more current data than those we present. The disadvantage is that references to Internet addresses can "break" as sites evolve, move, and die.
>
> Our solution to these challenges is to offer the best advice we can to help you search for the data, wherever they may be residing. We usually point you to a Web site. We'll sometimes suggest search terms and offer other guidance.
>
> Some words of caution, though: Data found on Internet sites may not be formatted in the best way for use in statistics software. Although you may see a data table in standard form, an attempt to copy the data may leave you with a single column of values. You may have to work in your favorite statistics or spreadsheet program to reformat the data into variables. You will also probably want to remove commas from large numbers and such extra symbols as money indicators ($, ¥, £); few statistics packages can handle these.

## JUST CHECKING

In the 2003 Tour de France, Lance Armstrong averaged 40.94 kilometers per hour (km/h) for the entire course, making it the fastest Tour de France in its 100-year history. In 2004, he made history again by winning the race for an unprecedented sixth time. In 2005, he became the only 7-time winner and once again set a new record for the fastest average speed. You can find data on all the Tour de France races on the DVD. Here are the first six and last nine lines of the data set. Keep in mind that the entire data set has nearly 100 entries.

**1.** List as many of the W's as you can for this data set.

**2.** Classify each variable as categorical or quantitative; if quantitative, identify the units.

| Year | Winner | Country of origin | Total time (h/min/s) | Avg. speed (km/h) | Stages | Total distance ridden (km) | Starting riders | Finishing riders |
|------|--------|-------------------|----------------------|-------------------|--------|----------------------------|-----------------|------------------|
| 1903 | Maurice Garin | France | 94.33.00 | 25.3 | 6 | 2428 | 60 | 21 |
| 1904 | Henri Cornet | France | 96.05.00 | 24.3 | 6 | 2388 | 88 | 23 |
| 1905 | Louis Trousselier | France | 112.18.09 | 27.3 | 11 | 2975 | 60 | 24 |
| 1906 | Rene Pottier | France | 185.47.26 | 24.5 | 13 | 4637 | 82 | 14 |
| 1907 | Lucien Petit-Breton | France | 156.22.30 | 28.5 | 14 | 4488 | 93 | 33 |
| 1908 | Lucien Petit-Breton | France | 156.09.31 | 28.7 | 14 | 4488 | 114 | 36 |
| ⋮ |  |  |  |  |  |  |  |  |
| 1999 | Lance Armstrong | USA | 91.32.16 | 40.30 | 20 | 3687 | 180 | 141 |
| 2000 | Lance Armstrong | USA | 92.33.08 | 39.56 | 21 | 3662 | 180 | 128 |
| 2001 | Lance Armstrong | USA | 86.17.28 | 40.02 | 20 | 3453 | 189 | 144 |
| 2002 | Lance Armstrong | USA | 82.05.12 | 39.93 | 20 | 3278 | 189 | 153 |
| 2003 | Lance Armstrong | USA | 83.41.12 | 40.94 | 20 | 3427 | 189 | 147 |
| 2004 | Lance Armstrong | USA | 83.36.02 | 40.53 | 20 | 3391 | 188 | 147 |
| 2005 | Lance Armstrong | USA | 86.15.02 | 41.65 | 21 | 3608 | 189 | 155 |
| 2006 | Oscar Periero | Spain | 89.40.27 | 40.78 | 20 | 3657 | 176 | 139 |
| 2007 | Alberto Cantadar | Spain | 91.00.26 | 38.97 | 20 | 3547 | 189 | 141 |

## WHAT CAN GO WRONG?

▶ **Don't label a variable as categorical or quantitative without thinking about the question you want it to answer.** The same variable can sometimes take on different roles.

▶ **Just because your variable's values are numbers, don't assume that it's quantitative.** Categories are often given numerical labels. Don't let that fool you into thinking they have quantitative meaning. Look at the context.

▶ **Always be skeptical.** One reason to analyze data is to discover the truth. Even when you are told a context for the data, it may turn out that the truth is a bit (or even a lot) different. The context colors our interpretation of the data, so those who want to influence what you think may slant the context. A survey that seems to be about all students may in fact report just the opinions of those who visited a fan Web site. The question that respondents answered may have been posed in a way that influenced their responses.

# WHAT HAVE WE LEARNED?

We've learned that data are information in a context.

▸ The W's help nail down the context: *Who, What, Why, Where, When,* and *hoW.*

▸ We must know at least the *Who, What,* and *Why* to be able to say anything useful based on the data. The *Who* are the *cases.* The *What* are the *variables.* A variable gives information about each of the cases. The *Why* helps us decide which way to treat the variables.

We treat variables in two basic ways, as *categorical* or *quantitative.*

▸ Categorical variables identify a category for each case. Usually, we think about the counts of cases that fall into each category. (An exception is an identifier variable that just names each case.)

▸ Quantitative variables record measurements or amounts of something; they must have *units.*

▸ Sometimes we treat a variable as categorical or quantitative depending on what we want to learn from it, which means that some variables can't be pigeonholed as one type or the other. That's an early hint that in Statistics we can't always pin things down precisely.

## Terms

| | |
|---|---|
| Context | 8. The context ideally tells *Who* was measured, *What* was measured, *How* the data were collected, *Where* the data were collected, and *When* and *Why* the study was performed. |
| Data | 8. Systematically recorded information, whether numbers or labels, together with its context. |
| Data table | 8. An arrangement of data in which each row represents a case and each column represents a variable. |
| Case | 9. A case is an individual about whom or which we have data. |
| Population | 9. All of the cases we wish we knew about. |
| Sample | 9. The cases we actually examine in seeking to understand the much larger population. |
| Variable | 9. A variable holds information about the same characteristic for many cases. |
| Units | 10. A quantity or amount adopted as a standard of measurement, such as dollars, hours, or grams. |
| Categorical variable | 10. A variable that names categories (whether with words or numerals) is called categorical. |
| Quantitative variable | 10. A variable in which the numbers act as numerical values is called quantitative. Quantitative variables always have units. |

## Skills

▸ Be able to identify the *Who, What, When, Where, Why,* and *How* of data, or recognize when some of this information has not been provided.

▸ Be able to identify the cases and variables in any data set.

▸ Be able to identify the population from which a sample was chosen.

▸ Be able to classify a variable as categorical or quantitative, depending on its use.

▸ For any quantitative variable, be able to identify the units in which the variable has been measured (or note that they have not been provided).

▸ Be able to describe a variable in terms of its *Who, What, When, Where, Why,* and *How* (and be prepared to remark when that information is not provided).

# ON THE COMPUTER

## Data

 **Activity: Examine the Data.** Take a look at your own data from your experiment (p. 12) and get comfortable with your statistics package as you find out about the experiment test results.

Most often we find statistics on a computer using a program, or *package*, designed for that purpose. There are many different statistics packages, but they all do essentially the same things. If you understand what the computer needs to know to do what you want and what it needs to show you in return, you can figure out the specific details of most packages pretty easily.

For example, to get your data into a computer statistics package, you need to tell the computer:

▶ Where to find the data. This usually means directing the computer to a file stored on your computer's disk or to data on a database. Or it might just mean that you have copied the data from a spreadsheet program or Internet site and it is currently on your computer's clipboard. Usually, the data should be in the form of a data table. Most computer statistics packages prefer the *delimiter* that marks the division between elements of a data table to be a *tab* character and the delimiter that marks the end of a case to be a *return* character.

▶ Where to put the data. (Usually this is handled automatically.)

▶ What to call the variables. Some data tables have variable names as the first row of the data, and often statistics packages can take the variable names from the first row automatically.

# EXERCISES

1. **Voters.**   A February 2007 Gallup Poll question asked, "In politics, as of today, do you consider yourself a Republican, a Democrat, or an Independent?" The possible responses were "Democrat", "Republican", "Independent", "Other", and "No Response". What kind of variable is the response?

2. **Mood.**   A January 2007 Gallup Poll question asked, "In general, do you think things have gotten better or gotten worse in this country in the last five years?" Possible answers were "Better", "Worse", "No Change", "Don't Know", and "No Response". What kind of variable is the response?

3. **Medicine.**   A pharmaceutical company conducts an experiment in which a subject takes 100 mg of a substance orally. The researchers measure how many minutes it takes for half of the substance to exit the bloodstream. What kind of variable is the company studying?

4. **Stress.**   A medical researcher measures the increase in heart rate of patients under a stress test. What kind of variable is the researcher studying?

*(Exercises 5–12) For each description of data, identify Who and What were investigated and the population of interest.*

5. **The news.**   Find a newspaper or magazine article in which some data are reported. For the data discussed in the article, answer the questions above. Include a copy of the article with your report.

6. **The Internet.**   Find an Internet source that reports on a study and describes the data. Print out the description and answer the questions above.

7. **Bicycle safety.**   Ian Walker, a psychologist at the University of Bath, wondered whether drivers treat bicycle riders differently when they wear helmets. He rigged his bicycle with an ultrasonic sensor that could measure how close each car was that passed him. He then rode on alternating days with and without a helmet. Out of 2500 cars passing him, he found that when he wore his helmet, motorists passed 3.35 inches closer to him, on average, than when his head was bare. [*NY Times*, Dec. 10, 2006]

8. **Investments.**   Some companies offer 401(k) retirement plans to employees, permitting them to shift part of their before-tax salaries into investments such as mutual funds. Employers typically match 50% of the employees' contribution up to about 6% of salary. One company, concerned with what it believed was a low employee participation rate in its 401(k) plan, sampled 30 other companies with similar plans and asked for their 401(k) participation rates.

9. **Honesty.**   Coffee stations in offices often just ask users to leave money in a tray to pay for their coffee, but many people cheat. Researchers at Newcastle University alternately taped two posters over the coffee station. During one week, it was a picture of flowers; during the other, it was a pair of staring eyes. They found that the average

contribution was significantly higher when the eyes poster was up than when the flowers were there. Apparently, the mere feeling of being watched—even by eyes that were not real—was enough to encourage people to behave more honestly. [*NY Times*, Dec. 10, 2006]

10. **Movies.** Some motion pictures are profitable and others are not. Understandably, the movie industry would like to know what makes a movie successful. Data from 120 first-run movies released in 2005 suggest that longer movies actually make *less* profit.

11. **Fitness.** Are physically fit people less likely to die of cancer? An article in the May 2002 issue of *Medicine and Science in Sports and Exercise* reported results of a study that followed 25,892 men aged 30 to 87 for 10 years. The most physically fit men had a 55% lower risk of death from cancer than the least fit group.

12. **Molten iron.** The Cleveland Casting Plant is a large, highly automated producer of gray and nodular iron automotive castings for Ford Motor Company. The company is interested in keeping the pouring temperature of the molten iron (in degrees Fahrenheit) close to the specified value of 2550 degrees. Cleveland Casting measured the pouring temperature for 10 randomly selected crankshafts.

*(Exercises 13–30) For each description of data, identify the W's, name the variables, specify for each variable whether its use indicates that it should be treated as categorical or quantitative, and, for any quantitative variable, identify the units in which it was measured (or note that they were not provided).*

13. **Weighing bears.** Because of the difficulty of weighing a bear in the woods, researchers caught and measured 54 bears, recording their weight, neck size, length, and sex. They hoped to find a way to estimate weight from the other, more easily determined quantities.

14. **Schools.** The State Education Department requires local school districts to keep these records on all students: age, race or ethnicity, days absent, current grade level, standardized test scores in reading and mathematics, and any disabilities or special educational needs.

15. **Arby's menu.** A listing posted by the Arby's restaurant chain gives, for each of the sandwiches it sells, the type of meat in the sandwich, the number of calories, and the serving size in ounces. The data might be used to assess the nutritional value of the different sandwiches.

16. **Firefighters.** A study was conducted to compare the abilities of men and women to perform the strenuous tasks required of a shipboard firefighter (*Human Factors* 24 [1982]). The study reports the pulling force (in newtons) that a firefighter was able to exert in pulling the starter cord of a P-250 water pump. The study also gives the weight and, of course, the sex of the firefighters.

17. **Babies.** Medical researchers at a large city hospital investigating the impact of prenatal care on newborn health collected data from 882 births during 1998–2000. They kept track of the mother's age, the number of weeks the pregnancy lasted, the type of birth (cesarean, induced, natural), the level of prenatal care the mother had (none, minimal, adequate), the birth weight and sex of the baby, and whether the baby exhibited health problems (none, minor, major).

18. **Flowers.** In a study appearing in the journal *Science*, a research team reports that plants in southern England are flowering earlier in the spring. Records of the first flowering dates for 385 species over a period of 47 years show that flowering has advanced an average of 15 days per decade, an indication of climate warming, according to the authors.

19. **Herbal medicine.** Scientists at a major pharmaceutical firm conducted an experiment to study the effectiveness of an herbal compound to treat the common cold. They exposed each patient to a cold virus, then gave them either the herbal compound or a sugar solution known to have no effect on colds. Several days later they assessed each patient's condition, using a cold severity scale ranging from 0 to 5. They found no evidence of the benefits of the compound.

20. **Tracking sales.** A start-up company is building a database of customers and sales information. For each customer, it records name, ID number, region of the country (1 = East, 2 = South, 3 = Midwest, 4 = West), date of last purchase, amount of purchase, and item purchased.

21. **Cars.** A survey of autos parked in student and staff lots at a large university recorded the make, country of origin, type of vehicle (car, van, SUV, etc.), and age.

22. **Vineyards.** Business analysts hoping to provide information helpful to grape growers compiled these data about vineyards: size (acres), number of years in existence, state, varieties of grapes grown, average case price, gross sales, and percent profit.

23. **Streams.** In performing research for an ecology class, students at a college in upstate New York collect data on streams each year. They record a number of biological, chemical, and physical variables, including the stream name, the substrate of the stream (limestone, shale, or mixed), the acidity of the water (pH), the temperature (°C), and the BCI (a numerical measure of biological diversity).

24. **Age and party.** The Gallup Poll conducted a representative telephone survey of 1180 American voters during the first quarter of 2007. Among the reported results were the voter's region (Northeast, South, etc.), age, party affiliation, and whether or not the person had voted in the 2006 midterm congressional election.

25. **Air travel.** The Federal Aviation Administration (FAA) monitors airlines for safety and customer service. For each flight, the carrier must report the type of aircraft, number of passengers, whether or not the flights departed and arrived on schedule, and any mechanical problems.

26. **Fuel economy.** The Environmental Protection Agency (EPA) tracks fuel economy of automobiles. Among the data the agency collects are the manufacturer (Ford, Toyota, etc.), vehicle type (car, SUV, etc.), weight, horsepower, and gas mileage (mpg) for city and highway driving.

**27. Refrigerators.** In 2006, *Consumer Reports* published an article evaluating refrigerators. It listed 41 models, giving the brand, cost, size (cu ft), type (such as top freezer), estimated annual energy cost, an overall rating (good, excellent, etc.), and the repair history for that brand (percentage requiring repairs over the past 5 years).

**28. Walking in circles.** People who get lost in the desert, mountains, or woods often seem to wander in circles rather than walk in straight lines. To see whether people naturally walk in circles in the absence of visual clues, researcher Andrea Axtell tested 32 people on a football field. One at a time, they stood at the center of one goal line, were blindfolded, and then tried to walk to the other goal line. She recorded each individual's sex, height, handedness, the number of yards each was able to walk before going out of bounds, and whether each wandered off course to the left or the right. No one made it all the way to the far end of the field without crossing one of the sidelines. [Stats No. 39, Winter 2004]

**29. Horse race 2006.** The Kentucky Derby is a horse race that has been run every year since 1875 at Churchill Downs, Louisville, Kentucky. The race started as a 1.5-mile race, but in 1896 it was shortened to 1.25 miles because experts felt that 3-year-old horses shouldn't run such a long race that early in the season. (It has been run in May every year but one—1901—when it took place on April 29). Here are the data for the first few and a few recent races.

| Date | Winner | Margin (lengths) | Jockey | Winner's Payoff ($) | Duration (min:sec) | Track Condition |
|------|--------|------------------|--------|---------------------|---------------------|------------------|
| May 17, 1875 | Aristides | 2 | O. Lewis | 2850 | 2:37.75 | Fast |
| May 15, 1876 | Vagrant | 2 | B. Swim | 2950 | 2:38.25 | Fast |
| May 22, 1877 | Baden-Baden | 2 | W. Walker | 3300 | 2:38.00 | Fast |
| May 21, 1878 | Day Star | 1 | J. Carter | 4050 | 2:37.25 | Dusty |
| May 20, 1879 | Lord Murphy | 1 | C. Shauer | 3550 | 2:37.00 | Fast |
| . . . . . . | | | | | | |
| May 4, 2002 | War Emblem | 4 | V. Espinoza | 1875000 | 2:01.13 | Fast |
| May 3, 2003 | Funny Cide | 1 3/4 | J. Santos | 800200 | 2:01.19 | Fast |
| May 1, 2004 | Smarty Jones | 2 3/4 | S. Elliott | 854800 | 2:04.06 | Sloppy |
| May 7, 2005 | Giacomo | 1/2 | M. Smith | 5854800 | 2:02.75 | Fast |
| May 6, 2006 | Barbaro | 6 1/2 | E. Prado | 1453200 | 2:01.36 | Fast |

**30. Indy 2006.** The 2.5-mile Indianapolis Motor Speedway has been the home to a race on Memorial Day nearly every year since 1911. Even during the first race, there were controversies. Ralph Mulford was given the checkered flag first but took three extra laps just to make sure he'd completed 500 miles. When he finished, another driver, Ray Harroun, was being presented with the winner's trophy, and Mulford's protests were ignored. Harroun averaged 74.6 mph for the 500 miles. In 2003, the winner, Gil de Ferran, averaged 153.6 mph.

Here are the data for the first few and four recent Indianapolis 500 races. Included also are the pole winners (the winners of the trial the day before, when each driver drives alone to determine the position on race day).

| Year | Winner | Pole Position | Average Speed (mph) | Pole Winner | Average Pole Speed (mph) |
|------|--------|---------------|---------------------|-------------|--------------------------|
| 1911 | Ray Harroun | 28 | 74.602 | Lewis Strang | . |
| 1912 | Joe Dawson | 7 | 78.719 | Gil Anderson | . |
| 1913 | Jules Goux | 7 | 75.933 | Caleb Bragg | . |
| 1914 | Rene Thomas | 15 | 82.474 | Jean Chassagne | . |
| 1915 | Ralph DePalma | 2 | 89.840 | Howard Wilcox | 98.90 |
| 1916 | Dario Resta | 4 | 84.001 | John Aitken | 96.69 |
| 1919 | Howdy Wilcox | 2 | 88.050 | Rene Thomas | 104.78 |
| 1920 | Gaston Chevrolet | 6 | 88.618 | Ralph DePalma | 99.15 |
| . . . | | | | | |
| 2003 | Gil de Ferran | 10 | 156.291 | Helio Castroneves | 231.725 |
| 2004 | Buddy Rice | 1 | 138.518 | Buddy Rice | 222.04 |
| 2005 | Dan Wheldon | 26 | 157.603 | Tony Kanaan | 227.566 |
| 2006 | Sam Harnish Jr. | 1 | 157.085 | Sam Harnish Jr. | 228.985 |

**JUST CHECKING**
**Answers**

1. Who—Tour de France races; What—year, winner, country of origin, total time, average speed, stages, total distance ridden, starting riders, finishing riders; How—official statistics at race; Where—France (for the most part); When—1903 to 2006; Why—to see progress in speeds of cycling racing?

2. 
| Variable | Type | Units |
|---|---|---|
| Variable: Year | Type—Quantitative or Categorical | Units—Years |
| Variable: Winner | Type—Categorical | |
| Variable: Country of Origin | Type—Categorical | |
| Variable: Total Time | Type—Quantitative | Units—Hours/minutes/seconds |
| Variable: Average Speed | Type—Quantitative | Units—Kilometers per hour |
| Variable: Stages | Type—Quantitative | Units—Counts (stages) |
| Variable: Total Distance | Type—Quantitative | Units—Kilometers |
| Variable: Starting Riders | Type—Quantitative | Units—Counts (riders) |
| Variable: Finishing Riders | Type—Quantitative | Units—Counts (riders) |

# CHAPTER 3

# Displaying and Describing Categorical Data

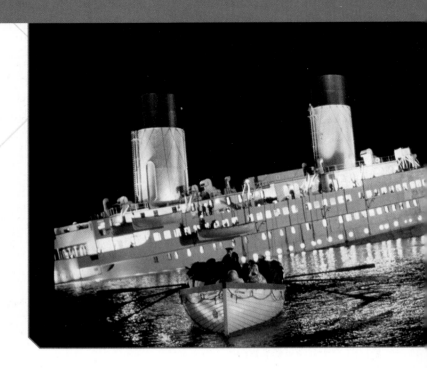

## Where are we going?

What is your class: Freshman, Sophomore, Junior, or Senior? What is your blood type? Which candidate do you plan to vote for?

Data are not just numbers—the answers to all these questions are categories. We'll study categorical variables like these, but things get even more interesting when we look at how categorical variables work together. Are men or women more likely to be Democrats? Are people with blue eyes more likely to be left-handed?

You often see categorical data displayed in pie charts or bar charts, or summarized in tables, sometimes in confusing ways. But, with a little skill, it's not hard to do it right.

| WHO | People on the *Titanic* |
|-----|-------------------------|
| WHAT | Survival status, age, sex, ticket class |
| WHEN | April 14, 1912 |
| WHERE | North Atlantic |
| HOW | A variety of sources and Internet sites |
| WHY | Historical interest |

**A S**  *Video:* **The Incident** tells the story of the Titanic, and includes rare film footage.

What happened on the *Titanic* at 11:40 on the night of April 14, 1912, is well known. Frederick Fleet's cry of "Iceberg, right ahead" and the three accompanying pulls of the crow's nest bell signaled the beginning of a nightmare that has become legend. By 2:15 a.m., the *Titanic,* thought by many to be unsinkable, had sunk, leaving more than 1500 passengers and crew members on board to meet their icy fate.

Here are some data about the passengers and crew aboard the *Titanic.* Each case (row) of the data table represents a person on board the ship. The variables

| Survival | Age | Sex | Class |
|----------|-----|-----|-------|
| Dead | Adult | Male | Third |
| Dead | Adult | Male | Crew |
| Dead | Adult | Male | Third |
| Dead | Adult | Male | Crew |
| Dead | Adult | Male | Crew |
| Dead | Adult | Male | Crew |
| Alive | Adult | Female | First |
| Dead | Adult | Male | Third |
| Dead | Adult | Male | Crew |

**Table 3.1**

Part of a data table showing four variables for nine people aboard the *Titanic.*

are the person's *Survival* (Dead or Alive) and the person's *Age* (Adult or Child), *Sex* (Male or Female), and ticket *Class* (First, Second, Third, or Crew).

The problem with a data table like this—and in fact with all data tables—is that you can't *see* what's going on. And seeing is just what we want to do. We need ways to show the data so that we can see patterns, relationships, trends, and exceptions.

## The Three Rules of Data Analysis

So, what should we do with data like these? There are three things you should always do first with data:

1. **Make a picture.** A display of your data will reveal things you are not likely to see in a table of numbers and will help you to *Think* clearly about the patterns and relationships that may be hiding in your data.
2. **Make a picture.** A well-designed display will *Show* the important features and patterns in your data. A picture will also show you the things you did not expect to see: the extraordinary (possibly wrong) data values or unexpected patterns.
3. **Make a picture.** The best way to *Tell* others about your data is with a well-chosen picture.

These are the three rules of data analysis. There are pictures of data throughout the book, and new kinds keep showing up. These days, technology makes drawing pictures of data easy, so there is no reason not to follow the three rules.

**FIGURE 3.1** *A Picture to Tell a Story*

*Florence Nightingale (1820–1910), a founder of modern nursing, was also a pioneer in health management, statistics, and epidemiology. She was the first female member of the British Statistical Society and was granted honorary membership in the newly formed American Statistical Association.*

*To argue forcefully for better hospital conditions for soldiers, she and her colleague, Dr. William Farr, invented this display, which showed that in the Crimean War, far more soldiers died of illness and infection than of battle wounds. Her campaign succeeded in improving hospital conditions and nursing for soldiers.*

*Florence Nightingale went on to apply statistical methods to a variety of important health issues and published more than 200 books, reports, and pamphlets during her long and illustrious career.*

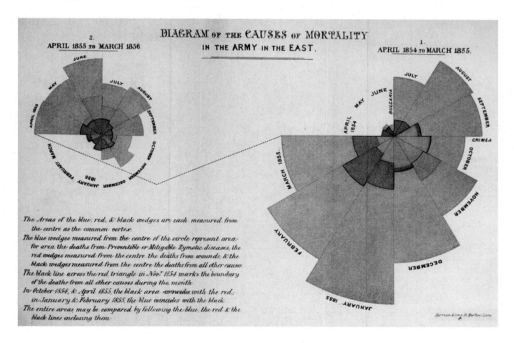

## Frequency Tables: Making Piles

**A S** **Activity: Make and examine a table of counts.** Even data on something as simple as hair color can reveal surprises when you organize it in a data table.

To make a picture of data, the first thing we have to do is to make piles. Making piles is the beginning of understanding about data. We pile together things that seem to go together, so we can see how the cases distribute across different

| Class | Count |
|--------|-------|
| First | 325 |
| Second | 285 |
| Third | 706 |
| Crew | 885 |

**Table 3.2**

A frequency table of the *Titanic* passengers.

| Class | % |
|--------|-------|
| First | 14.77 |
| Second | 12.95 |
| Third | 32.08 |
| Crew | 40.21 |

**Table 3.3**

A relative frequency table for the same data.

categories. For categorical data, piling is easy. We just count the number of cases corresponding to each category and pile them up.

One way to put all 2201 people on the *Titanic* into piles is by ticket *Class*, counting up how many had each kind of ticket. We can organize these counts into a **frequency table,** which records the totals and the category names.

Even when we have thousands of cases, a variable like ticket *Class*, with only a few categories, has a frequency table that's easy to read. A frequency table with dozens or hundreds of categories would be much harder to read. We use the names of the categories to label each row in the frequency table. For ticket *Class*, these are "First," "Second," "Third," and "Crew."

Counts are useful, but sometimes we want to know the fraction or **proportion** of the data in each category, so we divide the counts by the total number of cases. Usually we multiply by 100 to express these proportions as **percentages.** A **relative frequency table** displays the *percentages*, rather than the counts, of the values in each category. Both types of tables show how the cases are distributed across the categories. In this way, they describe the **distribution** of a categorical variable because they name the possible categories and tell how frequently each occurs.

## The Area Principle

**FIGURE 3.2**

*How many people were in each class on the* Titanic? *From this display, it looks as though the service must have been great, since most aboard were crew members. Although the* length *of each ship here corresponds to the correct number, the impression is all wrong. In fact, only about 40% were crew.*

Now that we have the frequency table, we're ready to follow the three rules of data analysis and make a picture of the data. But a bad picture can distort our understanding rather than help it. Here's a graph of the *Titanic* data. What impression do you get about who was aboard the ship?

It sure looks like most of the people on the *Titanic* were crew members, with a few passengers along for the ride. That doesn't seem right. What's wrong? The lengths of the ships *do* match the totals in the table. (You can check the scale at the bottom.) However, experience and psychological tests show that our eyes tend to be more impressed by the *area* than by other aspects of each ship image. So, even though the *length* of each ship matches up with one of the totals, it's the associated *area* in the image that we notice. Since there were about 3 times as many crew as second-class passengers, the ship depicting the number of crew is about 3 times longer than the ship depicting second-class passengers, but it occupies about 9 times the area. As you can see from the frequency table (Table 3.2), that just isn't a correct impression.

The best data displays observe a fundamental principle of graphing data called the **area principle.** The area principle says that the area occupied by a part of the graph should correspond to the magnitude of the value it represents. Violations of the area principle are a common way to lie (or, since most mistakes are unintentional, we should say err) with Statistics.

## Bar Charts

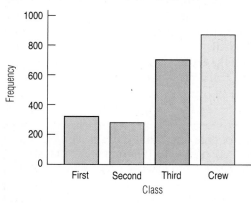

**FIGURE 3.3** *People on the* Titanic *by Ticket Class*
*With the area principle satisfied, we can see the true distribution more clearly.*

**A S**    *Activity:* **Bar Charts.**
Watch bar charts grow from data; then use your statistics package to create some bar charts for yourself.

For some reason, some computer programs give the name "bar chart" to any graph that uses bars. And others use different names according to whether the bars are horizontal or vertical. Don't be misled. "Bar chart" is the term for a *display of counts of a categorical variable* with bars.

Here's a chart that obeys the area principle. It's not as visually entertaining as the ships, but it does give an *accurate* visual impression of the distribution. The height of each bar shows the count for its category. The bars are the same width, so their heights determine their areas, and the areas are proportional to the counts in each class. Now it's easy to see that the majority of people on board were *not* crew, as the ships picture led us to believe. We can also see that there were about 3 times as many crew as second-class passengers. And there were more than twice as many third-class passengers as either first- or second-class passengers, something you may have missed in the frequency table. Bar charts make these kinds of comparisons easy and natural.

A **bar chart** displays the distribution of a categorical variable, showing the counts for each category next to each other for easy comparison. Bar charts should have small spaces between the bars to indicate that these are freestanding bars that could be rearranged into any order. The bars are lined up along a common base.

Usually they stick up like this 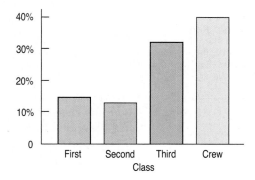, but sometimes they run sideways like this .

If we really want to draw attention to the relative *proportion* of passengers falling into each of these classes, we could replace the counts with percentages and use a **relative frequency bar chart.**

**FIGURE 3.4**
*The relative frequency bar chart looks the same as the bar chart (Figure 3.3), but shows the proportion of people in each category rather than the counts.*

## Pie Charts

Another common display that shows how a whole group breaks into several categories is a pie chart. **Pie charts** show the whole group of cases as a circle. They slice the circle into pieces whose size is proportional to the fraction of the whole in each category.

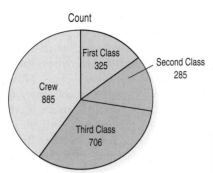

Count

**FIGURE 3.5** *Number of* Titanic *passengers in each class.*

Pie charts give a quick impression of how a whole group is partitioned into smaller groups. Because we're used to cutting up pies into 2, 4, or 8 pieces, pie charts are good for seeing relative frequencies near 1/2, 1/4, or 1/8. For example, you may be able to tell that the pink slice, representing the second-class passengers, is very close to 1/8 of the total. It's harder to see that there were about twice as many third-class as first-class passengers. Which category had the most passengers? Were there more crew or more third-class passengers? Comparisons such as these are easier in a bar chart.

> **Think before you draw**   Our first rule of data analysis is *Make a picture.* But what kind of picture? We don't have a lot of options—yet. There's more to Statistics than pie charts and bar charts, and knowing when to use each type of graph is a critical first step in data analysis. That decision depends in part on what type of data we have.
>
> It's important to check that the data are appropriate for whatever method of analysis you choose. Before you make a bar chart or a pie chart, always check the **Categorical Data Condition:** The data are counts or percentages of individuals in categories.
>
> If you want to make a relative frequency bar chart or a pie chart, you'll need to also make sure that the categories don't overlap, so that no individual is counted twice. If the categories do overlap, you can still make a bar chart, but the percentages won't add up to 100%. For the *Titanic* data, either kind of display is appropriate because the categories don't overlap.
>
> Throughout this course, you'll see that doing Statistics right means selecting the proper methods. That means you have to *Think* about the situation at hand. An important first step, then, is to check that the type of analysis you plan is appropriate. The Categorical Data Condition is just the first of many such checks.

# Contingency Tables: Children and First-Class Ticket Holders First?

**A S** *Activity:* **Children at Risk.** This activity looks at the fates of children aboard the *Titanic;* the subsequent activity shows how to make such tables on the computer.

We know how many tickets of each class were sold on the *Titanic,* and we know that only about 32% of all those aboard the *Titanic* survived. After looking at the distribution of each variable by itself, it's natural and more interesting to ask how they relate. Was there a relationship between the kind of ticket a passenger held and the passenger's chances of making it into the lifeboat? To answer this question, we need to look at the two categorical variables *Class* and *Survival* together.

To look at two categorical variables together, we often arrange the counts in a two-way table. Here is a two-way table of those aboard the *Titanic,* classified according to the class of ticket and whether the ticket holder survived or didn't. Because the table shows how the individuals are distributed along each variable, contingent on the value of the other variable, such a table is called a **contingency table.**

|  |  | Class | | | | |
|---|---|---|---|---|---|---|
|  |  | First | Second | Third | Crew | Total |
| Survival | **Alive** | 203 | 118 | 178 | 212 | **711** |
|  | **Dead** | 122 | 167 | 528 | 673 | **1490** |
|  | **Total** | **325** | **285** | **706** | **885** | **2201** |

**Table 3.4**

**Contingency table of ticket *Class* and *Survival*.** The bottom line of "Totals" is the same as the previous frequency table.

The margins of the table, both on the right and at the bottom, give totals. The bottom line of the table is just the frequency distribution of ticket *Class*. The right column of the table is the frequency distribution of the variable *Survival*. When presented like this, in the margins of a contingency table, the frequency distribution of one of the variables is called its **marginal distribution.**

Each **cell** of the table gives the count for a combination of values of the two variables. If you look down the column for second-class passengers to the first cell, you can see that 118 second-class passengers survived. Looking at the third-class passengers, you can see that more third-class passengers (178) survived. Were second-class passengers more likely to survive? Questions like this are easier to address by using percentages. The 118 survivors in second class were 41.4% of the total 285 second-class passengers, while the 178 surviving third-class passengers were only 25.2% of that class's total.

We know that 118 second-class passengers survived. We could display this number as a percentage, but as a percentage of what? The total number of passengers? (118 is 5.4% of the total, 2201.) The number of second-class passengers? (118 is 41.4% of the 285 second-class passengers.) The number of survivors? (118 is 16.6% of the 711 survivors.) All of these are possibilities, and all are potentially useful or interesting. You'll probably wind up calculating (or letting your technology calculate) lots of percentages. Most statistics programs offer a choice of total percent, row percent, or column percent for contingency tables. Unfortunately, they often put them all together with several numbers in each cell of the table. The resulting table holds lots of information, but it can be hard to understand:

*A bell-shaped artifact from the* Titanic.

**Table 3.5**

**Another contingency table of ticket** *Class.* This time we see not only the counts for each combination of *Class* and *Survival* (in bold) but the percentages these counts represent. For each count, there are three choices for the percentage: by row, by column, and by table total. There's probably too much information here for this table to be useful.

| | | | First | Second | Third | Crew | Total |
|---|---|---|---|---|---|---|---|
| | | | | | **Class** | | |
| Survival | Alive | Count | **203** | **118** | **178** | **212** | **711** |
| | | % of Row | 28.6% | 16.6% | 25.0% | 29.8% | 100% |
| | | % of Column | 62.5% | 41.4% | 25.2% | 24.0% | 32.3% |
| | | % of Table | 9.2% | 5.4% | 8.1% | 9.6% | 32.3% |
| | Dead | Count | **122** | **167** | **528** | **673** | **1490** |
| | | % of Row | 8.2% | 11.2% | 35.4% | 45.2% | 100% |
| | | % of Column | 37.5% | 58.6% | 74.8% | 76.0% | 67.7% |
| | | % of Table | 5.6% | 7.6% | 24.0% | 30.6% | 67.7% |
| | Total | Count | **325** | **285** | **706** | **885** | **2201** |
| | | % of Row | 14.8% | 12.9% | 32.1% | 40.2% | 100% |
| | | % of Column | 100% | 100% | 100% | 100% | 100% |
| | | % of Table | 14.8% | 12.9% | 32.1% | 40.2% | 100% |

To simplify the table, let's first pull out the percent of table values:

**Table 3.6**

**A contingency table of** *Class* **by** *Survival* **with only the table percentages.**

| | | First | Second | Third | Crew | Total |
|---|---|---|---|---|---|---|
| | | | | **Class** | | |
| Survival | Alive | 9.2% | 5.4% | 8.1% | 9.6% | 32.3% |
| | Dead | 5.6% | 7.6% | 24.0% | 30.6% | 67.7% |
| | Total | 14.8% | 12.9% | 32.1% | 40.2% | 100% |

These percentages tell us what percent of *all* passengers belong to each combination of column and row category. For example, we see that although 8.1% of the people aboard the *Titanic* were surviving third-class ticket holders, only 5.4%

were surviving second-class ticket holders. Is this fact useful? Comparing these percentages, you might think that the chances of surviving were better in third class than in second. But be careful. There were many more third-class than second-class passengers on the *Titanic,* so there were more third-class survivors. That group is a larger percentage of the passengers, but is that really what we want to know?

---

**Percent of what?**   The English language can be tricky when we talk about percentages. If you're asked, "What percent *of the survivors* were in second class?" it's pretty clear that we're interested only in survivors. It's as if we're restricting the *Who* in the question to the survivors, so we should look at the number of second-class passengers among all the survivors—in other words, the row percent.

But if you're asked, "What percent were second-class passengers who survived?" you have a different question. Be careful; here, the *Who* is everyone on board, so 2201 should be the denominator, and the answer is the table percent.

And if you're asked, "What percent of the second-class passengers survived?" you have a third question. Now the *Who* is the second-class passengers, so the denominator is the 285 second-class passengers, and the answer is the column percent.

Always be sure to ask "percent of what?" That will help you to know the *Who* and whether we want *row, column,* or *table* percentages.

---

## FOR EXAMPLE    Finding marginal distributions

**Question:** In January 2007, a Gallup poll asked 1008 Americans age 18 and over whether they planned to watch the upcoming Super Bowl. The pollster also asked those who planned to watch whether they were looking forward more to seeing the football game or the commercials. The results are summarized in the table:

|  |  | Sex | |  |
|---|---|---|---|---|
|  |  | **Male** | **Female** | Total |
| | **Game** | 279 | 200 | **479** |
| **Response** | **Commercials** | 81 | 156 | **237** |
| | **Won't watch** | 132 | 160 | **292** |
|  | Total | **492** | **516** | **1008** |

What's the marginal distribution of the responses?

To determine the percentages for the three responses, divide the count for each response by the total number of people polled:

$$\frac{479}{1008} = 47.5\%, \quad \frac{237}{1008} = 23.5\%, \quad \frac{292}{1008} = 29.0\%.$$

According to the poll, 47.5% of American adults were looking forward to watching the Super Bowl game, 23.5% were looking forward to watching the commercials, and 29% didn't plan to watch at all.

---

# Conditional Distributions

The more interesting questions are *contingent.* We'd like to know, for example, what percentage *of second-class passengers* survived and how that compares with the survival rate for third-class passengers.

It's more interesting to ask whether the chance of surviving the *Titanic* sinking *depended* on ticket class. We can look at this question in two ways. First, we could ask how the distribution of ticket *Class* changes between survivors and nonsurvivors. To do that, we look at the *row percentages:*

**Table 3.7**

The conditional distribution of ticket *Class* conditioned on each value of *Survival: Alive* and *Dead*.

|  |  | Class | | | | |
|---|---|---|---|---|---|---|
|  |  | First | Second | Third | Crew | Total |
| Survival | **Alive** | **203**<br>28.6% | **118**<br>16.6% | **178**<br>25.0% | **212**<br>29.8% | **711**<br>**100%** |
|  | **Dead** | **122**<br>8.2% | **167**<br>11.2% | **528**<br>35.4% | **673**<br>45.2% | **1490**<br>**100%** |

By focusing on each row separately, we see the distribution of class under the *condition* of surviving or not. The sum of the percentages in each row is 100%, and we divide that up by ticket class. In effect, we temporarily restrict the *Who* first to survivors and make a pie chart for them. Then we refocus the *Who* on the nonsurvivors and make their pie chart. These pie charts show the distribution of ticket classes *for each row* of the table: survivors and nonsurvivors. The distributions we create this way are called **conditional distributions,** because they show the distribution of one variable for just those cases that satisfy a condition on another variable.

**FIGURE 3.6**

*Pie charts of the conditional distributions of ticket* Class *for the survivors and nonsurvivors, separately. Do the distributions appear to be the same? We're concerned primarily with percentages here, so pie charts are a reasonable choice.*

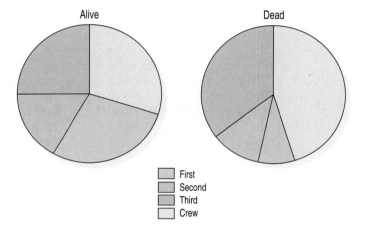

Alive      Dead

- First
- Second
- Third
- Crew

---

**FOR EXAMPLE**     Finding conditional distributions

**Recap:** The table shows results of a poll asking adults whether they were looking forward to the Super Bowl game, looking forward to the commercials, or didn't plan to watch.

|  |  | Sex | | |
|---|---|---|---|---|
|  |  | Male | Female | Total |
| Response | **Game** | 279 | 200 | 479 |
|  | **Commercials** | 81 | 156 | 237 |
|  | **Won't watch** | 132 | 160 | 292 |
|  | Total | **492** | **516** | **1008** |

**Question:** How do the conditional distributions of interest in the commercials differ for men and women?

Look at the group of people who responded "commercials" and determine what percent of them were male and female:

$$\frac{81}{237} = 34.2\%, \quad \frac{156}{237} = 65.8\%.$$

Women make up a sizeable majority of the adult Americans who look forward to seeing Super Bowl commercials more than the game itself. Nearly 66% of people who voiced a preference for the commercials were women, and only 34% were men.

But we can also turn the question around. We can look at the distribution of *Survival* for each category of ticket *Class*. To do this, we look at the *column percentages*. Those show us whether the chance of surviving was roughly the same *for each of the four classes*. Now the percentages in each column add to 100%, because we've restricted the *Who*, in turn, to each of the four ticket classes:

|  |  | Class | | | | |
|---|---|---|---|---|---|---|
|  |  | **First** | **Second** | **Third** | **Crew** | Total |
| **Alive** | **Count**<br>**% of Column** | 203<br>62.5% | 118<br>41.4% | 178<br>25.2% | 212<br>24.0% | 711<br>**32.3%** |
| **Dead** | **Count**<br>**% of Column** | 122<br>37.5% | 167<br>58.6% | 528<br>74.8% | 673<br>76.0% | 1490<br>**67.7%** |
| **Total** | **Count** | **325**<br>**100%** | **285**<br>**100%** | **706**<br>**100%** | **885**<br>**100%** | **2201**<br>**100%** |

**Table 3.8**

A contingency table of *Class* by *Survival,* with only counts and column percentages. Each column represents the conditional distribution of *Survival* for a given category of ticket *Class.*

Looking at how the percentages change across each row, it sure looks like ticket class mattered in whether a passenger survived. To make it more vivid, we could show the distribution of *Survival* for each ticket class in a display. Here's a side-by-side bar chart showing percentages of surviving and not for each category:

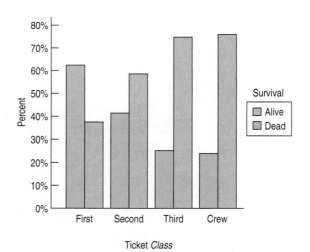

**FIGURE 3.7**

*Side-by-side bar chart showing the conditional distribution of* Survival *for each category of ticket* Class. *The corresponding pie charts would have only two categories in each of four pies, so bar charts seem the better alternative.*

These bar charts are simple because, for the variable *Survival,* we have only two alternatives: Alive and Dead. When we have only two categories, we really need to know only the percentage of one of them. Knowing the percentage that survived tells us the percentage that died. We can use this fact to simplify the display even more by dropping one category. Here are the percentages of dying *across the classes* displayed in one chart:

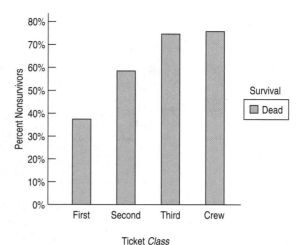

**FIGURE 3.8**

*Bar chart showing just nonsurvivor percentages for each value of ticket Class. Because we have only two values, the second bar doesn't add any information. Compare this chart to the side-by-side bar chart shown earlier.*

Now it's easy to compare the risks. Among first-class passengers, 37.5% perished, compared to 58.6% for second-class ticket holders, 74.8% for those in third class, and 76.0% for crew members.

If the risk had been about the same across the ticket classes, we would have said that survival was *independent* of class. But it's not. The differences we see among these conditional distributions suggest that survival may have depended on ticket class. You may find it useful to consider conditioning on each variable in a contingency table in order to explore the dependence between them.

It is interesting to know that *Class* and *Survival* are associated. That's an important part of the *Titanic* story. And we know how important this is because the margins show us the actual numbers of people involved.

Variables can be associated in many ways and to different degrees. The best way to tell whether two variables are associated is to ask whether they are *not*.[1] In a contingency table, when the distribution of *one* variable is the same for all categories of another, we say that the variables are **independent.** That tells us there's no association between these variables. We'll see a way to check for independence formally later in the book. For now, we'll just compare the distributions.

---

**FOR EXAMPLE**  |  Looking for associations between variables

**Recap:** The table shows results of a poll asking adults whether they were looking forward to the Super Bowl game, looking forward to the commercials, or didn't plan to watch.

|  |  | Sex |  |  |
|---|---|---|---|---|
|  |  | **Male** | **Female** | Total |
| **Response** | **Game** | 279 | 200 | 479 |
|  | **Commercials** | 81 | 156 | 237 |
|  | **Won't watch** | 132 | 160 | 292 |
|  | Total | **492** | **516** | **1008** |

**Question:** Does it seem that there's an association between interest in Super Bowl TV coverage and a person's sex?

First find the distribution of the three responses for the men (the column percentages):

$$\frac{279}{492} = 56.7\%;$$

$$\frac{81}{492} = 16.5\%;$$

$$\frac{132}{492} = 26.8\%.$$

*(continued)*

---

[1] This kind of "backwards" reasoning shows up surprisingly often in science—and in Statistics. We'll see it again.

For Example (*continued*)

Then do the same for the women who were polled, and display the two distributions with a side-by-side bar chart:

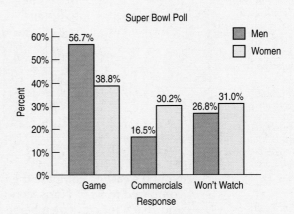

Based on this poll it appears that women were only slightly less interested than men in watching the Super Bowl telecast: 31% of the women said they didn't plan to watch, compared to just under 27% of men. Among those who planned to watch, however, there appears to be an association between the viewer's sex and what the viewer is most looking forward to. While more women are interested in the game (39%) than the commercials (30%), the margin among men is much wider: 57% of men said they were looking forward to seeing the game, compared to only 16.5% who cited the commercials.

## JUST CHECKING

A Statistics class reports the following data on Sex and Eye Color for students in the class:

|  |  | Eye Color | | | |
|---|---|---|---|---|---|
|  |  | Blue | Brown | Green/Hazel/Other | Total |
| Sex | Males | 6 | 20 | 6 | 32 |
|  | Females | 4 | 16 | 12 | 32 |
|  | Total | 10 | 36 | 18 | 64 |

1. What percent of females are brown-eyed?
2. What percent of brown-eyed students are female?
3. What percent of students are brown-eyed females?
4. What's the distribution of Eye Color?
5. What's the conditional distribution of Eye Color for the males?
6. Compare the percent who are female among the blue-eyed students to the percent of all students who are female.
7. Does it seem that Eye Color and Sex are independent? Explain.

# Segmented Bar Charts

We could display the *Titanic* information by dividing up bars rather than circles. The resulting **segmented bar chart** treats each bar as the "whole" and divides it proportionally into segments corresponding to the percentage in each group. We can clearly see that the distributions of ticket *Class* are different, indicating again that survival was not independent of ticket *Class*.

**FIGURE 3.9** *A segmented bar chart for* **Class** *by* **Survival**

*Notice that although the totals for survivors and nonsurvivors are quite different, the bars are the same height because we have converted the numbers to* percentages. *Compare this display with the side-by-side pie charts of the same data in Figure 3.6.*

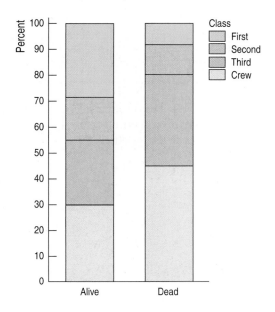

---

**STEP-BY-STEP EXAMPLE** | **Examining Contingency Tables**

Medical researchers followed 6272 Swedish men for 30 years to see if there was any association between the amount of fish in their diet and prostate cancer ("Fatty Fish Consumption and Risk of Prostate Cancer," *Lancet*, June 2001). Their results are summarized in this table:

*We asked for a picture of a man eating fish. This is what we got.*

|  | Prostate Cancer | |
|---|---|---|
|  | **No** | **Yes** |
| **Never/seldom** | 110 | 14 |
| **Small part of diet** | 2420 | 201 |
| **Moderate part** | 2769 | 209 |
| **Large part** | 507 | 42 |

(Fish Consumption — row labels)

**Table 3.9**

**Question:** Is there an association between fish consumption and prostate cancer?

THINK

**Plan** Be sure to state what the problem is about.

*I want to know if there is an association between fish consumption and prostate cancer.*

**Variables** Identify the variables and report the W's.

The individuals are 6272 Swedish men followed by medical researchers for 30 years. The variables record their fish consumption and whether or not they were diagnosed with prostate cancer.

Be sure to check the appropriate condition.

✔ **Categorical Data Condition:** I have counts for both fish consumption and cancer diagnosis. The categories of diet do not overlap, and the diagnoses do not overlap. It's okay to draw pie charts or bar charts.

 **Mechanics** It's a good idea to check the marginal distributions first before looking at the two variables together.

|  | | Prostate Cancer | | |
|---|---|---|---|---|
| | | **No** | **Yes** | Total |
| **Fish Consumption** | **Never/Seldom** | 110 | 14 | **124 (2.0%)** |
| | **Small part of diet** | 2420 | 201 | **2621 (41.8%)** |
| | **Moderate part** | 2769 | 209 | **2978 (47.5%)** |
| | **Large part** | 507 | 42 | **549 (8.8%)** |
| | Total | **5806 (92.6%)** | **466 (7.4%)** | **6272 (100%)** |

Two categories of the diet are quite small, with only 2.0% Never/Seldom eating fish and 8.8% in the "Large part" category. Overall, 7.4% of the men in this study had prostate cancer.

Then, make appropriate displays to see whether there is a difference in the relative proportions. These pie charts compare fish consumption for men who have prostate cancer to fish consumption for men who don't.

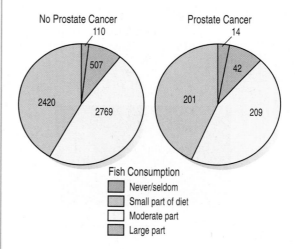

It's hard to see much difference in the pie charts. So, I made a display of the row percentages. Because there are only two alternatives, I chose to display the risk of prostate cancer for each group:

Both pie charts and bar charts can be used to compare conditional distributions. Here we compare prostate cancer rates based on differences in fish consumption.

**Conclusion** Interpret the patterns in the table and displays in context. If you can, discuss possible real-world consequences. Be careful not to overstate what you see. The results may not generalize to other situations.

Overall, there is a 7.4% rate of prostate cancer among men in this study. Most of the men (89.3%) ate fish either as a moderate or small part of their diet. From the pie charts, it's hard to see a difference in cancer rates among the groups. But in the bar chart, it looks like the cancer rate for those who never/seldom ate fish may be somewhat higher.

However, only 124 of the 6272 men in the study fell into this category, and only 14 of them developed prostate cancer. More study would probably be needed before we would recommend that men change their diets.[2]

This study is an example of looking at a sample of data to learn something about a larger population. We care about more than these particular 6272 Swedish men. We hope that learning about their experiences will tell us something about the value of eating fish in general. That raises the interesting question of what population we think this sample might represent. Do we hope to learn about all Swedish men? About all men? About the value of eating fish for all adult humans?[3] Often, it can be hard to decide just which population our findings may tell us about, but that also is how researchers decide what to look into in future studies.

---

[2] The original study actually used pairs of twins, which enabled the researchers to discern that the risk of cancer for those who never ate fish actually *was* substantially greater. Using pairs is a special way of gathering data. We'll discuss such study design issues and how to analyze the data in later chapters.

[3] Probably not, since we're looking only at prostate cancer risk.

# WHAT CAN GO WRONG?

▶ **Don't violate the area principle.** This is probably the most common mistake in a graphical display. It is often made in the cause of artistic presentation. Here, for example, are two displays of the pie chart of the *Titanic* passengers by class:

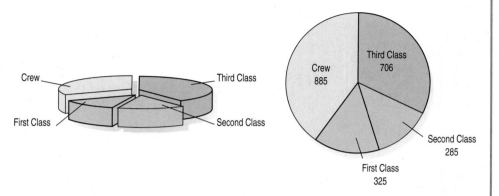

The one on the left looks pretty, doesn't it? But showing the pie on a slant violates the area principle and makes it much more difficult to compare fractions of the whole made up of each class—the principal feature that a pie chart ought to show.

▶ **Keep it honest.** Here's a pie chart that displays data on the percentage of high school students who engage in specified dangerous behaviors as reported by the Centers for Disease Control. What's wrong with this plot?

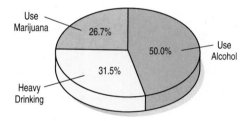

Try adding up the percentages. Or look at the 50% slice. Does it look right? Then think: What are these percentages of? Is there a "whole" that has been sliced up? In a pie chart, the proportions shown by each slice of the pie must add up to 100% and each individual must fall into only one category. Of course, showing the pie on a slant makes it even harder to detect the error.

Here's another. This bar chart shows the number of airline passengers searched in security screening, by year:

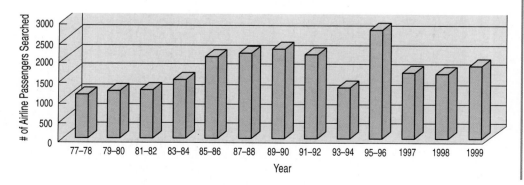

Looks like things didn't change much in the final years of the 20th century—until you read the bar labels and see that the last three bars represent single years while all the others are for *pairs* of years. Of course, the false depth makes it harder to see the problem.

▶ **Don't confuse similar-sounding percentages.** These percentages sound similar but are different:

   ▶ The percentage of the passengers who were both in first class and survived: This would be 203/2201, or 9.4%.
   ▶ The percentage of the first-class passengers who survived: This is 203/325, or 62.5%.
   ▶ The percentage of the survivors who were in first class: This is 203/711, or 28.6%.

In each instance, pay attention to the *Who* implicitly defined by the phrase. Often, there is a restriction to a smaller group (all aboard the *Titanic*, those in first class, and those who survived, respectively) before a percentage is found. Your discussion of results must make these differences clear.

▶ **Don't forget to look at the variables separately, too.** When you make a contingency table or display a conditional distribution, be sure you also examine the marginal distributions. It's important to know how many cases are in each category.

▶ **Be sure to use enough individuals.** When you consider percentages, take care that they are based on a large enough number of individuals. Take care not to make a report such as this one:

   *We found that 66.67% of the rats improved their performance with training. The other rat died.*

▶ **Don't overstate your case.** Independence is an important concept, but it is rare for two variables to be *entirely* independent. We can't conclude that one variable has no effect whatsoever on another. Usually, all we know is that little effect was observed in our study. Other studies of other groups under other circumstances could find different results.

## SIMPSON'S PARADOX

▶ **Don't use unfair or silly averages.** Sometimes averages can be misleading. Sometimes they just don't make sense at all. Be careful when averaging different variables that the quantities you're averaging are comparable. The Centerville sign says it all.

When using averages of proportions across several different groups, it's important to make sure that the groups really are comparable.

It's easy to make up an example showing that averaging across very different values or groups can give absurd results. Here's how that might work: Suppose there are two pilots, Moe and Jill. Moe argues that he's the better pilot of the two, since he managed to land 83% of his last 120 flights on time compared with Jill's 78%. But let's look at the data a little more closely. Here are the results for each of their last 120 flights, broken down by the time of day they flew:

|  |  | Class |  |  |  |  |
|---|---|---|---|---|---|---|
|  |  | First | Second | Third | Crew | Total |
| Survival | **Alive** | 203 | 118 | 178 | 212 | **711** |
|  | **Dead** | 122 | 167 | 528 | 673 | **1490** |
|  | Total | **325** | **285** | **706** | **885** | **2201** |

**Entering Centerville**

| | |
|---|---|
| Established | 1793 |
| Population | 7943 |
| Elevation | 710 |
| Average | 3,482 |

**Table 3.10**

On-time flights by *Time of Day* and *Pilot*. Look at the percentages within each *Time of Day* category. Who has a better on-time record during the day? At night? Who is better overall?

|  |  | Time of Day | | |
|---|---|---|---|---|
|  |  | **Day** | **Night** | **Overall** |
| Pilot | **Moe** | 90 out of 100<br>90% | 10 out of 20<br>50% | 100 out of 120<br>83% |
|  | **Jill** | 19 out of 20<br>95% | 75 out of 100<br>75% | 94 out of 120<br>78% |

*(continued)*

One famous example of Simpson's paradox arose during an investigation of admission rates for men and women at the University of California at Berkeley's graduate schools. As reported in an article in *Science,* about 45% of male applicants were admitted, but only about 30% of female applicants got in. It looked like a clear case of discrimination. However, when the data were broken down by school (Engineering, Law, Medicine, etc.), it turned out that, within each school, the women were admitted at nearly the same or, in some cases, much *higher* rates than the men. How could this be? Women applied in large numbers to schools with very low admission rates (Law and Medicine, for example, admitted fewer than 10%). Men tended to apply to Engineering and Science. Those schools have admission rates above 50%. When the *average* was taken, the women had a much lower *overall* rate, but the average didn't really make sense.

Look at the daytime and nighttime flights separately. For day flights, Jill had a 95% on-time rate and Moe only a 90% rate. At night, Jill was on time 75% of the time and Moe only 50%. So Moe is better "overall," but Jill is better both during the day and at night. How can this be?

What's going on here is a problem known as **Simpson's paradox,** named for the statistician who discovered it in the 1960s. It comes up rarely in real life, but there have been several well-publicized cases. As we can see from the pilot example, the problem is *unfair averaging* over different groups. Jill has mostly night flights, which are more difficult, so her *overall average* is heavily influenced by her nighttime average. Moe, on the other hand, benefits from flying mostly during the day, with its higher on-time percentage. With their very different patterns of flying conditions, taking an overall average is misleading. It's not a fair comparison.

The moral of Simpson's paradox is to be careful when you average across different levels of a second variable. It's always better to compare percentages or other averages *within* each level of the other variable. The overall average may be misleading.

# CONNECTIONS

All of the methods of this chapter work with *categorical variables*. You must know the *Who* of the data to know who is counted in each category and the *What* of the variable to know where the categories come from.

## WHAT HAVE WE LEARNED?

We've learned that we can summarize categorical data by counting the number of cases in each category, sometimes expressing the resulting distribution as percents. We can display the distribution in a bar chart or a pie chart. When we want to see how two categorical variables are related, we put the counts (and/or percentages) in a two-way table called a contingency table.

▸ We look at the marginal distribution of each variable (found in the margins of the table).
▸ We also look at the conditional distribution of a variable within each category of the other variable.
▸ We can display these conditional and marginal distributions by using bar charts or pie charts.
▸ If the conditional distributions of one variable are (roughly) the same for every category of the other, the variables are independent.

## Terms

**Frequency table**
**(Relative frequency table)**

21. A frequency table lists the categories in a categorical variable and gives the count (or percentage of observations for each category.

| | |
|---|---|
| Distribution | 22. The distribution of a variable gives |
| | ▸ the possible values of the variable and |
| | ▸ the relative frequency of each value. |
| Area principle | 22. In a statistical display, each data value should be represented by the same amount of area. |
| Bar chart (Relative frequency bar chart) | 23. Bar charts show a bar whose area represents the count (or percentage) of observations for each category of a categorical variable. |
| Pie chart | 23. Pie charts show how a "whole" divides into categories by showing a wedge of a circle whose area corresponds to the proportion in each category. |
| Categorical data condition | 24. The methods in this chapter are appropriate for displaying and describing categorical data. Be careful not to use them with quantitative data. |
| Contingency table | 24. A contingency table displays counts and, sometimes, percentages of individuals falling into named categories on two or more variables. The table categorizes the individuals on all variables at once, to reveal possible patterns in one variable that may be contingent on the category of the other. |
| Marginal distribution | 25. In a contingency table, the distribution of either variable alone is called the marginal distribution. The counts or percentages are the totals found in the margins (last row or column) of the table. |
| Conditional distribution | 26. The distribution of a variable restricting the *Who* to consider only a smaller group of individuals is called a conditional distribution. |
| Independence | 29. Variables are said to be independent if the conditional distribution of one variable is the same for each category of the other. We'll show how to check for independence in a later chapter. |
| Segmented bar chart | 31. A segmented bar chart displays the conditional distribution of a categorical variable within each category of another variable. |
| Simpson's paradox | 35. When averages are taken across different groups, they can appear to contradict the overall averages. This is known as "Simpson's paradox." |

## Skills

▸ Be able to recognize when a variable is categorical and choose an appropriate display for it.

▸ Understand how to examine the association between categorical variables by comparing conditional and marginal percentages.

▸ Be able to summarize the distribution of a categorical variable with a frequency table.

▸ Be able to display the distribution of a categorical variable with a bar chart or pie chart.

▸ Know how to make and examine a contingency table.

▸ Know how to make and examine displays of the conditional distributions of one variable for two or more groups.

▸ Be able to describe the distribution of a categorical variable in terms of its possible values and relative frequencies.

▸ Know how to describe any anomalies or extraordinary features revealed by the display of a variable.

▸ Be able to describe and discuss patterns found in a contingency table and associated displays of conditional distributions.

# ON THE COMPUTER

## Displaying Categorical Data on the Computer

Although every package makes a slightly different bar chart, they all have similar features:

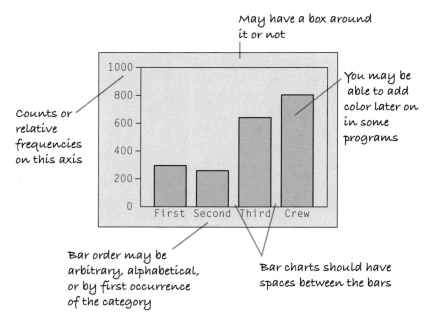

*May have a box around it or not*

*You may be able to add color later on in some programs*

*Counts or relative frequencies on this axis*

*Bar order may be arbitrary, alphabetical, or by first occurrence of the category*

*Bar charts should have spaces between the bars*

Sometimes the count or a percentage is printed above or on top of each bar to give some additional information. You may find that your statistics package sorts category names in annoying orders by default. For example, many packages sort categories alphabetically or by the order the categories are seen in the data set. Often, neither of these is the best choice.

### DATA DESK

To make a bar chart or pie chart, select the variable. In the **Plot** menu, choose **Bar Chart** or **Pie Chart.** To make a frequency table, in the **Calc** menu choose **Frequency Table.**

#### COMMENTS

These commands treat the data as categorical even if they are numerals. If you select a quantitative variable by mistake, you'll see an error message warning of too many categories.

### EXCEL

First make a pivot table (Excel's name for a frequency table). From the **Data** menu, choose **Pivot Table** and **Pivot Chart Report.**
When you reach the Layout window, drag your variable to the row area and drag your variable again to the data area. This tells Excel to count the occurrences of each category.
Once you have an Excel pivot table, you can construct bar charts and pie charts.
Click inside the Pivot Table.

Click the Pivot Table Chart Wizard button. Excel creates a bar chart.
A longer path leads to a pie chart; see your Excel documentation.

#### COMMENTS

Excel uses the pivot table to specify the category names and find counts within each category. If you already have that information, you can proceed directly to the Chart Wizard.

## EXCEL 2007

To make a bar chart:

▸ Select the variable in Excel you want to work with.
▸ Choose the **Column** command from the Insert tab in the Ribbon.
▸ Select the appropriate chart from the drop down dialog.

To change the bar chart into a pie chart:

▸ Right-click the chart and select **Change Chart Type...** from the menu. The Chart type dialog opens.
▸ Select a pie chart type.
▸ Click the **OK** button. Excel changes your bar chart into a pie chart.

## JMP

JMP makes a bar chart and frequency table together.
From the **Analyze** menu, choose **Distribution.**
In the Distribution dialog, drag the name of the variable into the empty variable window beside the label "Y, Columns"; click **OK.**
To make a pie chart, choose **Chart** from the **Graph** menu.
In the Chart dialog, select the variable name from the Columns list, click on the button labeled "Statistics," and select "N" from the drop-down menu.

Click the "**Categories, X, Levels**" button to assign the same variable name to the X-axis.
Under Options, click on the **second** button—labeled "**Bar Chart**"—and select "Pie" from the drop-down menu.

## MINITAB

To make a bar chart, choose **Bar Chart** from the **Graph** menu. Select "Counts of unique values" in the first menu, and select "Simple" for the type of graph. Click **OK.**

In the Chart dialog, enter the name of the variable that you wish to display in the box labeled "Categorical variables." Click **OK.**

## SPSS

To make a bar chart, open the **Chart Builder** from the **Graphs** menu.
Click the **Gallery** tab.
Choose **Bar Chart** from the list of chart types.
Drag the appropriate bar chart onto the canvas.
Drag a categorical variable onto the x-axis drop zone.
Click **OK**

COMMENT

A similar path makes a pie chart by choosing **Pie chart** from the list of chart types.

## TI-83/84 PLUS

The TI-83 won't do displays for categorical variables.

## TI-89

The TI-89 won't do displays for categorical variables.

# EXERCISES

**1. Graphs in the news.** Find a bar graph of categorical data from a newspaper, a magazine, or the Internet.
   a) Is the graph clearly labeled?
   b) Does it violate the area principle?
   c) Does the accompanying article tell the W's of the variable?
   d) Do you think the article correctly interprets the data? Explain.

**2. Graphs in the news II.** Find a pie chart of categorical data from a newspaper, a magazine, or the Internet.
   a) Is the graph clearly labeled?
   b) Does it violate the area principle?
   c) Does the accompanying article tell the W's of the variable?
   d) Do you think the article correctly interprets the data? Explain.

**3. Tables in the news.** Find a frequency table of categorical data from a newspaper, a magazine, or the Internet.
   a) Is it clearly labeled?
   b) Does it display percentages or counts?
   c) Does the accompanying article tell the W's of the variable?
   d) Do you think the article correctly interprets the data? Explain.

**4. Tables in the news II.** Find a contingency table of categorical data from a newspaper, a magazine, or the Internet.
   a) Is it clearly labeled?
   b) Does it display percentages or counts?
   c) Does the accompanying article tell the W's of the variables?
   d) Do you think the article correctly interprets the data? Explain.

**5. Movie genres.** The pie chart summarizes the genres of 120 first-run movies released in 2005.
   a) Is this an appropriate display for the genres? Why/why not?
   b) Which genre was least common?

Genre2
- Action/Adventure
- Comedy
- Drama
- Thriller/Horror

**6. Movie ratings.** The pie chart shows the ratings assigned to 120 first-run movies released in 2005.
   a) Is this an appropriate display for these data? Explain.
   b) Which was the most common rating?

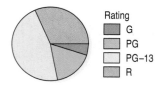

Rating
- G
- PG
- PG–13
- R

**7. Genres, again.** Here is a bar chart summarizing the 2005 movie genres, as seen in the pie chart in Exercise 5.
   a) Which genre was most common?
   b) Is it easier to see that in the pie chart or the bar chart? Explain.

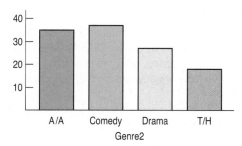

**8. Ratings, again.** Here is a bar chart summarizing the 2005 movie ratings, as seen in the pie chart in Exercise 6.
   a) Which was the least common rating?
   b) An editorial claimed that there's been a growth in PG-13 rated films that, according to the writer, "have too much sex and violence," at the expense of G-rated films that offer "good, clean fun." The writer offered the bar chart below as evidence to support his claim. Does the bar chart support his claim? Explain.

**9. Teen smokers.** In studying the behavior of teen smokers, the organization Monitoring the Future (www.monitoringthefuture.org) asked 2048 eighth graders who said they smoked cigarettes what brands they preferred. The results are shown in the table. Write a few sentences describing this distribution.

| Brand preference | Percent |
|---|---|
| Marlboro | 53.7 |
| Newport | 22.5 |
| Camel | 5.4 |
| Other (over 20 brands) | 8.7 |
| No usual brand | 9.7 |

**10. Sports.** Students in an introductory Statistics class were asked, "Do you play sports?" The table summarizes their responses. Write a few sentences summarizing this distribution.

| Response | Percent |
|---|---|
| No, not at all | 11.6 |
| Yes, but only for fun—informal | 43.2 |
| Yes, a club or intramural sport | 27.4 |
| Yes, I'm a varsity athlete | 17.9 |

**11. Magnet schools.** An article in the Winter 2003 issue of *Chance* magazine reported on the Houston Independent School District's magnet schools programs. Of the 1755 qualified applicants, 931 were accepted, 298 were wait-listed, and 526 were turned away for lack of space. Find the relative frequency distribution of the decisions made, and write a sentence describing it.

**12. Magnet schools again.** The *Chance* article about the Houston magnet schools program described in Exercise 11 also indicated that 517 applicants were black or Hispanic, 292 Asian, and 946 white. Summarize the relative frequency distribution of ethnicity with a sentence or two (in the proper context, of course).

**13. Causes of death 2003.** The Centers for Disease Control and Prevention (www.cdc.gov) lists causes of death in the United States during 2003:

| Cause of Death | Percent |
|---|---|
| Heart disease | 27.9 |
| Cancer | 22.8 |
| Circulatory diseases and stroke | 6.4 |
| Respiratory diseases | 5.2 |
| Accidents | 4.5 |

a) Is it reasonable to conclude that heart or respiratory diseases were the cause of approximately 33% of U.S. deaths in 2003?
b) What percent of deaths were from causes not listed here?
c) Create an appropriate display for these data.

**14. Plane crashes.** An investigation compiled information about recent nonmilitary plane crashes (www.planecrashinfo.com). The causes, to the extent that they could be determined, are summarized in the table.

| Cause | Percent |
|---|---|
| Pilot error | 40 |
| Other human error | 5 |
| Weather | 6 |
| Mechanical failure | 14 |
| Sabotage | 6 |

a) Is it reasonable to conclude that the weather or mechanical failures caused only about 20% of recent plane crashes?
b) In what percent of crashes were the causes not determined?
c) Create an appropriate display for these data.

**15. Ghosts.** A May 2001 Gallup Poll found that many Americans believe in ghosts and other supernatural phenomena. The poll was based on telephone responses from 1012 randomly selected adults. The table shows the percentages of people who expressed belief in various phenomena:

| Phenomenon | Percent Expressing Belief |
|---|---|
| Psychic healing | 54 |
| ESP | 50 |
| Ghosts | 38 |
| Astrology | 28 |
| Channeling | 15 |

a) Is it reasonable to conclude that 66% of those polled expressed belief in either ghosts or astrology?
b) Can you tell what percent of people did not believe in any of the phenomena listed? Explain.
c) Make a bar chart to display these results, and label it correctly.

**16. Illegal guns.** A study by the U.S. Bureau of Alcohol, Tobacco, and Firearms (BATF) (*USA Today,* 22 June 2000) surveyed 1530 investigations by the U.S. BATF into illegal gun trafficking from July 1996 through December 1998. The study reports the portion of cases that were the result of each of five gun-trafficking violations:

46% Straw purchase (legal gun buyer acting on behalf of an illegal buyer)

21% Unlicensed sellers

14% Gun shows and flea markets

14% Stolen from federally licensed dealers

10% Stolen from residences

a) State the W's for this study to the extent that the story gives them.
b) What do you notice about the percentages listed? What does that probably mean?
c) Make a bar chart to display these results, and label it correctly.

**17. Oil spills 2006.** Data from the International Tanker Owners Pollution Federation Limited (www.itopf.com) give the cause of spillage for 312 large oil tanker accidents from 1974–2006. Here are displays. Write a brief report interpreting what the displays show. Is a pie chart an appropriate display for these data? Why or why not?

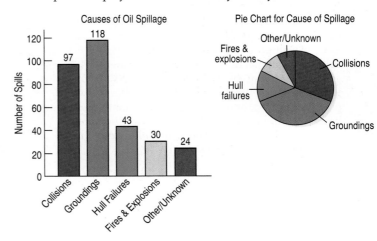

**18. Winter Olympics 2006.**   Twenty-six countries won medals in the 2006 Winter Olympics. The table lists them, along with the total number of medals each won:

| Country | Medals | Country | Medals |
|---------|--------|---------|--------|
| Germany | 29 | Finland | 9 |
| United States | 25 | Czech Republic | 4 |
| Canada | 24 | Estonia | 3 |
| Austria | 23 | Croatia | 3 |
| Russia | 22 | Australia | 2 |
| Norway | 19 | Poland | 2 |
| Sweden | 14 | Ukraine | 2 |
| Switzerland | 14 | Japan | 1 |
| South Korea | 11 | Belarus | 1 |
| Italy | 11 | Bulgaria | 1 |
| China | 11 | Great Britain | 1 |
| France | 9 | Slovakia | 1 |
| Netherlands | 9 | Latvia | 1 |

a) Try to make a display of these data. What problems do you encounter?
b) Can you find a way to organize the data so that the graph is more successful?

**19. Global Warming.**   The Pew Research Center for the People and the Press (http://people-press.org) has asked a representative sample of U.S. adults about global warming, repeating the question over time. In January of 2007, the responses reflected an increased belief that global warming is real and due to human activity. Here's a display of the percentages of respondents choosing each of the major alternatives offered:

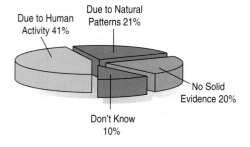

List the errors in this display.

**20. Modalities.**   A survey of athletic trainers (Scott F. Nadler, Michael Prybicien, Gerard A. Malanga, and Dan Sicher. "Complications from Therapeutic Modalities: Results of a National Survey of Athletic Trainers." *Archives of Physical Medical Rehabilitation* 84 [June 2003]) asked what modalities (treatment methods such as ice, whirlpool, ultrasound, or exercise) they commonly use to treat injuries. Respondents were each asked to list three modalities. The article included the following figure reporting the modalities used:

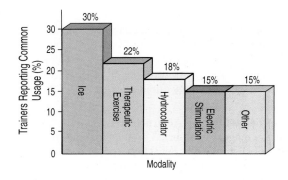

a) What problems do you see with the graph?
b) Consider the percentages for the named modalities. Do you see anything odd about them?

**21. Teen smokers, regionally.**   The Monitoring the Future study of teen smoking described in Exercise 9 looked at brand preferences by region of the country, as seen in the table below. Write a few sentences describing the similarities and differences in brand preferences among eighth graders in the two regions listed.

| Brand preference | South | West |
|------------------|-------|------|
| Marlboro | 58.4% | 58.0% |
| Newport | 22.5% | 10.1% |
| Camel | 3.3% | 9.5% |
| Other (over 20 brands) | 9.1% | 9.5% |
| No usual brand | 6.7% | 12.9% |

**22. Handguns.**   In an effort to reduce the number of gun-related homicides, some cities have run buyback programs in which the police offer cash (often $50) to anyone who turns in an operating handgun. *Chance* magazine looked at results from a four-year period in Milwaukee. The table shows what types of guns were turned in and what types were used in homicides during a four-year period. Write a few sentences comparing the two distributions.

| Caliber of gun | Buyback | Homicide |
|----------------|---------|----------|
| Small (.22, .25, .32) | 76.4% | 20.3% |
| Medium (.357, .38, 9 mm) | 19.3% | 54.7% |
| Large (.40, .44, .45) | 2.1% | 10.8% |
| Other | 2.2% | 14.2% |

**23. Movies by Genre and Rating.**   Here's a table that classifies movies released in 2005 by genre and MPAA rating:

| | G | PG | PG-13 | R | Total |
|---|---|---|---|---|---|
| **Action/Adventure** | 66.7 | 25 | 30.4 | 23.7 | **29.2** |
| **Comedy** | 33.3 | 60.0 | 35.7 | 10.5 | **31.7** |
| **Drama** | 0 | 15.0 | 14.3 | 44.7 | **23.3** |
| **Thriller/Horror** | 0 | 0 | 19.6 | 21.1 | **15.8** |
| Total | **100%** | **100%** | **100%** | **100%** | **100%** |

a) The table gives column percents. How could you tell that from the table itself?
b) What percentage of these movies were comedies?

c) What percentage of the PG-rated movies were comedies?
d) Which of the following can you learn from this table? Give the answer if you can find it from the table.

  i)   The percentage of PG-13 movies that were comedies
  ii)  The percentage of dramas that were R-rated
  iii) The percentage of dramas that were G-rated
  iv)  The percentage of 2005 movies that were PG-rated comedies

**T 24. The Last Picture Show.** Here's another table showing information about 120 movies released in 2005. This table gives percentages of the table total:

|  | G | PG | PG-13 | R | Total |
|---|---|---|---|---|---|
| Action/Adventure | 3.33% | 4.17 | 14.2 | 7.50 | 29.2 |
| Comedy | 1.67 | 10 | 16.7 | 3.33 | 31.7 |
| Drama | 0 | 2.50 | 6.67 | 14.2 | 23.3 |
| Thriller/Horror | 0 | 0 | 9.17 | 6.67 | 15.8 |
| Total | 5 | 16.7 | 46.7 | 31.7 | 100% |

a) How can you tell that this table holds table percentages (rather than row or column percentages)?
b) What was the most common genre/rating combination in 2005 movies?
c) How many of these movies were PG-rated comedies?
d) How many were G-rated?
e) An editorial about the movies noted, "More than three-quarters of the movies made today can be seen only by patrons 13 years old or older." Does this table support that assertion? Explain.

**25. Seniors.** Prior to graduation, a high school class was surveyed about its plans. The following table displays the results for white and minority students (the "Minority" group included African-American, Asian, Hispanic, and Native American students):

| Plans | White | Minority |
|---|---|---|
| 4-year college | 198 | 44 |
| 2-year college | 36 | 6 |
| Military | 4 | 1 |
| Employment | 14 | 3 |
| Other | 16 | 3 |

a) What percent of the graduates are white?
b) What percent of the graduates are planning to attend a 2-year college?
c) What percent of the graduates are white and planning to attend a 2-year college?
d) What percent of the white graduates are planning to attend a 2-year college?
e) What percent of the graduates planning to attend a 2-year college are white?

**26. Politics.** Students in an Intro Stats course were asked to describe their politics as "Liberal," "Moderate," or "Conservative." Here are the results:

| | | Politics | | | |
|---|---|---|---|---|---|
| | | L | M | C | Total |
| Sex | Female | 35 | 36 | 6 | 77 |
| | Male | 50 | 44 | 21 | 115 |
| | Total | 85 | 80 | 27 | 192 |

a) What percent of the class is male?
b) What percent of the class considers themselves to be "Conservative"?
c) What percent of the males in the class consider themselves to be "Conservative"?
d) What percent of all students in the class are males who consider themselves to be "Conservative"?

**27. More about seniors.** Look again at the table of post-graduation plans for the senior class in Exercise 25.
a) Find the conditional distributions (percentages) of plans for the white students.
b) Find the conditional distributions (percentages) of plans for the minority students.
c) Create a graph comparing the plans of white and minority students.
d) Do you see any important differences in the post-graduation plans of white and minority students? Write a brief summary of what these data show, including comparisons of conditional distributions.

**28. Politics revisited.** Look again at the table of political views for the Intro Stats students in Exercise 26.
a) Find the conditional distributions (percentages) of political views for the females.
b) Find the conditional distributions (percentages) of political views for the males.
c) Make a graphical display that compares the two distributions.
d) Do the variables *Politics* and *Sex* appear to be independent? Explain.

**29. Magnet schools revisited.** The *Chance* magazine article described in Exercise 11 further examined the impact of an applicant's ethnicity on the likelihood of admission to the Houston Independent School District's magnet schools programs. Those data are summarized in the table below:

| | | Admission Decision | | | |
|---|---|---|---|---|---|
| | | Accepted | Wait-listed | Turned away | Total |
| Ethnicity | Black/Hispanic | 485 | 0 | 32 | 517 |
| | Asian | 110 | 49 | 133 | 292 |
| | White | 336 | 251 | 359 | 946 |
| | Total | 931 | 300 | 524 | 1755 |

a) What percent of all applicants were Asian?
b) What percent of the students accepted were Asian?
c) What percent of Asians were accepted?
d) What percent of all students were accepted?

**30. More politics.**   Look once more at the table summarizing the political views of Intro Stats students in Exercise 26.
a) Produce a graphical display comparing the conditional distributions of males and females among the three categories of politics.
b) Comment briefly on what you see from the display in a.

**31. Back to school.**   Examine the table about ethnicity and acceptance for the Houston Independent School District's magnet schools program, shown in Exercise 29. Does it appear that the admissions decisions are made independent of the applicant's ethnicity? Explain.

**32. Cars.**   A survey of autos parked in student and staff lots at a large university classified the brands by country of origin, as seen in the table.

|  |  | Driver | |
|---|---|---|---|
|  |  | Student | Staff |
| Origin | American | 107 | 105 |
|  | European | 33 | 12 |
|  | Asian | 55 | 47 |

a) What percent of all the cars surveyed were foreign?
b) What percent of the American cars were owned by students?
c) What percent of the students owned American cars?
d) What is the marginal distribution of origin?
e) What are the conditional distributions of origin by driver classification?
f) Do you think that the origin of the car is independent of the type of driver? Explain.

**33. Weather forecasts.**   Just how accurate are the weather forecasts we hear every day? The following table compares the daily forecast with a city's actual weather for a year:

|  |  | Actual Weather | |
|---|---|---|---|
|  |  | Rain | No rain |
| Forecast | Rain | 27 | 63 |
|  | No rain | 7 | 268 |

a) On what percent of days did it actually rain?
b) On what percent of days was rain predicted?
c) What percent of the time was the forecast correct?
d) Do you see evidence of an association between the type of weather and the ability of forecasters to make an accurate prediction? Write a brief explanation, including an appropriate graph.

**34. Twins.**   In 2000, the *Journal of the American Medical Association (JAMA)* published a study that examined pregnancies that resulted in the birth of twins. Births were classified as preterm with intervention (induced labor or cesarean), preterm without procedures, or term/post-term. Researchers also classified the pregnancies by the level of prenatal medical care the mother received (inadequate, adequate, or intensive). The data,

from the years 1995–1997, are summarized in the table below. Figures are in thousands of births. (*JAMA* 284 [2000]:335–341)

**TWIN BIRTHS 1995–1997 (IN THOUSANDS)**

|  |  | Preterm (induced or cesarean) | Preterm (without procedures) | Term or post-term | Total |
|---|---|---|---|---|---|
| Level of Prenatal Care | Intensive | 18 | 15 | 28 | 61 |
|  | Adequate | 46 | 43 | 65 | 154 |
|  | Inadequate | 12 | 13 | 38 | 63 |
|  | Total | 76 | 71 | 131 | 278 |

a) What percent of these mothers received inadequate medical care during their pregnancies?
b) What percent of all twin births were preterm?
c) Among the mothers who received inadequate medical care, what percent of the twin births were preterm?
d) Create an appropriate graph comparing the outcomes of these pregnancies by the level of medical care the mother received.
e) Write a few sentences describing the association between these two variables.

**35. Blood pressure.**   A company held a blood pressure screening clinic for its employees. The results are summarized in the table below by age group and blood pressure level:

|  |  | Age | | |
|---|---|---|---|---|
|  |  | Under 30 | 30–49 | Over 50 |
| Blood Pressure | Low | 27 | 37 | 31 |
|  | Normal | 48 | 91 | 93 |
|  | High | 23 | 51 | 73 |

a) Find the marginal distribution of blood pressure level.
b) Find the conditional distribution of blood pressure level within each age group.
c) Compare these distributions with a segmented bar graph.
d) Write a brief description of the association between age and blood pressure among these employees.
e) Does this prove that people's blood pressure increases as they age? Explain.

**36. Obesity and exercise.**   The Centers for Disease Control and Prevention (CDC) has estimated that 19.8% of Americans over 15 years old are obese. The CDC conducts a survey on obesity and various behaviors. Here is a table on self-reported exercise classified by body mass index (BMI):

| Body Mass Index | | | |
|---|---|---|---|
| | Normal (%) | Overweight (%) | Obese (%) |
| **Inactive** | 23.8 | 26.0 | 35.6 |
| **Irregularly active** | 27.8 | 28.7 | 28.1 |
| **Regular, not intense** | 31.6 | 31.1 | 27.2 |
| **Regular, intense** | 16.8 | 14.2 | 9.1 |

*(Rows labeled under "Physical Activity")*

a) Are these percentages column percentages, row percentages, or table percentages?
b) Use graphical displays to show different percentages of physical activities for the three BMI groups.
c) Do these data prove that lack of exercise causes obesity? Explain.

**37. Anorexia.** Hearing anecdotal reports that some patients undergoing treatment for the eating disorder anorexia seemed to be responding positively to the antidepressant Prozac, medical researchers conducted an experiment to investigate. They found 93 women being treated for anorexia who volunteered to participate. For one year, 49 randomly selected patients were treated with Prozac and the other 44 were given an inert substance called a placebo. At the end of the year, patients were diagnosed as healthy or relapsed, as summarized in the table:

| | Prozac | Placebo | Total |
|---|---|---|---|
| **Healthy** | 35 | 32 | 67 |
| **Relapse** | 14 | 12 | 26 |
| **Total** | 49 | 44 | 93 |

Do these results provide evidence that Prozac might be helpful in treating anorexia? Explain.

**38. Antidepressants and bone fractures.** For a period of five years, physicians at McGill University Health Center followed more than 5000 adults over the age of 50. The researchers were investigating whether people taking a certain class of antidepressants (SSRIs) might be at greater risk of bone fractures. Their observations are summarized in the table:

| | Taking SSRI | No SSRI | Total |
|---|---|---|---|
| **Experienced fractures** | 14 | 244 | 258 |
| **No fractures** | 123 | 4627 | 4750 |
| **Total** | 137 | 4871 | 5008 |

Do these results suggest there's an association between taking SSRI antidepressants and experiencing bone fractures? Explain.

**39. Canadian languages 2007.** On its Web site, Statistics Canada (www12.statcan.ca) provides the following data on the Canadian population (in thousands). (Zeros indicate counts below 500.)

| Province | English only | French only | Both | Neither | Total |
|---|---|---|---|---|---|
| Newfoundland and Labrador | 486 | 0 | 21 | 1 | 508 |
| Prince Edward Island | 117 | 0 | 16 | 0 | 133 |
| Nova Scotia | 806 | 1 | 90 | 1 | 898 |
| New Brunswick | 407 | 66 | 246 | 0 | 720 |
| Quebec | 327 | 3831 | 2908 | 59 | 7126 |
| Ontario | 9691 | 42 | 1320 | 233 | 11,286 |
| Manitoba | 990 | 1 | 103 | 9 | 1104 |
| Saskatchewan | 911 | 0 | 49 | 3 | 963 |
| Alberta | 2705 | 2 | 203 | 31 | 2941 |
| British Columbia | 3494 | 2 | 269 | 104 | 3869 |
| Yukon Territory | 26 | 0 | 3 | 0 | 29 |
| Northwest Territories | 34 | 0 | 3 | 0 | 37 |
| Nunavut | 22 | 0 | 1 | 4 | 27 |
| Total | 20,015 | 3947 | 5232 | 446 | 29,639 |

a) What percent of Canadian citizens speak only English?
b) What percent of Canadian citizens speak French?
c) What percent of Quebec residents speak French?
d) What percent of French-speaking Canadians live in Quebec?
e) Do you think that language knowledge and province of residence are independent for Canadians? Explain.

**40. Pet ownership.** The U.S. Census Bureau reports the number of households owning various types of pets—specifically, dogs, cats, birds, and horses.

| INCOME DISTRIBUTION OF HOUSEHOLDS OWNING PETS (PERCENT) | | | | |
|---|---|---|---|---|
| | Pet | | | |
| | Dog | Cat | Bird | Horse |
| **Under $12,500** | 14 | 15 | 16 | 9 |
| **$12,500 to $24,999** | 20 | 20 | 21 | 21 |
| **$25,000 to $39,999** | 24 | 23 | 24 | 25 |
| **$40,000 to $59,999** | 22 | 22 | 21 | 22 |
| **$60,000 and over** | 20 | 20 | 18 | 23 |
| **Total** | 100 | 100 | 100 | 100 |

*(Rows labeled under "Income")*

a) Do you think the income distributions of the households that own these different animals would be roughly the same? Why or why not?
b) The table shows the percentages of income levels for each type of animal owned. Are these row percentages, column percentages, or table percentages?
c) Do the data support your initial guess? Explain.

**41. Working parents.** In July 1991 and again in April 2001, the Gallup Poll asked random samples of 1015 adults about their opinions on working parents. The table summarizes responses to this question:

*"Considering the needs of both parents and children, which of the following do you see as the ideal family in today's society?"*

On the basis of these results, do you think there was a change in people's attitudes during the 10 years between the two polls? Explain.

| | | Year | |
|---|---|---|---|
| | | **1991** | **2001** |
| | **Both work full time** | 142 | 131 |
| | **One works full time, other part time** | 274 | 244 |
| Response | **One works, other works at home** | 152 | 173 |
| | **One works, other stays home for kids** | 396 | 416 |
| | **No opinion** | 51 | 51 |

**42. Tattoos.** A study by the University of Texas Southwestern Medical Center examined 626 people to see if an increased risk of contracting hepatitis C was associated with having a tattoo. If the subject had a tattoo, researchers asked whether it had been done in a commercial tattoo parlor or elsewhere. Write a brief description of the association between tattooing and hepatitis C, including an appropriate graphical display.

| | Tattoo done in commercial parlor | Tattoo done elsewhere | No tattoo |
|---|---|---|---|
| **Has hepatitis C** | 17 | 8 | 18 |
| **No hepatitis C** | 35 | 53 | 495 |

**43. Drivers' licenses 2005.** The following table shows the number of licensed U.S. drivers by age and by sex (www.dot.gov):

| Age | Male Drivers (number) | Female Drivers (number) | Total |
|---|---|---|---|
| 19 and under | 4,777,694 | 4,553,946 | 9,331,640 |
| 20–24 | 8,611,161 | 8,398,879 | 17,010,040 |
| 25–29 | 8,879,476 | 8,666,701 | 17,546,177 |
| 30–34 | 9,262,713 | 8,997,662 | 18,260,375 |
| 35–39 | 9,848,050 | 9,576,301 | 19,424,351 |
| 40–44 | 10,617,456 | 10,484,149 | 21,101,605 |
| 45–49 | 10,492,876 | 10,482,479 | 20,975,355 |
| 50–54 | 9,420,619 | 9,475,882 | 18,896,501 |
| 55–59 | 8,218,264 | 8,265,775 | 16,484,039 |
| 60–64 | 6,103,792 | 6,147,569 | 12,251,361 |
| 65–69 | 4,571,157 | 4,643,913 | 9,215,070 |
| 70–74 | 3,617,908 | 3,761,039 | 7,378,947 |
| 75–79 | 2,890,155 | 3,192,408 | 6,082,563 |
| 80–84 | 1,907,743 | 2,222,412 | 4,130,155 |
| 85 and over | 1,170,817 | 1,406,271 | 2,577,088 |
| **Total** | **100,389,881** | **100,275,386** | **200,665,267** |

a) What percent of total drivers are under 20?
b) What percent of total drivers are male?
c) Write a few sentences comparing the number of male and female licensed drivers in each age group.
d) Do a driver's age and sex appear to be independent? Explain?

**44. Worldwide toy sales.** Around the world, toys are sold through different channels. For example, in some parts of the world toys are sold primarily through large toy store chains, while in other countries department stores sell more toys. The table below shows the percentages, by region, of the distribution of toys sold through various channels in 1999.

a) What percent of all toys sold through department stores were sold in Europe?
b) What percent of all toys worldwide were sold through catalogs?
c) Compare the distribution of channels for Europe with those for North America.
d) Summarize the distribution of toy sales by channel in a few sentences.

| REGIONAL TOY SALES BY CHANNEL OF DISTRIBUTION 1999 | | | | | | | |
|---|---|---|---|---|---|---|---|
| | | | | Type of Outlet | | | |
| | Toy chains | General merchandise | Toy, hobby, and game retailers | Department stores | Food, drug, and misc. outlets | Catalog sales | E-Tailers | Total |
| World (Total) | 17773.75 | 24883.25 | 10109.50 | 5987.60 | 12086.15 | 2843.80 | 710.95 | 74395.00 |
| **North America** | 6571.11 | 12516.40 | 1251.64 | 938.73 | 7822.75 | 1877.46 | 312.91 | 31291.00 |
| **Europe** | 5105.40 | 5105.40 | 2552.70 | 2042.16 | 1701.80 | 510.54 | 0.00 | 17018.00 |
| **Asia** | 4294.75 | 4122.96 | 4981.91 | 2233.27 | 1546.11 | 0.00 | 0.00 | 17179.00 |
| **Latin and South America** | 440.80 | 1129.55 | 523.45 | 440.80 | 220.40 | 0.00 | 0.00 | 2755.00 |
| **Oceania** | 218.55 | 728.50 | 291.40 | 87.42 | 101.99 | 29.14 | 0.00 | 1457.00 |
| **Other** | 1143.14 | 1280.44 | 508.40 | 245.22 | 693.10 | 426.66 | 398.04 | 4695.00 |

**45. Hospitals.** Most patients who undergo surgery make routine recoveries and are discharged as planned. Others suffer excessive bleeding, infection, or other post-surgical complications and have their discharges delayed. Suppose your city has a large hospital and a small hospital, each performing major and minor surgeries. You collect data to see how many surgical patients have their discharges delayed by post-surgical complications, and you find the results shown in the following table.

| | Discharge Delayed | |
|---|---|---|
| | **Large hospital** | **Small hospital** |
| **Major surgery** | 120 of 800 | 10 of 50 |
| **Minor surgery** | 10 of 200 | 20 of 250 |

(Procedure)

a) Overall, for what percent of patients was discharge delayed?
b) Were the percentages different for major and minor surgery?
c) Overall, what were the discharge delay rates at each hospital?
d) What were the delay rates at each hospital for each kind of surgery?
e) The small hospital advertises that it has a lower rate of postsurgical complications. Do you agree?
f) Explain, in your own words, why this confusion occurs.

**46. Delivery service.** A company must decide which of two delivery services it will contract with. During a recent trial period, the company shipped numerous packages with each service and kept track of how often deliveries did not arrive on time. Here are the data:

| Delivery Service | Type of Service | Number of Deliveries | Number of Late Packages |
|---|---|---|---|
| **Pack Rats** | **Regular** | 400 | 12 |
| | **Overnight** | 100 | 16 |
| **Boxes R Us** | **Regular** | 100 | 2 |
| | **Overnight** | 400 | 28 |

a) Compare the two services' overall percentage of late deliveries.
b) On the basis of the results in part a, the company has decided to hire Pack Rats. Do you agree that Pack Rats delivers on time more often? Why or why not? Be specific.
c) The results here are an instance of what phenomenon?

**47. Graduate admissions.** A 1975 article in the magazine *Science* examined the graduate admissions process at Berkeley for evidence of sex discrimination. The table below shows the number of applicants accepted to each of four graduate programs:

| | Males accepted (of applicants) | Females accepted (of applicants) |
|---|---|---|
| **1** | 511 of 825 | 89 of 108 |
| **2** | 352 of 560 | 17 of 25 |
| **3** | 137 of 407 | 132 of 375 |
| **4** | 22 of 373 | 24 of 341 |
| **Total** | **1022 of 2165** | **262 of 849** |

(Program)

a) What percent of total applicants were admitted?
b) Overall, was a higher percentage of males or females admitted?
c) Compare the percentage of males and females admitted in each program.
d) Which of the comparisons you made do you consider to be the most valid? Why?

**48. Be a Simpson!** Can you design a Simpson's paradox? Two companies are vying for a city's "Best Local Employer" award, to be given to the company most committed to hiring local residents. Although both employers hired 300 new people in the past year, Company A brags that it deserves the award because 70% of its new jobs went to local residents, compared to only 60% for Company B. Company B concedes that those percentages are correct, but points out that most of its new jobs were full-time, while most of Company A's were part-time. Not only that, says Company B, but a higher percentage of its full-time jobs went to local residents than did Company A's, and the same was true for part-time jobs. Thus, Company B argues, it's a better local employer than Company A.

Show how it's possible for Company B to fill a higher percentage of both full-time and part-time jobs with local residents, even though Company A hired more local residents overall.

**JUST CHECKING**
**Answers**

**1.** 50.0%
**2.** 44.4%
**3.** 25.0%
**4.** 15.6% Blue, 56.3% Brown, 28.1% Green/Hazel/Other
**5.** 18.8% Blue, 62.5% Brown, 18.8% Green/Hazel/Other
**6.** 40% of the blue-eyed students are female, while 50% of all students are female.
**7.** Since blue-eyed students appear less likely to be female, it seems that they may not be independent. (But the numbers are small.)

# CHAPTER 4

# Displaying and Summarizing Quantitative Data

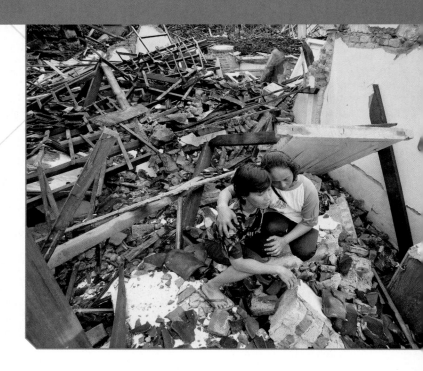

## Where are we going?

If someone asked you to summarize a variable, what would you say? You might start by making a picture. For quantitative data, that first picture would probably be a histogram. We've all looked at histograms, but what should we look *for*? We'll describe the histogram, and we'll often do more—reporting numerical summaries of the center and spread as well. Spread measures are a bit less common, but in Statistics they are even more important. This chapter is where we'll first encounter the single most important calculated value in all of Statistics.

Tsunamis are potentially destructive waves that can occur when the sea floor is suddenly and abruptly deformed. They are most often caused by earthquakes beneath the sea that shift the earth's crust, displacing a large mass of water.

The tsunami of December 26, 2004, with epicenter off the west coast of Sumatra, was caused by an earthquake of magnitude 9.0 on the Richter scale. It killed an estimated 297,248 people, making it the most disastrous tsunami on record. But was the earthquake that caused it truly extraordinary, or did it just happen at an unlucky place and time? The U.S. National Geophysical Data Center[1] has information on more than 2400 tsunamis dating back to 2000 B.C.E., and we have estimates of the magnitude of the underlying earthquake for 1240 of them. What can we learn from these data?

## Histograms

Let's start with a picture. For categorical variables, it is easy to draw the distribution because each category is a natural "pile." But for quantitative variables, there's no obvious way to choose piles. So, usually, we slice up all the possible values into equal-width bins. We then count the number of cases that fall into

[1] www.ngdc.noaa.gov

each bin. The bins, together with these counts, give the **distribution** of the quantitative variable and provide the building blocks for the histogram. By representing the counts as bars and plotting them against the bin values, the **histogram** displays the distribution at a glance.

For example, here are the *Magnitudes* (on the Richter scale) of the 2410 earthquakes in the NGDC data:

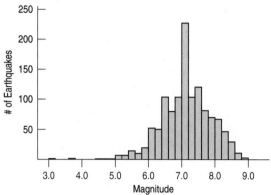

**FIGURE 4.1**

*A histogram of earthquake magnitudes shows the number of earthquakes with magnitudes (in Richter scale units) in each bin.*

Like a bar chart, a histogram plots the bin counts as the heights of bars. In this histogram of earthquake magnitudes, each bin has a width of 0.2, so, for example, the height of the tallest bar says that there were about 230 earthquakes with magnitudes between 7.0 and 7.2. In this way, the histogram displays the entire distribution of earthquake magnitudes.

> ## HOW DO HISTOGRAMS WORK?
>
> If you make a histogram by hand, you'll need to decide the endpoints of the bins. Usually, it helps to make them come out to "nice" numbers that are easy to think about. The standard rule for a value that falls exactly on a bin boundary is to put it into the next higher bin, so if a bin spans magnitudes 5.0 to 5.2, and the next goes from 5.2 to 5.4, you'd put an earthquake with magnitude 5.2 into the higher bin.
>
> Different features of the distribution may appear more obvious at different bin width choices. When you use technology, it's usually easy to vary the bin width interactively so you can make sure that a feature you think you see isn't a consequence of a certain bin width choice.

One surprising feature of the earthquake magnitudes is the spike around magnitude 7.0. Only one other bin holds even half that many earthquakes. These values include historical data for which the magnitudes were estimated by experts and not measured by modern seismographs. Perhaps the experts thought 7 was a typical and reasonable value for a tsunami-causing earthquake when they lacked detailed information. That would explain the overabundance of magnitudes right at 7.0 rather than spread out near that value.

Does the distribution look as you expected? It is often a good idea to *imagine* what the distribution might look like before you make the display. That way you'll be less likely to be fooled by errors in the data or when you accidentally graph the wrong variable.

From the histogram, we can see that these earthquakes typically have magnitudes around 7. Most are between 5.5 and 8.5, and some are as small as 3 and as big as 9. Now we can answer the question about the Sumatra tsunami. With a value of 9.0 it's clear that the earthquake that caused it was an extraordinarily powerful earthquake—one of the largest on record.[3]

The bar charts of categorical variables we saw in Chapter 3 had spaces between the bars to separate the counts of different categories. But in a histogram, the bins

---

[2] Technically, Richter scale values are in units of log dyne-cm. But the Richter scale is so common now that usually the units are assumed. The U.S. Geological Survey gives the background details of Richter scale measurements on its Web site www.usgs.gov/.
[3] Some experts now estimate the magnitude at between 9.1 and 9.3.

slice up *all the values* of the quantitative variable, so any spaces in a histogram are actual **gaps** in the data, indicating a region where there are no values.

Sometimes it is useful to make a **relative frequency histogram,** replacing the counts on the vertical axis with the *percentage* of the total number of cases falling in each bin. Of course, the shape of the histogram is exactly the same; only the vertical scale is different.

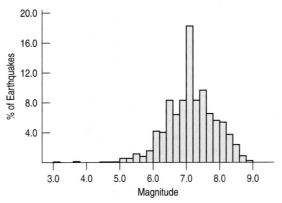

**FIGURE 4.2**

*A relative frequency histogram looks just like a frequency histogram except for the labels on the y-axis, which now show the percentage of earthquakes in each bin.*

## Stem-and-Leaf Displays

Histograms provide an easy-to-understand summary of the distribution of a quantitative variable, but they don't show the data values themselves. Here's a histogram of the pulse rates of 24 women, taken by a researcher at a health clinic:

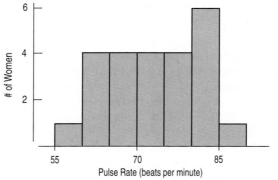

**FIGURE 4.3**

*The pulse rates of 24 women at a health clinic.*

The Stem-and-Leaf display was devised by John W. Tukey, one of the greatest statisticians of the 20th century. It is called a "Stemplot" in some texts and computer programs, but we prefer Tukey's original name for it.

The story seems pretty clear. We can see the entire span of the data and can easily see what a typical pulse rate might be. But is that all there is to these data?

A **stem-and-leaf display** is like a histogram, but it shows the individual values. It's also easier to make by hand. Here's a stem-and-leaf display of the same data:

**A S**   **Activity: Stem-and-Leaf Displays.** As you might expect of something called "stem-and-leaf," these displays grow as you consider each data value.

Turn the stem-and-leaf on its side (or turn your head to the right) and squint at it. It should look roughly like the histogram of the same data. Does it? Well, it's backwards because now the higher values are on the left, but other than that, it has the same shape.[4]

---

### HOW DO STEM-AND-LEAF DISPLAYS WORK?

Stem-and-leaf displays work like histograms, but they show more information. They use part of the number itself (called the stem) to name the bins. To make the "bars," they use the next digit of the number. For example, if we had a test score of 83, we could write it 8 | 3, where 8 serves as the stem and 3 as the leaf. Then, to display the scores 83, 76, and 88 together, we would write

```
8 | 38
7 | 6
```

For the pulse data, we have

```
8 | 0000448
7 | 22226666
6 | 04448888
5 | 6
    Pulse Rate
(5 | 6 means 56 beats/min)
```

This display is OK, but a little crowded. A histogram might split each line into two bars. With a stem-and-leaf, we can do the same by putting the leaves 0–4 on one line and 5–9 on another, as we saw above:

```
8 | 8
8 | 000044
7 | 6666
7 | 2222
6 | 8888
6 | 0444
5 | 6
    Pulse Rate
(8 | 8 means 88 beats/min)
```

We could have stretched out the scale even more, using 5 lines for each stem. Here's what that would look like just for the pulses from 60 to 69:[5]

```
6* | 8888
6S |
6F | 444
6T |
6O | 0
    Pulse Rate
(6F | 4 means 64 beats/min)
```

That's probably too spread out to be useful. Which resolution you choose is up to you. For numbers with three or more digits, you'll need to decide on the "resolution" as well. Usually you'll truncate (or round) the number to two places, using the first digit as the stem and the second as the leaf. So, if

---

[4] You could make the stem-and-leaf with the higher values on the bottom. Usually, though, higher on the top makes sense.

[5] The labels on the stems, O, T, F, S, * are reminders that those lines hold **0** and **O**ne, **T**wo and **T**hree, **F**our and **F**ive, **S**ix and **S**even, and * for the remaining 8 and 9 (and we were doing so well, too).

you had 432, 540, 571, and 638, you might display them as with an indication that 6 | 3 means 630.

```
6 | 3
5 | 4 7
4 | 3
```

When you make a stem-and-leaf by hand, make sure to give each digit the same width, in order to preserve the area principle. (That can lead to some fat 1's and thin 8's—but it makes the display honest.)

What does the line at the top of the display that says 8 | 8 mean? It stands for a pulse of 88 beats per minute (bpm). We've taken the tens place of the number and made that the "stem." Then we sliced off the ones place and made it a "leaf." The next line down is 8 | 000044. That shows that there were four pulse rates of 80 and two of 84 bpm. And as long as we are careful to write each leaf digit so that it takes up the same amount of room on the page, we'll preserve the area principle and have a proper data display.

Stem-and-leaf displays are especially useful when you make them by hand for batches of fewer than a few hundred data values. They are a quick way to display—and even to record—numbers. Because the leaves show the individual values, we can sometimes see even more in the data than the distribution's shape. Take another look at all the leaves of the pulse data. See anything unusual? At a glance you can see that they are all even. With a bit more thought you can see that they are all multiples of 4—something you couldn't possibly see from a histogram. How do you think the nurse took these pulses? Counting beats for a full minute or counting for only 15 seconds and multiplying by 4?

# Dotplots

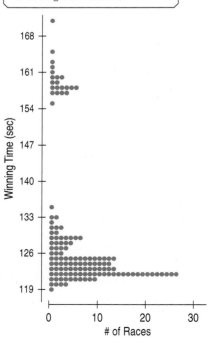

A **dotplot** is a simple display. It just places a dot along an axis for each case in the data. It's like a stem-and-leaf display, but with dots instead of digits for all the leaves. Dotplots are a great way to display a small data set (especially if you forget how to write the digits from 0 to 9). Here's a dotplot of the time (in seconds) that the winning horse took to win the Kentucky Derby in each race between the first Derby in 1875 and the 2007 Derby.

Dotplots show basic facts about the distribution. We can find the slowest and quickest races by finding times for the topmost and bottommost dots. It's also clear that there are two clusters of points, one just below 160 seconds and the other at about 122 seconds. Something strange happened to the Derby times. Once we know to look for it, we can find out that in 1896 the distance of the Derby race was changed from 1.5 miles to the current 1.25 miles. That explains the two clusters of winning times.

Some dotplots stretch out horizontally, with the counts on the vertical axis, like a histogram. Others, such as the one shown here, run vertically, like a stem-and-leaf display. Some dotplots place points next to each other when they would otherwise overlap. Others just place them on top of one another. Newspapers sometimes offer dotplots with the dots made up of little pictures.

**FIGURE 4.4**

*A dotplot of Kentucky Derby winning times plots each race as its own dot, showing the bimodal distribution.*

# Think Before You Draw, Again

Suddenly, we face a lot more options when it's time to invoke our first rule of data analysis and make a picture. You'll need to *Think* carefully to decide which type of graph to make. In the previous chapter you learned to check the Categorical Data Condition before making a pie chart or a bar chart. Now, before making a stem-and-leaf display, a histogram, or a dotplot, you need to check the

> **Quantitative Data Condition:** The data are values of a quantitative variable whose units are known.

Although a bar chart and a histogram may look somewhat similar, they're not the same display. You can't display categorical data in a histogram or quantitative data in a bar chart. Always check the condition that confirms what type of data you have before proceeding with your display.

Step back from a histogram or stem-and-leaf display. What can you say about the distribution? When you describe a distribution, you should always tell about three things: its **shape, center,** and **spread.**

# The Shape of a Distribution

The **mode** is sometimes defined as the single value that appears most often. That definition is fine for categorical variables because all we need to do is count the number of cases for each category. For quantitative variables, the mode is more ambiguous. What is the mode of the Kentucky Derby times? Well, seven races were timed at 122.2 seconds—more than any other race time. Should that be the mode? Probably not. For quantitative data, it makes more sense to use the term "mode" in the more general sense of the peak of the histogram rather than as a single summary value. In this sense, the important feature of the Kentucky Derby races is that there are two distinct modes, representing the two different versions of the race and warning us to consider those two versions separately.

1. *Does the histogram have a single, central hump or several separated humps?* These humps are called **modes.**[6] The earthquake magnitudes have a single mode at just about 7. A histogram with one peak, such as the earthquake magnitudes, is dubbed **unimodal;** histograms with two peaks are **bimodal,** and those with three or more are called **multimodal.**[7] For example, here's a bimodal histogram.

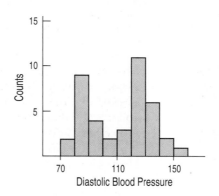

**FIGURE 4.5**

*A bimodal histogram has two apparent peaks.*

A histogram that doesn't appear to have any mode and in which all the bars are approximately the same height is called **uniform.**

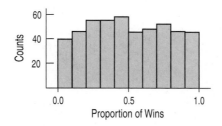

**FIGURE 4.6**

*In a uniform histogram, the bars are all about the same height. The histogram doesn't appear to have a mode.*

---

[6] Well, technically, it's the value on the horizontal axis of the histogram that is the mode, but anyone asked to point to the mode would point to the hump.

[7] Apparently, statisticians don't like to count past two.

You've heard of pie à la mode. Is there a connection between pie and the mode of a distribution? Actually, there is! The mode of a distribution is a *popular* value near which a lot of the data values gather. And "à la mode" means "in style"—*not* "with ice cream." That just happened to be a *popular* way to have pie in Paris around 1900.

2. *Is the histogram* **symmetric?** Can you fold it along a vertical line through the middle and have the edges match pretty closely, or are more of the values on one side?

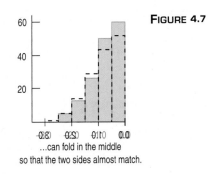

**FIGURE 4.7**

A symmetric histogram...

...can fold in the middle so that the two sides almost match.

The (usually) thinner ends of a distribution are called the **tails.** If one tail stretches out farther than the other, the histogram is said to be **skewed** to the side of the longer tail.

*Activity:* **Attributes of Distribution Shape.** This activity and the others on this page show off aspects of distribution shape through animation and examples, then let you make and interpret histograms with your statistics package.

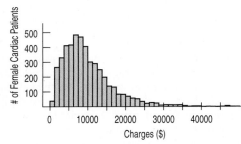

**FIGURE 4.8**

*Two skewed histograms showing data on two variables for all female heart attack patients in New York state in one year. The blue one (age in years) is skewed to the left. The purple one (charges in $) is skewed to the right.*

3. *Do any unusual features stick out?* Often such features tell us something interesting or exciting about the data. You should always mention any stragglers, or **outliers,** that stand off away from the body of the distribution. If you're collecting data on nose lengths and Pinocchio is in the group, you'd probably notice him, and you'd certainly want to mention it.

    Outliers can affect almost every method we discuss in this course. So we'll always be on the lookout for them. An outlier can be the most informative part of your data. Or it might just be an error. But don't throw it away without comment. Treat it specially and discuss it when you tell about your data. Or find the error and fix it if you can. Be sure to look for outliers. Always.

In the next chapter you'll learn a handy rule of thumb for deciding when a point might be considered an outlier.

**FIGURE 4.9**

*A histogram with outliers. There are three cities in the leftmost bar.*

Are there any gaps in the distribution? The Kentucky Derby data that we saw in the dotplot on page 52 has a large gap between two groups of times, one near 120 seconds and one near 160. Gaps help us see multiple modes and encourage us to notice when the data may come from different sources or contain more than one group.

---

**FOR EXAMPLE**    Describing Histograms

**Question:** A credit card company wants to see how much customers in a particular segment of their market use their credit card. They have provided you with data[8] on the amount spent by 500 selected customers during a 3-month period and have asked you to summarize the expenditures. Of course, you begin by making a histogram.

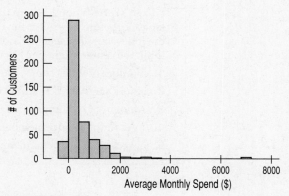

Describe the shape of this distribution.

The distribution of expenditures is unimodal and skewed to the high end. There is an extraordinarily large value at about $7000, and some of the expenditures are negative.

---

> **Toto, I've a feeling we're not in math class anymore...** When Dorothy and her dog Toto land in Oz, everything is more vivid and colorful, but also more dangerous and exciting. Dorothy has new choices to make. She can't always rely on the old definitions, and the yellow brick road has many branches. You may be coming to a similar realization about Statistics.
> When we summarize data, our goal is usually more than just developing a detailed knowledge of the data we have at hand. Scientists generally don't care about the particular guinea pigs they've treated, but rather about what their reactions say about how animals (and, perhaps, humans) would respond.
> When you look at data, you want to know what the data say about the world, so you'd like to know whether the patterns you see in histograms and summary statistics generalize to other individuals and situations. You'll want to calculate summary statistics accurately, but then you'll also want to think about what they may say beyond just describing the data. And your knowledge about the world matters when you think about the overall meaning of your analysis.
> It may surprise you that many of the most important concepts in Statistics are not defined as precisely as most concepts in mathematics. That's done on purpose, to leave room for judgment.
> Because we want to see broader patterns rather than focus on the details of the data set we're looking at, we deliberately leave some statistical concepts a bit vague. Whether a histogram is symmetric or skewed, whether it has one or more modes, whether a point is far enough from the rest of the data to be considered an outlier—these are all somewhat vague concepts. And they all require judgment. You

---

[8] These data are real, but cannot be further identified for obvious privacy reasons.

may be used to finding a single correct and precise answer, but in Statistics, there may be more than one interpretation. That may make you a little uncomfortable at first, but soon you'll see that this room for judgment brings you enormous power and responsibility. It means that using your own knowledge and judgment and supporting your findings with statistical evidence and justifications entitles you to your own opinions about what you see.

## JUST CHECKING

It's often a good idea to think about what the distribution of a data set might look like before we collect the data. What do you think the distribution of each of the following data sets will look like? Be sure to discuss its shape. Where do you think the center might be? How spread out do you think the values will be?

**1.** Number of miles run by Saturday morning joggers at a park.

**2.** Hours spent by U.S. adults watching football on Thanksgiving Day.

**3.** Amount of winnings of all people playing a particular state's lottery last week.

**4.** Ages of the faculty members at your school.

**5.** Last digit of phone numbers on your campus.

# The Center of the Distribution: The Median

Let's return to the tsunami earthquakes. But this time, let's look at just 25 years of data: 176 earthquakes that occurred from 1981 through 2005. These should be more accurately measured than prehistoric quakes because seismographs were in wide use. Try to put your finger on the histogram at the value you think is typical. (Read the value from the horizontal axis and remember it.) When we think of a typical value, we usually look for the **center** of the distribution. Where do you think the center of this distribution is? For a unimodal, symmetric distribution such as these earthquake data, it's easy. We'd all agree on the center of symmetry, where we would fold the histogram to match the two sides. But when the distribution is skewed or possibly multimodal, it's not immediately clear what we even mean by the center.

You might think of taking the average of the maximum and minimum values as a way of finding the center. This is called the **midrange,** but it's too sensitive to the outlying values to be safe for summarizing the whole distribution. A more reasonable choice of typical value is the value that is literally in the middle, with half the values below it and half above it.

### Using the Midrange

There actually is *one* everyday use of the midrange: Whenever you make a plot of data, you're likely to center the plot at the midrange, exactly halfway between the two extremes of the data.

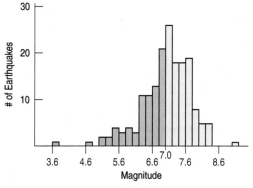

**FIGURE 4.10** *Tsunami-causing earthquakes (1981–2005).*

*The median splits the histogram into two halves of equal area.*

Histograms follow the area principle, and each half of the data has about 88 earthquakes, so each colored region has the same area in the display. The middle value that divides the histogram into two equal areas is called the **median.**

The median has the same units as the data. Be sure to include the units whenever you discuss the median.

For the recent tsunamis, there are 176 earthquakes, so the median is found at the $(176 + 1)/2 = 88.5$th place in the sorted data. That ".5" just says to average the two values on either side: the 88th and the 89th. The median earthquake magnitude is 7.0.

---

### FINDING THE MEDIAN BY HAND

Finding the median of a batch of $n$ numbers is easy as long as you remember to order the values first. If $n$ is odd, the median is the middle value. Counting in from the ends, we find this value in the $\dfrac{n + 1}{2}$ position.

When $n$ is even, there are two middle values. So, in this case, the median is the average of the two values in positions $\dfrac{n}{2}$ and $\dfrac{n}{2} + 1$.

Here are two examples:

Suppose the batch has these values: 14.1, 3.2, 25.3, 2.8, $-17.5$ 13.9, 45.8.
First we order the values: $-17.5$, 2.8, 3.2, 13.9, 14.1, 25.3, 45.8.
Since there are 7 values, the median is the $(7 + 1)/2 = 4$th value, counting from the top or bottom: 13.9.

Suppose we had the same batch with another value at 35.7. Then the ordered values are $-17.5$, 2.8, 3.2, 13.9, 14.1, 25.3, 35.7, 45.8.
The median is the average of the 8/2 or 4th, and the $(8/2) + 1$, or 5th, values. So the median is $(13.9 + 14.1)/2 = 14.0$.

---

The median is one way to find the center of the data. But there are many others. We'll look at an even more important measure later in this chapter.

Knowing the median, we could say that a typical tsunami-causing earthquake, worldwide, was about 7.0 on the Richter scale. How much does that really say? How well does the median describe the data? After all, not every earthquake has a Richter scale value of 7.0. Whenever we find the center of data, the next step is always to ask how well it actually summarizes the data.

## Spread: Home on the Range

If every earthquake that caused a tsunami registered 7.0 on the Richter scale, then knowing the median would tell us everything about the distribution of earthquake magnitudes worldwide. The more the data vary, however, the less the median alone can tell us. So we need to measure how much the data values vary around the center. In other words, how spread out are they? When we describe a distribution numerically, we always report a measure of its **spread** along with its center.

How should we measure the spread? We could simply look at the extent of the data. How far apart are the two extremes? The **range** of the data is defined as the *difference* between the maximum and minimum values:

$$Range = max - min.$$

Notice that the range is a *single number, not* an interval of values, as you might think from its use in common speech. The maximum magnitude of these earthquakes is 9.0 and the minimum is 3.7, so the *range* is $9.0 - 3.7 = 5.3$.

> Statistics pays close attention to what we *don't* know as well as what we do know. Understanding how spread out the data are is a first step in understanding what a summary *cannot* tell us about the data. It's the beginning of telling us what we don't know.

The range (like the midrange) has the disadvantage that a single extreme value can make it very large, giving a value that doesn't really represent the data overall.

# Spread: The Interquartile Range

A better way to describe the spread of a variable might be to ignore the extremes and concentrate on the middle of the data. We could, for example, find the range of just the middle half of the data. What do we mean by the middle half? Divide the data in half at the median. Now divide both halves in half again, cutting the data into four quarters. We call these new dividing points **quartiles.** One quarter of the data lies below the **lower quartile,** and one quarter of the data lies above the **upper quartile,** so half the data lies between them. The quartiles border the middle half of the data.

### FINDING QUARTILES BY HAND

A simple way to find the quartiles is to start by splitting the batch into two halves at the median. (When $n$ is odd, some statisticians include the median in both halves; others omit it.) The lower quartile is the median of the lower half, and the upper quartile is the median of the upper half.

Here are our two examples again.

The ordered values of the first batch were $-17.5$, 2.8, 3.2, 13.9, 14.1, 25.3, and 45.8, with a median of 13.9. Notice that 7 is odd; we'll include the median in both halves to get $-17.5$, 2.8, 3.2, 13.9 and 13.9, 14.1, 25.3, 45.8.

Each half has 4 values, so the median of each is the average of its 2nd and 3rd values. So, the lower quartile is $(2.8 + 3.2)/2 = 3.0$ and the upper quartile is $(14.1 + 25.3)/2 = 19.7$.

The second batch of data had the ordered values $-17.5$, 2.8, 3.2, 13.9, 14.1, 25.3, 35.7, and 45.8.

Here $n$ is even, so the two halves of 4 values are $-17.5$, 2.8, 3.2, 13.9 and 14.1, 25.3, 35.7, 45.8.

Now the lower quartile is $(2.8 + 3.2)/2 = 3.0$ and the upper quartile is $(25.3 + 35.7)/2 = 30.5$.

The difference between the quartiles tells us how much territory the middle half of the data covers and is called the **interquartile range.** It's commonly abbreviated IQR (and pronounced "eye-cue-are," not "ikker"):

$$IQR = upper\ quartile - lower\ quartile.$$

For the earthquakes, there are 88 values below the median and 88 values above the median. The midpoint of the lower half is the average of the 44th and 45th values in the ordered data; that turns out to be 6.6. In the upper half we average the 132nd and 133rd values, finding a magnitude of 7.6 as the third quartile. The *difference* between the quartiles gives the IQR:

$$IQR = 7.6 - 6.6 = 1.0.$$

Now we know that the middle half of the earthquake magnitudes extend for a (interquartile) range of 0.9 Richter scale units. This seems like a reasonable summary of the spread of the distribution, as we can see from the histogram:

**FIGURE 4.11**

*The IQR contains the middle 50% of the values of the distribution. It also gives a visual indication of the spread of the data. Here we see that the IQR is 1.0 Richter scale units.*

The IQR is almost always a reasonable summary of the spread of a distribution. Even if the distribution itself is skewed or has some outliers, the IQR should provide useful information. The one exception is when the data are strongly bimodal. In that case, we probably don't have a single collection of comparable data, so it isn't worthwhile to summarize it with only a few values.

For example, remember the dotplot of winning times in the Kentucky Derby (page 52)? The IQR of the Kentucky Derby winning times suddenly became much smaller in 1959. Why? That was the 85th year of the Derby. Until then, the first 21 years of races (at 1.5 miles) would have included the upper quartile. After that, there were enough races at the new 1.25-mile distance for the quartile to "jump" to the modern era. Before 1959 the IQR would have given a misleading impression of the variation in Kentucky Derby finishing times (at least for someone thinking about the modern race). The problem is that we really have data on two different races, and they shouldn't be summarized together.

The lower and upper quartiles are also known as the 25th and 75th **percentiles** of the data, respectively, since the lower quartile falls above 25% of the data and the upper quartile falls above 75% of the data. If we count this way, the median is the 50th percentile. We could, of course, define and calculate any percentile that we want. For example, the 10th percentile would be the number that falls above the lowest 10% of the data values.

---

**So, what is a quartile anyway?**   Finding the quartiles sounds easy, but surprisingly, the quartiles are not well defined. It's not always clear how to find a value such that exactly one quarter of the data lies above or below that value. We offer a simple rule in the Finding Quartiles by Hand box: Find the median of each half of the data split by the median. When *n* is odd, we include the median with each of the halves. Some other texts (and the TI calculators) omit the median before finding medians of each half of the data. Both methods are commonly used. If you are willing to do a bit more calculating, there are several other methods that locate a quartile somewhere between adjacent data values. We know of at least six different rules for finding quartiles. Remarkably, each one is in use in some software package or calculator. Throughout the book you'll see other calculations that can give different values, depending on reasonable choices in how they are computed. This is just another reminder that Statistics is about understanding the world, not about calculating the right number. The "answer" to a statistical question is a sentence about the issue raised in the question.

So don't worry too much about getting the "exact" value for a quartile. All of the methods agree pretty closely when the data set is large. When the data set is small, different rules will disagree more, but in that case there's little need to summarize the data anyway. Remember, the quartiles are just summary values of the data set. In fact, the main use for quartiles is in calculating the IQR, a measure of how spread out the data are.

# 5-Number Summary

The **5-number summary** of a distribution reports its median, quartiles, and extremes (maximum and minimum). The 5-number summary for the recent tsunami earthquake *Magnitudes* looks like this:

| | |
|---|---|
| Max | 9.0 |
| Q3 | 7.6 |
| Median | 7.0 |
| Q1 | 6.6 |
| Min | 3.7 |

It's good idea to report the number of data values and the identity of the cases (the *Who*). Here there are 176 earthquakes.

---

**STEP-BY-STEP EXAMPLE** | **Shape, Center, and Spread: Flight Cancellations**

The U.S. Bureau of Transportation Statistics (www.bts.gov) reports data on airline flights. Let's look at data giving the percentage of flights cancelled each month between 1995 and 2005.

**Question:** How often are flights cancelled?

| | |
|---|---|
| **WHO** | Months |
| **WHAT** | Percentage of flights cancelled at U.S. Airports |
| **WHEN** | 1995–2005 |
| **WHERE** | United States |

**Variable:** Identify the *variable*, and decide how you wish to display it.

To identify a variable, report the W's.

Select an appropriate display based on the nature of the data and what you want to know.

I want to learn about the monthly percentage of flight cancellations at U.S airports.

I have data from the U.S. Bureau of Transportation Statistics giving the percentage of flights cancelled at U.S. Airports each month between 1995 and 2005.

✓ **Quantitative Data Condition:** Percentages are quantitative. A histogram and numerical summaries would be appropriate.

**Mechanics:** We usually make histograms with a computer or graphing calculator.

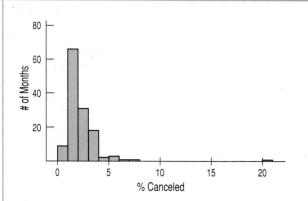

The histogram shows a distribution skewed to the high end and one extreme outlier, a month in which more than 20% of flights were cancelled.

 It's always a good idea to think about what you expect to see so that you can check whether the histogram looks like what you expected.

With 132 cases, we probably have more data than you'd choose to work with by hand. The results given here are from technology.

In most months, fewer than 5% of flights are cancelled and usually only about 2 or 3%. That seems reasonable.

| Count | 132 |
|---|---|
| Max | 20.240 |
| Q3 | 2.615 |
| Median | 1.755 |
| Q1 | 1.445 |
| Min | 0.770 |
| IQR | 1.170 |

**TELL** **Interpretation:** Describe the shape, center, and spread of the distribution. Report on the symmetry, number of modes, and any gaps or outliers. You should also mention any concerns you may have about the data.

The distribution of cancellations is skewed, and this makes sense: The values can't fall below 0%, but can increase almost arbitrarily due to bad weather or other events.

The median is 1.76% and the IQR is 1.17%. So most months are close to the median. In fact, I know from the upper quartile that in only 1/4 of the months were more than 2.6% of flights cancelled.

There is one extraordinary value: 20.2%. Looking it up, I find that the extraordinary month was September 2001. The attacks of September 11 shut down air travel for several days, accounting for this outlier.

# Summarizing Symmetric Distributions: The Mean

Medians do a good job of summarizing the center of a distribution even when the shape is skewed or when there is an outlier, as with the flight cancellations. But when we have symmetric data, there's another alternative. You probably already know how to average values. In fact, to find the median when $n$ is even, we said you should average the two middle values, and you didn't even flinch.

The earthquake magnitudes are pretty close to symmetric, so we can also summarize their center with a mean. The mean tsunami earthquake magnitude is 6.96—about what we might expect from the histogram. You already know how to average values, but this is a good place to introduce notation that we'll use throughout the book. We use the Greek capital letter sigma, $\Sigma$, to mean "sum" (sigma is "S" in Greek), and we'll write

$$\bar{y} = \frac{Total}{n} = \frac{\sum y}{n}.$$

In Algebra you used letters to represent values in a problem, but it didn't matter what letter you picked. You could call the width of a rectangle $X$ or you could call it $w$ (or *Fred*, for that matter). But in Statistics, the notation is part of the vocabulary. For example, in Statistics $n$ is always the number of data values. Always.

We have already begun to point out such special notation conventions: $n$, Q1, and Q3. Think of them as part of the terminology you need to learn in this course.

Here's another one: Whenever we put a bar over a symbol, it means "find the mean."

The formula says to add up all the values of the variable and divide that sum by the number of data values, $n$—just as you've always done.[9]

Once we've averaged the data, you'd expect the result to be called the *average*, but that would be too easy. Informally, we speak of the "average person" but we don't add up people and divide by the number of people. To make this distinction, the value we calculated is called the mean, $\bar{y}$, and pronounced "y-bar."

The **mean** feels like the center because it is the point where the histogram balances:

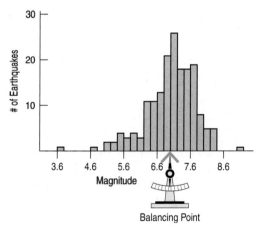

**FIGURE 4.12**
*The mean is located at the balancing point of the histogram.*

In everyday language, sometimes "average" *does* mean what we want it to mean. We don't talk about your grade point mean or a baseball player's batting mean or the Dow Jones Industrial mean. So we'll continue to say "average" when that seems most natural. When we do, though, you may assume that what we mean is the mean.

The center of balance makes sense when the data are symmetric. But data are not always this well behaved. If the distribution is skewed or has outliers, the center is not so well defined and the mean may not be what we want. For example, the mean of the flight cancellations doesn't give a very good idea of the typical percentage of cancellations.

---

[9] You may also see the variable called $x$ and the equation written $\bar{x} = \frac{Total}{n} = \frac{\sum x}{n}$. Don't let that throw you. You are free to name the variable anything you want, but we'll generally use $y$ for variables like this that we want to summarize, model, or predict. (Later we'll talk about variables that are used to explain, model, or predict $y$. We'll call them $x$.)

**FIGURE 4.13**

*The median splits the area of the histogram in half at 1.75%. Because the distribution is skewed to the right, the mean (2.28%) is higher than the median. The points at the right have pulled the mean toward them away from the median.*

**A S** *Activity:* **The Center of a Distribution.** Compare measures of center by dragging points up and down and seeing the consequences. Another activity shows how to find summaries with your statistics package.

The mean is 2.28%, but nearly 70% of months had cancellation rates below that, so the mean doesn't feel like a good overall summary. Why is the balancing point so high? The large outlying value pulls it to the right. For data like these, the median is a better summary of the center.

Because the median considers only the order of the values, it is **resistant** to values that are extraordinarily large or small; it simply notes that they are one of the "big ones" or the "small ones" and ignores their distance from the center.

For the tsunami earthquake magnitudes, it doesn't seem to make much difference—the mean is 6.96; the median is 7.0. When the data are symmetric, the mean and median will be close, but when the data are skewed, the median is likely to be a better choice. So, why not just use the median? Well, for one, the median can go overboard. It's not just resistant to occasional outliers, but can be unaffected by changes in up to half the data values. By contrast, the mean includes input from each data value and gives each one equal weight. It's also easier to work with, so when the distribution is unimodal and symmetric, we'll use the mean.

Of course, to choose between mean and median, we'll start by looking at the data. If the histogram is symmetric and there are no outliers, we'll prefer the mean. However, if the histogram is skewed or has outliers, we're usually better off with the median. If you're not sure, report both and discuss why they might differ.

**FOR EXAMPLE**     Describing center

**Recap:** You want to summarize the expenditures of 500 credit card company customers, and have looked at a histogram.

**Question:** You have found the mean expenditure to be $478.19 and the median to be $216.28. Which is the more appropriate measure of center, and why?

(*continued*)

> For Example (*continued*)
>
> Because the distribution of expenditures is skewed, the median is the more appropriate measure of center. The median is the middle value, with half the expenditures above and half below it, and, unlike the mean, it's not affected by the large outlying value or by the skewness of the distribution.

> **When to expect skewness**   Even without making a histogram, we can expect some variables to be skewed. When values of a quantitative variable are bounded on one side but not the other, the distribution may be skewed. For example, incomes and waiting times can't be less than zero, so they are often skewed to the right. Amounts of things (dollars, employees) are often skewed to the right for the same reason. If a test is too easy, the distribution will be skewed to the left, because many scores will bump against 100%. And combinations of things are often skewed. In the case of the cancelled flights, flights are more likely to be cancelled in January (due to snowstorms) and in August (thunderstorms). Combining values across months leads to a skewed distribution.

# What About Spread? The Standard Deviation

> **A S**   *Activity:* **The Spread of a Distribution.** What happens to measures of spread when data values change may not be quite what you expect.

> **NOTATION ALERT:**
>
> $s^2$ always means the variance, and $s$ always denotes the standard deviation.

The IQR is always a reasonable summary of spread, but because it uses only the two quartiles of the data, it ignores much of the information about how individual values vary. A more powerful approach uses the **standard deviation,** which takes into account how far *each* value is from the mean. Like the mean, the standard deviation is appropriate only for symmetric data.

One way to think about spread is to examine how far each data value is from the mean. This difference is called a *deviation.* We could just average the deviations, but the positive and negative differences always cancel each other out. So the average deviation is always zero—not very helpful.

To keep them from canceling out, we *square* each deviation. Squaring always gives a positive value, so the sum won't be zero. That's great. Squaring also emphasizes larger differences—a feature that turns out to be both good and bad.

When we add up these squared deviations and find their average (almost), we call the result the **variance:**

$$s^2 = \frac{\sum (y - \bar{y})^2}{n - 1}.$$

Why almost? It *would* be a mean if we divided the sum by $n$. Instead, we divide by $n - 1$. Why? The simplest explanation is "to drive you crazy." But there are good technical reasons, some of which we'll see later.

The variance will play an important role later in this book, but it has a problem as a measure of spread. Whatever the units of the original data are, the variance is in *squared* units. We want measures of spread to have the same units as the data. And we probably don't want to talk about squared dollars, or $mpg^2$. So, to get back to the original units, we take the square root of $s^2$. The result, $s$, is the **standard deviation.**

Putting it all together, the standard deviation of the data is found by the following formula:

$$s = \sqrt{\frac{\sum (y - \bar{y})^2}{n - 1}}.$$

You will almost always rely on a calculator or computer to do the calculating.

### FINDING THE STANDARD DEVIATION BY HAND

To find the standard deviation, start with the mean, $\bar{y}$. Then find the *deviations* by taking $\bar{y}$ from each value: $(y - \bar{y})$. Square each deviation: $(y - \bar{y})^2$.

Now you're nearly home. Just add these up and divide by $n - 1$. That gives you the variance, $s^2$. To find the standard deviation, $s$, take the square root. Here we go:

Suppose the batch of values is 4, 3, 10, 12, 8, 9, and 3.

The mean is $\bar{y} = 7$. So the deviations are found by subtracting 7 from each value:

| Original Values | Deviations | Squared Deviations |
|:---:|:---|:---:|
| 4 | $4 - 7 = -3$ | $(-3)^2 = 9$ |
| 3 | $3 - 7 = -4$ | $(-4)^2 = 16$ |
| 10 | $10 - 7 = 3$ | 9 |
| 12 | $12 - 7 = 5$ | 25 |
| 8 | $8 - 7 = 1$ | 1 |
| 9 | $9 - 7 = 2$ | 4 |
| 3 | $3 - 7 = -4$ | 16 |

Add up the squared deviations: $9 + 16 + 9 + 25 + 1 + 4 + 16 = 80$.

Now divide by $n - 1$:                  $80/6 = 13.33$.

Finally, take the square root:           $s = \sqrt{13.33} = 3.65$

# Thinking About Variation

**A S**    *Activity:* **Displaying Spread.** What does the standard deviation look like on a histogram? How about the IQR?

Why do banks favor a single line that feeds several teller windows rather than separate lines for each teller? The average waiting time is the same. But the time you can expect to wait is less variable when there is a single line, and people prefer consistency.

Statistics is about variation, so spread is an important fundamental concept in Statistics. Measures of spread help us to be precise about what we *don't* know. If many data values are scattered far from the center, the IQR and the standard deviation will be large. If the data values are close to the center, then these measures of spread will be small. If all our data values were exactly the same, we'd have no question about summarizing the center, and all measures of spread would be zero—and we wouldn't need Statistics. You might think this would be a big plus, but it would make for a boring world. Fortunately (at least for Statistics), data do vary.

Measures of spread tell how well other summaries describe the data. That's why we always (always!) report a spread along with any summary of the center.

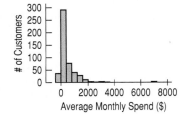

### FOR EXAMPLE     Describing spread

**Recap:** The histogram has shown you that the distribution of credit card expenditures is skewed, and you have used the median to describe the center. The quartiles are $73.84 and $624.80.

**Question:** What is the IQR and why is it a suitable measure of spread?

For these data, the interquartile range (IQR) is $624.80 − $73.84 = $550.97. Like the median, the IQR is not affected by the outlying value or by the skewness of the distribution, so it is an appropriate measure of spread for the given expenditures.

## JUST CHECKING

6. The U.S. Census Bureau reports the median family income in its summary of census data. Why do you suppose they use the median instead of the mean? What might be the disadvantages of reporting the mean?

7. You've just bought a new car that claims to get a highway fuel efficiency of 31 miles per gallon. Of course, your mileage will "vary." If you had to guess, would you expect the IQR of gas mileage attained by all cars like yours to be 30 mpg, 3 mpg, or 0.3 mpg? Why?

8. A company selling a new MP3 player advertises that the player has a mean lifetime of 5 years. If you were in charge of quality control at the factory, would you prefer that the standard deviation of lifespans of the players you produce be 2 years or 2 months? Why?

# What to *Tell* About a Quantitative Variable— A Summary

**A S** | **Activity: Playing with Summaries.** Here's a Statistics game about summaries that even some experienced statisticians find . . . well, challenging. Your intuition may be better. Give it a try!

**How "Accurate" Should We Be?**
Don't think you should report means and standard deviations to a zillion decimal places; such implied accuracy is really meaningless. Although there is no ironclad rule, statisticians commonly report summary statistics to one or two decimal places more than the original data have.

What should you *Tell* about a quantitative variable?

▶ Start by making a histogram or stem-and-leaf display, and discuss the shape of the distribution.

▶ Next, discuss the center *and* spread.

 ▶ If the shape is skewed, report the median and IQR. You may want to include the mean and standard deviation as well, but you should point out why the mean and median differ.

 ▶ If the shape is symmetric, report the mean and standard deviation and possibly the median and IQR as well. For unimodal symmetric data, the IQR is usually a bit larger than the standard deviation. If that's not true of your data set, look again to make sure that the distribution isn't skewed and there are no outliers.

 ▶ We always pair the median with the IQR and the mean with the standard deviation. It's not useful to report one without the other. Reporting a center without a spread is dangerous. You may think you know more than you do about the distribution. Reporting only the spread leaves us wondering where we are.

▶ Also, discuss any unusual features.

 ▶ If there are multiple modes, try to understand why. If you can identify a reason for separate modes (for example, women and men typically have heart attacks at different ages), it may be a good idea to split the data into separate groups.

 ▶ If there are any clear outliers, you should point them out. If you are reporting the mean and standard deviation, report them with the outliers present and with the outliers removed. The differences may be revealing. (Of course, the median and IQR won't be affected very much by the outliers.)

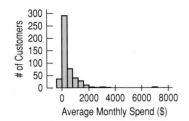

**Recap:** You have provided the credit card company's board of directors with a histogram of customer expenditures, and you have summarized the center and spread with the median and IQR. Knowing a little Statistics, the directors now insist on having the mean and standard deviation as summaries of the spending data.

**Question:** Although you know that the mean is $478.19 and the standard deviation is $741.87, you need to explain to them why these are not suitable summary statistics for these expenditures data. What would you give as reasons?

*The high outlier at $7000 pulls the mean up substantially and inflates the standard deviation. Locating the mean value on the histogram shows that it is not a typical value at all, and the standard deviation suggests that expenditures vary much more than they do. The median and IQR are more resistant to the presence of skewness and outliers, giving more realistic descriptions of center and spread.*

---

**STEP-BY-STEP EXAMPLE**    **Summarizing a Distribution**

One of the authors owned a 1989 Nissan Maxima for 8 years. Being a statistician, he recorded the car's fuel efficiency (in mpg) each time he filled the tank. He wanted to know what fuel efficiency to expect as "ordinary" for his car. (Hey, he's a statistician, what would you expect?[10]) Knowing this, he was able to predict when he'd need to fill the tank again and to notice if the fuel efficiency suddenly got worse, which could be a sign of trouble.

**Question:** How would you describe the distribution of *Fuel efficiency* for this car?

| | |
|---|---|
| **THINK** | |

**Plan** State what you want to find out.

*I want to summarize the distribution of Nissan fuel efficiency.*

**Variable** Identify the variable and report the W's.

Be sure to check the appropriate condition.

*The data are the fuel efficiency values in miles per gallon for the first 100 fill-ups of a 1989 Nissan Maxima between 1989 and 1992.*

✔ **Quantitative Data Condition:** *The fuel efficiencies are quantitative with units miles per gallon. Histograms and boxplots are appropriate displays for displaying the distribution. Numerical summaries are appropriate as well.*

**SHOW**

**Mechanics** Make a histogram and boxplot. Based on the shape, choose appropriate numerical summaries.

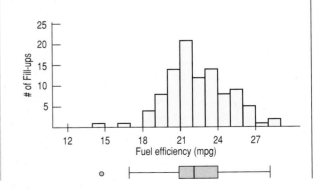

---

[10] He also recorded the time of day, temperature, price of gas, and phase of the moon. (OK, maybe not phase of the moon.) His data are on the DVD.

REALITY CHECK

A value of 22 mpg seems reasonable for such a car. The spread is reasonable, although the range looks a bit large.

A histogram of the data shows a fairly symmetric distribution with a low outiler.

| Count | 100 |
|--------|---------|
| Mean | 22.4 mpg |
| StdDev | 2.45 |
| Q1 | 20.8 |
| Median | 22.0 |
| Q3 | 24.0 |
| IQR | 3.2 |

The mean and median are close, so the outlier doesn't seen to be a problem. I can use the mean and standard deviation.

TELL

**Conclusion** Summarize and interpret your findings in context. Be sure to discuss the distribution's shape, center, spread, and unusual features (if any).

The distribution of mileage is unimodal and symmetric with a mean of 22.4 mpg. There is a low outlier that should be investigated, but it does not influence the mean very much. The standard deviation is 2.4 mpg. The boxplot shows that half of the time the car had a fuel efficiency between about 21 and 24 mpg.

---

**Are my quartiles "right"?**   When you calculate a mean, the computation is clear: You sum all the values and divide by the sample size. You may round your answer less or more than someone else (we recommend one more decimal place than the data), but all books and technologies agree on how to find the mean.

Some statistics, however, are more problematic. For example, the first quartile is defined as the value such that a quarter of the data falls at or below it. That seems simple enough, but let's look more closely. If we have 8 distinct data values—say 1, 2, 3, 4, 5, 6, 7, and 8—then *any* value between 2 and 3 (but not including 3) would satisfy the definition, slicing off exactly a quarter of the data values (specifically, 1 and 2). And if we have 9 data values (say 1 to 9), there's *no value* for which exactly a quarter of the values lie below it.

The *concept* of a quartile is simple, and with enough data values we can get very close to realizing it in the data. But for small amounts of data, we're forced to make a choice about just how to approximate that concept. You'll find that different books and technologies find quartiles in slightly different ways. A review of statistics programs found nine different ways to compute quartiles! All of them are reasonable approximations to the concept of a quartile, and those differences rarely matter to how we *understand* what the data are telling us. But the differences in value can be startling, and you may be surprised (and worried) if your answer doesn't match the one in the back of the book.

Differences in numeric results can also arise from decisions in the middle of calculations. For example, if you round off the value you computed for the mean before you calculate the sums of squared differences in a standard deviation, your result probably won't agree with a computer program that calculates with many digits after the decimal point. (We do recommend that you carry as many digits as you can for intermediate calculations to minimize this effect.)

Don't be overly concerned with these discrepancies, especially if the differences are small. They don't mean that your answer is "wrong," and they usually won't change any conclusion you might draw about the data. Sometimes (in footnotes and in the answers in the back of the book), we'll note alternative results, but we could never list all the possible values, so we'll rely on your common sense to focus on the meaning rather than on the digits.

# WHAT CAN GO WRONG?

A data display should tell a story about the data. To do that, it must speak in a clear language, making plain what variable is displayed, what any axis shows, and what the values of the data are. And it must be consistent in those decisions.

A display of quantitative data can go wrong in many ways. The most common failures arise from only a few basic errors:

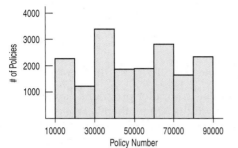

**FIGURE 4.14**

*It's not appropriate to display these data with a histogram.*

▶ **Don't make a histogram of a categorical variable.** Just because the variable contains numbers doesn't mean that it's quantitative. Here's a histogram of the insurance policy numbers of some workers. It's not very informative because the policy numbers are just labels. A histogram or stem-and-leaf display of a categorical variable makes no sense. A bar chart or pie chart would be more appropriate.

▶ **Don't look for shape, center, and spread of a bar chart.** A bar chart showing the sizes of the piles displays the distribution of a categorical variable, but the bars could be arranged in any order left to right. Concepts like symmetry, center, and spread make sense only for quantitative variables.

▶ **Don't use bars in every display—save them for histograms and bar charts.** In a bar chart, the bars indicate how many cases of a categorical variable are piled in each category. Bars in a histogram indicate the number of cases piled in each interval of a quantitative variable. In both bar charts and histograms, the bars represent counts of data values. Some people create other displays that use bars to represent individual data values. Beware: Such graphs are neither bar charts nor histograms. For example, a student was asked to make a histogram from data showing the number of juvenile bald eagles seen during each of the 13 weeks in the winter of 2003–2004 at a site in Rock Island, IL. Instead, he made this plot:

**FIGURE 4.15**

*This isn't a histogram or a bar chart. It's an ill-conceived graph that uses bars to represent individual data values (number of eagles sighted) week by week.*

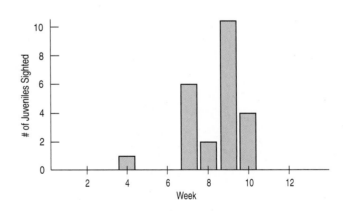

Look carefully. That's not a histogram. A histogram shows *What* we've measured along the horizontal axis and counts of the associated *Who*'s represented as bar heights. This student has it backwards: He used bars to show counts of birds for each week.[11] We need counts of weeks. A correct histogram should have a tall bar at "0" to show there were many weeks when no eagles were seen, like this:

*(continued)*

---

[11] Edward Tufte, in his book *The Visual Display of Quantitative Information*, proposes that graphs should have a high data-to-ink ratio. That is, we shouldn't waste a lot of ink to display a single number when a dot would do the job.

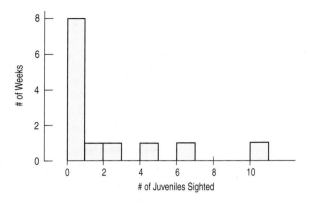

**FIGURE 4.16**

*A histogram of the eagle-sighting data shows the number of weeks in which different counts of eagles occurred. This display shows the distribution of juvenile-eagle sightings.*

▶ **Choose a bin width appropriate to the data.** Computer programs usually do a pretty good job of choosing histogram bin widths. Often, there's an easy way to adjust the width, sometimes interactively. Here are the tsunami earthquakes with two (rather extreme) choices for the bin size:

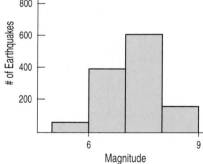

The task of summarizing a quantitative variable is relatively simple, and there is a simple path to follow. However, you need to watch out for certain features of the data that make summarizing them with a number dangerous. Here's some advice:

▶ **Don't forget to do a reality check.** Don't let the computer or calculator do your thinking for you. Make sure the calculated summaries make sense. For example, does the mean look like it is in the center of the histogram? Think about the spread: An IQR of 50 mpg would clearly be wrong for gas mileage. And no measure of spread can be negative. The standard deviation can take the value 0, but only in the very unusual case that all the data values equal the same number. If you see an IQR or standard deviation equal to 0, it's probably a sign that something's wrong with the data.

▶ **Don't forget to sort the values before finding the median or percentiles.** It seems obvious, but when you work by hand, it's easy to forget to sort the data first before counting in to find medians, quartiles, or other percentiles. Don't report that the median of the five values 194, 5, 1, 17, and 893 is 1 just because 1 is the middle number.

▶ **Don't worry about small differences when using different methods.** Finding the 10th percentile or the lower quartile in a data set sounds easy enough. But it turns out that the definitions are not exactly clear. If you compare different statistics packages or calculators, you may find that they give slightly different answers for the same data. These differences, though, are unlikely to be important in interpreting the data, the quartiles, or the IQR, so don't let them worry you.

▶ **Don't compute numerical summaries of a categorical variable.** Neither the mean zip code nor the standard deviation of social security numbers is meaningful. If the variable is categorical, you should instead report summaries such as percentages of individuals in each category. It is easy to make this mistake when using technology to do the summaries for you. After all, the computer doesn't care what the numbers mean.

| Gold Card Customers—Regions National Bank | | |
|---|---|---|
| Month | April 2007 | May 2007 |
| Average Zip Code | 45,034.34 | 38,743.34 |

▶ **Don't report too many decimal places.** Statistical programs and calculators often report a ridiculous number of digits. A general rule for numerical summaries is to report one or two more digits than the number of digits in the data. For example, earlier we saw a dotplot of the Kentucky Derby race times. The mean and standard deviation of those times could be reported as

$$\bar{y} = 130.63401639344262 \text{ sec}$$

$$s = 13.66448201942662 \text{ sec}$$

but the race times are reported only to the nearest quarter second, so the extra digits are meaningless.

▶ **Don't round in the middle of a calculation.** Don't *report* too many decimal places, but it's best not to do any rounding until the end of your calculations. Even though you might report the mean of the earthquakes as 7.08, it's really 7.08339. Use the more precise number in your calculations if you're finding the standard deviation by hand—or be prepared to see small differences in your final result.

▶ **Watch out for multiple modes.** The summaries of the Kentucky Derby times are meaningless for another reason. As we saw in the dotplot, the Derby initially was a longer race. It would make much more sense to report that the old 1.5 mile Derby had a mean time of 159.6 seconds, while the current Derby has a mean time of 124.6 seconds. If the distribution has multiple modes, consider separating the data into different groups and summarizing each group separately.

▶ **Beware of outliers.** The median and IQR are resistant to outliers, but the mean and standard deviation are not. To help spot outliers,

▶ **Don't forget to: Make a picture (make a picture, make a picture).** The sensitivity of the mean and standard deviation to outliers is one reason you should always make a picture of the data. Summarizing a variable with its mean and standard deviation when you have not looked at a histogram or dotplot to check for outliers or skewness invites disaster. You may find yourself drawing absurd or dangerously wrong conclusions about the data. And, of course, you should demand no less of others. Don't accept a mean and standard deviation blindly without some evidence that the variable they summarize is unimodal, symmetric, and free of outliers.

# CONNECTIONS

Distributions of quantitative variables, like those of categorical variables, show the possible values and their relative frequencies. A histogram shows the distribution of values in a quantitative variable with adjacent bars. Don't confuse histograms with bar charts, which display categorical variables. For categorical data, the mode is the category with the biggest count. For quantitative data, modes are peaks in the histogram.

The shape of the distribution of a quantitative variable is an important concept in most of the subsequent chapters. We will be especially interested in distributions that are unimodal and symmetric.

In addition to their shape, we summarize distributions with center and spread, usually pairing a measure of center with a measure of spread: median with IQR and mean with standard deviation. We favor the mean and standard deviation when the shape is unimodal and symmetric, but choose the median and IQR for skewed distributions or when there are outliers we can't otherwise set aside.

## WHAT HAVE WE LEARNED?

We've learned how to make a picture of quantitative data to help us see the story the data have to *Tell*.

▶ We can display the distribution of quantitative data with a *histogram*, a *stem-and-leaf* display, or a *dotplot*.

▶ We *Tell* what we see about the distribution by talking about *shape*, *center*, *spread*, and any *unusual features*.

We've learned how to summarize distributions of quantitative variables numerically.

▶ Measures of center for a distribution include the median and the mean.

We write the formula for the mean as $\bar{y} = \dfrac{\sum y}{n}$.

▶ Measures of spread include the range, IQR, and standard deviation.

The standard deviation is computed as $s = \sqrt{\dfrac{\sum (y - \bar{y})^2}{n - 1}}$.

The median and IQR are not usually given as formulas.

▶ We'll report the median and IQR when the distribution is skewed. If it's symmetric, we'll summarize the distribution with the mean and standard deviation (and possibly the median and IQR as well). Always pair the median with the IQR and the mean with the standard deviation.

We've learned to *Think* about the type of variable we're summarizing.

▶ All the methods of this chapter assume that the data are quantitative.

▶ The **Quantitative Data Condition** serves as a check that the data are, in fact, quantitative. One good way to be sure is to know the measurement units. You'll want those as part of the *Think* step of your answers.

## Terms

| | |
|---|---|
| Distribution | 49. The distribution of a quantitative variable slices up all the possible values of the variable into equal- width bins and gives the number of values (or counts) falling into each bin. |
| Histogram (relative frequency histogram) | 49, 50. A histogram uses adjacent bars to show the distribution of a quantitative variable. Each bar represents the frequency (or relative frequency) of values falling in each bin. |
| Gap | 50. A region of the distribution where there are no values. |
| Stem-and-leaf display | 50. A stem-and-leaf display shows quantitative data values in a way that sketches the distribution of the data. It's best described in detail by example. |

| Dotplot | 52. A dotplot graphs a dot for each case against a single axis. |
| Shape | 53. To describe the shape of a distribution, look for |

- single vs. multiple modes.
- symmetry vs. skewness.
- outliers and gaps.

| Center | 53, 56. The place in the distribution of a variable that you'd point to if you wanted to attempt the impossible by summarizing the entire distribution with a single number. Measures of center include the mean and median. |
| Spread | 53, 57. A numerical summary of how tightly the values are clustered around the center. Measures of spread include the IQR and standard deviation. |
| Mode | 53. A hump or local high point in the shape of the distribution of a variable. The apparent location of modes can change as the scale of a histogram is changed. |
| Unimodal | 53. Having one mode. This is a useful term for describing the shape of a histogram when it's generally mound-shaped. Distributions with two modes are called **bimodal.** Those with more than two are **multimodal.** |
| Uniform | 53. A distribution that's roughly flat is said to be uniform. |
| Symmetric | 54. A distribution is symmetric if the two halves on either side of the center look approximately like mirror images of each other. |
| Tails | 54. The tails of a distribution are the parts that typically trail off on either side. Distributions can be characterized as having long tails (if they straggle off for some distance) or short tails (if they don't). |
| Skewed | 54. A distribution is skewed if it's not symmetric and one tail stretches out farther than the other. Distributions are said to be **skewed left** when the longer tail stretches to the left, and **skewed right** when it goes to the right. |
| Outliers | 54. Outliers are extreme values that don't appear to belong with the rest of the data. They may be unusual values that deserve further investigation, or they may be just mistakes; there's no obvious way to tell. Don't delete outliers automatically—you have to think about them. Outliers can affect many statistical analyses, so you should always be alert for them. |
| Median | 56. The median is the middle value, with half of the data above and half below it. If $n$ is even, it is the average of the two middle values. It is usually paired with the IQR. |
| Range | 57. The difference between the lowest and highest values in a data set. *Range = max − min*. |
| Quartile | 58. The lower quartile (Q1) is the value with a quarter of the data below it. The upper quartile (Q3) has three quarters of the data below it. The median and quartiles divide data into four parts with equal numbers of data values. |
| Interquartile range (IQR) | 58. The IQR is the difference between the first and third quartiles. *IQR = Q3 − Q1*. It is usually reported along with the median. |
| Percentile | 59. The $i$th percentile is the number that falls above $i$% of the data. |
| 5-Number Summary | 60. The 5-number summary of a distribution reports the minimum value, Q1, the median, Q3, and the maximum value. |
| Mean | 62. The mean is found by summing all the data values and dividing by the count: |

$$\bar{y} = \frac{Total}{n} = \frac{\sum y}{n}.$$

It is usually paired with the standard deviation.

| Resistant | 63. A calculated summary is said to be resistant if it is affected only a limited amount by outliers. |
| Variance | 65. The variance is the sum of squared deviations from the mean, divided by the count minus 1: |

$$s^2 = \frac{\sum (y - \bar{y})^2}{n - 1}$$

It is useful in calculations later in the book.

**Standard deviation**

64. The standard deviation is the square root of the variance:

$$s = \sqrt{\frac{\sum (y - \bar{y})^2}{n - 1}}.$$

It is usually reported along with the mean.

# Skills

- ▸ Be able to identify an appropriate display for any quantitative variable.
- ▸ Be able to guess the shape of the distribution of a variable by knowing something about the data.
- ▸ Be able to select a suitable measure of center and a suitable measure of spread for a variable based on information about its distribution.
- ▸ Know the basic properties of the median: The median divides the data into the half of the data values that are below the median and the half that are above.
- ▸ Know the basic properties of the mean: The mean is the point at which the histogram balances.
- ▸ Know that the standard deviation summarizes how spread out all the data are around the mean.
- ▸ Understand that the median and IQR resist the effects of outliers, while the mean and standard deviation do not.
- ▸ Understand that in a skewed distribution, the mean is pulled in the direction of the skewness (toward the longer tail) relative to the median.

- ▸ Know how to display the distribution of a quantitative variable with a stem-and-leaf display (drawn by hand for smaller data sets), a dotplot, or a histogram (made by computer for larger data sets).
- ▸ Know how to compute the mean and median of a set of data.
- ▸ Know how to compute the standard deviation and IQR of a set of data.

- ▸ Be able to describe the distribution of a quantitative variable in terms of its shape, center, and spread.
- ▸ Be able to describe any anomalies or extraordinary features revealed by the display of a variable.
- ▸ Know how to describe summary measures in a sentence. In particular, know that the common measures of center and spread have the same units as the variable that they summarize, and should be described in those units.
- ▸ Be able to describe the distribution of a quantitative variable with a description of the shape of the distribution, a numerical measure of center, and a numerical measure of spread. Be sure to note any unusual features, such as outliers, too.

# ON THE COMPUTER

## Displaying and Summarizing Quantitative Variables

Almost any program that displays data can make a histogram, but some will do a better job of determining where the bars should start and how they should partition the span of the data.

*The vertical scale may be counts or proportions. Sometimes it isn't clear which. But the shape of the histogram is the same either way.*

*Most packages choose the number of bars for you automatically. Often you can adjust that choice.*

*The axis should be clearly labeled so you can tell what "pile" each bar represents. You should be able to tell the lower and upper bounds of each bar.*

Many statistics packages offer a prepackaged collection of summary measures. The result might look like this:

```
Variable: Weight
N = 234
Mean = 143.3        Median = 139
St. Dev = 11.1      IQR = 14
```

Alternatively, a package might make a table for several variables and summary measures:

| Variable | N | mean | median | stdev | IQR |
|---|---|---|---|---|---|
| Weight | 234 | 143.3 | 139 | 11.1 | 14 |
| Height | 234 | 68.3 | 68.1 | 4.3 | 5 |
| Score | 234 | 86 | 88 | 9 | 5 |

**A S**  *Case Study:*
**Describing Distribution Shapes.** Who's safer in a crash—passengers or the driver? Investigate with your statistics package.

It is usually easy to read the results and identify each computed summary. You should be able to read the summary statistics produced by any computer package.

Packages often provide many more summary statistics than you need. Of course, some of these may not be appropriate when the data are skewed or have outliers. It is your responsibility to check a histogram or stem-and-leaf display and decide which summary statistics to use.

It is common for packages to report summary statistics to many decimal places of "accuracy." Of course, it is rare data that have such accuracy in the original measurements. The ability to calculate to six or seven digits beyond the decimal point doesn't mean that those digits have any meaning. Generally, it's a good idea to round these values, allowing perhaps one more digit of precision than was given in the original data.

Displays and summaries of quantitative variables are among the simplest things you can do in most statistics packages.

## DATA DESK

To make a histogram:
▸  Select the variable to display.
▸  In the **Plot** menu, choose **Histogram.**

To calculate summaries:
▸  In the **Calc** menu, open the **summaries** submenu. **Options** offer separate tables, a single unified table, and other formats.

## EXCEL

Excel cannot make histograms or dotplots without a third-party add-in.

To calculate summaries,

Click on an empty cell. Type an equals sign and choose "**Average**" from the popup list of functions that appears to the left of the text editing box. Enter the data range in the box that says "**Number 1.**" Click the **OK** button.

To compute the standard deviation of a column of data directly, use the **STDEV** from the popup list of functions in the same way.

### COMMENTS

Excel's Data Analysis add-in does offer something called a histogram, but it just makes a crude frequency table, and the Chart Wizard cannot then create a statistically appropriate histogram. The DDXL add-in provided on our DVD adds these and other capabilities to Excel.

Excel's STDEV function should not be used for data values larger in magnitude than 100,000 or for lists of more than a few thousand values. It is programmed with an unstable formula that can generate rounding errors when these limits are exceeded.

## EXCEL 2007

In Excel 2007 there is another way to find some of the standard summary statistics. For example, to compute the mean:
▸  Click on an empty cell.
▸  Go to the Formulas tab in the Ribbon. Click on the drop down arrow next to "AutoSum" and choose "**Average**".
▸  Enter the data range in the formula displayed in the empty box you selected earlier.
▸  Press **Enter.** This computes the mean for the values in that range.

To compute the standard deviation:
▸  Click on an empty cell.
▸  Go to the Formulas tab in the Ribbon and click the drop down arrow next to "AutoSum" and select "**More functions...**"
▸  In the dialog window that opens, select "**STDEV**" from the list of functions and click **OK.** A new dialog window opens. Enter a range of fields into the text fields and click **OK.**

Excel 2007 computes the standard deviation for the values in that range and places it in the specified cell of the spreadsheet.

## JMP

To make a histogram and find summary statistics:
▸  Choose **Distribution** from the **Analyze** menu.
▸  In the **Distribution** dialog, drag the name of the variable that you wish to analyze into the empty window beside the label "**Y, Columns.**"

▸  Click **OK.** JMP computes standard summary statistics along with displays of the variables.

## MINITAB

To make a histogram:
▶ Choose **Histogram** from the **Graph** menu.
▶ Select "Simple" for the type of graph and click **OK.**
▶ Enter the name of the quantitative variable you wish to display in the box labeled "Graph variables." Click **OK.**

To calculate summary statistics:
▶ Choose **Basic statistics** from the **Stat** menu. From the **Basic Statistics** submenu, choose **Display Descriptive Statistics.**
▶ Assign variables from the variable list box to the Variables box. MINITAB makes a Descriptive Statistics table.

## SPSS

To make a histogram in SPSS open the Chart Builder from the Graphs menu.
▶ Click the **Gallery** tab
▶ Choose **Histogram** from the ist of chart types.
▶ Drag the histogram onto the canvas.
▶ Drag a scale variable to the y-axis drop zone.
▶ Click **OK**

To calculate summary statistics:
▶ Choose **Explore** from the **Descriptive Statistics** submenu of the **Analyze** menu. In the Explore dialog, assign one or more variables from the source list to the Dependent List and click the **OK** button.

## TI-83/84 PLUS

To make a histogram:
▶ Turn a **STATPLOT** on.
▶ Choose the **histogram icon** and specify the List where the data are stored.
▶ **ZoomStat,** then adjust the **WINDOW** appropriately.
To calculate summary statistics:
▶ Choose **1-VarStats** from the **STAT CALC** menu and specify the List where the data are stored. You must scroll down to see the 5-number summary.
▶ To make a boxplot, set up a **STAT PLOT** using the boxplot icon.

### COMMENTS

If the data are stored as a frequency table (say, with data values in L1 and frequencies in L2), set up the Plot with Xlist: L1 and Freq: L2.

## TI-89

To make a histogram:
▶ Select F2 **(Plots),** then 1: **Plot Setup.** Select a plot and press F1 to define it.
▶ Select plot type 4: **Histogram.** Use VAR-LINK to select the data list.
▶ Enter a number for the histogram bucket (bar) width.
▶ Press ENTER to complete the plot definition. Press F5 to display the histogram.
▶ Press •F2 to adjust the window appropriately, then press •F3 **(Graph).**
To calculate summary statistics:
▶ To compute summary statistics, press F4 **(Calc).** Input the name of the list using VAR-LINK. Press ENTER.
▶ Use the down arrow to scroll through the output.
▶ To create a boxplot, press F2 **(Plots)** then ENTER. Select a plot to define and press F1. Select either 3: **Box Plot** or 4: **Mod Box Plot** (to identify outliers). Select the mark type of your choice (for outliers). Press ENTER to finish.
▶ Press F5 to display the graph.

### COMMENTS

If the data are stored as a frequency table (say, with data values in list1 and frequencies in list2), change Use Freq and Categories to YES and use VAR-LINK to select list2 as the frequency variable on the plot definition screen.
If the data are stored as a frequency table (say, with data values in list1 and frequencies in list2), use VAR-LINK to select list2 as the frequency variable in 1-Var Stats.
For the plot, change Use Freq and Categories to YES and use VAR-LINK to select list2 as the frequency variable on the plot definition screen.

# EXERCISES

1. **Statistics in print.** Find a histogram that shows the distribution of a variable in a newspaper or magazine article.
   a) Does the article identify the W's?
   b) Discuss whether the display is appropriate for the data.
   c) Discuss what the display reveals about the variable and its distribution.
   d) Does the article accurately describe and interpret the data? Explain.

2. **Not a histogram.** Find a graph other than a histogram that shows the distribution of a quantitative variable in a newspaper or magazine article.
   a) Does the article identify the W's?
   b) Discuss whether the display is appropriate for the data.
   c) Discuss what the display reveals about the variable and its distribution.
   d) Does the article accurately describe and interpret the data? Explain.

3. **In the news.** Find an article in a newspaper or a magazine that discusses an "average."
   a) Does the article discuss the W's for the data?
   b) What are the units of the variable?
   c) Is the average used the median or the mean? How can you tell?
   d) Is the choice of median or mean appropriate for the situation? Explain.

4. **In the news II.** Find an article in a newspaper or a magazine that discusses a measure of spread.
   a) Does the article discuss the W's for the data?
   b) What are the units of the variable?
   c) Does the article use the range, IQR, or standard deviation?
   d) Is the choice of measure of spread appropriate for the situation? Explain.

5. **Thinking about shape.** Would you expect distributions of these variables to be uniform, unimodal, or bimodal? Symmetric or skewed? Explain why.
   a) The number of speeding tickets each student in the senior class of a college has ever had.
   b) Players' scores (number of strokes) at the U.S. Open golf tournament in a given year.
   c) Weights of female babies born in a particular hospital over the course of a year.
   d) The length of the average hair on the heads of students in a large class.

6. **More shapes.** Would you expect distributions of these variables to be uniform, unimodal, or bimodal? Symmetric or skewed? Explain why.
   a) Ages of people at a Little League game.
   b) Number of siblings of people in your class.
   c) Pulse rates of college-age males.
   d) Number of times each face of a die shows in 100 tosses.

7. **Sugar in cereals.** The histogram displays the sugar content (as a percent of weight) of 49 brands of breakfast cereals.

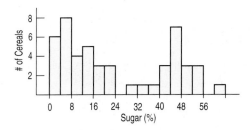

   a) Describe this distribution.
   b) What do you think might account for this shape?

8. **Singers.** The display shows the heights of some of the singers in a chorus, collected so that the singers could be positioned on stage with shorter ones in front and taller ones in back.

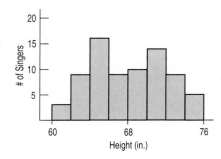

   a) Describe the distribution.
   b) Can you account for the features you see here?

9. **Vineyards.** The histogram shows the sizes (in acres) of 36 vineyards in the Finger Lakes region of New York.

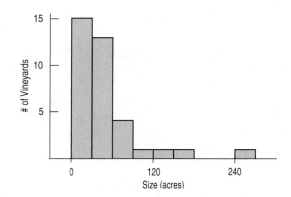

   a) Approximately what percentage of these vineyards are under 60 acres?
   b) Write a brief description of this distribution (shape, center, spread, unusual features).

**10. Run times.** One of the authors collected the times (in minutes) it took him to run 4 miles on various courses during a 10-year period. Here is a histogram of the times.

Describe the distribution and summarize the important features. What is it about running that might account for the shape you see?

**11. Heart attack stays.** The histogram shows the lengths of hospital stays (in days) for all the female patients admitted to hospitals in New York during one year with a primary diagnosis of acute myocardial infarction (heart attack).

a) From the histogram, would you expect the mean or median to be larger? Explain.
b) Write a few sentences describing this distribution (shape, center, spread, unusual features).

**12. E-mails.** A university teacher saved every e-mail received from students in a large Introductory Statistics class during an entire term. He then counted, for each student who had sent him at least one e-mail, how many e-mails each student had sent.

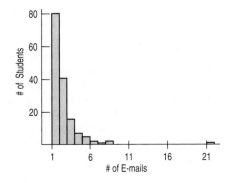

a) From the histogram, would you expect the mean or the median to be larger? Explain.
b) Write a few sentences describing this distribution (shape, center, spread, unusual features).

**13. Super Bowl points.** How many points do football teams score in the Super Bowl? Here are the total numbers of points scored by both teams in each of the first 41 Super Bowl games:

45, 47, 23, 30, 29, 27, 21, 31, 22, 38, 46, 37, 66, 50, 37, 47, 44, 47, 54, 56, 59, 52, 36, 65, 39, 61, 69, 43, 75, 44, 56, 55, 53, 39, 41, 37, 69, 61, 45, 31, 46

a) Find the median.
b) Find the quartiles.

**14. Super Bowl wins.** In the Super Bowl, by how many points does the winning team outscore the losers? Here are the winning margins for the first 41 Super Bowl games:

25, 19, 9, 16, 3, 21, 7, 17, 10, 4, 18, 17, 4, 12, 17, 5, 10, 29, 22, 36, 19, 32, 4, 45, 1, 13, 35, 17, 23, 10, 14, 7, 15, 7, 27, 3, 27, 3, 3, 11, 12

a) Find the median.
b) Find the quartiles.

**15. Oil production.** The histogram shows amount of oil produced (in gallons) from an acre of land in the United States from 36 different crops.

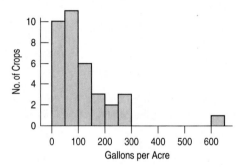

Which summary statistics would you choose to summarize the center and spread in these data? Why?

**16. Paper consumption.** The histogram shows the 2004 per capita consumption of paper for 195 countries around the world (in *kg per person per year*). (www.swivel.com)

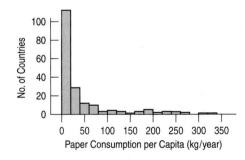

Which summary statistics would you choose to summarize the center and spread in these data? Why?

**17. Pizza prices.** The histogram shows the distribution of the prices of a small, plain pizza (in $) for 156 weeks in Dallas, Texas.

Which summary statistics would you choose to summarize the center and spread in these data? Why?

**T** **18. Neck size.** The histogram shows the neck sizes (in inches) of 250 men recruited for a health study in Utah.

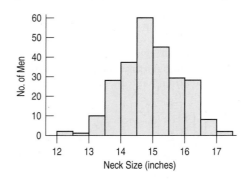

Which summary statistics would you choose to summarize the center and spread in these data? Why?

**T** **19. Pizza prices again.** Look again at the histogram of the pizza prices in Exercise 17.
a) Is the mean closer to $2.40, $2.60, or $2.80? Why?
b) Is the standard deviation closer to $0.15, $0.50, or $1.00? Explain.

**T** **20. Neck sizes again.** Look again at the histogram of men's neck sizes in Exercise 18.
a) Is the mean closer to 14, 15, or 16 inches? Why?
b) Is the standard deviation closer to 1 inch, 3 inches, or 5 inches? Explain.

**T** **21. Movie lengths.** The histogram shows the running times in minutes of 122 feature films released in 2005.

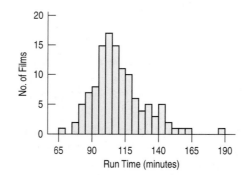

a) You plan to see a movie this weekend. Based on these movies, how long do you expect a typical movie to run?
b) Would you be surprised to find that your movie ran for 2 1/2 hours (150 minutes)?

c) Which would you expect to be higher, the mean or the median run time for all movies? Why?

**T** **22. Golf drives.** The display shows the average drive distance (in yards) for 202 professional golfers on the men's PGA tour.

a) Describe this distribution.
b) Approximately what proportion of professional male golfers drive, on average, less than 280 yards?
c) Estimate the mean by examining the histogram.
d) Do you expect the mean to be smaller than, approximately equal to, or larger than the median? Why?

**23. Summaries.** Here are costs of 10 electric smoothtop ranges rated very good or excellent by *Consumer Reports* in August 2002:

$850  900  1400  1200  1050  1000  750  1250  1050  565

Find these statistics *by hand* (no calculator!):
a) mean
b) median and quartiles
c) range and IQR

**24. More summaries.** Here are the annual numbers of deaths from tornadoes in the United States from 1990 through 2000 (www.noaa.gov):

53  39  39  33  69  30  25  67  130  94  40

Find these statistics *by hand* (no calculator!):
a) mean
b) median and quartiles
c) range and IQR

**25. Mistake.** A clerk entering salary data into a company spreadsheet accidentally put an extra "0" in the boss's salary, listing it as $2,000,000 instead of $200,000. Explain how this error will affect these summary statistics for the company payroll:
a) measures of center: median and mean.
b) measures of spread: range, IQR, and standard deviation.

**26. Cold weather.** A meteorologist preparing a talk about global warming compiled a list of weekly low temperatures (in degrees Fahrenheit) he observed at his southern Florida home last year. The coldest temperature for any week was 36°F but he inadvertently recorded the Celsius value of 2°. Assuming that he correctly listed all the other temperatures, explain how this error will affect these summary statistics:
a) measures of center: mean and median.
b) measures of spread: range, IQR, and standard deviation.

**27. Movie budgets.** The histogram shows the budgets (in millions of dollars) of major release movies in 2005.

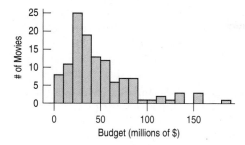

An industry publication reports that the average movie costs $35 million to make, but a watchdog group concerned with rising ticket prices says that the average cost is $46.8 million. What statistic do you think each group is using? Explain.

**28. Sick days.** During contract negotiations, a company seeks to change the number of sick days employees may take, saying that the annual "average" is 7 days of absence per employee. The union negotiators counter that the "average" employee misses only 3 days of work each year. Explain how both sides might be correct, identifying the measure of center you think each side is using and why the difference might exist.

**29. Standard deviation I.** For each lettered part, a through c, examine the two given sets of numbers. Without doing any calculations, decide which set has the larger standard deviation and explain why. Then check by finding the standard deviations *by hand*.

| | Set 1 | Set 2 |
|---|---|---|
| a) | 3, 5, 6, 7, 9 | 2, 4, 6, 8, 10 |
| b) | 10, 14, 15, 16, 20 | 10, 11, 15, 19, 20 |
| c) | 2, 6, 6, 9, 11, 14 | 82, 86, 86, 89, 91, 94 |

**30. Standard deviation II.** For each lettered part, a through c, examine the two given sets of numbers. Without doing any calculations, decide which set has the larger standard deviation and explain why. Then check by finding the standard deviations *by hand*.

| | Set 1 | Set 2 |
|---|---|---|
| a) | 4, 7, 7, 7, 10 | 4, 6, 7, 8, 10 |
| b) | 100, 140, 150, 160, 200 | 10, 50, 60, 70, 110 |
| c) | 10, 16, 18, 20, 22, 28 | 48, 56, 58, 60, 62, 70 |

**31. Payroll.** A small warehouse employs a supervisor at $1200 a week, an inventory manager at $700 a week, six stock boys at $400 a week, and four drivers at $500 a week.
a) Find the mean and median wage.
b) How many employees earn more than the mean wage?
c) Which measure of center best describes a typical wage at this company, the mean or the median?
d) Which measure of spread would best describe the payroll, the range, the IQR, or the standard deviation? Why?

**32. Singers.** The frequency table shows the heights (in inches) of 130 members of a choir.

| Height | Count | Height | Count |
|---|---|---|---|
| 60 | 2 | 69 | 5 |
| 61 | 6 | 70 | 11 |
| 62 | 9 | 71 | 8 |
| 63 | 7 | 72 | 9 |
| 64 | 5 | 73 | 4 |
| 65 | 20 | 74 | 2 |
| 66 | 18 | 75 | 4 |
| 67 | 7 | 76 | 1 |
| 68 | 12 | | |

a) Find the median and IQR.
b) Find the mean and standard deviation.
c) Display these data with a histogram.
d) Write a few sentences describing the distribution of heights.

**33. Gasoline.** In March 2006, 16 gas stations in Grand Junction, Colorado, posted these prices for a gallon of regular gasoline:

| | | | |
|---|---|---|---|
| 2.22 | 2.21 | 2.45 | 2.24 |
| 2.27 | 2.28 | 2.27 | 2.23 |
| 2.26 | 2.46 | 2.29 | 2.32 |
| 2.36 | 2.38 | 2.33 | 2.27 |

a) Make a stem-and-leaf display of these gas prices. Use split stems; for example, use two 2.2 stems, one for prices between $2.20 and $2.24, the other for prices from $2.25 to $2.29.
b) Describe the shape, center, and spread of this distribution.
c) What unusual feature do you see?

**34. The Great One.** During his 20 seasons in the NHL, Wayne Gretzky scored 50% more points than anyone who ever played professional hockey. He accomplished this amazing feat while playing in 280 fewer games than Gordie Howe, the previous record holder. Here are the number of games Gretzky played during each season:

79, 80, 80, 80, 74, 80, 80, 79, 64, 78, 73, 78, 74, 45, 81, 48, 80, 82, 82, 70

a) Create a stem-and-leaf display for these data, using split stems.
b) Describe the shape of the distribution.
c) Describe the center and spread of this distribution.
d) What unusual feature do you see? What might explain this?

**35. Sip size.** Researchers in Cornell University's Food Sciences department study how people experience foods. One study considered how much liquid people typically take into their mouths in one "sip" (in milliliters). The researchers also recorded the height (meters) and weight (kilograms) of the participants. Here are histograms of three of the variables from that study:

a) For which of the variables depicted in the histograms would you be most satisfied to summarize the center with a mean? Explain.
b) For which of the variables depicted in the histograms would you most strenuously insist on using an IQR rather than a standard deviation to summarize spread? Explain.

**36. How tall?** Students in a large class were asked to estimate the teacher's height in inches. Here's a histogram of their estimates:

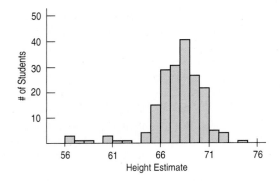

You want a good guess of the professor's true height (or at least a good guess of how tall the students think the professor is). How would you summarize these data? Why? What might explain guesses as low as 56"?

**37. States.** The stem-and-leaf display shows populations of the 50 states and Washington, DC, in millions of people, according to the 2000 census.

```
3 | 4
2 |
2 | 1
1 | 69
1 | 0122
0 | 5555666667888
0 | 1111111111111122222333333344444
```
State Populations (1 | 2 means 12 million)

a) What measures of center and spread are most appropriate?
b) Without doing any calculations, which must be larger, the median or the mean? Explain how you know.
c) From the stem-and-leaf display, find the median and the interquartile range.
d) Write a few sentences describing this distribution.

**38. Wayne Gretzky.** In Exercise 34 you examined the number of games played by hockey great Wayne Gretzky during his 20-year career in the NHL
a) Would you use the median or the mean to describe the center of this distribution? Why?
b) Find the median.
c) Without actually finding the mean, would you expect it to be higher or lower than the median? Explain.

**39. Home runs.** The stem-and-leaf display shows the number of home runs hit by Mark McGwire during the 1986–2001 seasons. Describe the distribution, mentioning its shape and any unusual features.

```
7 | 0
6 | 5
5 | 28
4 | 29
3 | 22399
2 | 29
1 |
0 | 399
```
Home Runs
(7 | 0 means 70)

**40. Bird species.** The Cornell Lab of Ornithology holds an annual Christmas Bird Count (www.birdsource.org), in which bird watchers at various locations around the country see how many different species of birds they can spot. Here are some of the counts reported from sites in Texas during the 1999 event:

| | | | | | | |
|---|---|---|---|---|---|---|
| 228 | 178 | 186 | 162 | 206 | 166 | 163 |
| 183 | 181 | 206 | 177 | 175 | 167 | 162 |
| 160 | 160 | 157 | 156 | 153 | 153 | 152 |

a) Create a stem-and-leaf display of these data.
b) Write a brief description of the distribution. Be sure to discuss the overall shape as well as any unusual features.

**41. Hurricanes 2006.** The data below give the number of hurricanes classified as major hurricanes in the Atlantic Ocean each year from 1944 through 2006, as reported by *NOAA* (www.nhc.noaa.gov):

3, 2, 1, 2, 4, 3, 7, 2, 3, 3, 2, 5, 2, 2, 4, 2, 2, 6, 0, 2, 5, 1, 3, 1, 0, 3, 2, 1, 0, 1, 2, 3, 2, 1, 2, 2, 2, 3, 1, 1, 1, 3, 0, 1, 3, 2, 1, 2, 1, 1, 0, 5, 6, 1, 3, 5, 3, 3, 2, 3, 6, 7, 2

a) Create a dotplot or stem-and-leaf display of these data.
b) Describe the distribution.

**42. Horsepower.** Create a stem-and-leaf display for these horsepowers of autos reviewed by *Consumer Reports* one year, and describe the distribution:

| | | | | |
|---|---|---|---|---|
| 155 | 103 | 130 | 80 | 65 |
| 142 | 125 | 129 | 71 | 69 |
| 125 | 115 | 138 | 68 | 78 |
| 150 | 133 | 135 | 90 | 97 |
| 68 | 105 | 88 | 115 | 110 |
| 95 | 85 | 109 | 115 | 71 |
| 97 | 110 | 65 | 90 | |
| 75 | 120 | 80 | 70 | |

**43. Home runs, again.** Students were asked to make a histogram of the number of home runs hit by Mark McGwire from 1986 to 2001 (see Exercise 39). One student submitted the following display:

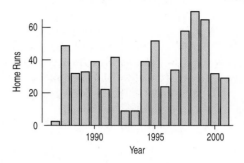

a) Comment on this graph.
b) Create your own histogram of the data.

**44. Return of the birds.** Students were given the assignment to make a histogram of the data on bird counts reported in Exercise 40. One student submitted the following display:

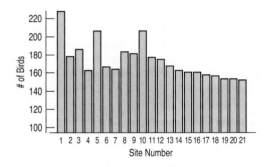

a) Comment on this graph.
b) Create your own histogram of the data.

**45. Acid rain.** Two researchers measured the pH (a scale on which a value of 7 is neutral and values below 7 are acidic) of water collected from rain and snow over a 6-month period in Allegheny County, Pennsylvania. Describe their data with a graph and a few sentences:

| 4.57 | 5.62 | 4.12 | 5.29 | 4.64 | 4.31 | 4.30 | 4.39 | 4.45 |
| 5.67 | 4.39 | 4.52 | 4.26 | 4.26 | 4.40 | 5.78 | 4.73 | 4.56 |
| 5.08 | 4.41 | 4.12 | 5.51 | 4.82 | 4.63 | 4.29 | 4.60 | |

**46. Marijuana 2003.** In 2003 the Council of Europe published a report entitled *The European School Survey Project on Alcohol and Other Drugs* (www.espad.org). Among other issues, the survey investigated the percentages of 16-year-olds who had used marijuana. Shown here are the results for 20 European countries. Create an appropriate graph of these data, and describe the distribution.

| Country | Percentage | Country | Percentage |
|---------|-----------|---------|-----------|
| Austria | 21% | Italy | 27% |
| Belgium | 32% | Latvia | 16% |
| Bulgaria | 21% | Lithuania | 13% |
| Croatia | 22% | Malta | 10% |
| Cyprus | 4% | Netherlands | 28% |
| Czech | | Norway | 9% |
| Republic | 44% | Poland | 18% |
| Denmark | 23% | Portugal | 15% |
| Estonia | 23% | Romania | 3% |
| Faroe | | Russia | 22% |
| Islands | 9% | Slovak | |
| Finland | 11% | Republic | 27% |
| France | 22% | Slovenia | 28% |
| Germany | 27% | Sweden | 7% |
| Greece | 6% | Switzerland | 40% |
| Greenland | 27% | Turkey | 4% |
| Hungary | 16% | Ukraine | 21% |
| Iceland | 13% | United | |
| Ireland | 39% | Kingdom | 38% |
| Isle of Man | 39% | | |

**47. Final grades.** A professor (of something other than Statistics!) distributed the following histogram to show the distribution of grades on his 200-point final exam. Comment on the display.

**48. Final grades revisited.** After receiving many complaints about his final-grade histogram from students currently taking a Statistics course, the professor from Exercise 47 distributed the following revised histogram:

a) Comment on this display.
b) Describe the distribution of grades.

**49. Zip codes.** Holes-R-Us, an Internet company that sells piercing jewelry, keeps transaction records on its sales. At a recent sales meeting, one of the staff presented a histogram of the zip codes of the last 500 customers, so that the staff might understand where sales are coming from. Comment on the usefulness and appropriateness of the display.

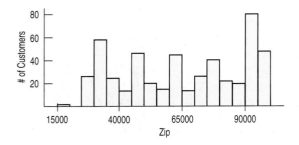

**50. Industry codes.** A recently hired investment analyst has been assigned to analyze the companies that make up the Fortune 800, a collection of the largest U.S. companies. He codes each company by the type of industry to which they belong. Here is a table showing some of the industry types and the corresponding codes he uses:

| Industry | Industry Code |
| --- | --- |
| Financial services | 1 |
| Food/drink/tobacco | 2 |
| Health | 3 |
| Insurance | 4 |
| Retailing | 6 |
| Forest products | 9 |
| Aerospace/defense | 11 |
| Energy | 12 |
| Capital goods | 14 |
| Computers/communications | 16 |
| Entertainment/information | 17 |
| Consumer nondurables | 18 |
| Electric utilities | 19 |

The analyst produces the following histogram of the industry codes for the companies:

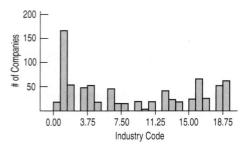

a) What might account for the gaps seen in the histogram?
b) Is the histogram unimodal?
c) What advice might you give the analyst about the appropriateness of this display?

**51. Math scores 2005.** The National Center for Education Statistics (http://nces.ed.gov/nationsreportcard/) reported 2005 average mathematics achievement scores for eighth graders in all 50 states:

| State | Score | State | Score |
| --- | --- | --- | --- |
| Alabama | 225 | Montana | 241 |
| Alaska | 236 | Nebraska | 238 |
| Arizona | 230 | Nevada | 230 |
| Arkansas | 236 | New Hampshire | 246 |
| California | 230 | New Jersey | 244 |
| Colorado | 239 | New Mexico | 224 |
| Connecticut | 242 | New York | 238 |
| Delaware | 240 | North Carolina | 241 |
| Florida | 239 | North Dakota | 243 |
| Georgia | 234 | Ohio | 242 |
| Hawaii | 230 | Oklahoma | 234 |
| Idaho | 242 | Oregon | 238 |
| Illinois | 233 | Pennsylvania | 241 |
| Indiana | 240 | Rhode Island | 233 |
| Iowa | 240 | South Carolina | 238 |
| Kansas | 246 | South Dakota | 242 |
| Kentucky | 231 | Tennessee | 232 |
| Louisiana | 230 | Texas | 242 |
| Maine | 241 | Utah | 239 |
| Maryland | 238 | Vermont | 244 |
| Massachusetts | 247 | Virginia | 240 |
| Michigan | 238 | Washington | 242 |
| Minnesota | 246 | West Virginia | 231 |
| Mississippi | 227 | Wisconsin | 241 |
| Missouri | 235 | Wyoming | 243 |

a) Find the median, the IQR, the mean, and the standard deviation of these state averages.
b) Which summary statistics would you report for these data? Why?
c) Write a brief summary of the performance of eighth graders nationwide.

**52. Prisons 2005.** A report from the U.S. Department of Justice (www.ojp.usdoj.gov/bjs/) gave the following percent changes in federal prison populations in 20 northeastern and midwestern states during 2005:

| State | Percent Change During 2005 |
| --- | --- |
| Connecticut | −0.3 |
| Maine | 0.0 |
| Massachusetts | 5.5 |
| New Hampshire | 3.3 |
| New Jersey | 2.2 |
| New York | −1.6 |
| Pennsylvania | 3.5 |
| Rhode Island | 6.5 |
| Vermont | 5.6 |
| Illinois | 2.0 |
| Indiana | 1.9 |
| Iowa | 2.5 |
| Kansas | 1.1 |
| Michigan | 1.4 |

*(continued)*

| | |
|---|---|
| Minnesota | 6.0 |
| Missouri | −0.8 |
| Nebraska | 7.9 |
| North Dakota | 4.4 |
| Ohio | 2.3 |
| South Dakota | 11.9 |
| Wisconsin | −1.0 |

a) Graph these data.
b) Calculate appropriate summary statistics.
c) Write a few sentences about these data. (Remember: shape, center, spread, unusual features.)

**T 53. Gasoline usage 2004.** The California Energy Commission (www.energy.ca.gov/gasoline/) collects data on the amount of gasoline sold in each state. The following data show the per capita (gallons used per person) consumption in the year 2004. Using appropriate graphical displays and summary statistics, write a report on the gasoline use by state in the year 2004.

| State | Gallons per Capita |
|---|---|
| Alabama | 529.4 |
| Alaska | 461.7 |
| Arizona | 381.9 |
| Arkansas | 512.0 |
| California | 414.4 |
| Colorado | 435.7 |
| Connecticut | 435.7 |
| Delaware | 541.6 |
| Florida | 496.0 |
| Georgia | 537.1 |
| Hawaii | 358.7 |
| Idaho | 454.8 |
| Illinois | 408.3 |
| Indiana | 491.7 |
| Iowa | 555.1 |
| Kansas | 511.8 |
| Kentucky | 526.6 |
| Louisiana | 507.8 |
| Maine | 576.3 |
| Maryland | 447.5 |
| Massachusetts | 458.5 |
| Michigan | 482.0 |
| Minnesota | 527.7 |
| Mississippi | 558.5 |
| Missouri | 550.5 |
| Montana | 544.4 |
| Nebraska | 470.1 |
| Nevada | 367.9 |
| New Hampshire | 544.4 |
| New Jersey | 488.2 |
| New Mexico | 508.8 |
| New York | 293.4 |
| North Carolina | 505.0 |

| | |
|---|---|
| North Dakota | 553.7 |
| Ohio | 451.1 |
| Oklahoma | 614.2 |
| Oregon | 418.4 |
| Pennsylvania | 386.8 |
| Rhode Island | 454.6 |
| South Carolina | 578.6 |
| South Dakota | 564.4 |
| Tennessee | 552.5 |
| Texas | 532.7 |
| Utah | 460.6 |
| Vermont | 545.5 |
| Virginia | 526.9 |
| Washington | 423.6 |
| West Virginia | 426.7 |
| Wisconsin | 449.8 |
| Wyoming | 615.0 |

**T 54. Boomtowns.** In 2006, *Inc.* magazine (www.inc.com) listed its choice of "boomtowns" in the United States — larger cities that are growing rapidly. Here is the magazines top 20, along with their job growth percentages:

| City | 1-Year Job Growth (%) |
|---|---|
| Las Vegas, NV | 7.50 |
| Fort Lauderdale, FL | 4.20 |
| Orlando, FL | 4.50 |
| West Palm Beach-Boca Raton, FL | 3.40 |
| San Bernadino-Riverside, CA | 1.90 |
| Phoenix, AZ | 4.40 |
| Northern Virginia, VA | 3.10 |
| Washington, DC-Arlington-Alexandria, VA | 3.20 |
| Tampa-St. Petersburg, FL | 2.60 |
| Camden-Burlington Counties, NJ | 2.60 |
| Jacksonville, FL | 2.60 |
| Charlotte, NC | 3.30 |
| Raleigh-Cary, NC | 2.80 |
| Richmond, VA | 2.90 |
| Salt Lake City, UT | 3.30 |
| Putnam-Rockland-Westchester counties, New York | 2.30 |
| Santa Ana-Anaheim-Irvine, CA | 1.70 |
| Miami-Miami Beach, FL | 2.20 |
| Sacramento, CA | 1.50 |
| San Diego, CA | 1.40 |

a) Make a suitable display of the growth rates.
b) Summarize the typical growth rate among these cities with a median and mean. Why do they differ?
c) Given what you know about the distribution, which of the measures in b) does the better job of summarizing the growth rates? Why?
d) Summarize the spread of the growth rate distribution with a standard deviation and with an IQR.

*(continued)*

e) Given what you know about the distribution, which of the measures in d) does the better job of summarizing the growth rates? Why?

f) Suppose we subtract from each of the preceding growth rates the predicted U.S. average growth rate of 1.20%, so that we can look at how much these growth rates exceed the U.S. rate. How would this change the values of the summary statistics you calculated above? (*Hint:* You need not recompute any of the summary statistics from scratch.)

g) If we were to omit Las Vegas from the data, how would you expect the mean, median, standard deviation, and IQR to change? Explain your expectations for each.

h) Write a brief report about all of these growth rates.

**55. Customer database.** A philanthropic organization has a database of millions of donors that it contacts by mail to raise money for charities. One of the variables in the database, *Title*, contains the title of the person or persons printed on the address label. The most common are Mr., Ms., Miss, and Mrs., but there are also Ambassador and Mrs., Your Imperial Majesty, and Cardinal, to name a few others. In all, there are more than 100 different titles, each with a corresponding numeric code. Here are a few of them:

| Code | Title |
|------|-------|
| 000 | MR. |
| 001 | MRS. |
| 002 | MR. and MRS. |
| 003 | MISS |
| 004 | DR. |
| 005 | MADAME |
| 006 | SERGEANT |
| 009 | RABBI |
| 010 | PROFESSOR |
| 126 | PRINCE |
| 127 | PRINCESS |
| 128 | CHIEF |
| 129 | BARON |
| 130 | SHEIK |
| 131 | PRINCE AND PRINCESS |
| 132 | YOUR IMPERIAL MAJESTY |
| 1035 | M. ET MME. |
| 1210 | PROF. |

An intern who was asked to analyze the organization's fundraising efforts presented these summary statistics for the variable *Title:*

| | |
|------|------|
| Mean | 54.41 |
| StdDev | 957.50 |
| Median | 1 |
| IQR | 2 |
| *n* | 94,649 |

a) What does the mean of 54.41 mean?

b) What are the typical reasons that cause measures of the center and spread to be as different as those in this table?

c) Is that why these are so different?

**56. Zip codes revisited.** Here are some summary statistics to go with the histogram of the zip codes of 500 customers from the Holes-R-Us Internet Jewelry Salon that we saw in Exercise 49:

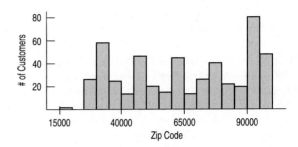

| | |
|--------|----------|
| Count | 500 |
| Mean | 64,970.0 |
| StdDev | 23,523.0 |
| Median | 64,871 |
| IQR | 44,183 |
| Q1 | 46,050 |
| Q3 | 90,233 |

a) Is the mean or median a better summary of the center of the zip code distribution? Why?

b) Is the standard deviation or the IQR a better summary of the spread? Why?

c) What can these statistics tell you about the company's sales?

## JUST CHECKING
### Answers

(Thoughts will vary.)

1. Roughly symmetric, slightly skewed to the right. Center around 3 miles? Few over 10 miles.

2. Bimodal. Center between 1 and 2 hours? Many people watch no football; others watch most of one or more games. Probably only a few values over 5 hours.

3. Strongly skewed to the right, with almost everyone at $0; a few small prizes, with the winner an outlier.

4. Fairly symmetric, somewhat uniform, perhaps slightly skewed to the right. Center in the 40s? Few ages below 25 or above 70.

5. Uniform, symmetric. Center near 5. Roughly equal counts for each digit 0–9.

6. Incomes are probably skewed to the right and not symmetric, making the median the more appropriate measure of center. The mean will be influenced by the high end of family incomes and not reflect the "typical" family income as well as the median would. It will give the impression that the typical income is higher than it is.

7. An IQR of 30 mpg would mean that only 50% of the cars get gas mileages in an interval 30 mpg wide. Fuel economy doesn't vary that much. 3 mpg is reasonable. It seems plausible that 50% of the cars will be within about 3 mpg of each other. An IQR of 0.3 mpg would mean that the gas mileage of half the cars varies little from the estimate. It's unlikely that cars, drivers, and driving conditions are that consistent.

8. We'd prefer a standard deviation of 2 months. Making a consistent product is important for quality. Customers want to be able to count on the MP3 player lasting somewhere close to 5 years, and a standard deviation of 2 years would mean that life-spans were highly variable.

# Understanding and Comparing Distributions

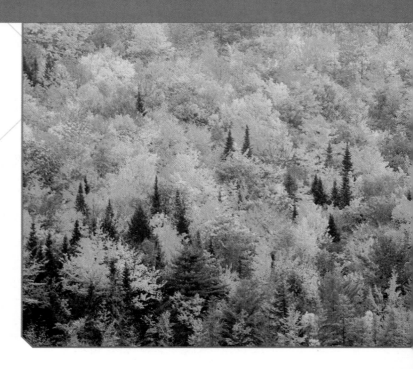

## Where are we going?

We can answer much more interesting questions about variables when we compare distributions for different groups. Are heart attack rates the same for men and women? Is that expensive beverage container really worth the price? Are wind patterns the same throughout the year? These are the kinds of questions where Statistics can really help. Some simple graphical displays and summaries can start us thinking about patterns, trends, and models—something we'll do throughout the rest of this book.

| | |
|---|---|
| **WHO** | Days during 1989 |
| **WHAT** | Average daily wind speed (mph), Average barometric pressure (mb), Average daily temperature (deg Celsius) |
| **WHEN** | 1989 |
| **WHERE** | Hopkins Forest, in Western Massachusetts |
| **WHY** | Long-term observations to study ecology and climate |

The Hopkins Memorial Forest is a 2500-acre reserve in Massachusetts, New York, and Vermont managed by the Williams College Center for Environmental Studies (CES). As part of their mission, CES monitors forest resources and conditions over the long term. They post daily measurements at their Web site.[1] You can go there, download, and analyze data for any range of days. We'll focus for now on 1989. As we'll see, some interesting things happened that year.

One of the variables measured in the forest is wind speed. Three remote anemometers generate far too much data to report, so, as summaries, you'll find minimum, maximum, and average wind speed (in mph) for each day.

Wind is caused as air flows from areas of high pressure to areas of low pressure. Centers of low pressure often accompany storms, so both high winds and low pressure are associated with some of the fiercest storms. Wind speeds can vary greatly during a day and from day to day, but if we step back a bit farther, we can see patterns. By modeling these patterns, we can understand things about *Average Wind Speed* that we may not have known.

In Chapter 3 we looked at the association between two categorical variables using contingency tables and displays. Here we'll explore different ways of examining the relationship between two variables when one is quantitative, and the other is categorical and indicates groups to compare. We are given wind speed

---

[1] www.williams.edu/CES/hopkins.htm

averages for each day of 1989. But we can collect the days together into different size groups and compare the wind speeds among them. If we consider *Time* as a categorical variable in this way, we'll gain enormous flexibility for our analysis and for our understanding. We'll discover new insights as we change the granularity of the grouping variable—from viewing the whole year's data at one glance, to comparing seasons, to looking for patterns across months, and, finally, to looking at the data day by day.

## The Big Picture

Let's start with the "big picture." Here's a histogram of the *Average Wind Speed* for every day in 1989. Because of the skewness, we'll report the median and IQR.

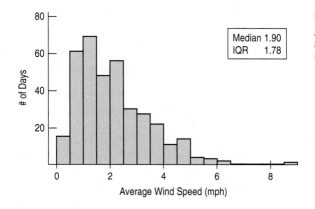

> Median 1.90
> IQR    1.78

**FIGURE 5.1**

*A histogram of daily* Average Wind Speed *for 1989. It is unimodal and skewed to the right, with a possible high outlier.*

We can see that the distribution is unimodal and skewed to the right. That high value may be an outlier. Median daily wind speed is about 1.90 mph, and the IQR is reported to be 1.78 mph. But even these seem somehow unsatisfying as a summary. Can we say more?

## 5-Number Summary

One good way to summarize a distribution with just a few values is with a **5-number summary,** which reports its median, quartiles, and extremes (maximum and minimum). For the *Average Wind Speed,* we have

| | |
|---|---|
| Max | 8.67 |
| Q3 | 2.93 |
| Median | 1.90 |
| Q1 | 1.15 |
| Min | 0.20 |

The 5-number summary provides a good overview of the distribution. For a start, we can see that the median wind speed is 1.91 mph, and we know that is a good summary because the IQR is only (2.93 − 1.15 =) 1.78 mph, so most days have winds close to the median. To put it another way, on half of the days the average wind speed is between 1.15 and 2.93 mph, because the quartiles frame the middle half of the data. The median and IQR are better summaries for these data because the distribution is skewed. (For comparison, the mean is 2.13 mph, pulled up by those windier days, and the standard deviation is 1.33 mph.)

We can also see a rather windy 8.67-mph day. Was that unusually windy or just the windiest day of the year? To answer that, we'll need to work with the summaries a bit more.

Roller coasters[2] are a thrill ride in many amusement parks worldwide. And thrill seekers want a coaster that goes fast. Here is information on the distribution of speeds of some of the fastest coasters in the world:

| Median | 65 mph |
|---|---|
| Min | 40 |
| Max | 120 |
| Q1 | 55 |
| Q3 | 74 |
| Mean | 66.5 |
| StdDev | 13.9 |
| IQR | 19 |

**Question:** Describe the shape of this distribution, and summarize what a roller coaster fan might want to know about roller coaster speeds.

The distribution of roller coaster speeds is unimodal and slightly skewed to the high end. It seems to have an extraordinary value at 120 mph. The median speed is 65 mph, and the IQR is (74 − 55 =) 19 mph. The mean speed is larger than the median, showing the effect of the distribution's skewness and the pull of the large value. Half of these coasters run at between 55 and 74 mph, so that is a typical range of speeds. But the fastest one runs at a remarkable 120 mph.

# Boxplots and 5-Number Summaries

Once we have a 5-number summary of a (quantitative) variable, we can display that information in a **boxplot.** To make a boxplot of the average wind speeds, follow these steps:

1. Draw a single vertical axis spanning the extent of the data.[3] Draw short horizontal lines at the lower and upper quartiles and at the median. Then connect them with vertical lines to form a box. The box can have any width that looks OK.[4]
2. To help us construct the boxplot, we erect "fences" around the main part of the data. We place the upper fence 1.5 IQRs above the upper quartile and the lower fence 1.5 IQRs below the lower quartile. For the wind speed data, we compute

$$Upper\ fence = Q3 + 1.5\ IQR = 2.93 + 1.5 \times 1.78 = 5.60\ mph$$

and

$$Lower\ fence = Q1 + 1.5\ IQR = 1.15 - 1.5 \times 1.78 = -1.52\ mph$$

The fences are just for construction and are not part of the display. We show them here with dotted lines for illustration. You should never include them in your boxplot.

3. We use the fences to grow "whiskers." Draw lines from the ends of the box up and down to *the most extreme data values found within the fences.* If a data value falls outside one of the fences, we do *not* connect it with a whisker.

[2] See the roller coaster data base at www.rcdb.com
[3] The axis could also run horizontally.
[4] Some computer programs draw wider boxes for larger data sets. That can be useful when comparing groups.

**4.**

**4.** Finally, we add the **outliers** by displaying any data values beyond the fences with special symbols. (We often use a different symbol for **"far outliers"**— data values farther than 3 IQRs from the quartiles.)

What does a boxplot show? The center of a boxplot is (remarkably enough) a box that shows the middle half of the data, between the quartiles. The height of the box is equal to the IQR. If the median is roughly centered between the quartiles, then the middle half of the data is roughly symmetric. If the median is not centered, the distribution is skewed. The whiskers show skewness as well if they are not roughly the same length. Any outliers are displayed individually, both to keep them out of the way for judging skewness and to encourage you to give them special attention. They may be mistakes, or they may be the most interesting cases in your data.

For the Hopkins Forest data, the central box contains each day whose *Average Wind Speed* is between 1.15 and 2.93 miles per hour (see Figure 5.2). From the shape of the box, it looks like the central part of the distribution of wind speeds is roughly symmetric, but the longer upper whisker indicates that the distribution stretches out at the upper end. We also see a few very windy days. Boxplots are particularly good at pointing out outliers. These extraordinarily windy days may deserve more attention. We'll give them that extra attention shortly.

**A S** **Boxplots.** Watch a boxplot under construction.

The prominent statistician John W. Tukey, the originator of the boxplot, was asked by one of the authors why the outlier nomination rule cut at 1.5 IQRs beyond each quartile. He answered that the reason was that 1 IQR would be too small and 2 IQRs would be too large. That works for us.

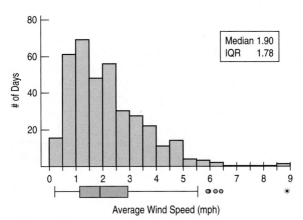

Median 1.90
IQR 1.78

**FIGURE 5.2**

*By turning the boxplot and putting it on the same scale as the histogram, we can compare both displays of the daily wind speeds and see how each represents the distribution.*

# Comparing Groups with Histograms

It is almost always more interesting to compare groups. Is it windier in the winter or the summer? Are any months particularly windy? Are weekends a special problem? Let's split the year into two groups: April through September (Spring/ Summer) and October through March (Fall/Winter). Here are histograms of the average daily wind speed for Spring/Summer (on the left) and Fall/Winter (on the right):

**FIGURE 5.3**

*Histograms of Average Wind Speed for days in Spring/Summer (left) and Fall/Winter (right) show very different patterns.*

Average Wind Speed (mph)

The shapes, centers, and spreads of these two distributions are strikingly different. During spring and summer (histogram on the left), the distribution is skewed to the right. A typical day during these warmer months has an average wind speed of only 1 to 2 mph, and few have average speeds above 3 mph. In the colder months, however (histogram on the right), the shape is less strongly skewed and more spread out. The typical wind speed is higher, and days with wind speeds above 3 mph are not unusual. There are several noticeable high values.

| Summaries for *Average Wind Speed* by Season | | | | |
| --- | --- | --- | --- | --- |
| Group | Mean | StdDev | Median | IQR |
| Fall/Winter | 2.71 | 1.36 | 2.47 | 1.87 |
| Spring/Summer | 1.56 | 1.01 | 1.34 | 1.32 |

# Comparing Groups with Boxplots

Are some months windier than others? Even residents may not have a good idea of which parts of the year are the most windy. (Do you know for your hometown?) We're not interested just in the centers, but also in the spreads. Are wind speeds equally variable from month to month, or do some months show more variation?

Earlier, we compared histograms of the wind speeds for two halves of the year. To look for seasonal trends, though, we'll group the daily observations by month. Histograms are a fine way to display one distribution or two. But it would be hard to see patterns by comparing 12 histograms. Boxplots offer an ideal balance of information and simplicity, hiding the details while displaying the overall summary information. So we often plot them side by side for groups or categories we wish to compare.

By placing boxplots side by side, we can easily see which groups have higher medians, which have the greater IQRs, where the central 50% of the data is located in each group, and which have the greater overall range. And, when the boxes are in an order, we can get a general idea of patterns in both the centers and the spreads. Equally important, we can see past any outliers in making these comparisons because they've been displayed separately.

Here are boxplots of the *Average Daily Wind Speed* by month:

**FIGURE 5.4**

*Boxplots of the average daily wind speed for each month show seasonal patterns in both the centers and spreads.*

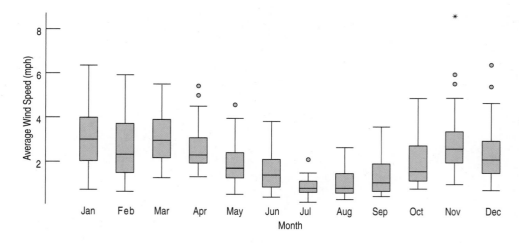

Here we see that wind speeds tend to decrease in the summer. The months in which the winds are both strongest and most variable are November through March. And there was one remarkably windy day in November.

When we looked at a boxplot for wind speeds of the entire year, there were only 5 outliers. Now, when we group the days by *Month,* the boxplots display more days as outliers and call out one in November as a far outlier. The boxplots show different outliers than before because our outlier nomination rule for box-plots depends on the quartiles of the data being displayed. Some days that seemed ordinary when placed against the entire year's data looked like outliers for the month that they're in. That windy day in July certainly wouldn't stand out in November or December, but for July it was remarkable.

---

**FOR EXAMPLE**    Comparing distributions

**Recap:**  We looked at the speeds of the fastest roller coasters in the world. There are two main types of roller coasters: those with wooden tracks and those with steel tracks. Do they typically run at different speeds? Here are boxplots:

**Question:**  Compare the speeds of wood and steel roller coasters.

*Overall, wooden-track roller coasters are slower than steel-track coasters. In fact, the fastest half of the steel coasters are faster than three quarters of the wooden coasters. Although the IQRs of the two groups are similar, the range of speeds among steel coasters is larger than the range for wooden coasters. The distribution of speeds of wooden coasters appears to be roughly symmetric, but the speeds of the steel coasters are skewed to the right and there is a high outlier at 120 mph. We should look into why that steel coaster is so fast.*

---

**STEP-BY-STEP EXAMPLE**    **Comparing Groups**

Of course, we can compare groups even when they are not in any particular order. Most scientific studies compare two or more groups. It is almost always a good idea to start an analysis of data from such studies by comparing boxplots for the groups. Here's an example:

For her class project, a student compared the efficiency of various coffee containers. For her study, she decided to try 4 different containers and to test each of them 8 different times. Each time, she heated water to 180 °F, poured it into a container, and sealed it. (We'll learn the details of how to set up experiments in Chapter 13.) After 30 minutes she measured the temperature again and recorded the difference in temperature. Because these are temperature differences, smaller differences mean that the liquid stayed hot—just what we would want in a coffee mug.

**Question:**  What can we say about the effectiveness of these four mugs?

**Plan** State what you want to find out.

**Variables** Identify the *variables* and report the W's.

Be sure to check the appropriate condition.

I want to compare the effectiveness of the different mugs in maintaining temperature. I have 8 measurements of Temperature Change for each of the mugs.

✓ **Quantitative Data Condition:** The Temperature Changes are quantitative, with units of °F. Boxplots are appropriate displays for comparing the groups. Numerical summaries of each group are appropriate as well.

**Mechanics** Report the 5-number summaries of the four groups. Including the IQR is a good idea as well.

|          | Min    | Q1    | Median | Q3    | Max   | IQR   |
|----------|--------|-------|--------|-------|-------|-------|
| CUPPS    | 6 °F   | 6     | 8.25   | 14.25 | 18.50 | 8.25  |
| Nissan   | 0      | 1     | 2      | 4.50  | 7     | 3.50  |
| SIGG     | 9      | 11.50 | 14.25  | 21.75 | 24.50 | 10.25 |
| Starbucks| 6      | 6.50  | 8.50   | 14.25 | 17.50 | 7.75  |

Make a picture. Because we want to compare the distributions for four groups, boxplots are an appropriate choice.

**Conclusion** Interpret what the boxplots and summaries say about the ability of these mugs to retain heat. Compare the shapes, centers, and spreads, and note any outliers.

The individual distributions are all slightly skewed to the high end. The Nissan cup does the best job of keeping liquids hot, with a median loss of only 2 °F, and the SIGG cup does the worst, typically losing 14 °F. The difference is large enough to be important: A coffee drinker would be likely to notice a 14 ° drop in temperature. And the mugs are clearly different: 75% of the Nissan tests showed less heat loss than any of the other mugs in the study. The IQR of results for the Nissan cup is also the smallest of these test cups, indicating that it is a consistent performer.

### JUST CHECKING

The Bureau of Transportation Statistics of the U.S. Department of Transportation collects and publishes statistics on airline travel (www.transtats.bts.gov). Here are three displays of the % of flights arriving late each month from 1995 through 2005:

1. Describe what the histogram says about late arrivals.

2. What does the boxplot of late arrivals suggest that you can't see in the histogram?

3. Describe the patterns shown in the boxplots by month. At what time of year are flights least likely to be late? Can you suggest reasons for this pattern?

## Outliers

When we looked at boxplots for the *Average Wind Speed* by *Month,* we noticed that several days stood out as possible outliers and that one very windy day in November seemed truly remarkable. What should we do with such outliers?

Cases that stand out from the rest of the data almost always deserve our attention. An outlier is a value that doesn't fit with the rest of the data, but exactly how different it should be to be treated specially is a judgment call. Boxplots provide a rule of thumb to highlight these unusual points, but that rule doesn't tell you what to do with them.

So, what *should* we do with outliers? The first thing to do is to try to understand them in the context of the data. A good place to start is with a histogram. Histograms show us more detail about a distribution than a boxplot can, so they give us a better idea of how the outlier fits (or doesn't fit) in with the rest of the data.

A histogram of the *Average Wind Speed* in November shows a slightly skewed main body of data and that very windy day clearly set apart from the other days. When considering whether a case is an outlier, we often look at the gap between that case and the rest of the data. A large gap suggests that the case really is quite different. But a case that just happens to be the largest or smallest value at the end of a possibly stretched-out tail may be best thought of as just . . . the largest or smallest value. After all, *some* case has to be the largest or smallest.

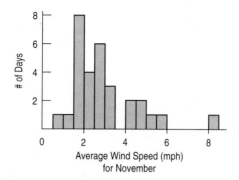

**FIGURE 5.5**
*The* Average Wind Speed *in November is slightly skewed with a high outlier.*

Some outliers are simply unbelievable. If a class survey includes a student who claims to be 170 inches tall (about 14 feet, or 4.3 meters), you can be pretty sure that's an error.

Once you've identified likely outliers, you should always investigate them. Some outliers are just errors. A decimal point may have been misplaced, digits transposed, or digits repeated or omitted. The units may be wrong. (Was that outlying height reported in centimeters rather than in inches [170 cm = 65 in.]?) Or a number may just have been transcribed incorrectly, perhaps copying an adjacent value on the original data sheet. If you can identify the correct value, then you should certainly correct it. One important reason to look into outliers is to correct errors in your data.

Many outliers are not wrong; they're just different. Such cases often repay the effort to understand them. You can learn more from the extraordinary cases than from summaries of the overall data set.

---

**FOR EXAMPLE** | Checking out the outliers

**Recap:** We've looked at the speeds of roller coasters and found a difference between steel- and wooden-track coasters. We also noticed an extraordinary value.

**Question:** The fastest coaster in this collection turns out to be the "Top Thrill Dragster" at Cedar Point amusement park. What might make this roller coaster unusual? You'll have to do some research, but that's often what happens with outliers.

The Top Thrill Dragster is easy to find in an Internet search. We learn that it is a "hydraulic launch" coaster. That is, it doesn't get its remarkable speed just from gravity, but rather from a kick start by a hydraulic piston. That could make it different from the other roller coasters.

(You might also discover that it is no longer the fastest roller coaster in the world.)

**14-year-old widowers?** Careful attention to outliers can often reveal problems in data collection and management. Two researchers, Ansley Coale and Fred Stephan, looking at data from the 1950 census noticed that the number of widowed 14-year-old boys had increased from 85 in 1940 to a whopping 1600 in 1950. The number of divorced 14-year-old boys had increased, too, from 85 to 1240. Oddly, the number of teenaged widowers and divorcees *decreased* for every age group after 14, from 15 to 19. When Coale and Stephan also noticed a large increase in the number of young Native Americans in the Northeast United States, they began to look for data problems. Data in the 1950 census were recorded on computer cards. (For a picture of a computer card, see p. 11.) Cards are hard to read and mistakes are easy to make. It turned out that data punches had been shifted to the right by one column on hundreds of cards. Because each card column meant something different, the shift turned 43-year-old widowed males into 14-year-olds, 42-year-old divorcees into 14-year-olds, and children of white parents into Native Americans. Not all outliers have such a colorful (or famous) story, but it is always worthwhile to investigate them. And, as in this case, the explanation is often surprising. (A. Coale and F. Stephan, "The case of the Indians and the teen–age widows." *J. Am. Stat. Assoc.* 57 [Jun 1962]: 338–347.)

What about that windy November day? Was it really that windy, or could there have been a problem with the anemometers? A quick Internet search for weather on November 21, 1989, finds that there was a severe storm:

# WIND, SNOW, COLD GIVE N.E. A TASTE OF WINTER

*Published on November 22, 1989*
*Author: Andrew Dabilis, Globe Staff*

An intense storm roared like the Montreal Express through New England yesterday, bringing frigid winds of up to 55 m.p.h., 2 feet of snow in some parts of Vermont and a preview of winter after weeks of mild weather. Residents throughout the region awoke yesterday to an icy vortex that lifted an airplane off the runway in Newark and made driving dangerous in New England because of rapidly shifting winds that seemed to come from all directions.

When we have outliers, we still need to decide what to *Tell* about the data. If we can correct an error, we'll just summarize the corrected data (and note the correction). But if we see no way to correct an outlying value, or if we confirm that it is correct, our best path is to report summaries and analyses with *and* without the outlier. In this way a reader can judge for him- or herself what influence the outlier has and decide what to think about the data.

There are two things we should *never* do with outliers. The first is to silently leave an outlier in place and proceed as if nothing were unusual. Analyses of data with outliers are very likely to be influenced by those outliers—sometimes to a large and misleading degree. The other is to drop an outlier from the analysis without comment just because it's unusual. If you want to exclude an outlier, you must discuss your decision and, to the extent you can, justify your decision. When you can't be sure of the status of a case, consider reporting the analysis both with and without the outlier, and discuss the difference.

**A S** *Case Study:* **Are passengers or drivers safer in a crash?** Practice the skills of this chapter by comparing these two groups.

# Timeplots: Order, Please!

The Hopkins Forest wind speeds are reported as daily averages. Previously, we grouped the days into months or seasons, but we could look at the wind speed values day by day. Whenever we have data measured over time, it is a good idea to look for patterns by plotting the data in time order. Here are the daily average wind speeds plotted over time:

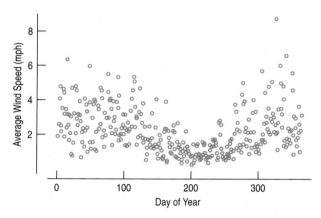

**FIGURE 5.6**

*A timeplot of* Average Wind Speed *shows the overall pattern and changes in variation.*

A display of values against time is sometimes called a **timeplot.** This timeplot reflects the pattern that we saw when we plotted the wind speeds by month. But without the arbitrary divisions between months, we can see a calm period during the summer, starting around day 200 (the middle of July), when the wind is relatively mild and doesn't vary greatly from day to day. We can also see that the wind becomes both more variable and stronger during the early and late parts of the year.

## *SMOOTHING TIMEPLOTS

Timeplots often show a great deal of point-to-point variation, as this one does. We usually want to see past this variation to understand any underlying smooth trends, and then also think about how the values vary around that trend—the timeplot version of center and spread. You could take your pencil, squint at the plot a bit to blur things, and sketch a smooth curve. And you'd probably do a pretty good job. But we can also ask a computer to do it for us.

There are many ways for computers to run a smooth trace through a timeplot. Some follow local bumps, others emphasize long-term trends. Some provide an equation that gives a typical value for any given time point, others just offer a smooth trace. For our purposes here, it doesn't matter all that much. You can try the methods offered by your favorite program and pick the one that looks best for the timeplot you are looking at and the questions you'd like to answer.

You'll often see timeplots drawn with all the points connected, especially in financial publications. This trace through the data falls at one extreme, following every bump as the data unfold. For the wind speeds, the daily fluctuations are so large that connecting the points doesn't help us a great deal:

**FIGURE 5.7**

*The* Average Wind Speeds *of Figure 5.6, drawn by connecting all the points. Sometimes this can help in seeing the underlying pattern, but here there is too much daily variation for this to be very useful.*

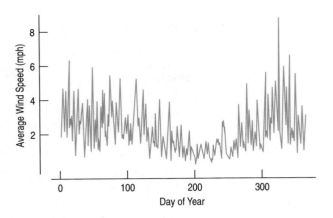

A smooth trace can highlight long-term patterns and help us see them through the more local variation. Here are the daily average wind speed values with a smooth trace found by a method called *lowess,* available in many statistics programs:

**FIGURE 5.8**

*The* Average Wind Speeds *of Figure 5.6, with a smooth trace added to help your eye see the long-term pattern.*

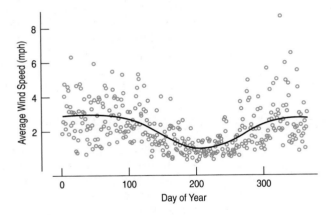

With the smooth trace, it's a bit easier to see a pattern. The trace helps our eye follow the main trend and alerts us to points that don't fit the overall pattern.

**FOR EXAMPLE**     Timeplots and smoothing

**Recap:** We have looked at the current speeds of the world's fastest roller coasters. Have coasters been getting faster? Our data include coasters going back to 1909. Here's a timeplot with a *lowess* smooth trace:

**Question:** What does the timeplot say about the trend in roller coaster speeds?

Roller coasters do seem to have been getting faster. Speeds were stagnant, or even declining, until 1970, but have increased (on average) since then. The increase seems to have been more rapid since 1990, pushed along by a few outliers.

> **HOW DO SMOOTHERS WORK?**
>
> If you planned to go camping in the Hopkins Forest around July 15 and wanted to know how windy it was likely to be, you'd probably look at a typical value for mid-July. Maybe you'd consider all the wind speeds for July, or maybe only those from July 10th to July 20th. That's just the kind of thing we do when we smooth a timeplot.
>
> One simple way to smooth is with a **moving average.** To find a smooth value for a particular time, we average the values around that point in an interval called the "window." To find the value for the next point, we *move* the window by one point in time and take the new *average*. The size of the window you choose affects how smooth the resulting trace will be. For the Hopkins Forest winds, we might use a 5-day moving average. Stock analysts often use a 50- or 200-day moving average to help them (attempt) to see the underlying pattern in stock price movements.
>
> Can we use smoothing to predict the future? We have only the values of a stock in the past, but (unfortunately) none of the future values. We could use the recent past as our window and take the simple average of those values. A more sophisticated method, **exponential smoothing,** gives more weight to the recent past values and less and less weight to values as they recede into the past.

# Looking into the Future

It is always tempting to try to extend what we see in a timeplot into the future. Sometimes that makes sense. Most likely, the Hopkins Forest climate follows regular seasonal patterns. It's probably safe to predict a less windy June next year and a windier November. But we certainly wouldn't predict another storm on November 21.

Other patterns are riskier to extend into the future. If a stock has been rising, will it continue to go up? No stock has ever increased in value indefinitely, and no stock analyst has consistently been able to forecast when a stock's value will turn around. Stock prices, unemployment rates, and other economic, social, or psychological concepts are much harder to predict than physical quantities. The path a ball will follow when thrown from a certain height at a given speed and direction is well understood. The path interest rates will take is much less clear. Unless we have strong (nonstatistical) reasons for doing otherwise, we should resist the temptation to think that any trend we see will continue, even into the near future.

Statistical models often tempt those who use them to think beyond the data. We'll pay close attention later in this book to understanding when, how, and how much we can justify doing that.

# *Re-expressing Data: A First Look[5]

### RE-EXPRESSING TO IMPROVE SYMMETRY

When the data are skewed, it can be hard to summarize them simply with a center and spread, and hard to decide whether the most extreme values are outliers or

---

[5] This section is optional in that it's not required for other parts of the book. But we recommend that you at least look at these ideas. They can make what you've already learned useful in many more situations.

just part of the stretched-out tail. How can we say anything useful about such data? The secret is to *re-express* the data by applying a simple function to each value.

Many relationships and "laws" in the sciences and social sciences include functions such as logarithms, square roots, and reciprocals. Similar relationships often show up in data. Here's a simple example:

In 1980 large companies' chief executive officers (CEOs) made, on average, about 42 times what workers earned. In the next two decades, CEO compensation soared when compared to the average worker. By 2000 that multiple had jumped[6] to 525. What does the distribution of the compensation of Fortune 500 companies' CEOs look like? Here's a histogram and boxplot for 2005 compensation:

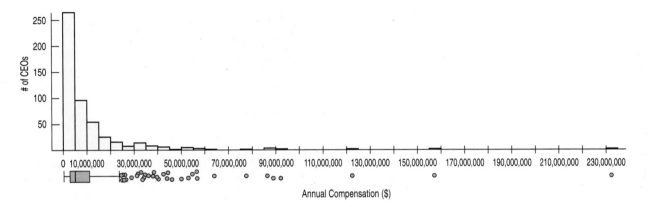

**FIGURE 5.9**

*Compensation paid to CEOs of the Fortune 500 companies in 2005. The distribution seems to have outliers. But maybe it just has a long tail on the right.*

We have 500 CEOs and about 48 possible histogram bins, most of which are empty—but don't miss the tiny bars straggling out to the right. The boxplot indicates that some CEOs received extraordinarily high compensations, while the majority received relatively "little." But look at the values of the bins. The first bin, with about half the CEOs, covers the range $0 to $5,000,000. Imagine receiving a salary survey with these categories:

> What is your income?
> a) $0 to $5,000,000
> b) $5,000,001 to $10,000,000
> c) $10,000,001 to $15,000,000
> d) More than $15,000,000

The reason that the histogram seems to leave so much of the area blank is that the salaries are spread all along the axis from about $15,000,000 to $240,000,000. After $50,000,000 there are so few for each bin that it's very hard to see the tiny bars. What we *can* see from this histogram and boxplot is that this distribution is highly skewed to the right.

Total compensation for CEOs consists of their base salaries, bonuses, and extra compensation, usually in the form of stock or stock options. Data that add together several variables, such as the compensation data, can easily have skewed distributions. It's often a good idea to separate the component variables and examine them individually to understand the data, but we don't have that information for these CEOs.

---

[6] *Sources:* United for a Fair Economy, *Business Week* annual CEO pay surveys, Bureau of Labor Statistics, "Average Weekly Earnings of Production Workers, Total Private Sector." Series ID: EEU00500004.

It can be hard to decide what we mean by the "center" of a skewed distribution, so it's hard to pick a typical value to summarize the distribution. What would you say was a typical CEO total compensation? The mean value is $10,307,000, while the median is "only" $4,700,000. Each tells us something different about the data.

One approach is to re-express, or transform, the data by applying a simple function to make the skewed distribution more symmetric. For example, we could take the square root or logarithm of each compensation value. Taking logs works pretty well for the CEO compensations, as you can see:

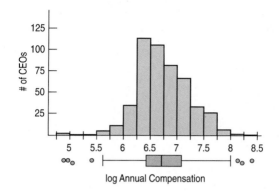

**FIGURE 5.10**

*The logarithms of 2005 CEO compensations are much more nearly symmetric.*

The histogram of the logs of the total CEO compensations is much more nearly symmetric, so we can see that a typical log compensation is between 6, which corresponds to $1,000,000, and 7, corresponding to $10,000,000. And it's easier to talk about a typical value for the logs. The mean log compensation is 6.73, while the median is 6.67. (That's $5,370,317 and $4,677,351, respectively.) Notice that nearly all the values are between 6.0 and 8.0—in other words, between $1,000,000 and $100,000,000 a year, but who's counting?

Against the background of a generally symmetric main body of data, it's easier to decide whether the largest compensations are outliers. In fact, the three most highly compensated CEOs are identified as outliers by the boxplot rule of thumb even after this re-expression. It's perhaps impressive to be an outlier CEO in annual compensation. It's even more impressive to be an outlier in the log scale![7]

Variables that are skewed to the right often benefit from a re-expression by square roots, logs, or reciprocals. Those skewed to the left may benefit from squaring the data. Because computers and calculators can do the calculating, re-expressing data is quite easy. Consider re-expression as a helpful tool whenever you have skewed data.

---

**Dealing with logarithms**   You have probably learned about logs in math courses and seen them in psychology or science classes. In this book, we use them only for making data behave better. Base 10 logs are the easiest to understand, but natural logs are often used as well. (Either one is fine.) You can think of base 10 logs as roughly one less than the number of digits you need to write the number. So 100, which is the smallest number to require 3 digits, has a $\log_{10}$ of 2. And 1000 has a $\log_{10}$ of 3. The $\log_{10}$ of 500 is between 2 and 3, but you'd need a calculator to find that it's approximately 2.7. All salaries of "six figures" have $\log_{10}$ between 5 and 6. Logs are incredibly useful for making skewed data more symmetric. But don't worry—there's no need to find your mother's slide rule. Nobody does logs without technology and neither should you. Often, remaking a histogram or other display of the data is as easy as pushing another button.

---

[7] That's Terry S. Semel of Yahoo, Barry Diller of IAC/InterActiveCorp, and William W. McGuire of UnitedHealth Group, in case you're interested.

## RE-EXPRESSING TO EQUALIZE SPREAD ACROSS GROUPS

Researchers measured the concentration (nanograms per milliliter) of cotinine in the blood of three groups of people: nonsmokers who have not been exposed to smoke, nonsmokers who have been exposed to smoke (ETS), and smokers. Cotinine is left in the blood when the body metabolizes nicotine, so this measure gives a direct measurement of the effect of passive smoke exposure. The boxplots of the cotinine levels of the three groups tell us that the smokers have higher cotinine levels, but if we want to compare the levels of the passive smokers to those of the nonsmokers, we're in trouble, because on this scale the cotinine levels for both nonsmoking groups are too low to be seen.

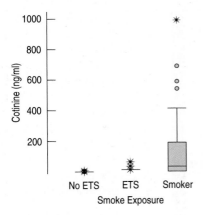

**FIGURE 5.11**

*Cotinine levels (nanograms per milliliter) for three groups with different exposures to tobacco smoke. Can you compare the ETS (exposed to smoke) and No-ETS groups?*

Re-expressing can help alleviate the problem of comparing groups that have very different spreads. For measurements like the cotinine data, whose values can't be negative and whose distributions are skewed to the high end, a good first guess at a re-expression is the logarithm.

After taking logs, we can compare the groups and see that the nonsmokers exposed to environmental smoke (the ETS group) do show increased levels of (log) cotinine, although not the high levels found in the blood of smokers.

Notice that the same re-expression has also improved the symmetry of the cotinine distribution for smokers and pulled in most of the apparent outliers in all of the groups. It is not unusual for a re-expression that improves one aspect of data to improve others as well. We'll talk about other ways to re-express data as the need arises throughout the book. We'll explore some common re-expressions more thoroughly in Chapter 10.

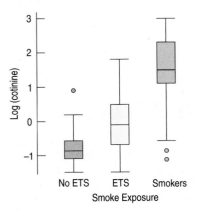

**FIGURE 5.12**

*Blood cotinine levels after taking logs. What a difference a log makes!*

## WHAT CAN GO WRONG?

▶ **Avoid inconsistent scales.** Parts of displays should be mutually consistent—no fair changing scales in the middle or plotting two variables on different scales but on the same display. When comparing two groups, be sure to compare them on the same scale.

▶ **Label clearly.** Variables should be identified clearly and axes labeled so a reader knows what the plot displays.

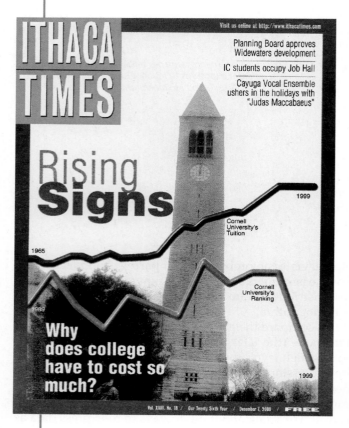

Here's a remarkable example of a plot gone wrong. It illustrated a news story about rising college costs. It uses time-plots, but it gives a misleading impression. First think about the story you're being told by this display. Then try to figure out what has gone wrong.

What's wrong? Just about everything.

▶ The horizontal scales are inconsistent. Both lines show trends over time, but exactly for what years? The tuition sequence starts in 1965, but rankings are graphed from 1989. Plotting them on the same (invisible) scale makes it seem that they're for the same years.

▶ The vertical axis isn't labeled. That hides the fact that it's inconsistent. Does it graph dollars (of tuition) or ranking (of Cornell University)?

This display violates three of the rules. And it's even worse than that: It violates a rule that we didn't even bother to mention.

▶ The two inconsistent scales for the vertical axis don't point in the same direction! The line for Cornell's rank shows that it has "plummeted" from 15th place to 6th place in academic rank. Most of us think that's an *improvement*, but that's not the message of this graph.

▶ **Beware of outliers.** If the data have outliers and you can correct them, you should do so. If they are clearly wrong or impossible, you should remove them and report on them. Otherwise, consider summarizing the data both with and without the outliers.

▶ **Be careful when comparing groups that have very different spreads.** As the cotinine data showed, a simple re-expression can often make comparisons across groups with very different spreads much easier.

## CONNECTIONS

We discussed the value of summarizing a distribution with shape, center, and spread in Chapter 4, and we developed several ways to measure these attributes. Now we've seen the value of comparing distributions for different groups and of looking at patterns in a quantitative variable measured over time. Although it can be interesting to summarize a single variable for a single group, it is almost always more interesting to compare groups and look for patterns across several groups and over time. We'll continue to make comparisons like these throughout the rest of our work.

# WHAT HAVE WE LEARNED?

▸ We've learned the value of comparing groups and looking for patterns among groups and over time.

▸ We've seen that boxplots are very effective for comparing groups graphically. When we compare groups, we discuss their shape, center, and spreads, and any unusual features.

▸ We've experienced the value of identifying and investigating outliers. And we've seen that when we group data in different ways, it can allow different cases to emerge as possible outliers.

▸ We've graphed data that have been measured over time against a time axis and looked for long-term trends both by eye and with a data smoother.

## Terms

**5-number summary**

89. A 5-number summary for a variable consists of:
▸ The minimum and maximum
▸ The quartiles: Q1 and Q3
▸ The median

**Boxplot**

90. A boxplot displays the 5-number summary as a central box with whiskers that extend to the non-outlying data values. Boxplots are particularly effective for comparing groups and for displaying outliers.

**Outlier**

91, 95. Any point more than 1.5 IQR from either end of the box in a boxplot is nominated as an *outlier.*

**Far Outlier**

91. If a point is more than 3.0 IQR from either end of the box in a boxplot, it is nominated as a *far outlier.*

**Comparing distributions**

91. When comparing the distributions of several groups, consider their:
▸ Shape
▸ Center
▸ Spread

**Comparing boxplots**

92. When comparing groups with boxplots,
▸ Compare the shapes. Do the boxes look symmetric or skewed? Are there differences between groups?
▸ Compare the medians. Which group has the higher center? Is there any pattern to the medians?
▸ Compare the IQRs. Which group is more spread out? Is there any pattern to how the IQRs change?
▸ Using the IQRs as a background measure of variation, do the medians seem to be different, or do they just vary much as you'd expect from the overall variation?
▸ Check for possible outliers. Identify them if you can and discuss why they might be unusual. Of course, correct them if you find that they are errors.

**Timeplot**

98. A timeplot displays data that change over time. Often, successive values are connected with lines to show trends more clearly. Sometimes a smooth curve is added to the plot to help show long-term patterns and trends.

## Skills

▸ Be able to select a suitable display for comparing groups. Understand that histograms show distributions well, but are difficult to use when comparing more than two or three groups. Boxplots are more effective for comparing several groups, in part because they show much less information about the distribution of each group.

▸ Understand that how you group data can affect what kinds of patterns and relationships you are likely to see. Know how to select groupings to show the information that is important for your analysis.

▸ Be aware of the effects of skewness and outliers on measures of center and spread. Know how to select appropriate measures for comparing groups based on their displayed distributions.

▸ Understand that outliers can emerge at different groupings of data and that, whatever their source, they deserve special attention.

▸ Recognize when it is appropriate to make a timeplot. Be able to choose between connecting consecutive points in a timeplot to show the sequence clearly and adding a smooth trace, which helps long-term trends emerge from the background scatter.

▸ Know how to make side-by-side histograms on comparable scales to compare the distributions of two groups.

▸ Know how to make side-by-side boxplots to compare the distributions of two or more groups.

▸ Know how to describe differences among groups in terms of patterns and changes in their center, spread, shape, and unusual values.

▸ Know how to make a timeplot of data that have been measured over time.

▸ Know how to add a smooth trace to a timeplot.

▸ Know how to compare the distributions of two or more groups by comparing their shapes, centers, and spreads. Be prepared to explain your choice of measures of center and spread for comparing the groups.

▸ Be able to describe trends and patterns in the centers and spreads of groups—especially if there is a natural order to the groups, such as a time order.

▸ Be prepared to discuss patterns in a timeplot in terms of both the general trend of the data and the changes in how spread out the pattern is. Be able to use a smooth trace as a general guide to the long-term patterns.

▸ Be cautious about assuming that trends over time will continue into the future.

▸ Be able to describe the distribution of a quantitative variable in terms of its shape, center, and spread.

▸ Be able to describe any anomalies or extraordinary features revealed by the display of a variable.

▸ Know how to compare the distributions of two or more groups by comparing their shapes, centers, and spreads.

▸ Know how to describe patterns over time shown in a timeplot.

▸ Be able to discuss any outliers in the data, noting how they deviate from the overall pattern of the data.

# ON THE COMPUTER

## Comparing Distributions

Most programs for displaying and analyzing data can display plots to compare the distributions of different groups. Typically, these are boxplots displayed side-by-side.

*Side-by-side boxplots should be on the same y-axis scale so they can be compared.*

*Some programs offer a graphical way to assess how much the medians differ by drawing a band around the median or by "notching" the boxes.*

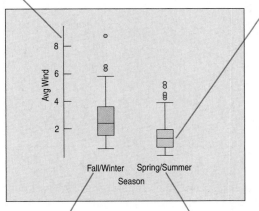

*Boxes are typically labeled with a group name. Often they are placed in alphabetical order by group name—not the most useful order.*

There are two ways to organize data when we want to compare groups. Each group can be in its own variable (or list, on a calculator). In this form, the experiment comparing coffee cups would have four lists, one for each type of cup:

| CUPPS | SIGG | Nissan | Starbucks |
|---|---|---|---|
| 6 | 2 | 12 | 13 |
| 6 | 1.5 | 16 | 7 |
| 6 | 2 | 9 | 7 |
| 18.5 | 3 | 23 | 17.5 |
| 10 | 0 | 11 | 10 |
| 17.5 | 7 | 20.5 | 15.5 |
| 11 | 0.5 | 12.5 | 6 |
| 6.5 | 6 | 24.5 | 6 |

But there's another way to think about and organize the data. What is the variable of interest (the *What*) in this experiment? It's the number of degrees lost by the water in each cup. And the *Who* is each time she tested a cup. We could gather all of the temperature values into one variable and put the names of the cups in a second variable listing the individual results, one on each row. Now, the *Who* is clearer—it's an experimental run, one row of the table. Most statistics packages prefer data on groups organized in this way.

That's actually the way we've thought about the wind speed data in this chapter, treating wind speeds as one variable and the groups (whether seasons, months, or days) as a second variable.

| Container | Temperature Difference | Container | Temperature Difference |
|-----------|------------------------|-----------|------------------------|
| CUPPS | 6 | SIGG | 12 |
| CUPPS | 6 | SIGG | 16 |
| CUPPS | 6 | SIGG | 9 |
| CUPPS | 18.5 | SIGG | 23 |
| CUPPS | 10 | SIGG | 11 |
| CUPPS | 17.5 | SIGG | 20.5 |
| CUPPS | 11 | SIGG | 12.5 |
| CUPPS | 6.5 | SIGG | 24.5 |
| Nissan | 2 | Starbucks | 13 |
| Nissan | 1.5 | Starbucks | 7 |
| Nissan | 2 | Starbucks | 7 |
| Nissan | 3 | Starbucks | 17.5 |
| Nissan | 0 | Starbucks | 10 |
| Nissan | 7 | Starbucks | 15.5 |
| Nissan | 0.5 | Starbucks | 6 |
| Nissan | 6 | Starbucks | 6 |

## DATA DESK

If the data are in separate variables, select the variables and choose **Boxplot side by side** from the **Plot** menu. The boxes will appear in the order in which the variables were selected. If the data are a single quantitative variable and a second variable holding group names, select the quantitative variable as Y and the group variable as X. Then choose **Boxplot y by x** from the **Plot** menu. The boxes will appear in alphabetical order by group name.

Data Desk offers options for assessing whether any pair of medians differ.

## EXCEL

Excel cannot make boxplots.

COMMENT

The DDXL add-on provided on the DVD adds the ability to make boxplots to Excel.

## JMP

Choose **Fit y by x.** Assign a continuous response variable to **Y, Response** and a nominal group variable holding the group names to **X, Factor,** and click **OK.** JMP will offer (among other things) dotplots of the data. Click the red triangle and, under **Display Options,** select Boxplots. *Note:* if the variables are of the wrong type, the display options might not offer boxplots.

## MINITAB

Choose **Boxplot...** from the **Graph** menu. If your data are in the form of one quantitative variable and one group variable, choose **One Y** and **with Groups.** If your data are in separate columns of the worksheet, choose **Multiple Y's.**

## SPSS

To make a boxplot in SPSS open the **Chart Builder** from the Graphs menu.
Click the **Gallery** tab.
Choose **Boxplot** from the list of chart types.
Drag a single or 2-D (side-by-side) boxplot onto the canvas.
Drag a scale variable to the *y*-axis drop zone.

To make side-by-side boxplots, drag a categorical variable to the *x*-axis drop zone.
Click **OK**.

**TI-83/84 PLUS**

To make a boxplot, set up a **STAT PLOT** by using the boxplot icon.

**TI-89**

For the plot, change Use Freq and Categories to YES and use VAR-LINK to select list2 as the frequency variable on the plot definition screen.

To create a boxplot, press F2 **(Plots),** then ENTER. Select a plot to define and press F1. Select either 3: **Box Plot** or 4: **Mod Box Plot** (to identify outliers). Select the mark type of your choice (for outliers). Press ENTER to finish.
Press F5 to display the graph.

# EXERCISES

1. **In the news.**   Find an article in a newspaper or a magazine that compares two or more groups of data.
   a) Does the article discuss the W's?
   b) Is the choice of graphics appropriate for the situation? Explain.
   c) Discuss what the display reveals about the groups.
   d) Does the article accurately describe and interpret the data? Explain.

2. **In the news.**   Find an article in a newspaper or a magazine that shows a time plot.
   a) Does the article discuss the W's?
   b) Is the timeplot appropriate for the data? Explain.
   c) Discuss what the timeplot reveals about the variable.
   d) Does the article accurately describe and interpret the data? Explain.

3. **Time on the Internet.**   Find data on the Internet (or elsewhere) that give results recorded over time. Make an appropriate display and discuss what it shows.

4. **Groups on the Internet.**   Find data on the Internet (or elsewhere) for two or more groups. Make appropriate displays to compare the groups, and interpret what you find.

5. **Pizza prices.**   A company that sells frozen pizza to stores in four markets (Denver, Baltimore, Dallas, and Chicago) in the United States wants to examine the prices that the stores charge for pizza slices. Here are boxplots comparing data from a sample of stores in each market:

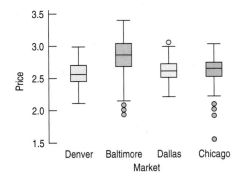

a) Do prices appear to be the same in the four markets? Explain.
b) Does the presence of any outliers affect your overall conclusions about prices in the four markets?

6. **Costs.**   To help travelers know what to expect, researchers collected the prices of commodities in 16 cities throughout the world. Here are boxplots comparing the prices of a ride on public transportation, a newspaper, and a cup of coffee in the 16 cities (prices are all in $US).

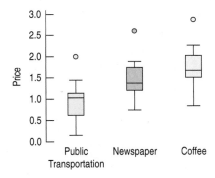

a) On average, which commodity is the most expensive?
b) Is a newspaper always more expensive than a ride on public transportation? Explain.
c) Does the presence of outliers affect your conclusions in a) or b)?

7. **Golf courses.**   One measure of the difficulty of a golf course is its length: the total distance (in yards) from tee to hole for all 18 holes. Here are the histogram and summary statistics for the lengths of all the golf courses in Vermont:

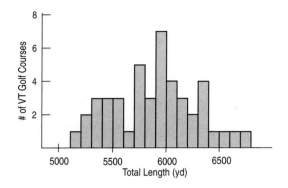

| Count | 45 |
|---|---|
| Mean | 5892.91 yd |
| StdDev | 386.59 |
| Min | 5185 |
| Q1 | 5585.75 |
| Median | 5928 |
| Q3 | 6131 |
| Max | 6796 |

a) What is the range of these lengths?
b) Between what lengths do the central 50% of these courses lie?
c) What summary statistics would you use to describe these data?
d) Write a brief description of these data (shape, center, and spread).

**8. Men's Combined.** The Men's Combined skiing event consists of a downhill and a slalom. Here are the total times (adding the two race times) for the 2006 Olympics:

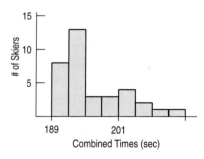

| Count | 35 |
|---|---|
| Mean | 196.079 |
| StdDev | 5.80009 |
| Min | 189.350 |
| Q1 | 192.238 |
| Median | 193.270 |
| Q3 | 200.625 |
| Max | 211.890 |

a) What is the range of these lengths?
b) Between what values do the central 50% of these times lie?

c) What summary statistics would you use to describe these data?
d) Write a brief description of the data (shape, center, and spread).

**9. Still rockin'.** Crowd Management Strategies monitors accidents at rock concerts. In their database, they list the names and other variables of victims whose deaths were attributed to "crowd crush" at rock concerts. Here are the histogram and boxplot of the victims' ages for data from 1999 to 2000:

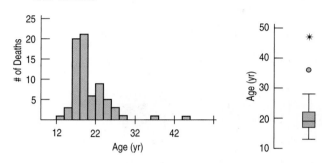

a) What features of the distribution can you see in both the histogram and the boxplot?
b) What features of the distribution can you see in the histogram that you could not see in the boxplot?
c) What summary statistic would you choose to summarize the center of this distribution? Why?
d) What summary statistic would you choose to summarize the spread of this distribution? Why?

**10. Slalom times.** The Men's Combined skiing event consists of a downhill and a slalom. Here are two displays of the slalom times in the Men's Combined of the 2006 Winter Olympics:

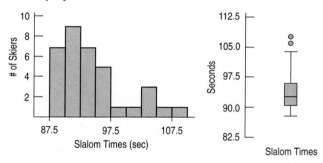

a) What features of the distribution can you see in both the histogram and the boxplot?
b) What features of the distribution can you see in the histogram that you could not see in the boxplot?
c) What summary statistic would you choose to summarize the center of this distribution? Why?
d) What summary statistic would you choose to summarize the spread of this distribution? Why?

**11. Cereals.** Sugar is a major ingredient in many breakfast cereals. The following boxplot and histogram display the sugar content as a percentage of weight for 49 brands of cereal:

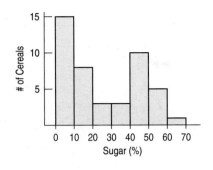

a) What is the median sugar content?
b) What is the range of the sugar contents of these cereals.
c) Describe the shape of the distribution.
d) What aspect of breakfast cereals might account for this shape?

**12. Tendon transfers.** People with spinal cord injuries may lose function in some, but not all, of their muscles. The ability to push oneself up is particularly important for shifting position when seated and for transferring into and out of wheelchairs. Surgeons compared two operations to restore the ability to push up in children. Two years after surgery, scores rating pushing strength for 16 arms that had been operated on had a distribution displayed here with a histogram and boxplot. (Mulcahey, M. J., Lutz, Cheryl, Kozen, Scott, Betz, Randel, "Prospective Evaluation of Biceps to Triceps and Deltoid to Triceps for Elbow Extension in Tetraplegia," *Journal of Hand Surgery,* 28, 6, 2003)

a) Describe the shape of this distribution.
b) What is the median of the distribution?
c) What is the range of the strength scores?

**13. More cereal.** Let's look once more at the sugar content of the cereals described in Exercise 11. The following box-plots compare cereals marketed primarily to adults with children's cereals:

a) Are all children's cereals higher in sugar than adult cereals?
b) Which group of cereals varies more in sugar content? Explain.

**14. Tendon transfer II.** The point of the tendon transfer experiment described in Exercise 12 was to compare two different surgical procedures: biceps transfers and deltoid transfers. Here are boxplots showing the results. There were 8 surgeries using each procedure:

a) Which method had the higher (better) median score?
b) Was that method always best?
c) Which method produced the most consistent results? Explain.

**15. Population growth.** Here is a "back-to-back" stem-and-leaf display that shows two data sets at once—one going to the left, one to the right. The display compares the percent change in population for two regions of the United States (based on census figures for 1990 and 2000). The fastest growing states were Nevada at 66% and Arizona at 40%. To show the distributions better, this display breaks each stem into two lines, putting leaves 0–4 on one stem and leaves 5–9 on the other.

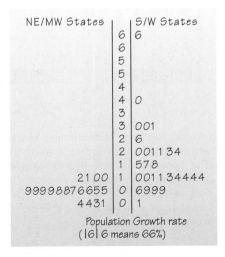

a) Use the data displayed in the stem-and-leaf display to construct comparative boxplots.
b) Write a few sentences describing the difference in growth rates for the two regions of the United States.

**16. Camp sites.** Shown below are the histogram and summary statistics for the number of camp sites at public parks in Vermont.

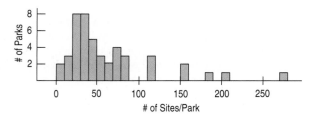

| Count | 46 |
|-------|-----|
| Mean | 62.8 sites |
| Median | 43.5 |
| StdDev | 56.2 |
| Min | 0 |
| Max | 275 |
| Q1 | 28 |
| Q3 | 78 |

a) Which statistics would you use to identify the center and spread of this distribution? Why?
b) How many parks would you classify as outliers? Explain.
c) Create a boxplot for these data.
d) Write a few sentences describing the distribution.

**17. Hospital stays.** The U.S. National Center for Health Statistics compiles data on the length of stay by patients in short-term hospitals and publishes its findings in *Vital and Health Statistics*. Data from a sample of 39 male patients and 35 female patients on length of stay (in days) are displayed in the histograms below.

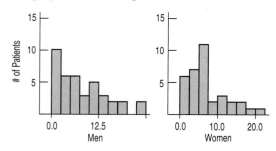

a) What would you suggest be changed about these histograms to make them easier to compare?
b) Describe these distributions by writing a few sentences comparing the duration of hospitalization for men and women.
c) Can you suggest a reason for the peak in women's length of stay?

**18. Deaths 2003.** A National Vital Statistics Report (www.cdc.gov/nchs/) indicated that nearly 300,000 black Americans died in 2003 compared with just over 2 million white Americans. Here are histograms displaying the distributions of their ages at death.

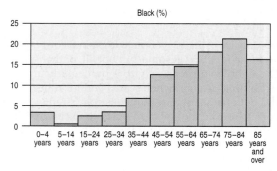

a) Describe the overall shapes of these distributions.
b) How do the distributions differ?
c) Look carefully at the bar definitions. Where do these plots violate the rules for statistical graphs?

**T 19. Women's basketball.** Here are boxplots of the points scored during the first 10 games of the season for both Scyrine and Alexandra:

a) Summarize the similarities and differences in their performance so far.
b) The coach can take only one player to the state championship. Which one should she take? Why?

**20. Gas prices.** Here are boxplots of weekly gas prices at a service station in the Midwestern United States (prices in $ per gallon):

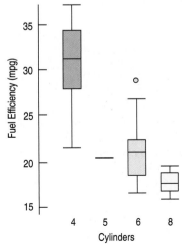

a) Compare the distribution of prices over the three years.
b) In which year were the prices least stable? Explain.

**T 21. Marriage age.** In 1975, did men and women marry at the same age? Here are boxplots of the age at first marriage for a sample of U.S. citizens then. Write a brief report discussing what these data show.

**T 22. Fuel economy.** Describe what these boxplots tell you about the relationship between the number of cylinders a car's engine has and the car's fuel economy (mpg):

**23. Fuel economy II.** The Environmental Protection Agency provides fuel economy and pollution information on over 2000 car models. Here is a boxplot of *Combined Fuel Economy*

(using an average of driving conditions) in *miles per gallon* by vehicle *Type* (car, van, or SUV). Summarize what you see about the fuel economies of the three vehicle types.

**24. Fuel economy III.** The Environmental Protection Agency provides fuel economy and pollution information on over 2000 car models. Here is a boxplot of *Combined Fuel Economy* (using an average of driving conditions) in *miles per gallon* by whether the car has two- or four-wheel drive. Summarize what you see about the fuel economies of these two types of vehicles.

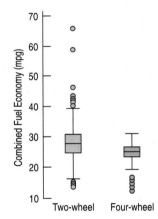

**T 25. Wines.** The boxplots display case prices (in dollars) of varieties of wines produced by vineyards along three of the Finger Lakes:

a) Which lake region produces the most expensive wine?
b) Which lake region produces the cheapest wine?
c) In which region are the wines generally more expensive?
d) Write a few sentences describing these wine prices.

**T 26. Ozone.** Ozone levels (in parts per billion, ppb) were recorded at sites in New Jersey monthly between 1926 and 1971. Here are boxplots of the data for each month (over the 46 years), lined up in order (January=1):

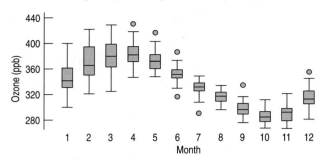

a) In what month was the highest ozone level ever recorded?
b) Which month has the largest IQR?
c) Which month has the smallest range?
d) Write a brief comparison of the ozone levels in January and June.
e) Write a report on the annual patterns you see in the ozone levels.

**27. Wild-card Summer Olympics.** Seventy-one swimmers finished the qualifying first day of the men's 100-m swim in the 2000 Olympics in Sydney. The average time was 52.65 seconds, with a standard deviation of 7.66 seconds. The median time was 51.34 seconds and the IQR was 2.58 seconds.
a) Without looking at a graphical display, what shape would you expect the distributions of times to have?
b) What might account for the difference between these two sets of statistics?
c) Here is the histogram of the actual times. Write a couple of sentences summarizing what you see.[8]

[8] IOC president Juan Antonio Samaranch initiated a special program in the 2000 Olympics. As a way of spreading sports around the world, a handful of athletes were allowed to compete even though they didn't meet qualifying standards. Eric Moussambani of Equatorial Guinea, who trains in a 20-m pool with no lane markers in his African homeland, became an international celebrity after completing his swim in more than twice the time of the next slowest competitor. He carried the national flag in the opening ceremony, leading an 11-person team that also included a female swimmer. He actually won his heat of 3 swimmers when the other 2 failed to qualify.

**28. Unemployment.** In May of 2001, the U.S. Bureau of Labor Statistics (BLS) issued a news release that said,

*In April, 223 metropolitan areas recorded unemployment rates below the U.S. average of 4.2 percent (not seasonally adjusted), while 99 areas registered higher rates.*

Sketch what the distribution of unemployment rates for the 322 metropolitan areas reported on by BLS probably looks like.

**29. Test scores.** Three Statistics classes all took the same test. Histograms of the scores for each class are shown below.

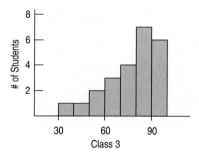

a) Which class had the highest mean score?
b) Which class had the highest median score?
c) For which class are the mean and median most different? Which is higher? Why?
d) Which class had the smallest standard deviation?
e) Which class had the smallest IQR?

**30. Test scores.** Look again at the histograms of test scores for the three Statistics classes in Exercise 29.
a) Overall, which class do you think performed best on the test? Why?
b) How would you describe the shape of each distribution?
c) Match each class with the corresponding boxplot below.

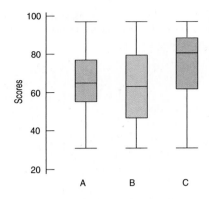

**31. Graduation?** A survey of major universities asked what percentage of incoming freshmen usually graduate "on time" in 4 years. Use the summary statistics given to answer the questions that follow.

|  | % on Time |
|---|---|
| Count | 48 |
| Mean | 68.35 |
| Median | 69.90 |
| StdDev | 10.20 |
| Min | 43.20 |
| Max | 87.40 |
| Range | 44.20 |
| 25th %tile | 59.15 |
| 75th %tile | 74.75 |

a) Would you describe this distribution as symmetric or skewed? Explain.
b) Are there any outliers? Explain.
c) Create a boxplot of these data.
d) Write a few sentences about the graduation rates.

**T 32. Vineyards.** Here are summary statistics for the sizes (in acres) of Finger Lakes vineyards:

| Count | 36 |
|---|---|
| Mean | 46.50 acres |
| StdDev | 47.76 |
| Median | 33.50 |
| IQR | 36.50 |
| Min | 6 |
| Q1 | 18.50 |
| Q3 | 55 |
| Max | 250 |

a) Would you describe this distribution as symmetric or skewed? Explain.
b) Are there any outliers? Explain.
c) Create a boxplot of these data.
d) Write a few sentences about the sizes of the vineyards.

**33. Caffeine.** A student study of the effects of caffeine asked volunteers to take a memory test 2 hours after drinking soda. Some drank caffeine-free cola, some drank regular cola (with caffeine), and others drank a mixture of the two (getting a half-dose of caffeine). Here are the

5-number summaries for each group's scores (number of items recalled correctly) on the memory test:

|  | n | Min | Q1 | Median | Q3 | Max |
|---|---|---|---|---|---|---|
| No caffeine | 15 | 16 | 20 | 21 | 24 | 26 |
| Low caffeine | 15 | 16 | 18 | 21 | 24 | 27 |
| High caffeine | 15 | 12 | 17 | 19 | 22 | 24 |

a) Describe the W's for these data.
b) Name the variables and classify each as categorical or quantitative.
c) Create parallel boxplots to display these results as best you can with this information.
d) Write a few sentences comparing the performances of the three groups.

**34. SAT scores.** Here are the summary statistics for Verbal SAT scores for a high-school graduating class:

|  | n | Mean | Median | SD | Min | Max | Q1 | Q3 |
|---|---|---|---|---|---|---|---|---|
| Male | 80 | 590 | 600 | 97.2 | 310 | 800 | 515 | 650 |
| Female | 82 | 602 | 625 | 102.0 | 360 | 770 | 530 | 680 |

a) Create parallel boxplots comparing the scores of boys and girls as best you can from the information given.
b) Write a brief report on these results. Be sure to discuss the shape, center, and spread of the scores.

**T 35. Derby speeds 2007.** How fast do horses run? Kentucky Derby winners top 30 miles per hour, as shown in this graph. The graph shows the percentage of Derby winners that have run *slower* than each given speed. Note that few have won running less than 33 miles per hour, but about 86% of the winning horses have run less than 37 miles per hour. (A cumulative frequency graph like this is called an "ogive.")

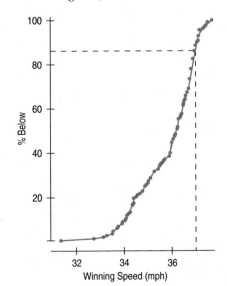

a) Estimate the median winning speed.
b) Estimate the quartiles.
c) Estimate the range and the IQR.

d) Create a boxplot of these speeds.
e) Write a few sentences about the speeds of the Kentucky Derby winners.

**36. Cholesterol.** The Framingham Heart Study recorded the cholesterol levels of more than 1400 men. Here is an ogive of the distribution of these cholesterol measures. (An ogive shows the percentage of cases at or below a certain value.) Construct a boxplot for these data and write a few sentences describing the distribution.

**37. Reading scores.** A class of fourth graders takes a diagnostic reading test, and the scores are reported by reading grade level. The 5-number summaries for the 14 boys and 11 girls are shown:

| | | | | | |
|---|---|---|---|---|---|
| **Boys:** | 2.0 | 3.9 | 4.3 | 4.9 | 6.0 |
| **Girls:** | 2.8 | 3.8 | 4.5 | 5.2 | 5.9 |

a) Which group had the highest score?
b) Which group had the greatest range?
c) Which group had the greatest interquartile range?
d) Which group's scores appear to be more skewed? Explain.
e) Which group generally did better on the test? Explain.
f) If the mean reading level for boys was 4.2 and for girls was 4.6, what is the overall mean for the class?

**38. Rainmakers?** In an experiment to determine whether seeding clouds with silver iodide increases rainfall, 52 clouds were randomly assigned to be seeded or not. The amount of rain they generated was then measured (in acre-feet). Here are the summary statistics:

| | n | Mean | Median | SD | IQR | Q1 | Q3 |
|---|---|---|---|---|---|---|---|
| Unseeded | 26 | 164.59 | 44.20 | 278.43 | 138.60 | 24.40 | 163 |
| Seeded | 26 | 441.98 | 221.60 | 650.79 | 337.60 | 92.40 | 430 |

a) Which of the summary statistics are most appropriate for describing these distributions. Why?
b) Do you see any evidence that seeding clouds may be effective? Explain.

**39. Law enforcement 2004.** Some federal employees have the authority to carry firearms and make arrests. Obviously, some danger is associated with these jobs, but how much? The table below summarizes the rates of assault and injury (or death) for these employees for 2004. (www.ojp.usdoj.gov/bjs)

| Agency | Assaults (per 100) | Injured (per 100) |
|---|---|---|
| Bureau of Indian Affairs | 33.8 | 5.3 |
| National Park Service | 5.2 | 1.5 |
| U.S. Marshals Service | 1.5 | 0.7 |
| U.S. Customs and Border Protection | 0.9 | 0.2 |
| U.S. Postal Inspection Service | 0.8 | 0.3 |
| U.S. Capitol Police | 0.7 | 0.2 |
| Drug Enforcement Administration | 0.7 | 0.1 |
| Treasury IG for Tax Administration | 0.6 | 0 |
| U.S. Secret Service | 0.5 | 0.2 |
| U.S. Immigration and Customs Enforcement | 0.5 | 0.2 |
| Federal Bureau of Investigation | 0.2 | 0 |
| Bureau of Alcohol, Tobacco, Firearms and Explosives | 0.2 | 0 |
| U.S. Fish and Wildlife Service | 0.1 | 0.1 |
| Internal Revenue Service | 0 | 0 |

a) Create a display of these data.
b) Describe the data (shape, center, spread, unusual features).
c) Which agencies are outliers?

**40. Cholesterol.** A study examining the health risks of smoking measured the cholesterol levels of people who had smoked for at least 25 years and people of similar ages who had smoked for no more than 5 years and then stopped. Create appropriate graphical displays for both groups, and write a brief report comparing their cholesterol levels. Here are the data:

| Smokers | | | | Ex-Smokers | | |
|---|---|---|---|---|---|---|
| 225 | 211 | 209 | 284 | 250 | 134 | 300 |
| 258 | 216 | 196 | 288 | 249 | 213 | 310 |
| 250 | 200 | 209 | 280 | 175 | 174 | 328 |
| 225 | 256 | 243 | 200 | 160 | 188 | 321 |
| 213 | 246 | 225 | 237 | 213 | 257 | 292 |
| 232 | 267 | 232 | 216 | 200 | 271 | 227 |
| 216 | 243 | 200 | 155 | 238 | 163 | 263 |
| 216 | 271 | 230 | 309 | 192 | 242 | 249 |
| 183 | 280 | 217 | 305 | 242 | 267 | 243 |
| 287 | 217 | 246 | 351 | 217 | 267 | 218 |
| 200 | 280 | 209 | | 217 | 183 | 228 |

**41. Industrial experiment.** Engineers at a computer production plant tested two methods for accuracy in drilling holes into a PC board. They tested how fast they could set the drilling machine by running 10 boards at each of two different speeds. To assess the results, they measured the distance (in inches) from the center of a target on the board to the center of the hole. The data and summary statistics are shown in the table:

| Distance (in.) | Speed | Distance (in.) | Speed |
|---|---|---|---|
| 0.000101 | Fast | 0.000098 | Slow |
| 0.000102 | Fast | 0.000096 | Slow |
| 0.000100 | Fast | 0.000097 | Slow |
| 0.000102 | Fast | 0.000095 | Slow |
| 0.000101 | Fast | 0.000094 | Slow |
| 0.000103 | Fast | 0.000098 | Slow |
| 0.000104 | Fast | 0.000096 | Slow |
| 0.000102 | Fast | 0.975600 | Slow |
| 0.000102 | Fast | 0.000097 | Slow |
| 0.000100 | Fast | 0.000096 | Slow |
| Mean | 0.000102 | Mean | 0.097647 |
| StdDev | 0.000001 | StdDev | 0.308481 |

Write a report summarizing the findings of the experiment. Include appropriate visual and verbal displays of the distributions, and make a recommendation to the engineers if they are most interested in the accuracy of the method.

**42. Eye and hair color.** A survey of 1021 school-age children was conducted by randomly selecting children from several large urban elementary schools. Two of the questions concerned eye and hair color. In the survey, the following codes were used:

| Hair Color | Eye Color |
|---|---|
| 1 = Blond | 1 = Blue |
| 2 = Brown | 2 = Green |
| 3 = Black | 3 = Brown |
| 4 = Red | 4 = Grey |
| 5 = Other | 5 = Other |

The Statistics students analyzing the data were asked to study the relationship between eye and hair color. They produced this plot:

Is their graph appropriate? If so, summarize the findings. If not, explain why not.

**43. MPG.** A consumer organization compared gas mileage figures for several models of cars made in the United States with autos manufactured in other countries. The data are shown in the table:

| Gas Mileage (mpg) | Country | Gas Mileage (mpg) | Country |
|---|---|---|---|
| 16.9 | U.S. | 26.8 | U.S. |
| 15.5 | U.S. | 33.5 | U.S. |
| 19.2 | U.S. | 34.2 | U.S. |
| 18.5 | U.S. | 16.2 | Other |
| 30.0 | U.S. | 20.3 | Other |
| 30.9 | U.S. | 31.5 | Other |
| 20.6 | U.S. | 30.5 | Other |
| 20.8 | U.S. | 21.5 | Other |
| 18.6 | U.S. | 31.9 | Other |
| 18.1 | U.S. | 37.3 | Other |
| 17.0 | U.S. | 27.5 | Other |
| 17.6 | U.S. | 27.2 | Other |
| 16.5 | U.S. | 34.1 | Other |
| 18.2 | U.S. | 35.1 | Other |
| 26.5 | U.S. | 29.5 | Other |
| 21.9 | U.S. | 31.8 | Other |
| 27.4 | U.S. | 22.0 | Other |
| 28.4 | U.S. | 17.0 | Other |
| 28.8 | U.S. | 21.6 | Other |

a) Create graphical displays for these two groups.
b) Write a few sentences comparing the distributions.

**44. Baseball.** American League baseball teams play their games with the designated hitter rule, meaning that pitchers do not bat. The League believes that replacing the pitcher, typically a weak hitter, with another player in the batting order produces more runs and generates more interest among fans. Following are the average number of runs scored in American League and National League stadiums for the first half of the 2001 season:

| Average Runs | League | Average Runs | League |
|---|---|---|---|
| 11.1 | American | 14.0 | National |
| 10.8 | American | 11.6 | National |
| 10.8 | American | 10.4 | National |
| 10.3 | American | 10.9 | National |
| 10.3 | American | 10.2 | National |
| 10.1 | American | 9.5 | National |
| 10.0 | American | 9.5 | National |
| 9.5 | American | 9.5 | National |
| 9.4 | American | 9.5 | National |
| 9.3 | American | 9.1 | National |
| 9.2 | American | 8.8 | National |
| 9.2 | American | 8.4 | National |
| 9.0 | American | 8.3 | National |
| 8.3 | American | 8.2 | National |
| | | 8.1 | National |
| | | 7.9 | National |

a) Create an appropriate graphical display of these data.
b) Write a few sentences comparing the average number of runs scored per game in the two leagues. (Remember: shape, center, spread, unusual features!)

c) Coors Field, in Denver, stands a mile above sea level, an altitude far greater than that of any other major league ball park. Some believe that the thinner air makes it harder for pitchers to throw curve balls and easier for batters to hit the ball a long way. Do you see any evidence that the 14 runs scored per game there is unusually high? Explain.

**T** **45. Fruit Flies.** Researchers tracked a population of 1,203,646 fruit flies, counting how many died each day for 171 days. Here are three timeplots offering different views of these data. One shows the number of flies alive on each day, one the number who died that day, and the third the mortality rate—the fraction of the number alive who died. On the last day studied, the last 2 flies died, for a mortality rate of 1.0.

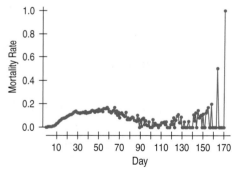

a) On approximately what day did the most flies die?
b) On what day during the first 100 days did the largest *proportion* of flies die?
c) When did the number of fruit flies alive stop changing very much from day to day?

**T** **46. Drunk driving 2005.** Accidents involving drunk drivers account for about 40% of all deaths on the nation's highways. The table tracks the number of alcohol-related fatalities for 24 years. (www.madd.org)

| Year | Deaths (thousands) | Year | Deaths (thousands) |
|------|-----|------|-----|
| 1982 | 26.2 | 1994 | 17.3 |
| 1983 | 24.6 | 1995 | 17.7 |
| 1984 | 24.8 | 1996 | 17.7 |
| 1985 | 23.2 | 1997 | 16.7 |
| 1986 | 25.0 | 1998 | 16.7 |
| 1987 | 24.1 | 1999 | 16.6 |
| 1988 | 23.8 | 2000 | 17.4 |
| 1989 | 22.4 | 2001 | 17.4 |
| 1990 | 22.6 | 2002 | 17.5 |
| 1991 | 20.2 | 2003 | 17.1 |
| 1992 | 18.3 | 2004 | 16.9 |
| 1993 | 17.9 | 2005 | 16.9 |

a) Create a stem-and-leaf display or a histogram of these data.
b) Create a timeplot.
c) Using features apparent in the stem-and-leaf display (or histogram) and the timeplot, write a few sentences about deaths caused by drunk driving.

**T** **47. Hurricanes again 2006.** Here are the number of Atlantic hurricanes classified as major for the years 1944 to 2006. (www.nhc.noaa.gov)

3, 2, 1, 2, 4, 3, 7, 2, 3, 3, 2, 5, 2, 2, 4, 2, 2, 6, 0, 2, 5, 1, 3, 1, 0, 3, 2, 1, 0, 1, 2, 3, 2, 1, 2, 2, 2, 3, 1, 1, 1, 3, 0, 1, 3, 2, 1, 2, 1, 1, 0, 5, 6, 1, 3, 5, 3, 3, 2, 3, 6, 7, 2

Create a timeplot of the data and summarize what you see. (Use a smoother if your software has one available.)

**T** **48. Sunspots.** Sunspots have fascinated people for hundreds of years. (The first recordings of sunspots date from ancient Greece and China.) These dark spots on the sun seem to come and go, and for about 150 years astronomers have noted that there appears to be a cycle. The data set *sunspots* on the DVD holds yearly average numbers of sunspots for the years 1701 to 2005. Find more information about sunspots at http://solarscience.msfc.nasa.gov/SunspotCycle.shtml.

a) Make a timeplot of the sunspot data.
b) With the help of a smoother, discuss the cycle that astronomers see. (*Hint:* Because of the amount of data, you may have to adjust the "span" or "window" of the smoother to be smaller than the default, to see the "cycle.")

**T** **49. Assets.** Here is a histogram of the assets (in millions of dollars) of 79 companies chosen from the *Forbes* list of the nation's top corporations:

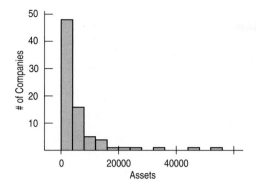

a) What aspect of this distribution makes it difficult to summarize, or to discuss, center and spread?
b) What would you suggest doing with these data if we want to understand them better?

**50. Music library.** Students were asked how many songs they had in their digital music library. Here's a display of the responses:

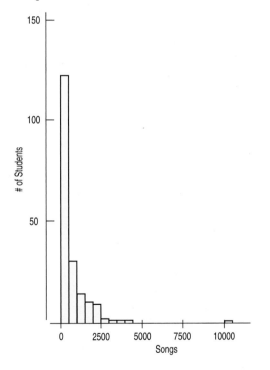

a) What aspect of this distribution makes it difficult to summarize, or to discuss, center and spread?
b) What would you suggest doing with these data if we want to understand them better?

**51. Assets again.** Here are the same data you saw in Exercise 49 after re-expressions as the square root of assets and the logarithm of assets:

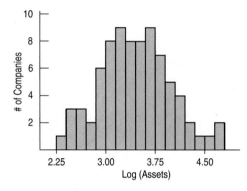

a) Which re-expression do you prefer? Why?
b) In the square root re-expression, what does the value 50 actually indicate about the company's assets?
c) In the logarithm re-expression, what does the value 3 actually indicate about the company's assests?

**52. Rainmakers.** The table lists the amount of rainfall (in acre-feet) from the 26 clouds seeded with silver iodide discussed in Exercise 38:

| | |
|------|-----|
| 2745 | 200 |
| 1697 | 198 |
| 1656 | 129 |
| 978  | 119 |
| 703  | 118 |
| 489  | 115 |
| 430  | 92  |
| 334  | 40  |
| 302  | 32  |
| 274  | 31  |
| 274  | 17  |
| 255  | 7   |
| 242  | 4   |

a) Why is acre-feet a good way to measure the amount of precipitation produced by cloud seeding?
b) Plot these data, and describe the distribution.
c) Create a re-expression of these data that produces a more advantageous distribution.
d) Explain what your re-expressed scale means.

**53. Stereograms.** Stereograms appear to be composed entirely of random dots. However, they contain separate images that a viewer can "fuse" into a three-dimensional (3D) image by staring at the dots while defocusing the eyes. An experiment was performed to determine whether knowledge of the embedded image affected the time required for subjects to fuse the images. One group of subjects (group NV) received no information or just verbal information about the shape of the embedded object. A second group (group VV) received both verbal information and visual information (specifically, a drawing of the object). The experimenters measured how many seconds it took for the subject to report that he or she saw the 3D image.

a) What two variables are discussed in this description?
b) For each variable, is it quantitative or categorical? If quantitative, what are the units?
c) The boxplots compare the fusion times for the two treatment groups. Write a few sentences comparing these distributions. What does the experiment show?

**54. Stereograms, revisited.** Because of the skewness of the distributions of fusion times, we might consider a re-expression. Here are the boxplots of the *log* of fusion times. Is it better to analyze the original fusion times or the log fusion times? Explain.

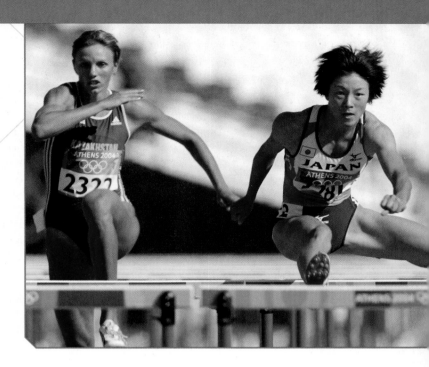

# CHAPTER

# 6

# The Standard Deviation as a Ruler and the Normal Model

## Where are we going?

A college admissions officer is looking at the files of two candidates, one with a total SAT score of 1500, another with an ACT score of 21. Which candidate scored better? How do we compare things when they're measured on different scales?

To answer a question like this, we need to standardize the results. To do that, we need to know two things. First, we need a base value for comparison—we'll often use the mean for that. Next, we need to know how far away we are from the mean. So, we'll need some sort of ruler. Fortunately, the standard deviation is just the thing we need.

The idea of measuring distances from means by counting standard deviations shows up throughout Statistics, and it starts right here.

The women's heptathlon in the Olympics consists of seven track and field events: the 200-m and 800-m runs, 100-m high hurdles, shot put, javelin, high jump, and long jump. To determine who should get the gold medal, somehow the performances in all seven events have to be combined into one score. How can performances in such different events be compared? They don't even have the same units; the races are recorded in minutes and seconds and the throwing and jumping events in meters. In the 2004 Olympics, Austra Skujyte of Lithuania put the shot 16.4 meters, about 3 meters farther than the average of all contestants. Carolina Kluft won the long jump with a 6.78-m jump, about a meter better than the average. Which performance deserves more points? Even though both events are measured in meters, it's not clear how to compare them. The solution to the problem of how to compare scores turns out to be a useful method for comparing all sorts of values whether they have the same units or not.

| | Event | |
|---|---|---|
| | Long Jump | Shot Put |
| Mean (all contestants) | 6.16 m | 13.29 m |
| SD | 0.23 m | 1.24 m |
| $n$ | 26 | 28 |
| Kluft | 6.78 m | 14.77 m |
| Skujyte | 6.30 m | 16.40 m |

# The Standard Deviation as a Ruler

The trick in comparing very different-looking values is to use standard deviations. The standard deviation tells us how the whole collection of values varies, so it's a natural ruler for comparing an individual value to the group. Over and over during this course, we will ask questions such as "How far is this value from the mean?" or "How different are these two statistics?" The answer in every case will be to measure the distance or difference in standard deviations.

The concept of the standard deviation as a ruler is not special to this course. You'll find statistical distances measured in standard deviations throughout Statistics, up to the most advanced levels.[1] This approach is one of the basic tools of statistical thinking.

| Long Jump | | Shot Put | |
|---|---|---|---|
| Stem | Leaf | Stem | Leaf |
| 67 | 8 | 16 | 4 |
| 66 | | 15 | |
| 65 | 1 | 15 | |
| 64 | 2 | 14 | 56778 |
| 63 | 0566 | 14 | 24 |
| 62 | 11235 | 13 | 5789 |
| 61 | 0569 | 13 | 012234 |
| 60 | 2223 | 12 | 55 |
| 59 | 0278 | 12 | 0144 |
| 58 | 4 | 11 | 59 |
| 57 | 0 | 11 | 23 |

**FIGURE 6.1**

*Stem-and-leaf displays for both the long jump and the shot put in the 2004 Olympic Heptathlon. Carolina Kluft (blue scores) won the long jump, and Austra Skujyte (red scores) won the shot put. Which heptathlete did better for both events combined?*

In order to compare the two events, let's start with a picture. This time we'll use stem-and-leaf displays, so we can see the individual distances. The two winning performances on the top of each stem-and-leaf display appear to be about the same distance from the center of the pack. But look again carefully. What do we mean by the *same distance*? The two displays have different scales. Each line in the stem-and-leaf for the shot put represents half a meter, but for the long jump each line is only a tenth of a meter. It's only because our eyes naturally adjust the scales and use the standard deviation as the ruler that we see each as being about the same distance from the center of the data.

| | Event | |
|---|---|---|
| | Long Jump | Shot Put |
| Mean | 6.16 m | 13.29 m |
| SD | 0.23 m | 1.24 m |
| Kluft | 6.78 m | 14.77 m |
| z-score | 2.70 = (6.78−6.16)/0.23 | 1.19 = (14.77−13.29)/1.24 |
| Skujyte | 6.30 m | 16.40m |
| z-score | 0.61 = (6.30−6.16)/0.23 | 2.51 = (16.40−13.29)/1.24 |
| Total z-score 2 events: | | |
| Kluft: | 2.70 + 1.19 = 3.89 | |
| Skujyte: | 0.61 + 2.51 = 3.12 | |

How can we make this more precise? How many standard deviations is Kluft's 6.78-m long jump from the mean? The mean is 6.16 m and the standard deviation is 0.23 m, so 6.78 m is 2.70 SDs above the mean (see the table for more details). Skujyte's shot put is nearly as impressive at 2.51 SDs above the mean.

Expressing the distance in standard deviations **standardizes** the performances. To standardize a value, we simply subtract the mean performance in that event and then divide this difference by the standard deviation. We can write the calculation as

$$z = \frac{y - \bar{y}}{s}.$$

---

[1] Other measures of spread could be used as well, but the standard deviation is the most common measure, and it is almost always used as the ruler.

These values are called **standardized values,** and are commonly denoted with the letter $z$. Usually, we just call them **$z$-scores.**

Standardized values have *no units. $z$*-scores measure the distance of each data value from the mean in standard deviations. A $z$-score of 2 tells us that a data value is 2 standard deviations above the mean. It doesn't matter whether the original variable was measured in inches, dollars, or seconds. Data values below the mean have negative $z$-scores, so a $z$-score of $-1.6$ means that the data value was 1.6 standard deviations below the mean. Of course, regardless of the direction, the farther a data value is from the mean, the more unusual it is, so a $z$-score of $-1.3$ is more extraordinary than a $z$-score of 1.2. Looking at the $z$-scores, we can see that even though both were winning scores, Kluft's long jump with a $z$-score of 2.70 is slightly more impressive than Skujyte's shot put with a $z$-score of 2.51.

---

**FOR EXAMPLE**    Standardizing skiing times

The men's combined skiing event in the winter Olympics consists of two races: a downhill and a slalom. Times for the two events are added together, and the skier with the lowest total time wins. In the 2006 Winter Olympics, the mean slalom time was 94.2714 seconds with a standard deviation of 5.2844 seconds. The mean downhill time was 101.807 seconds with a standard deviation of 1.8356 seconds. Ted Ligety of the United States, who won the gold medal with a combined time of 189.35 seconds, skied the slalom in 87.93 seconds and the downhill in 101.42 seconds.

**Question:** On which race did he do better compared with the competition?

For the slalom, Ligety's z-score is found by subtracting the mean time from his time and then dividing by the standard deviation.

$$z_{Slalom} = \frac{87.93 - 94.2714}{5.2844} = -1.2$$

Similarly, his z-score for the downhill is

$$z_{Downhill} = \frac{101.42 - 101.807}{1.8356} = -0.21$$

The z-scores show that Ligety's time in the slalom is farther below the mean than his time in the downhill. His performance in the slalom was more remarkable.

---

By using the standard deviation as a ruler to measure statistical distance from the mean, we can compare values that are measured on different variables, with different scales, with different units, or for different individuals. To determine the winner of the heptathlon, the judges must combine performances on seven very different events. Because they want the score to be absolute, and *not* dependent on the particular athletes in each Olympics, they use predetermined tables, but they could combine scores by standardizing each, and then adding the $z$-scores together to reach a total score. The only trick is that they'd have to switch the sign of the $z$-score for running events, because unlike throwing and jumping, it's better to have a running time below the mean (with a negative $z$-score).

To combine the scores Skujyte and Kluft earned in the long jump and the shot put, we standardize both events. That gives Kluft her 2.70 $z$-score in the long jump and a 1.19 in the shot put, for a total of 3.89. Skujyte's shot put gave her a 2.51, but her long jump was only 0.61 SDs above the mean, so her total is 3.12.

Is this the result we wanted? Yes. Both won one event, but Kluft's shot put was second best, while Skujyte's long jump was seventh. The $z$-scores measure how far each result is from the event mean in standard deviation units.

**FOR EXAMPLE** Combining z-scores

**Question:** In the 2006 winter Olympics men's combined event, Ivica Kostelic of Croatia skied the slalom in 89.44 seconds and the downhill in 100.44 seconds. He thus beat Ted Ligety in the downhill, but not in the slalom. Maybe he should have won the gold medal. Considered in terms of standardized scores, which skier did better?

Kostelic's z-scores are

$$z_{Slalom} = \frac{89.44 - 94.2714}{5.2844} = -0.91$$

and

$$z_{Downhill} = \frac{100.44 - 101.807}{1.8356} = -0.74$$

The sum of his z-scores is approximately –1.65. Ligety's z-score sum is only about –1.41. Because the standard deviation of the downhill times is so much smaller, Kostelic's better performance there means that he would have won the event if standardized scores were used.

And because they are both in standard deviation units, we can combine them. Not coincidentally, Kluft went on to win the gold medal for the entire seven-event heptathlon, while Skujyte got the silver.

When we standardize data to get a z-score, we do two things. First, we shift the data by subtracting the mean. Then, we rescale the values by dividing by their standard deviation. We often shift and rescale data. What happens to a grade distribution if *everyone* gets a five-point bonus? Everyone's grade goes up, but does the shape change? (*Hint:* Has anyone's distance from the mean changed?) If we switch from feet to meters, what happens to the distribution of heights of students in your class? Even though your intuition probably tells you the answers to these questions, we need to see exactly how shifting and rescaling work.

### JUST CHECKING

1. Your Statistics teacher has announced that the lower of your two tests will be dropped. You got a 90 on test 1 and an 80 on test 2. You're all set to drop the 80 until she announces that she grades "on a curve." She standardized the scores in order to decide which is the lower one. If the mean on the first test was 88 with a standard deviation of 4 and the mean on the second was 75 with a standard deviation of 5,
   a) Which one will be dropped?
   b) Does this seem "fair"?

## Shifting Data

Since the 1960s, the Centers for Disease Control's National Center for Health Statistics has been collecting health and nutritional information on people of all ages and backgrounds. A recent survey, the National Health and Nutrition

| WHO | 80 male partici-pants of the NHANES sur-vey between the ages of 19 and 24 who measured between 68 and 70 inches tall |
|------|------|
| **WHAT** | Their weights |
| **UNIT** | Kilograms |
| **WHEN** | 2001–2002 |
| **WHERE** | United States |
| **WHY** | To study nutri-tion, and health issues and trends |
| **HOW** | National survey |

Examination Survey (NHANES) 2001–2002,[2] measured a wide variety of vari-ables, including body measurements, cardiovascular fitness, blood chemistry, and demographic information on more than 11,000 individuals.

Included in this group were 80 men between 19 and 24 years old of average height (between 5'8" and 5'10" tall). Here are a histogram and boxplot of their weights:

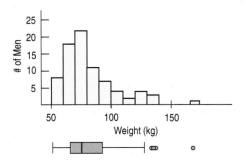

**FIGURE 6.2**

*Histogram and boxplot for the men's weights. The shape is skewed to the right with several high outliers.*

**A S** *Activity:* **Changing the Baseline.** What happens when we shift data? Do measures of center and spread change?

Their mean weight is 82.36 kg. For this age and height group, the National Institutes of Health recommends a maximum healthy weight of 74 kg, but we can see that some of the men are heavier than the recommended weight. To compare their weights to the recommended maximum, we could subtract 74 kg from each of their weights. What would that do to the center, shape, and spread of the histogram? Here's the picture:

**FIGURE 6.3**

*Subtracting 74 kilograms shifts the entire histogram down but leaves the spread and the shape exactly the same.*

Doctors' height and weight charts sometimes give ideal weights for various heights that include 2-inch heels. If the mean height of adult women is 66 inches including 2-inch heels, what is the mean height of women without shoes? Each woman is shorter by 2 inches when barefoot, so the mean is decreased by 2 inches, to 64 inches.

On average, they weigh 82.36 kg, so on average they're 8.36 kg overweight. And, after subtracting 74 from each weight, the mean of the new distribution is 82.36 − 74 = 8.36 kg. In fact, when we **shift** the data by adding (or subtracting) a constant to each value, all measures of position (center, percentiles, min, max) will increase (or decrease) by the same constant.

What about the spread? What does adding or subtracting a constant value do to the spread of the distribution? Look at the two histograms again. Adding or subtracting a constant changes each data value equally, so the entire distribution just shifts. Its shape doesn't change and neither does the spread. None of the measures of spread we've discussed—not the range, not the IQR, not the standard deviation—changes.

> *Adding (or subtracting) a constant to every data value adds (or subtracts) the same constant to measures of position, but leaves measures of spread unchanged.*

---

[2] www.cdc.gov/nchs/nhanes.htm

# Rescaling Data

Not everyone thinks naturally in metric units. Suppose we want to look at the weights in pounds instead. We'd have to **rescale** the data. Because there are about 2.2 pounds in every kilogram, we'd convert the weights by multiplying each value by 2.2. Multiplying or dividing each value by a constant changes the measurement units. Here are histograms of the two distributions, plotted on the same scale, so you can see the effect of multiplying:

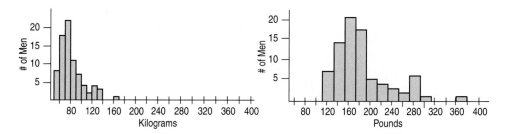

**FIGURE 6.4**

*Men's weights in both kilograms and pounds. How do the distributions and numerical summaries change?*

> **A S**    *Simulation:* **Changing the Units.** Change the center and spread values for a distribution and watch the summaries change (or not, as the case may be).

What happens to the shape of the distribution? Although the histograms don't look exactly alike, we see that the shape really hasn't changed: Both are unimodal and skewed to the right.

What happens to the mean? Not too surprisingly, it gets multiplied by 2.2 as well. The men weigh 82.36 kg on average, which is 181.19 pounds. As the boxplots and 5-number summaries show, all measures of position act the same way. They all get multiplied by this same constant.

What happens to the spread? Take a look at the boxplots. The spread in pounds (on the right) is larger. How much larger? If you guessed 2.2 times, you've figured out how measures of spread get rescaled.

> *When we multiply (or divide) all the data values by any constant, all measures of position (such as the mean, median, and percentiles) and measures of spread (such as the range, the IQR, and the standard deviation) are multiplied (or divided) by that same constant.*

|  | Weight (kg) | Weight (lb) |
|---|---|---|
| Min | 54.3 | 119.46 |
| Q1 | 67.3 | 148.05 |
| Median | 76.85 | 169.07 |
| Q3 | 92.3 | 203.05 |
| Max | 161.5 | 355.30 |
|  |  |  |
| IQR | 25 | 55 |
| SD | 22.27 | 48.99 |

**FIGURE 6.5**

*The boxplots (drawn on the same scale) show the weights measured in kilograms (on the left) and pounds (on the right). Because 1 kg is 2.2 lb, all the points in the right box are 2.2 times larger than the corresponding points in the left box. So each measure of position and spread is 2.2 times as large when measured in pounds rather than kilograms.*

**FOR EXAMPLE**    Rescaling the slalom

**Recap:** The times in the men's combined event at the winter Olympics are reported in minutes and seconds. Previously, we converted these to seconds and found the mean and standard deviation of the slalom times to be 94.2714 seconds and 5.2844 seconds, respectively.

**Question:** Suppose instead that we had reported the times in minutes—that is, that each individual time was divided by 60. What would the resulting mean and standard deviation be?

Dividing all the times by 60 would divide both the mean and the standard deviation by 60:

$$\text{Mean} = 94.2714/60 = 1.5712 \text{ minutes};$$
$$\text{SD} = 5.2844/60 = 0.0881 \text{ minutes}.$$

## JUST CHECKING

2. In 1995 the Educational Testing Service (ETS) adjusted the scores of SAT tests. Before ETS recentered the SAT Verbal test, the mean of all test scores was 450.
    a) How would adding 50 points to each score affect the mean?
    b) The standard deviation was 100 points. What would the standard deviation be after adding 50 points?
    c) Suppose we drew boxplots of test takers' scores a year before and a year after the recentering. How would the boxplots of the two years differ?

3. A company manufactures wheels for in-line skates. The diameters of the wheels have a mean of 3 inches and a standard deviation of 0.1 inches. Because so many of their customers use the metric system, the company decided to report their production statistics in millimeters (1 inch = 25.4 mm). They report that the standard deviation is now 2.54 mm. A corporate executive is worried about this increase in variation. Should he be concerned? Explain.

# Back to z-scores

**A S**  *Activity:* **Standardizing.**
What if we both shift and rescale? The result is so nice that we give it a name.

Standardizing data into z-scores is just shifting them by the mean and rescaling them by the standard deviation. Now we can see how standardizing affects the distribution. When we subtract the mean of the data from every data value, we shift the mean to zero. As we have seen, such a shift doesn't change the standard deviation.

When we *divide* each of these shifted values by s, however, the standard deviation should be divided by s as well. Since the standard deviation was s to start with, the new standard deviation becomes 1.

How, then, does standardizing affect the distribution of a variable? Let's consider the three aspects of a distribution: the shape, center, and spread.

*z*-scores have mean 0 and standard deviation 1.

▸ *Standardizing into z-scores does not change the **shape** of the distribution of a variable.*
▸ *Standardizing into z-scores changes the **center** by making the mean 0.*
▸ *Standardizing into z-scores changes the **spread** by making the standard deviation 1.*

**STEP-BY-STEP EXAMPLE** | Working with Standardized Variables

Many colleges and universities require applicants to submit scores on standardized tests such as the SAT Writing, Math, and Critical Reading (Verbal) tests. The college your little sister wants to apply to says that while there is no minimum score required, the middle 50% of their students have combined SAT scores between 1530 and 1850. You'd feel confident if you knew her score was in their top 25%, but unfortunately she took the ACT test, an alternative standardized test.

**Question:** How high does her ACT need to be to make it into the top quarter of equivalent SAT scores?

To answer that question you'll have to standardize all the scores, so you'll need to know the mean and standard deviations of scores for some group on both tests. The college doesn't report the mean or standard deviation for their applicants on either test, so we'll use the group of all test takers nationally. For college-bound seniors, the average combined SAT score is about 1500 and the standard deviation is about 250 points. For the same group, the ACT average is 20.8 with a standard deviation of 4.8.

| | | |
|---|---|---|
|  | **Plan** State what you want to find out. | I want to know what ACT score corresponds to the upper-quartile SAT score. I know the mean and standard deviation for both the SAT and ACT scores based on all test takers, but I have no individual data values. |
| | **Variables** Identify the variables and report the W's. | |
| | Check the appropriate conditions. | ✓ **Quantitative Data Condition:** Scores for both tests are quantitative but have no meaningful units other than points. |
|  | **Mechanics** Standardize the variables. | The middle 50% of SAT scores at this college fall between 1530 and 1850 points. To be in the top quarter, my sister would have to have a score of at least 1850. That's a z-score of |
| | | $$z = \frac{(1850 - 1500)}{250} = 1.40$$ |
| | | So an SAT score of 1850 is 1.40 standard deviations above the mean of all test takers. |
| | The *y*-value we seek is *z* standard deviations above the mean. | For the ACT, 1.40 standard deviations above the mean is $20.8 + 1.40\,(4.8) = 27.52$. |
|  | **Conclusion** Interpret your results in context. | To be in the top quarter of applicants in terms of combined SAT score, she'd need to have an ACT score of at least 27.52. |

# When Is a *z*-score BIG?

*"All models are wrong—but some are useful."*

—George Box, famous statistician

**Is Normal Normal?**
Don't be misled. The name "Normal" doesn't mean that these are the *usual* shapes for histograms. The name follows a tradition of positive thinking in Mathematics and Statistics in which functions, equations, and relationships that are easy to work with or have other nice properties are called "normal," "common," "regular," "natural," or similar terms. It's as if by calling them ordinary, we could make them actually occur more often and simplify our lives.

**NOTATION ALERT:**

$N(\mu, \sigma)$ always denotes a Normal model. The $\mu$, pronounced "mew," is the Greek letter for "m," and always represents the mean in a model. The $\sigma$, sigma, is the lowercase Greek letter for "s," and always represents the standard deviation in a model.

**Is the Standard Normal a standard?**
Yes. We call it the "Standard Normal" because it models standardized values. It is also a "standard" because this is the particular Normal model that we almost always use.

A *z*-score gives us an indication of how unusual a value is because it tells us how far it is from the mean. If the data value sits right at the mean, it's not very far at all and its *z*-score is 0. A *z*-score of 1 tells us that the data value is 1 standard deviation above the mean, while a *z*-score of –1 tells us that the value is 1 standard deviation below the mean. How far from 0 does a *z*-score have to be to be interesting or unusual? There is no universal standard, but the larger the score is (negative or positive), the more unusual it is. We know that 50% of the data lie between the quartiles. For symmetric data, the standard deviation is usually a bit smaller than the IQR, and it's not uncommon for at least half of the data to have *z*-scores between −1 and 1. But no matter what the shape of the distribution, a *z*-score of 3 (plus or minus) or more is rare, and a *z*-score of 6 or 7 shouts out for attention.

To say more about how big we expect a *z*-score to be, we need to *model* the data's distribution. A model will let us say much more precisely how often we'd be likely to see *z*-scores of different sizes. Of course, like all models of the real world, the model will be wrong—wrong in the sense that it can't match reality exactly. But it can still be useful. Like a physical model, it's something we can look at and manipulate in order to learn more about the real world.

Models help our understanding in many ways. Just as a model of an airplane in a wind tunnel can give insights even though it doesn't show every rivet,[3] models of data give us summaries that we can learn from and use, even though they don't fit each data value exactly. It's important to remember that they're only *models* of reality and not reality itself. But without models, what we can learn about the world at large is limited to only what we can say about the data we have at hand.

There is no universal standard for *z*-scores, but there is a model that shows up over and over in Statistics. You may have heard of "bell-shaped curves." Statisticians call them Normal models. **Normal models** are appropriate for distributions whose shapes are unimodal and roughly symmetric. For these distributions, they provide a measure of how extreme a *z*-score is. Fortunately, there is a Normal model for every possible combination of mean and standard deviation. We write $N(\mu, \sigma)$ to represent a Normal model with a mean of $\mu$ and a standard deviation of $\sigma$. Why the Greek? Well, *this* mean and standard deviation are not numerical summaries of data. They are part of the model. They don't come from the data. Rather, they are numbers that we choose to help specify the model. Such numbers are called **parameters** of the model.

We don't want to confuse the parameters with summaries of the data such as $\bar{y}$ and $s$, so we use special symbols. In Statistics, we almost always use Greek letters for parameters. By contrast, summaries of data are called **statistics** and are usually written with Latin letters.

If we model data with a Normal model and standardize them using the corresponding $\mu$ and $\sigma$, we still call the standardized value a **z-score**, and we write

$$z = \frac{y - \mu}{\sigma}.$$

Usually it's easier to standardize data first (using its mean and standard deviation). Then we need only the model $N(0,1)$. The Normal model with mean 0 and standard deviation 1 is called the **standard Normal model** (or the **standard Normal distribution**).

But be careful. You shouldn't use a Normal model for just any data set. Remember that standardizing won't change the shape of the distribution. If the distribution is not unimodal and symmetric to begin with, standardizing won't make it Normal.

---

[3] In fact, the model is useful *because* it doesn't have every rivet. It is because models offer a simpler view of reality that they are so useful as we try to understand reality.

**A S** *Activity:* **Working with Normal Models.** Learn more about the Normal model and see what data drawn at random from a Normal model might look like.

When we use the Normal model, we assume that the distribution of the data is, well, Normal. Practically speaking, there's no way to check whether this **Normality Assumption** is true. In fact, it almost certainly is not true. Real data don't behave like mathematical models. Models are idealized; real data are real. The good news, however, is that to use a Normal model, it's sufficient to check the following condition:

> **Nearly Normal Condition.** The shape of the data's distribution is unimodal and symmetric. Check this by making a histogram (or a Normal probability plot, which we'll explain later).

Don't model data with a Normal model without checking whether the condition is satisfied.

All models make **assumptions.** Whenever we model—and we'll do that often—we'll be careful to point out the assumptions that we're making. And, what's even more important, we'll check the associated **conditions** in the data to make sure that those assumptions are reasonable.

# The 68–95–99.7 Rule

**One in a Million**

These magic 68, 95, 99.7 values come from the Normal model. As a model, it can give us corresponding values for any *z*-score. For example, it tells us that fewer than 1 out of a million values have *z*-scores smaller than –5.0 or larger than +5.0. So if someone tells you you're "one in a million" they must really admire your *z*-score.

Normal models give us an idea of how extreme a value is by telling us how likely it is to find one that far from the mean. We'll soon show how to find these numbers precisely—but one simple rule is usually all we need.

It turns out that in a Normal model, about 68% of the values fall within 1 standard deviation of the mean, about 95% of the values fall within 2 standard deviations of the mean, and about 99.7%—almost all—of the values fall within 3 standard deviations of the mean. These facts are summarized in a rule that we call (let's see . . .) the **68–95–99.7 Rule.**[4]

**FIGURE 6.6**

*Reaching out one, two, and three standard deviations on a Normal model gives the 68–95–99.7 Rule.*

**FOR EXAMPLE** Using the 68–95–99.7 Rule

**Question:** In the 2006 Winter Olympics men's combined event, Jean-Baptiste Grange of France skied the slalom in 88.46 seconds—about 1 standard deviation faster than the mean. If a Normal model is useful in describing slalom times, about how many of the 35 skiers finishing the event would you expect skied the slalom *faster* than Jean-Baptiste?

From the 68–95–99.7 Rule, we expect 68% of the skiers to be within one standard deviation of the mean. Of the remaining 32%, we expect half on the high end and half on the low end. 16% of 35 is 5.6, so, conservatively, we'd expect about 5 skiers to do better than Jean-Baptiste.

---

[4] This rule is also called the "Empirical Rule" because it originally came from observation. The rule was first published by Abraham de Moivre in 1733, 75 years before the Normal model was discovered. Maybe it should be called "de Moivre's Rule," but that wouldn't help us remember the important numbers, 68, 95, and 99.7.

## JUST CHECKING

**4.** As a group, the Dutch are among the tallest people in the world. The average Dutch man is 184 cm tall—just over 6 feet (and the average Dutch woman is 170.8 cm tall—just over 5'7"). If a Normal model is appropriate and the standard deviation for men is about 8 cm, what percentage of all Dutch men will be over 2 meters (6'6") tall?

**5.** Suppose it takes you 20 minutes, on average, to drive to school, with a standard deviation of 2 minutes. Suppose a Normal model is appropriate for the distributions of driving times.
   **a)** How often will you arrive at school in less than 22 minutes?
   **b)** How often will it take you more than 24 minutes?
   **c)** Do you think the distribution of your driving times is unimodal and symmetric?
   **d)** What does this say about the accuracy of your predictions? Explain.

# The First Three Rules for Working with Normal Models

   **1.** Make a picture.
   **2.** Make a picture.
   **3.** Make a picture.

Although we're thinking about models, not histograms of data, the three rules don't change. To help you think clearly, a simple hand-drawn sketch is all you need. Even experienced statisticians sketch pictures to help them think about Normal models. You should too.

Of course, when we have data, we'll also need to make a histogram to check the **Nearly Normal Condition** to be sure we can use the Normal model to model the data's distribution. Other times, we may be told that a Normal model is appropriate based on prior knowledge of the situation or on theoretical considerations.

### HOW TO SKETCH A NORMAL CURVE THAT LOOKS NORMAL

To sketch a good Normal curve, you need to remember only three things:

▸ The Normal curve is bell-shaped and symmetric around its mean. Start at the middle, and sketch to the right and left from there.

▸ Even though the Normal model extends forever on either side, you need to draw it only for 3 standard deviations. After that, there's so little left that it isn't worth sketching.

▸ The place where the bell shape changes from curving downward to curving back up—the *inflection point*—is exactly one standard deviation away from the mean.

**STEP-BY-STEP EXAMPLE**   |   **Working with the 68–95–99.7 Rule**

The SAT Reasoning Test has three parts: Writing, Math, and Critical Reading (Verbal). Each part has a distribution that is roughly unimodal and symmetric and is designed to have an overall mean of about 500 and a standard deviation of 100 for all test takers. In any one year, the mean and standard deviation may differ from these target values by a small amount, but they are a good overall approximation.

**Question:** Suppose you earned a 600 on one part of your SAT. Where do you stand among all students who took that test?

You could calculate your *z*-score and find out that it's $z = (600 - 500)/100 = 1.0$, but what does that tell you about your percentile? You'll need the Normal model and the 68–95–99.7 Rule to answer that question.

---

 **THINK**

**Plan** State what you want to know.

I want to see how my SAT score compares with the scores of all other students. To do that, I'll need to model the distribution.

**Variables** Identify the variable and report the W's.

Let y = my SAT score. Scores are quantitative but have no meaningful units other than points.

Be sure to check the appropriate conditions.

✔ **Nearly Normal Condition:** If I had data, I would check the histogram. I have no data, but I am told that the SAT scores are roughly unimodal and symmetric.

Specify the parameters of your model.

I will model SAT score with a N(500, 100) model.

---

 **SHOW**

**Mechanics** Make a picture of this Normal model. (A simple sketch is all you need.)

Locate your score.

My score of 600 is 1 standard deviation above the mean. That corresponds to one of the points of the 68–95–99.7 Rule.

---

**TELL**

**Conclusion** Interpret your result in context.

About 68% of those who took the test had scores that fell no more than 1 standard deviation from the mean, so 100% − 68% = 32% of all students had scores more than 1 standard deviation away. Only half of those were on the high side, so about 16% (half of 32%) of the test scores were better than mine. My score of 600 is higher than about 84% of all scores on this test.

The bounds of SAT scoring at 200 and 800 can also be explained by the 68–95–99.7 Rule. Since 200 and 800 are three standard deviations from 500, it hardly pays to extend the scoring any farther on either side. We'd get more information only on $100 - 99.7 = 0.3\%$ of students.

**The Worst-Case Scenario**   Suppose we encounter an observation that's 5 standard deviations above the mean. Should we be surprised? We've just seen that when a Normal model is appropriate, such a value is exceptionally rare. After all, 99.7% of all the values should be within 3 standard deviations of the mean, so anything farther away would be unusual indeed.

But our handy 68–95–99.7 Rule applies only to Normal models, and the Normal is such a *nice* shape. What if we're dealing with a distribution that's strongly skewed (like the CEO salaries), or one that is uniform or bimodal or something really strange? A Normal model has 68% of its observations within one standard deviation of the mean, but a bimodal distribution could even be entirely empty in the middle. In that case could we still say anything at all about an observation 5 standard deviations above the mean?

Remarkably, even with really weird distributions, the worst case can't get all that bad. A Russian mathematician named Pafnuty Tchebycheff[5] answered the question by proving this theorem:

*In any distribution, at least $1 - \dfrac{1}{k^2}$ of the values must lie within $\pm k$ standard deviations of the mean.*

What does that mean?

▶ For $k = 1$, $1 - \dfrac{1}{1^2} = 0$; if the distribution is far from Normal, it's possible that none of the values are within 1 standard deviation of the mean. We should be really cautious about saying anything about 68% unless we think a Normal model is justified. (Tchebycheff's theorem really is about the worst case; it tells us nothing about the middle; only about the extremes.)

▶ For $k = 2$, $1 - \dfrac{1}{2^2} = \dfrac{3}{4}$; no matter how strange the shape of the distribution, at least 75% of the values must be within 2 standard deviations of the mean. Normal models may expect 95% in that 2-standard-deviation interval, but even in a worst-case scenario it can never go lower than 75%.

▶ For $k = 3$, $1 - \dfrac{1}{3^2} = \dfrac{8}{9}$; in any distribution, at least 89% of the values lie within 3 standard deviations of the mean.

What we see is that values beyond 3 standard deviations from the mean are uncommon, Normal model or not. Tchebycheff tells us that at least 96% of all values must be within 5 standard deviations of the mean. While we can't always apply the 68–95–99.7 Rule, we can be sure that the observation we encountered 5 standard deviations above the mean is unusual.

# Finding Normal Percentiles by Hand

An SAT score of 600 is easy to assess, because we can think of it as one standard deviation above the mean. If your score was 680, though, where do you stand among the rest of the people tested? Your z-score is 1.80, so you're somewhere between 1 and 2 standard deviations above the mean. We figured out that no more than 16% of

[5] He may have made the worst case for deviations clear, but the English spelling of his name is not. You'll find his first name spelled Pavnutii or Pavnuty and his last name spelled Chebsheff, Cebysev, and other creative versions.

people score better than 600. By the same logic, no more than 2.5% of people score better than 700. Can we be more specific than "between 16% and 2.5%"?

| z | .00 | .01 |
|---|---|---|
| ⋮ | ⋮ | ⋮ |
| 1.7 | .9554 | .9564 |
| 1.8 → | .9641 | .9649 |
| 1.9 | .9713 | .9719 |
| ⋮ | ⋮ | ⋮ |

**FIGURE 6.7**

*A table of Normal percentiles (Table Z in Appendix D) lets us find the percentage of individuals in a Standard Normal distribution falling below any specified z-score value.*

When the value doesn't fall exactly 1, 2, or 3 standard deviations from the mean, we can look it up in a table of **Normal percentiles.**[6] Nobody wants to lug around a bunch of tables, so we make a table only for the *standard Normal.* That means we have to convert our data to z-scores before using the table. Your SAT score of 680 has a z-score of $(680 - 500)/100 = 1.80$. In the piece of the table shown, we find your z-score by looking down the left column for the first two digits, 1.8, and across the top row for the third digit, 0. The table gives the percentile as 0.9641. That means that 96.4% of the z-scores are less than 1.80. Only 3.6% of people, then, scored better than 680 on the SAT.

---

**FOR EXAMPLE** | **Finding Normal percentiles**

**Question:** Ivan Heimschild of Slovakia completed the winter Olympics downhill race in 103.12 seconds. His z-score is 0.72. If the distribution of downhill times can be modeled by a Normal model, what proportion of the 35 skiers in the event would you expect to have skied *slower* than Heimschild in this event?

Table Z gives proportions to the left of a given z-score value, but here we want a proportion to the right. We can do that two ways:

The proportion of values in a Normal model to the left of a z-score of 0.72 is 0.7642. So the proportion of values to the right is 1.0 − 0.7642 = 0.2358.

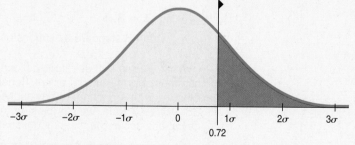

Alternatively, because the Normal model is symmetric, we can find the proportion directly, by looking for the proportion to the left of −0.72 which, of course, is also 0.2358.

To find the number of skiers we expect out of 35, we multiply: 0.2358 × 35 = 8.25, so we'd expect about 8 skiers to have done worse in this event.

(In fact, exactly 8 skiers were slower than Heimschild.)

---

[6] See Table Z in Appendix D. Many calculators and statistics computer packages do this, too.

# Finding Normal Percentiles Using Technology

These days, finding percentiles from a Normal probability table is a "desert island" method—something we might do if we desperately needed a Normal percentile and were stranded miles from the mainland with only a Normal probability table. (Of course, you might feel just that way during a Statistics exam, so it's a good idea to know how to do it.) Fortunately, most of the time, we can use a calculator, a computer, or the Internet. Graphing calculators, such as the TI-84, find Normal percentiles and offer to draw the picture as well. Most statistics programs have functions to find Normal percentiles, and values of z-scores are easy to find on the Internet (search for *z-scores,* or *normal probability tables*).

The *ActivStats* Multimedia Assistant provided on the DVD that accompanies this book offers two methods. The "Normal Model Tool" introduced along with the Normal model makes it easy to see how areas under parts of the Normal model correspond to particular cut points. The tool is especially useful for problems in which you want to find the area *between* two z-scores.

The tool also allows you to work in the original units if you wish, without converting everything to z-scores. This can be particularly helpful for understanding statements about relative frequencies.

*ActivStats* also offers a Normal table in which the picture of the Normal model is interactive.[7] Grab the z-score cut point with your mouse and drag it to the value you are interested in. The table will adjust accordingly.

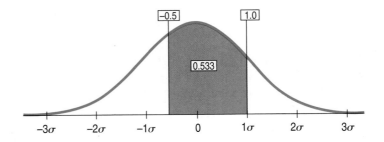

**FIGURE 6.8**
*The* ActivStats *Normal model tool makes it easy to see how areas under parts of the Normal model correspond to particular cut points.*

With a tool like the *ActivStats* Normal model tool, it's easy to answer a question like "What percentage of all test takers score between 950 and 1080 on the combined SAT?" You can leave the units as they are and just enter the mean and standard deviation on the Normal model tool, sliding the cut points to 950 and 1080. Alternatively, you could convert both values to z-scores and slide the area to match those scores on the Standard Normal model tool. In either case, you would read the percentage right off the picture.

## OTHER MODELS

Of course, the Normal is not the only model for data. There are models for skewed data (watch out for $\chi^2$ later in the book), and we'll see models for variables that can take on only a few values (Binomial and Poisson, to name two). But the Normal will return in an important and surprising way.

---

[7] Now it's time to open the DVD that accompanies the book if you haven't done so already. You'll find the instructions for using the tools there. You can also get to the tools directly in the Appendix following the last chapter of the *ActivStats* Lesson Book.

---

**STEP-BY-STEP EXAMPLE**   **Practice—Working with Normal Models Part I**

The Normal model is our first model for data. It's the first in a series of modeling situations where we step away from the data at hand to make more general statements about the world. We'll become more practiced in thinking about and learning the details of models as we progress through the book. To give you some practice in thinking about the Normal model, here are several problems that ask you to find percentiles in detail.

**Question: What proportion of SAT scores fall between 450 and 600?**

---

**Plan** State the problem.

**Variables** Name the variable.

Check the appropriate conditions and specify which Normal model to use.

I want to know the proportion of SAT scores between 450 and 600.

Let y = SAT score.

✓ **Nearly Normal Condition:** We are told that SAT scores are nearly Normal.

I'll model SAT scores with a N(500, 100) model, using the mean and standard deviation specified for them.

---

**Mechanics** Make a picture of this Normal model. Locate the desired values and shade the region of interest.

Locate the desired values. The easiest way is to use a technology that allows you to input the raw data values directly.

Alternatively, you can convert 450 and 600 to z-scores before using technology or a table to find the two areas. Then you need to subtract them to find the area *between* the two values.

I can see directly from this picture that about 53.3% of scores fall between 450 and 600 under the Normal model.

Standardizing the two scores, I find that

$$z = \frac{(y - \mu)}{\sigma} = \frac{(600 - 500)}{100} = 1.00$$

and

$$z = \frac{(450 - 500)}{100} = -0.50$$

From Table Z, the area (z < 1.0) = 0.8413 and area (z < −0.5) = 0.3085, so the proportion of z-scores between them is 0.8413 − 0.3085 = 0.5328, or 53.28%.

---

**Conclusion** Interpret your result in context.

The Normal model estimates that about 53.3% of SAT scores fall between 450 and 600.

# From Percentiles to Scores: *z* in Reverse

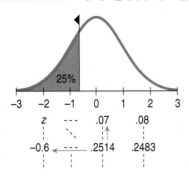

Finding areas from *z*-scores is the simplest way to work with the Normal model. But sometimes we start with areas and are asked to work backward to find the corresponding *z*-score or even the original data value.

For instance, what *z*-score represents the first quartile in a Normal model? In our first set of examples we knew the *z*-score and used the table or technology to find the percentile. Now we want to find the cut point for the 25th percentile.

Make a picture like the one shown, shading the leftmost 25% of the area. Look in Table Z for an area of 0.2500. The exact area is not there, but 0.2514 is pretty close. That shows up in the table with −0.6 in the left margin and .07 in the top margin. The *z*-score for Q1, then, is approximately *z* = −0.67.

Computers and calculators will determine the cut point more precisely (and more easily).

---

**STEP-BY-STEP EXAMPLE** | **Working with Normal Models Part II**

**Question: Suppose a college says it admits only people with SAT Verbal test scores among the top 10%. How high a score does it take to be eligible?**

| | | |
|---|---|---|
|  **THINK** | **Plan** State the problem. | How high an SAT Verbal score do I need to be in the top 10% of all test takers? |
| | **Variable** Define the variable. | Let *y* = my SAT score. |
| | Check to see if a Normal model is appropriate, and specify which Normal model to use. | ✓  **Nearly Normal Condition:** I am told that SAT scores are nearly Normal. I'll model them with N(500, 100). |

| | | |
|---|---|---|
|  **SHOW** | **Mechanics** Make a picture of this Normal model. Locate the desired percentile approximately by shading the rightmost 10% of the area. | 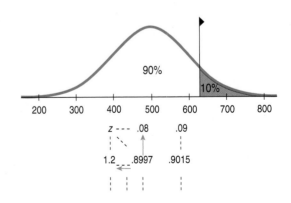 |
| | The college takes the top 10%, so its cutoff score is the 90th percentile. Find the corresponding *z*-score using your calculator. (**OR**: Use Table Z. Locate 0.90 (or as close to it as you can) in the *interior* of the table. Here the 1.2 is in the left margin and the .08 is in the margin above the entry. Putting them together gives 1.28.) | The cut point is *z* = 1.28. |
| | Convert the *z*-score back to the original units. | A *z*-score of 1.28 is 1.28 standard deviations above the mean. Since the SD is 100, that's 128 SAT points. The cutoff is 128 points above the mean of 500, or 628. |

**Conclusion** Interpret your results in the proper context.

Because the school wants SAT Verbal scores in the top 10%, the cutoff is 628. (Actually, since SAT scores are reported only in multiples of 10, I'd have to score at least a 630.)

---

**STEP-BY-STEP EXAMPLE**   **More Working with Normal Models**

Working with Normal percentiles can be a little tricky, depending on how the problem is stated. Here are a few more worked examples of the kind you're likely to see.

> *A cereal manufacturer has a machine that fills the boxes. Boxes are labeled "16 ounces," so the company wants to have that much cereal in each box, but since no packaging process is perfect, there will be minor variations. If the machine is set at exactly 16 ounces and the Normal model applies (or at least the distribution is roughly symmetric), then about half of the boxes will be underweight, making consumers unhappy and exposing the company to bad publicity and possible lawsuits. To prevent underweight boxes, the manufacturer has to set the mean a little higher than 16.0 ounces.*
>
> *Based on their experience with the packaging machine, the company believes that the amount of cereal in the boxes fits a Normal model with a standard deviation of 0.2 ounces. The manufacturer decides to set the machine to put an average of 16.3 ounces in each box. Let's use that model to answer a series of questions about these cereal boxes.*

**Question 1:** What fraction of the boxes will be underweight?

---

**Plan** State the problem.

What proportion of boxes weigh less than 16 ounces?

**Variable** Name the variable.

Let $y$ = weight of cereal in a box.

Check to see if a Normal model is appropriate.

✓  **Nearly Normal Condition:** I have no data, so I cannot make a histogram, but I am told that the company believes the distribution of weights from the machine is Normal.

Specify which Normal model to use.

I'll use a $N(16.3, 0.2)$ model.

---

**Mechanics** Make a picture of this Normal model. Locate the value you're interested in on the picture, label it, and shade the appropriate region.

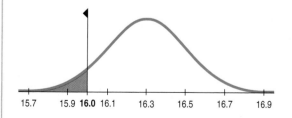

**REALITY CHECK** Estimate from the picture the percentage of boxes that are underweight. (This will be useful later to check that your answer makes sense.) It looks like a low percentage. Less than 20% for sure.

I want to know what fraction of the boxes will weigh less than 16 ounces.

| Convert your cutoff value into a z-score. | $$z = \frac{y - \mu}{\sigma} = \frac{16 - 16.3}{0.2} = -1.50$$ |
| Find the area with your calculator (or use the Normal table). | Area $(y < 16)$ = Area $(z < -1.50)$ = 0.0668 |

**Conclusion** State your conclusion, and check that it's consistent with your earlier guess. It's below 20%—seems okay.

*I estimate that approximately 6.7% of the boxes will contain less than 16 ounces of cereal.*

---

**Question 2:** The company's lawyers say that 6.7% is too high. They insist that no more than 4% of the boxes can be underweight. So the company needs to set the machine to put a little more cereal in each box. What mean setting do they need?

---

**Plan** State the problem.

*What mean weight will reduce the proportion of underweight boxes to 4%?*

**Variable** Name the variable.

*Let y = weight of cereal in a box.*

Check to see if a Normal model is appropriate.

✔ **Nearly Normal Condition:** I am told that a Normal model applies.

Specify which Normal model to use. This time you are not given a value for the mean!

*I don't know $\mu$, the mean amount of cereal. The standard deviation for this machine is 0.2 ounces. The model is $N(\mu, 0.2)$.*

REALITY CHECK  We found out earlier that setting the machine to $\mu = 16.3$ ounces made 6.7% of the boxes too light. We'll need to raise the mean a bit to reduce this fraction.

*No more than 4% of the boxes can be below 16 ounces.*

---

**Mechanics** Make a picture of this Normal model. Center it at $\mu$ (since you don't know the mean), and shade the region below 16 ounces.

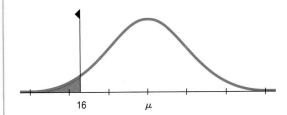

Using your calculator (or the Normal table), find the z-score that cuts off the lowest 4%.

*The z-score that has 0.04 area to the left of it is $z = -1.75$.*

Use this information to find $\mu$. It's located 1.75 standard deviations to the right of 16. Since $\sigma$ is 0.2, that's $1.75 \times 0.2$, or 0.35 ounces more than 16.

*For 16 to be 1.75 standard deviations below the mean, the mean must be*

$$16 + 1.75\,(0.2) = 16.35 \text{ ounces.}$$

| | |
|---|---|
| **Conclusion** Interpret your result in context.<br>(This makes sense; we knew it would have to be just a bit higher than 16.3.) | The company must set the machine to average 16.35 ounces of cereal per box. |

**Question 3:** The company president vetoes that plan, saying the company should give away less free cereal, not more. Her goal is to set the machine no higher than 16.2 ounces and still have only 4% underweight boxes. The only way to accomplish this is to reduce the standard deviation. What standard deviation must the company achieve, and what does that mean about the machine?

**Plan** State the problem.

What standard deviation will allow the mean to be 16.2 ounces and still have only 4% of boxes underweight?

**Variable** Name the variable.

Let y = weight of cereal in a box.

Check conditions to be sure that a Normal model is appropriate.

✓ **Nearly Normal Condition:** The company believes that the weights are described by a Normal model.

Specify which Normal model to use. This time you don't know $\sigma$.

I know the mean, but not the standard deviation, so my model is N(16.2, $\sigma$).

REALITY CHECK  We know the new standard deviation must be less than 0.2 ounces.

**Mechanics** Make a picture of this Normal model. Center it at 16.2, and shade the area you're interested in. We want 4% of the area to the left of 16 ounces.

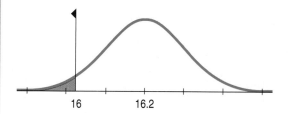

Find the z-score that cuts off the lowest 4%.

Solve for $\sigma$. (We need 16 to be 1.75 $\sigma$'s below 16.2, so 1.75 $\sigma$ must be 0.2 ounces. You could just start with that equation.)

I know that the z-score with 4% below it is $z = -1.75$.

$$z = \frac{y - \mu}{\sigma}$$

$$-1.75 = \frac{16 - 16.2}{\sigma}$$

$$1.75\,\sigma = 0.2$$

$$\sigma = 0.114$$

**Conclusion** Interpret your result in context.

As we expected, the standard deviation is lower than before—actually, quite a bit lower.

The company must get the machine to box cereal with a standard deviation of only 0.114 ounces. This means the machine must be more consistent (by nearly a factor of 2) in filling the boxes.

# Are You Normal? Find Out with a Normal Probability Plot

In the examples we've worked through, we've assumed that the underlying data distribution was roughly unimodal and symmetric, so that using a Normal model makes sense. When you have data, you must *check* to see whether a Normal model is reasonable. How? Make a picture, of course! Drawing a histogram of the data and looking at the shape is one good way to see if a Normal model might work.

There's a more specialized graphical display that can help you to decide whether the Normal model is appropriate: the **Normal probability plot.** If the distribution of the data is roughly Normal, the plot is roughly a diagonal straight line. Deviations from a straight line indicate that the distribution is not Normal. This plot is usually able to show deviations from Normality more clearly than the corresponding histogram, but it's usually easier to understand *how* a distribution fails to be Normal by looking at its histogram.

Some data on a car's fuel efficiency provide an example of data that are nearly Normal. The overall pattern of the Normal probability plot is straight. The two trailing low values correspond to the values in the histogram that trail off the low end. They're not quite in line with the rest of the data set. The Normal probability plot shows us that they're a bit lower than we'd expect of the lowest two values in a Normal model.

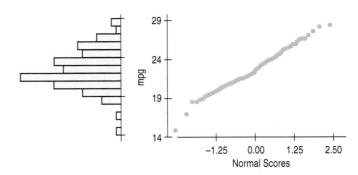

**FIGURE 6.9**

*Histogram and Normal probability plot for gas mileage (mpg) recorded by one of the authors over the 8 years he owned a 1989 Nissan Maxima. The vertical axes are the same, so each dot on the probability plot would fall into the bar on the histogram immediately to its left.*

By contrast, the Normal probability plot of the men's *Weights* from the NHANES Study is far from straight. The weights are skewed to the high end, and the plot is curved. We'd conclude from these pictures that approximations using the 68–95–99.7 Rule for these data would not be very accurate.

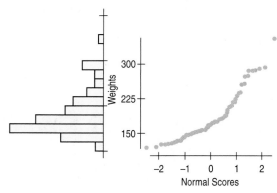

**FIGURE 6.10**

*Histogram and Normal probability plot for men's weights. Note how a skewed distribution corresponds to a bent probability plot.*

# How Does a Normal Probability Plot Work?

Why does the Normal probability plot work like that? We looked at 100 fuel efficiency measures for the author's Nissan car. The smallest of these has a $z$-score of $-3.16$. The Normal model can tell us what value to expect for the smallest $z$-score in a batch of 100 if a Normal model were appropriate. That turns out to be $-2.58$. So our first data value is smaller than we would expect from the Normal.

We can continue this and ask a similar question for each value. For example, the 14th-smallest fuel efficiency has a $z$-score of almost exactly $-1$, and that's just what we should expect (well, $-1.1$ to be exact). A Normal probability plot takes each data value and plots it against the $z$-score you'd expect that point to have if the distribution were perfectly Normal.[8]

When the values match up well, the line is straight. If one or two points are surprising from the Normal's point of view, they don't line up. When the entire distribution is skewed or different from the Normal in some other way, the values don't match up very well at all and the plot bends.

It turns out to be tricky to find the values we expect. They're called *Normal scores,* but you can't easily look them up in the tables. That's why probability plots are best made with technology and not by hand.

The best advice on using Normal probability plots is to see whether they are straight. If so, then your data look like data from a Normal model. If not, make a histogram to understand how they differ from the model.

> **A S**   *Activity:* **Assessing Normality.** This activity guides you through the process of checking the Nearly Normal condition using your statistics package.

---

[8] Sometimes the Normal probability plot switches the two axes, putting the data on the $x$-axis and the $z$-scores on the $y$-axis.

# WHAT CAN GO WRONG?

▶ **Don't use a Normal model when the distribution is not unimodal and symmetric.** Normal models are so easy and useful that it is tempting to use them even when they don't describe the data very well. That can lead to wrong conclusions. Don't use a Normal model without first checking the **Nearly Normal Condition.** Look at a picture of the data to check that it is unimodal and symmetric. A histogram, or a Normal probability plot, can help you tell whether a Normal model is appropriate.

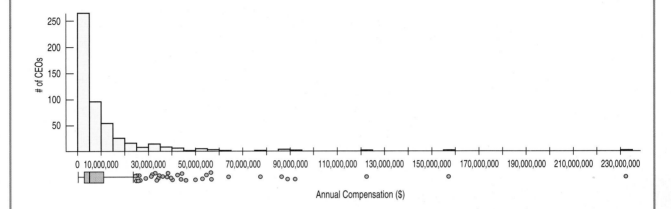

The CEOs (p. 101) had a mean total compensation of $10,307,311.87 with a standard deviation of $17,964,615.16. Using the Normal model rule, we should expect about 68% of the CEOs to have compensations between −$7,657,303.29 and $28,271,927.03. In fact, more than 90% of the CEOs have annual compensations in this range. What went wrong? The distribution is skewed, not symmetric. Using the 68–95–99.7 Rule for data like these will lead to silly results.

▶ **Don't use the mean and standard deviation when outliers are present.** Both means and standard deviations can be distorted by outliers, and no model based on distorted values will do a good job. A z-score calculated from a distribution with outliers may be misleading. It's always a good idea to check for outliers. How? Make a picture.

▶ **Don't round your results in the middle of a calculation.** We *reported* the mean of the heptathletes' long jump as 6.16 meters. More precisely, it was 6.16153846153846 meters.

You should use all the precision available in the data for all the intermediate steps of a calculation. Using the more precise value for the mean (and also carrying 15 digits for the SD), the z-score calculation for Kluft's long jump comes out to

$$z = (6.78 - 6.16153846153846)/0.2297597407326585$$

$$= 2.691775053755667700$$

We'd report that as 2.692. So, . . .

▶ **Do what we say, not what we do.** When we showed the z-score calculations for Kluft, we rounded the mean to 6.16 m and the SD to 0.23 m. Then, to make the story clearer we used *those values* in the displayed calculation. But that gave a z-score of 2.70, not 2.692.

We'll continue to show simplified calculations in the book to make the story simpler. When you calculate with full precision, your results may differ slightly from ours. So, we also advise . . .

▶ **Don't worry about minor differences in results.** Because various calculators and programs may carry different precision in calculations, your answers may differ slightly from those we show in the text and in the Step-By-Steps, or even from the values given in the answers in the back of the book. Those differences aren't anything to worry about. They're not the main story Statistics tries to tell.

# CONNECTIONS

Changing the center and spread of a variable is equivalent to changing its *units*. Indeed, the only part of the data's context changed by standardizing is the units. All other aspects of the context do not depend on the choice or modification of measurement units. This fact points out an important distinction between the numbers the data provide for calculation and the meaning of the variables and the relationships among them. Standardizing can make the numbers easier to work with, but it does not alter the meaning.

Another way to look at this is to note that standardizing may change the center and spread values, but it does not affect the *shape* of a distribution. A histogram or boxplot of standardized values looks just the same as the histogram or boxplot of the original values except, perhaps, for the numbers on the axes.

When we summarized *shape, center,* and *spread* for histograms, we compared them to unimodal, symmetric shapes. You couldn't ask for a nicer example than the Normal model. And if the shape *is* like a Normal, we'll use the the mean and standard deviation to standardize the values.

# WHAT HAVE WE LEARNED?

We've learned that the story data can tell may be easier to understand after shifting or rescaling the data.

▸ Shifting data by adding or subtracting the same amount from each value affects measures of center and position but not measures of spread.

▸ Rescaling data by multiplying or dividing every value by a constant, changes all the summary statistics—center, position, and spread.

We've learned the power of standardizing data.

▸ Standardizing uses the standard deviation as a ruler to measure distance from the mean, creating z-scores.

▸ Using these z-scores, we can compare apples and oranges—values from different distributions or values based on different units.

▸ And a z-score can identify unusual or surprising values among data.

We've learned that the 68–95–99.7 Rule can be a useful rule of thumb for understanding distributions:

▸ For data that are unimodal and symmetric, about 68% fall within 1 SD of the mean, 95% fall within 2 SDs of the mean, and 99.7% fall within 3 SDs of the mean (see p. 130).

Again we've seen the importance of *Thinking* about whether a method will work:

▸ **Normality Assumption:** We sometimes work with Normal tables (Table Z). Those tables are based on the Normal model.

▸ Data can't be exactly Normal, so we check the **Nearly Normal Condition** by making a histogram (is it unimodal, symmetric, and free of outliers?) or a Normal probability plot (is it straight enough?). (See p. 141.)

## Terms

Standardizing

122. We standardize to eliminate units. Standardized values can be compared and combined even if the original variables had different units and magnitudes.

Standardized value

123. A value found by subtracting the mean and dividing by the standard deviation.

Shifting

124. Adding a constant to each data value adds the same constant to the mean, the median, and the quartiles, but does not change the standard deviation or IQR.

| | |
|---|---|
| **Rescaling** | 125. Multiplying each data value by a constant multiplies both the measures of position (mean, median, and quartiles) and the measures of spread (standard deviation and IQR) by that constant. |
| **Normal model** | 129. A useful family of models for unimodal, symmetric distributions. |
| **Parameter** | 129. A numerically valued attribute of a model. For example, the values of $\mu$ and $\sigma$ in a $N(\mu, \sigma)$ model are parameters. |
| **Statistic** | 129. A value calculated from data to summarize aspects of the data. For example, the mean, $\bar{y}$ and standard deviation, $s$, are statistics. |
| **z-score** | 129. A z-score tells how many standard deviations a value is from the mean; z-scores have a mean of 0 and a standard deviation of 1. When working with data, use the statistics $\bar{y}$ and $s$: |

$$z = \frac{y - \bar{y}}{s}.$$

When working with models, use the parameters $\mu$ and $\sigma$:

$$z = \frac{y - \mu}{\sigma}.$$

| | |
|---|---|
| **Standard Normal model** | 129. A Normal model, $N(\mu, \sigma)$ with mean $\mu = 0$ and standard deviation $\sigma = 1$. Also called the **standard Normal distribution**. |
| **68–95–99.7 Rule** | 130. In a Normal model, about 68% of values fall within 1 standard deviation of the mean, about 95% fall within 2 standard deviations of the mean, and about 99.7% fall within 3 standard deviations of the mean. |
| **Nearly Normal Condition** | 131. A distribution is nearly Normal if it is unimodal and symmetric. We can check by looking at a histogram or a Normal probability plot. |
| **Normal percentile** | 133. The Normal percentile corresponding to a z-score gives the percentage of values in a standard Normal distribution found at that z-score or below. |
| **Normal probability plot** | 141. A display to help assess whether a distribution of data is approximately Normal. If the plot is nearly straight, the data satisfy the **Nearly Normal Condition**. |

## Skills

- ▸ Understand how adding (subtracting) a constant or multiplying (dividing) by a constant changes the center and/or spread of a variable.
- ▸ Recognize when standardization can be used to compare values.
- ▸ Understand that standardizing uses the standard deviation as a ruler.
- ▸ Recognize when a Normal model is appropriate.

- ▸ Know how to calculate the z-score of an observation.
- ▸ Know how to compare values of two different variables using their z-scores.
- ▸ Be able to use Normal models and the 68–95–99.7 Rule to estimate the percentage of observations falling within 1, 2, or 3 standard deviations of the mean.
- ▸ Know how to find the percentage of observations falling below any value in a Normal model using a Normal table or appropriate technology.
- ▸ Know how to check whether a variable satisfies the **Nearly Normal Condition** by making a Normal probability plot or a histogram.

- ▸ Know what z-scores mean.
- ▸ Be able to explain how extraordinary a standardized value may be by using a Normal model.

# ON THE COMPUTER

## Normal Plots

The best way to tell whether your data can be modeled well by a Normal model is to make a picture or two. We've already talked about making histograms. Normal probability plots are almost never made by hand because the values of the Normal scores are tricky to find. But most statistics software make Normal plots, though various packages call the same plot by different names and array the information differently.

### DATA DESK

To make a "Normal Probability Plot" in Data Desk,
▸  Select the Variable.
▸  Choose **Normal Prob Plot** from the **Plot** menu.

COMMENTS

Data Desk places the ordered data values on the vertical axis and the Normal scores on the horizontal axis.

### EXCEL

Excel offers a "Normal probability plot" as part of the Regression command in the Data Analysis extension, but (as of this writing) it is not a correct Normal probability plot and should not be used.

### JMP

To make a "Normal Quantile Plot" in JMP,
▸  Make a histogram using **Distributions** from the **Analyze** menu.
▸  Click on the drop-down menu next to the variable name.
▸  Choose **Normal Quantile Plot** from the drop-down menu.
▸  JMP opens the plot next to the histogram.

COMMENTS

JMP places the ordered data on the vertical axis and the Normal scores on the horizontal axis. The vertical axis aligns with the histogram's axis, a useful feature.

### MINITAB

To make a "Normal Probability Plot" in MINITAB,
▸  Choose **Probability Plot** from the **Graph** menu.
▸  Select "Single" for the type of plot. Click **OK**.
▸  Enter the name of the variable in the "Graph variables" box. Click **OK**.

COMMENTS

MINITAB places the ordered data on the horizontal axis and the Normal scores on the vertical axis.

### SPSS

To make a Normal "P-P plot" in SPSS,
▸  Choose **P-P** from the **Graphs** menu.
▸  Select the variable to be displayed in the source list.
▸  Click the arrow button to move the variable into the target list.
▸  Click the **OK** button.

COMMENTS

SPSS places the ordered data on the horizontal axis and the Normal scores on the vertical axis. You may safely ignore the options in the P-P dialog.

## TI-83/84 PLUS

To create a "Normal Percentile Plot" on the TI-83,
- Set up a **STAT PLOT** using the last of the Types.
- Specify your datalist, and the axis you choose to represent the data.

Although most people wouldn't open a statistics package just to find a Normal model value they could find in a table, you *would* use a calculator for that function. So . . .

To find what percent of a Normal model lies between two z-scores, choose **normalcdf** from the **DISTRibutions** menu and enter the command normalcdf(zLeft, zRight).

To find the z-score that corresponds to a given percentile in a Normal model, choose **invNorm** from the **DISTRibutions** menu and enter the command **invNorm(percentile).**

### COMMENTS

We often want to find Normal percentages from a certain z-score to infinity. On the calculator, indicate "infinity" as a very large z-score, say, 99. For example, the percentage of a Normal model over 2 standard deviations above the mean can be evaluated with **normalcdf(2, 99).**

## TI-89

- To create a "Normal Prob Plot", press F2 and select choice 2: **Norm Prob Plot.** Select a plot number and use VAR-LINK to enter the data list. Select X or Y for the data axis. Press ENTER to calculate the z-scores.
- Press F2 and select choice 1: **Plot Setup.** Turn off any undesired plots (either F3 (Clear) or F4 (✓)). Press F5 to display the plot.
- To find what percent of a Normal model lies between two z-scores, press F5 (**Distr**). Then select 4: **Normal Cdf.** Enter the lower and upper z-scores, specify mean 0 and standard deviation 1, and press ENTER.
- To find the z-score for a given percentile, press F5 (**Distr**). Then arrow down to 2: **Inverse** press the right arrow to see the sub menu and select 1: **Inverse Normal.** Enter the area to the left of the desired point, mean 0 and standard deviation 1, and press ENTER.

### COMMENTS

Normal models strictly go to infinity on either end, which is 1EE99 on the calculator. In practice, any "large" number will work. For example, the percentage of the Normal model over two standard deviations above the mean can use Lower Value 2 and Upper Value 99. To find area more than 2 standard deviations below the mean, use Lower Value −99, and Upper value −2.

# EXERCISES

1. **Shipments.** A company selling clothing on the Internet reports that the packages it ships have a median weight of 68 ounces and an IQR of 40 ounces.
   a) The company plans to include a sales flyer weighing 4 ounces in each package. What will the new median and IQR be?
   b) If the company recorded the shipping weights of these new packages in pounds instead of ounces, what would the median and IQR be?

2. **Hotline.** A company's customer service hotline handles many calls relating to orders, refunds, and other issues. The company's records indicate that the median length of calls to the hotline is 4.4 minutes with an IQR of 2.3 minutes.

   a) If the company were to describe the duration of these calls in seconds instead of minutes, what would the median and IQR be?
   b) In an effort to speed up the customer service process, the company decides to streamline the series of push-button menus customers must navigate, cutting the time by 24 seconds. What will the median and IQR of the length of hotline calls become?

3. **Payroll.** Here are the summary statistics for the weekly payroll of a small company: lowest salary = $300, mean salary = $700, median = $500, range = $1200, IQR = $600, first quartile = $350, standard deviation = $400.
   a) Do you think the distribution of salaries is symmetric, skewed to the left, or skewed to the right? Explain why.

b) Between what two values are the middle 50% of the salaries found?

c) Suppose business has been good and the company gives every employee a $50 raise. Tell the new value of each of the summary statistics.

d) Instead, suppose the company gives each employee a 10% raise. Tell the new value of each of the summary statistics.

4. **Hams.**   A specialty foods company sells "gourmet hams" by mail order. The hams vary in size from 4.15 to 7.45 pounds, with a mean weight of 6 pounds and standard deviation of 0.65 pounds. The quartiles and median weights are 5.6, 6.2, and 6.55 pounds.

a) Find the range and the IQR of the weights.

b) Do you think the distribution of the weights is symmetric or skewed? If skewed, which way? Why?

c) If these weights were expressed in ounces (1 pound = 16 ounces) what would the mean, standard deviation, quartiles, median, IQR, and range be?

d) When the company ships these hams, the box and packing materials add 30 ounces. What are the mean, standard deviation, quartiles, median, IQR, and range of weights of boxes shipped (in ounces)?

e) One customer made a special order of a 10-pound ham. Which of the summary statistics of part d might *not* change if that data value were added to the distribution?

5. **SAT or ACT?**   Each year thousands of high-school students take either the SAT or the ACT, standardized tests used in the college admissions process. Combined SAT Math and Verbal scores go as high as 1600, while the maximum ACT composite score is 36. Since the two exams use very different scales, comparisons of performance are difficult. A convenient rule of thumb is $SAT = 40 \times ACT + 150$; that is, multiply an ACT score by 40 and add 150 points to estimate the equivalent SAT score. An admissions officer reported the following statistics about the ACT scores of 2355 students who applied to her college one year. Find the summaries of equivalent SAT scores.

Lowest score = 19    Mean = 27    Standard deviation = 3

Q3 = 30              Median = 28    IQR = 6

6. **Cold U?**   A high school senior uses the Internet to get information on February temperatures in the town where he'll be going to college. He finds a Web site with some statistics, but they are given in degrees Celsius. The conversion formula is $°F = 9/5 °C + 32$. Determine the Fahrenheit equivalents for the summary information below.

Maximum temperature = 11 °C    Range = 33°

Mean = 1°      Standard deviation = 7°

Median = 2°     IQR = 16°

7. **Stats test.**   Suppose your Statistics professor reports test grades as z-scores, and you got a score of 2.20 on the midterm exam. Write a sentence explaining what that means.

8. **Checkup.**   One of the authors has an adopted grandson whose birth family members are very short. After examining him at his 2-year checkup, the boy's pediatrician said that the z-score for his height relative to American

2-year-olds was −1.88. Write a sentence explaining what that means.

9. **Stats test, again.**   Nicole's score on the Stats midterm was 80 points. The class average was 75 and the standard deviation was 5 points. What was her z-score?

10. **Horsepower.**   Cars currently sold in the United States have an average of 135 horsepower, with a standard deviation of 40 horsepower. What's the z-score for a car with 195 horsepower?

11. **Stats test, part III.**   The average score on the Stats midterm was 75 points with a standard deviation of 5 points, and Gregor's z-score was −2. How many points did he score?

12. **Mensa.**   People with z-scores greater than 2.5 on an IQ test are sometimes classified as geniuses. If IQ test scores have a mean of 100 and a standard deviation of 16 points, what IQ score do you need to be considered a genius?

13. **Temperatures.**   A town's January high temperatures average 36 °F with a standard deviation of 10°, while in July the mean high temperature is 74° and the standard deviation is 8°. In which month is it more unusual to have a day with a high temperature of 55°? Explain.

14. **Placement exams.**   An incoming freshman took her college's placement exams in French and mathematics. In French, she scored 82 and in math 86. The overall results on the French exam had a mean of 72 and a standard deviation of 8, while the mean math score was 68, with a standard deviation of 12. On which exam did she do better compared with the other freshmen?

15. **Combining test scores.**   The first Stats exam had a mean of 65 and a standard deviation of 10 points; the second had a mean of 80 and a standard deviation of 5 points. Derrick scored an 80 on both tests. Julie scored a 70 on the first test and a 90 on the second. They both totaled 160 points on the two exams, but Julie claims that her total is better. Explain.

16. **Combining scores again.**   The first Stat exam had a mean of 80 and a standard deviation of 4 points; the second had a mean of 70 and a standard deviation of 15 points. Reginald scored an 80 on the first test and an 85 on the second. Sara scored an 88 on the first but only a 65 on the second. Although Reginald's total score is higher, Sara feels she should get the higher grade. Explain her point of view.

17. **Final exams.**   Anna, a language major, took final exams in both French and Spanish and scored 83 on each. Her roommate Megan, also taking both courses, scored 77 on the French exam and 95 on the Spanish exam. Overall, student scores on the French exam had a mean of 81 and a standard deviation of 5, and the Spanish scores had a mean of 74 and a standard deviation of 15.

a) To qualify for language honors, a major must maintain at least an 85 average for all language courses taken. So far, which student qualifies?

b) Which student's overall performance was better?

**18. MP3s.** Two companies market new batteries targeted at owners of personal music players. DuraTunes claims a mean battery life of 11 hours, while RockReady advertises 12 hours.
a) Explain why you would also like to know the standard deviations of the battery lifespans before deciding which brand to buy.
b) Suppose those standard deviations are 2 hours for DuraTunes and 1.5 hours for RockReady. You are headed for 8 hours at the beach. Which battery is most likely to last all day? Explain.
c) If your beach trip is all weekend, and you probably will have the music on for 16 hours, which battery is most likely to last? Explain.

**19. Cattle.** The Virginia Cooperative Extension reports that the mean weight of yearling Angus steers is 1152 pounds. Suppose that weights of all such animals can be described by a Normal model with a standard deviation of 84 pounds.
a) How many standard deviations from the mean would a steer weighing 1000 pounds be?
b) Which would be more unusual, a steer weighing 1000 pounds or one weighing 1250 pounds?

**Ⓣ 20. Car speeds.** John Beale of Stanford, CA, recorded the speeds of cars driving past his house, where the speed limit read 20 mph. The mean of 100 readings was 23.84 mph, with a standard deviation of 3.56 mph. (He actually recorded every car for a two-month period. These are 100 representative readings.)
a) How many standard deviations from the mean would a car going under the speed limit be?
b) Which would be more unusual, a car traveling 34 mph or one going 10 mph?

**21. More cattle.** Recall that the beef cattle described in Exercise 19 had a mean weight of 1152 pounds, with a standard deviation of 84 pounds.
a) Cattle buyers hope that yearling Angus steers will weigh at least 1000 pounds. To see how much over (or under) that goal the cattle are, we could subtract 1000 pounds from all the weights. What would the new mean and standard deviation be?
b) Suppose such cattle sell at auction for 40 cents a pound. Find the mean and standard deviation of the sale prices for all the steers.

**Ⓣ 22. Car speeds again.** For the car speed data of Exercise 20, recall that the mean speed recorded was 23.84 mph, with a standard deviation of 3.56 mph. To see how many cars are speeding, John subtracts 20 mph from all speeds.
a) What is the mean speed now? What is the new standard deviation?
b) His friend in Berlin wants to study the speeds, so John converts all the original miles-per-hour readings to kilometers per hour by multiplying all speeds by 1.609 (km per mile). What is the mean now? What is the new standard deviation?

**23. Cattle, part III.** Suppose the auctioneer in Exercise 21 sold a herd of cattle whose minimum weight was 980 pounds, median was 1140 pounds, standard deviation 84 pounds, and IQR 102 pounds. They sold for 40 cents a pound, and the auctioneer took a $20 commission on each animal. Then, for example, a steer weighing 1100 pounds would net the owner $0.40(1100) - 20 = \$420$. Find the minimum, median, standard deviation, and IQR of the net sale prices.

**24. Caught speeding.** Suppose police set up radar surveillance on the Stanford street described in Exercise 20. They handed out a large number of tickets to speeders going a mean of 28 mph, with a standard deviation of 2.4 mph, a maximum of 33 mph, and an IQR of 3.2 mph. Local law prescribes fines of $100, plus $10 per mile per hour over the 20 mph speed limit. For example, a driver convicted of going 25 mph would be fined $100 + 10(5) = \$150$. Find the mean, maximum, standard deviation, and IQR of all the potential fines.

**25. Professors.** A friend tells you about a recent study dealing with the number of years of teaching experience among current college professors. He remembers the mean but can't recall whether the standard deviation was 6 months, 6 years, or 16 years. Tell him which one it must have been, and why.

**26. Rock concerts.** A popular band on tour played a series of concerts in large venues. They always drew a large crowd, averaging 21,359 fans. While the band did not announce (and probably never calculated) the standard deviation, which of these values do you think is most likely to be correct: 20, 200, 2000, or 20,000 fans? Explain your choice.

**27. Guzzlers?** Environmental Protection Agency (EPA) fuel economy estimates for automobile models tested recently predicted a mean of 24.8 mpg and a standard deviation of 6.2 mpg for highway driving. Assume that a Normal model can be applied.
a) Draw the model for auto fuel economy. Clearly label it, showing what the 68–95–99.7 Rule predicts about miles per gallon.
b) In what interval would you expect the central 68% of autos to be found?
c) About what percent of autos should get more than 31 mpg?
d) About what percent of cars should get between 31 and 37.2 mpg?
e) Describe the gas mileage of the worst 2.5% of all cars.

**28. IQ.** Some IQ tests are standardized to a Normal model, with a mean of 100 and a standard deviation of 16.
a) Draw the model for these IQ scores. Clearly label it, showing what the 68–95–99.7 Rule predicts about the scores.
b) In what interval would you expect the central 95% of IQ scores to be found?
c) About what percent of people should have IQ scores above 116?
d) About what percent of people should have IQ scores between 68 and 84?
e) About what percent of people should have IQ scores above 132?

**29. Small steer.** In Exercise 19 we suggested the model $N(1152, 84)$ for weights in pounds of yearling Angus steers. What weight would you consider to be unusually low for such an animal? Explain.

**30. High IQ.** Exercise 28 proposes modeling IQ scores with $N(100, 16)$. What IQ would you consider to be unusually high? Explain.

**T 31. Winter Olympics 2006 downhill.** Fifty-three men qualified for the men's alpine downhill race in Torino. The gold medal winner finished in 1 minute, 48.8 seconds. All competitors' times (in seconds) are found in the following list:

| | | | | |
|---|---|---|---|---|
| 108.80 | 109.52 | 109.82 | 109.88 | 109.93 |
| 110.00 | 110.04 | 110.12 | 110.29 | 110.33 |
| 110.35 | 110.44 | 110.45 | 110.64 | 110.68 |
| 110.70 | 110.72 | 110.84 | 110.88 | 110.88 |
| 110.90 | 110.91 | 110.98 | 111.37 | 111.48 |
| 111.51 | 111.55 | 111.70 | 111.72 | 111.93 |
| 112.17 | 112.55 | 112.87 | 112.90 | 113.34 |
| 114.07 | 114.65 | 114.70 | 115.01 | 115.03 |
| 115.73 | 116.10 | 116.58 | 116.81 | 117.45 |
| 117.54 | 117.56 | 117.69 | 118.77 | 119.24 |
| 119.41 | 119.79 | 120.93 | | |

a) The mean time was 113.02 seconds, with a standard deviation of 3.24 seconds. If the Normal model is appropriate, what percent of times will be less than 109.78 seconds?
b) What is the actual percent of times less than 109.78 seconds?
c) Why do you think the two percentages don't agree?
d) Create a histogram of these times. What do you see?

**32. Rivets.** A company that manufactures rivets believes the shear strength (in pounds) is modeled by $N(800, 50)$.
a) Draw and label the Normal model.
b) Would it be safe to use these rivets in a situation requiring a shear strength of 750 pounds? Explain.
c) About what percent of these rivets would you expect to fall below 900 pounds?
d) Rivets are used in a variety of applications with varying shear strength requirements. What is the maximum shear strength for which you would feel comfortable approving this company's rivets? Explain your reasoning.

**33. Trees.** A forester measured 27 of the trees in a large woods that is up for sale. He found a mean diameter of 10.4 inches and a standard deviation of 4.7 inches. Suppose that these trees provide an accurate description of the whole forest and that a Normal model applies.
a) Draw the Normal model for tree diameters.
b) What size would you expect the central 95% of all trees to be?
c) About what percent of the trees should be less than an inch in diameter?
d) About what percent of the trees should be between 5.7 and 10.4 inches in diameter?
e) About what percent of the trees should be over 15 inches in diameter?

**T 34. Car speeds, the picture.** For the car speed data of Exercise 20, here is the histogram, boxplot, and Normal probability plot of the 100 readings. Do you think it is appropriate to apply a Normal model here? Explain.

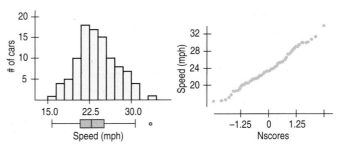

**35. Trees, part II.** Later on, the forester in Exercise 33 shows you a histogram of the tree diameters he used in analyzing the woods that was for sale. Do you think he was justified in using a Normal model? Explain, citing some specific concerns.

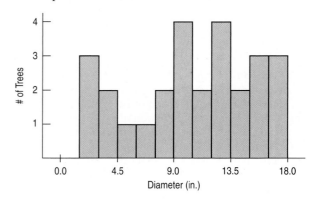

**36. Check the model.** Recall from Exercise 20 that the mean of the 100 car speeds in Exercise 34 was 23.84 mph, with a standard deviation of 3.56 mph.
a) Using a Normal model, what values should border the middle 95% of all car speeds?
b) Here are some summary statistics.

| Percentile | | Speed |
|---|---|---|
| 100% | **Max** | 34.060 |
| 97.5% | | 30.976 |
| 90.0% | | 28.978 |
| 75.0% | **Q3** | 25.785 |
| 50.0% | **Median** | 23.525 |
| 25.0% | **Q1** | 21.547 |
| 10.0% | | 19.163 |
| 2.5% | | 16.638 |
| 0.0% | **Min** | 16.270 |

From your answer in part a, how well does the model do in predicting those percentiles? Are you surprised? Explain.

**T 37. Receivers.** NFL data from the 2006 football season reported the number of yards gained by each of the league's 167 wide receivers:

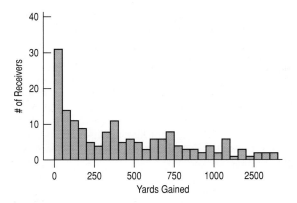

The mean is 435 yards, with a standard deviation of 384 yards.

a) According to the Normal model, what percent of receivers would you expect to gain fewer yards than 2 standard deviations below the mean number of yards?
b) For these data, what does that mean?
c) Explain the problem in using a Normal model for these data.

**38. Customer database.** A large philanthropic organization keeps records on the people who have contributed to their cause. In addition to keeping records of past giving, the organization buys demographic data on neighborhoods from the U.S. Census Bureau. Eighteen of these variables concern the ethnicity of the neighborhood of the donor. Here are a histogram and summary statistics for the percentage of whites in the neighborhoods of 500 donors:

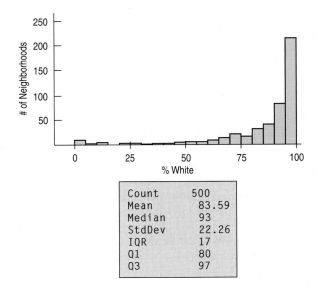

| Count | 500 |
|---|---|
| Mean | 83.59 |
| Median | 93 |
| StdDev | 22.26 |
| IQR | 17 |
| Q1 | 80 |
| Q3 | 97 |

a) Which is a better summary of the percentage of white residents in the neighborhoods, the mean or the median? Explain.
b) Which is a better summary of the spread, the IQR or the standard deviation? Explain.
c) From a Normal model, about what percentage of neighborhoods should have a percent white within one standard deviation of the mean?

d) What percentage of neighborhoods actually have a percent white within one standard deviation of the mean?
e) Explain the discrepancy between parts c and d.

**39. Normal models.** What percent of a standard Normal model is found in each region? Be sure to draw a picture first.
a) $z > 1.5$
b) $z < 2.25$
c) $-1 < z < 1.15$
d) $|z| > 0.5$

**40. Normal models, again.** What percent of a standard Normal model is found in each region? Draw a picture first.
a) $z > -2.05$
b) $z < -0.33$
c) $1.2 < z < 1.8$
d) $|z| < 1.28$

**41. More Normal models.** In a standard Normal model, what value(s) of $z$ cut(s) off the region described? Don't forget to draw a picture.
a) the highest 20%
b) the highest 75%
c) the lowest 3%
d) the middle 90%

**42. Yet another Normal model.** In a standard Normal model, what value(s) of $z$ cut(s) off the region described? Remember to draw a picture first.
a) the lowest 12%
b) the highest 30%
c) the highest 7%
d) the middle 50%

**43. Normal cattle.** Using $N(1152, 84)$, the Normal model for weights of Angus steers in Exercise 19, what percent of steers weigh
a) over 1250 pounds?
b) under 1200 pounds?
c) between 1000 and 1100 pounds?

**44. IQs revisited.** Based on the Normal model $N(100, 16)$ describing IQ scores, what percent of people's IQs would you expect to be
a) over 80?
b) under 90?
c) between 112 and 132?

**45. More cattle.** Based on the model $N(1152, 84)$ describing Angus steer weights, what are the cutoff values for
a) the highest 10% of the weights?
b) the lowest 20% of the weights?
c) the middle 40% of the weights?

**46. More IQs.** In the Normal model $N(100, 16)$, what cutoff value bounds
a) the highest 5% of all IQs?
b) the lowest 30% of the IQs?
c) the middle 80% of the IQs?

**47. Cattle, finis.** Consider the Angus weights model $N(1152, 84)$ one last time.
a) What weight represents the 40th percentile?
b) What weight represents the 99th percentile?
c) What's the IQR of the weights of these Angus steers?

**48. IQ, finis.** Consider the IQ model $N(100, 16)$ one last time.
a) What IQ represents the 15th percentile?
b) What IQ represents the 98th percentile?
c) What's the IQR of the IQs?

**49. Parameters.** Every Normal model is defined by its parameters: the mean and the standard deviation. For each model described below, find the missing parameter. As always, start by drawing a picture.
a) $\mu = 20$, 45% above 30; $\sigma = ?$
b) $\mu = 88$, 2% below 50; $\sigma = ?$
c) $\sigma = 5$, 80% below 100; $\mu = ?$
d) $\sigma = 15.6$, 10% above 17.2; $\mu = ?$

**50. Parameters II.** Every Normal model is defined by its parameters: the mean and the standard deviation. For each model described below, find the missing parameter. Don't forget to draw a picture.
a) $\mu = 1250$, 35% below 1200; $\sigma = ?$
b) $\mu = 0.64$, 12% above 0.70; $\sigma = ?$
c) $\sigma = 0.5$, 90% above 10.0; $\mu = ?$
d) $\sigma = 220$, 3% below 202; $\mu = ?$

**51. Cholesterol.** Assume the cholesterol levels of adult American women can be described by a Normal model with a mean of 188 mg/dL and a standard deviation of 24.
a) Draw and label the Normal model.
b) What percent of adult women do you expect to have cholesterol levels over 200 mg/dL?
c) What percent of adult women do you expect to have cholesterol levels between 150 and 170 mg/dL?
d) Estimate the interquartile range of the cholesterol levels.
e) Above what value are the highest 15% of women's cholesterol levels?

**52. Tires.** A tire manufacturer believes that the treadlife of its snow tires can be described by a Normal model with a mean of 32,000 miles and standard deviation of 2500 miles.
a) If you buy a set of these tires, would it be reasonable for you to hope they'll last 40,000 miles? Explain.
b) Approximately what fraction of these tires can be expected to last less than 30,000 miles?
c) Approximately what fraction of these tires can be expected to last between 30,000 and 35,000 miles?
d) Estimate the IQR of the treadlives.
e) In planning a marketing strategy, a local tire dealer wants to offer a refund to any customer whose tires fail to last a certain number of miles. However, the dealer does not want to take too big a risk. If the dealer is willing to give refunds to no more than 1 of every 25 customers, for what mileage can he guarantee these tires to last?

**53. Kindergarten.** Companies that design furniture for elementary school classrooms produce a variety of sizes for kids of different ages. Suppose the heights of kindergarten children can be described by a Normal model with a mean of 38.2 inches and standard deviation of 1.8 inches.
a) What fraction of kindergarten kids should the company expect to be less than 3 feet tall?

b) In what height interval should the company expect to find the middle 80% of kindergarteners?
c) At least how tall are the biggest 10% of kindergarteners?

**54. Body temperatures.** Most people think that the "normal" adult body temperature is 98.6 °F. That figure, based on a 19th-century study, has recently been challenged. In a 1992 article in the *Journal of the American Medical Association,* researchers reported that a more accurate figure may be 98.2 °F. Furthermore, the standard deviation appeared to be around 0.7 °F. Assume that a Normal model is appropriate.
a) In what interval would you expect most people's body temperatures to be? Explain.
b) What fraction of people would be expected to have body temperatures above 98.6 °F?
c) Below what body temperature are the coolest 20% of all people?

**55. Undercover?** We learned in the chapter that the average Dutch man is 184 cm tall. The standard deviation of Caucasian adult male heights is about 7 cm. The average Greek 18-year-old in Athens is 167.8 cm tall. How easily could the average Dutch man hide in Athens? (Let's assume he dyes his hair, if necessary.) That is, would his height make him sufficiently extraordinary that he'd stand out easily? Assume heights are nearly Normal.

**56. Big mouth!** A Cornell University researcher measured the mouth volumes of 31 men and 30 women. She found a mean of 66 cc for men (SD = 17 cc) and a mean of 54 cc for women (SD = 14.5 cc). The man with the largest mouth had a mouth volume of 111.2 cc. The woman with the largest mouth had a mouth volume of 95.8 cc.
a) Which had the more extraordinarily large mouth?
b) If the distribution of mouth volumes is nearly Normal, what percentage of men and of women should have even larger mouths than these?

**57. First steps.** While only 5% of babies have learned to walk by the age of 10 months, 75% are walking by 13 months of age. If the age at which babies develop the ability to walk can be described by a Normal model, find the parameters (mean and standard deviation).

**58. Trout.** Wildlife biologists believe that the weights of adult trout can be described by a Normal model. They collected data from fishermen, finding that 22% of the trout caught were thrown back because they were below the 2-pound minimum, and only 6% weighed over 5 pounds. What mean and standard deviation should define the model?

**59. Eggs.** Hens usually begin laying eggs when they are about 6 months old. Young hens tend to lay smaller eggs, often weighing less than the desired minimum weight of 54 grams.
a) The average weight of the eggs produced by the young hens is 50.9 grams, and only 28% of their eggs exceed the desired minimum weight. If a Normal model is appropriate, what would the standard deviation of the egg weights be?

b) By the time these hens have reached the age of 1 year, the eggs they produce average 67.1 grams, and 98% of them are above the minimum weight. What is the standard deviation for the appropriate Normal model for these older hens?

c) Are egg sizes more consistent for the younger hens or the older ones? Explain.

d) A certain poultry farmer finds that 8% of his eggs are underweight and that 12% weigh over 70 grams. Estimate the mean and standard deviation of his eggs.

**60. Tomatoes.**   Agricultural scientists are working on developing an improved variety of Roma tomatoes. Marketing research indicates that customers are likely to bypass Romas that weigh less than 70 grams. The current variety of Roma plants produces fruit that averages 74 grams, but 11% of the tomatoes are too small. It is reasonable to assume that a Normal model applies.

a) What is the standard deviation of the weights of Romas now being grown?

b) Scientists hope to reduce the frequency of undersized tomatoes to no more than 4%. One way to accomplish this is to raise the average size of the fruit. If the standard deviation remains the same, what target mean should they have as a goal?

c) The researchers produce a new variety with a mean weight of 75 grams, which meets the 4% goal. What is the standard deviation of the weights of these new Romas?

d) Based on their standard deviations, compare the tomatoes produced by the two varieties.

### JUST CHECKING
### Answers

**1. a)** On the first test, the mean is 88 and the SD is 4, so $z = (90 - 88)/4 = 0.5$. On the second test, the mean is 75 and the SD is 5, so $z = (80 - 75)/5 = 1.0$. The first test has the lower $z$-score, so it is the one that will be dropped.

**b)** The second test is 1 standard deviation above the mean, farther away than the first test, so it's the better score relative to the class.

**2. a)** The mean would increase to 500.

**b)** The standard deviation is still 100 points.

**c)** The two boxplots would look nearly identical (the shape of the distribution would remain the same), but the later one would be shifted 50 points higher.

**3.** The standard deviation is now 2.54 millimeters, which is the same as 0.1 inches. Nothing has changed. The standard deviation has "increased" only because we're reporting it in millimeters now, not inches.

**4.** The mean is 184 centimeters, with a standard deviation of 8 centimeters. 2 meters is 200 centimeters, which is 2 standard deviations above the mean. We expect 5% of the men to be more than 2 standard deviations below or above the mean, so half of those, 2.5%, are likely to be above 2 meters.

**5. a)** We know that 68% of the time we'll be within 1 standard deviation (2 min) of 20. So 32% of the time we'll arrive in less than 18 or more than 22 minutes. Half of those times (16%) will be greater than 22 minutes, so 84% will be less than 22 minutes.

**b)** 24 minutes is 2 standard deviations above the mean. Because of the 95% rule, we know 2.5% of the times will be more than 24 minutes.

**c)** Traffic incidents may occasionally increase the time it takes to get to school, so the driving times may be skewed to the right, and there may be outliers.

**d)** If so, the Normal model would not be appropriate and the percentages we predict would not be accurate.

## Exploring and Understanding Data

### Quick Review

It's time to put it all together. Real data don't come tagged with instructions for use. So let's step back and look at how the key concepts and skills we've seen work together. This brief list and the review exercises that follow should help you check your understanding of Statistics so far.

▶ We treat data two ways: as categorical and as quantitative.

▶ To describe categorical data:

- Make a picture. Bar graphs work well for comparing counts in categories.

- Summarize the distribution with a table of counts or relative frequencies (percents) in each category.

- Pie charts and segmented bar charts display divisions of a whole.

- Compare distributions with plots side by side.

- Look for associations between variables by comparing marginal and conditional distributions.

▶ To describe quantitative data:

- Make a picture. Use histograms, boxplots, stem-and-leaf displays, or dotplots. Stem-and-leafs are great when working by hand and good for small data sets. Histograms are a good way to see the distribution. Boxplots are best for comparing several distributions.

- Describe distributions in terms of their shape, center, and spread, and note any unusual features such as gaps or outliers.

- The shape of most distributions you'll see will likely be uniform, unimodal, or bimodal. It may be multimodal. If it is unimodal, then it may be symmetric or skewed.

- A 5-number summary makes a good numerical description of a distribution: min, Q1, median, Q3, and max.

- If the distribution is skewed, be sure to include the median and interquartile range (IQR) when you describe its center and spread.

- A distribution that is severely skewed may benefit from re-expressing the data. If it is skewed to the high end, taking logs often works well.

- If the distribution is unimodal and symmetric, describe its center and spread with the mean and standard deviation.

- Use the standard deviation as a ruler to tell how unusual an observed value may be, or to compare or combine measurements made on different scales.

- Shifting a distribution by adding or subtracting a constant affects measures of position but not measures of spread. Rescaling by multiplying or dividing by a constant affects both.

- When a distribution is roughly unimodal and symmetric, a Normal model may be useful. For Normal models, the 68–95–99.7 Rule is a good rule of thumb.

- If the Normal model fits well (check a histogram or Normal probability plot), then Normal percentile tables or functions found in most statistics technology can provide more detailed values.

Need more help with some of this? It never hurts to reread sections of the chapters! And in the following pages we offer you more opportunities[1] to review these concepts and skills.

The exercises that follow use the concepts and skills you've learned in the first six chapters. To be more realistic and more useful for your review, they don't tell you which of the concepts or methods you need. But neither will the exam.

---

[1] If you doubted that we are teachers, this should convince you. Only a teacher would call additional homework exercises "opportunities."

# REVIEW EXERCISES

1. **Bananas.** Here are the prices (in cents per pound) of bananas reported from 15 markets surveyed by the U.S. Department of Agriculture.

| | | |
|---|---|---|
| 51 | 52 | 45 |
| 48 | 53 | 52 |
| 50 | 49 | 52 |
| 48 | 43 | 46 |
| 45 | 42 | 50 |

a) Display these data with an appropriate graph.
b) Report appropriate summary statistics.
c) Write a few sentences about this distribution.

2. **Prenatal care.** Results of a 1996 American Medical Association report about the infant mortality rate for twins carried for the full term of a normal pregnancy are shown below, broken down by the level of prenatal care the mother had received.

| Full-Term Pregnancies, Level of Prenatal Care | Infant Mortality Rate Among Twins (deaths per thousand live births) |
|---|---|
| Intensive | 5.4 |
| Adequate | 3.9 |
| Inadequate | 6.1 |
| **Overall** | 5.1 |

a) Is the overall rate the average of the other three rates? Should it be? Explain.
b) Do these results indicate that adequate prenatal care is important for pregnant women? Explain.
c) Do these results suggest that a woman pregnant with twins should be wary of seeking too much medical care? Explain.

3. **Singers.** The boxplots shown display the heights (in inches) of 130 members of a choir.

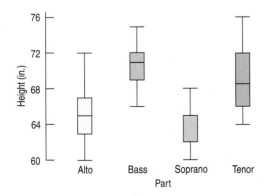

a) It appears that the median height for sopranos is missing, but actually the median and the upper quartile are equal. How could that happen?
b) Write a few sentences describing what you see.

4. **Dialysis.** In a study of dialysis, researchers found that "of the three patients who were currently on dialysis, 67% had developed blindness and 33% had their toes amputated." What kind of display might be appropriate for these data? Explain.

5. **Beanstalks.** Beanstalk Clubs are social clubs for very tall people. To join, a man must be over 6′2″ tall, and a woman over 5′10″. The National Health Survey suggests that heights of adults may be Normally distributed, with mean heights of 69.1″ for men and 64.0″ for women. The respective standard deviations are 2.8″ and 2.5″.
a) You are probably not surprised to learn that men are generally taller than women, but what does the greater standard deviation for men's heights indicate?
b) Who are more likely to qualify for Beanstalk membership, men or women? Explain.

6. **Bread.** Clarksburg Bakery is trying to predict how many loaves to bake. In the last 100 days, they have sold between 95 and 140 loaves per day. Here is a histogram of the number of loaves they sold for the last 100 days.

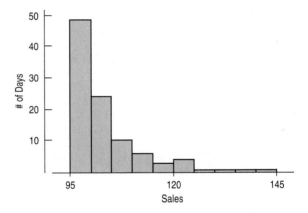

a) Describe the distribution.
b) Which should be larger, the mean number of sales or the median? Explain.
c) Here are the summary statistics for Clarksburg Bakery's bread sales. Use these statistics and the histogram above to create a boxplot. You may approximate the values of any outliers.

| Summary of Sales | |
|---|---|
| Median | 100 |
| Min | 95 |
| Max | 140 |
| 25th %tile | 97 |
| 75th %tile | 105.5 |

d) For these data, the mean was 103 loaves sold per day, with a standard deviation of 9 loaves. Do these statistics suggest that Clarksburg Bakery should expect to sell between 94 and 112 loaves on about 68% of the days? Explain.

**7. State University.** Public relations staff at State U. collected data on people's opinions of various colleges and universities in their state. They phoned 850 local residents. After identifying themselves, the callers asked the survey participants their ages, whether they had attended college, and whether they had a favorable opinion of the university. The official report to the university's directors claimed that, in general, people had very favorable opinions about their university.
a) Identify the W's of these data.
b) Identify the variables, classify each as categorical or quantitative, and specify units if relevant.
c) Are you confident about the report's conclusion? Explain.

**8. Acid rain.** Based on long-term investigation, researchers have suggested that the acidity (pH) of rainfall in the Shenandoah Mountains can be described by the Normal model N(4.9, 0.6).
a) Draw and carefully label the model.
b) What percent of storms produce rainfall with pH over 6?
c) What percent of storms produce rainfall with pH under 4?
d) The lower the pH, the more acidic the rain. What is the pH level for the most acidic 20% of all storms?
e) What is the pH level for the least acidic 5% of all storms?
f) What is the IQR for the pH of rainfall?

**9. Fraud detection.** A credit card bank is investigating the incidence of fraudulent card use. The bank suspects that the type of product bought may provide clues to the fraud. To examine this situation, the bank looks at the Standard Industrial Code (SIC) of the business related to the transaction. This is a code that was used by the U.S. Census Bureau and Statistics Canada to identify the type of every registered business in North America.[2] For example, 1011 designates Meat and Meat Products (except Poultry), 1012 is Poultry Products, 1021 is Fish Products, 1031 is Canned and Preserved Fruits and Vegetables, and 1032 is Frozen Fruits and Vegetables.

A company intern produces the following histogram of the SIC codes for 1536 transactions:

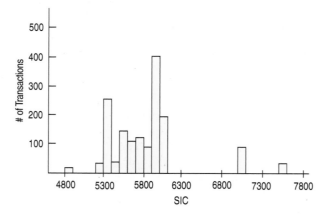

He also reports that the mean SIC is 5823.13 with a standard deviation of 488.17.
a) Comment on any problems you see with the use of the mean and standard deviation as summary statistics.
b) How well do you think the Normal model will work on these data? Explain.

**10. Streams.** As part of the course work, a class at an upstate NY college collects data on streams each year. Students record a number of biological, chemical, and physical variables, including the stream name, the substrate of the stream (*limestone, shale, or mixed*), the pH, the temperature (°C), and the BCI, a measure of biological diversity.

| Group | Count | % |
|---|---|---|
| Limestone | 77 | 44.8 |
| Mixed | 26 | 15.1 |
| Shale | 69 | 40.1 |

a) Name each variable, indicating whether it is categorical or quantitative, and giving the units if available.
b) These streams have been classified according to their substrate—the composition of soil and rock over which they flow—as summarized in the table. What kind of graph might be used to display these data?

**11. Cramming.** One Thursday, researchers gave students enrolled in a section of basic Spanish a set of 50 new vocabulary words to memorize. On Friday the students took a vocabulary test. When they returned to class the following Monday, they were retested—without advance warning. Both sets of test scores for the 28 students are shown below.

| Fri | Mon | Fri | Mon |
|---|---|---|---|
| 42 | 36 | 50 | 47 |
| 44 | 44 | 34 | 34 |
| 45 | 46 | 38 | 31 |
| 48 | 38 | 43 | 40 |
| 44 | 40 | 39 | 41 |
| 43 | 38 | 46 | 32 |
| 41 | 37 | 37 | 36 |
| 35 | 31 | 40 | 31 |
| 43 | 32 | 41 | 32 |
| 48 | 37 | 48 | 39 |
| 43 | 41 | 37 | 31 |
| 45 | 32 | 36 | 41 |
| 47 | 44 | | |

a) Create a graphical display to compare the two distributions of scores.
b) Write a few sentences about the scores reported on Friday and Monday.
c) Create a graphical display showing the distribution of the *changes* in student scores.
d) Describe the distribution of changes.

---

[2] Since 1997 the SIC has been replaced by the NAICS, a code of six letters.

**12. Computers and Internet.** A U.S. Census Bureau report (August 2000, *Current Population Survey*) found that 51.0% of homes had a personal computer and 41.5% had access to the Internet. A newspaper concluded that 92.5% of homes had either a computer or access to the Internet. Do you agree? Explain.

**13. Let's play cards.** You pick a card from a deck (see description in Chapter 11) and record its denomination (7, say) and its suit (maybe spades).
a) Is the variable *suit* categorical or quantitative?
b) Name a game you might be playing for which you would consider the variable *denomination* to be categorical. Explain.
c) Name a game you might be playing for which you would consider the variable *denomination* to be quantitative. Explain.

**14. Accidents.** In 2001, Progressive Insurance asked customers who had been involved in auto accidents how far they were from home when the accident happened. The data are summarized in the table.

| Miles from Home | % of Accidents |
|---|---|
| Less than 1 | 23 |
| 1 to 5 | 29 |
| 6 to 10 | 17 |
| 11 to 15 | 8 |
| 16 to 20 | 6 |
| Over 20 | 17 |

a) Create an appropriate graph of these data.
b) Do these data indicate that driving near home is particularly dangerous? Explain.

**15. Hard water.** In an investigation of environmental causes of disease, data were collected on the annual mortality rate (deaths per 100,000) for males in 61 large towns in England and Wales. In addition, the water hardness was recorded as the calcium concentration (parts per million, ppm) in the drinking water.
a) What are the variables in this study? For each, indicate whether it is quantitative or categorical and what the units are.
b) Here are histograms of calcium concentration and mortality. Describe the distributions of the two variables.

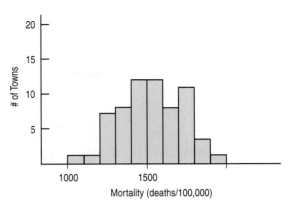

**16. Hard water II.** The data set from England and Wales also notes for each town whether it was south or north of Derby. Here are some summary statistics and a comparative boxplot for the two regions.

| Summary of Mortality | | | | |
|---|---|---|---|---|
| Group | Count | Mean | Median | StdDev |
| North | 34 | 1631.59 | 1631 | 138.470 |
| South | 27 | 1388.85 | 1369 | 151.114 |

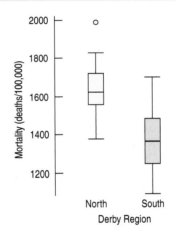

a) What is the overall mean mortality rate for the two regions?
b) Do you see evidence of a difference in mortality rates? Explain.

**17. Seasons.** Average daily temperatures in January and July for 60 large U.S. cities are graphed in the histograms below.

a) What aspect of these histograms makes it difficult to compare the distributions?

b) What differences do you see between the distributions of January and July average temperatures?

c) Differences in temperatures (July–January) for each of the cities are displayed in the boxplot above. Write a few sentences describing what you see.

**18. Old Faithful.** It is a common belief that Yellowstone's most famous geyser erupts once an hour at very predictable intervals. The histogram below shows the time gaps (in minutes) between 222 successive eruptions. Describe this distribution.

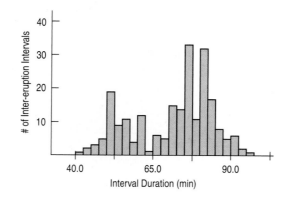

**19. Old Faithful?** Does the duration of an eruption have an effect on the length of time that elapses before the next eruption?

a) The histogram below shows the duration (in minutes) of those 222 eruptions. Describe this distribution.

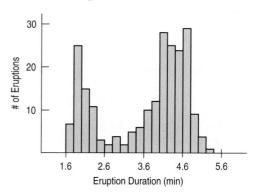

b) Explain why it is not appropriate to find summary statistics for this distribution.

c) Let's classify the eruptions as "long" or "short," depending upon whether or not they last at least 3 minutes. Describe what you see in the comparative boxplots.

**20. Teen drivers.** In its *Traffic Safety Facts 2005*, the National Highway Traffic Safety Administration reported that 6.3% of licensed drivers were between the ages of 15 and 20, yet this age group was behind the wheel in 15.9% of all fatal crashes. Use these statistics to explain the concept of independence.

**T 21. Liberty's nose.** Is the Statue of Liberty's nose too long? Her nose measures 4'6", but she is a large statue, after all. Her arm is 42 feet long. That means her arm is $42/45 = 9.3$ times as long as her nose. Is that a reasonable ratio? Shown in the table are arm and nose lengths of 18 girls in a Statistics class, and the ratio of arm-to-nose length for each.

| Arm (cm) | Nose (cm) | Arm/Nose Ratio |
|----------|-----------|----------------|
| 73.8 | 5.0 | 14.8 |
| 74.0 | 4.5 | 16.4 |
| 69.5 | 4.5 | 15.4 |
| 62.5 | 4.7 | 13.3 |
| 68.6 | 4.4 | 15.6 |
| 64.5 | 4.8 | 13.4 |
| 68.2 | 4.8 | 14.2 |
| 63.5 | 4.4 | 14.4 |
| 63.5 | 5.4 | 11.8 |
| 67.0 | 4.6 | 14.6 |
| 67.4 | 4.4 | 15.3 |
| 70.7 | 4.3 | 16.4 |
| 69.4 | 4.1 | 16.9 |
| 71.7 | 4.5 | 15.9 |
| 69.0 | 4.4 | 15.7 |
| 69.8 | 4.5 | 15.5 |
| 71.0 | 4.8 | 14.8 |
| 71.3 | 4.7 | 15.2 |

a) Make an appropriate plot and describe the distribution of the ratios.
b) Summarize the ratios numerically, choosing appropriate measures of center and spread.
c) Is the ratio of 9.3 for the Statue of Liberty unrealistically low? Explain.

**22. Winter Olympics 2006 speed skating.** The top 25 women's 500-m speed skating times are listed in the table below:

| Skater | Country | Time |
|--------|---------|------|
| Svetlana Zhurova | Russia | 76.57 |
| Wang Manli | China | 76.78 |
| Hui Ren | China | 76.87 |
| Tomomi Okazaki | Japan | 76.92 |
| Lee Sang-Hwa | South Korea | 77.04 |
| Jenny Wolf | Germany | 77.25 |
| Wang Beixing | China | 77.27 |
| Sayuri Osuga | Japan | 77.39 |
| Sayuri Yoshii | Japan | 77.43 |
| Chiara Simionato | Italy | 77.68 |
| Jennifer Rodriguez | United States | 77.70 |
| Annette Gerritsen | Netherlands | 78.09 |
| Xing Aihua | China | 78.35 |
| Sanne van der Star | Netherlands | 78.59 |
| Yukari Watanabe | Japan | 78.65 |
| Shannon Rempel | Canada | 78.85 |
| Amy Sannes | United States | 78.89 |
| Choi Seung-Yong | South Korea | 79.02 |
| Judith Hesse | Germany | 79.03 |
| Kim You-Lim | South Korea | 79.25 |
| Kerry Simpson | Canada | 79.34 |
| Krisy Myers | Canada | 79.43 |
| Elli Ochowicz | United States | 79.48 |
| Pamela Zoellner | Germany | 79.56 |
| Lee Bo-Ra | South Korea | 79.73 |

a) The mean finishing time was 78.21 seconds, with a standard deviation of 1.03 second. If the Normal model is appropriate, what percent of the times should be within 0.5 second of 78.21?
b) What percent of the times actually fall within this interval?
c) Explain the discrepancy between a and b.

**23. Sample.** A study in South Africa focusing on the impact of health insurance identified 1590 children at birth and then sought to conduct follow-up health studies 5 years later. Only 416 of the original group participated in the 5-year follow-up study. This made researchers concerned that the follow-up group might not accurately resemble the total group in terms of health insurance. The table in the next column summarizes the two groups by race and by presence of medical insurance when the child was born. Carefully explain how this study demonstrates Simpson's paradox. (*Birth to Ten Study*, Medical Research Council, South Africa)

| | | Number (%) Insured | |
|---|---|---|---|
| | | **Follow-up** | **Not traced** |
| Race | **Black** | 36 of 404 (8.9%) | 91 of 1048 (8.7%) |
| | **White** | 10 of 12 (83.3%) | 104 of 126 (82.5%) |
| | **Overall** | 46 of 416 (11.1%) | 195 of 1174 (16.6%) |

**24. Sluggers.** Roger Maris's 1961 home run record stood until Mark McGwire hit 70 in 1998. Listed below are the home run totals for each season McGwire played. Also listed are Babe Ruth's home run totals.

**McGwire:** 3*, 49, 32, 33, 39, 22, 42, 9*, 9*, 39, 52, 58, 70, 65, 32*, 27*

**Ruth:** 54, 59, 35, 41, 46, 25, 47, 60, 54, 46, 49, 46, 41, 34, 22

a) Find the 5-number summary for McGwire's career.
b) Do any of his seasons appear to be outliers? Explain.
c) McGwire played in only 18 games at the end of his first big league season, and missed major portions of some other seasons because of injuries to his back and knees. Those seasons might not be representative of his abilities. They are marked with asterisks in the list above. Omit these values and make parallel boxplots comparing McGwire's career to Babe Ruth's.
d) Write a few sentences comparing the two sluggers.
e) Create a side-by-side stem-and-leaf display comparing the careers of the two players.
f) What aspects of the distributions are apparent in the stem-and-leaf displays that did not clearly show in the boxplots?

**25. Be quick!** Avoiding an accident when driving can depend on reaction time. That time, measured from the moment the driver first sees the danger until he or she gets his foot on the brake pedal, is thought to follow a Normal model with a mean of 1.5 seconds and a standard deviation of 0.18 seconds.

a) Use the 68–95–99.7 Rule to draw the Normal model.
b) Write a few sentences describing driver reaction times.
c) What percent of drivers have a reaction time less than 1.25 seconds?
d) What percent of drivers have reaction times between 1.6 and 1.8 seconds?
e) What is the interquartile range of reaction times?
f) Describe the reaction times of the slowest 1/3 of all drivers.

**26. Music and memory.** Is it a good idea to listen to music when studying for a big test? In a study conducted by some Statistics students, 62 people were randomly assigned to listen to rap music, Mozart, or no music while attempting to memorize objects pictured on a page. They were then asked to list all the objects they could remember. Here are the 5-number summaries for each group:

|  | n | Min | Q1 | Median | Q3 | Max |
|---|---|---|---|---|---|---|
| Rap | 29 | 5 | 8 | 10 | 12 | 25 |
| Mozart | 20 | 4 | 7 | 10 | 12 | 27 |
| None | 13 | 8 | 9.5 | 13 | 17 | 24 |

a) Describe the W's for these data: *Who, What, Where, Why, When, How.*
b) Name the variables and classify each as categorical or quantitative.
c) Create parallel boxplots as best you can from these summary statistics to display these results.
d) Write a few sentences comparing the performances of the three groups.

**T 27. Mail.** Here are the number of pieces of mail received at a school office for 36 days.

| | | |
|---|---|---|
| 123 | 70 | 90 |
| 80 | 78 | 72 |
| 52 | 103 | 138 |
| 112 | 92 | 93 |
| 118 | 118 | 106 |
| 95 | 131 | 59 |
| 151 | 115 | 97 |
| 100 | 128 | 130 |
| 66 | 135 | 76 |
| 143 | 100 | 88 |
| 110 | 75 | 60 |
| 115 | 105 | 85 |

a) Plot these data.
b) Find appropriate summary statistics.
c) Write a brief description of the school's mail deliveries.
d) What percent of the days actually lie within one standard deviation of the mean? Comment.

**T 28. Birth order.** Is your birth order related to your choice of major? A Statistics professor at a large university polled his students to find out what their majors were and what position they held in the family birth order. The results are summarized in the table.

a) What percent of these students are oldest or only children?
b) What percent of Humanities majors are oldest children?
c) What percent of oldest children are Humanities students?
d) What percent of the students are oldest children majoring in the Humanities?

| | Birth Order* | | | | |
|---|---|---|---|---|---|
| | **1** | **2** | **3** | **4+** | **Total** |
| Math/Science | 34 | 14 | 6 | 3 | 57 |
| Agriculture | 52 | 27 | 5 | 9 | 93 |
| Humanities | 15 | 17 | 8 | 3 | 43 |
| Other | 12 | 11 | 1 | 6 | 30 |
| **Total** | **113** | **69** | **20** | **21** | **223** |

(Major labels the rows)

\* 1 = oldest or only child

**29. Engines.** One measure of the size of an automobile engine is its "displacement," the total volume (in liters or cubic inches) of its cylinders. Summary statistics for several models of new cars are shown. These displacements were measured in cubic inches.

| Summary of Displacement | |
|---|---|
| Count | 38 |
| Mean | 177.29 |
| Median | 148.5 |
| StdDev | 88.88 |
| Range | 275 |
| 25th %tile | 105 |
| 75th %tile | 231 |

a) How many cars were measured?
b) Why might the mean be so much larger than the median?
c) Describe the center and spread of this distribution with appropriate statistics.
d) Your neighbor is bragging about the 227-cubic-inch engine he bought in his new car. Is that engine unusually large? Explain.
e) Are there any engines in this data set that you would consider to be outliers? Explain.
f) Is it reasonable to expect that about 68% of car engines measure between 88 and 266 cubic inches? (That's $177.289 \pm 88.8767$.) Explain.
g) We can convert all the data from cubic inches to cubic centimeters (cc) by multiplying by 16.4. For example, a 200-cubic-inch engine has a displacement of 3280 cc. How would such a conversion affect each of the summary statistics?

**T 30. Birth order revisited.** Consider again the data on birth order and college majors in Exercise 28.
a) What is the marginal distribution of majors?
b) What is the conditional distribution of majors for the oldest children?

c) What is the conditional distribution of majors for the children born second?

d) Do you think that college major appears to be independent of birth order? Explain.

**31. Herbal medicine.** Researchers for the Herbal Medicine Council collected information on people's experiences with a new herbal remedy for colds. They went to a store that sold natural health products. There they asked 100 customers whether they had taken the cold remedy and, if so, to rate its effectiveness (on a scale from 1 to 10) in curing their symptoms. The Council concluded that this product was highly effective in treating the common cold.

a) Identify the W's of these data.

b) Identify the variables, classify each as categorical or quantitative, and specify units if relevant.

c) Are you confident about the Council's conclusion? Explain.

**32. Pay.** According to the *2006 National Occupational Employment and Wage Estimates for Management Occupations*, the mean hourly wage for Chief Executives was $69.52 and the median hourly wage was "over $70.00." By contrast, for General and Operations Managers, the mean hourly wage was $47.73 and the median was $40.97. Are these wage distributions likely to be symmetric, skewed left, or skewed right? Explain. (Bureau of Labor Statistics)

**33. Age and party 2007.** The Pew Research Center conducts surveys regularly asking respondents which political party they identify with. Among their results is the following table relating preferred political party and age. (http://people-press.org/reports/)

| | | Party | | | |
|---|---|---|---|---|---|
| | | **Republican** | **Democrat** | **Others** | Total |
| Age | **18–29** | 2636 | 2738 | 4765 | 10139 |
| | **30–49** | 6871 | 6442 | 8160 | 21473 |
| | **50–64** | 3896 | 4286 | 4806 | 12988 |
| | **65+** | 3131 | 3718 | 2934 | 9784 |
| | **Total** | **16535** | **17183** | **20666** | **54384** |

a) What percent of people surveyed were Republicans?

b) Do you think this might be a reasonable estimate of the percentage of all voters who are Republicans? Explain.

c) What percent of people surveyed were under 30 or over 65?

d) What percent of people were classified as "Other" and under the age of 30?

e) What percent of the people classified as "Other" were under 30?

f) What percent of people under 30 were classified as "Other"?

**34. Engines, again.** Horsepower is another measure commonly used to describe auto engines. Here are the summary statistics and histogram displaying horsepowers of the same group of 38 cars.

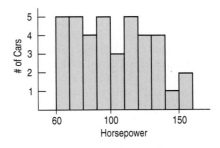

| Summary of Horsepower | |
|---|---|
| Count | 38 |
| Mean | 101.7 |
| Median | 100 |
| StdDev | 26.4 |
| Range | 90 |
| 25th %tile | 78 |
| 75th %tile | 125 |

a) Describe the shape, center, and spread of this distribution.

b) What is the interquartile range?

c) Are any of these engines outliers in terms of horsepower? Explain.

d) Do you think the 68–95–99.7 Rule applies to the horsepower of auto engines? Explain.

e) From the histogram, make a rough estimate of the percentage of these engines whose horsepower is within one standard deviation of the mean.

f) A fuel additive boasts in its advertising that it can "add 10 horsepower to any car." Assuming that is true, what would happen to each of these summary statistics if this additive were used in all the cars?

**35. Age and party II.** Consider again the Pew Research Center results on age and political party in Exercise 33.

a) What is the marginal distribution of party affiliation?

b) Create segmented bar graphs displaying the conditional distribution of party affiliation for each age group.

c) Summarize these poll results in a few sentences that might appear in a newspaper article about party affiliation in the United States.

d) Do you think party affiliation is independent of the voter's age? Explain.

**36. Public opinion.** For many years Martha Stewart was a popular expert in home decorating, an arbiter of good taste, and a very successful businesswoman. In June 2002 she first came under attack amidst rumors of insider stock trading. At that time, a series of Gallup polls each contacted over 1000 people to ask about their overall opinion of her. Those polled could answer favorable, unfavorable, or that they did not know who she was. Results are summarized in the table on the following page.

|  |  | Poll Date |  |  |
|---|---|---|---|---|
|  |  | Oct. 1999 | June 2002 | July 2002 |
| **Opinion** | **Favorable** | 49% | 46% | 30% |
|  | **Unfavorable** | 16% | 27% | 39% |
|  | **Don't know** | 32% | 23% | 27% |

a) Each poll should total 100%. Can you think of a reason why these do not?

b) How could the number of people who do not know who Martha Stewart is *increase* from June to July? Did people forget her? Or is the poll perhaps flawed? Explain how these results could be valid.

c) Display these results in a bar graph.

d) Display these results with pie charts.

e) Display these results with a timeplot.

f) Which display do you think best depicts these data? Why?

g) Write a few sentences describing Martha Stewart's public image at that time.

**T 37. Bike safety 2003.** The Bicycle Helmet Safety Institute website includes a report on the number of bicycle fatalities per year in the United States. The table below shows the counts for the years 1994–2003.

| Year | Bicycle fatalities |
|---|---|
| 1994 | 796 |
| 1995 | 828 |
| 1996 | 761 |
| 1997 | 811 |
| 1998 | 757 |
| 1999 | 750 |
| 2000 | 689 |
| 2001 | 729 |
| 2002 | 663 |
| 2003 | 619 |

a) What are the W's for these data?

b) Display the data in a stem-and-leaf display.

c) Display the data in a timeplot.

d) What is apparent in the stem-and-leaf display that is hard to see in the timeplot?

e) What is apparent in the timeplot that is hard to see in the stem-and-leaf display?

f) Write a few sentences about bicycle fatalities in the United States.

**T 38. Profits.** Here is a stem-and-leaf display showing profits as a percent of sales for 29 of the *Forbes* 500 largest U.S. corporations. The stems are split; each stem represents a span of 5%, from a loss of 9% to a profit of 25%.

```
-0 | 9 9
-0 | 1 2 3 4
 0 | 1 1 1 1 2 3 4 4 4
 0 | 5 5 5 5 6 7 9
 1 | 0 0 1 1 3
 1 |
 2 | 2
 2 | 5
```
**Profits (% of sales)**
(–0|3 means a loss of 3%)

a) Find the 5-number summary.

b) Draw a boxplot for these data.

c) Find the mean and standard deviation.

d) Describe the distribution of profits for these corporations.

**39. Some assembly required.** A company that markets build-it-yourself furniture sells a computer desk that is advertised with the claim "less than an hour to assemble." However, through postpurchase surveys the company has learned that only 25% of its customers succeeded in building the desk in under an hour; 5% said it took them over 2 hours. The company assumes that consumer assembly time follows a Normal model.

a) Find the mean and standard deviation of the assembly time model.

b) One way the company could solve this problem would be to change the advertising claim. What assembly time should the company quote in order that 60% of customers succeed in finishing the desk by then?

c) Wishing to maintain the "less than an hour" claim, the company hopes that revising the instructions and labeling the parts more clearly can improve the 1-hour success rate to 60%. If the standard deviation stays the same, what new lower mean time does the company need to achieve?

d) Months later, another postpurchase survey shows that new instructions and part labeling did lower the mean assembly time, but only to 55 minutes. Nonetheless, the company did achieve the 60%-in-an-hour goal, too. How was that possible?

**40. Crime and punishment.** Because of the development of statistics and the methods of analysis you are learning about in this book, the 20th century has been called "The First Measured Century" in a series of documentaries on PBS. On the following page are two of their graphs.

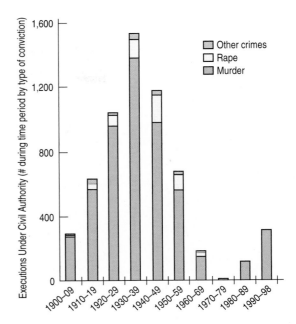

a) Write a few sentences describing the homicide rate in the United States during the 20th century.

b) Write a few sentences describing the use of capital punishment in the United States.

c) Could these two graphs be used to support the argument that capital punishment serves as a deterrent? If yes, explain how the graphs demonstrate that support. If no, explain why not.

# PART II

# Exploring Relationships Between Variables

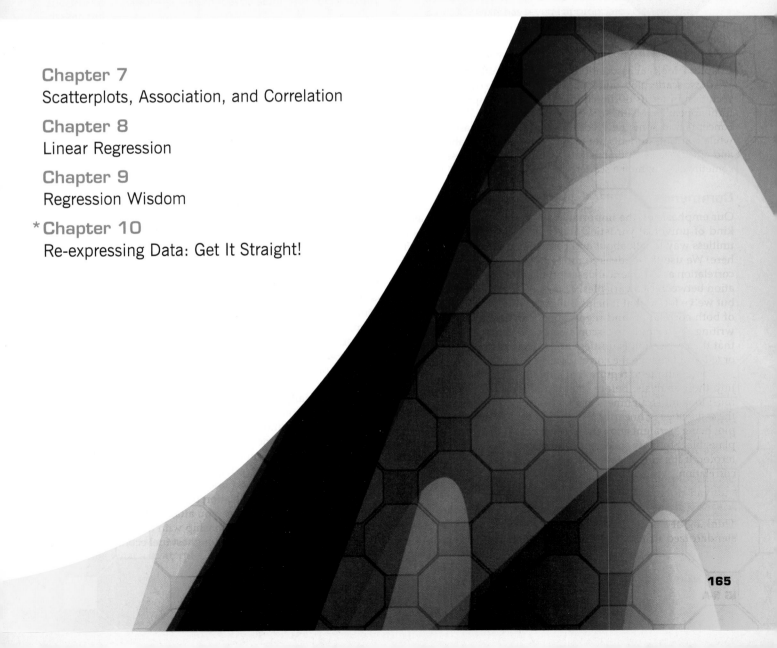

### Printed Test Bank and Resource Guide

The *Printed Test Bank and Resource Guide* introduces a worksheet that will carry over into Chapter 8. It leads students through an investigation of heights and weights for female students and encourages them to consider what correlation can reveal about these data and whether regression can tell us more. And there are three chapter quizzes.

### Web Links

▶ Find current Web links for a correlation-guessing game and a correlation slider at the book's Web site, www.aw-bc .com/dvb.

▶ Many sources will have bivariate data. The Data and Story Library's organization makes it easy to find examples of data suitable for discussing correlation. (www.stat.cmu .edu/DASL/)

# Instructor's Guide

# CHAPTER 8

# Linear Regression

## What's It About?

In Chapter 7 we saw how to use correlation to quantify the strength of a linear association; now we see how to use it to find a line that models the association. We build on the concepts from Chapter 7 and show students how to find the equation of this regression line, first from summary statistics and correlation, and later by reading the output of software-generated regression analyses.

We show that if we standardize both variables, the "best fit" line has slope equal to $r$. This makes several things clear, among them the concept of "regression to the mean."

We help students interpret the slope, the $y$-intercept, and the value of $R^2$ in context. As always, we caution students about possible misuses and misinterpretations of these ideas.

## Comments

The simple fact that $r$ is the slope of the line that best fits the scatterplot of $z$-scores is the key to a myriad of important insights. The concept of regression, the equation of the regression line, the meaning of $R^2$, and even our previous assertion that correlation is never greater than 1 (or less than –1) all grow out of this basic fact.

## Looking Ahead

Our central goal in this chapter is to develop the concepts, mechanics, and interpretation of linear regression. Many other issues can arise, and though these are important, we mention them but briefly here. We'll need entire chapters for those discussions. We devote Chapter 9 to a detailed examination of What Can Go Wrong?, and Chapter 10 to the question of dealing with one of our nemeses, nonlinearity in the data.

We'll return to these issues at the very end of the course, when we look at inference for regression in Chapter 27.

## Class Do's

Be sure to emphasize the model theme again. In Chapter 6 we saw the usefulness of the Normal model as a theoretical

approximation of real data; now we look at how to use a line to model a relationship we see in a scatterplot.

Open the discussion with a question about what might constitute a "good" line through a scatterplot. At first, talk in general about the model using examples involving means and standard deviations. Help students understand the general nature of a linear association by exploring several ideas:

▶ The first important idea is that at the mean of the $x$-variable, we should expect the line to be at the mean of the $y$-variable. In other words, the line should go through the mean–mean point.

▶ The model line may not pass through any of the points, but it should be close to a lot of them. Minor discrepancies between the line and the points are of less concern to us than huge gaps. Define the residual for a point.

▶ Discuss the goal of finding the "best" line. Point out that we want to somehow minimize the magnitude of these residuals. Talk about the least squares criterion.

To write an equation of a best-fit line, we need only know two things—a point on the line and a slope—and we have both. A point on the line? The mean–mean point! The slope? Easy to find, knowing the standard deviations of both variables and their correlation. Armed with the slope, we can use the known point to produce the equation.

Always insist that students use meaningful variable names in writing the equations for their models. In the interest of understanding and clear communication, we want $\widehat{shipfee} = 2.33 + 0.82\,weight$, not $\hat{y} = 2.33 + 0.82x$. You can probably guess what the first equation means even without knowing anything about the data that led to it. The second equation provides no such insight.

Spend time on the interpretations of slope, intercept, and $R^2$—always in context. Insisting on real variable names will help students be clear that with regression we are no longer dealing with standardized variables. We are now working with the data in their natural units. The regression slope is in "$y$-units *per* $x$-unit." The intercept is in $y$ units. Encourage students to write the phrase "*y*-units *per x*-unit" and then fill in the name of the *y* units and the name of the *x* units. The resulting phrase usually describes well what the regression is about. (We see phrases like "dollars per year of employment" or "grams of protein per ounce.")

Often the best (indeed, the only reasonable) interpretation of the intercept is as a starting value. Caution students that if *x* = 0 makes no sense (a baby with zero weight, the economy in the year "0"), then the interpretation of the intercept as a predicted value for *x* = 0 doesn't make much sense.

Remind students frequently that the line only *models* the relationship—it isn't the "truth." As George Box said, "All models are wrong, but some are useful." Be sure that the interpretations students make show they understand the distinction between models and reality. "Weight increases 6 pounds for every inch of height" is not a correct interpretation of slope. We always need some weasel words: "The model suggests that weight increases about 6 pounds, on average, for every additional inch of height." The same is true of estimates made with the model. Students should say something like, "the model predicts this person may weigh about 145 pounds," not "The person weighs . . .".

Students have trouble with the distinction between assessing the *appropriateness* of the model and the *strength* of the model. These are very different issues. "Appropriate" refers to whether the underlying relationship is linear. Look at the scatterplot or (better) the residuals plot. If there is no sign of a pattern (especially curvature), then a linear model is appropriate. But how strong is the association? Look at $R^2$. See how much of the variability the model explains. These two issues are not the same. An appropriate linear model can have a low $R^2$. The underlying relationship appears to be linear, but weak. And for a different relationship, the wrong model can have a high $R^2$. Imagine a scatterplot showing a series of points lying along a slight, but distinct, curve. A line may fit them pretty well (high $R^2$) but not be appropriate (because of the curve). Also look at $s_e$ to see how well the model fits the data. Compare $s_e$ with $s_y$ to see how much the model improves our ability to predict values of *y*.

Spend some time discussing the idea that the slope of the regression line for *z*-scores is the correlation. Concentrate on getting students to understand the concept of regression. Consider as an example a mythical college where the correlation between the SAT scores of freshmen and the GPAs they earn is 0.50. What should the college predict about the freshman GPA of an applicant who has an average SAT score? Or someone who has an above-average GPA?

▸ It's common sense that students with average SAT scores should be expected to achieve average GPAs. And remember, the line goes through the mean–mean point.

▸ When there's a positive association, we'd predict *y* to be above the mean when *x* is above the mean. Students with above-average SAT scores should be expected to achieve above-average GPAs.

▸ From there, we ask how far above the mean we should predict a student's GPA will be if he is two standard deviations above the mean in SAT score. Initially, students will say that if *x* is at +2 SD, then *y* should also be at +2 SD. Further discussion should convince them that a model's prediction must depend on the strength of the association. It's unusual for anything to be two standard deviations above the mean. Predicting that will happen is risky, and we statisticians are

a cautious lot. We'll venture that far out on a limb only if we have pretty strong assurance that it's safe. In fact, only if the correlation is 1. If the correlation is near 0, we stick close to the safety of the trunk—the mean. We would not feel comfortable predicting GPAs far above average for students whose shoe sizes are two standard deviations above the mean (assuming we think those two variables are unrelated . . .). It turns out that the correlation is our guide. With a correlation of 0.5, we are willing to go halfway, predicting GPAs will be $0.5 \times 2 = 1$ standard deviation above the mean for students who entered that college 2 standard deviations above the mean in SAT score. This caution, this backing off, is called "regression to the mean."

We need to be sure students understand that the line for predicting *x* from *y* is not the inverse of the line for predicting *y* from *x*. Especially tricky is that fact that if we regress standardized *y* on standardized *x*, we'll get a slope of *r*, while if we reverse the roles and regress standardized *x* on standardized *y* we don't get a slope of $1/r$, but r again. Ironically, it's usually the more mathematically oriented students that have trouble with this. They want to backsolve the equation for the new slope rather than refit the line. Have them write the equations of both lines. They should see, for example, that the weight predicted from a height of 70 inches does not itself predict a height of 70 inches. This provides another opportunity to deal with the concept of regression to the mean.

Here's another time that we want students to check on an assumption. Among other things, linear regression assumes that there is an underlying linear association between the two variables. As is always the case with assumptions, we cannot be sure that is true, but we can check to see if it is plausible. We eyeball the scatterplot or, even better, the residuals plot to see if there is a sign of curvature. The Straight Enough Condition affirms the assumption and allows us to proceed. It is worth noting that we make this check of residuals after the fact. First we do the regression, and then we look at the residuals to decide whether we should use that model.

## The Importance of What You Don't Say

*Dependent Variable.* Though still used in some disciplines, the terms independent and dependent variables are potentially confusing for two reasons. First, so-called "independent" variables aren't statistically independent of anything. Second, saying that one variable depends on another sounds like causation—one of the major misinterpretations we are trying to help students avoid. Unfortunately, these terms are standard in statistical software, so students should get used to seeing them. That's why we've sometimes used the term "dependent variable" in the generic computer output we show in the text and exercises.

## Class Examples

1. Use *ActivStats* to give students an opportunity to play with the least squares idea. (You may also find some effective demos or applets online.)

2. We can use cricket chirps to estimate temperature. Just count the number of chirps per minute, divide by 4, and add 40. This will give you the temperature (Fahrenheit) of the cricket's location. How could we discover such a relationship? We collect data on temperature and chirps, and

make a scatterplot. If there's evidence of a strong linear association, then the next question is about the line. Someone claims that for crickets it's

$$\widehat{dgF} = 40 + 0.25 \, chirps.$$

Interpret the slope.

3. Use the heights and weights (from Chapter 7) or distance and airfares data (here) as contexts for developing regression concepts. You can write equations of the regression line, and interpret slope, $y$-intercept, $R^2$, and residuals.

| Atlanta to: | Distance (mi) | Fare ($) |
|---|---|---|
| **Baltimore** | 568 | 219 |
| **Boston** | 933 | 222 |
| **Dallas** | 720 | 249 |
| **Denver** | 1190 | 308 |
| **Detroit** | 602 | 249 |
| **Kansas City** | 683 | 141 |
| **Las Vegas** | 1719 | 252 |
| **Miami** | 589 | 229 |
| **Memphis** | 327 | 183 |
| **Minneapolis** | 894 | 209 |
| **New Orleans** | 419 | 199 |
| **NY** | 749 | 248 |
| **Oklahoma City** | 749 | 301 |
| **Orlando** | 392 | 238 |
| **Philadelphia** | 657 | 205 |
| **St Louis** | 461 | 232 |
| **Salt Lake City** | 1565 | 371 |
| **Seattle** | 2150 | 343 |

| Summary Statistics | | |
|---|---|---|
| Mean | 853.7 | 244.33 |
| St Dev | 497.8 | 56.37 |
| Correlation | 0.694 | |

4. Interpreting $R^2$ can be a problem. Students are eager to say, "Height explains 46% of a person's weight" instead of "Differences in height account for 46% of the *variability* in weight" or some similar statement about variability. They have trouble both hearing and understanding the difference. An easier-to-understand example can help. Suppose we open a pizza place, selling our plain pizzas for $8 and adding $1.50 per topping. Create a scatterplot graphing cost of pizza against the number of toppings. Because this association is perfect, we easily know the equation of the line. Since all the points lie on the line, we know that $r = 1.00$. Ask students which statement describes this situation:
   A: The number of toppings accounts for 100% of the cost of the pizza.
   B: Differences in the number of toppings account for 100% of the variation in the cost of pizzas.
   Students should now see that the first statement is false. It attributes all of the cost to the toppings, ignoring the base price of a plain pizza. The second correctly explains the situation.

5. The final step in the process is learning to read regression output. Here's the output for the airfares data in (3). Discuss how to find correlation and write the regression equation.

Dependent variable is: Fare
R squared = 48.2%
s = 41.82 with 18 − 2 = 16 degrees of freedom

| Variable | Coefficient | SE(Coeff) | t-ratio | P-value |
|---|---|---|---|---|
| Intercept | 177.215 | 19.99 | 8.86 | ≤0.0001 |
| Distance | 0.078619 | 0.0204 | 3.86 | 0.0014 |

6. You can also use the airfares data to discuss reversing the direction of prediction. This output provides an equation to predict how far you can fly if you are willing to spend a certain amount. Show that the results are not the same as those obtained by backsolving the other equation.

Dependent variable is: Distance
R squared = 48.2%
s = 369.3 with 18 − 2 = 16 degrees of freedom

| Variable | Coefficient | SE(Coeff) | t-ratio | P-value |
|---|---|---|---|---|
| Intercept | −644.287 | 397.9 | −1.62 | 0.1249 |
| Fare | 6.13101 | 1.589 | 3.86 | 0.0014 |

7. If you have access to computer labs and software, use a data set (of your own or from the DVD) to teach students how to perform and interpret a regression analysis. You can use our sample with the *Cars* data and a computer software package, or adapt the basic ideas to create a similar lab exercise.

## RESOURCES

### ActivStats

▶ Chapter 8—"Least Squares Regression." The tool that encourages students to position a line on a scatterplot and view the sum of squared residuals offers an intuitive demonstration that there really is a unique line that minimizes the sum of squared residuals.

### Printed Test Bank and Resource Guide

The *Printed Test Bank and Resource Guide* shows you the algebra to demonstrate our assertion that the least squares line passes through $(\bar{x}, \bar{y})$ (which we assert rather lightly in the chapter) just for those students who really want to know. (We don't recommend it as a classroom activity.) There are two worksheets that guide students through regression analyses. The first works well with calculators. The second requires no technology at all, as it provides computer output and asks for interpretations. Then there's a *DataDesk* lab that leads students through an analysis with the computer. An investigative task poses questions based on a regression analysis and calls for a written report. Then, of course, you'll find chapter quizzes.

### Web Links

▶ Four lessons at the NCTM's Illuminations Web site investigate linear relationships, correlation, and regression lines.

# Regression Wisdom

## What's It About?

Chapter 8 briefly touched on What Can Go Wrong? with regression. Now we examine those issues in greater detail. We look at pattern changes in scatterplots; the dangers of extrapolation; the possible effects of outliers, high leverage, and influential points; the problem of regression on summary data; and the mistake of inferring causation. The exercises offer students more practice with regression while helping them learn to notice and deal with potential problems.

## Comments

Earlier in this Guide we described Statistics as the *art* of distilling meaning from data. In choosing that term, we mean to imply that what we do is not merely algorithmic or formulaic. We have to *Think*. We have to consider the circumstances, check the conditions, and choose our approach wisely, and then interpret the results carefully. We cannot rush into regression full speed ahead; there are many pitfalls. Chapter 8 taught students the concepts, the mechanics, and the correct interpretations of simple regression mostly by looking at situations where everything works. The real world, though, is rarely so cooperative. We want students to be cautious when applying regression techniques and interpreting the results. This chapter offers insights into many of the common problems that can arise, and provides ways of dealing with them. In some sense, there's nothing dramatically new here; after all, we are still just doing linear regression. But what we're aiming at is much deeper—the wisdom to use our statistical tools properly.

## Looking Ahead

Having dealt with many of the things that can go wrong, we are left with one remaining problem: What can we do when we see that the relationship between two quantitative variables is curved? When the scatterplot, or, more likely, the residuals plot reveals that a linear model is not appropriate, we need to find another approach. Re-expressing the data can often achieve linearity. We tackle that topic in Chapter 10.

You may find it worthwhile to glance far ahead, to Chapter 27, where we return to regression to do inference. While you won't be discussing inference with your students until the end of the course, looking at the issues there will help you know what to emphasize in the current chapter.

## Class Do's

Emphasize the fact that we always need to *Think* before rushing into regression. Plot the data. Look for trouble. Think of a way to deal with any problems.

Changes in a pattern over time may be a signal that something has changed in the underlying situation. Think about what might have changed historically. Divide the data into subsets that show a consistent trend. Answer the questions you have about the situation by creating a model for the relevant subset of the data. Don't extrapolate much—or at all—if you can avoid it.

Beware of unusual points. They come in three flavors:

▸ Least harmful are the points that confirm the pattern, but are extreme examples—high-leverage points with small residuals. A person who is really tall and weighs a lot may fit the overall pattern perfectly. The slope and intercept may be largely unaffected by that point (it's still the same line). Such a point, however, will increase the value of $R^2$, possibly misleading you into believing that the model is stronger than the rest of the data may warrant. Of course, it is best to check that the model for the other points *is* the same. If the other points don't determine a clear model, one extreme point can completely dictate the model. Be wary of overstating your case on the strength of one point.

▸ Outliers that aren't high-leverage points but still show up with large residuals may not affect the slope much but are clearly not consistent with the pattern seen in the other points. They often change the intercept. Never throw them away without just cause. Sometimes we know or strongly suspect that a datum might be inappropriate to use—mistakes in measurement, an individual known to be somehow different from the rest of the group, etc. However, it's not defensible to pare away anomalous measurements just to strengthen a model.

▸ Most troublesome are influential points. These are high-leverage points that aren't consistent with the model that describes the other points. These distort the model and may mislead us about the underlying relationship between the variables. They are hardest to detect. Influential points may have very small residuals, precisely *because* they are influential. A point that is an outlier in the *x* direction may exert so much leverage that it pulls the regression line toward it. We need to look at the scatterplot, covering up a point or two at a time to see if our perception of the pattern changes. When we suspect a point is influential we should omit that point and recalculate the regression. If the slope of the line changes dramatically we know that the omitted point was influential. We can be pretty sure that a model for all the data won't be worth much, so we need to set any influential points aside and find a model for the remaining points. But what should we do with the influential points? We need to *Think* more about those. They may simply be a mistake, or they may represent a fluke occurrence. However, we cannot overlook the possibility that data inconsistent with the rest of the pattern reflect a real and important aspect of the situation that we do not clearly understand. Often the points that *don't* fit the model tell us the most about it.

▸ We must be careful when we interpret $R^2$. It still measures the percentage of variability accounted for by our model. But now it describes the model's effectiveness in accounting for variability *in the re-expressed variables*, not the original. Recall, too, that correlation measures the strength of a *linear* association, so we should talk about $r$ only if we find a re-expression that makes the relationship linear.

Remind students that in order to write the correct equation for their model, they must pay careful attention to the re-expression they used. Just knowing that the coefficients of the linear model are 1.2 and 0.55 is not enough. If they used a logarithmic re-expression, the correct model is not $\hat{y} = 1.2 + 0.55x$, it's $\log(\hat{y}) = 1.2 + 0.55x$. While students should know that this model represents exponential growth, they do not need to be able to convert the equation into exponential form. They *do* need to be able to make predictions from the equation, though. For example, a student must be able to start with a value of $x = 2$, find $\log(\hat{y}) = 1.2 + 0.55x = 1.2 + 0.55(2) = 2.3$, and then "backsolve" to get $\hat{y} = 10^{2.3} \approx 200$.

## The Importance of What You Don't Say

***The "Best" Model, or the "Right" Model.*** We are looking for useful models. A useful model describes the relationship without leaving information behind (showing up as a pattern in the residuals plot). If the relationship is strong, it will describe much of the variability in the response variable (high $R^2$), but that alone is not the sign of a useful model. When the association is weak, $R^2$ may be small even for an appropriate model.

***Don't Use $R^2$ to Assert Linearity.*** Although $R^2$ applies to linear relationships, a high $R^2$ does not confirm linearity. A distinctly nonlinear relationship can have a high $R^2$, and a linear relationship with a lot of scatter can have a low $R^2$.

## Class Examples

1. Start off with one example of straightening a scatterplot using re-expression. The *Cars91* data set provides a good example to show in class (and it's repeated in the reading). We try to use horsepower to predict fuel economy, but there's a curve in the scatterplot, seen more clearly in the residuals. We try the reciprocal, gallons per hundred miles. Much better. Create the equation and backsolve some estimates.

2. For a calculator or software example, consider the population growth in the United States.

| Year | Population (millions) | Year | Population (millions) |
|------|------|------|------|
| 1800 | 5 | 1925 | 114 |
| 1825 | 11 | 1950 | 151 |
| 1850 | 23 | 1975 | 215 |
| 1875 | 44 | 2000 | 285 |
| 1900 | 76 | | |

This example is instructive in several ways. We scale the years as we enter the data. We could use 1, 2, 3, 4, . . . or 0, 25, 50, . . . (Caution students about using 0 or negative numbers as data values if they might want to try a logarithmic re-expression. This can be particularly insidious with computer software. Taking logs of 0 or negative values can make them "go missing" and just disappear quietly from the analysis.) We begin with the scatterplot and see a clear curve, concave upward. Now we use our Ladder of Powers. First we'll try the 0 power, the logarithm of the population. We start there because we suspect that population might increase by a roughly equal percentage each year (and hence that growth is exponential), or simply because it's a good place to start if we're not sure what to do. The change in the new scatterplot is dramatic. There's still a curve, but it bends the wrong way. This is a clear indication that we have gone too far on the ladder and should retreat toward the original data (the "1" rung). That suggests the $\frac{1}{2}$ power, so we find the square roots of the populations and plot them against the years. This scatterplot looks very straight, so we now fit a line. Remember to include the square root of population in the equation of the line. The line appears to fit well on the scatterplot. We check the residuals plot and see that the model still shows lingering curvature, but a trace of the residuals indicates that they are small and our $R^2$ value is high. This is a good model—not perfect, but apparently useful. Again, be sure to practice making estimates by backsolving.

3. If you have access to technology, have students practice the re-expression search-and-check using the ladder of powers or the log–log approach. Select some of the exercises in the text, data sets from the DVD, or use the class worksheet we provide among the resource materials. As with most classroom investigations, it's helpful to have students working in groups, where they can discuss their strategies and results while helping each other understand the concepts and develop facility with the technology.

4. Chapter 9's example on predicting life expectancy in a country from the number of television sets per person is a good one. Not only $\sqrt{x}$ does predict $y$ well, but the silly misinterpretation of solving world health problems by sending TVs rather than doctors is memorable.

5. It's too expensive for most farmers to own livestock scales, so they have "weight tapes" for estimating the weights of their animals. These tapes look like a standard tape measure. The farmer simply measures the animal's girth by tossing the tape over its back and around the largest part of the chest. But instead of reading off, say, 77 inches, a beef cattle tape will read 1309 pounds. A quick inspection shows that the scale is not linear—each extra inch does not represent a constant increase in the number of pounds. Ask students to describe how such a tape might have been created. (Weight tapes are available for beef cows, dairy cows, calves, pigs, and horses. Find them at a farm supply store, or at online livestock supply sites.)

## RESOURCES

### *ActivStats*

▸ Chapter 10–Re-expressing Data

### *Decisions Through Data*

▸ Video Unit 10–Exponential Growth

### *Printed Test Bank and Resource Guide*

The *Printed Test Bank and Resource Guide* offers a classroom worksheet. There's an Investigative Task predicting the weights of alligators from their (easier to measure or estimate) lengths. There are two chapter quizzes. And, since this is the end of Part II, there are three Part Tests on material from Chapters 7–10.

# CHAPTER 7

# Scatterplots, Association, and Correlation

## Where are we going?

Is the price of sneakers related to how long they last? Is your alertness in class related to how much (or little) sleep you got the night before?

In this chapter we'll look at relationships between two quantitative variables. We'll start by looking at scatterplots and describing the essence of what we see—the direction, form, and strength of the association. Then, as we did for histograms, we'll find a quantitative summary of what we learned from the display. We'll use the correlation to measure the strength of the association we see in the scatterplot.

| | |
|---|---|
| **WHO** | Years 1970–2005 |
| **WHAT** | Mean error in the position of Atlantic hurricanes as predicted 72 hours ahead by the NHC |
| **UNITS** | nautical miles |
| **WHEN** | 1970–2005 |
| **WHERE** | Atlantic and Gulf of Mexico |
| **WHY** | NHC wants to improve prediction models. |

Hurricane Katrina killed 1,836 people[1] and caused well over 100 billion dollars in damage—the most ever recorded. Much of the damage caused by Katrina was due to its almost perfectly deadly aim at New Orleans.

Where will a hurricane go? People want to know if a hurricane is coming their way, and the National Hurricane Center (NHC) of the National Oceanic and Atmospheric Administration (NOAA) tries to predict the path a hurricane will take. But hurricanes tend to wander around aimlessly and are pushed by fronts and other weather phenomena in their area, so they are notoriously difficult to predict. Even relatively small changes in a hurricane's track can make big differences in the damage it causes.

To improve hurricane prediction, NOAA[2] relies on sophisticated computer models, and has been working for decades to improve them. How well are they doing? Have predictions improved in recent years? Has the improvement been consistent? Here's a timeplot of the mean error, in nautical miles, of the NHC's 72-hour predictions of Atlantic hurricanes since 1970:

---

[1] In addition, 705 are still listed as missing.
[2] www.nhc.noaa.gov

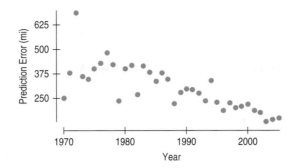

**FIGURE 7.1**

*A plot of the average error in nautical miles of the predicted position of Atlantic hurricanes for predictions made by the National Hurricane Center of NOAA, plotted against the Year in which the predictions were made.*

Clearly, predictions have improved. The plot shows a fairly steady decline in the average error, from almost 500 nautical miles in the late 1970s to about 150 nautical miles in 2005. We can also see a few years when predictions were unusually good and that 1972 was a really bad year for predicting hurricane tracks.

This timeplot is an example of a more general kind of display called a **scatterplot.** Scatterplots may be the most common displays for data. By just looking at them, you can see patterns, trends, relationships, and even the occasional extraordinary value sitting apart from the others. As the great philosopher Yogi Berra[3] once said, "You can observe a lot by watching."[4] Scatterplots are the best way to start observing the relationship between two *quantitative* variables.

Relationships between variables are often at the heart of what we'd like to learn from data:

▶ Are grades actually higher now than they used to be?

▶ Do people tend to reach puberty at a younger age than in previous generations?

▶ Does applying magnets to parts of the body relieve pain? If so, are stronger magnets more effective?

▶ Do students learn better with the use of computer technology?

Questions such as these relate two quantitative variables and ask whether there is an **association** between them. Scatterplots are the ideal way to *picture* such associations.

# Looking at Scatterplots

How would you describe the association of hurricane *Prediction Error* and *Year*? Everyone looks at scatterplots. But, if asked, many people would find it hard to say what to look for in a scatterplot. What do *you* see? Try to describe the scatterplot of *Prediction Error* against *Year*.

You might say that the **direction** of the association is important. Over time, the NHC's prediction errors have decreased. A pattern like this that runs from the upper left to the lower right is said to be **negative.** A pattern running the other way is called **positive.**

The second thing to look for in a scatterplot is its **form.** If there is a straight line relationship, it will appear as a cloud or swarm of points stretched out in a generally consistent, straight form. For example, the scatterplot of *Prediction Error* vs. *Year* has such an underlying **linear** form, although some points stray away from it.

---

[3] Hall of Fame catcher and manager of the New York Mets and Yankees.
[4] But then he also said "I really didn't say everything I said." So we can't really be sure.

**A S** *Activity:* **Heights of Husbands and Wives.** Husbands are usually taller than their wives. Or are they?

**A S** *Activity:* **Making and Understanding Scatterplots.** See the best way to make scatterplots—using a computer.

Look for **Direction:** What's my sign—positive, negative, or neither?

Scatterplots can reveal many kinds of patterns. Often they will not be straight, but straight line patterns are both the most common and the most useful for statistics.

If the relationship isn't straight, but curves gently, while still increasing or decreasing steadily, :: :...: , we can often find ways to make it more nearly

straight. But if it curves sharply—up and then down, for example —there is much less we can say about it with the methods of this book.

The third feature to look for in a scatterplot is how strong the relationship is. At one extreme, do the points appear tightly clustered in a single stream (whether straight, curved, or bending all over the place)? Or, at the other extreme, does the swarm of points seem to form a vague cloud through which we can

barely discern any trend or pattern? The *Prediction error* vs. *Year* plot shows moderate scatter around a generally straight form. This indicates that the linear trend of improving prediction is pretty consistent and moderately strong.

Finally, always look for the unexpected. Often the most interesting thing to see in a scatterplot is something you never thought to look for. One example of such a surprise is an **outlier** standing away from the overall pattern of the scatterplot. Such a point is almost always interesting and always deserves special attention. In the scatterplot of prediction errors, the year 1972 stands out as a year with very high prediction errors. An Internet search shows that it was a relatively quiet hurricane season. However, it included the very unusual—and deadly—hurricane Agnes, which combined with another low-pressure center to ravage the northeastern United States, killing 122 and causing 1.3 billion 1972 dollars in damage. Possibly, Agnes was also unusually difficult to predict.

You should also look for clusters or subgroups that stand away from the rest of the plot or that show a trend in a different direction. Deviating groups should raise questions about why they are different. They may be a clue that you should split the data into subgroups instead of looking at them all together.

**Look for Form:** straight, curved, something exotic, or no pattern?

**Look for Strength:** how much scatter?

**Look for Unusual Features:** Are there outliers or subgroups?

---

**FOR EXAMPLE** | Describing the scatterplot of hurricane winds and pressure

Hurricanes develop low pressure at their centers. This pulls in moist air, pumps up their rotation, and generates high winds. Standard sea-level pressure is around 1013 millibars (mb), or 29.9 inches of mercury. Hurricane Katrina had a central pressure of 920 mb and sustained winds of 110 knots.

Here's a scatterplot of *maximum wind speed* (kts) vs. *central pressure* (mb):

A scatterplot of Max Wind Speed *(in knots) vs.* Central Pressure *(in mb) for 163 hurricanes that have hit the United States since 1851.*

> **Question:** Describe what this plot shows.
>
> The scatterplot shows a negative direction; in general, lower central pressure is found in hurricanes that have higher maximum wind speeds. This association is linear and moderately strong.

## Scatterplot Details

*Descartes was a philosopher, famous for his statement* cogito ergo sum: *I think, therefore I am.*

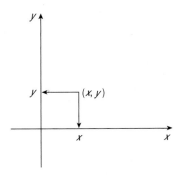

Scatterplots were among the first modern mathematical displays. The idea of using two axes at right angles to define a field on which to display values can be traced back to René Descartes (1596–1650), and the playing field he defined in this way is formally called a *Cartesian plane*, in his honor.

The two axes Descartes specified characterize the scatterplot. The axis that runs up and down is, by convention, called the $y$-axis, and the one that runs from side to side is called the $x$-axis. You can count on these names. If someone refers to the $y$-axis, you may be sure they mean the vertical, up-and-down axis, and when they refer to the $x$-axis, they mean the horizontal axis.[5]

To make a scatterplot of two quantitative variables, assign one to the $y$-axis and the other to the $x$-axis. Be sure to label the axes clearly, and indicate the scales of the axes with numbers. Scatterplots display *quantitative* variables. Each variable has units, which should appear with the display to define what it's showing.

Each point is placed on a scatterplot at a position that corresponds to values of these two variables. Its horizontal location is specified by its $x$-value and its vertical location is specified by its $y$-value. Together, these are known as *coordinates* and written $(x, y)$.

Scatterplots made by computer programs (such as the two we've seen in this chapter) often do not—and usually should not—show the *origin*, the point at $x = 0, y = 0$ where the axes meet. If both variables have values near or on both sides of zero, then the origin will be part of the display. If the values are far from zero, though, there's no reason to include the origin. In fact, it's far better to focus on the part of the Cartesian plane that contains the data. In our example about hurricanes, none of the prediction errors or years were anywhere near 0, so the computer drew the scatterplot (Figure 7.1) with axes that don't quite meet.

## Roles for Variables

Which variable should go on the $x$-axis and which on the $y$-axis? What we want to know about the relationship can tell us how to make the plot. We often have questions such as

▷ Do baseball teams that score more runs sell more tickets to their games?

▷ Do older houses sell for less than newer ones of comparable size and quality?

▷ Do students who score higher on their SAT tests have higher grade point averages in college?

▷ Can we estimate a person's percent body fat more simply by just measuring waist or wrist size?

---

[5] The $y$- and $x$-axes are also called the "ordinate" and the "abscissa," respectively—but we can never remember which is which because statisticians don't use these terms. In Statistics (and in all statistics computer programs), the axes are generically called "$x$" and "$y$," but are usually labeled with the names of the corresponding variables.

In these examples, the two variables play different roles. We'll call the variable of interest the **response variable** and the other the **explanatory** or **predictor variable.** We'll continue our practice of naming the variable of interest *y*. Naturally we'll plot it on the *y*-axis and place the explanatory variable on the *x*-axis. Sometimes, we'll call them the *x*- and *y*-**variables.** When you make a scatterplot, you can assume that those who view it will think this way, so choose which variables to assign to which axes carefully.

The roles that we choose for variables are more about how we *think* about them than about the variables themselves. Just placing a variable on the *x*-axis doesn't necessarily mean that it explains or predicts *anything*. And the variable on the *y*-axis may not respond to it in any way. We plotted prediction error on the *y*-axis against year on the *x*-axis because the National Hurricane Center is interested in how their predictions have changed over time. Could we have plotted them the other way? In this case, it's hard to imagine reversing the roles—knowing the prediction error and wanting to guess in what year it happened. But for some scatterplots, it can make sense to use either choice, so you have to think about how the choice of role helps to answer the question you have.

The *x*- and *y*-variables have sometimes been referred to as the *independent* and *dependent* variables, respectively. The idea was that the *y*-variable depended on the *x*-variable and the *x*-variable acted independently to make *y* respond. These names, however, conflict with other uses of the same terms in Statistics. We'll use the terms "explanatory" and "response" when we're thinking about a relationship in those terms, but we'll often just say *x-variable* and *y-variable*.

**A S** *Self-Test:* Scatterplot **Check.** Can you identify a scatterplot's direction, form, and strength?

# Correlation

| | |
|---|---|
| **WHO** | Students |
| **WHAT** | Height (inches), weight (pounds) |
| **WHERE** | Ithaca, NY |
| **WHY** | Data for class |
| **HOW** | Survey |

Data collected from students in Statistics classes included their *Height* (in inches) and *Weight* (in pounds). It's no great surprise to discover that there is a positive association between the two. As you might suspect, taller students tend to weigh more. (If we had reversed the roles and chosen height as the explanatory variable, we might say that heavier students tend to be taller.)[6] And the form of the scatterplot is fairly straight as well, although there seems to be a high outlier, as the plot shows.

**FIGURE 7.2** *Weight vs. Height of Statistics students.*
*Plotting* Weight *vs.* Height *in different units doesn't change the shape of the pattern.*

**A S** *Activity:* **Correlation.** Here's a good example of how correlation works to summarize the strength of a linear relationship and disregard scaling.

The pattern in the scatterplots looks straight and is clearly a positive association, but how strong is it? If you had to put a number (say, between 0 and 1) on the strength, what would it be? Whatever measure you use shouldn't depend on

---

[6] The son of one of the authors, when told (as he often was) that he was tall for his age, used to point out that, actually, he was young for his height.

the choice of units for the variables. After all, if we measure heights and weights in centimeters and kilograms instead, it doesn't change the direction, form, or strength, so it shouldn't change the number.

Since the units shouldn't matter to our measure of strength, we can remove them by standardizing each variable. Now, for each point, instead of the values $(x, y)$ we'll have the standardized coordinates $(z_x, z_y)$. Remember that to standardize values, we subtract the mean of each variable and then divide by its standard deviation:

$$(z_x, z_y) = \left( \frac{x - \bar{x}}{s_x}, \frac{y - \bar{y}}{s_y} \right).$$

Because standardizing makes the means of both variables 0, the center of the new scatterplot is at the origin. The scales on both axes are now standard deviation units.

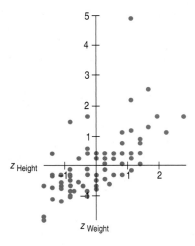

**FIGURE 7.3**

*A scatterplot of standardized heights and weights.*

Standardizing shouldn't affect the appearance of the plot. Does the plot of z-scores (Figure 7.3) look like the previous plots? Well, no. The underlying linear pattern seems steeper in the standardized plot. That's because the scales of the axes are now the same, so the length of one standard deviation is the same vertically and horizontally. When we worked in the original units, we were free to make the plot as tall and thin

or as squat and wide

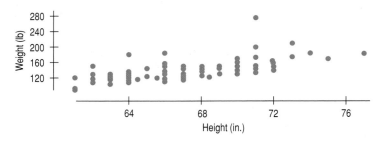

as we wanted to, but that can change the impression the plot gives. By contrast, equal scaling gives a neutral way of drawing the scatterplot and a fairer impression of the strength of the association.[7]

Which points in the scatterplot of the $z$-scores give the impression of a positive association? In a positive association, $y$ tends to increase as $x$ increases. So, the points in the upper right and lower left (colored green) strengthen that impression. For these points, $z_x$ and $z_y$ have the same sign, so the product $z_x z_y$ is positive. Points far from the origin (which make the association look more positive) have bigger products.

The red points in the upper left and lower right quadrants tend to weaken the positive association (or support a negative association). For these points, $z_x$ and $z_y$ have opposite signs. So the product $z_x z_y$ for these points is negative. Points far from the origin (which make the association look more negative) have a negative product even larger in magnitude.

Points with $z$-scores of zero on either variable don't vote either way, because $z_x z_y = 0$. They're colored blue.

To turn these products into a measure of the strength of the association, just add up the $z_x z_y$ products for every point in the scatterplot:

$$\sum z_x z_y.$$

This summarizes the direction *and* strength of the association for all the points. If most of the points are in the green quadrants, the sum will tend to be positive. If most are in the red quadrants, it will tend to be negative.

But the *size* of this sum gets bigger the more data we have. To adjust for this, the natural (for statisticians anyway) thing to do is to divide the sum by $n - 1$.[8] The ratio is the famous **correlation coefficient:**

$$r = \frac{\sum z_x z_y}{n - 1}.$$

For the students' heights and weights, the correlation is 0.644. There are a number of alternative formulas for the correlation coefficient, using $x$ and $y$ in their original units, that you may encounter elsewhere.[9] They can be more convenient for computing correlation by hand, but the form using $z$-scores is best for understanding what correlation means.

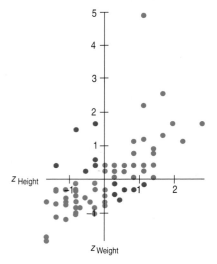

**FIGURE 7.4**

*In this scatterplot of z-scores, points are colored according to how they affect the association: green for positive, red for negative, and blue for neutral.*

---

**A S**  **Activity: Correlation and Relationship Strength.** What does a correlation of 0.8 look like? How about 0.3?

---

**NOTATION ALERT:**

The letter $r$ is always used for correlation, so you can't use it for anything else in Statistics. Whenever you see an $r$, it's safe to assume it's a correlation.

---

[7] When we draw a scatterplot, what often looks best is to make the length of the $x$-axis slightly larger than the length of the $y$-axis. This is an aesthetic choice, probably related to the Golden Ratio of the Greeks.

[8] Yes, the same $n - 1$ as in the standard deviation calculation. And we offer the same promise to explain it later.

[9] Like here, for example:

$$r = \frac{\sum (x - \bar{x})(y - \bar{y})}{\sqrt{\sum (x - \bar{x})^2 \sum (y - \bar{y})^2}} = \frac{\sum (x - \bar{x})(y - \bar{y})}{(n - 1) s_x s_y}.$$

## FINDING THE CORRELATION COEFFICIENT BY HAND

To find the correlation coefficient by hand, use a formula in original units, such as the second one in footnote 9 on page 172. This saves the work of having to standardize each individual data value first. Start with the summary statistics for both variables: $\bar{x}$, $\bar{y}$, $s_x$, and $s_y$. Then find the deviations as we did for the standard deviation, but now in both $x$ and $y$: $(x - \bar{x})$ and $(y - \bar{y})$. For each data pair, multiply these deviations together: $(x - \bar{x})(y - \bar{y})$. Add the products up for all data pairs. Finally, divide the sum by the product of $(n - 1) \times s_x \times s_y$ to get the correlation coefficient.

Here we go:
Suppose the data pairs are

| $x$ | 6 | 10 | 14 | 19 | 21 |
|---|---|---|---|---|---|
| $y$ | 5 | 3 | 7 | 8 | 12 |

Then $\bar{x} = 14$, $\bar{y} = 7$, $s_x = 6.20$, and $s_y = 3.39$.

| Deviations in $x$ | Deviations in $y$ | Product |
|---|---|---|
| $6 - 14 = -8$ | $5 - 7 = -2$ | $-8 \times -2 = 16$ |
| $10 - 14 = -4$ | $3 - 7 = -4$ | 16 |
| $14 - 14 = \phantom{-}0$ | $7 - 7 = \phantom{-}0$ | 0 |
| $19 - 14 = \phantom{-}5$ | $8 - 7 = \phantom{-}1$ | 5 |
| $21 - 14 = \phantom{-}7$ | $12 - 7 = \phantom{-}5$ | 35 |

Add up the products: $16 + 16 + 0 + 5 + 35 = 72$.
Finally, divide by $(n - 1) \times s_x \times s_y = (5 - 1) \times 6.20 \times 3.39 = 84.07$
The ratio is the correlation coefficient:

$$r = 72/84.07 = 0.856$$

# Correlation Conditions

**Correlation** measures the strength of the *linear* association between two *quantitative* variables. Before you use correlation, you must check several *conditions:*

▷ **Quantitative Variables Condition:** Are both variables quantitative? Correlation applies only to quantitative variables. Don't apply correlation to categorical data masquerading as quantitative. Check that you know the variables' units and what they measure.

▷ **Straight Enough Condition:** Is the form of the scatterplot straight enough that a linear relationship makes sense? Sure, you can *calculate* a correlation coefficient for any pair of variables. But correlation measures the strength only of the *linear* association, and will be misleading if the relationship is not linear. What is "straight enough"? How non-straight would the scatterplot have to be to fail the condition? This is a judgment call that you just have to think about. Do you think that the underlying relationship is curved? If so, then summarizing its strength with a correlation would be misleading.

▷ **Outlier Condition:** Outliers can distort the correlation dramatically. An outlier can make an otherwise weak correlation look big or hide a strong correlation. It can even give an otherwise positive association a negative correlation coefficient (and vice versa). When you see an outlier, it's often a good idea to report the correlation with and without that point.

**A S**  *Simulation:* **Correlation and Linearity.** How much does straightness matter?

**A S**  *Case Study:* **Mortality and Education.** Is the mortality rate lower in cities with higher education levels?

Each of these conditions is easy to check with a scatterplot. Many correlations are reported without supporting data or plots. Nevertheless, you should still think about the conditions. And you should be cautious in interpreting (or accepting others' interpretations of) the correlation when you can't check the conditions for yourself.

**FOR EXAMPLE** Correlating wind speed and pressure

**Recap:** We looked at the scatterplot displaying hurricane wind speeds and central pressures.

The correlation coefficient for these wind speeds and pressures is $r = -0.879$.

**Question:** Check the conditions for using correlation. If you feel they are satisfied, interpret this correlation.

▶ Quantitative Variables Condition: Both wind speed and central pressure are quantitative variables, measured (respectively) in knots and millibars.

▶ Straight Enough Condition: The pattern in the scatterplot is quite straight.

▶ Outlier Condition: A few hurricanes seem to straggle away from the main pattern, but they don't appear to be extreme enough to be called outliers. It may be worthwhile to check on them, however.

The conditions for using correlation are satisfied. The correlation coefficient of $r = -0.879$ indicates quite a strong negative linear association between the wind speeds of hurricanes and their central pressures.

## JUST CHECKING

Your Statistics teacher tells you that the correlation between the scores (points out of 50) on Exam 1 and Exam 2 was 0.75.

**1.** Before answering any questions about the correlation, what would you like to see? Why?

**2.** If she adds 10 points to each Exam 1 score, how will this change the correlation?

**3.** If she standardizes scores on each exam, how will this affect the correlation?

**4.** In general, if someone did poorly on Exam 1, are they likely to have done poorly or well on Exam 2? Explain.

**5.** If someone did poorly on Exam 1, can you be sure that they did poorly on Exam 2 as well? Explain.

**STEP-BY-STEP EXAMPLE** | **Looking at Association**

When your blood pressure is measured, it is reported as two values: systolic blood pressure and diastolic blood pressure.

**Questions:** How are these variables related to each other? Do they tend to be both high or both low? How strongly associated are they?

**Plan** State what you are trying to investigate.

I'll examine the relationship between two measures of blood pressure.

**Variables** Identify the two quantitative variables whose relationship we wish to examine. Report the W's, and be sure both variables are recorded for the same individuals.

The variables are systolic and diastolic blood pressure (SBP and DBP), recorded in millimeters of mercury (mm Hg) for each of 1406 participants in the Framingham Heart Study, a famous health study in Framingham, MA.[10]

**Plot** Make the scatterplot. Use a computer program or graphing calculator if you can.

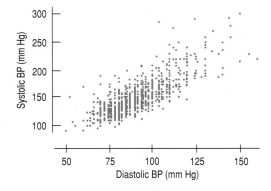

Check the conditions.

✓ **Quantitative Variables Condition:** Both SBP and DBP are quantitative and measured in mm Hg.
✓ **Straight Enough Condition:** The scatterplot looks straight.
✓ **Outlier Condition:** There are a few straggling points, but none far enough from the body of the data to be called outliers.

**REALITY CHECK** Looks like a strong positive linear association. We shouldn't be surprised if the correlation coefficient is positive and fairly large.

I have two quantitative variables that satisfy the conditions, so correlation is a suitable measure of association.

 **Mechanics** We usually calculate correlations with technology. Here we have 1406 cases, so we'd never try it by hand.

The correlation coefficient is $r = 0.792$.

---

[10] www.nhlbi.nih.gov/about/framingham

**Conclusion** Describe the direction, form, and strength you see in the plot, along with any unusual points or features. Be sure to state your interpretations in the proper context.

> The scatterplot shows a positive direction, with higher SBP going with higher DBP. The plot is generally straight, with a moderate amount of scatter. The correlation of 0.792 is consistent with what I saw in the scatterplot. A few cases stand out with unusually high SBP compared with their DBP. It seems far less common for the DBP to be high by itself.

# Correlation Properties

Here's a useful list of facts about the correlation coefficient:

**A S**  *Activity:* **Construct Scatterplots with a Given Correlation.** Try to make a scatterplot that has a given correlation. How close can you get?

▷ The sign of a correlation coefficient gives the direction of the association.

▷ Correlation is always between $-1$ and $+1$. Correlation *can* be exactly equal to $-1.0$ or $+1.0$, but these values are unusual in real data because they mean that all the data points fall *exactly* on a single straight line.

▷ Correlation treats $x$ and $y$ symmetrically. The correlation of $x$ with $y$ is the same as the correlation of $y$ with $x$.

▷ Correlation has no units. This fact can be especially appropriate when the data's units are somewhat vague to begin with (IQ score, personality index, socialization, and so on). Correlation is sometimes given as a percentage, but you probably shouldn't do that because it suggests a percentage of *something*—and correlation, lacking units, has no "something" of which to be a percentage.

**Height and Weight, Again**
We could have measured the students' weights in stones. In the now outdated UK system of measures, a stone is a measure equal to 14 pounds. And we could have measured heights in hands. Hands are still commonly used to measure the heights of horses. A hand is 4 inches. But no matter what *units* we use to measure the two variables, the *correlation* stays the same.

▷ Correlation is not affected by changes in the center or scale of either variable. Changing the units or baseline of either variable has no effect on the correlation coefficient. Correlation depends only on the z-scores, and they are unaffected by changes in center or scale.

▷ Correlation measures the strength of the *linear* association between the two variables. Variables can be strongly associated but still have a small correlation if the association isn't linear.

▷ Correlation is sensitive to outliers. A single outlying value can make a small correlation large or make a large one small.

> **How strong is strong?** You'll often see correlations characterized as "weak," "moderate," or "strong," but be careful. There's no agreement on what those terms mean. The same numerical correlation might be strong in one context and weak in another. You might be thrilled to discover a correlation of 0.7 between the new summary of the economy you've come up with and stock market prices, but you'd consider it a design failure if you found a correlation of "only" 0.7 between two tests intended to measure the same skill. Deliberately vague terms like "weak," "moderate," or "strong" that describe a linear association can be useful additions to the numerical summary that correlation provides. But be sure to include the correlation and show a scatterplot, so others can judge for themselves.

**Recap:** We found a correlation of $r = -0.879$ between hurricane wind speeds in knots and their central pressures in millibars.

**Question:** Suppose we wanted to consider the wind speeds in miles per hour (1 mile per hour = 0.869 knots) and central pressures in inches of mercury (1 inch of mercury = 33.86 millibars). How would that conversion affect the conditions, the value of $r$, and our interpretation of the correlation coefficient?

*Not at all! Correlation is based on standardized values (z-scores), so the conditions, the value of $r$, and the proper interpretation are all unaffected by changes in units.*

# Warning: Correlation ≠ Causation

Whenever we have a strong correlation, it's tempting to try to explain it by imagining that the predictor variable has *caused* the response to change. Humans are like that; we tend to see causes and effects in everything.

Sometimes this tendency can be amusing. A scatterplot of the human population ($y$) of Oldenburg, Germany, in the beginning of the 1930s plotted against the number of storks nesting in the town ($x$) shows a tempting pattern.

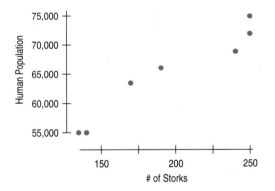

**FIGURE 7.5**

*The number of storks in Oldenburg, Germany, plotted against the population of the town for 7 years in the 1930s. The association is clear. How about the causation?* (Ornithologishe Monatsberichte, 44, no. 2)

Anyone who has seen the beginning of the movie *Dumbo* remembers Mrs. Jumbo anxiously waiting for the stork to bring her new baby. Even though you know it's silly, you can't help but think for a minute that this plot shows that storks are the culprits. The two variables are obviously related to each other (the correlation is 0.97!), but that doesn't prove that storks bring babies.

It turns out that storks nest on house chimneys. More people means more houses, more nesting sites, and so more storks. The causation is actually in the *opposite* direction, but you can't tell from the scatterplot or correlation. You need additional information—not just the data—to determine the real mechanism.

A scatterplot of the damage (in dollars) caused to a house by fire would show a strong correlation with the number of firefighters at the scene. Surely the damage doesn't cause firefighters. And firefighters do seem to cause damage, spraying water all around and chopping holes. Does that mean we shouldn't call the fire department? Of course not. There is an underlying variable that leads to both more damage and more firefighters: the size of the blaze.

A hidden variable that stands behind a relationship and determines it by simultaneously affecting the other two variables is called a **lurking variable.** You can often debunk claims made about data by finding a lurking variable behind the scenes.

> **Does cancer cause smoking?** Even if the correlation of two variables is due to a causal relationship, the correlation itself cannot tell us what causes what.
> Sir Ronald Aylmer Fisher (1890–1962) was one of the greatest statisticians of the 20th century. Fisher testified in court (in testimony paid for by the tobacco companies) that a causal relationship might underlie the correlation of smoking and cancer:
>
> "Is it possible, then, that lung cancer . . . is one of the causes of smoking cigarettes? I don't think it can be excluded . . . the pre-cancerous condition is one involving a certain amount of slight chronic inflammation . . . .
> A slight cause of irritation . . . is commonly accompanied by pulling out a cigarette, and getting a little compensation for life's minor ills in that way. And . . . is not unlikely to be associated with smoking more frequently."
>
> Ironically, the proof that smoking indeed is the cause of many cancers came from experiments conducted following the principles of experiment design and analysis that Fisher himself developed—and that we'll see in Chapter 13.

Scatterplots and correlation coefficients *never* prove causation. That's one reason it took so long for the U.S. Surgeon General to get warning labels on cigarettes. Although there was plenty of evidence that increased smoking was *associated* with increased levels of lung cancer, it took years to provide evidence that smoking actually *causes* lung cancer.

# Correlation Tables

It is common in some fields to compute the correlations between every pair of variables in a collection of variables and arrange these correlations in a table. The rows and columns of the table name the variables, and the cells hold the correlations.

Correlation tables are compact and give a lot of summary information at a glance. They can be an efficient way to start to look at a large data set, but a dangerous one. By presenting all of these correlations without any checks for linearity and outliers, the correlation table risks showing truly small correlations that have been inflated by outliers, truly large correlations that are hidden by outliers, and correlations of any size that may be meaningless because the underlying form is not linear.

| | Assets | Sales | Market Value | Profits | Cash Flow | Employees |
|---|---|---|---|---|---|---|
| Assets | 1.000 | | | | | |
| Sales | 0.746 | 1.000 | | | | |
| Market Value | 0.682 | 0.879 | 1.000 | | | |
| Profits | 0.602 | 0.814 | 0.968 | 1.000 | | |
| Cash Flow | 0.641 | 0.855 | 0.970 | 0.989 | 1.000 | |
| Employees | 0.594 | 0.924 | 0.818 | 0.762 | 0.787 | 1.000 |

**Table 7.1**

A correlation table of data reported by *Forbes* magazine for large companies. From this table, can you be sure that the variables are linearly associated and free from outliers?

The diagonal cells of a correlation table always show correlations of exactly 1. (Can you see why?) Correlation tables are commonly offered by statistics packages on computers. These same packages often offer simple ways to make all the scatterplots that go with these correlations.

# Straightening Scatterplots

Correlation is a suitable measure of strength for straight relationships only. When a scatterplot shows a bent form that consistently increases or decreases, we can often straighten the form of the plot by re-expressing one or both variables.

Some camera lenses have an adjustable aperture, the hole that lets the light in. The size of the aperture is expressed in a mysterious number called the f/stop. Each increase of one f/stop number corresponds to a halving of the light that is allowed to come through. The f/stops of one digital camera are

| **f/stop:** | 2.8 | 4 | 5.6 | 8 | 11 | 16 | 22 | 32 |

When you halve the shutter speed, you cut down the light, so you have to open the aperture one notch. We could experiment to find the best f/stop value for each shutter speed. A table of recommended shutter speeds and f/stops for a camera lists the relationship like this:

| **Shutter speed:** | 1/1000 | 1/500 | 1/250 | 1/125 | 1/60 | 1/30 | 1/15 | 1/8 |
|---|---|---|---|---|---|---|---|---|
| **f/stop:** | 2.8 | 4 | 5.6 | 8 | 11 | 16 | 22 | 32 |

The correlation of these shutter speeds and f/stops is 0.979. That sounds pretty high. You might assume that there must be a strong linear relationship. But when we check the scatterplot (we *always* check the scatterplot), it shows that something is not quite right:

**FIGURE 7.6**

*A scatterplot of f/stop vs. Shutter Speed shows a bent relationship.*

We can see that the f/stop is not *linearly* related to the shutter speed. Can we find a transformation of f/stop that straightens out the line? What if we look at the *square* of the f/stop against the shutter speed?

**FIGURE 7.7**

*Re-expressing f/stop by squaring straightens the plot.*

The second plot looks much more nearly straight. In fact, the correlation is now 0.998, but the increase in correlation is not important. (The original value of

0.979 should please almost anyone who sought a large correlation.) What is important is that the *form* of the plot is now straight, so the correlation is now an appropriate measure of association.[11]

We can often find transformations that straighten a scatterplot's form. Here, we found the square. Chapter 10 discusses simple ways to find a good re-expression.

---

## WHAT CAN GO WRONG?

▶ **Don't say "correlation" when you mean "association."** How often have you heard the word "correlation"? Chances are pretty good that when you've heard the term, it's been misused. When people want to sound scientific, they often say "correlation" when talking about the relationship between two variables. It's one of the most widely misused Statistics terms, and given how often statistics are misused, that's saying a lot. One of the problems is that many people use the specific term *correlation* when they really mean the more general term *association*. "Association" is a deliberately vague term describing the relationship between two variables.

   "Correlation" is a precise term that measures the strength and direction of the linear relationship between quantitative variables.

▶ **Don't confuse correlation with causation.** One of the most common mistakes people make in interpreting statistics occurs when they observe a high correlation between two variables and jump to the perhaps tempting conclusion that one thing must be causing the other. Scatterplots and correlations *never* demonstrate causation. At best, these statistical tools can only reveal an association between variables, and that's a far cry from establishing cause and effect. While it's true that some associations may be causal, the nature and direction of the causation can be very hard to establish, and there's always the risk of overlooking lurking variables.

▶ **Don't correlate categorical variables.** People who misuse the term "correlation" to mean "association" often fail to notice whether the variables they discuss are quantitative. Be sure to check the **Quantitative Variables Condition.**

▶ **Make sure the association is linear.** Not all associations between quantitative variables are linear. Correlation can miss even a strong nonlinear association. A student project evaluating the quality of brownies baked at different temperatures reports a correlation of −0.05 between judges' scores and baking temperature. That seems to say there is no relationship—until we look at the scatterplot:

**FIGURE 7.8**

*The relationship between brownie taste* Score *and* Baking Temperature *is strong, but not at all linear.*

There is a strong association, but the relationship is not linear. Don't forget to check the Straight Enough Condition.

---

[11] Sometimes we can do a "reality check" on our choice of re-expression. In this case, a bit of research reveals that f/stops are related to the diameter of the open shutter. Since the amount of light that enters is determined by the *area* of the open shutter, which is related to the diameter by squaring, the square re-expression seems reasonable. Not all re-expressions have such nice explanations, but it's a good idea to think about them.

▶ **Don't assume the relationship is linear just because the correlation coefficient is high.** Recall that the correlation of f/stops and shutter speeds is 0.979 and yet the relationship is clearly not straight. Although the relationship must be straight for the correlation to be an appropriate measure, a high correlation is no guarantee of straightness. Nor is it safe to use correlation to judge the best re-expression. It's important to look at the scatterplot.

**FIGURE 7.9**

*A scatterplot of f/stop vs. Shutter Speed shows a bent relationship even though the correlation is r = 0.979.*

▶ **Beware of outliers.** You can't interpret a correlation coefficient safely without a background check for outliers. Here's a silly example:

The relationship between IQ and shoe size among comedians shows a surprisingly strong positive correlation of 0.50. To check assumptions, we look at the scatterplot:

**FIGURE 7.10**

*A scatterplot of IQ vs. Shoe Size. From this "study," what is the relationship between the two? The correlation is 0.50. Who does that point (the green x) in the upper right-hand corner belong to?*

The outlier is Bozo the Clown, known for his large shoes, and widely acknowledged to be a comic "genius." Without Bozo, the correlation is near zero.

Even a single outlier can dominate the correlation value. That's why you need to check the Outlier Condition.

# CONNECTIONS

Scatterplots are the basic tool for examining the relationship between two quantitative variables. We start with a picture when we want to understand the distribution of a single variable, and we always make a scatterplot to begin to understand the relationship between two quantitative variables.

We used z-scores as a way to measure the statistical distance of data values from their means. Now we've seen the z-scores of $x$ and $y$ working together to build the correlation coefficient. Correlation is a summary statistic like the mean and standard deviation—only it summarizes the strength of a linear relationship. And we interpret it as we did z-scores, using the standard deviations as our rulers in both $x$ and $y$.

# WHAT HAVE WE LEARNED?

In recent chapters we learned how to listen to the story told by data from a single variable. Now we've turned our attention to the more complicated (and more interesting) story we can discover in the association between two quantitative variables.

We've learned to begin our investigation by looking at a scatterplot. We're interested in the *direction* of the association, the *form* it takes, and its *strength*.

We've learned that, although not every relationship is linear, when the scatterplot is straight enough, the *correlation coefficient* is a useful numerical summary.

▸ The sign of the correlation tells us the direction of the association.

▸ The magnitude of the correlation tells us of the *strength* of a linear association. Strong associations have correlations near −1 or +1, and very weak associations near 0.

▸ Correlation has no units, so shifting or scaling the data, standardizing, or even swapping the variables has no effect on the numerical value.

Once again we've learned that doing Statistics right means we have to *Think* about whether our choice of methods is appropriate.

▸ The correlation coefficient is appropriate only if the underlying relationship is linear.

▸ We'll check the **Straight Enough Condition** by looking at a scatterplot.

▸ And, as always, we'll watch out for outliers!

Finally, we've learned not to make the mistake of assuming that a high correlation or strong association is evidence of a cause-and-effect relationship. Beware of lurking variables!

**A S** *Simulation: Correlation, Center, and Scale.* If you have any lingering doubts that shifting and rescaling the data won't change the correlation, watch nothing happen right before your eyes!

## Terms

**Scatterplots**

167. A scatterplot shows the relationship between two quantitative variables measured on the same cases.

**Association**

▸ 167. **Direction:** A positive direction or association means that, in general, as one variable increases, so does the other. When increases in one variable generally correspond to decreases in the other, the association is negative.

▸ 167. **Form:** The form we care about most is straight, but you should certainly describe other patterns you see in scatterplots.

▸ 168. **Strength:** A scatterplot is said to show a strong association if there is little scatter around the underlying relationship.

**Outlier**

168. A point that does not fit the overall pattern seen in the scatterplot.

**Response variable, Explanatory variable, *x*-variable, *y*-variable**

169. In a scatterplot, you must choose a role for each variable. Assign to the *y*-axis the response variable that you hope to predict or explain. Assign to the *x*-axis the explanatory or predictor variable that accounts for, explains, predicts, or is otherwise responsible for the *y*-variable.

**Correlation Coefficient**

172. The correlation coefficient is a numerical measure of the direction and strength of a linear association.

$$r = \frac{\sum z_x z_y}{n - 1}.$$

**Lurking variable**

177. A variable other than *x* and *y* that simultaneously affects both variables, accounting for the correlation between the two.

## Skills

▸ Recognize when interest in the pattern of a possible relationship between two quantitative variables suggests making a scatterplot.

▸ Know how to identify the roles of the variables and that you should place the response variable on the *y*-axis and the explanatory variable on the *x*-axis.

- ▸ Know the conditions for correlation and how to check them.

- ▸ Know that correlations are between $-1$ and $+1$, and that each extreme indicates a perfect linear association.

- ▸ Understand how the magnitude of the correlation reflects the strength of a linear association as viewed in a scatterplot.

- ▸ Know that correlation has no units.

- ▸ Know that the correlation coefficient is not changed by changing the center or scale of either variable.

- ▸ Understand that causation cannot be demonstrated by a scatterplot or correlation.

- ▸ Know how to make a scatterplot by hand (for a small set of data) or with technology.

- ▸ Know how to compute the correlation of two variables.

- ▸ Know how to read a correlation table produced by a statistics program.

- ▸ Be able to describe the direction, form, and strength of a scatterplot.

- ▸ Be prepared to identify and describe points that deviate from the overall pattern.

- ▸ Be able to use correlation as part of the description of a scatterplot.

- ▸ Be alert to misinterpretations of correlation.

- ▸ Understand that finding a correlation between two variables does not indicate a causal relationship between them. Beware the dangers of suggesting causal relationships when describing correlations.

# ON THE COMPUTER

## Scatterplots and Correlation

Statistics packages generally make it easy to look at a scatterplot to check whether the correlation is appropriate. Some packages make this easier than others.

Many packages allow you to modify or enhance a scatterplot, altering the axis labels, the axis numbering, the plot symbols, or the colors used. Some options, such as color and symbol choice, can be used to display additional information on the scatterplot.

### DATA DESK

To make a scatterplot of two variables, select one variable as Y and the other as X and choose **Scatterplot** from the **Plot** menu. Then find the correlation by choosing **Correlation** from the scatterplot's HyperView menu.

Alternatively, select the two variables and choose **Pearson Product-Moment** from the **Correlations** submenu of the **Calc** menu.

### COMMENTS

We prefer that you look at the scatterplot first and then find the correlation. But if you've found the correlation first, click on the correlation value to drop down a menu that offers to make the scatterplot.

## EXCEL

To make a Scatterplot with the Excel Chart Wizard,

▸ Click on the **Chart Wizard** Button in the menu bar. Excel opens the Chart Wizard's Chart Type Dialog window.

▸ Make sure the **Standard Types** tab is selected, and select **XY (Scatter)** from the choices offered.

▸ Specify the **scatterplot without lines** from the choices offered in the Chart subtype selections. The **Next** button takes you to the Chart Source Data dialog.

▸ If it is not already frontmost, click on the **Data Range** tab, and enter the data range in the space provided.

▸ By convention, we always represent variables in columns. The Chart Wizard refers to variables as Series. Be sure the **Column** option is selected.

▸ Excel places the leftmost column of those you select on the x-axis of the scatterplot. If the column you wish to see on the x-axis is not the leftmost column in your spreadsheet, click on the **Series** tab and edit the specification of the individual axis series.

▸ Click the **Next** button. The Chart Options dialog appears.

▸ Select the **Titles** tab. Here you specify the title of the chart and names of the variables displayed on each axis.

▸ Type the chart title in the **Chart title:** edit box.

▸ Type the x-axis variable name in the **Value (X) Axis:** edit box. Note that you must name the columns correctly here. Naming another variable will not alter the plot, only mislabel it.

▸ Type the y-axis variable name in the **Value (Y) Axis:** edit box.

▸ Click the **Next** button to open the chart location dialog.

▸ Select the **As new sheet:** option button.

▸ Click the **Finish** button.

Often, the resulting scatterplot will not be useful. By default, Excel includes the origin in the plot even when the data are far from zero. You can adjust the axis scales.

To change the scale of a plot axis in Excel,

▸ Double-click on the axis. The **Format Axis Dialog** appears.

▸ If the **scale tab** is not the frontmost, select it.

▸ Enter new minimum or new maximum values in the spaces provided. You can drag the dialog box over the scatterplot as a straightedge to help you read the maximum and minimum values on the axes.

▸ Click the **OK** button to view the rescaled scatterplot.

▸ Follow the same steps for the x-axis scale.

Compute a correlation in Excel with the **CORREL** function from the drop-down menu of functions. If CORREL is not on the menu, choose **More Functions** and find it among the statistical functions in the browser.

In the dialog that pops up, enter the range of cells holding one of the variables in the space provided.

Enter the range of cells for the other variable in the space provided.

## EXCEL 2007

To make a scatterplot in Excel 2007:

▸ Select the columns of data to use in the scatterplot. You can select more than one column by holding down the control key while clicking.

▸ In the Insert tab, click on the **Scatter** button and select the **Scatter with only Markers** chart from the menu.

Unfortunately, the plot this creates is often statistically useless. To make the plot useful, we need to change the display:

▸ With the chart selected click on the **Gridlines** button in the Layout tab to cause the Chart Tools tab to appear.

▸ Within Primary Horizontal Gridlines, select **None**. This will remove the gridlines from the scatterplot.

▸ To change the axis scaling, click on the numbers of each axis of the chart, and click on the **Format Selection** button in the Layout tab.

▸ Select the **Fixed** option instead of the Auto option, and type a value more suited for the scatterplot. You can use the popup dialog window as a straightedge to approximate the appropriate values.

Excel 2007 automatically places the leftmost of the two columns you select on the x-axis, and the rightmost one on the y-axis. If that's not what you'd prefer for your plot, you'll want to switch them.

To switch the X and Y-variables:

▸ Click the chart to access the **Chart Tools** tabs.

▸ Click on the **Select Data** button in the Design tab.

▸ In the popup window's Legend Entries box, click on **Edit.**

▸ Highlight and delete everything in the Series X Values line, and select new data from the spreadsheet. (Note that selecting the column would inadvertently select the title of the column, which would not work well here.)

▸ Do the same with the Series Y Values line.

▸ Press **OK**, then press **OK** again.

## JMP

To make a scatterplot and compute correlation, choose **Fit Y by X** from the **Analyze** menu.

In the Fit Y by X dialog, drag the Y variable into the **"Y, Response"** box, and drag the X variable into the **"X, Factor"** box. Click the **OK** button.

Once JMP has made the scatterplot, click on the red triangle next to the plot title to reveal a menu of options. Select **Density Ellipse** and select .95. JMP draws an ellipse around the data and reveals the **Correlation** tab. Click the blue triangle next to Correlation to reveal a table containing the correlation coefficient.

## MINITAB

To make a scatterplot, choose **Scatterplot** from the **Graph** menu. Choose "Simple" for the type of graph. Click **OK.** Enter variable names for the *Y*-variable and *X*-variable into the table. Click **OK.**

To compute a correlation coefficient, choose **Basic Statistics** from the **Stat** menu. From the Basic Statistics submenu, choose **Correlation.** Specify the names of at least two quantitative variables in the "Variables" box. Click **OK** to compute the correlation table.

## SPSS

To make a scatterplot in SPSS, open the Chart Builder from the Graphs menu. Then

- Click the Gallery tab.
- Choose Scatterplot from the list of chart types.
- Drag the scatterplot onto the canvas.
- Drag a scale variable you want as the response variable to the *y*-axis drop zone.
- Drag a scale variable you want as the factor or predictor to the *x*-axis drop zone.
- Click OK.

To compute a correlation coefficient, choose **Correlate** from the **Analyze** menu. From the Correlate submenu, choose **Bivariate.** In the Bivariate Correlations dialog, use the arrow button to move variables between the source and target lists. Make sure the **Pearson** option is selected in the Correlation Coefficients field.

## TI-83/84 PLUS

To create a scatterplot, set up the **STAT PLOT** by choosing the **scatterplot** icon (the first option). Specify the lists where the data are stored as Xlist and Ylist. Set the graphing **WINDOW** to the appropriate scale and **GRAPH** (or take the easy way out and just ZoomStat!).

To find the correlation, go to **STAT CALC** menu and select **8: LinReg(a + bx).** Then specify the lists where the data are stored. The final command you will enter should look like **LinReg(a + bx) L1, L2.**

COMMENTS

Notice that if you **TRACE** the scatterplot, the calculator will tell you the *x*- and *y*-value at each point.

If the calculator does not tell you the correlation after you enter a LinReg command, try this: Hit **2nd CATALOG.** You now see a list of everything the calculator knows how to do. Scroll down until you find **DiagnosticOn.** Hit **ENTER** twice. (It should say Done.) Now and forevermore (or until you change batteries), you can find a correlation by using your calculator.

## TI-89

To create a scatterplot, press F2 **(Plots).** Select choice 1: **Plot Setup.** Select a plot to define and press F1. Select **Plot Type 1: Scatter.** Select a mark type. Specify the lists where the data are stored as Xlist and Ylist, using VAR-LINK. Press ENTER to finish. Press F5 to display the plot.

To find the correlation, press F4 **(CALC),** then arrow to **3: Regressions,** press the right arrow, and select **1:LinReg(a + bx).** Then specify the lists where the data are stored. You can also select a *y*-function to store the equation of the line.

COMMENTS

Notice that if you **TRACE** (press F3) the scatterplot, the calculator will tell you the *x*- and *y*-value at each point.

# EXERCISES

**1. Association.**   Suppose you were to collect data for each pair of variables. You want to make a scatterplot. Which variable would you use as the explanatory variable and which as the response variable? Why? What would you expect to see in the scatterplot? Discuss the likely direction, form, and strength.
a) Apples: weight in grams, weight in ounces
b) Apples: circumference (inches), weight (ounces)
c) College freshmen: shoe size, grade point average
d) Gasoline: number of miles you drove since filling up, gallons remaining in your tank

**2. Association.**   Suppose you were to collect data for each pair of variables. You want to make a scatterplot. Which variable would you use as the explanatory variable and which as the response variable? Why? What would you expect to see in the scatterplot? Discuss the likely direction, form, and strength.
a) T-shirts at a store: price each, number sold
b) Scuba diving: depth, water pressure
c) Scuba diving: depth, visibility
d) All elementary-school students: weight, score on a reading test

**3. Association.**   Suppose you were to collect data for each pair of variables. You want to make a scatterplot. Which variable would you use as the explanatory variable and which as the response variable? Why? What would you expect to see in the scatterplot? Discuss the likely direction, form, and strength.
a) When climbing a mountain: altitude, temperature
b) For each week: ice cream cone sales, air-conditioner sales
c) People: age, grip strength
d) Drivers: blood alcohol level, reaction time

**4. Association.**   Suppose you were to collect data for each pair of variables. You want to make a scatterplot. Which variable would you use as the explanatory variable and which as the response variable? Why? What would you expect to see in the scatterplot? Discuss the likely direction, form, and strength.
a) Long-distance calls: time (minutes), cost
b) Lightning strikes: distance from lightning, time delay of the thunder
c) A streetlight: its apparent brightness, your distance from it
d) Cars: weight of car, age of owner

**5. Scatterplots.**   Which of the scatterplots at the top of the next column show
a) little or no association?
b) a negative association?
c) a linear association?
d) a moderately strong association?
e) a very strong association?

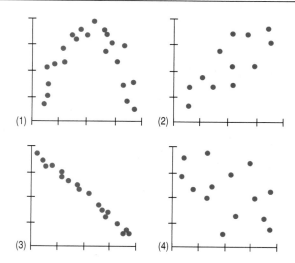

(1)   (2)

(3)   (4)

**6. Scatterplots.**   Which of the scatterplots below show
a) little or no association?
b) a negative association?
c) a linear association?
d) a moderately strong association?
e) a very strong association?

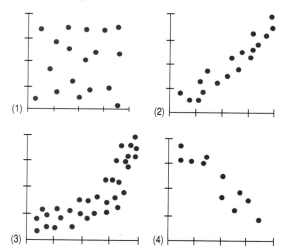

(1)   (2)

(3)   (4)

**7. Performance IQ scores vs. brain size.**   A study examined brain size (measured as pixels counted in a digitized magnetic resonance image [MRI] of a cross section of the brain) and IQ (4 Performance scales of the Weschler IQ test) for college students. The scatterplot shows the Performance IQ scores vs. the brain size. Comment on the association between brain size and IQ as seen in the scatterplot on the next page.

Performance IQ vs Brain Size (pixels)

**8. Kentucky Derby 2006.** The fastest horse in Kentucky Derby history was Secretariat in 1973. The scatterplot shows speed (in miles per hour) of the winning horses each year.

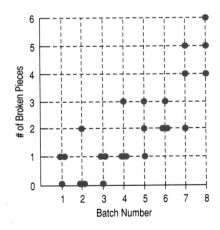

What do you see? In most sporting events, performances have improved and continue to improve, so surely we anticipate a positive direction. But what of the form? Has the performance increased at the same rate throughout the last 130 years?

**9. Firing pottery.** A ceramics factory can fire eight large batches of pottery a day. Sometimes a few of the pieces break in the process. In order to understand the problem better, the factory records the number of broken pieces in each batch for 3 days and then creates the scatterplot shown.

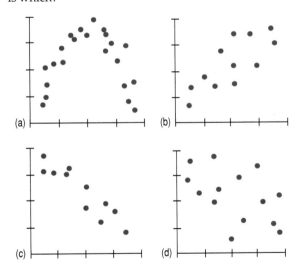

a) Make a histogram showing the distribution of the number of broken pieces in the 24 batches of pottery examined.
b) Describe the distribution as shown in the histogram. What feature of the problem is more apparent in the histogram than in the scatterplot?
c) What aspect of the company's problem is more apparent in the scatterplot?

**10. Coffee sales.** Owners of a new coffee shop tracked sales for the first 20 days and displayed the data in a scatterplot (by day):

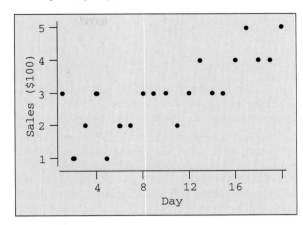

a) Make a histogram of the daily sales since the shop has been in business.
b) State one fact that is obvious from the scatterplot, but not from the histogram.
c) State one fact that is obvious from the histogram, but not from the scatterplot.

**11. Matching.** Here are several scatterplots. The calculated correlations are $-0.923$, $-0.487$, $0.006$, and $0.777$. Which is which?

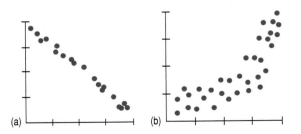

**12. Matching.** Here and on the next page are several scatterplots. The calculated correlations are $-0.977$, $-0.021$, $0.736$, and $0.951$. Which is which?

(c)  (d)

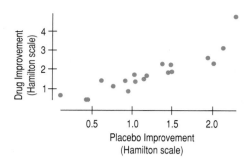

13. **Politics.** A candidate for office claims that "there is a correlation between television watching and crime." Criticize this statement on statistical grounds.

14. **Car thefts.** The National Insurance Crime Bureau reports that Honda Accords, Honda Civics, and Toyota Camrys are the cars most frequently reported stolen, while Ford Tauruses, Pontiac Vibes, and Buick LeSabres are stolen least often. Is it reasonable to say that there's a correlation between the type of car you own and the risk that it will be stolen?

15. **Roller coasters.** Roller coasters get all their speed by dropping down a steep initial incline, so it makes sense that the height of that drop might be related to the speed of the coaster. Here's a scatterplot of top *Speed* and largest *Drop* for 75 roller coasters around the world.

a) Does the scatterplot indicate that it is appropriate to calculate the correlation? Explain.
b) In fact, the correlation of *Speed* and *Drop* is 0.91. Describe the association.

16. **Antidepressants.** A study compared the effectiveness of several antidepressants by examining the experiments in which they had passed the FDA requirements. Each of those experiments compared the active drug with a placebo, an inert pill given to some of the subjects. In each experiment some patients treated with the placebo had improved, a phenomenon called the *placebo effect.* Patients' depression levels were evaluated on the Hamilton Depression Rating Scale, where larger numbers indicate greater improvement. The scatterplot at the top of the next column compares mean improvement levels for the antidepressants and placebos for several experiments.

a) Is it appropriate to calculate the correlation? Explain.
b) The correlation is 0.898. Explain what we have learned about the results of these experiments.

17. **Hard water.** In a study of streams in the Adirondack Mountains, the following relationship was found between the water's pH and its hardness (measured in grains):

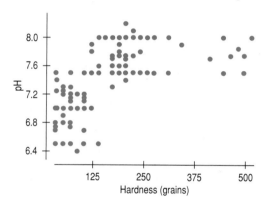

Is it appropriate to summarize the strength of association with a correlation? Explain.

18. **Traffic headaches.** A study of traffic delays in 68 U.S. cities found the following relationship between total delays (in total hours lost) and mean highway speed:

Is it appropriate to summarize the strength of association with a correlation? Explain.

19. **Cold nights.** Is there an association between time of year and the nighttime temperature in North Dakota? A researcher assigned the numbers 1–365 to the days January 1–December 31 and recorded the temperature at 2:00 a.m. for each. What might you expect the correlation between *DayNumber* and *Temperature* to be? Explain.

**20. Association.** A researcher investigating the association between two variables collected some data and was surprised when he calculated the correlation. He had expected to find a fairly strong association, yet the correlation was near 0. Discouraged, he didn't bother making a scatterplot. Explain to him how the scatterplot could still reveal the strong association he anticipated.

**21. Prediction units.** The errors in predicting hurricane tracks (examined in this chapter) were given in nautical miles. An ordinary mile is 0.86898 nautical miles. Most people living on the Gulf Coast of the United States would prefer to know the prediction errors in miles rather than nautical miles. Explain why converting the errors to miles would not change the correlation between *Prediction Error* and *Year*.

**22. More predictions.** Hurricane Katrina's hurricane force winds extended 120 miles from its center. Katrina was a big storm, and that affects how we think about the prediction errors. Suppose we add 120 miles to each error to get an idea of how far from the predicted track we might still find damaging winds. Explain what would happen to the correlation between *Prediction Error* and *Year*, and why.

**23. Correlation errors.** Your Economics instructor assigns your class to investigate factors associated with the gross domestic product (*GDP*) of nations. Each student examines a different factor (such as *Life Expectancy*, *Literacy Rate*, etc.) for a few countries and reports to the class. Apparently, some of your classmates do not understand Statistics very well because you know several of their conclusions are incorrect. Explain the mistakes in their statements below.
a) "My correlation of −0.772 shows that there is almost no association between *GDP* and *Infant Mortality Rate*."
b) "There was a correlation of 0.44 between *GDP* and *Continent*."

**24. More correlation errors.** Students in the Economics class discussed in Exercise 23 also wrote these conclusions. Explain the mistakes they made.
a) "There was a very strong correlation of 1.22 between *Life Expectancy* and *GDP*."
b) "The correlation between *Literacy Rate* and *GDP* was 0.83. This shows that countries wanting to increase their standard of living should invest heavily in education."

**25. Height and reading.** A researcher studies children in elementary school and finds a strong positive linear association between height and reading scores.
a) Does this mean that taller children are generally better readers?
b) What might explain the strong correlation?

**26. Cellular telephones and life expectancy.** A survey of the world's nations in 2004 shows a strong positive correlation between percentage of the country using cell phones and life expectancy in years at birth.
a) Does this mean that cell phones are good for your health?
b) What might explain the strong correlation?

**27. Correlation conclusions I.** The correlation between *Age* and *Income* as measured on 100 people is $r = 0.75$. Explain whether or not each of these possible conclusions is justified:
a) When *Age* increases, *Income* increases as well.
b) The form of the relationship between *Age* and *Income* is straight.
c) There are no outliers in the scatterplot of *Income* vs. *Age*.
d) Whether we measure *Age* in years or months, the correlation will still be 0.75.

**28. Correlation conclusions II.** The correlation between *Fuel Efficiency* (as measured by miles per gallon) and *Price* of 150 cars at a large dealership is $r = -0.34$. Explain whether or not each of these possible conclusions is justified:
a) The more you pay, the lower the fuel efficiency of your car will be.
b) The form of the relationship between *Fuel Efficiency* and *Price* is moderately straight.
c) There are several outliers that explain the low correlation.
d) If we measure *Fuel Efficiency* in kilometers per liter instead of miles per gallon, the correlation will increase.

**29. Baldness and heart disease.** Medical researchers followed 1435 middle-aged men for a period of 5 years, measuring the amount of *Baldness* present (none = 1, little = 2, some = 3, much = 4, extreme = 5) and presence of *Heart Disease* (No = 0, Yes = 1). They found a correlation of 0.089 between the two variables. Comment on their conclusion that this shows that baldness is not a possible cause of heart disease.

**30. Sample survey.** A polling organization is checking its database to see if the two data sources it used sampled the same zip codes. The variable *Datasource* = 1 if the data source is MetroMedia, 2 if the data source is DataQwest, and 3 if it's RollingPoll. The organization finds that the correlation between five-digit zip code and *Datasource* is −0.0229. It concludes that the correlation is low enough to state that there is no dependency between *Zip Code* and *Source of Data*. Comment.

**31. Income and housing.** The Office of Federal Housing Enterprise Oversight (www.ofheo.gov) collects data on various aspects of housing costs around the United States. Here is a scatterplot of the *Housing Cost Index* versus the *Median Family Income* for each of the 50 states. The correlation is 0.65.

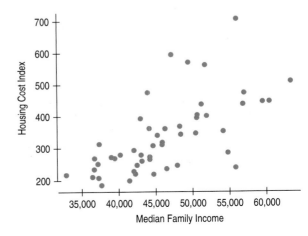

a) Describe the relationship between the *Housing Cost Index* and the *Median Family Income* by state.

b) If we standardized both variables, what would the correlation coefficient between the standardized variables be?

c) If we had measured *Median Family Income* in thousands of dollars instead of dollars, how would the correlation change?

d) Washington, DC, has a Housing Cost Index of 548 and a median income of about $45,000. If we were to include DC in the data set, how would that affect the correlation coefficient?

e) Do these data provide proof that by raising the median income in a state, the Housing Cost Index will rise as a result? Explain.

**32. Interest rates and mortgages.**   Since 1980, average mortgage interest rates have fluctuated from a low of under 6% to a high of over 14%. Is there a relationship between the amount of money people borrow and the interest rate that's offered? Here is a scatterplot of *Total Mortgages* in the United States (in millions of 2005 dollars) versus *Interest Rate* at various times over the past 26 years. The correlation is −0.84.

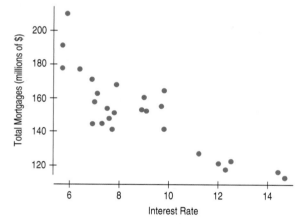

a) Describe the relationship between *Total Mortgages* and *Interest Rate*.

b) If we standardized both variables, what would the correlation coefficient between the standardized variables be?

c) If we were to measure *Total Mortgages* in thousands of dollars instead of millions of dollars, how would the correlation coefficient change?

d) Suppose in another year, interest rates were 11% and mortgages totaled $250 million. How would including that year with these data affect the correlation coefficient?

e) Do these data provide proof that if mortgage rates are lowered, people will take out more mortgages? Explain.

**33. Lunchtime.**   Does how long children remain at the lunch table help predict how much they eat? The table gives data on 20 toddlers observed over several months at a nursery school. "Time" is the average number of minutes a child spent at the table when lunch was served. "Calories" is the average number of calories the child consumed during lunch, calculated from careful observation of what the child ate each day.

| Calories | Time |
|----------|------|
| 472 | 21.4 |
| 498 | 30.8 |
| 465 | 37.7 |
| 456 | 33.5 |
| 423 | 32.8 |
| 437 | 39.5 |
| 508 | 22.8 |
| 431 | 34.1 |
| 479 | 33.9 |
| 454 | 43.8 |
| 450 | 42.4 |
| 410 | 43.1 |
| 504 | 29.2 |
| 437 | 31.3 |
| 489 | 28.6 |
| 436 | 32.9 |
| 480 | 30.6 |
| 439 | 35.1 |
| 444 | 33.0 |
| 408 | 43.7 |

a) Find the correlation for these data.

b) Suppose we were to record time at the table in hours rather than in minutes. How would the correlation change? Why?

c) Write a sentence or two explaining what this correlation means for these data. Remember to write about food consumption by toddlers rather than about correlation coefficients.

d) One analyst concluded, "It is clear from this correlation that toddlers who spend more time at the table eat less. Evidently something about being at the table causes them to lose their appetites." Explain why this explanation is not an appropriate conclusion from what we know about the data.

**34. Vehicle weights.**   The Minnesota Department of Transportation hoped that they could measure the weights of big trucks without actually stopping the vehicles by using a newly developed "weight-in-motion" scale. To see if the new device was accurate, they conducted a calibration test. They weighed several stopped trucks (static weight) and assumed that this weight was correct. Then they weighed the trucks again while they were moving to see how well the new scale could estimate the actual weight. Their data are given in the table on the next page.

**WEIGHT OF A TRUCK**
(THOUSANDS OF POUNDS)

| Weight-in-Motion | Static Weight |
|---|---|
| 26.0 | 27.9 |
| 29.9 | 29.1 |
| 39.5 | 38.0 |
| 25.1 | 27.0 |
| 31.6 | 30.3 |
| 36.2 | 34.5 |
| 25.1 | 27.8 |
| 31.0 | 29.6 |
| 35.6 | 33.1 |
| 40.2 | 35.5 |

a) Make a scatterplot for these data.
b) Describe the direction, form, and strength of the plot.
c) Write a few sentences telling what the plot says about the data. (*Note:* The sentences should be about weighing trucks, not about scatterplots.)
d) Find the correlation.
e) If the trucks were weighed in kilograms, how would this change the correlation? (1 kilogram = 2.2 pounds)
f) Do any points deviate from the overall pattern? What does the plot say about a possible recalibration of the weight-in-motion scale?

**T** **35. Fuel economy 2007.** Here are advertised horsepower ratings and expected gas mileage for several 2007 vehicles. (http://www.kbb.com/KBB/ReviewsAndRatings)

| Vehicle | Horsepower | Highway Gas Mileage (mpg) |
|---|---|---|
| Audi A4 | 200 | 32 |
| BMW 328 | 230 | 30 |
| Buick LaCrosse | 200 | 30 |
| Chevy Cobalt | 148 | 32 |
| Chevy TrailBlazer | 291 | 22 |
| Ford Expedition | 300 | 20 |
| GMC Yukon | 295 | 21 |
| Honda Civic | 140 | 40 |
| Honda Accord | 166 | 34 |
| Hyundai Elantra | 138 | 36 |
| Lexus IS 350 | 306 | 28 |
| Lincoln Navigator | 300 | 18 |
| Mazda Tribute | 212 | 25 |
| Toyota Camry | 158 | 34 |
| Volkswagen Beetle | 150 | 30 |

a) Make a scatterplot for these data.
b) Describe the direction, form, and strength of the plot.
c) Find the correlation between horsepower and miles per gallon.
d) Write a few sentences telling what the plot says about fuel economy.

**36. Drug abuse.** A survey was conducted in the United States and 10 countries of Western Europe to determine the percentage of teenagers who had used marijuana and other drugs. The results are summarized in the table.

| Country | Percent Who Have Used | |
|---|---|---|
| | Marijuana | Other Drugs |
| Czech Rep. | 22 | 4 |
| Denmark | 17 | 3 |
| England | 40 | 21 |
| Finland | 5 | 1 |
| Ireland | 37 | 16 |
| Italy | 19 | 8 |
| No. Ireland | 23 | 14 |
| Norway | 6 | 3 |
| Portugal | 7 | 3 |
| Scotland | 53 | 31 |
| USA | 34 | 24 |

a) Create a scatterplot.
b) What is the correlation between the percent of teens who have used marijuana and the percent who have used other drugs?
c) Write a brief description of the association.
d) Do these results confirm that marijuana is a "gateway drug," that is, that marijuana use leads to the use of other drugs? Explain.

**T** **37. Burgers.** Fast food is often considered unhealthy because much of it is high in both fat and sodium. But are the two related? Here are the fat and sodium contents of several brands of burgers. Analyze the association between fat content and sodium.

| Fat (g) | 19 | 31 | 34 | 35 | 39 | 39 | 43 |
|---|---|---|---|---|---|---|---|
| Sodium (mg) | 920 | 1500 | 1310 | 860 | 1180 | 940 | 1260 |

**T** **38. Burgers.** In the previous exercise you analyzed the association between the amounts of fat and sodium in fast food hamburgers. What about fat and calories? Here are data for the same burgers:

| Fat (g) | 19 | 31 | 34 | 35 | 39 | 39 | 43 |
|---|---|---|---|---|---|---|---|
| Calories | 410 | 580 | 590 | 570 | 640 | 680 | 660 |

**T** **39. Attendance 2006.** American League baseball games are played under the designated hitter rule, meaning that weak-hitting pitchers do not come to bat. Baseball owners believe that the designated hitter rule means more runs scored, which in turn means higher attendance. Is there evidence that more fans attend games if the teams score more runs? Data collected from American League games during the 2006 season indicate a correlation of 0.667 between runs scored and the number of people at the game. (http://mlb.mlb.com)

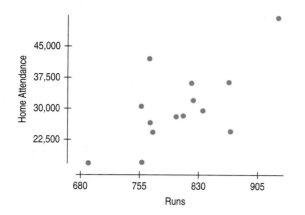

a) Does the scatterplot indicate that it's appropriate to calculate a correlation? Explain.
b) Describe the association between attendance and runs scored.
c) Does this association prove that the owners are right that more fans will come to games if the teams score more runs?

**40. Second inning 2006.** Perhaps fans are just more interested in teams that win. The displays below are based on American League teams for the 2006 season. (http://espn.go.com) Are the teams that win necessarily those which score the most runs?

|  | **CORRELATION** | | |
|---|---|---|---|
|  | Wins | Runs | Attend |
| Wins | 1.000 | | |
| Runs | 0.605 | 1.000 | |
| Attend | 0.697 | 0.667 | 1.000 |

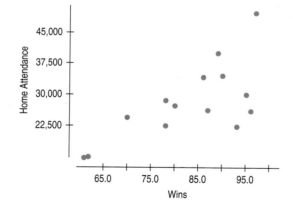

a) Do winning teams generally enjoy greater attendance at their home games? Describe the association.
b) Is attendance more strongly associated with winning or scoring runs? Explain.
c) How strongly is scoring more runs associated with winning more games?

**41. Thrills.** People who responded to a July 2004 Discovery Channel poll named the 10 best roller coasters in the United States. The table below shows the length of the initial drop (in feet) and the duration of the ride (in seconds). What do these data indicate about the

height of a roller coaster and the length of the ride you can expect?

| Roller Coaster | State | Drop (ft) | Duration (sec) |
|---|---|---|---|
| Incredible Hulk | FL | 105 | 135 |
| Millennium Force | OH | 300 | 105 |
| Goliath | CA | 255 | 180 |
| Nitro | NJ | 215 | 240 |
| Magnum XL-2000 | OH | 195 | 120 |
| The Beast | OH | 141 | 65 |
| Son of Beast | OH | 214 | 140 |
| Thunderbolt | PA | 95 | 90 |
| Ghost Rider | CA | 108 | 160 |
| Raven | IN | 86 | 90 |

**42. Oil production 2005.** The following table shows the oil production of the United States from 1949 to 2005 (in thousands of barrels per year):

| Year | Production (thousands of barrels) | Year | Production (thousands of barrels) |
|---|---|---|---|
| 1949 | 1,841,940 | 1978 | 3,178,216 |
| 1950 | 1,973,574 | 1979 | 3,121,310 |
| 1951 | 2,247,711 | 1980 | 3,146,365 |
| 1952 | 2,289,836 | 1981 | 3,128,624 |
| 1953 | 2,357,082 | 1982 | 3,156,715 |
| 1954 | 2,314,988 | 1983 | 3,170,999 |
| 1955 | 2,484,428 | 1984 | 3,249,696 |
| 1956 | 2,617,283 | 1985 | 3,274,553 |
| 1957 | 2,616,901 | 1986 | 3,168,252 |
| 1958 | 2,448,987 | 1987 | 3,047,377 |
| 1959 | 2,574,590 | 1988 | 2,979,126 |
| 1960 | 2,574,933 | 1989 | 2,778,772 |
| 1961 | 2,621,758 | 1990 | 2,684,689 |
| 1962 | 2,676,189 | 1991 | 2,707,039 |
| 1963 | 2,752,723 | 1992 | 2,624,631 |
| 1964 | 2,786,822 | 1993 | 2,499,033 |
| 1965 | 2,848,514 | 1994 | 2,431,476 |
| 1966 | 3,027,763 | 1995 | 2,394,269 |
| 1967 | 3,215,742 | 1996 | 2,366,016 |
| 1968 | 3,329,042 | 1997 | 2,354,831 |
| 1969 | 3,371,751 | 1998 | 2,281,920 |
| 1970 | 3,517,450 | 1999 | 2,146,732 |
| 1971 | 3,453,914 | 2000 | 2,130,706 |
| 1972 | 3,455,368 | 2001 | 2,117,512 |
| 1973 | 3,360,903 | 2002 | 2,097,124 |
| 1974 | 3,202,585 | 2003 | 2,073,454 |
| 1975 | 3,056,779 | 2004 | 1,983,300 |
| 1976 | 2,976,180 | 2005 | 1,890,107 |
| 1977 | 3,009,265 | | |

a) Find the correlation between *Year* and *Production*.

b) A reporter concludes that a low correlation between *Year* and *Production* shows that oil production has remained steady over the 57-year period. Do you agree with this interpretation? Explain.

**43. Planets (more or less).** On August 24, 2006, the International Astronomical Union voted that Pluto is not a planet. Some members of the public have been reluctant to accept that decision. Let's look at some of the data. (We'll see more in the next chapter.) Is there any pattern to the locations of the planets? The table shows the average distance of each of the traditional nine planets from the sun.

| Planet | Position Number | Distance from Sun (million miles) |
|---|---|---|
| Mercury | 1 | 36 |
| Venus | 2 | 67 |
| Earth | 3 | 93 |
| Mars | 4 | 142 |
| Jupiter | 5 | 484 |
| Saturn | 6 | 887 |
| Uranus | 7 | 1784 |
| Neptune | 8 | 2796 |
| Pluto | 9 | 3666 |

a) Make a scatterplot and describe the association. (Remember: direction, form, and strength!)
b) Why would you not want to talk about the correlation between a planet's *Position* and *Distance* from the sun?
c) Make a scatterplot showing the logarithm of *Distance* vs. *Position*. What is better about this scatterplot?

**44. Flights.** The number of flights by U.S. Airlines has grown rapidly. Here are the number of flights flown in each year from 1995 to 2005.
a) Find the correlation of *Flights* with *Year*.
b) Make a scatterplot and describe the trend.
c) Note two reasons that the correlation you found in (a) is not a suitable summary of the strength of the association. Can you account for these violations of the conditions?

| Year | Flights |
|---|---|
| 1995 | 5,327,435 |
| 1996 | 5,351,983 |
| 1997 | 5,411,843 |
| 1998 | 5,384,721 |
| 1999 | 5,527,884 |
| 2000 | 5,683,047 |
| 2001 | 5,967,780 |
| 2002 | 5,271,359 |
| 2003 | 6,488,539 |
| 2004 | 7,129,270 |
| 2005 | 7,140,596 |

**JUST CHECKING**
**Answers**

1. We know the scores are quantitative. We should check to see if the Straight Enough Condition and the Outlier Condition are satisfied by looking at a scatterplot of the two scores.

2. It won't change.

3. It won't change.

4. They are likely to have done poorly. The positive correlation means that low scores on Exam 1 are associated with low scores on Exam 2 (and similarly for high scores).

5. No. The general association is positive, but individual performances may vary.

# CHAPTER 8

# Linear Regression

## Where are we going?

We know that lower pressure in storms is associated with higher wind speeds. In fact, for hurricanes, the correlation is $-0.88$. If we know that a hurricane has a central pressure of 860 mb, how high would we expect the winds to be? The correlation alone won't tell us the answer.

We need a model to be able to use one variable to predict another. Using linear regression, we can understand the relationship between two quantitative variables better and make predictions.

| WHO | Items on the Burger King menu |
|---|---|
| **WHAT** | Protein content and total fat content |
| **UNITS** | Grams of protein Grams of fat |
| **HOW** | Supplied by BK on request or at their Web site |

**A S**   *Video:* **Manatees and Motorboats.** Are motorboats killing more manatees in Florida? Here's the story on video.

The Whopper™ has been Burger King's signature sandwich since 1957. One Double Whopper with cheese provides 53 grams of protein—all the protein you need in a day. It also supplies 1020 calories and 65 grams of fat. The Daily Value (based on a 2000-calorie diet) for fat is 65 grams. So after a Double Whopper you'll want the rest of your calories that day to be fat-free.[1]

Of course, the Whopper isn't the only item Burger King sells. How are fat and protein related on the entire BK menu? The scatterplot of the *Fat* (in grams) versus the *Protein* (in grams) for foods sold at Burger King shows a positive, moderately strong, linear relationship.

**FIGURE 8.1**

*Total Fat versus Protein for 30 items on the BK menu. The Double Whopper is in the upper right corner. It's extreme, but is it out of line?*

---

[1] Sorry about the fries.

*"Statisticians, like artists, have the bad habit of falling in love with their models."*

—George Box, famous statistician

If you want 25 grams of protein in your lunch, how much fat should you expect to consume at Burger King? The correlation between *Fat* and *Protein* is 0.83, a sign that the linear association seen in the scatterplot is fairly strong. But *strength* of the relationship is only part of the picture. The correlation says, "The linear association between these two variables is fairly strong," but it doesn't tell us *what the line is.*

Of course, we *can* say more. We can **model** the relationship with a line and give its equation. The equation will let us predict the fat content for any Burger King food, given its amount of protein.

We met our first model in Chapter 6. We saw there that we can specify a Normal model with two parameters: its mean ($\mu$) and standard deviation ($\sigma$).

For the Burger King foods, we'd choose a linear model to describe the relationship between *Protein* and *Fat*. The **linear model** is just an equation of a straight line through the data. Of course, no line can go through all the points, but a linear model can summarize the general pattern with only a couple of parameters. Like all models of the real world, the line will be wrong—wrong in the sense that it can't match reality *exactly.* But it can help us understand how the variables are associated.

## Residuals

Not only can't we draw a line through all the points, the best line might not even hit *any* of the points. Then how can it be the "best" line? We want to find the line that somehow comes *closer* to all the points than any other line. Some of the points will be above the line and some below. For example, the line might suggest that a BK Broiler chicken sandwich with 30 grams of protein should have 36 grams of fat when, in fact, it actually has only 25 grams of fat. We call the estimate made from a model the **predicted value,** and write it as $\hat{y}$ (called *y-hat*) to distinguish it from the true value *y* (called, uh, *y*). The difference between the observed value and its associated predicted value is called the **residual.** The residual value tells us how far off the model's prediction is at that point. The BK Broiler chicken residual would be $y - \hat{y} = 25 - 36 = -11$ g of fat.

To find the residuals, we always subtract the predicted value from the observed one. The negative residual tells us that the actual fat content of the BK Broiler chicken is about 11 grams *less* than the model predicts for a typical Burger King menu item with 30 grams of protein.

Our challenge now is how to find the right line.

> *residual = observed value − predicted value*
> A *negative* residual means the predicted value's too big—an **overestimate.** And a *positive* residual shows that the model makes an **underestimate.** These may seem backwards until you think about them.

## "Best Fit" Means Least Squares

When we draw a line through a scatterplot, some residuals are positive and some negative. We can't assess how well the line fits by adding up all the residuals—the positive and negative ones would just cancel each other out. We faced the same issue when we calculated a standard deviation to measure spread. And we deal with it the same way here: by squaring the residuals. Squaring makes them all positive. Now we can add them up. Squaring also emphasizes the large residuals. After all, points near the line are consistent with the model, but we're more concerned about points far from the line. When we add all the squared residuals together, that sum indicates how well the line we drew fits the data—the smaller the sum, the better the fit. A different line will produce a different sum, maybe bigger, maybe smaller. The **line of best fit** is the line for which the sum of the squared residuals is smallest, the **least squares** line.

You might think that finding this line would be pretty hard. Surprisingly, it's not, although it was an exciting mathematical discovery when Legendre published it in 1805 (see note below).

> **Who's on First**
> In 1805, Legendre was the first to publish the "least squares" solution to the problem of fitting a line to data when the points don't all fall exactly on the line. The main challenge was how to distribute the errors "fairly." After considerable thought, he decided to minimize the sum of the squares of what we now call the residuals. When Legendre published his paper, though, Gauss claimed he had been using the method since 1795. Gauss later referred to the "least squares" solution as "*our* method" (*principium nostrum*), which certainly didn't help his relationship with Legendre.

# The Linear Model

**NOTATION ALERT:**

"Putting a hat on it" is standard Statistics notation to indicate that something has been predicted by a model. Whenever you see a hat over a variable name or symbol, you can assume it is the predicted version of that variable or symbol (and look around for the model).

In a linear model, we use $b_1$ for the slope and $b_0$ for the $y$-intercept.

You may remember from Algebra that a straight line can be written as

$$y = mx + b.$$

We'll use this form for our linear model, but in Statistics we use slightly different notation:

$$\hat{y} = b_0 + b_1 x.$$

We write $\hat{y}$ ($y$-hat) to emphasize that the points that satisfy this equation are just our *predicted* values, not the actual data values (which scatter around the line).[2] If the model is a good one, the data values will scatter closely around it.

We write $b_1$ and $b_0$ for the slope and intercept of the line. The $b$'s are called the **coefficients** of the linear model. The coefficient $b_1$ is the **slope,** which tells how rapidly $\hat{y}$ changes with respect to $x$. The coefficient $b_0$ is the **intercept,** which tells where the line hits (intercepts) the $y$-axis.

For the Burger King menu items, the best fit line is

$$\widehat{Fat} = 6.8 + 0.97 \, Protein.$$

What does this mean? The slope, 0.97, says that an additional gram of protein is associated with an additional 0.97 grams of fat, on average. Less formally, we might say that Burger King foods pack about 0.97 grams of fat per gram of protein. Slopes are always expressed in $y$-units per $x$-unit. They tell how the $y$-variable changes (in its units) for a one-unit change in the $x$-variable. When you see a phrase like "students per teacher" or "kilobytes per second," think slope.

How about the intercept, 6.8? Algebraically, that's the value the line takes when $x$ is zero. Here, our model predicts that even a BK item with no protein would have, on average, about 6.8 grams of fat. Is that reasonable? Well, the apple pie, with 2 grams of protein, has 14 grams of fat, so it's not impossible. But often 0 is not a plausible value for $x$ (the year 0, a baby born weighing 0 grams, . . .). Then the intercept serves only as a starting value for our predictions, and we don't interpret it as a meaningful predicted value.

**A S** *Simulation:* **Interpreting Equations.** This demonstrates how to use and interpret linear equations.

---

[2] We change from $mx + b$ to $b_0 + b_1 x$ for a reason: Eventually we'll want to add more $x$'s to the model to make it more realistic, and we don't want to use up the entire alphabet. What would we use after $m$? The next letter is $n$ and that one's already taken. $o$? See our point? Sometimes subscripts are the best approach.

**FOR EXAMPLE**    A regression model for hurricanes

In Chapter 7 we looked at the relationship between the central pressure and maximum wind speed of Atlantic hurricanes. We saw that the scatterplot was straight enough, and then found a correlation of −0.879, but we had no model to describe how these two important variables are related or to allow us to predict wind speed from pressure. Since the conditions we need to check for regression are the same ones we checked before, we can use technology to find the regression model. It looks like this:

$$\widehat{MaxWindSpeed} = 955.27 - 0.897\,CentralPressure$$

**Question:** Interpret this model. What does the slope mean in this context? Does the intercept have a meaningful interpretation?

*The negative slope says that as CentralPressure falls, MaxWindSpeed increases. That makes sense from our general understanding of how hurricanes work: Low central pressure pulls in moist air, driving the rotation and the resulting destructive winds. The slope's value says that, on average, the maximum wind speed increases by about 0.897 knots for every 1-millibar drop in central pressure.*

    *It's not meaningful, however, to interpret the intercept as the wind speed predicted for a central pressure of 0—that would be a vacuum. Instead, it is merely a starting value for the model.*

# The Least Squares Line

> **Slope**
> $$b_1 = r\frac{s_y}{s_x}$$

How do we find the actual values of slope and intercept for the least squares line? The formulas are simple. The model is built from the summary statistics you already know: the correlation (to tell us the strength of the linear association), the standard deviations (to give us the units), and the means (to tell us where to put the line). The slope of the line is just

$$b_1 = r\frac{s_y}{s_x}.$$

We've already seen that the correlation tells us the *sign* as well as the strength of the relationship, so it's no surprise that the slope inherits this sign as well.

**Units of *y* per unit of *x***
Get into the habit of identifying the units by writing down "*y*-units per *x*-unit," with the unit names put in place. You'll find it'll really help you to Tell about the line in context.

Correlations don't have units, but slopes do. How *x* and *y* are measured—what units they have—doesn't affect their correlation, but can change their slope. If children grow an average of 3 inches per year, that's the same as 0.21 millimeters per day. For the slope, it matters whether you express age in days or years and whether you measure height in inches or millimeters. Changing the units of *x* and *y* affects their standard deviations directly. And that's how the slope gets its units—from the ratio of the two standard deviations. So, the units of the slope are a ratio too. The units of the slope are always the units of *y per* unit of *x*.

What about the intercept? If you had to predict the *y*-value for a data point whose *x*-value was average, what would you say? The best fit line always predicts $\bar{y}$ for points whose *x*-value is $\bar{x}$. Putting that into our equation, we find

$$\bar{y} = b_0 + b_1\bar{x},$$

or, rearranging the terms,

$$b_0 = \bar{y} - b_1\bar{x}.$$

**Intercept**
$$b_0 = \bar{y} - b_1\bar{x}$$

Knowing the slope and the fact that the line goes through the point $(\bar{x}, \bar{y})$ tells us how to find the intercept.

| Protein | Fat |
|---------|-----|
| $\bar{x} = 17.2\,g$ | $\bar{y} = 23.5\,g$ |
| $s_x = 14.0\,g$ | $s_y = 16.4\,g$ |
| | $r = 0.83$ |

### FOR EXAMPLE     Finding the regression equation

Let's try out the slope and intercept formulas on the "BK data" and see how to find the line. We checked the conditions when we calculated the correlation. We'll need the summary statistics (located conveniently in the margin). So, the slope is

$$b_1 = r\frac{s_y}{s_x} = 0.83 \times \frac{16.4 \text{ g fat}}{14.0 \text{ g protein}} = 0.97 \text{ grams of fat } per \text{ gram of protein.}$$

The intercept is

$$b_0 = \bar{y} - b_1\bar{x} = 23.5 \text{ g fat} - 0.97\frac{\text{g fat}}{\text{g protein}} \times 17.2 \text{ g protein} = 6.8 \text{ g fat.}$$

Putting these results back into the equation gives

$$\widehat{Fat} = 6.8 \text{ g fat} + 0.97\frac{\text{g fat}}{\text{g protein}} Protein,$$

or more simply,

$$\widehat{Fat} = 6.8 + 0.97\, Protein.$$

With an estimated linear model, it's easy to predict fat content for any menu item we want. For example, for the BK Broiler chicken sandwich with 30 grams of protein, we can plug in 30 grams for the amount of protein and see that the predicted fat content is 6.8 + 0.97(30) = 35.9 grams of fat. Because the BK Broiler chicken sandwich actually has 25 grams of fat, its residual is

$$Fat - \widehat{Fat} = 25 - 35.9 = -10.9 \text{ g.}$$

Least squares lines are commonly called regression lines. In a few pages we'll see that this name is an accident of history. For now, you just need to know that "regression" almost always means "the linear model fit by least squares."

To use a regression model, we should check the same conditions for regressions as we did for correlation: the **Quantitative Variables Condition**, the **Straight Enough Condition,** and the **Outlier Condition.**

**FIGURE 8.2**

*Burger King menu items with the regression line.*

## STEP-BY-STEP EXAMPLE | Calculating a Regression Equation

Wildfires are an ongoing source of concern shared by several government agencies. In 2004, the Bureau of Land Management, Bureau of Indian Affairs, Fish and Wildlife Service, National Park Service, and USDA Forest Service spent a combined total of $890,233,000 on fire suppression, down from nearly twice that much in 2002. These government agencies join together in the National Interagency Fire Center, whose Web site (www.nifc.gov) reports statistics about wildfires.

**Question:** Has the annual number of wildfires been changing, on average? If so, how fast and in what way?

**Plan** State the problem.

I want to know how the number of wildfires in the continental United States has changed in the past two decades.

**Variables** Identify the variables and report the W's

I have data giving the number of wildfires for each year (in thousands of fires) from 1982 to 2005.

Just as we did for correlation, check the conditions for a regression by making a picture. Never fit a regression without looking at the scatterplot first.

✔ **Quantitative Variables Condition:** Both the number of fires and the year are quantitative.

*Note:* It's common (and usually simpler) not to use four-digit numbers to identify years. Here we have chosen to number the years beginning in 1982, so 1982 is represented as year 0 and 2005 as year 23.

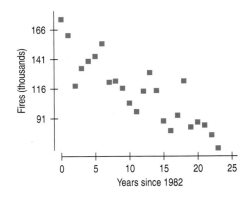

✔ **Straight Enough Condition:** The scatterplot shows a strong linear relationship with a negative association.

✔ **Outlier Condition:** No outliers are evident in the scatterplot.

Because these conditions are satisfied, it is OK to model the relationship with a regression line.

**Mechanics** Find the equation of the regression line. Summary statistics give the building blocks of the calculation.

(We generally report summary statistics to one more digit of accuracy than the data. We do the same for intercept and predicted values, but for slopes we usually report an additional digit. Remember, though, not to round off until you finish computing an answer.)[3]

**Year:**

$$\bar{x} = 11.5 \ (\text{representing } 1993.5)$$
$$s_x = 7.07 \ \text{years}$$

**Fires:**

$$\bar{y} = 114.098 \ \text{fires}$$
$$s_y = 28.342 \ \text{fires}$$

**Correlation:**

$$r = -0.862$$

Find the slope, $b_1$.

$$b_1 = r\frac{s_y}{s_x} = -0.862\frac{28.342}{7.07}$$
$$= -3.4556 \ \text{fires per year}$$

Find the intercept, $b_0$.

$$b_0 = \bar{y} - b_1\bar{x} = 114.098 - (-3.4556)11.5$$
$$= 153.837$$

So the least squares line is

$$\hat{y} = 153.837 - 3.4556x,$$

Write the equation of the model, using meaningful variable names.

$$\text{or } \widehat{Fires} = 153.837 - 3.4556 \ year$$

**Conclusion** Interpret what you have found in the context of the question. Discuss in terms of the variables and their units.

During the period from 1982 to 2005, the annual number of fires declined at an average rate of about 3,456 (3.456 thousand) fires per year. For prediction, the model uses a base estimation of 153,837 fires in 1982.

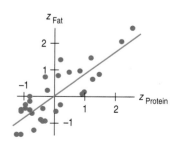

**A S** *Activity:* **Find a Regression Equation.** Now that we've done it by hand, try it with technology using the statistics package paired with your version of *ActivStats*.

## Correlation and the Line

In Chapter 7, we learned a lot about how correlation worked by looking at a scatterplot of the standardized variables. Let's see what else standardizing can tell us. Here's a scatterplot of $z_y$ (standardized *Fat*) vs. $z_x$ (standardized *Protein*) for the BK items along with their least squares line. What's the slope of this line?

We know that the slope $b_1 = r\frac{s_y}{s_x}$, but here we are working with standardized variables whose standard deviations are both 1. So for the regression of $z_y$ on $z_x$, $b_1 = r$.

**FIGURE 8.3**

*The Burger King scatterplot in z-scores.*

[3] We warned you in Chapter 6 that we'll round in the intermediate steps of a calculation to show the steps more clearly. If you repeat these calculations yourself on a calculator or statistics program, you may get somewhat different results. When calculated with more precision, the intercept is 153,809 and the slope is −3.453.

What about the intercept? Look at the plot. We know that $b_0 = \bar{y} - b_1\bar{x}$. But standardized variables have zero means, so we just get $b_0 = 0$; the line goes through the origin.

Wow! This line has an equation that's about as simple as we could possibly hope for:

$$\hat{z} = rz_x.$$

Great. It's simple, but what does it tell us? It says that in moving one standard deviation from the mean in $x$, we can expect to move about $r$ standard deviations away from the mean in $y$. Now that we're thinking about regression lines, the correlation is more than just a vague measure of strength of association: It's a great way to think about what regression tells us.

Let's be more specific. For the BK menu items, the correlation is 0.83. If we standardize both protein and fat, we can write

$$\hat{z}_{Fat} = 0.83z_{Protein}.$$

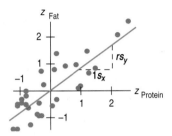

**FIGURE 8.4**

*Standardized* Fat *vs. standardized* Protein *with the regression line. Each one-standard-deviation change in* Protein *results in a predicted change of r standard deviations in* Fat.

We ordinarily don't standardize variables to perform a regression, but it's useful to think about what this equation says. It tells us that for every standard deviation above (or below) the mean a menu item is in protein, we'd predict that its fat content is 0.83 standard deviations above (or below) the mean fat content.

A double hamburger has 31 grams of protein, about 1 SD above the mean. How much fat do you expect it to have? Putting 1.0 in for $\hat{z}_{xy}$ in the model gives a $\hat{z}_y$ value of 0.83. If you trust the model, you'd expect the fat content to be about 0.83 fat SDs above the mean fat level. In general, menu items that are one standard deviation away from the mean in $x$ are, on average, $r$ standard deviations away from the mean in $y$.

If $r = 0$, there's no linear relationship. The line is horizontal, and no matter how many standard deviations you move in $x$, the predicted value for $y$ doesn't change. On the other hand, if $r = 1.0$ or $-1.0$, there's a perfect linear association. In that case, moving any number of standard deviations in $x$ moves the prediction exactly the same number of standard deviations in $y$.

### JUST CHECKING

A scatterplot of house *Price* (in thousands of dollars) vs. house *Size* (in thousands of square feet) for houses sold recently in Saratoga, NY shows a relationship that is straight, with only moderate scatter and no outliers. The correlation between house *Price* and house *Size* is 0.77, and the equation of the regression model is

$$\widehat{Price} = -3.117 + 94.454 \; Size.$$

1. What does the slope of 94.454 mean?
2. What are the units of the slope?
3. Your house is 2000 sq ft bigger than your neighbor's house. How much more do you expect it to be worth?

## How Big Can Predicted Values Get?

Suppose you were told that a new male student was about to join the class, and you were asked to guess his height in inches. What would be your guess? A good guess would be the mean height of male students. Now suppose you are also told that this student has a grade point average (*GPA*) of 3.9—about 2 SDs above

*Sir Francis Galton was the first to speak of "regression," although others had fit lines to data by the same method.*

the mean *GPA.* Would that change your guess? Probably not. There's no association between *GPA* and *Height,* so knowing the *GPA* value doesn't tell you anything and doesn't move your guess. (And the formula tells us that as well, since it says that we should guess $0 \times 2$ SDs from the mean.)

On the other hand, if you were told that, measured in centimeters, the student's height was 2 SDs above the mean, you'd know his height in inches. There's a perfect correlation between *Height in Inches* and *Height in Centimeters,* so you know he's 2 SDs above mean height in inches as well. (The formula would tell us to guess $1.0 \times 2$ SDs from the mean.)

What if you're told that the student is 2 SDs above the mean in *Shoe Size*? Would you still guess that he's of average *Height*? You might guess that he's taller than average, since there's a positive correlation between *Height* and *Shoe Size.* But would you guess that he's 2 SDs above the mean? When there was no correlation, we didn't move away from the mean at all. With a perfect correlation, we moved our guess the full 2 SDs. Any correlation between these extremes should lead us to guess somewhere between 0 and 2 SDs above the mean. (To be exact, the formula tells us to guess $2 \times r$ standard deviations away from the mean.)

You won't ever guess more than 2 SDs away, since *r* can't be bigger than 1.0. So, each predicted *y* tends to be closer to its mean (in standard deviations) than its corresponding *x* was. This property of the linear model is called **regression to the mean,** and that's where we got the term **regression line.**

### The First Regression

Sir Francis Galton related the heights of sons to the heights of their fathers with a regression line. The slope of his line was less than 1. That is, sons of tall fathers were tall, but not as much above the average height as their fathers had been above their mean. Sons of short fathers were short, but generally not as far from their mean as their fathers. Galton interpreted the slope correctly as indicating a "regression" toward the mean height—and "regression" stuck as a description of the method he had used to find the line.

### JUST CHECKING

Remember the homes in Saratoga? Our analysis found a correlation of $r = 0.77$ between the house *Price* (in thousands of dollars) and the house *Size* (in thousands of square feet).

**4.** You go to an open house and find that the house is 1 standard deviation above the mean in size. What would you guess about its price?

**5.** You read an ad for a house priced 2 standard deviations below the mean. What would you guess about its size?

**6.** A friend tells you about a house whose size in square meters (he's European) is 1.5 standard deviations above the mean. What would you guess about its size in square feet?

## Residuals Revisited

### Why *e* for "Residual"?

The flip answer is that *r* is already taken, but the truth is that *e* stands for "error." No, that doesn't mean it's a mistake. Statisticians often refer to variability not explained by a model as error.

The linear model we are using assumes that the relationship between the two variables is a perfect straight line. The residuals are the part of the data that *hasn't* been modeled. We can write

$$Data = Model + Residual$$

or, equivalently,

$$Residual = Data - Model.$$

Or, in symbols,

$$e = y - \hat{y}.$$

When we want to know how well the model fits, we can ask instead what the model missed. To see that, we look at the residuals.

**FOR EXAMPLE**    Katrina's residual

**Recap:** The linear model relating hurricanes' wind speeds to their central pressures was

$$\widehat{MaxWindSpeed} = 955.27 - 0.897 CentralPressure$$

Let's use this model to make predictions and see how those predictions do.

**Question:** Hurricane Katrina had a central pressure measured at 920 millibars. What does our regression model predict for her maximum wind speed? How good is that prediction, given that Katrina's actual wind speed was measured at 110 knots?

Substituting 920 for the central pressure in the regression model equation gives

$$\widehat{MaxWindSpeed} = 955.27 - 0.897(920) = 130.03$$

The regression model predicts a maximum wind speed of 130 knots for Hurricane Katrina.

The residual for this prediction is the observed value minus the predicted value:

$$110 - 130 = -20 kts.$$

In the case of Hurricane Katrina, the model predicts a wind speed 20 knots higher than was actually observed.

Residuals help us to see whether the model makes sense. When a regression model is appropriate, it should model the underlying relationship. Nothing interesting should be left behind. So after we fit a regression model, we usually plot the residuals in the hope of finding . . . nothing.

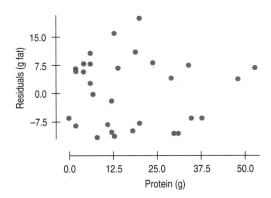

**FIGURE 8.5**
*The residuals for the BK menu regression look appropriately boring.*

A scatterplot of the residuals versus the $x$-values should be the most boring scatterplot you've ever seen. It shouldn't have any interesting features, like a direction or shape. It should stretch horizontally, with about the same amount of scatter throughout. It should show no bends, and it should have no outliers. If you see any of these features, find out what the regression model missed.

Most computer statistics packages plot the residuals against the predicted values $\hat{y}$, rather than against $x$. When the slope is negative, the two versions are mirror images. When the slope is positive, they're virtually identical except for the axis labels. Since all we care about is the patterns (or, better, lack of patterns) in the plot, it really doesn't matter which way we plot the residuals.

# The Residual Standard Deviation

If the residuals show no interesting pattern when we plot them against $x$, we can look at how big they are. After all, we're trying to make them as small as possible. Since their mean is always zero, though, it's only sensible to look at how much they vary. The standard deviation of the residuals, $s_e$, gives us a measure of how much the points spread around the regression line. Of course, for this summary to make sense, the residuals should all share the same underlying spread. That's why we check to make sure that the residual plot has about the same amount of scatter throughout.

This gives us a new assumption: the **Equal Variance Assumption.** The associated condition to check is the **Does the Plot Thicken? Condition.** We check to make sure that the spread is about the same throughout. We can check that either in the original scatterplot of $y$ against $x$ or in the scatterplot of residuals.

We estimate the standard deviation of the residuals in almost the way you'd expect:

> Why $n - 2$ rather than $n - 1$? We used $n - 1$ for $s$ when we estimated the mean. Now we're estimating both a slope and an intercept. Looks like a pattern—and it is. We subtract one more for each parameter we estimate.

$$s_e = \sqrt{\frac{\Sigma e^2}{n - 2}}.$$

We don't need to subtract the mean because the mean of the residuals $\bar{e} = 0$.

For the Burger King foods, the standard deviation of the residuals is 9.2 grams of fat. That looks about right in the scatterplot of residuals. The residual for the BK Broiler chicken was $-11$ grams, just over one standard deviation.

It's a good idea to make a histogram of the residuals. If we see a unimodal, symmetric histogram, then we can apply the 68–95–99.7 Rule to see how well the regression model describes the data. In particular, we know that 95% of the residuals should be no larger in size than $2s_e$. The Burger King residuals look like this:

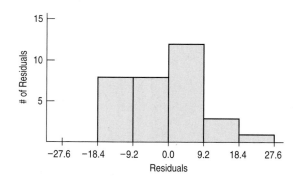

Sure enough, most are less than 2(9.2), or 18.4, g of fat in size.

# $R^2$—The Variation Accounted For

> **Why Is Correlation "$r$"?**
> In his original paper on correlation, Galton used $r$ for the "index of correlation" that we now call the correlation coefficient. He calculated it from the regression of $y$ on $x$ or of $x$ on $y$ after standardizing the variables, just as we have done. It's fairly clear from the text that he used $r$ to stand for (standardized) regression.

The variation in the residuals is the key to assessing how well the model fits. Let's compare the variation of the response variable with the variation of the residuals. The total *Fat* has a standard deviation of 16.4 grams. The standard deviation of the residuals is 9.2 grams. If the correlation were 1.0 and the model predicted the *Fat* values perfectly, the residuals would all be zero and have no variation. We couldn't possibly do any better than that.

On the other hand, if the correlation were zero, the model would simply predict 23.5 grams of *Fat* (the mean) for all menu items. The residuals from that prediction would just be the observed *Fat* values minus their mean. These residuals would have the same variability as the original data because, as we know, just subtracting the mean doesn't change the spread.

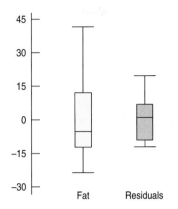

**FIGURE 8.6**

*Compare the variability of total Fat with the residuals from the regression. The means have been subtracted to make it easier to compare spreads. The variation left in the residuals is unaccounted for by the model, but it's less than the variation in the original data.*

How well does the BK regression model do? Look at the boxplots. The variation in the residuals is smaller than in the data, but certainly bigger than zero. That's nice to know, but how much of the variation is still left in the residuals? If you had to put a number between 0% and 100% on the fraction of the variation left in the residuals, what would you say?

All regression models fall somewhere between the two extremes of zero correlation and perfect correlation. We'd like to gauge where our model falls. Can we use the correlation to do that? Well, a regression model with correlation −0.5 is doing as well as one with correlation +0.5. They just have different directions. But if we *square* the correlation coefficient, we'll get a value between 0 and 1, and the direction won't matter. The squared correlation, $r^2$, gives the fraction of the data's variation accounted for by the model, and $1 - r^2$ is the fraction of the original variation left in the residuals. For the Burger King model, $r^2 = 0.83^2 = 0.69$, and $1 - r^2$ is 0.31, so 31% of the variability in total *Fat* has been left in the residuals. How close was that to your guess?

All regression analyses include this statistic, although by tradition, it is written with a capital letter, $R^2$, and pronounced "R-squared." An $R^2$ of 0 means that none of the variance in the data is in the model; all of it is still in the residuals. It would be hard to imagine using that model for anything.

Because $R^2$ is a fraction of a whole, it is often given as a percentage.[4] For the Burger King data, $R^2$ is 69%.

When interpreting a regression model, you need to *Tell* what $R^2$ means. According to our linear model, 69% of the variability in the fat content of Burger King sandwiches is accounted for by variation in the protein content.

Is a correlation of 0.80 twice as strong as a correlation of 0.40? Not if you think in terms of $R^2$. A correlation of 0.80 means an $R^2$ of $0.80^2 = 64\%$. A correlation of 0.40 means an $R^2$ of $0.40^2 = 16\%$—only a quarter as much of the variability accounted for. A correlation of 0.80 gives an $R^2$ *four* times as strong as a correlation of 0.40 and accounts for four times as much of the variability.

> **How can we see that $R^2$ is really the fraction of variance accounted for by the model?** It's a simple calculation. The variance of the fat content of the Burger King foods is $16.4^2 = 268.42$. If we treat the residuals as data, the variance of the residuals is 83.195.[5] As a fraction, that's $83.195/268.42 = 0.31$, or 31%. That's the fraction of the variance that is *not* accounted for by the model. The fraction that is accounted for is $100\% - 31\% = 69\%$, just the value we got for $R^2$.

---

[4] By contrast, we usually give correlation coefficients as decimal values between −1.0 and 1.0.

[5] This isn't quite the same as squaring the $s_e$ that we discussed on the previous page, but it's very close. We'll deal with the distinction in Chapter 27.

---

**FOR EXAMPLE**      Interpreting $R^2$

**Recap:** Our regression model that predicts maximum wind speed in hurricanes based on the storm's central pressure has $R^2 = 77.3\%$.

**Question:** What does that say about our regression model?

An $R^2$ of 77.3% indicates that 77.3% of the variation in maximum wind speed can be accounted for by the hurricane's central pressure. Other factors, such as temperature and whether the storm is over water or land, may account for some of the remaining variation.

---

## JUST CHECKING

Back to our regression of house *Price* (in thousands of $) on house *Size* (in thousands of square feet):

$$\widehat{Price} = -3.117 + 94.454 \, Size.$$

The $R^2$ value is reported as 59.5%, and the standard deviation of the residuals is 53.79.

**7.** What does the $R^2$ value mean about the relationship of price and size?

**8.** Is the correlation of price and size positive or negative? How do you know?

**9.** You find that your house is worth $100,000 more than the regression model predicts. Should you be very surprised (as well as pleased)?

---

# How Big Should $R^2$ Be?

**Some Extreme Tales**

One major company developed a method to differentiate between proteins. To do so, they had to distinguish between regressions with $R^2$ of 99.99% and 99.98%. For this application, 99.98% was not high enough.

The president of a financial services company reports that although his regressions give $R^2$ below 2%, they are highly successful because those used by his competition are even lower.

$R^2$ is always between 0% and 100%. But what's a "good" $R^2$ value? The answer depends on the kind of data you are analyzing and on what you want to do with it. Just as with correlation, there is no value for $R^2$ that automatically determines that the regression is "good." Data from scientific experiments often have $R^2$ in the 80% to 90% range and even higher. Data from observational studies and surveys, though, often show relatively weak associations because it's so difficult to measure responses reliably. An $R^2$ of 50% to 30% or even lower might be taken as evidence of a useful regression. The standard deviation of the residuals can give us more information about the usefulness of the regression by telling us how much scatter there is around the line.

As we've seen, an $R^2$ of 100% is a perfect fit, with no scatter around the line. The $s_e$ would be zero. All of the variance is accounted for by the model and none is left in the residuals at all. This sounds great, but it's too good to be true for real data.[6]

Along with the slope and intercept for a regression, you should always report $R^2$ so that readers can judge for themselves how successful the regression is at

---

[6] If you see an $R^2$ of 100%, it's a good idea to figure out what happened. You may have discovered a new law of Physics, but it's much more likely that you accidentally regressed two variables that measure the same thing.

fitting the data. Statistics is about variation, and $R^2$ measures the success of the regression model in terms of the fraction of the variation of $y$ accounted for by the regression. $R^2$ is the first part of a regression that many people look at because, along with the scatterplot, it tells whether the regression model is even worth thinking about.

# Regression Assumptions and Conditions

The linear regression model is perhaps the most widely used model in all of Statistics. It has everything we could want in a model: two easily estimated parameters, a meaningful measure of how well the model fits the data, and the ability to predict new values. It even provides a self-check in plots of the residuals, to help us avoid silly mistakes.

Like all models, though, linear models don't apply all the time, so we'd better think about whether they're reasonable. It makes no sense to make a scatterplot of categorical variables, and even less to perform a regression on them. Always check the **Quantitative Variables Condition** to be sure a regression is appropriate.

The linear model makes several assumptions. First, and foremost, is the **Linearity Assumption**—that the relationship between the variables is, in fact, linear. You can't verify an assumption, but you can check the associated condition. A quick look at the scatterplot will help you check the **Straight Enough Condition.** You don't need a *perfectly* straight plot, but it must be straight enough for the linear model to make sense. If you try to model a curved relationship with a straight line, you'll usually get exactly what you deserve.

If the scatterplot is not straight enough, stop here. You can't use a linear model for *any* two variables, even if they are related. They must have a *linear* association, or the model won't mean a thing.

For the standard deviation of the residuals to summarize the scatter, all the residuals should share the same spread, so we need the **Equal Variance Assumption.** The **Does the Plot Thicken? Condition** checks for changing spread in the scatterplot.

Check the **Outlier Condition.** Outlying points can dramatically change a regression model. Outliers can even change the sign of the slope, misleading us about the underlying relationship between the variables. We'll see examples in the next chapter.

Even though we've checked the conditions in the scatterplot of the data, a scatterplot of the residuals can sometimes help us see any violations even more clearly. And examining the residuals is the best way to look for additional patterns and interesting quirks in the data.

> **Make a Picture**
>
> To use regression, first check that
>
> - the scatterplot is straight enough.
>
> After you've fit the regression, make a residual plot and check that there are no obvious patterns. In particular, check that
>
> - there are no obvious bends,
> - the spread of the residuals is about the same throughout, and
> - there are no obvious outliers.

---

**STEP-BY-STEP EXAMPLE** | **Regression**

Even if you hit the fast food joints for lunch, you should have a good breakfast. Nutritionists, concerned about "empty calories" in breakfast cereals, recorded facts about 77 cereals, including their *Calories* per serving and *Sugar* content (in grams).

**Question:** How are calories and sugar content related in breakfast cereals?

**Plan** State the problem.

I am interested in the relationship between sugar content and calories in cereals.

**Variables** Name the variables and report the W's.

✓ **Quantitative Variables Condition:** I have two quantitative variables, *Calories* and *Sugar* content per serving, measured on 77 breakfast cereals. The units of measurement are calories and grams of sugar, respectively.

Check the conditions for a regression by making a picture. Never fit a regression without looking at the scatterplot first.

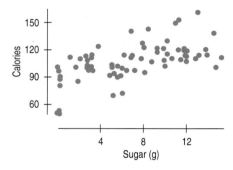

✓ **Outlier Condition:** There are no obvious outliers or groups.

✓ The **Straight Enough Condition** is satisfied; I will fit a regression model to these data.

✓ The **Does the Plot Thicken? Condition** is satisfied. The spread around the line looks about the same throughout.

**Mechanics** If there are no clear violations of the conditions, fit a straight line model of the form $\hat{y} = b_0 + b_1 x$ to the data. Summary statistics give the building blocks of the calculation.

**Calories**

$\bar{y} = 107.0$ calories

$s_y = 19.5$ calories

**Sugar**

$\bar{x} = 7.0$ grams

$s_x = 4.4$ grams

**Correlation**

$r = 0.564$

Find the slope.

$$b_1 = r\frac{s_y}{s_x} = 0.564\frac{19.5}{4.4}$$

$= 2.50$ calories per gram of sugar.

Find the intercept.

$b_0 = \bar{y} - b_1\bar{x} = 107 - 2.50(7) = 89.5$ calories.

So the least squares line is

$\hat{y} = 89.5 + 2.50\, x,$

Write the equation, using meaningful variable names.

or $\widehat{Calories} = 89.5 + 2.50\ Sugar.$

State the value of $R^2$.

Squaring the correlation gives

$R^2 = 0.564^2 = 0.318$ or $31.8\%$.

**Conclusion** Describe what the model says in words and numbers. Be sure to use the names of the variables and their units.

The key to interpreting a regression model is to start with the phrase "$b_1$ $y$-units per $x$-unit," substituting the estimated value of the slope for $b_1$ and the names of the respective units. The intercept is then a starting or base value.

$R^2$ gives the fraction of the variability of $y$ accounted for by the linear regression model.

Find the standard deviation of the residuals, $s_e$, and compare it to the original $s_y$.

The scatterplot shows a positive, linear relationship and no outliers. The least squares regression line fit through these data has the equation

$$\widehat{Calories} = 89.5 + 2.50\ Sugar.$$

The slope says that cereals have about 2.50 Calories more per gram of Sugar.

The intercept predicts that sugar-free cereals would average about 89.5 calories.

The $R^2$ says that 31.8% of the variability in Calories is accounted for by variation in Sugar content.

$s_e = 16.2$ calories. That's smaller than the original SD of 19.5, but still fairly large.

 **Check Again** Even though we looked at the scatterplot *before* fitting a regression model, a plot of the residuals is essential to any regression analysis because it is the best check for additional patterns and interesting quirks in the data.

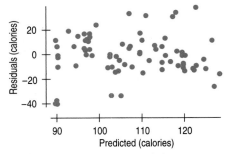

The residuals show a horizontal direction, a shapeless form, and roughly equal scatter for all predicted values. The linear model appears to be appropriate.

# Reality Check: Is the Regression Reasonable?

Statistics don't come out of nowhere. They are based on data. The results of a statistical analysis should reinforce your common sense, not fly in its face. If the results are surprising, then either you've learned something new about the world or your analysis is wrong.

Whenever you perform a regression, think about the coefficients and ask whether they make sense. Is a slope of 2.5 calories per gram of sugar reasonable? That's hard to say right off. We know from the summary statistics that a typical cereal has about 100 calories and 7 grams of sugar. A gram of sugar contributes some calories (actually, 4, but you don't need to know that), so calories should go up with increasing sugar. The direction of the slope seems right.

To see if the *size* of the slope is reasonable, a useful trick is to consider its order of magnitude. We'll start by asking if deflating the slope by a factor of 10 seems reasonable. Is 0.25 calories per gram of sugar enough? The 7 grams of sugar found in the average cereal would contribute less than 2 calories. That seems too small.

Now let's try inflating the slope by a factor of 10. Is 25 calories per gram reasonable? Then the average cereal would have 175 calories from sugar alone. The average cereal has only 100 calories per serving, though, so that slope seems too big.

We have tried inflating the slope by a factor of 10 and deflating it by 10 and found both to be unreasonable. So, like Goldilocks, we're left with the value in the middle that's just right. And an increase of 2.5 calories per gram of sugar is certainly *plausible*.

The small effort of asking yourself whether the regression equation is plausible is repaid whenever you catch errors or avoid saying something silly or absurd about the data. It's too easy to take something that comes out of a computer at face value and assume that it makes sense.

Always be skeptical and ask yourself if the answer is reasonable.

---

### FOR EXAMPLE    Causation and regression

**Recap:** Our regression model predicting hurricane wind speeds from the central pressure was reasonably successful. The negative slope indicates that, in general, storms with lower central pressures have stronger winds.

**Question:** Can we conclude that lower central barometric pressure *causes* the higher wind speeds in hurricanes?

No. While it may be true that lower pressure causes higher winds, a regression model for observed data such as these cannot demonstrate causation. Perhaps higher wind speeds reduce the barometric pressure, or perhaps both pressure and wind speed are both driven by some other variable we have not observed.

(As it happens, in hurricanes it is reasonable to say that the low central pressure at the eye is responsible for the high winds because it draws moist, warm air into the center of the storm, where it swirls around, generating the winds. But as is often the case, things aren't quite that simple. The winds themselves contribute to lowering the pressure at the center of the storm as it becomes organized into a hurricane. The lesson is that to understand causation in hurricanes, we must do more than just model the relationship of two variables; we must study the mechanism itself.)

---

## WHAT CAN GO WRONG?

There are many ways in which data that appear at first to be good candidates for regression analysis may be unsuitable. And there are ways that people use regression that can lead them astray. Here's an overview of the most common problems. We'll discuss them at length in the next chapter.

▶ **Don't fit a straight line to a nonlinear relationship.** Linear regression is suited only to relationships that are, well, *linear*. Fortunately, we can often improve the linearity easily by using re-expression. We'll come back to that topic in Chapter 10.

▶ **Beware of extraordinary points.** Data points can be extraordinary in a regression in two ways: They can have $y$-values that stand off from the linear pattern suggested by the bulk of the data, or extreme $x$-values. Both kinds of extraordinary points require attention.

▶ **Don't invert the regression.** The BK regression model was $\widehat{Fat} = 6.8 + 0.97Protein$. Knowing protein content, we can predict the amount of fat. But that doesn't let us switch the regression around. We can't use this model to predict protein values from fat values. To model $y$ from $x$, the least squares slope is $b_1 = r\frac{s_y}{s_x}$. To model $x$ in terms of $y$, we'd find $b_1 = r\frac{s_x}{s_y}$. That's not the reciprocal of the first slope (unless the correlation is 1.0). To swap the predictor–response roles of the variables in a regression (which can sometimes make sense), we must fit a new regression equation.

▶ **Don't extrapolate beyond the data.** A linear model will often do a reasonable job of summarizing a relationship in the narrow range of observed $x$-values. Once we have a working model for the relationship, it's tempting to use it. But beware of predicting $y$-values for $x$-values that lie outside the range of the original data. The model may no longer hold there, so such *extrapolations* too far from the data are dangerous.

▶ **Don't infer that $x$ causes $y$ just because there is a good linear model for their relationship.** When two variables are strongly correlated, it is often tempting to assume a causal relationship between them. Putting a regression line on a scatterplot tempts us even further, but it doesn't make the assumption of causation any more valid.

▶ **Don't choose a model based on $R^2$ alone.** Although $R^2$ measures the *strength* of the linear association, a high $R^2$ does not demonstrate the *appropriateness* of the regression. A single outlier, or data that separate into two groups rather than a single cloud of points, can make $R^2$ seem quite large when, in fact, the linear regression model is simply inappropriate. Conversely, a low $R^2$ value may be due to a single outlier as well. It may be that most of the data fall roughly along a straight line, with the exception of a single point. Always look at the scatterplot.

$R^2$ does **not** mean that protein accounts for 69% of the fat in a BK food item. It is the *variation* in fat content that is accounted for by the linear model.

# CONNECTIONS

We've talked about the importance of models before, but have seen only the Normal model as an example. The linear model is one of the most important models in Statistics. Chapter 7 talked about the assignment of variables to the $y$- and $x$-axes. That didn't matter to correlation, but it does matter to regression because $y$ is predicted by $x$ in the regression model.

The connection of $R^2$ to correlation is obvious, although it may not be immediately clear that just by squaring the correlation we can learn the fraction of the variability of $y$ accounted for by a regression on $x$. We'll return to this in subsequent chapters.

We made a big fuss about knowing the units of your quantitative variables. We didn't need units for correlation, but without the units we can't define the slope of a regression. A regression makes no sense if you don't know the *Who*, the *What*, and the *Units* of both your variables.

We've summed squared deviations before when we computed the standard deviation and variance. That's not coincidental. They are closely connected to regression.

When we first talked about models, we noted that deviations away from a model were often interesting. Now we have a formal definition of these deviations as residuals.

## WHAT HAVE WE LEARNED?

We've learned that when the relationship between quantitative variables is fairly straight, a linear model can help summarize that relationship and give us insights about it:

▶ The regression (best fit) line doesn't pass through all the points, but it is the best compromise in the sense that the sum of squares of the residuals is the smallest possible.

We've learned several things the correlation, $r$, tells us about the regression:

▶ The slope of the line is based on the correlation, adjusted for the units of $x$ and $y$:

$$b_1 = r\frac{s_y}{s_x}.$$

We've learned to interpret that slope in context:

▸ For each SD of $x$ that we are away from the $x$ mean, we expect to be $r$ SDs of $y$ away from the $y$ mean.

▸ Because $r$ is always between $-1$ and $+1$, each predicted $y$ is fewer SDs away from its mean than the corresponding $x$ was, a phenomenon called regression to the mean.

▸ The square of the correlation coefficient, $R^2$, gives us the fraction of the variation of the response accounted for by the regression model. The remaining $1 - R^2$ of the variation is left in the residuals.

The residuals also reveal how well the model works:

▸ If a plot of residuals against predicted values shows a pattern, we should re-examine the data to see why.

▸ The standard deviation of the residuals

$$s_e = \sqrt{\frac{\Sigma e^2}{n - 2}}$$

quantifies the amount of scatter around the line.

Of course, the linear model makes no sense unless the **Linearity Assumption** is satisfied. We check the **Straight Enough Condition** and **Outlier Condition** with a scatterplot, as we did for correlation, and also with a plot of residuals against either the $x$ or the predicted values. For the standard deviation of the residuals to make sense as a summary, we have to make the **Equal Variance Assumption**. We check it by looking at both the original scatterplot and the residual plot for the **Does the Plot Thicken? Condition.**

## Terms

**Model**
195. An equation or formula that simplifies and represents reality.

**Linear model**
195. A linear model is an equation of the form

$$\hat{y} = b_0 + b_1 x.$$

To interpret a linear model, we need to know the variables (along with their W's) and their units.

**Predicted value**
195. The value of $\hat{y}$ found for a given $x$-value in the data. A predicted value is found by substituting the $x$-value in the regression equation. The predicted values are the values on the fitted line; the points $(x, \hat{y})$ all lie exactly on the fitted line. The predicted values are found from the linear model that we fit:

$$\hat{y} = b_0 + b_1 x.$$

**Residuals**
195. Residuals are the differences between data values and the corresponding values predicted by the regression model—or, more generally, values predicted by any model.

$$\text{Residual} = \text{obeserved value} - \text{predicted value} = e = y - \hat{y}$$

**Regression line**
**Line of best fit**
195. The particular linear equation

$$\hat{y} = b_0 + b_1 x$$

that satisfies the least squares criterion is called the least squares regression line. Casually, we often just call it the regression line, or the line of best fit.

**Least squares**
195. The least squares criterion specifies the unique line that minimizes the variance of the residuals or, equivalently, the sum of the squared residuals.

**Slope**
196. The slope, $b_1$, gives a value in "$y$-units *per* $x$-unit." Changes of one unit in $x$ are associated with changes of $b_1$ units in predicted values of $y$. The slope can be found by

$$b_1 = r\frac{s_y}{s_x}.$$

**Intercept**
196. The intercept, $b_0$, gives a starting value in $y$-units. It's the $\hat{y}$-value when $x$ is 0. You can find it from $b_0 = \bar{y} - b_1\bar{x}$.

**Regression to the mean**

202. Because the correlation is always less than 1.0 in magnitude, each predicted $\hat{y}$ tends to be fewer standard deviations from its mean than its corresponding $x$ was from its mean. This is called regression to the mean.

$s_e$

204. The standard deviation of the residuals is found by $s_e = \sqrt{\dfrac{\Sigma e^2}{n-2}}$. When the assumptions and conditions are met, the residuals can be well described by using this standard deviation and the 68–95–99.7 Rule.

$R^2$

▸ 204. $R^2$ is the square of the correlation between $y$ and $x$.

▸ $R^2$ gives the fraction of the variability of $y$ accounted for by the least squares linear regression on $x$.

▸ $R^2$ is an overall measure of how successful the regression is in linearly relating $y$ to $x$.

# Skills

▸ Be able to identify response ($y$) and explanatory ($x$) variables in context.

▸ Understand how a linear equation summarizes the relationship between two variables.

▸ Recognize when a regression should be used to summarize a linear relationship between two quantitative variables.

▸ Be able to judge whether the slope of a regression makes sense.

▸ Know how to examine your data for violations of the **Straight Enough Condition** that would make it inappropriate to compute a regression.

▸ Understand that the least squares slope is easily affected by extreme values.

▸ Know that residuals are the differences between the data values and the corresponding values predicted by the line and that the *least squares criterion* finds the line that minimizes the sum of the squared residuals.

▸ Know how to use a plot of residuals against predicted values to check the **Straight Enough Condition,** the **Does the Plot Thicken? Condition,** and the **Outlier Condition.**

▸ Understand that the standard deviation of the residuals, $s_e$, measures variability around the line. A large $s_e$ means the points are widely scattered; a small $s_e$ means they lie close to the line.

▸ Know how to find a regression equation from the summary statistics for each variable and the correlation between the variables.

▸ Know how to find a regression equation using your statistics software and how to find the slope and intercept values in the regression output table.

▸ Know how to use regression to predict a value of $y$ for a given $x$.

▸ Know how to compute the residual for each data value and how to display the residuals.

▸ Be able to write a sentence explaining what a linear equation says about the relationship between $y$ and $x$, basing it on the fact that the slope is given in *y-units per x-unit.*

▸ Understand how the correlation coefficient and the regression slope are related. Know how $R^2$ describes how much of the variation in $y$ is accounted for by its linear relationship with $x$.

▸ Be able to describe a prediction made from a regression equation, relating the predicted value to the specified $x$-value.

▸ Be able to write a sentence interpreting $s_e$ as representing typical errors in predictions—the amounts by which actual $y$-values differ from the $\hat{y}$'s estimated by the model.

# ON THE COMPUTER

## Regression

All statistics packages make a table of results for a regression. These tables may differ slightly from one package to another, but all are essentially the same—and all include much more than we need to know for now. Every computer regression table includes a section that looks something like this:

**A S** **Finding Least Squares Lines.** We almost always use technology to find regressions. Practice now—just in time for the exercises.

The slope and intercept coefficient are given in a table such as this one. Usually the slope is labeled with the name of the x-variable, and the intercept is labeled "Intercept" or "Constant." So the regression equation shown here is

$$\widehat{Fat} = 6.83077 + 0.97138 Protein.$$

It is not unusual for statistics packages to give many more digits of the estimated slope and intercept than could possibly be estimated from the data. (The original data were reported to the nearest gram.) Ordinarily, you should round most of the reported numbers to one digit more than the precision of the data, and the slope to two. We will learn about the other numbers in the regression table later in the book. For now, all you need to be able to do is find the coefficients, the $s_e$, and the $R^2$ value.

### DATA DESK

Select the y-variable and the x-variable. In the **Plot** menu choose **Scatterplot**. From the scatterplot HyperView menu, choose **Add Regression Line** to display the line. From the HyperView menu, choose **Regression** to compute the regression.

#### COMMENTS

Alternatively, find the regression first with the **Regression** command in the **Calc** menu. Click on the x-variable's name to open a menu that offers the scatterplot.

### EXCEL

Make a scatterplot of the data. With the scatterplot frontmost, select **Add Trendline . . .** from the **Chart** menu. Click the **Options** tab and select **Display Equation on Chart.** Click **OK.**

#### COMMENTS

The computer section for Chapter 7 shows how to make a scatterplot. We don't repeat those steps here.

## EXCEL 2007

▸ Click on a blank cell in the spreadsheet.
▸ Go to the **Formulas** tab in the Ribbon and click **More Functions → Statistical.**
▸ Choose the **CORREL** function from the drop-down menu of functions.
▸ In the dialog that pops up, enter the range of one of the variables in the space provided.
▸ Enter the range of the other variable in the space provided.
▸ Click **OK.**

### COMMENTS

The correlation is computed in the selected cell. Correlations computed this way will update if any of the data values are changed.

Before you interpret a correlation coefficient, always make a scatterplot to check for nonlinearity and outliers. If the variables are not linearly related, the correlation coefficient cannot be interpreted.

## JMP

Choose **Fit Y by X** from the **Analyze** menu. Specify the y-variable in the Select Columns box and click the **"Y, Response"** button. Specify the x-variable and click the **"X, Factor"** button. Click **OK** to make a scatterplot. In the scatterplot window, click on the red triangle beside the heading labeled "Bivariate Fit . . ." and choose **"Fit Line."** JMP draws the least squares regression line on the scatterplot and displays the results of the regression in tables below the plot.

## MINITAB

Choose **Regression** from the **Stat** menu. From the Regression submenu, choose **Fitted Line Plot.** In the Fitted Line Plot dialog, click in the **Response Y** box, and assign the y-variable from the Variable list. Click in the **Predictor X** box, and assign the x-variable from the Variable list. Make sure that the Type of Regression Model is set to Linear. Click the **OK** button.

## SPSS

Choose **Interactive** from the **Graphs** menu. From the interactive Graphs submenu, choose **Scatterplot.** In the Create Scatterplot dialog, drag the y-variable into the **y-axis target,** and the x-variable into the **x-axis target.** Click on the **Fit** tab. Choose **Regression** from the **Method** popup menu. Click the **OK** button.

## TI-83/84 PLUS

To find the equation of the regression line (add the line to a scatterplot), choose **LinReg(a+bx),** tell it the list names, and then add a comma to specify a function name (from **VARS Y-Vars 1:Function**). The final command looks like

**LinReg (a+bx) L1, L2, Y1.**

To make a residuals plot, set up a **STATPLOT** as a scatterplot. Specify your explanatory datalist as Xlist. For Ylist, import the name **RESID** from the **LIST NAMES** menu. **ZoomStat** will now create the residuals plot.

### COMMENTS

Each time you execute a **LinReg** command, the calculator automatically computes the residuals and stores them in a data list named RESID. If you want to see them, go to **STAT EDIT.** Space through the names of the lists until you find a blank. Import RESID from the LIST NAMES menu. Now every time you have the calculator compute a regression analysis, it will show you the residuals.

## TI-89

To find the equation of the regression line (and add the line to a scatterplot), choose **LinReg (a+bx)** from the **Calc Regressions** menu and tell it the list names and a function to store the equation. To make a residuals plot, define a **PLOT** as a scatterplot.

Specify your explanatory datalist as Xlist. For Ylist, find the list name **resid** from VAR-LINK by arrowing to the **STATVARS** portion. Then press ② **(r)** and locate the list. Press ENTER to finish the plot definition and F5 to display the plot.

### COMMENTS

Each time you execute a **LinReg** command, the calculator automatically computes the residuals and stores them in a data list named RESID. If you don't want to see this (or any other calculator-generated list) anymore, press F1 (Tools) and select choice 3: Setup Editor. Leaving the box for lists to display blank will reset the calculator to show only lists 1 through 6.

# EXERCISES

1. **Cereals.** For many people, breakfast cereal is an important source of fiber in their diets. Cereals also contain potassium, a mineral shown to be associated with maintaining a healthy blood pressure. An analysis of the amount of fiber (in grams) and the potassium content (in milligrams) in servings of 77 breakfast cereals produced the regression model $\widehat{Potassium} = 38 + 27Fiber$. If your cereal provides 9 grams of fiber per serving, how much potassium does the model estimate you will get?

2. **Horsepower.** In Chapter 7's Exercise 35 we examined the relationship between the fuel economy (mpg) and horsepower for 15 models of cars. Further analysis produces the regression model $\widehat{mpg} = 46.87 - 0.084HP$. If the car you are thinking of buying has a 200-horsepower engine, what does this model suggest your gas mileage would be?

3. **More cereal.** Exercise 1 describes a regression model that estimates a cereal's potassium content from the amount of fiber it contains. In this context, what does it mean to say that a cereal has a negative residual?

4. **Horsepower, again.** Exercise 2 describes a regression model that uses a car's horsepower to estimate its fuel economy. In this context, what does it mean to say that a certain car has a positive residual?

5. **Another bowl.** In Exercise 1, the regression model $\widehat{Potassium} = 38 + 27Fiber$ relates fiber (in grams) and potassium content (in milligrams) in servings of breakfast cereals. Explain what the slope means.

6. **More horsepower.** In Exercise 2, the regression model $\widehat{mpg} = 46.87 - 0.084HP$ relates cars' horsepower to their fuel economy (in mpg). Explain what the slope means.

7. **Cereal again.** The correlation between a cereal's fiber and potassium contents is $r = 0.903$. What fraction of the variability in potassium is accounted for by the amount of fiber that servings contain?

8. **Another car.** The correlation between a car's horsepower and its fuel economy (in mpg) is $r = -0.869$. What fraction of the variability in fuel economy is accounted for by the horsepower?

9. **Last bowl!** For Exercise 1's regression model predicting potassium content (in milligrams) from the amount of fiber (in grams) in breakfast cereals, $s_e = 30.77$. Explain in this context what that means.

10. **Last tank!** For Exercise 2's regression model predicting fuel economy (in mpg) from the car's horsepower, $s_e = 3.287$. Explain in this context what that means.

11. **Regression equations.** Fill in the missing information in the table below.

| | $\bar{x}$ | $s_x$ | $\bar{y}$ | $s_y$ | $r$ | $\hat{y} = b_0 + b_1x$ |
|---|---|---|---|---|---|---|
| a) | 10 | 2 | 20 | 3 | 0.5 | |
| b) | 2 | 0.06 | 7.2 | 1.2 | -0.4 | |
| c) | 12 | 6 | | | -0.8 | $\hat{y} = 200 - 4x$ |
| d) | | 2.5 | 1.2 | | 100 | $\hat{y} = -100 + 50x$ |

12. **More regression equations.** Fill in the missing information in the table below.

| | $\bar{x}$ | $s_x$ | $\bar{y}$ | $s_y$ | $r$ | $\hat{y} = b_0 + b_1x$ |
|---|---|---|---|---|---|---|
| a) | 30 | 4 | 18 | 6 | -0.2 | |
| b) | 100 | 18 | 60 | 10 | 0.9 | |
| c) | | 0.8 | 50 | 15 | | $\hat{y} = -10 + 15x$ |
| d) | | | 18 | 4 | -0.6 | $\hat{y} = 30 - 2x$ |

13. **Residuals.** Tell what each of the residual plots below indicates about the appropriateness of the linear model that was fit to the data.

14. **Residuals.** Tell what each of the residual plots below indicates about the appropriateness of the linear model that was fit to the data.

15. **Real estate.** A random sample of records of sales of homes from Feb. 15 to Apr. 30, 1993, from the files maintained by the Albuquerque Board of Realtors gives the *Price* and *Size* (in square feet) of 117 homes. A regression to predict *Price* (in thousands of dollars) from *Size* has an R-squared of 71.4%. The residuals plot indicated that a linear model is appropriate.
    a) What are the variables and units in this regression?
    b) What units does the slope have?
    c) Do you think the slope is positive or negative? Explain.

16. **Roller coaster.** People who responded to a July 2004 Discovery Channel poll named the 10 best roller coasters in the United States. A table in the last chapter's exercises shows the length of the initial drop (in feet) and the duration of the ride (in seconds). A regression to predict *Duration* from *Drop* has $R^2 = 12.4\%$.
    a) What are the variables and units in this regression?
    b) What units does the slope have?
    c) Do you think the slope is positive or negative? Explain.

17. **What slope?** If you create a regression model for predicting the *Weight* of a car (in pounds) from its *Length* (in feet), is the slope most likely to be 3, 30, 300, or 3000? Explain.

18. **What slope?** If you create a regression model for estimating the *Height* of a pine tree (in feet) based on the *Circumference* of its trunk (in inches), is the slope most likely to be 0.1, 1, 10, or 100? Explain.

**19. Real estate again.** The regression of *Price* on *Size* of homes in Albuquerque had $R^2 = 71.4\%$, as described in Exercise 15. Write a sentence (in context, of course) summarizing what the $R^2$ says about this regression.

**20. Coasters again.** Exercise 16 examined the association between the *Duration* of a roller coaster ride and the height of its initial *Drop*, reporting that $R^2 = 12.4\%$. Write a sentence (in context, of course) summarizing what the $R^2$ says about this regression.

**21. Misinterpretations.** A Biology student who created a regression model to use a bird's *Height* when perched for predicting its *Wingspan* made these two statements. Assuming the calculations were done correctly, explain what is wrong with each interpretation.
a) My $R^2$ of 93% shows that this linear model is appropriate.
b) A bird 10 inches tall will have a wingspan of 17 inches.

**22. More misinterpretations.** A Sociology student investigated the association between a country's *Literacy Rate* and *Life Expectancy*, then drew the conclusions listed below. Explain why each statement is incorrect. (Assume that all the calculations were done properly.)
a) The *Literacy Rate* determines 64% of the *Life Expectancy* for a country.
b) The slope of the line shows that an increase of 5% in *Literacy Rate* will produce a 2-year improvement in *Life Expectancy*.

**23. Real estate redux.** The regression of *Price* on *Size* of homes in Albuquerque had $R^2 = 71.4\%$, as described in Exercise 15.
a) What is the correlation between *Size* and *Price*?
b) What would you predict about the *Price* of a home one standard deviation above average in *Size*?
c) What would you predict about the *Price* of a home two standard deviations below average in *Size*?

**24. Another ride.** The regression of *Duration* of a roller coaster ride on the height of its initial *Drop*, described in Exercise 16, had $R^2 = 12.4\%$.
a) What is the correlation between *Drop* and *Duration*?
b) What would you predict about the *Duration* of the ride on a coaster whose initial *Drop* was 1 standard deviation below the mean *Drop*?
c) What would you predict about the *Duration* of the ride on a coaster whose initial *Drop* was 3 standard deviations above the mean *Drop*?

**25. ESP.** People who claim to "have ESP" participate in a screening test in which they have to guess which of several images someone is thinking of. You and a friend both took the test. You scored 2 standard deviations above the mean, and your friend scored 1 standard deviation below the mean. The researchers offer everyone the opportunity to take a retest.
a) Should you choose to take this retest? Explain.
b) Now explain to your friend what his decision should be and why.

**26. SI jinx.** Players in any sport who are having great seasons, turning in performances that are much better than anyone might have anticipated, often are pictured on the cover of *Sports Illustrated*. Frequently, their performances then falter somewhat, leading some athletes to believe in

a "*Sports Illustrated* jinx." Similarly, it is common for phenomenal rookies to have less stellar second seasons—the so-called "sophomore slump." While fans, athletes, and analysts have proposed many theories about what leads to such declines, a statistician might offer a simpler (statistical) explanation. Explain.

**27. More real estate.** Consider the Albuquerque home sales from Exercise 15 again. The regression analysis gives the model $\widehat{Price} = 47.82 + 0.061\,Size$.
a) Explain what the slope of the line says about housing prices and house size.
b) What price would you predict for a 3000-square-foot house in this market?
c) A real estate agent shows a potential buyer a 1200-square-foot home, saying that the asking price is $6000 less than what one would expect to pay for a house of this size. What is the asking price, and what is the $6000 called?

**28. Last ride.** Consider the roller coasters described in Exercise 16 again. The regression analysis gives the model $\widehat{Duration} = 91.033 + 0.242\,Drop$.
a) Explain what the slope of the line says about how long a roller coaster ride may last and the height of the coaster.
b) A new roller coaster advertises an initial drop of 200 feet. How long would you predict the rides last?
c) Another coaster with a 150-foot initial drop advertises a 2-minute ride. Is this longer or shorter than you'd expect? By how much? What's that called?

**29. Cigarettes.** Is the nicotine content of a cigarette related to the "tars"? A collection of data (in milligrams) on 29 cigarettes produced the scatterplot, residuals plot, and regression analysis shown:

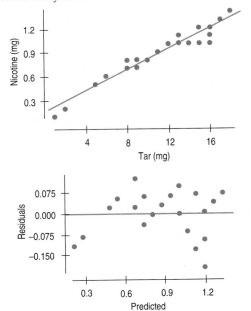

Dependent variable is: nicotine
R squared = 92.4%

| Variable | Coefficient |
|---|---|
| Constant | 0.154030 |
| Tar | 0.065052 |

a) Do you think a linear model is appropriate here? Explain.
b) Explain the meaning of $R^2$ in this context.

**30. Attendance 2006.** In the previous chapter you looked at the relationship between the number of wins by American League baseball teams and the average attendance at their home games for the 2006 season. Here are the scatterplot, the residuals plot, and part of the regression analysis:

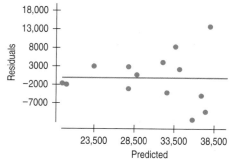

Dependent variable is: Home Attendance
R squared = 48.5%

| Variable | Coefficient |
|----------|-------------|
| Constant | −14364.5 |
| Wins | 538.915 |

a) Do you think a linear model is appropriate here? Explain.
b) Interpret the meaning of $R^2$ in this context.
c) Do the residuals show any pattern worth remarking on?
d) The point in the upper right of the plots is the New York Yankees. What can you say about the residual for the Yankees?

**31. Another cigarette.** Consider again the regression of *Nicotine* content on *Tar* (both in milligrams) for the cigarettes examined in Exercise 29.
a) What is the correlation between *Tar* and *Nicotine*?
b) What would you predict about the average *Nicotine* content of cigarettes that are 2 standard deviations below average in *Tar* content?
c) If a cigarette is 1 standard deviation above average in *Nicotine* content, what do you suspect is true about its *Tar* content?

**32. Second inning 2006.** Consider again the regression of *Average Attendance* on *Wins* for the baseball teams examined in Exercise 30.
a) What is the correlation between *Wins* and *Average Attendance*?
b) What would you predict about the *Average Attendance* for a team that is 2 standard deviations above average in *Wins*?
c) If a team is 1 standard deviation below average in attendance, what would you predict about the number of games the team has won?

**33. Last cigarette.** Take another look at the regression analysis of tar and nicotine content of the cigarettes in Exercise 29.
a) Write the equation of the regression line.
b) Estimate the *Nicotine* content of cigarettes with 4 milligrams of *Tar*.
c) Interpret the meaning of the slope of the regression line in this context.
d) What does the *y*-intercept mean?
e) If a new brand of cigarette contains 7 milligrams of tar and a nicotine level whose residual is −0.5 mg, what is the nicotine content?

**34. Last inning 2006.** Refer again to the regression analysis for average attendance and games won by American League baseball teams, seen in Exercise 30.
a) Write the equation of the regression line.
b) Estimate the *Average Attendance* for a team with 50 *Wins*.
c) Interpret the meaning of the slope of the regression line in this context.
d) In general, what would a negative residual mean in this context?
e) The St. Louis Cardinals, the 2006 World Champions, are not included in these data because they are a National League team. During the 2006 regular season, the Cardinals won 83 games and averaged 42,588 fans at their home games. Calculate the residual for this team, and explain what it means.

**35. Income and housing revisited.** In Chapter 7, Exercise 31, we learned that the Office of Federal Housing Enterprise Oversight (OFHEO) collects data on various aspects of housing costs around the United States. Here's a scatterplot (by state) of the *Housing Cost Index* (HCI) versus the *Median Family Income* (MFI) for the 50 states. The correlation is $r = 0.65$. The mean HCI is 338.2, with a standard deviation of 116.55. The mean MFI is $46,234, with a standard deviation of $7072.47.

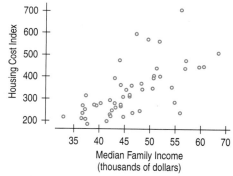

a) Is a regression analysis appropriate? Explain.
b) What is the equation that predicts Housing Cost Index from median family income?
c) For a state with MFI = $44,993, what would be the predicted HCI?
d) Washington, DC, has an MFI of $44,993 and an HCI of 548.02. How far off is the prediction in b) from the actual HCI?
e) If we standardized both variables, what would be the regression equation that predicts standardized HCI from standardized MFI?

f) If we standardized both variables, what would be the regression equation that predicts standardized MFI from standardized HCI?

**36. Interest rates and mortgages again.** In Chapter 7, Exercise 32, we saw a plot of total mortgages in the United States (in millions of 2005 dollars) versus the interest rate at various times over the past 26 years. The correlation is $r = -0.84$. The mean mortgage amount is $151.9 million and the mean interest rate is 8.88%. The standard deviations are $23.86 million for mortgage amounts and 2.58% for the interest rates.

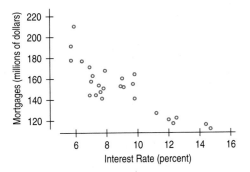

a) Is a regression model appropriate for predicting mortgage amount from interest rates? Explain.
b) What is the equation that predicts mortgage amount from interest rates?
c) What would you predict the mortgage amount would be if the interest rates climbed to 20%?
d) Do you have any reservations about your prediction in part c?
e) If we standardized both variables, what would be the regression equation that predicts standardized mortgage amount from standardized interest rates?
f) If we standardized both variables, what would be the regression equation that predicts standardized interest rates from standardized mortgage amount?

**37. Online clothes.** An online clothing retailer keeps track of its customers' purchases. For those customers who signed up for the company's credit card, the company also has information on the customer's *Age* and *Income*. A random sample of 500 of these customers shows the following scatterplot of *Total Yearly Purchases* by *Age*:

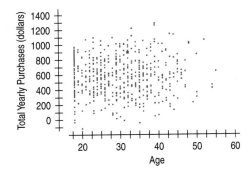

The correlation between *Total Yearly Purchases* and *Age* is $r = 0.037$. Summary statistics for the two variables are:

|  | Mean | SD |
|---|---|---|
| Age | 29.67 yrs | 8.51 yrs |
| Total Yearly Purchase | $572.52 | $253.62 |

a) What is the linear regression equation for predicting *Total Yearly Purchase* from *Age*?
b) Do the assumptions and conditions for regression appear to be met?
c) What is the predicted average *Total Yearly Purchase* for an 18-year-old? For a 50-year-old?
d) What percent of the variability in *Total Yearly Purchases* is accounted for by this model?
e) Do you think the regression might be a useful one for the company? Explain.

**38. Online clothes II.** For the online clothing retailer discussed in the previous problem, the scatterplot of *Total Yearly Purchases* by *Income* shows

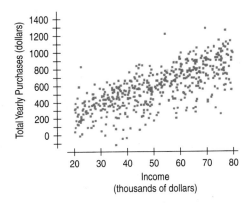

The correlation between *Total Yearly Purchases* and *Income* is 0.722. Summary statistics for the two variables are:

|  | Mean | SD |
|---|---|---|
| Income | $50,343.40 | $16,952.50 |
| Total Yearly Purchase | $572.52 | $253.62 |

a) What is the linear regression equation for predicting *Total Yearly Purchase* from *Income*?
b) Do the assumptions and conditions for regression appear to be met?
c) What is the predicted average *Total Yearly Purchase* for someone with a yearly *Income* of $20,000? For someone with an annual *Income* of $80,000?
d) What percent of the variability in *Total Yearly Purchases* is accounted for by this model?
e) Do you think the regression might be a useful one for the company? Comment.

**39. SAT scores.** The SAT is a test often used as part of an application to college. SAT scores are between 200 and 800, but have no units. Tests are given in both Math and Verbal areas. Doing the SAT-Math problems also involves the ability to read and understand the questions, but can a person's verbal score be used to predict the math score?

Verbal and math SAT scores of a high school graduating class are displayed in the scatterplot, with the regression line added.

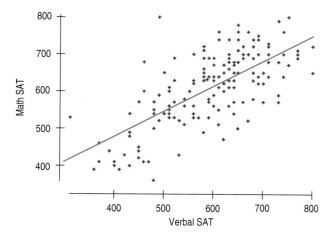

a) Describe the relationship.
b) Are there any students whose scores do not seem to fit the overall pattern?
c) For these data, $r = 0.685$. Interpret this statistic.
d) These verbal scores averaged 596.3, with a standard deviation of 99.5, and the math scores averaged 612.2, with a standard deviation of 96.1. Write the equation of the regression line.
e) Interpret the slope of this line.
f) Predict the math score of a student with a verbal score of 500.
g) Every year some student scores a perfect 1600. Based on this model, what would that student's residual be for her math score?

**40. Success in college.**   Colleges use SAT scores in the admissions process because they believe these scores provide some insight into how a high school student will perform at the college level. Suppose the entering freshmen at a certain college have mean combined *SAT Scores* of 1833, with a standard deviation of 123. In the first semester these students attained a mean *GPA* of 2.66, with a standard deviation of 0.56. A scatterplot showed the association to be reasonably linear, and the correlation between *SAT* score and *GPA* was 0.47.
a) Write the equation of the regression line.
b) Explain what the *y*-intercept of the regression line indicates.
c) Interpret the slope of the regression line.
d) Predict the GPA of a freshman who scored a combined 2100.
e) Based upon these statistics, how effective do you think SAT scores would be in predicting academic success during the first semester of the freshman year at this college? Explain.
f) As a student, would you rather have a positive or a negative residual in this context? Explain.

**41. SAT, take 2.**   Suppose we wanted to use SAT math scores to estimate verbal scores based on the information in Exercise 39.

a) What is the correlation?
b) Write the equation of the line of regression predicting verbal scores from math scores.
c) In general, what would a positive residual mean in this context?
d) A person tells you her math score was 500. Predict her verbal score.
e) Using that predicted verbal score and the equation you created in Exercise 39, predict her math score.
f) Why doesn't the result in part e come out to 500?

**42. Success, part 2.**   Based on the statistics for college freshmen given in Exercise 40, what SAT score might be expected among freshmen who attained a first-semester GPA of 3.0?

**T  43. Wildfire damage.**   In an example earlier in the chapter, we saw that the number of wildfires in the United States has been declining. But has the damage done by wildfires also been declining? Here's a scatterplot of the amount of land lost to wildfires (in millions of acres) during the same period, along with a least squares line:

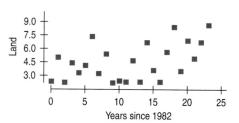

Dependent variable is: Land
R squared = 22.4%    $s_e = 1.857$
| Variable | Coefficient |
|---|---|
| Intercept | 2.97372 |
| Year | 0.138008 |

a) Do you think a linear model is appropriate for these data? Explain.
b) Interpret the slope in this context.
c) Can we interpret the intercept? Why or why not?
d) What does the value of $s_e$ say about the size of the residuals? What does it say about the effectiveness of the model?
e) What does $R^2$ mean in this context?

**T  44. Fire damage.**   We saw in Exercise 43 that even though the number of fires was falling, the amount of damage due to wildfires has been increasing. Could it be that individual fires are getting bigger? Here's a regression that examines the trend in *Acres per Fire,* together with some supporting plots:

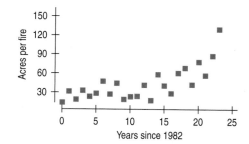

Dependent variable is: Acres/Fire
R squared = 53.9%
s = 18.86

| Variable | Coefficient |
|----------|-------------|
| Constant | −5577.77 |
| Year | 2.81988 |

a) Does this information help to account for the apparent contradiction between our first analysis that showed decreases in the number of fires and the analysis of Exercise 43 that showed increasing damage? Explain. (Be careful not to claim more than you can support.)
b) What does the residuals plot say about this regression? Discuss the assumptions and conditions for the regression shown here.

**T 45. Used cars 2007.** Classified ads in the *Ithaca Journal* offered several used Toyota Corollas for sale. Listed below are the ages of the cars and the advertised prices.

| Age (yr) | Price Advertised ($) |
|----------|----------------------|
| 1 | 13,990 |
| 1 | 13,495 |
| 3 | 12,999 |
| 4 | 9500 |
| 4 | 10,495 |
| 5 | 8995 |
| 5 | 9495 |
| 6 | 6999 |
| 7 | 6950 |
| 7 | 7850 |
| 8 | 6999 |
| 8 | 5995 |
| 10 | 4950 |
| 10 | 4495 |
| 13 | 2850 |

a) Make a scatterplot for these data.
b) Describe the association between *Age* and *Price* of a used Corolla.
c) Do you think a linear model is appropriate?
d) Computer software says that $R^2 = 94.4\%$. What is the correlation between *Age* and *Price*?
e) Explain the meaning of $R^2$ in this context.
f) Why doesn't this model explain 100% of the variability in the price of a used Corolla?

**T 46. Drug abuse.** In the exercises of the last chapter you examined results of a survey conducted in the United States and 10 countries of Western Europe to determine the percentage of teenagers who had used marijuana and other drugs. Below is the scatterplot. Summary statistics showed that the mean percent that had used marijuana was 23.9%, with a standard deviation of 15.6%. An average of 11.6% of teens had used other drugs, with a standard deviation of 10.2%.

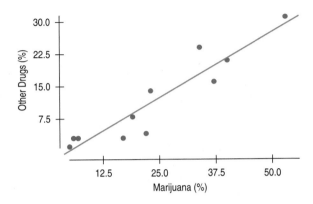

a) Do you think a linear model is appropriate? Explain.
b) For this regression, $R^2$ is 87.3%. Interpret this statistic in this context.
c) Write the equation you would use to estimate the percentage of teens who use other drugs from the percentage who have used marijuana.
d) Explain in context what the slope of this line means.
e) Do these results confirm that marijuana is a "gateway drug," that is, that marijuana use leads to the use of other drugs?

**T 47. More used cars 2007.** Use the advertised prices for Toyota Corollas given in Exercise 45 to create a linear model for the relationship between a car's *Age* and its *Price*.
a) Find the equation of the regression line.
b) Explain the meaning of the slope of the line.
c) Explain the meaning of the *y*-intercept of the line.
d) If you want to sell a 7-year-old Corolla, what price seems appropriate?
e) You have a chance to buy one of two cars. They are about the same age and appear to be in equally good condition. Would you rather buy the one with a positive residual or the one with a negative residual? Explain.
f) You see a "For Sale" sign on a 10-year-old Corolla stating the asking price as $3500. What is the residual?
g) Would this regression model be useful in establishing a fair price for a 20-year-old car? Explain.

**48. Veggie burgers.** Recently Burger King introduced a meat-free burger. The nutrition label is shown here:

## Nutrition Facts

| Calories | 330 |
|---|---|
| Fat | 10g* |
| Sodium | 760g |
| Sugars | 5g |
| Protein | 14g |
| Carbohydrates | 43g |
| Dietary Fiber | 4g |
| Cholesterol | 0 |

\* (2 grams of saturated fat)

RECOMMENDED DAILY VALUES*
(based on a 2,000-calorie/day diet)

| Iron | 20% |
|---|---|
| Vitamin A | 10% |
| Vitamin C | 10% |
| Calcium | 6% |

a) Use the regression model created in this chapter, $\widehat{Fat} = 6.8 + 0.97\ Protein$, to predict the fat content of this burger from its protein content.
b) What is its residual? How would you explain the residual?
c) Write a brief report about the *Fat* and *Protein* content of this new menu item. Be sure to talk about the variables by name and in the correct units.

**49. Burgers.** In the last chapter, you examined the association between the amounts of *Fat* and *Calories* in fast-food hamburgers. Here are the data:

| Fat (g) | 19 | 31 | 34 | 35 | 39 | 39 | 43 |
|---|---|---|---|---|---|---|---|
| Calories | 410 | 580 | 590 | 570 | 640 | 680 | 660 |

a) Create a scatterplot of *Calories* vs. *Fat*.
b) Interpret the value of $R^2$ in this context.
c) Write the equation of the line of regression.
d) Use the residuals plot to explain whether your linear model is appropriate.
e) Explain the meaning of the *y*-intercept of the line.
f) Explain the meaning of the slope of the line.
g) A new burger containing 28 grams of fat is introduced. According to this model, its residual for calories is +33. How many calories does the burger have?

**50. Chicken.** Chicken sandwiches are often advertised as a healthier alternative to beef because many are lower in fat. Tests on 11 brands of fast-food chicken sandwiches produced the following summary statistics and scatterplot from a graphing calculator:

| | Fat (g) | Calories |
|---|---|---|
| Mean | 20.6 | 472.7 |
| St. Dev. | 9.8 | 144.2 |
| Correlation | 0.947 | |

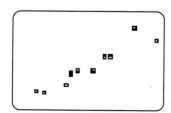

a) Do you think a linear model is appropriate in this situation?
b) Describe the strength of this association.
c) Write the equation of the regression line.
d) Explain the meaning of the slope.
e) Explain the meaning of the *y*–intercept.
f) What does it mean if a certain sandwich has a negative residual?
g) If a chicken sandwich and a burger each advertised 35 grams of fat, which would you expect to have more calories? (See Exercise 49.)
h) McDonald's Filet-O-Fish sandwich has 26 grams of fat and 470 calories. Does the fat–calorie relationship in this sandwich appear to be very different from that found in chicken sandwiches or in burgers (see Exercise 49)? Explain.

**51. A second helping of burgers.** In Exercise 49 you created a model that can estimate the number of *Calories* in a burger when the *Fat* content is known.
a) Explain why you cannot use that model to estimate the fat content of a burger with 600 calories.
b) Using an appropriate model, estimate the fat content of a burger with 600 calories.

**T 52. Cost of living 2006.** The *Worldwide Cost of Living Survey City Rankings* determine the cost of living in the 25 most expensive cities in the world. (www.finfacts.com/ costofliving.htm) These rankings scale New York City as 100, and express the cost of living in other cities as a percentage of the New York cost. For example, the table indicates that in Tokyo the cost of living was 34.7% higher than New York in 2005, but dropped to only 19.1% higher in 2006.

| City | 2006 | 2005 |
|---|---|---|
| Moscow | 123.9 | 119.0 |
| Seoul | 121.7 | 115.4 |
| Tokyo | 119.1 | 134.7 |
| Hong Kong | 116.3 | 109.5 |
| London | 110.6 | 120.3 |
| Osaka | 108.3 | 121.8 |
| Geneva | 103.0 | 113.5 |
| Copenhagen | 101.1 | 110.0 |
| Zurich | 100.8 | 112.1 |
| Oslo | 100.0 | 105.3 |
| New York City | 100.0 | 100.0 |
| St. Petersburg | 99.7 | 99.5 |
| Milan | 96.9 | 104.9 |
| Beijing | 94.9 | 95.6 |
| Istanbul | 93.1 | 93.8 |
| Paris | 93.1 | 102.2 |
| Singapore | 92.0 | 88.0 |
| Dublin | 91.8 | 100.0 |
| Sydney | 91.3 | 95.2 |
| Shanghai | 91.2 | 90.4 |
| Rome | 89.8 | 97.3 |
| Kiev | 89.8 | 84.5 |
| Vienna | 89.8 | 97.8 |
| Tel Aviv | 89.7 | 87.6 |
| Helsinki | 87.8 | 95.2 |

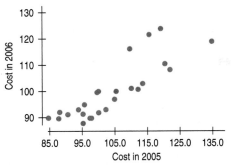

a) Here is a scatterplot. Describe the association between costs of living in 2005 and 2006.
b) The correlation is 0.846. Find and interpret the value of $R^2$.
c) The regression equation predicting the 2006 cost of living from the 2005 figure is $\widehat{Cost06} = 22.45 + 0.746Cost05$. Use this equation to find the residual for Moscow.
d) Explain what the residual means.

**53. Cell phones.** Most people prefer digital cell phone service to analog because it is clearer and more private. Nonetheless, many calls are switched to analog channels because digital lines are busy, or because the calls are between people with different carriers. These analog calls require more power, so they are harder on phone batteries. How much battery time do you lose when making analog calls?

*Consumer Reports* tested seven popular brands of cell phones, comparing digital and analog talk times. The scatterplot appears to show a linear relationship with $r = 0.94$ and regression equation $\widehat{An} = -5.1 + 0.44Dig$.
a) If you have a cell phone claiming to provide 200 minutes of digital calls between battery chargings, how many minutes of analog calling would you expect to get?
b) How much faith do you place in that prediction? Explain.
c) Explain what the slope of the line means in this context.
d) If a certain brand of battery has a positive residual, what does that mean in this context?

**Ⓣ 54. Candy 2006.** The table shows the increase in Halloween candy sales over a 7-year period as reported by the National Confectioners Association (www.ecandy.com). Using these data, estimate the amount of candy sold in 2006. Discuss the appropriateness of your model and your faith in the estimate. Then comment on the fact that NCA reported 2006 sales of $2.136 million. (Enter *Year* as 95, 96, . . . , 101.)

| Year | Halloween Candy Sales (millions of dollars) |
|------|---------------------------------------------|
| 1995 | 1.474 |
| 1996 | 1.660 |
| 1997 | 1.708 |
| 1998 | 1.787 |
| 1999 | 1.896 |
| 2000 | 1.985 |
| 2001 | 2.035 |

**55. El Niño.** Concern over the weather associated with El Niño has increased interest in the possibility that the climate on earth is getting warmer. The most common theory relates an increase in atmospheric levels of carbon dioxide ($CO_2$), a greenhouse gas, to increases in temperature. Here is a scatterplot showing the mean annual $CO_2$ concentration in the atmosphere, measured in parts per million (ppm) at the top of Mauna Loa in Hawaii, and the mean annual air temperature over both land and sea across the globe, in degrees Celsius (C).

A regression predicting *Temperature* from $CO_2$ produces the following output table (in part):

Dependent variable is: Temperature
R-squared = 33.4%

| Variable | Coefficient |
|----------|-------------|
| Intercept | 15.3066 |
| $CO_2$ | 0.004 |

a) What is the correlation between $CO_2$ and *Temperature*?
b) Explain the meaning of R-squared in this context.
c) Give the regression equation.
d) What is the meaning of the slope in this equation?
e) What is the meaning of the y-intercept of this equation?
f) Here is a scatterplot of the residuals vs. $CO_2$. Does this plot show evidence of the violation of any assumptions behind the regression? If so, which ones?

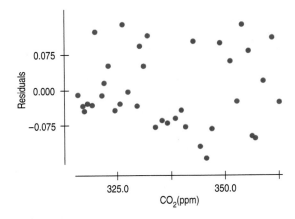

g) $CO_2$ levels will probably reach 364 ppm this year. What mean *Temperature* does the regression predict from that information?

**56. Birthrates 2005.** The table shows the number of live births per 1000 women aged 15–44 years in the United States, starting in 1965. (National Center for Health Statistics, www.cdc.gov/nchs/)

| Year | 1965 | 1970 | 1975 | 1980 | 1985 | 1990 | 1995 | 2000 | 2005 |
|------|------|------|------|------|------|------|------|------|------|
| Rate | 19.4 | 18.4 | 14.8 | 15.9 | 15.6 | 16.4 | 14.8 | 14.4 | 14.0 |

a) Make a scatterplot and describe the general trend in *Birthrates*. (Enter *Year* as years since 1900: 65, 70, 75, etc.)
b) Find the equation of the regression line.
c) Check to see if the line is an appropriate model. Explain.
d) Interpret the slope of the line.
e) The table gives rates only at 5-year intervals. Estimate what the rate was in 1978.
f) In 1978 the birthrate was actually 15.0. How close did your model come?
g) Predict what the *Birthrate* will be in 2010. Comment on your faith in this prediction.
h) Predict the *Birthrate* for 2025. Comment on your faith in this prediction.

**57. Body fat.** It is difficult to determine a person's body fat percentage accurately without immersing him or her in water. Researchers hoping to find ways to make a good estimate immersed 20 male subjects, then measured their waists and recorded their weights.

| Waist (in.) | Weight (lb) | Body Fat (%) | Waist (in.) | Weight (lb) | Body Fat (%) |
|-------------|-------------|--------------|-------------|-------------|--------------|
| 32 | 175 | 6  | 33 | 188 | 10 |
| 36 | 181 | 21 | 40 | 240 | 20 |
| 38 | 200 | 15 | 36 | 175 | 22 |
| 33 | 159 | 6  | 32 | 168 | 9  |
| 39 | 196 | 22 | 44 | 246 | 38 |
| 40 | 192 | 31 | 33 | 160 | 10 |
| 41 | 205 | 32 | 41 | 215 | 27 |
| 35 | 173 | 21 | 34 | 159 | 12 |
| 38 | 187 | 25 | 34 | 146 | 10 |
| 38 | 188 | 30 | 44 | 219 | 28 |

a) Create a model to predict *%Body Fat* from *Weight*.
b) Do you think a linear model is appropriate? Explain.
c) Interpret the slope of your model.
d) Is your model likely to make reliable estimates? Explain.
e) What is the residual for a person who weighs 190 pounds and has 21% body fat?

**58. Body fat again.** Would a model that uses the person's *Waist* size be able to predict the *%Body Fat* more accurately than one that uses *Weight*? Using the data in Exercise 57, create and analyze that model.

**59. Heptathlon 2004.** We discussed the women's 2004 Olympic heptathlon in Chapter 6. Here are the results from the high jump, 800-meter run, and long jump for the 26 women who successfully completed all three events in the 2004 Olympics (www.espn.com):

| Name | Country | High Jump (m) | 800-m (sec) | Long Jump (m) |
|------|---------|---------------|-------------|---------------|
| Carolina Klüft | SWE | 1.91 | 134.15 | 6.51 |
| Austra Skujyte | LIT | 1.76 | 135.92 | 6.30 |
| Kelly Sotherton | GBR | 1.85 | 132.27 | 6.51 |
| Shelia Burrell | USA | 1.70 | 135.32 | 6.25 |
| Yelena Prokhorova | RUS | 1.79 | 131.31 | 6.21 |
| Sonja Kesselschlaeger | GER | 1.76 | 135.21 | 6.42 |
| Marie Collonville | FRA | 1.85 | 133.62 | 6.19 |
| Natalya Dobrynska | UKR | 1.82 | 137.01 | 6.23 |
| Margaret Simpson | GHA | 1.79 | 137.72 | 6.02 |
| Svetlana Sokolova | RUS | 1.70 | 133.23 | 5.84 |
| J J Shobha | IND | 1.67 | 137.28 | 6.36 |
| Claudia Tonn | GER | 1.82 | 130.77 | 6.35 |
| Naide Gomes | POR | 1.85 | 140.05 | 6.10 |
| Michelle Perry | USA | 1.70 | 133.69 | 6.02 |
| Aryiro Strataki | GRE | 1.79 | 137.90 | 5.97 |
| Karin Ruckstuhl | NED | 1.85 | 133.95 | 5.90 |
| Karin Ertl | GER | 1.73 | 138.68 | 6.03 |
| Kylie Wheeler | AUS | 1.79 | 137.65 | 6.36 |
| Janice Josephs | RSA | 1.70 | 138.47 | 6.21 |
| Tiffany Lott Hogan | USA | 1.67 | 145.10 | 6.15 |
| Magdalena Szczepanska | POL | 1.76 | 133.08 | 5.98 |
| Irina Naumenko | KAZ | 1.79 | 134.57 | 6.16 |
| Yuliya Akulenko | UKR | 1.73 | 142.58 | 6.02 |
| Soma Biswas | IND | 1.70 | 132.27 | 5.92 |
| Marsha Mark-Baird | TRI | 1.70 | 141.21 | 6.22 |
| Michaela Hejnova | CZE | 1.70 | 145.68 | 5.70 |

Let's examine the association among these events. Perform a regression to predict high-jump performance from the 800-meter results.

a) What is the regression equation? What does the slope mean?

b) What percent of the variability in high jumps can be accounted for by differences in 800-m times?

c) Do good high jumpers tend to be fast runners? (Be careful—low times are good for running events and high distances are good for jumps.)

d) What does the residuals plot reveal about the model?

e) Do you think this is a useful model? Would you use it to predict high-jump performance? (Compare the residual standard deviation to the standard deviation of the high jumps.)

**T** **60. Heptathlon 2004 again.** We saw the data for the women's 2004 Olympic heptathlon in Exercise 59. Are the two jumping events associated? Perform a regression of the long-jump results on the high-jump results.

a) What is the regression equation? What does the slope mean?

b) What percentage of the variability in long jumps can be accounted for by high-jump performances?

c) Do good high jumpers tend to be good long jumpers?

d) What does the residuals plot reveal about the model?

e) Do you think this is a useful model? Would you use it to predict long-jump performance? (Compare the residual standard deviation to the standard deviation of the long jumps.)

**T** **61. Hard water.** In an investigation of environmental causes of disease, data were collected on the annual mortality rate (deaths per 100,000) for males in 61 large towns in England and Wales. In addition, the water hardness was recorded as the calcium concentration (parts per million, ppm) in the drinking water. The following display shows the relationship between *Mortality* and *Calcium* concentration for these towns:

a) Describe what you see in this scatterplot, in context.

b) Here is the regression analysis of *Mortality* and *Calcium* concentration. What is the regression equation?

Dependent variable is: Mortality
R-squared = 43%
s = 143.0

| Variable | Coefficient | SE(Coeff) | t-ratio | P-value |
|---|---|---|---|---|
| Intercept | 1676 | 29.30 | 57.2 | <0.0001 |
| Calcium | -3.23 | 0.48 | -6.66 | <0.0001 |

c) Interpret the slope and *y*-intercept of the line, in context.

d) The largest residual, with a value of −348.6, is for the town of Exeter. Explain what this value means.

e) The hardness of Derby's municipal water is about 100 ppm of calcium. Use this equation to predict the mortality rate in Derby.

f) Explain the meaning of *R*-squared in this situation.

**62. Gators.** Wildlife researchers monitor many wildlife populations by taking aerial photographs. Can they estimate the weights of alligators accurately from the air? Here is a regression analysis of the *Weight* of alligators (in pounds) and their *Length* (in inches) based on data collected about captured alligators.

Dependent variable is: Weight
R-squared = 83.6%
s = 54.01

| Variable | Coefficient | SE(Coeff) | t-ratio | P-value |
|---|---|---|---|---|
| Intercept | −393 | 47.53 | −8.27 | <0.0001 |
| Length | 5.9 | 0.5448 | 10.8 | <0.0001 |

a) Did they choose the correct variable to use as the dependent variable and the predictor? Explain.

b) What is the correlation between an alligator's length and weight?

c) Write the regression equation.

d) Interpret the slope of the equation in this context.

e) Do you think this equation will allow the scientists to make accurate predictions about alligators? What part of the regression analysis indicates this? What additional concerns do you have?

**63. Least squares.** Consider the four points (10,10), (20,50), (40,20), and (50,80). The least squares line is $\hat{y} = 7.0 + 1.1x$. Explain what "least squares" means, using these data as a specific example.

**64. Least squares.** Consider the four points (200,1950), (400,1650), (600,1800), and (800,1600). The least squares line is $\hat{y} = 1975 - 0.45x$. Explain what "least squares" means, using these data as a specific example.

### JUST CHECKING
### Answers

1.  An increase in home size of 1000 square feet is associated with an increase in price of $94,454, on average.

2.  Units are thousands of dollars per thousand square feet.

3.  About $188,908, on average

4.  You should expect the price to be 0.77 standard deviations above the mean.

5.  You should expect the size to be $2(0.77) = 1.54$ standard deviations below the mean.

6.  The home is 1.5 standard deviations above the mean in size no matter how size is measured.

7.  Differences in the size of houses account for about 59.5% of the variation in the house prices.

8.  It's positive. The correlation and the slope have the same sign.

9.  No, the standard deviation of the residuals is 53.79 thousand dollars. We shouldn't be surprised by any residual smaller than 2 standard deviations, and a residual of $100,000 is less than 2(53,790).

# CHAPTER 9

# Regression Wisdom

## Where are we going?

What happens when we fit a regression model to data that aren't straight? How bad will the predictions be? How can we tell if the model is appropriate or not? Questions like these are as important as fitting the model itself. In this chapter we'll see how to tell whether a regression model is sensible and what to do if it isn't.

*A S* **Activity: Construct a Plot with a Given Slope.** How's your feel for regression lines? Can you make a scatterplot that has a specified slope?

egression may be the most widely used Statistics method. It is used every day throughout the world to predict customer loyalty, numbers of admissions at hospitals, sales of automobiles, and many other things. Because regression is so widely used, it's also widely abused and misinterpreted. This chapter presents examples of regressions in which things are not quite as simple as they may have seemed at first, and shows how you can still use regression to discover what the data have to say.

## Getting the "Bends": When the Residuals Aren't Straight

No regression analysis is complete without a display of the residuals to check that the linear model is reasonable. Because the residuals are what is "left over" after the model describes the relationship, they often reveal subtleties that were not clear from a plot of the original data. Sometimes these are additional details that help confirm or refine our understanding. Sometimes they reveal violations of the regression conditions that require our attention.

We can't *know* whether the **Linearity Assumption** is true, but we can see if it's *plausible* by checking the **Straight Enough Condition.**

The fundamental assumption in working with a linear model is that the relationship you are modeling is, in fact, linear. That sounds obvious, but when you fit a regression, you can't take it for granted. Often it's hard to tell from the scatterplot you looked at before you fit the regression model. Sometimes you can't see a bend in the relationship until you plot the residuals.

Jessica Meir and Paul Ponganis study emperor penguins at the Scripps Institution of Oceanography's Center for Marine Biotechnology and Biomedicine at the University of California at San Diego. Says Jessica:

> *Emperor penguins are the most accomplished divers among birds, making routine dives of 5–12 minutes, with the longest recorded dive over 27 minutes. These birds can also dive to depths of over 500 meters! Since air-breathing animals like penguins must hold their breath while submerged, the duration of any given dive depends on how much oxygen is in the bird's body at the beginning of the dive, how quickly that oxygen gets used, and the lowest level of oxygen the bird can tolerate. The rate of oxygen depletion is primarily determined by the penguin's heart rate. Consequently, studies of heart rates during dives can help us understand how these animals regulate their oxygen consumption in order to make such impressive dives.*

The researchers equip emperor penguins with devices that record their heart rates during dives. Here's a scatterplot of the *Dive Heart Rate* (beats per minute) and the *Duration* (minutes) of dives by these high-tech penguins:

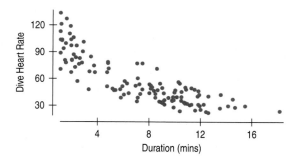

**FIGURE 9.1**

*The scatterplot of* Dive Heart Rate *in beats per minute (bpm) vs.* Duration *(minutes) shows a strong, roughly linear, negative association.*

The scatterplot looks fairly linear with a moderately strong negative association ($R^2 = 71.5\%$). The linear regression equation

$$\widehat{DiveHeartRate} = 96.9 - 5.47\ Duration$$

says that for longer dives, the average *Dive Heart Rate* is lower by about 5.47 beats per dive minute, starting from a value of 96.9 beats per minute.

The scatterplot of the residuals against *Duration* holds a surprise. The Linearity Assumption says we should not see a pattern, but instead there's a bend, starting high on the left, dropping down in the middle of the plot, and rising again at the right. Graphs of residuals often reveal patterns such as this that were easy to miss in the original scatterplot.

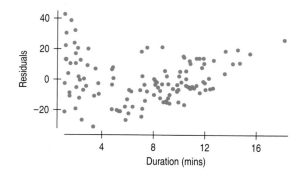

**FIGURE 9.2**

*Plotting the residuals against* Duration *reveals a bend. It was also in the original scatterplot, but here it's easier to see.*

Now looking back at the original scatterplot, you may see that the scatter of points isn't really straight. There's a slight bend to that plot, but the bend is much easier to see in the residuals. Even though it means rechecking the Straight Enough Condition *after* you find the regression, it's always a good idea to check your scatterplot of the residuals for bends that you might have overlooked in the original scatterplot.

## Sifting Residuals for Groups

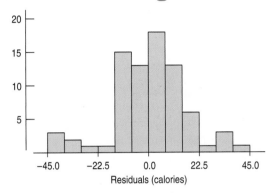

**FIGURE 9.3**

*A histogram of the regression residuals shows small modes both above and below the central large mode. These may be worth a second look.*

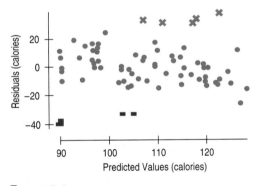

**FIGURE 9.4**

*A scatterplot of the residuals vs. predicted values for the cereal regression. The green "x" points are cereals whose calorie content is higher than the linear model predicts. The red "–" points show cereals with fewer calories than the model predicts. Is there something special about these cereals?*

In the Step-By-Step analysis in Chapter 8 to predict *Calories* from *Sugar* content in breakfast cereals, we examined a scatterplot of the residuals. Our first impression was that it had no particular structure—a conclusion that supported using the regression model. But let's look again.

Here's a histogram of the residuals. How would you describe its shape? It looks like there might be small modes on both sides of the central body of the data. One group of cereals seems to stand out as having large negative residuals, with fewer calories than we might have predicted, and another stands out with large positive residuals. The calories in these cereals were overestimated by the model. Whenever we suspect multiple modes, we ask whether they are somehow different.

Here's the residual plot from Chapter 8, with the points in those modes marked. Now we can see that those two groups stand away from the central pattern in the scatterplot. The high-residual cereals are Just Right Fruit & Nut; Muesli Raisins, Dates & Almonds; Peaches & Pecans; Mueslix Crispy Blend; and Nutri-Grain Almond Raisin. Do these cereals seem to have something in common? They all present themselves as "healthy." This might be surprising, but in fact, "healthy" cereals often contain more fat, and therefore more calories, than we might expect from looking at their sugar content alone.

The low-residual cereals are Puffed Rice, Puffed Wheat, three bran cereals, and Golden Crisps. You might not have grouped these cereals together before. What they have in common is a low calorie count *relative to their sugar content*—even though their sugar contents are quite different.

These observations may not lead us to question the overall linear model, but they do help us understand that other factors may be part of the story. An examination of residuals often leads us to discover groups of observations that are different from the rest.

When we discover that there is more than one group in a regression, we may decide to analyze the groups separately, using a different model for each group. Or we can stick with the original model and simply note that there are groups that are a little different. Either way, the model will be wrong, but useful, so it will improve our understanding of the data.

## Subsets

> Here's an important unstated condition for fitting models: **All the data must come from the same population.**

Cereal manufacturers aim cereals at different segments of the market. Supermarkets and cereal manufacturers try to attract different customers by placing different types of cereals on certain shelves. Cereals for kids tend to be on the "kid's shelf," at their eye level. Toddlers wouldn't be likely to grab a box from this shelf and beg, "Mom, can we please get this All-Bran with Extra Fiber?"

Should we take this extra information into account in our analysis? Figure 9.5 shows a scatterplot of *Calories* and *Sugar*, colored according to the shelf on which the cereals were found and with a separate regression line fit for each. The top shelf is clearly different. We might want to report two regressions, one for the top shelf and one for the bottom two shelves.[1]

**FIGURE 9.5**

*Calories and Sugar colored according to the shelf on which the cereal was found in a supermarket, with regression lines fit for each shelf individually. Do these data appear homogeneous? That is, do all the cereals seem to be from the same population of cereals? Or are there different kinds of cereals that we might want to consider separately?*

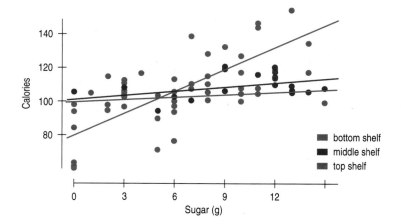

# Extrapolation: Reaching Beyond the Data

**A S** *Case Study:* **Predicting Manatee Kills.** Can we use regression to predict the number of manatees that will be killed by power boats this year?

*"Prediction is difficult, especially about the future."*
— Niels Bohr, Danish physicist

Linear models give a predicted value for each case in the data. Put a new *x*-value into the equation, and it gives a predicted value, $\hat{y}$, to go with it. But when the new *x*-value lies far from the data we used to build the regression, how trustworthy is the prediction?

The simple answer is that the farther the new *x*-value is from $\bar{x}$, the less trust we should place in the predicted value. Once we venture into new *x* territory, such a prediction is called an **extrapolation**. Extrapolations are dubious because they require the very questionable assumption that nothing about the relationship between *x* and *y* changes even at extreme values of *x* and beyond.

Extrapolations can get us into deep trouble. When the *x*-variable is *Time*, extrapolation becomes an attempt to peer into the future. People have always wanted to see into the future, and it doesn't take a crystal ball to foresee that they always will. In the past, seers, oracles, and wizards were called on to predict the future. Today mediums, fortune-tellers, and Tarot card readers still find many customers.

FOXTROT © 2002 Bill Amend. Reprinted with permission of UNIVERSAL PRESS SYNDICATE. All rights reserved.

---

[1] More complex models can take into account both sugar content and shelf information. This kind of *multiple regression* model is a natural extension of the model we're using here. You can learn about such models in Chapter 29 on the DVD.

Those with a more scientific outlook may use a linear model as their digital crystal ball. Linear models are based on the *x*-values of the data at hand and cannot be trusted beyond that span. Some physical phenomena do exhibit a kind of "inertia" that allows us to guess that current systematic behavior will continue, but regularity can't be counted on in phenomena such as stock prices, sales figures, hurricane tracks, or public opinion.

Extrapolating from current trends is so tempting that even professional forecasters make this mistake, and sometimes the errors are striking. In the mid-1970s, oil prices surged and long lines at gas stations were common. In 1970, oil cost about $17 a barrel (in 2005 dollars)—about what it had cost for 20 years or so. But then, within just a few years, the price surged to over $40. In 1975, a survey of 15 top econometric forecasting models (built by groups that included Nobel prize–winning economists) found predictions for 1985 oil prices that ranged from $300 to over $700 a barrel (in 2005 dollars). How close were these forecasts?

Here's a scatterplot of oil prices from 1972 to 1981 (in 2005 dollars).

> ### When the Data Are Years...
>
> ... we usually don't enter them as four-digit numbers. Here we used 0 for 1970, 10 for 1980, and so on. Or we may simply enter two digits, using 82 for 1982, for instance. Rescaling years like this often makes calculations easier and equations simpler. We recommend you do it, too. But be careful: If 1982 is 82, then 2004 is 104 (not 4), right?

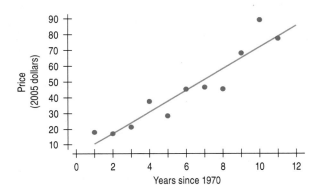

**FIGURE 9.6**

*The scatterplot shows an average increase in the price of a barrel of oil of over $7 per year from 1971 to 1982.*

The regression model

$$\widehat{Price} = -0.85 + 7.39 \, Years \; since \; 1970$$

says that prices had been going up 7.39 dollars per year, or nearly $74 in 10 years. If you assume that they would *keep going up*, it's not hard to imagine almost any price you want.

So, how did the forecasters do? Well, in the period from 1982 to 1998 oil prices didn't exactly continue that steady increase. In fact, they went down so much that by 1998, prices (adjusted for inflation) were the lowest they'd been since before World War II:

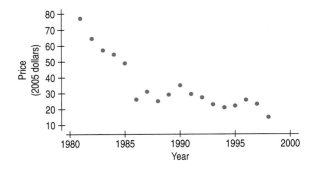

**FIGURE 9.7**

*This scatterplot of oil prices from 1981 to 1998 shows a fairly constant **decrease** of about $3 per barrel per year.*

Not one of the experts' models predicted that.

Of course, these decreases clearly couldn't continue, or oil would be free by now. The Energy Information Administration offered two *different* 20-year forecasts for oil prices after 1998, and both called for relatively modest increases in oil prices. So, how accurate have *these* forecasts been? Here's a timeplot of the EIA's predictions and the actual prices (in 2005 dollars):

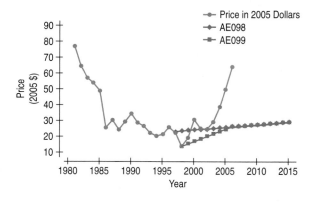

**FIGURE 9.8**

*Here are the EIA forecasts with the actual prices from 1981 to 2006. Neither forecast predicted the sharp run-up in the past few years.*

Oops! They seemed to have missed the sharp run-up in oil prices in the past few years.

Where do you think oil prices will go in the next decade? *Your* guess may be as good as anyone's!

Of course, knowing that extrapolation is dangerous doesn't stop people. The temptation to see into the future is hard to resist. So our more realistic advice is this:

*If you must extrapolate into the future, at least don't believe that the prediction will come true.*

# Outliers, Leverage, and Influence

The outcome of the 2000 U.S. presidential election was determined in Florida amid much controversy. The main race was between George W. Bush and Al Gore, but two minor candidates played a significant role. To the political right of the main party candidates was Pat Buchanan, while to the political left was Ralph Nader. Generally, Nader earned more votes than Buchanan throughout the state. We would expect counties with larger vote totals to give more votes to each candidate. Here's a regression relating *Buchanan's* vote totals by county in the state of Florida to *Nader's*:

Dependent variable is: Buchanan
R-squared = 42.8%

| Variable | Coefficient |
|----------|-------------|
| Intercept | 50.3 |
| Nader | 0.14 |

The regression model,

$$\widehat{Buchanan} = 50.3 + 0.14\ Nader,$$

says that, in each county, Buchanan received about 0.14 times (or 14% of) the vote Nader received, starting from a base of 50.3 votes.

This seems like a reasonable regression, with an $R^2$ of almost 43%. But we've violated all three Rules of Data Analysis by going straight to the regression table without making a picture.

Here's a scatterplot that shows the vote for Buchanan in each county of Florida plotted against the vote for Nader. The striking **outlier** is Palm Beach County.

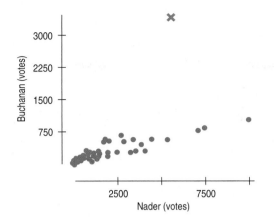

**FIGURE 9.9**

*Votes received by Buchanan against votes for Nader in all Florida counties in the presidential election of 2000. The red "x" point is Palm Beach County, home of the "butterfly ballot."*

*"Nature is nowhere accustomed more openly to display her secret mysteries than in cases where she shows traces of her workings apart from the beaten path."*

—William Harvey
(1657)

The so-called "butterfly ballot," used only in Palm Beach County, was a source of controversy. It has been claimed that the format of this ballot confused voters so that some who intended to vote for the Democrat, Al Gore, punched the wrong hole next to his name and, as a result, voted for Buchanan.

The scatterplot shows a strong, positive, linear association, and one striking point. With Palm Beach removed from the regression, the $R^2$ jumps from 42.8% to 82.1% and the slope of the line changes to 0.1, suggesting that Buchanan received only about 10% of the vote that Nader received. With more than 82% of the variability of the Buchanan vote accounted for, the model when Palm Beach is omitted certainly fits better. Palm Beach County now stands out, not as a Buchanan stronghold, but rather as a clear violation of the model that begs for explanation.

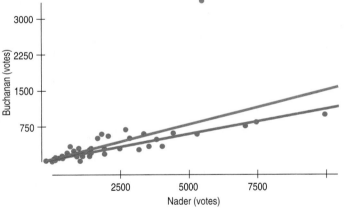

**FIGURE 9.10**

*The red line shows the effect that one unusual point can have on a regression.*

One of the great values of models is that, by establishing an idealized behavior, they help us to see when and how data values are unusual. In regression, a point can stand out in two different ways. First, a data value can have a large residual, as Palm Beach County does in this example. Because they seem to be different from the other cases, points whose residuals are large always deserve special attention.

A data point can also be unusual if its *x*-value is far from the mean of the *x*-values. Such a point is said to have high **leverage.** The physical image of a lever is exactly right. We know the line must pass through $(\bar{x}, \bar{y})$, so you can picture that point as the fulcrum of the lever. Just as sitting farther from the hinge on a see-saw gives you more leverage to pull it your way, points with values far from $\bar{x}$ pull more strongly on the regression line.

A point with high leverage has the potential to change the regression line. But it doesn't always use that potential. If the point lines up with the pattern of the

*"Give me a place to stand and I will move the Earth."*

—Archimedes
(287–211 BCE)

other points, then including it doesn't change our estimate of the line. By sitting so far from $\bar{x}$, though, it may strengthen the relationship, inflating the correlation and $R^2$. How can you tell if a high-leverage point actually changes the model? Just fit the linear model twice, both with and without the point in question. We say that a point is **influential** if omitting it from the analysis gives a very different model.[2]

Influence depends on both leverage and residual; a case with high leverage whose $y$-value sits right on the line fit to the rest of the data is not influential. Removing that case won't change the slope, even if it does affect $R^2$. A case with modest leverage but a very large residual (such as Palm Beach County) can be influential. Of course, if a point has enough leverage, it can pull the line right to it. Then it's highly influential, but its residual is small. The only way to be sure is to fit both regressions.

Unusual points in a regression often tell us more about the data and the model than any other points. We face a challenge: The best way to identify unusual points is against the background of a model, but good models are free of the influence of unusual points. (That insight's at least 400 years old. See the sidebar.) Don't give in to the temptation to simply delete points that don't fit the line. You can take points out and discuss what the model looks like with and without them, but arbitrarily deleting points can give a false sense of how well the model fits the data. Your goal should be understanding the data, not making $R^2$ as big as you can.

In 2000, George W. Bush won Florida (and thus the presidency) by only a few hundred votes, so Palm Beach County's residual is big enough to be meaningful. It's the rare unusual point that determines a presidency, but all are worth examining and trying to understand.

A point with so much influence that it pulls the regression line close to it can make its residual deceptively small. Influential points like that can have a shocking effect on the regression. Here's a plot of *IQ* against *Shoe Size*, again from the fanciful study of intelligence and foot size in comedians we saw in Chapter 7. The linear regression output shows

Dependent variable is: IQ
R-squared = 24.8%

| Variable | Coefficient |
|----------|-------------|
| Intercept | 93.3265 |
| Shoe size | 2.08318 |

Although this is a silly example, it illustrates an important and common potential problem: Almost all of the variance accounted for ($R^2 = 24.8\%$) is due to *one* point, namely, Bozo. Without Bozo, there is little correlation between *Shoe Size* and *IQ*. Look what happens to the regression when we take him out:

Dependent variable is: IQ
R-squared = 0.7%

| Variable | Coefficient |
|----------|-------------|
| Intercept | 105.458 |
| Shoe size | −0.460194 |

The $R^2$ value is now 0.7%—a very weak linear relationship (as one might expect!). One single point exhibits a great influence on the regression analysis.

What would have happened if Bozo hadn't shown his comic genius on IQ tests? Suppose his measured *IQ* had been only 50. The slope of the line would then drop from 0.96 IQ points/shoe size to −0.69 IQ points/shoe size. No

**FIGURE 9.11**

*Bozo's extraordinarily large shoes give his data point high leverage in the regression. Wherever Bozo's IQ falls, the regression line will follow.*

**FIGURE 9.12**

*If Bozo's IQ were low, the regression slope would change from positive to negative. A single influential point can change a regression model drastically.*

> **A S** **Activity: Leverage.** You may be surprised to see how sensitive to a single influential point a regression line is.

> *"For whoever knows the ways of Nature will more easily notice her deviations; and, on the other hand, whoever knows her deviations will more accurately describe her ways."*
>
> —Francis Bacon (1561–1626)

---

[2] Some textbooks use the term *influential point* for any observation that influences the slope, intercept, or $R^2$. We'll reserve the term for points that influence the slope.

matter where Bozo's *IQ* is, the line tends to follow it because his *Shoe Size,* being so far from the mean *Shoe Size,* makes this a high-leverage point.

Even though this example is far fetched, similar situations occur all the time in real life. For example, a regression of sales against floor space for hardware stores that looked primarily at small-town businesses could be dominated in a similar way if Home Depot were included.

> **Warning:** Influential points can hide in plots of residuals. Points with high leverage pull the line close to them, so they often have small residuals. You'll see influential points more easily in scatterplots of the original data or by finding a regression model with and without the points.

# JUST CHECKING

Each of these scatterplots shows an unusual point. For each, tell whether the point is a high-leverage point, would have a large residual, or is influential.

**1.**

**2.**

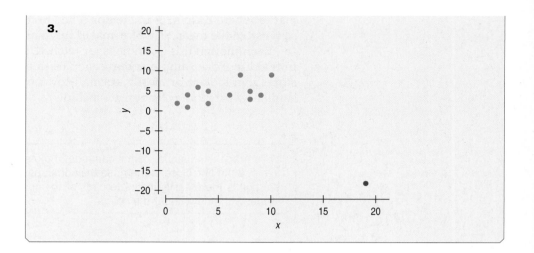

3.

# Lurking Variables and Causation

> One common way to interpret a regression slope is to say that "a change of 1 unit in $x$ results in a change of $b_1$ units in $y$." This way of saying things encourages causal thinking. Beware.

In Chapter 7, we tried to make it clear that no matter how strong the correlation is between two variables, there's no simple way to show that one variable causes the other. Putting a regression line through a cloud of points just increases the temptation to think and to say that the $x$-variable *causes* the $y$-variable. Just to make sure, let's repeat the point again: No matter how strong the association, no matter how large the $R^2$ value, no matter how straight the line, there is no way to conclude from a regression alone that one variable *causes* the other. There's always the possibility that some third variable is driving both of the variables you have observed. With observational data, as opposed to data from a designed experiment, there is no way to be sure that a **lurking variable** is not the cause of any apparent association.

Here's an example: The scatterplot shows the *Life Expectancy* (average of men and women, in years) for each of 41 countries of the world, plotted against the square root of the number of *Doctors* per person in the country. (The square root is here to make the relationship satisfy the Straight Enough Condition, as we saw back in Chapter 7.)

**FIGURE 9.13**

*The relationship between* Life Expectancy *(years) and availability of* Doctors *(measured as* √doctors per person*) for countries of the world is strong, positive, and linear.*

The strong positive association ($R^2 = 62.4\%$) seems to confirm our expectation that more *Doctors* per person improves healthcare, leading to longer lifetimes and a greater *Life Expectancy*. The strength of the association would *seem* to argue that we should send more doctors to developing countries to increase life expectancy.

That conclusion is about the consequences of a change. Would sending more doctors increase life expectancy? Specifically, do doctors *cause* greater life expectancy? Perhaps, but these are observed data, so there may be another explanation for the association.

Here's a similar-looking scatterplot. This time the *x*-variable is the square root of the number of *Televisions* per person in each country. The positive association in this scatterplot is even *stronger* than the association in the previous plot ($R^2 = 72.3\%$). We can fit the linear model, and quite possibly use the number of TVs as a way to predict life expectancy. Should we conclude that increasing the number of TVs actually extends lifetimes? If so, we should send TVs instead of doctors to developing countries. Not only is the correlation with life expectancy higher, but TVs are much cheaper than doctors.

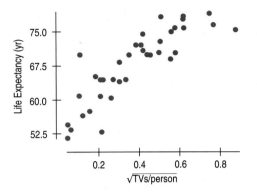

**FIGURE 9.14**

*To increase life expectancy, don't send doctors, send TVs; they're cheaper and more fun. Or maybe that's not the right interpretation of this scatterplot of life expectancy against availability of TVs (as √TVs per person).*

What's wrong with this reasoning? Maybe we were a bit hasty earlier when we concluded that doctors *cause* longer lives. Maybe there's a lurking variable here. Countries with higher standards of living have both longer life expectancies *and* more doctors (and more TVs). Could higher living standards cause changes in the other variables? If so, then improving living standards might be expected to prolong lives, increase the number of doctors, and increase the number of TVs.

From this example, you can see how easy it is to fall into the trap of mistakenly inferring causality from a regression. For all we know, doctors (or TVs!) *do* increase life expectancy. But we can't tell that from data like these, no matter how much we'd like to. Resist the temptation to conclude that *x* causes *y* from a regression, no matter how obvious that conclusion seems to you.

# Working with Summary Values

Scatterplots of statistics summarized over groups tend to show less variability than we would see if we measured the same variable on individuals. This is because the summary statistics themselves vary less than the data on the individuals do—a fact we will make more specific in coming chapters.

In Chapter 7 we looked at the heights and weights of individual students. There we saw a correlation of 0.644, so $R^2$ is 41.5%.

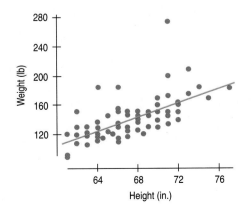

**FIGURE 9.15**

*Weight (lb) against Height (in.) for a sample of men. There's a strong, positive, linear association.*

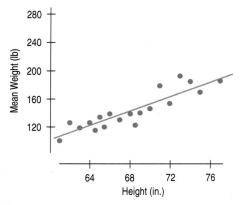

**FIGURE 9.16**

Mean Weight *(lb)* shows a stronger linear association with Height *than do the weights of individuals. Means vary less than individual values.*

Suppose, instead of data on individuals, we knew only the mean weight for each height value. The scatterplot of mean weight by height would show less scatter. And the $R^2$ would increase to 80.1%.

Scatterplots of summary statistics show less scatter than the baseline data on individuals and can give a false impression of how well a line summarizes the data. There's no simple correction for this phenomenon. Once we're given summary data, there's no simple way to get the original values back.

In the life expectancy and TVs example, we have no good measure of exposure to doctors or to TV on an individual basis. But if we did, we should expect the scatterplot to show more variability and the corresponding $R^2$ to be smaller. The bottom line is that you should be a bit suspicious of conclusions based on regressions of summary data. They may look better than they really are.

**FOR EXAMPLE**     Using several of these methods together

Motorcycles designed to run off-road, often known as dirt bikes, are specialized vehicles.

We have data on 104 dirt bikes available for sale in 2005. Some cost as little as $3000, while others are substantially more expensive. Let's investigate how the size and type of engine contribute to the cost of a dirt bike. As always, we start with a scatterplot.

Here's a scatterplot of the manufacturer's suggested retail price (*MSRP*) in dollars against the engine *Displacement*, along with a regression analysis:

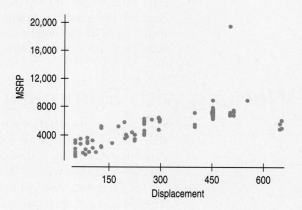

Dependent variable is: MSRP
R-squared = 49.9% s = 1737

| Variable | Coefficient |
|---|---|
| Intercept | 2273.67 |
| Displacement | 10.0297 |

**Question:** What do you see in the scatterplot?

*There is a strong positive association between the engine displacement of dirt bikes and the manufacturer's suggested retail price. One of the dirt bikes is an outlier; its price is more than double that of any other bike.*

The outlier is the Husqvarna TE 510 Centennial. Most of its components are handmade exclusively for this model, including extensive use of carbon fiber throughout. That may explain its $19,500 price tag! Clearly, the TE 510 is not like the other bikes. We'll set it aside for now and look at the data for the remaining dirt bikes.

**Question:** What effect will removing this outlier have on the regression? Describe how the slope, $R^2$, and $s_e$ will change.

The TE 510 was an influential point, tilting the regression line upward. With that point removed, the regression slope will get smaller. With that dirt bike omitted, the pattern becomes more consistent, so the value of $R^2$ should get larger and the standard deviation of the residuals, $s_e$, should get smaller.

With the outlier omitted, here's the new regression and a scatterplot of the residuals:

Dependent variable is: MSRP
R-squared = 61.3%  s = 1237

| Variable | Coefficient |
| --- | --- |
| Intercept | 2411.02 |
| Displacement | 9.05450 |

**Question:** What do you see in the residuals plot?

The points at the far right don't fit well with the other dirt bikes. Overall, there appears to be a bend in the relationship, so a linear model may not be appropriate.

Let's try a re-expression. (You'll learn how to do this in Chapter 10.) Here's a scatterplot showing *MSRP* against the cube root of *Displacement* to make the relationship closer to straight. (Since displacement is measured in cubic centimeters, its cube root has the simple units of centimeters.) In addition, we've colored the plot according to the cooling method used in the bike's engine: liquid or air. Each group is shown with its own regression line, as we did for the cereals on different shelves.

*(continued)*

For Example (*continued*)

**Question:** What does this plot say about dirt bikes?

There appears to be a positive, linear relationship between *MSRP* and the cube root of *Displacement*. In general, the larger the engine a bike has, the higher the suggested price. Liquid-cooled dirt bikes, however, typically cost more than air-cooled bikes with comparable displacement. A few liquid-cooled bikes appear to be much less expensive than we might expect, given their engine displacements. [Jiang Lu, Joseph B. Kadane, and Peter Boatwright, "The Dirt on Bikes: An Illustration of CART Models for Brand Differentiation," provides data on 2005-model bikes.]

# WHAT CAN GO WRONG?

This entire chapter has held warnings about things that can go wrong in a regression analysis. So let's just recap. When you make a linear model,

▶ **Make sure the relationship is straight.** Check the Straight Enough Condition. Always examine the residuals for evidence that the Linearity Assumption has failed. It's often easier to see deviations from a straight line in the residuals plot than in the scatterplot of the original data. Pay special attention to the most extreme residuals because they may have something to add to the story told by the linear model.

▶ **Be on guard for different groups in your regression.** Check for evidence that the data consist of separate subsets. If you find subsets that behave differently, consider fitting a different linear model to each subset.

▶ **Beware of extrapolating.** Beware of extrapolation beyond the *x*-values that were used to fit the model. Although it's common to use linear models to extrapolate, the practice is dangerous.

▶ **Beware especially of extrapolating into the future!** Be especially cautious about extrapolating into the future with linear models. To predict the future, you must assume that future changes will continue at the same rate you've observed in the past. Predicting the future is particularly tempting and particularly dangerous.

▶ **Look for unusual points.** Unusual points always deserve attention, and may well reveal more about your data than the rest of the points combined. Always look for them and try to understand why they stand apart. A scatterplot of the data is a good way to see high-leverage and influential points. A scatterplot of the residuals against the predicted values is a good tool for finding points with large residuals.

▶ **Beware of high-leverage points, and especially of those that are influential.** Influential points can alter the regression model a great deal. The resulting model may say more about one or two points than about the overall relationship.

▶ **Consider comparing two regressions.** To see the impact of outliers on a regression, it's often wise to run two regressions, one with and one without the extraordinary points, and then to discuss the differences.

▶ **Treat unusual points honestly.** If you remove enough carefully selected points, you can always get a regression with a high $R^2$ eventually. But it won't give you much understanding. Some data are not related simply enough for a linear model to fit very well. When that happens, report the failure and stop.

▶ **Beware of lurking variables.** Think about lurking variables before interpreting a linear model. It's particularly tempting to explain a strong regression by thinking that the *x*-variable *causes* the *y*-variable. A linear model alone can never demonstrate such causation, in part because it cannot eliminate the chance that a lurking variable has caused the variation in both *x* and *y*.

▶ **Watch out when dealing with data that are summaries.** Be cautious in working with data values that are themselves summaries, such as means or medians. Such statistics are less variable than the data on which they are based, so they tend to inflate the impression of the strength of a relationship.

# CONNECTIONS

We are always alert to things that can go wrong if we use statistics without thinking carefully. Regression opens new vistas of potential problems. But each one relates to issues we've thought about before.

It is always important that our data be from a single homogeneous group and not made up of disparate groups. We looked for multiple modes in single variables. Now we check scatterplots for evidence of subgroups in our data. As with modes, it's often best to split the data and analyze the groups separately.

Our concern with unusual points and their potential influence also harks back to our earlier concern with outliers in histograms and boxplots—and for many of the same reasons. As we've seen here, regression offers such points new scope for mischief.

The risks of interpreting linear models as causal or predictive arose in Chapters 7 and 8. And they're important enough to mention again in later chapters.

## WHAT HAVE WE LEARNED?

We've learned that there are many ways in which a data set may be unsuitable for a regression analysis.

▶ Watch out for more than one group hiding in your regression analysis. If you find subsets of the data that behave differently, consider fitting a different regression model to each subset.

▶ The **Straight Enough Condition** says that the relationship should be reasonably straight to fit a regression. Somewhat paradoxically, sometimes it's easier to see that the relationship is not straight *after* fitting the regression by examining the residuals. The same is true of outliers.

▶ The **Outlier Condition** actually means two things: Points with large residuals or high leverage (especially both) can influence the regression model significantly. It's a good idea to perform the regression analysis with and without such points to see their impact.

And we've learned that even a good regression doesn't mean we should believe that the model says more than it really does.

▶ Extrapolation far from $\bar{x}$ can lead to silly and useless predictions.

▶ Even an $R^2$ near 100% doesn't indicate that $x$ causes $y$ (or the other way around). Watch out for lurking variables that may affect both $x$ and $y$.

▶ Be careful when you interpret regressions based on *summaries* of the data sets. These regressions tend to look stronger than the regression based on all the individual data.

## Terms

**Extrapolation**    230. Although linear models provide an easy way to predict values of $y$ for a given value of $x$, it is unsafe to predict for values of $x$ far from the ones used to find the linear model equation. Such extrapolation may pretend to see into the future, but the predictions should not be trusted.

**Outlier**    232. Any data point that stands away from the others can be called an outlier. In regression, outliers can be extraordinary in two ways: by having a large residual or by having high leverage.

**Leverage**    233. Data points whose $x$-values are far from the mean of $x$ are said to exert leverage on a linear model. High-leverage points pull the line close to them, and so they can have a large effect on the line, sometimes completely determining the slope and intercept. With high enough leverage, their residuals can be deceptively small.

**Influential point**    234. If omitting a point from the data results in a very different regression model, then that point is called an influential point.

**Re-expression**    239. A re-expression of one or both variables can straighten a bent relationship.

Lurking variable

236. A variable that is not explicitly part of a model but affects the way the variables in the model appear to be related is called a lurking variable. Because we can never be certain that observational data are not hiding a lurking variable that influences both *x* and *y*, it is never safe to conclude that a linear model demonstrates a causal relationship, no matter how strong the linear association.

## Skills

▸ Understand that we cannot fit linear models or use linear regression if the underlying relationship between the variables is not itself linear.

▸ Understand that data used to find a model must be homogeneous. Look for subgroups in data before you find a regression, and analyze each separately.

▸ Know the danger of extrapolating beyond the range of the *x*-values used to find the linear model, especially when the extrapolation tries to predict into the future.

▸ Understand that points can be unusual by having a large residual or by having high leverage.

▸ Understand that an influential point can change the slope and intercept of the regression line.

▸ Look for lurking variables whenever you consider the association between two variables. Understand that a strong association does not mean that the variables are causally related.

▸ Know how to display residuals from a linear model by making a scatterplot of residuals against predicted values or against the *x*-variable, and know what patterns to look for in the picture.

▸ Know how to look for high-leverage and influential points by examining a scatterplot of the data and how to look for points with large residuals by examining a scatterplot of the residuals against the predicted values or against the *x*-variable. Understand how fitting a regression line with and without influential points can add to your understanding of the regression model.

▸ Know how to look for high-leverage points by examining the distribution of the *x*-values or by recognizing them in a scatterplot of the data, and understand how they can affect a linear model.

▸ Include diagnostic information such as plots of residuals and leverages as part of your report of a regression.

▸ Report any high-leverage points.

▸ Report any outliers. Consider reporting analyses with and without outliers, to assess their influence on the regression.

▸ Include appropriate cautions about extrapolation when reporting predictions from a linear model.

▸ Discuss possible lurking variables.

# ON THE COMPUTER

## Regression Diagnosis

Most statistics technology offers simple ways to check whether your data satisfy the conditions for regression. We have already seen that these programs can make a simple scatterplot. They can also help us check the conditions by plotting residuals.

### DATA DESK

Click on the **HyperView** menu on the **Regression** output table. A menu drops down to offer scatterplots of residuals against predicted values, Normal probability plots of residuals, or just the ability to save the residuals and predicted values.
Click on the name of a predictor in the regression table to be offered a scatterplot of the residuals against that predictor.

COMMENTS

If you change any of the variables in the regression analysis, Data Desk will offer to update the plots of residuals.

## EXCEL

The Data Analysis add-in for Excel includes a Regression command. The dialog box it shows offers to make plots of residuals.

**COMMENTS**

Do not use the Normal probability plot offered in the regression dialog. It is not what it claims to be and is wrong.

## JMP

From the **Analyze** menu, choose **Fit Y by X.** Select **Fit Line.** Under Linear Fit, Select **Plot Residuals.** You can also choose

to **Save Residuals.** Subsequently, from the **Distribution** menu, choose **Normal quantile plot** or **histogram** for the residuals.

## MINITAB

From the **Stat** menu, choose **Regression.** From the **Regression** submenu, select **Regression** again. In the Regression dialog, enter the response variable name in the "Response" box and the predictor variable name in the "Predictor" box. To specify saved results, in the Regression dialog, click **Storage.** Check

"Residuals" and "Fits." Click **OK.** To specify displays, in the Regression dialog, click **Graphs.** Under "Residual Plots," select "Individual plots" and check "Residuals versus fits." Click **OK.** Now back in the Regression dialog, click **OK.** Minitab computes the regression and the requested saved values and graphs.

## SPSS

From the **Analyze** menu, choose **Regression.** From the Regression submenu, choose **Linear.** After assigning variables to their roles in the regression, click the "**Plots ...**" button. In the Plots dialog, you can specify a Normal probability plot of residuals and scatterplots of various versions of standardized residuals and predicted values.

**COMMENTS**

A plot of ***ZRESID** against ***PRED** will look most like the residual plots we've discussed. SPSS standardizes the residuals by dividing by their standard deviation. (There's no need to subtract their mean; it must be zero.) The standardization doesn't affect the scatterplot.

## TI-83/84 PLUS

To make a residuals plot, set up a **STATPLOT** as a scatterplot. Specify your explanatory datalist as **Xlist.** For **Ylist,** import the name **RESID** from the **LIST NAMES** menu. **ZoomStat** will now create the residuals plot.

**COMMENTS**

Each time you execute a **LinReg** command, the calculator automatically computes the residuals and stores them in a data list named **RESID.** If you want to see them, go to **STAT EDIT.** Space through the names of the lists until you find a blank. Import **RESID** from the **LIST NAMES** menu. Now every time you have the calculator compute a regression analysis, it will show you the residuals.

## TI-89

To make a residuals plot, define a Plot as a scatterplot. Specify your explanatory datalist as **Xlist.** For **Ylist,** find the list name resid from **VAR-LINK** by arrowing to the **STATVARS** portion. Then press ② **(r)** and locate the list. Press [ENTER] to finish the plot definition and [F5] to display the plot.

**COMMENTS**

Each time you execute a **LinReg** command, the calculator automatically computes the residuals and stores them in a data list named **RESID.** If you don't want to see this (or any other calculator-generated list) anymore, press [F1] (Tools) and select choice 3: Setup Editor. Leaving the box for lists to display blank will reset the calculator to show only lists 1 through 6.

# EXERCISES

**1. Marriage age 2003.** Is there evidence that the age at which women get married has changed over the past 100 years? The scatterplot shows the trend in age at first marriage for American women. (www.census.gov)

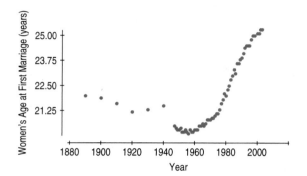

a) Do you think there is a clear pattern? Describe the trend.
b) Is the association strong?
c) Is the correlation high? Explain.
d) Do you think a linear model is appropriate for these data? Explain.

**2. Smoking 2004.** The Centers for Disease Control and Prevention track cigarette smoking in the United States. How has the percentage of people who smoke changed since the danger became clear during the last half of the 20th century? The scatterplot shows percentages of smokers among men 18–24 years of age, as estimated by surveys, from 1965 through 2004. (www.cdc.gov/nchs/)

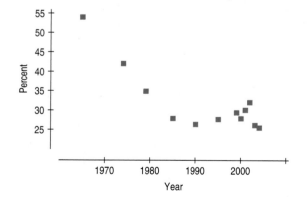

a) Do you think there is a clear pattern? Describe the trend.
b) Is the association strong?
c) Is a linear model appropriate for these data? Explain.

**3. Human Development Index.** The United Nations Development Programme (UNDP) collects data in the developing world to help countries solve global and national development challenges. In the UNDP annual Human Development Report, you can find data on over 100 variables for each of 177 countries worldwide. One summary measure used by the agency is the Human Development Index (HDI), which attempts to summarize in a single number the progress in health, education, and economics of a country. In 2006, the HDI was as high as 0.965 for Norway and as low as 0.331 for Niger. The gross domestic product per capita (GDPPC), by contrast, is often used to summarize the *overall* economic strength of a country. Is the HDI related to the GDPPC? Here is a scatterplot of *HDI* against *GDPPC*.

a) Explain why fitting a linear model to these data might be misleading.
b) If you fit a linear model to the data, what do you think a scatterplot of residuals versus predicted *HDI* will look like?
c) There is an outlier (Luxembourg) with a *GDPPC* of around $70,000. Will setting this point aside improve the model substantially? Explain.

**4. HDI Revisited.** The United Nations Development Programme (UNDP) uses the Human Development Index (HDI) in an attempt to summarize in one number the progress in health, education, and economics of a country. The number of cell phone subscribers per 1000 people is positively associated with economic progress in a country. Can the number of cell phone subscribers be used to predict the HDI? Here is a scatterplot of HDI against cell phone subscribers:

a) Explain why fitting a linear model to these data might be misleading.
b) If you fit a linear model to the data, what do you think a scatterplot of residuals versus predicted *HDI* will look like?

**5. Good model?**    In justifying his choice of a model, a student wrote, "I know this is the correct model because $R^2 = 99.4\%$."
   a) Is this reasoning correct? Explain.
   b) Does this model allow the student to make accurate predictions? Explain.

**6. Bad model?**    A student who has created a linear model is disappointed to find that her $R^2$ value is a very low 13%.
   a) Does this mean that a linear model is not appropriate? Explain.
   b) Does this model allow the student to make accurate predictions? Explain.

**7. Movie Dramas.**    Here's a scatterplot of the production budgets (in millions of dollars) vs. the running time (in minutes) for major release movies in 2005. Dramas are plotted in red and all other genres are plotted in black. A separate least squares regression line has been fitted to each group. For the following questions, just examine the plot:

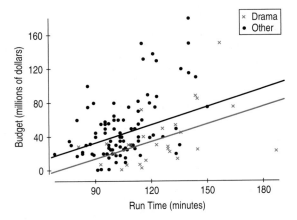

a) What are the units for the slopes of these lines?
b) In what way are dramas and other movies similar with respect to this relationship?
c) In what way are dramas different from other genres of movies with respect to this relationship?

**8. Movie Ratings.**    Does the cost of making a movie depend on its audience? Here's a scatterplot of the same data we examined in Exercise 7. Movies with an R rating are colored purple, those with a PG-13 rating are red, and those with a PG rating are green. Regression lines have been found for each group. (The black points are G-rated, but there were too few to fit a line reliably.)

a) In what ways is the relationship between run times and budgets similar for the three different ratings groups?
b) How do the costs of R-rated movies differ from those of PG-13 and PG rated movies? Discuss both the slopes and the intercepts.
c) The film *King Kong*, with a run time of 187 minutes, is the red point sitting at the lower right. If it were omitted from this analysis, how might that change your conclusions about PG-13 movies?

**9. Oakland passengers.**    The scatterplot below shows the number of passengers departing from Oakland (CA) airport month by month since the start of 1997. Time is shown as years since 1990, with fractional years used to represent each month. (Thus, June of 1997 is 7.5—halfway through the 7th year after 1990.) www.oaklandairport.com

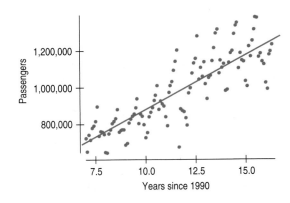

Here's a regression and the residuals plotted against *Years since 1990*:

Dependent variable is: Passengers
R-squared = 71.1%   s = 104330

| Variable | Coefficient |
|----------|-------------|
| Constant | 282584 |
| Year-1990 | 59704.4 |

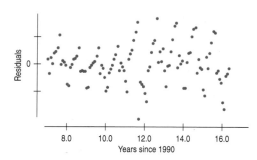

a) Interpret the slope and intercept of the regression model.

b) What does the value of $R^2$ say about how successful the model is?

c) Interpret $s_e$ in this context.

d) Would you use this model to predict the numbers of passengers in 2010 (*YearsSince1990* = 20)? Explain.

e) There's a point near the middle of this time span with a large negative residual. Can you explain this outlier?

**T** **10. Tracking hurricanes.**   In a previous chapter, we saw data on the errors (in nautical miles) made by the National Hurricane Center in predicting the path of hurricanes. The following scatterplot shows the trend in the 24-hour tracking errors since 1970. (www.nhc.noaa.gov)

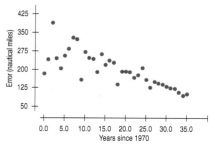

Dependent variable is: Error
R-squared = 63.0%   s = 42.87

| Variable | Coefficient |
|---|---|
| Intercept | 292.089 |
| Years-1970 | −5.22924 |

a) Interpret the slope and intercept of the regression model.

b) Interpret $s_e$ in this context.

c) The Center had a stated goal of achieving an average tracking error of 125 nautical miles in 2009. Will they make it? Why do you think so?

d) What if their goal were an average tracking error of 90 nautical miles?

e) What cautions would you state about your conclusion?

**11. Unusual points.**   Each of the four scatterplots that follow shows a cluster of points and one "stray" point. For each, answer these questions:

1) In what way is the point unusual? Does it have high leverage, a large residual, or both?

2) Do you think that point is an influential point?

3) If that point were removed from the data, would

the correlation become stronger or weaker? Explain.

4) If that point were removed from the data, would the slope of the regression line increase or decrease? Explain.

a)

b)

c)

d)

**12. More unusual points.**   Each of the following scatterplots shows a cluster of points and one "stray" point. For each, answer these questions:

1) In what way is the point unusual? Does it have high leverage, a large residual, or both?

2) Do you think that point is an influential point?

3) If that point were removed from the data, would the correlation become stronger or weaker? Explain.

4) If that point were removed from the data, would the slope of the regression line increase or decrease? Explain.

a)

b)

c)

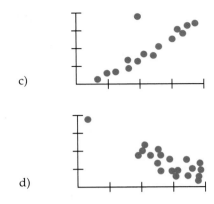

d)

**13. The extra point.** The scatterplot shows five blue data points at the left. Not surprisingly, the correlation for these points is $r = 0$. Suppose *one* additional data point is added at one of the five positions suggested below in green. Match each point (a–e) with the correct new correlation from the list given.
1) −0.90
2) −0.40
3) 0.00
4) 0.05
5) 0.75

**14. The extra point revisited.** The original five points in Exercise 13 produce a regression line with slope 0. Match each of the green points (a–e) with the slope of the line after that one point is added:
1) −0.45
2) −0.30
3) 0.00
4) 0.05
5) 0.85

**15. What's the cause?** Suppose a researcher studying health issues measures blood pressure and the percentage of body fat for several adult males and finds a strong positive association. Describe three different possible cause-and-effect relationships that might be present.

**16. What's the effect?** A researcher studying violent behavior in elementary-school children asks the children's parents how much time each child spends playing computer games and has their teachers rate each child on the level of aggressiveness they display while playing with other children. Suppose that the researcher finds a moderately strong positive correlation. Describe three different possible cause-and-effect explanations for this relationship.

**17. Reading.** To measure progress in reading ability, students at an elementary school take a reading comprehension test every year. Scores are measured in "grade-level" units; that is, a score of 4.2 means that a student is reading at slightly above the expected level for a fourth grader. The school principal prepares a report to parents that includes a graph showing the mean reading score for each grade. In his comments he points out that the strong positive trend demonstrates the success of the school's reading program.

a) Does this graph indicate that students are making satisfactory progress in reading? Explain.
b) What would you estimate the correlation between *Grade* and *Average Reading Level* to be?
c) If, instead of this plot showing average reading levels, the principal had produced a scatterplot of the reading levels of all the individual students, would you expect the correlation to be the same, higher, or lower? Explain.
d) Although the principal did not do a regression analysis, someone as statistically astute as you might do that. (But don't bother.) What value of the slope of that line would you view as demonstrating acceptable progress in reading comprehension? Explain.

**18. Grades.** A college admissions officer, defending the college's use of SAT scores in the admissions process, produced the graph below. It shows the mean GPAs for last year's freshmen, grouped by SAT scores. How strong is the evidence that *SAT Score* is a good predictor of *GPA*? What concerns you about the graph, the statistical methodology or the conclusions reached?

**19. Heating.** After keeping track of his heating expenses for several winters, a homeowner believes he can estimate the monthly cost from the average daily Fahrenheit temperature by using the model $\widehat{Cost} = 133 - 2.13\ Temp$. The residuals plot for his data is shown.

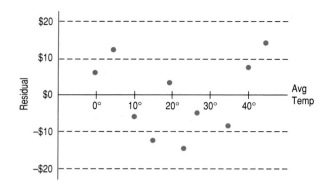

a) Interpret the slope of the line in this context.
b) Interpret the y-intercept of the line in this context.
c) During months when the temperature stays around freezing, would you expect cost predictions based on this model to be accurate, too low, or too high? Explain.
d) What heating cost does the model predict for a month that averages 10°?
e) During one of the months on which the model was based, the temperature did average 10°. What were the actual heating costs for that month?
f) Do you think the homeowner should use this model? Explain.
g) Would this model be more successful if the temperature were expressed in degrees Celsius? Explain.

20. **Speed.**   How does the speed at which you drive affect your fuel economy? To find out, researchers drove a compact car for 200 miles at speeds ranging from 35 to 75 miles per hour. From their data, they created the model *Fuel Efficiency* = 32 − 0.1 *Speed* and created this residual plot:

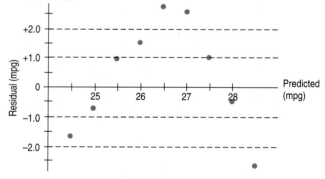

a) Interpret the slope of this line in context.
b) Explain why it's silly to attach any meaning to the y-intercept.
c) When this model predicts high *Fuel Efficiency,* what can you say about those predictions?
d) What *Fuel Efficiency* does the model predict when the car is driven at 50 mph?
e) What was the actual *Fuel Efficiency* when the car was driven at 45 mph?
f) Do you think there appears to be a strong association between *Speed* and *Fuel Efficiency*? Explain.
g) Do you think this is the appropriate model for that association? Explain.

**T** 21. **Interest rates.**   Here's a plot showing the federal rate on 3-month Treasury bills from 1950 to 1980, and a regres-

sion model fit to the relationship between the *Rate* (in %) and *Years since 1950.* (www.gpoaccess.gov/eop/)

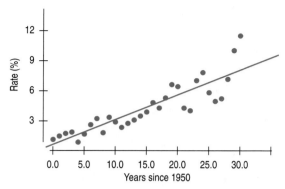

Dependent variable is: Rate
R-squared = 77.4%   s = 1.239

| Variable | Coefficient |
|---|---|
| Intercept | 0.640282 |
| Year-1950 | 0.247637 |

a) What is the correlation between *Rate* and *Year*?
b) Interpret the slope and intercept.
c) What does this model predict for the interest rate in the year 2000?
d) Would you expect this prediction to have been accurate? Explain.

**T** 22. **Ages of couples 2003.**   The graph shows the ages of both men and women at first marriage. (www.census. gov)

Clearly, the pattern for men is similar to the pattern for women. But are the two lines getting closer together?

Here's a timeplot showing the *difference* in average age (men's age − women's age) at first marriage, the regression analysis, and the associated residuals plot.

Dependent variable is: Age Difference
R-squared = 75.1%   s = 0.2333

| Variable | Coefficient |
|----------|-------------|
| Constant | 35.0617 |
| Year | −0.016565 |

a) What is the correlation between *Age Difference* and *Year*?
b) Interpret the slope of this line.
c) Predict the average age difference in 2015.
d) Describe reasons why you might not place much faith in that prediction.

**T 23. Interest rates revisited.** In Exercise 21 you investigated the federal rate on 3-month Treasury bills between 1950 and 1980. The scatterplot below shows that the trend changed dramatically after 1980, so we've built a new regression model for the data since 1980.

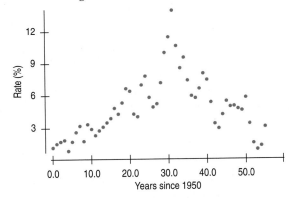

Dependent variable is: Rate
R-squared = 74.5%   s = 1.630

| Variable | Coefficient |
|----------|-------------|
| Intercept | 21.0688 |
| Year-50 | −0.356578 |

a) How does this model compare to the one in Exercise 21?
b) What does this model estimate the interest rate to have been in 2000? How does this compare to the rate you predicted in Exercise 21?
c) Do you trust this newer predicted value? Explain.
d) Given these two models, what would you predict the interest rate on 3-month Treasury bills will be in 2020?

**T 24. Ages of couples, again.** Has the trend of decreasing difference in age at first marriage seen in Exercise 22 gotten stronger recently? Here are the scatterplot and residual plot for the data from 1975 through 2003, along with a regression for just those years.

Dependent variable is: Men − Women
R-squared = 65.6%   s = 0.1869

| Variable | Coefficient |
|----------|-------------|
| Intercept | 4.88424 |
| Year | −0.029959 |

a) Why is $R^2$ higher for the first model (in Exercise 22)?
b) Is this linear model appropriate for the post-1975 data? Explain.
c) What does the slope say about marriage ages since 1975?
d) Explain why it's not reasonable to interpret the *y*-intercept.

**25. Gestation.** For women, pregnancy lasts about 9 months. In other species of animals, the length of time from conception to birth varies. Is there any evidence that the gestation period is related to the animal's lifespan? The first scatterplot shows *Gestation Period* (in days) vs. *Life Expectancy* (in years) for 18 species of mammals. The highlighted point at the far right represents humans.

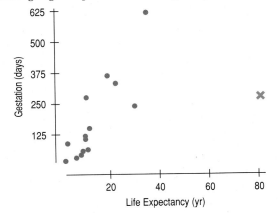

a) For these data, $r = 0.54$, not a very strong relationship. Do you think the association would be stronger or weaker if humans were removed? Explain.
b) Is there reasonable justification for removing humans from the data set? Explain.
c) Here are the scatterplot and regression analysis for the 17 nonhuman species. Comment on the strength of the association.

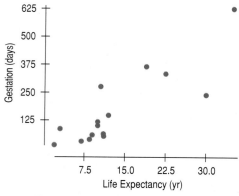

Dependent variable is: Gestation
R-squared = 72.2%

| Variable | Coefficient |
|---|---|
| Constant | −39.5172 |
| LifExp | 15.4980 |

d) Interpret the slope of the line.
e) Some species of monkeys have a life expectancy of about 20 years. Estimate the expected gestation period of one of these monkeys.

**T** **26. Swim the lake 2006.** People swam across Lake Ontario 42 times between 1974 and 2006 (www.soloswims.com). We might be interested in whether they are getting any faster or slower. Here are the regression of the crossing *Times* (minutes) against the *Year* of the crossing and the residuals plot:

Dependent variable is: Time
R-squared = 1.3%     s = 443.8

| Variable | Coefficient |
|---|---|
| Intercept | −8950.40 |
| Year | 5.14171 |

a) What does the $R^2$ mean for this regression?
b) Are the swimmers getting faster or slower? Explain.
c) The outlier seen in the residuals plot is a crossing by Vicki Keith in 1987 in which she swam a round trip, North to South and then back again. Clearly, this swim doesn't belong with the others. Do you think that removing it would change the model a lot? Explain.

**27. Elephants and hippos.** We removed humans from the scatterplot in Exercise 25 because our species was an outlier in life expectancy. The resulting scatterplot shows two points that now may be of concern. The point in the upper right corner of this scatterplot is for elephants, and the other point at the far right is for hippos.
a) By removing one of these points, we could make the association appear to be stronger. Which point? Explain.
b) Would the slope of the line increase or decrease?
c) Should we just keep removing animals to increase the strength of the model? Explain.
d) If we remove elephants from the scatterplot, the slope of the regression line becomes 11.6 days per year. Do you think elephants were an influential point? Explain.

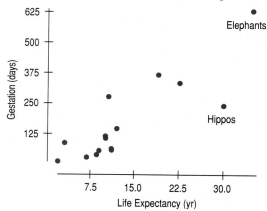

**T** **28. Another swim 2006.** In Exercise 26 we saw that Vicki Keith's round-trip swim of Lake Ontario was an obvious outlier among the other one-way times. Here is the new regression after this unusual point is removed:

Dependent variable is: Time
R-squared = 4.1%     s = 292.6

| Variable | Coefficient |
|---|---|
| Intercept | −11048.7 |
| Year | 6.17091 |

a) In this new model, the value of $s_e$ is much smaller. Explain what that means in this context.
b) Now would you be willing to say that the Lake Ontario swimmers are getting faster (or slower)?

**T** **29. Marriage age 2003 revisited.** Suppose you wanted to predict the trend in marriage age for American women into the early part of this century.
a) How could you use the data graphed in Exercise 1 to get a good prediction? Marriage ages in selected years starting in 1900 are listed below. Use all or part of these data to create an appropriate model for predicting the average age at which women will first marry in 2010.

1900–1950 (10-yr intervals): 21.9, 21.6, 21.2, 21.3, 21.5, 20.3
1955–2000 (5-yr intervals): 20.2, 20.2, 20.6, 20.8, 21.1, 22.0, 23.3, 23.9, 24.5, 25.1

b) How much faith do you place in this prediction? Explain.

c) Do you think your model would produce an accurate prediction about your grandchildren, say, 50 years from now? Explain.

**30. Unwed births.** The National Center for Health Statistics reported the data below, showing the percentage of all births that are to unmarried women for selected years between 1980 and 1998. Create a model that describes this trend. Justify decisions you make about how to best use these data.

| Year | 1980 | 1985 | 1990 | 1991 | 1992 | 1993 | 1994 | 1995 | 1996 | 1997 | 1998 |
|------|------|------|------|------|------|------|------|------|------|------|------|
| % | 18.4 | 22.0 | 28.0 | 29.5 | 30.1 | 31.0 | 32.6 | 32.2 | 32.4 | 32.4 | 32.8 |

**31. Life Expectancy 2004.** Data from the World Bank for 26 Western Hemisphere countries can be used to examine the association between female *Life Expectancy* and the average *Number of Children* women give birth to. (http://devdata.worldbank.org/data-query/)

| Country | Births/ Woman | Life Exp. | Country | Births/ Woman | Life Exp. |
|---------|------|------|---------|------|------|
| Argentina | 2.3 | 74.6 | Guatemala | 4.4 | 67.6 |
| Bahamas | 2.3 | 70.5 | Honduras | 3.6 | 68.2 |
| Barbados | 1.7 | 75.4 | Jamaica | 2.4 | 70.8 |
| Belize | 3.0 | 71.9 | Mexico | 2.2 | 75.1 |
| Bolivia | 3.7 | 64.5 | Nicaragua | 3.2 | 70.1 |
| Brazil | 2.3 | 70.9 | Panama | 2.6 | 75.1 |
| Canada | 1.5 | 79.8 | Paraguay | 3.7 | 71.2 |
| Chile | 2.0 | 78.0 | Peru | 2.8 | 70.4 |
| Colombia | 2.4 | 72.6 | Puerto Rico | 1.9 | 77.5 |
| Costa Rica | 24.9 | 78.7 | United States | 2.0 | 77.4 |
| Dominican | | | Uruguay | 2.1 | 75.2 |
| Republic | 2.8 | 67.8 | Venezuela | 2.7 | 73.7 |
| Ecuador | 2.7 | 74.5 | Virgin | | |
| El Salvador | 2.8 | 71.1 | Islands | 2.2 | 78.6 |

a) Create a scatterplot relating these two variables, and describe the association.
b) Are there any countries that do not seem to fit the overall pattern?
c) Find the correlation, and interpret the value of $R^2$.
d) Find the equation of the regression line.
e) Is the line an appropriate model? Describe what you see in the residuals plot.
f) Interpret the slope and the *y*-intercept of the line.
g) If government leaders wanted to increase life expectancy in their country, should they encourage women to have fewer children? Explain.

**32. Tour de France 2007.** We met the Tour de France data set in Chapter 2 (in Just Checking). One hundred years ago, the fastest rider finished the course at an average speed of about 25.3 kph (around 15.8 mph). In 2005, Lance Armstrong averaged 41.65 kph (25.88 mph) for the fastest average winning speed in history.
a) Make a scatterplot of *Avg Speed* against *Year*. Describe the relationship of *Avg Speed* by *Year*, being careful to point out any unusual features in the plot.
b) Find the regression equation of *Avg Speed* on *Year*.
c) Are the conditions for regression met? Comment.

**33. Inflation 2006.** The Consumer Price Index (CPI) tracks the prices of consumer goods in the United States, as shown in the table (ftp://ftp.bis.gov). It indicates, for example, that the average item costing $17.70 in 1926 cost $201.60 in the year 2006.

| Year | CPI | Year | CPI |
|------|------|------|------|
| 1914 | 10.0 | 1962 | 30.2 |
| 1918 | 15.1 | 1966 | 32.4 |
| 1922 | 16.8 | 1970 | 38.8 |
| 1926 | 17.7 | 1974 | 49.3 |
| 1930 | 16.7 | 1978 | 65.2 |
| 1934 | 13.4 | 1982 | 96.5 |
| 1938 | 14.1 | 1986 | 109.6 |
| 1942 | 16.3 | 1990 | 130.7 |
| 1946 | 19.5 | 1994 | 148.2 |
| 1950 | 24.1 | 1998 | 163.0 |
| 1954 | 26.9 | 2002 | 179.9 |
| 1958 | 28.9 | 2006 | 201.6 |

a) Make a scatterplot showing the trend in consumer prices. Describe what you see.
b) Be an economic forecaster: Project increases in the cost of living over the next decade. Justify decisions you make in creating your model.

**34. Second stage 2007.** Look once more at the data from the Tour de France. In Exercise 32 we looked at the whole history of the race, but now let's consider just the post–World War II era.
a) Find the regression of *Avg Speed* by *Year* only for years from 1947 to the present. Are the conditions for regression met?
b) Interpret the slope.
c) In 1979 Bernard Hinault averaged 39.8 kph, while in 2005 Lance Armstrong averaged 41.65 kph. Which was the more remarkable performance and why?

**JUST CHECKING**
**Answers**

1. Not high leverage, not influential, large residual
2. High leverage, not influential, small residual
3. High leverage, influential, not large residual

# CHAPTER 10

# Re-expressing Data: Get It Straight!

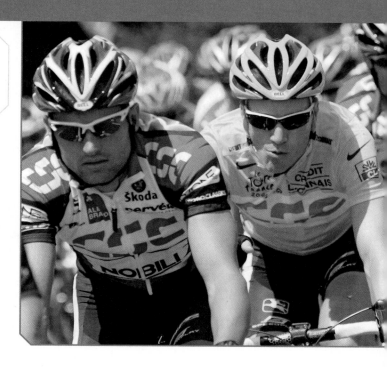

## Where are we going?

What should we do when the data don't satisfy one of the conditions we're checking? What can we do if they are really skewed, or fail to satisfy the Straight Enough Condition?

Re-expressing the data—replacing the original by a simple function of it such as a logarithm or reciprocal—can often improve things. That makes the methods in this book far more useful because they can be applied to many more kinds of data.

And technology makes it all pretty easy.

---

**A S** *Activity:* **Re-expressing Data.** Should you re-express data? Actually, you already do.

ow fast can you go on a bicycle? If you measure your speed, you probably do it in miles per hour or kilometers per hour. In a 12-mile-long time trial in the 2005 Tour de France, Dave Zabriskie *averaged* nearly 35 mph (54.7 kph), beating Lance Armstrong by 2 seconds. You probably realize that's a tough act to follow. It's fast. You can tell that at a glance because you have no trouble thinking in terms of distance covered per time. OK, then, if you averaged 12.5 mph (20.1 kph) for a mile *run,* would *that* be fast? Would it be fast for a 100-m dash? Even if you run the mile often, you probably have to stop and calculate. Although we measure the speed of bicycles in distance per time, we don't usually measure running speed that way. Instead, we use the *reciprocal,* time per distance (minutes per mile, seconds per 100 meters, etc.).

Running a mile in under 5 minutes (12 mph) is fast. A mile at 16 mph would be a world record (that's a 3-minute, 45-second, mile). There's no single *natural* way to measure speed. Sometimes we use time over distance; other times we use the reciprocal, distance over time. Neither one is *correct.* We're just used to thinking that way in each case.

So, how does this insight help us understand data? All quantitative data come to us measured in some way, with units specified. And we know it's important to keep track of the units and use them when we *Tell* what we've learned from the data. But maybe the units we have aren't the best choice. It's not that meters are better (or worse) than fathoms or leagues. What we're talking about is re-expressing the data differently by applying a function, as we do when we take a reciprocal.

As with speeds, some expressions of the data may be easier to think about. And some may be much easier to analyze with Statistics methods. We've seen that symmetric distributions are easier to summarize and straight scatterplots are easier to model with regressions. We often look to re-express our data if doing so makes them more suitable for our methods.

What kinds of functions should we consider? It turns out that there's a simple family of functions, including the square root, logarithm, and reciprocal, that can do the job most of the time. And you already use some of them, even though you may not know it. For example, the Richter scale of earthquake strength (logs), the decibel scale for sound intensity (logs), the f/stop scale for camera aperture openings (squares), and the gauges of shotguns (square roots) all include simple functions of this sort.

# Straight to the Point

We know from common sense and from physics that heavier cars need more fuel, but exactly how does a car's weight affect its fuel efficiency? Here are the *Weight* (in pounds) and *Fuel Efficiency* (in miles per gallon) for 38 cars:

**FIGURE 10.1**

Fuel Efficiency *(mpg) vs.* Weight *for 38 cars as reported by* Consumer Reports. *The plot shows a negative direction, roughly linear shape, and strong relationship.*

Even though the $R^2$ is 81.6% we know that we should examine the residuals:

**FIGURE 10.2**

*The residuals from a regression of* Fuel Efficiency *on* Weight *reveal a bent shape when plotted against the predicted values. Looking back at the original scatterplot, you may be able to see the bend.*

**FIGURE 10.3**

*Extrapolating the regression line gives an absurd answer for vehicles that weigh as little as 6000 pounds.*

Hmm . . . . The residuals don't show the random scatter we were hoping for. The shape is clearly bent. Looking back at the first scatterplot, you can probably see the slight bending. Think about the regression line through the points. How heavy would a car have to be to have a predicted gas mileage of 0? It looks like the *Fuel Efficiency* would go negative at about 6000 pounds. A Hummer H2 weighs about 6400 pounds. The H2 is hardly known for fuel efficiency, but it does get more than the *minus* 5 mpg this regression predicts. Extrapolation is always dangerous, but it's more dangerous the more the model is wrong, because wrong models tend to do even worse the farther you get from the middle of the data.

The bend in the relationship between *Fuel Efficiency* and *Weight* is the kind of failure to satisfy the conditions for an analysis that we can repair by re-expressing the data. Instead of looking at miles per gallon, we could take the reciprocal and work with gallons per hundred miles.[1]

> Scan through any Physics book. Most equations have powers, reciprocals, or logs.

**"Gallons per hundred miles—what an absurd way to measure fuel efficiency! Who would ever do it that way?"** Not all re-expressions are easy to understand, but in this case the answer is "Everyone except U.S. drivers." Most of the world measures fuel efficiency in liters per 100 kilometers (L/100 km). This is the same reciprocal form (fuel amount per distance driven) and differs from gallons per 100 miles only by a constant multiple of about 2.38. It has been suggested that most of the world says, "I've got to go 100 km; how much gas do I need?" But Americans say, "I've got 10 gallons in the tank. How far can I drive?" In much the same way, re-expressions "think" about the data differently but don't change what they mean.

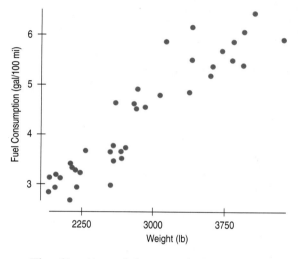

**FIGURE 10.4**

*The reciprocal (1/y) is measured in gallons per mile. Gallons per 100 miles gives more meaningful numbers. The reciprocal is more nearly linear against Weight than the original variable, but the re-expression changes the direction of the relationship.*

The direction of the association is positive now, since we're measuring gas consumption and heavier cars consume more gas per mile. The relationship is much straighter, as we can see from a scatterplot of the regression residuals.

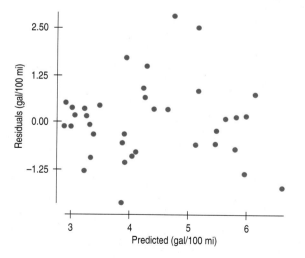

**FIGURE 10.5**

*The residuals from the regression of Fuel Consumption (gal/100 mi) on Weight show less of a pattern than before.*

This is more the kind of boring scatterplot (no direction, no particular shape, no outliers, no bends) that we hope to see in a scatterplot of residuals, so we have

---

[1] Multiplying by 100 to get gallons per 100 miles simply makes the numbers easier to think about: You might have a good idea of how many gallons your car needs to drive 100 miles, but probably a much poorer sense of how much gas you need to go just 1 mile.

reason to think that the Straight Enough Condition is now satisfied. Now here's the payoff: What does the reciprocal model say about the Hummer? The regression line fit to *Fuel Consumption vs. Weight* predicts somewhere near 9.7 for a car weighing 6400 pounds. What does this mean? It means the car is predicted to use 9.7 gallons for every 100 miles, or in other words,

$$\frac{100 \; miles}{9.7 \; gallons} = 10.3 \; mpg.$$

That's a much more reasonable prediction and very close to the reported value of 11.0 miles per gallon (of course, *your* mileage may vary . . . ).

# Goals of Re-expression

We re-express data for several reasons. Each of these goals helps make the data more suitable for analysis by our methods.

## GOAL 1

***Make the distribution of a variable (as seen in its histogram, for example) more symmetric.*** It's easier to summarize the center of a symmetric distribution, and for nearly symmetric distributions, we can use the mean and standard deviation. If the distribution is unimodal, then the resulting distribution may be closer to the Normal model, allowing us to use the 68–95–99.7 Rule.

Here are the *Assets* of 77 companies selected from the Forbes 500 list (in $100,000):

| | |
|---|---|
| **WHO** | 77 large companies |
| **WHAT** | Assets, sales, and market sector |
| **UNITS** | $100,000 |
| **HOW** | Public records |
| **WHEN** | 1986 |
| **WHY** | By *Forbes* magazine in reporting on the Forbes 500 for that year |

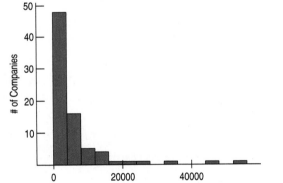

**FIGURE 10.6**

*The distribution of the* Assets *of large companies is skewed to the right. Data on wealth often look like this.*

The skewed distribution is made much more symmetric by taking logs.

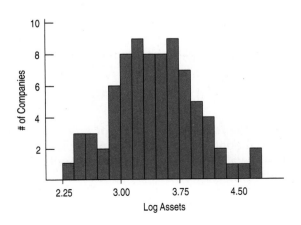

**FIGURE 10.7**

*Taking logs makes the distribution more nearly symmetric.*

**A S** **Simulation: Re-expression in Action.** Slide the re-expression power and watch the histogram change.

## GOAL 2

***Make the spread of several groups (as seen in side-by-side boxplots) more alike, even if their centers differ.*** Groups that share a common spread are easier to compare. We'll see methods later in the book that can be applied only to groups with a common standard deviation. We saw an example of re-expression for comparing groups with boxplots in Chapter 5.

Here are the *Assets* of these companies by *Market Sector:*

**FIGURE 10.8**

Assets *of large companies by* Market Sector. *It's hard to compare centers or spreads, and there seem to be a number of high outliers.*

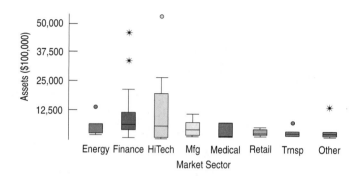

Taking logs makes the individual boxplots more symmetric and gives them spreads that are more nearly equal.

**FIGURE 10.9**

*After re-expressing by logs, it's much easier to compare across market sectors. The boxplots are more nearly symmetric, most have similar spreads, and the companies that seemed to be outliers before are no longer extraordinary. Two new outliers have appeared in the finance sector. They are the only companies in that sector that are not banks. Perhaps they don't belong there.*

Doing this makes it easier to compare assets across market sectors. It can also reveal problems in the data. Some companies that looked like outliers on the high end turned out to be more typical. But two companies in the finance sector now stick out. Unlike the rest of the companies in that sector, they are not banks. They may have been placed in the wrong sector, but we couldn't see that in the original data.

## GOAL 3

***Make the form of a scatterplot more nearly linear.*** Linear scatterplots are easier to model. We saw an example of scatterplot straightening in Chapter 7. The greater value of re-expression to straighten a relationship is that we can fit a linear model once the relationship is straight.

Here are *Assets* of the companies plotted against the logarithm of *Sales:*

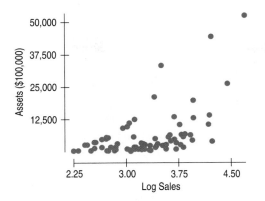

**FIGURE 10.10**

Assets *vs. log* Sales *shows a positive association (bigger sales go with bigger assets) but a bent shape. Note also that the points go from tightly bunched at the left to widely scattered at the right; the plot "thickens."*

The plot's shape is bent. Taking logs makes things much more linear.

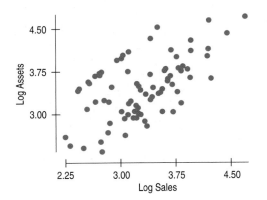

**FIGURE 10.11**

*Log* Assets *vs. log* Sales *shows a clean, positive, linear association. And the variability at each value of x is about the same.*

## GOAL 4

***Make the scatter in a scatterplot spread out evenly rather than thickening at one end.*** Having an even scatter is a condition of many methods of Statistics, as we'll see in later chapters. This goal is closely related to Goal 2, but it often comes along with Goal 3. Indeed, a glance back at the scatterplot (Figure 10.10) shows that the plot for *Assets* is much more spread out on the right than on the left, while the plot for log *Assets* has roughly the same variation in log *Assets* for any *x*-value.

**FOR EXAMPLE** | Recognizing when a re-expression can help

In Chapter 9, we saw the awesome ability of emperor penguins to slow their heart rates while diving. Here are three displays relating to the diving heart rates:

*(continued)*

For Example (*continued*)

(The boxplots show the diving heart rates for each of the 9 penguins whose dives were tracked. The names are those given by the researchers; EP = emperor penguin.)

**Question:**   What features of each of these displays suggest that a re-expression might be helpful?

The scatterplot shows a curved relationship, concave upward, between the duration of the dives and penguins' heart rates. Re-expressing either variable may help to straighten the pattern.

The histogram of heart rates is skewed to the high end. Re-expression often helps to make skewed distributions more nearly symmetric.

The boxplots each show skewness to the high end as well. The medians are low in the boxes, and several show high outliers.

# The Ladder of Powers

**A S**   *Activity:* **Re-expression in Action** Here's the animated version of the Ladder of Powers. Slide the power and watch the change.

How can we pick a re-expression to use? Some kinds of data favor certain re-expressions. But even starting from a suggested one, it's always a good idea to look around a bit. Fortunately, the re-expressions line up in order, so it's easy to slide up and down to find the best one. The trick is to choose our re-expressions from a simple family that includes the most common ways to re-express data. More important, the members of the family line up in order, so that the farther you move away from the original data (the "1" position), the greater is the effect on the data. This fact lets you search systematically for a re-expression that works, stepping a bit farther from "1" or taking a step back toward "1" as you see the results.

Where to start? It turns out that certain kinds of data are more likely to be helped by particular re-expressions. Knowing that gives you a good place to start your search for a re-expression. We call this collection of re-expressions the **Ladder of Powers.**

| Power | Name | Comment |
|---|---|---|
| 2 | The square of the data values, $y^2$. | Try this for unimodal distributions that are skewed to the left. |
| 1 | The raw data—no change at all. This is "home base." The farther you step from here up or down the ladder, the greater the effect. | Data that can take on both positive and negative values with no bounds are less likely to benefit from re-expression. |
| 1/2 | The square root of the data values, $\sqrt{y}$. | Counts often benefit from a square root re-expression. For counted data, start here. |

*(Table continues on next page)*

| Power | Name | Comment |
|---|---|---|
| "0" | Although mathematicians define the "0-th" power differently,[2] for us the place is held by the logarithm. You may feel uneasy about logarithms. Don't worry; the computer or calculator does the work.[3] | Measurements that cannot be negative, and especially values that grow by percentage increases such as salaries or populations, often benefit from a log re-expression. When in doubt, start here. If your data have zeros, try adding a small constant to all values before finding the logs. |
| $-1/2$ | The (negative) reciprocal square root, $-1/\sqrt{y}$. | An uncommon re-expression, but sometimes useful. Changing the sign to take the *negative* of the reciprocal square root preserves the direction of relationships, making things be a bit simpler. |
| $-1$ | The (negative) reciprocal, $-1/y$. | Ratios of two quantities (miles per hour, for example) often benefit from a reciprocal. (You have about a 50–50 chance that the original ratio was taken in the "wrong" order for simple statistical analysis and would benefit from re-expression.) Often, the reciprocal will have simple units (hours per mile). Change the sign if you want to preserve the direction of relationships. If your data have zeros, try adding a small constant to all values before finding the reciprocal. |

## JUST CHECKING

1. You want to model the relationship between the number of birds counted at a nesting site and the temperature (in degrees Celsius). The scatterplot of counts vs. temperature shows an upwardly curving pattern, with more birds spotted at higher temperatures. What transformation (if any) of the bird counts might you start with?

2. You want to model the relationship between prices for various items in Paris and in Hong Kong. The scatterplot of Hong Kong prices vs. Parisian prices shows a generally straight pattern with a small amount of scatter. What transformation (if any) of the Hong Kong prices might you start with?

3. You want to model the population growth of the United States over the past 200 years. The scatterplot shows a strongly upwardly curved pattern. What transformation (if any) of the population might you start with?

> Scientific laws often include simple re-expressions. For example, in Psychology, Fechner's Law states that sensation increases as the logarithm of stimulus intensity ($S = k \log R$).

The Ladder of Powers orders the effects that the re-expressions have on data. If you try, say, taking the square roots of all the values in a variable and it helps, but not enough, then move farther down the ladder to the logarithm or reciprocal root. Those re-expressions will have a similar, but even stronger, effect on your data. If you go too far, you can always back up. But don't forget—when you take a negative power, the *direction* of the relationship will change. That's OK. You can always change the sign of the response variable if you want to keep the same direction.

---

[2] You may remember that for any nonzero number $y$, $y^0 = 1$. This is not a very exciting transformation for data; every data value would be the same. We use the logarithm in its place.

[3] Your calculator or software package probably gives you a choice between "base 10" logarithms and "natural (base $e$)" logarithms. Don't worry about that. It doesn't matter at all which you use; they have exactly the same effect on the data. If you want to choose, base 10 logarithms can be a bit easier to interpret.

A generation ago, before desktop computers and powerful calculators were available, finding a suitable re-expression was a major undertaking, often given as an end-of-semester project. Now, it's usually no harder than the push of a button, making it easy to search for a suitable re-expression.

## FOR EXAMPLE | Trying a re-expression

**Recap:** We've seen curvature in the relationship between emperor penguins' diving heart rates and the duration of the dive. Let's start the process of finding a good re-expression. Heart rate is in beats per minute; maybe heart "speed" in minutes per beat would be a better choice. Here are the corresponding displays for this reciprocal re-expression (as we often do, we've changed the sign to preserve the order of the data values):

**Question:** Were the re-expressions successful?

*The scatterplot bends less than before, but now may be slightly concave downward. The histogram is now slightly skewed to the low end. Most of the boxplots have no outliers. These boxplots seem better than the ones for the raw heart rates.*

*Overall, it looks like I may have moved a bit "too far" on the ladder of powers. Halfway between "1" (the original data) and "−1" (the reciprocal) is "0", which represents the logarithm. I'd try that for comparison.*

## STEP-BY-STEP EXAMPLE | Re-expressing to Straighten a Scatterplot

Standard (monofilament) fishing line comes in a range of strengths, usually expressed as "test pounds." Five-pound test line, for example, can be expected to withstand a pull of up to five pounds without breaking. The convention in selling fishing line is that the price of a spool doesn't vary with strength. Instead, the length of line on the spool varies. Higher test pound line is thicker, though, so spools of fishing line hold about the same amount of material. Some spools hold line that is thinner and longer, some fatter and shorter. Let's look at the *Length* and *Strength* of spools of monofilament line manufactured by the same company and sold for the same price at one store.

**Questions:** How are the *Length* on the spool and the *Strength* related? And what re-expression will straighten the relationship?

**Plan** State the problem.

**Variables** Identify the variables and report the W's.

I want to fit a linear model for the length and strength of monofilament fishing line.

I have the *length* and "pound test" strength of monofilament fishing line sold by a single vendor at a particular store. Each case is a different strength of line, but all spools of line sell for the same price.

Let *Length* = length (in yards) of fishing line on the spool

*Strength* = the test strength (in pounds).

**Plot** Check that even if there is a curve, the overall pattern does not reach a minimum or maximum, and then turn around and go back. An up-and-down curve can't be fixed by re-expression.

The plot shows a negative direction and an association that has little scatter but is not straight.

**Mechanics** Try a re-expression.

The lesson of the Ladder of Powers is that if we're moving in the right direction but have not had sufficient effect, we should go farther along the ladder. This example shows improvement, but is still not straight.

(Because *Length* is an amount of something and cannot be negative, we probably should have started with logs. This plot is here in part to illustrate how the Ladder of Powers works.)

Here's a plot of the square root of *Length* against *Strength*:

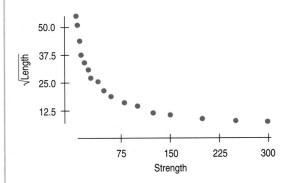

The plot is less bent, but still not straight.

Stepping from the 1/2 power to the "0" power, we try the logarithm of *Length* against *Strength*.

The scatterplot of the logarithm of *Length* against *Strength* is even less bent:

The straightness is improving, so we know we're moving in the right direction. But since the plot of the logarithms is not yet straight, we know we haven't gone far enough. To keep the direction consistent, change the sign and re-express to −1/*Length*.

This is much better, but still not straight, so I'll take another step to the "−1" power, or reciprocal.

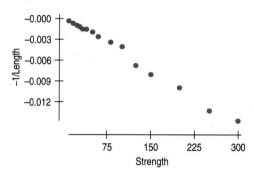

Maybe now I moved too far along the ladder.

A half-step back is the −1/2 power: the reciprocal square root.

We may have to choose between two adjacent re-expressions. For most data analyses, it really doesn't matter which we choose.

**Conclusion** Specify your choice of re-expression. If there's some natural interpretation (as for gallons per 100 miles), give that.

It's hard to choose between the last two alternatives. Either of the last two choices is good enough. I'll choose the −1/2 power.

Now that the re-expressed data satisfy the Straight Enough Condition, we can fit a linear model by least squares. We find that

$$\frac{-1}{\sqrt{\widehat{Length}}} = -0.023 - 0.000373 \; Strength.$$

We can use this model to predict the length of a spool of, say, 35-pound test line:

$$\frac{-1}{\sqrt{\widehat{Length}}} = -0.023 - 0.000373 \times 35 = -0.036$$

We could leave the result in these units ($-1/\sqrt{\text{yards}}$). Sometimes the new units may be as meaningful as the original, but here we want to transform the predicted value back into yards. Fortunately, each of the re-expressions in the Ladder of Powers can be reversed.

To reverse the process, we first take the reciprocal: $\sqrt{\widehat{Length}} = -1/-0.036 = 27.778$. Then squaring gets us back to the original units:

$$\widehat{Length} = 27.778^2 = 771.6 \; yards.$$

This may be the most painful part of the re-expression. Getting back to the original units can sometimes be a little work. Nevertheless, it's worth the effort to always consider re-expression. Re-expressions extend the reach of all of your Statistics tools by helping more data to satisfy the conditions they require. Just think how much more useful this course just became!

---

**FOR EXAMPLE**   Comparing re-expressions

**Recap:** We've concluded that, in trying to straighten the relationship between *Diving Heart Rate* and *Dive Duration* for emperor penguins, using the reciprocal re-expression goes a bit "too far" on the ladder of powers. Now we try the logarithm. Here are the resulting displays:

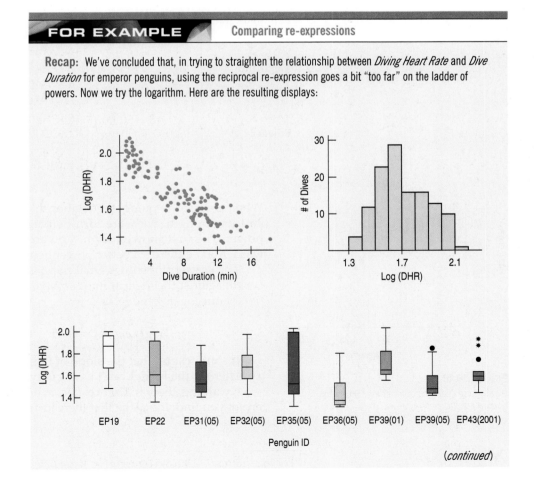

*(continued)*

For Example *(continued)*

**Questions:** Comment on these displays. Now that we've looked at the original data (rung 1 on the Ladder), the reciprocal (rung -1), and the logarithm (rung 0), which re-expression of *Diving Heart Rate* would you choose?

*The scatterplot is now more linear and the histogram is symmetric. The boxplots are still a bit skewed to the high end, but less so than for the original Diving Heart Rate values. The logarithm seems like the best compromise re-expression, improving several different aspects of the data.*

# Plan B: Attack of the Logarithms

The Ladder of Powers is often successful at finding an effective re-expression. Sometimes, though, the curvature is more stubborn, and we're not satisfied with the residuals plots. What then?

When none of the data values is zero or negative, logarithms can be a helpful ally in the search for a useful model. Try taking the logs of *both* the *x*- and *y*-variables. Then re-express the data using some combination of *x* or log(*x*) vs. *y* or log(*y*). You may find that one of these works pretty well.

| Model Name | *x*-axis | *y*-axis | Comment |
|---|---|---|---|
| **Exponential** | *x* | log(*y*) | This model is the "0" power in the ladder approach, useful for values that grow by percentage increases. |
| **Logarithmic** | log(*x*) | *y* | A wide range of *x*-values, or a scatterplot descending rapidly at the left but leveling off toward the right, may benefit from trying this model. |
| **Power** | log(*x*) | log(*y*) | The Goldilocks model: When one of the ladder's powers is too big and the next is too small, this one may be just right. |

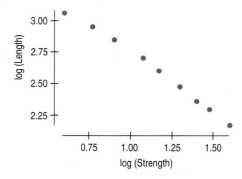

**FIGURE 10.12**

*Plotting log (Length) against log (Strength) gives a straighter shape.*

When we tried to model the relationship between the length of fishing line and its strength, we were torn between the "−1" power and the "−1/2" power. The first showed slight upward curvature, and the second downward. Maybe there's a better power between those values.

The scatterplot shows what happens when we graph the logarithm of *Length* against the logarithm of *Strength*. Technology reveals that the equation of our log–log model is

$$\widehat{\log(Length)} = 3.65 - 0.90 \log(Strength).$$

It's interesting that the slope of this line (−0.90) is a power[4] we didn't try. After all, the ladder can't have every imaginable rung.

A warning, though! Don't expect to be able to straighten every curved scatterplot you find. It may be that there just isn't a very effective re-expression to

---

[4] For logarithms, $-0.90 \log(Strength) = \log(Strength^{-0.90})$.

be had. You'll certainly encounter situations when nothing seems to work the way you wish it would. Don't set your sights too high—you won't find a perfect model. Keep in mind: We seek a *useful* model, not perfection (or even "the best").

## Multiple Benefits

We often choose a re-expression for one reason and then discover that it has helped other aspects of an analysis. For example, we might re-express a variable to make its histogram more nearly symmetric. It wouldn't be surprising to find that the same re-expression also straightens scatterplots or makes spreads more nearly equal. This phenomenon is one reason we encourage that data re-expression be used more often. Sometimes there's an obvious "best" or "right" re-expression for a variable. For example, it makes sense that things that tend to grow by a constant percentage, so that larger values increase faster (populations, bacteria counts, wealth), grow exponentially. Logarithms straighten out the exponential trend and pull in the long right tail in the histogram.

We saw just this phenomenon in the companies example earlier. Each of our goals was met by re-expressing *Assets* with logarithms. That single re-expression improved all four of the goals at the same time. Multiple successes like this turn out not to be all that unusual.

Measurement errors are often larger when measuring larger quantities than when measuring smaller ones. (The error in your height may be only a centimeter or two, but the error in the height of a tree could be ten times that much.) Again, logarithms are likely to help. Measurements of rates (e.g., time to complete a task) are often plagued by infinities for those who never finish. The reciprocal of "minutes per task" is "tasks per minute"—a speed measure. And the unfinished tasks that once took "infinite" time now simply rate a zero speed. Here once more the re-expression seems natural.

In other cases, the only evidence we have to favor re-expression is that it seems to work well and that it leads to simpler models. Often we can find a re-expression for a variable that simplifies our analysis in several ways at once, making the distribution symmetric, making the relationship linear in terms of other variables of interest, or stabilizing its variance. If so, re-expressing the variable certainly simplifies our efforts to analyze and understand it.

## Why Not Just Use a Curve?

When a clearly curved pattern shows up in the scatterplot, why not just fit a curve to the data? We saw earlier that the association between the *Weight* of a car and its *Fuel Efficiency* was not a straight line. Instead of trying to find a way to straighten the plot, why not find a curve that seems to describe the pattern well?

We can find "curves of best fit" using essentially the same approach that led us to linear models. You won't be surprised, though, to learn that the mathematics and the calculations are considerably more difficult for curved models. Many calculators and computer packages do have the ability to fit curves to data, but this approach has many drawbacks.

Straight lines are easy to understand. We know how to think about the slope and the *y*-intercept, for example. We often want some of the other benefits mentioned earlier, such as making the spread around the model more nearly the same everywhere. In later chapters you will learn more advanced statistical methods for analyzing linear associations.

We give all of that up when we fit a model that is not linear. For many reasons, then, it is usually better to re-express the data to straighten the plot.

# WHAT CAN GO WRONG?

▶ **Don't expect your model to be perfect.** In Chapter 6 we quoted statistician George Box: "All models are wrong, but some are useful." Be aware that the real world is a messy place and data can be uncooperative. Don't expect to find one elusive re-expression that magically irons out every kink in your scatterplot and produces perfect residuals. You aren't looking for the Right Model, because that mythical creature doesn't exist. Find a useful model and use it wisely.

▶ **Don't choose a model based on $R^2$ alone.** You've tried re-expressing your data to straighten a curved relationship and found a model with a high $R^2$. Beware: That doesn't mean the pattern is straight now. Here's a plot of a relationship with an $R^2$ of 98.3%.

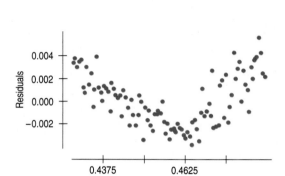

The $R^2$ is about as high as we could ask for, but if you look closely, you'll see that there's a consistent bend. Plotting the residuals from the least squares line makes the bend much easier to see.

Remember the basic rule of data analysis: *Make a picture.* Before you fit a line, always look at the pattern in the scatterplot. After you fit the line, check for linearity again by plotting the residuals.

▶ **Beware of multiple modes.** Re-expression can often make a skewed unimodal histogram more nearly symmetric, but it cannot pull separate modes together. A suitable re-expression may, however, make the separation of the modes clearer, simplifying their interpretation and making it easier to separate them to analyze individually.

▶ **Watch out for scatterplots that turn around.** Re-expression can straighten many bent relationships, but not those that go up and then down or down and then up. You should refuse to analyze such data with methods that require a linear form.

**FIGURE 10.13**

*The shape of the scatterplot of Birth Rates (births per 100,000 women) in the United States shows an oscillation that cannot be straightened by re-expressing the data.*

▶ **Watch out for negative data values.** It's impossible to re-express negative values by any power that is not a whole number on the Ladder of Powers or to re-express values that are zero for negative powers. Most statistics programs will just mark the result of trying to re-express such values "missing" if they can't be re-expressed. But that might mean that when you try a re-expression, you inadvertently lose a bunch of data values. The effect of that loss may be surprising and may substantially change your analysis. Because you are likely to be working with a computer package or calculator, take special care that you do not lose otherwise good data values when you choose a re-expression.

One possible cure for zeros and small negative values is to add a constant ($\frac{1}{2}$ and $\frac{1}{6}$ are often used) to bring all the data values above zero.

▶ **Watch for data far from 1.** Data values that are all very far from 1 may not be much affected by re-expression unless the range is very large. Re-expressing numbers between 1 and 100 will have a much greater effect than re-expressing numbers between 100,001 and 100,100. When all your data values are large (for example, working with years), consider subtracting a constant to bring them back near 1. (For example, consider "years since 1950" as an alternative variable for re-expression. Unless your data start at 1950, then avoid creating a zero by using "years since 1949".)

▶ **Don't stray too far from the ladder.** Finally, it's wise not to stray too far from the powers that we suggest in the Ladder of Powers. Taking the $y$-values to an extremely high power may artificially inflate $R^2$, but it won't give a useful or meaningful model, so it doesn't really simplify anything. It's better to stick to powers between 2 and $-2$. Even in that range, you should prefer the simpler powers in the ladder to those in the cracks. A square root is easier to understand than the 0.413 power. That simplicity may compensate for a slightly less straight relationship.

# CONNECTIONS

We have seen several ways to model or summarize data. Each requires that the data have a particular simple structure. We seek symmetry for summaries of center and spread and to use a Normal model. We seek equal variation across groups when we compare groups with boxplots or want to compare their centers. We seek linear shape in a scatterplot so we can use correlation to summarize the scatter and regression to fit a linear model.

Data do often satisfy the requirements to use Statistics methods. But often they do not. Our choice is to stop with just displays, to use much more complex methods, or to re-express the data so that we can use the simpler methods we have developed.

In this fundamental sense, this chapter connects to everything we have done thus far and to all of the methods we will introduce throughout the rest of the book. Re-expression greatly extends the reach and applicability of all of these methods.

## WHAT HAVE WE LEARNED?

We've learned that when the conditions for regression are not met, a simple re-expression of the data may help. There are several reasons to consider a re-expression:

▶ To make the distribution of a variable more symmetric (as we saw in Chapter 5)
▶ To make the spread across different groups more similar
▶ To make the form of a scatterplot straighter
▶ To make the scatter around the line in a scatterplot more consistent

We've learned that when seeking a useful re-expression, taking logs is often a good, simple starting point. To search further, the Ladder of Powers or the log–log approach can help us find a good re-expression.

We've come to understand that our models won't be perfect, but that re-expression can lead us to a useful model.

# Terms

**Re-express data**   255. We re-express data by taking the logarithm, the square root, the reciprocal, or some other mathematical operation on all values of a variable.

**Ladder of Powers**   258. The Ladder of Powers places in order the effects that many re-expressions have on the data.

# Skills

▶ Recognize when a well-chosen re-expression may help you improve and simplify your analysis.

▶ Understand the value of re-expressing data to improve symmetry, to make the scatter around a line more constant, or to make a scatterplot more linear.

▶ Recognize when the pattern of the data indicates that no re-expression can improve the structure of the data.

▶ Know how to re-express data with powers and how to find an effective re-expression for your data using your statistics software or calculator.

▶ Be able to reverse any of the common re-expressions to put a predicted value or residual back into the original units.

▶ Be able to describe a summary or display of a re-expressed variable, making clear how it was re-expressed and giving its re-expressed units.

▶ Be able to describe a regression model fit to re-expressed data in terms of the re-expressed variables.

# ON THE COMPUTER

# Re-expression

Computers and calculators make it easy to re-express data. Most statistics packages offer a way to re-express and compute with variables. Some packages permit you to specify the power of a re-expression with a slider or other moveable control, possibly while watching the consequences of the re-expression on a plot or analysis. This, of course, is a very effective way to find a good re-expression.

## DATA DESK

To re-express a variable in Data Desk, select the variable and Choose the function to re-express it from the **Manip > Transform** menu. Square root, log, reciprocal, and reciprocal root are immediately available. For others, make a derived variable and type the function. Data Desk makes a new derived variable that holds the re-expressed values. Any value changed in the original variable will immediately be re-expressed in the derived variable.

### COMMENTS

Or choose **Manip > Transform > Dynamic > Box-Cox** to generate a continuously changeable variable and a slider that specifies the power. Set plots to **Automatic Update** in their HyperView menus and watch them change dynamically as you drag the slider.

## EXCEL

To re-express a variable in Excel, use Excel's built-in functions as you would for any calculation. Changing a value in the original column will change the re-expressed value.

## JMP

To re-express a variable in JMP, double-click to the right of the last column of data to create a new column. Name the new column and select it. Choose **Formula** from the **Cols** menu. In the Formula dialog, choose the transformation and variable that you wish to assign to the new column. Click the **OK** button. JMP places the re-expressed data in the new column.

### COMMENTS

The log and square root re-expressions are found in the **Transcendental** menu of functions in the formula dialog.

## MINITAB

To re-express a variable in MINITAB, choose **Calculator** from the **Calc** menu. In the Calculator dialog, specify a name for the new re-expressed variable. Use the **Functions List,** the calculator buttons, and the **Variables list** box to build the expression. Click **OK.**

## SPSS

To re-express a variable in SPSS, Choose **Compute** from the **Transform** menu. Enter a name in the Target Variable field. Use the calculator and Function List to build the expression.

Move a variable to be re-expressed from the source list to the Numeric Expression field. Click the **OK** button.

## TI-83/84 PLUS

To re-express data stored in a list, perform the re-expression on the whole list and store it in another list. For example, to use the logarithms of the data in L1, enter the command **log(L1) STO L2.**

## TI-89

To re-express data stored in a list, perform the re-expression on the whole list and store it in another list. For example, to use the common (base 10) logarithms of the data in list1, on the home screen, enter the command **log(list1)** [STO▶] **list2.**

### COMMENTS

▶  To find the log command, press [CATALOG] then [4] (L) arrow to log, and press [ENTER].
▶  Natural logs are **LN** (press [2nd][X]).
▶  For square roots, press [2nd][x]

# EXERCISES

**1. Residuals.**   Suppose you have fit a linear model to some data and now take a look at the residuals. For each of the following possible residuals plots, tell whether you would try a re-expression and, if so, why.

**2. Residuals.**   Suppose you have fit a linear model to some data and now take a look at the residuals. For each of the following possible residuals plots, tell whether you would try a re-expression and, if so, why.

**3. Airline passengers revisited.** In Chapter 9, Exercise 9, we created a linear model describing the trend in the number of passengers departing from Oakland (CA) airport each month since the start of 1997. Here's the residual plot, but with lines added to show the order of the values in time:

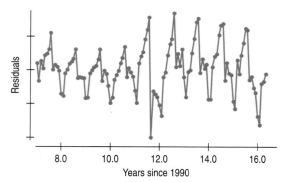

a) Can you account for the pattern shown here?
b) Would a re-expression help us deal with this pattern? Explain.

**4. Hopkins winds, revisited.** In Chapter 5, we examined the wind speeds in the Hopkins forest over the course of a year. Here's the scatterplot we saw then:

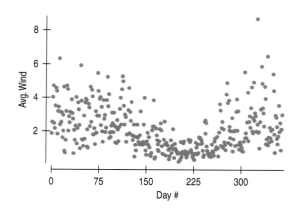

a) Describe the pattern you see here.
b) Should we try re-expressing either variable to make this plot straighter? Explain.

**5. Models.** For each of the models listed below, predict $y$ when $x = 2$.
a) $\hat{y} = 1.2 + 0.8x$
b) $\ln \hat{y} = 1.2 + 0.8x$
c) $\sqrt{\hat{y}} = 1.2 + 0.8x$
d) $\frac{1}{\hat{y}} = 1.2 + 0.8x$
e) $\hat{y} = 1.2x^{0.8}$

**6. More models.** For each of the models listed below, predict $y$ when $x = 2$.
a) $\hat{y} = 1.2 + 0.8 \log x$
b) $\log \hat{y} = 1.2 + 0.8x$
c) $\hat{y} = 1.2 + 0.8\sqrt{x}$
d) $\hat{y} = 1.2(0.8^x)$
e) $\hat{y} = 0.8x^2 + 1.2x + 1$

**7. Gas mileage.** As the example in the chapter indicates, one of the important factors determining a car's *Fuel Efficiency* is its *Weight*. Let's examine this relationship again, for 11 cars.
a) Describe the association between these variables shown in the scatterplot.

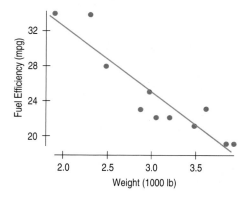

b) Here is the regression analysis for the linear model. What does the slope of the line say about this relationship?

Dependent variable is: Fuel Efficiency
R-squared = 85.9%

| Variable | Coefficient |
|---|---|
| Intercept | 47.9636 |
| Weight | −7.65184 |

c) Do you think this linear model is appropriate? Use the residuals plot to explain your decision.

**8. Crowdedness.** In a *Chance* magazine article (Summer 2005), Danielle Vasilescu and Howard Wainer used data from the United Nations Center for Human Settlements to investigate aspects of living conditions for several countries. Among the variables they looked at were the country's per capita gross domestic product (*GDP*, in $) and *Crowdedness*, defined as the average number of persons per room living in homes there. This scatterplot displays these data for 56 countries:

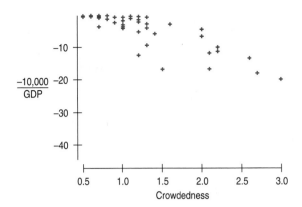

a) Explain why you should re-express these data before trying to fit a model.
b) What re-expression of *GDP* would you try as a starting point?

**9. Gas mileage revisited.** Let's try the re-expressed variable *Fuel Consumption* (gal/100 mi) to examine the fuel efficiency of the 11 cars in Exercise 7. Here are the revised regression analysis and residuals plot:

Dependent variable is: Fuel Consumption
R-squared = 89.2%

| Variable | Coefficient |
|----------|-------------|
| Intercept | 0.624932 |
| Weight | 1.17791 |

a) Explain why this model appears to be better than the linear model.
b) Using the regression analysis above, write an equation of this model.
c) Interpret the slope of this line.
d) Based on this model, how many miles per gallon would you expect a 3500-pound car to get?

**10. Crowdedness again.** In Exercise 8 we looked at United Nations data about a country's *GDP* and the average number of people per room (*Crowdedness*) in housing there. For a re-expression, a student tried the reciprocal −10000/*GDP*, representing the number of people per $10,000 of gross domestic product. Here are the results, plotted against *Crowdedness:*

a) Is this a useful re-expression? Explain.
b) What re-expression would you suggest this student try next?

**11. Earnings/price ratio.** Investors often judge the value of a stock by considering the company's earnings (after taxes) relative to the stock price. If the ratio is high, then the stock may be a good buy. Here's a scatterplot of the one stock's earnings/price ratio since 1950:

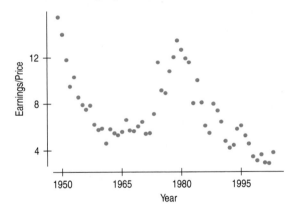

Clearly, the relationship is not linear. Can it be made nearly linear with a re-expression? If so, which one would you suggest? If not, why not?

**12. Treasury Bills.** The 3-month Treasury bill interest rate is watched by investors and economists. Here's a scatterplot of the 3-month Treasury bill rate since 1950:

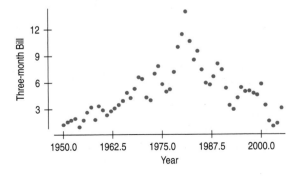

Clearly, the relationship is not linear. Can it be made nearly linear with a re-expression? If so, which one would you suggest? If not, why not?

**13. GDP.** The scatterplot shows the gross domestic product (GDP) of the United States in billions of dollars plotted against years since 1950.

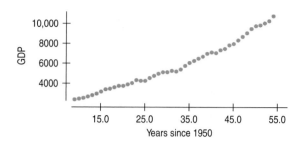

A linear model fit to the relationship looks like this:

Dependent variable is: GDP
R-squared = 97.2%   s = 406.6

| Variable | Coefficient |
|----------|-------------|
| Intercept | 240.171 |
| Year-1950 | 177.689 |

a) Does the value 97.2% suggest that this is a good model? Explain.
b) Here's a scatterplot of the residuals. Now do you think this is a good model for these data? Explain?

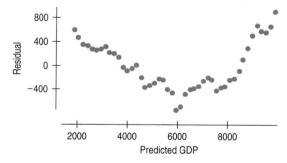

**14. Catapults.** Ancient torsion catapults were machines for throwing rocks or other projectiles. These catapults used a pair of torsion springs made of a bundle of horsehair rope to accelerate the projectile. Greek engineers used re-expressions. They determined that they could design catapults of almost any size, provided they observed the relationship $D = 1.1W^{1/3}$, where $D$ is the diameter of the spring hole in dactyls and $W$ is the weight of the shot in drachmae. (Recall that the 1/3 power is the same as taking a cube root.) The largest stone-thrower ever built was made by Archimedes and was reported to be able to launch a rock weighing 3 talents. (One talent = 7895 drachmae. )[5] Estimate the size of the torsion spring hole of Archimedes' catapult. (Source: Kenneth Reinschmidt, letter in *Science*, 28 May 2004)

**15. Better GDP model?** Consider again the post-1950 trend in U.S. GDP we examined in Exercise 13. Here are a regression and residual plot when we use the log of GDP in the model. Is this a better model for GDP? Explain.

Dependent variable is: LogGDP
R-squared = 99.4%   s = 0.0150

| Variable | Coefficient |
|----------|-------------|
| Intercept | 3.29092 |
| Year-1950 | 0.013881 |

**16. Pressure.** Scientist Robert Boyle examined the relationship between the volume in which a gas is contained and the pressure in its container. He used a cylindrical container with a moveable top that could be raised or lowered to change the volume. He measured the *Height* in inches by counting equally spaced marks on the cylinder, and measured the *Pressure* in inches of mercury (as in a barometer). Some of his data are listed in the table. Create an appropriate model.

| Height | 48 | 44 | 40 | 36 | 32 | 28 |
|--------|------|------|------|------|------|------|
| Pressure | 29.1 | 31.9 | 35.3 | 39.3 | 44.2 | 50.3 |
| Height | 24 | 20 | 18 | 16 | 14 | 12 |
| Pressure | 58.8 | 70.7 | 77.9 | 87.9 | 100.4 | 117.6 |

**17. Brakes.** The table below shows stopping distances in feet for a car tested 3 times at each of 5 speeds. We hope to create a model that predicts *Stopping Distance* from the *Speed* of the car.

| Speed (mph) | Stopping Distances (ft) |
|-------------|-------------------------|
| 20 | 64, 62, 59 |
| 30 | 114, 118, 105 |
| 40 | 153, 171, 165 |
| 50 | 231, 203, 238 |
| 60 | 317, 321, 276 |

a) Explain why a linear model is not appropriate.
b) Re-express the data to straighten the scatterplot.
c) Create an appropriate model.
d) Estimate the stopping distance for a car traveling 55 mph.
e) Estimate the stopping distance for a car traveling 70 mph.
f) How much confidence do you place in these predictions? Why?

**18. Pendulum.** A student experimenting with a pendulum counted the number of full swings the pendulum made in 20 seconds for various lengths of string. Her data are shown on the next page.

---

[5] We don't know what these ancient units mean either, but you should be able to answer the question anyway.

| Length (in.) | 6.5 | 9 | 11.5 | 14.5 | 18 | 21 | 24 | 27 | 30 | 37.5 |
|---|---|---|---|---|---|---|---|---|---|---|
| Number of Swings | 22 | 20 | 17 | 16 | 14 | 13 | 13 | 12 | 11 | 10 |

a) Explain why a linear model is not appropriate for using the *Length* of a pendulum to predict the *Number of Swings* in 20 seconds.
b) Re-express the data to straighten the scatterplot.
c) Create an appropriate model.
d) Estimate the number of swings for a pendulum with a 4-inch string.
e) Estimate the number of swings for a pendulum with a 48-inch string.
f) How much confidence do you place in these predictions? Why?

**T** 19. **Baseball salaries 2005.** Ballplayers have been signing ever larger contracts. The highest salaries (in millions of dollars per season) for some notable players are given in the following table.

| Player | Year | Salary (million $) |
|---|---|---|
| Nolan Ryan | 1980 | 1.0 |
| George Foster | 1982 | 2.0 |
| Kirby Puckett | 1990 | 3.0 |
| Jose Canseco | 1990 | 4.7 |
| Roger Clemens | 1991 | 5.3 |
| Ken Griffey, Jr. | 1996 | 8.5 |
| Albert Belle | 1997 | 11.0 |
| Pedro Martinez | 1998 | 12.5 |
| Mike Piazza | 1999 | 12.5 |
| Mo Vaughn | 1999 | 13.3 |
| Kevin Brown | 1999 | 15.0 |
| Carlos Delgado | 2001 | 17.0 |
| Alex Rodriguez | 2001 | 22.0 |
| Manny Ramirez | 2004 | 22.5 |
| Alex Rodriguez | 2005 | 26.0 |

a) Examine a scatterplot of the data. Does it look straight?
b) Find the regression of *Salary* vs. *Year* and plot the residuals? Do they look straight?
c) Re-express the data, if necessary, to straighten the relationship.
d) What model would you report for the trend in salaries?

**T** 20. **Planet distances and years 2006.** At a meeting of the International Astronomical Union (IAU) in Prague in 2006, Pluto was determined not to be a planet, but rather the largest member of the Kuiper belt of icy objects. Let's examine some facts. In the next column is a table of the 9 sun-orbiting objects formerly known as planets:

| Planet | Position Number | Distance from Sun (million miles) | Length of Year (Earth years) |
|---|---|---|---|
| Mercury | 1 | 36 | 0.24 |
| Venus | 2 | 67 | 0.61 |
| Earth | 3 | 93 | 1.00 |
| Mars | 4 | 142 | 1.88 |
| Jupiter | 5 | 484 | 11.86 |
| Saturn | 6 | 887 | 29.46 |
| Uranus | 7 | 1784 | 84.07 |
| Neptune | 8 | 2796 | 164.82 |
| Pluto | 9 | 3707 | 247.68 |

a) Plot the *Length* of the year against the *Distance* from the sun. Describe the shape of your plot.
b) Re-express one or both variables to straighten the plot. Use the re-expressed data to create a model describing the length of a planet's year based on its distance from the sun.
c) Comment on how well your model fits the data.

**T** 21. **Planet distances and order 2006.** Let's look again at the pattern in the locations of the planets in our solar system seen in the table in Exercise 20.
a) Re-express the distances to create a model for the *Distance* from the sun based on the planet's *Position*.
b) Based on this model, would you agree with the International Astronomical Union that Pluto is not a planet? Explain.

**T** 22. **Planets 2006, part 3.** The asteroid belt between Mars and Jupiter may be the remnants of a failed planet. If so, then Jupiter is really in position 6, Saturn is in 7, and so on. Repeat Exercise 21, using this revised method of numbering the positions. Which method seems to work better?

**T** 23. **Eris: Planets 2006, part 4.** In July 2005, astronomers Mike Brown, Chad Trujillo, and David Rabinowitz announced the discovery of a sun-orbiting object, since named Eris,[6] that is 5% larger than Pluto. Eris orbits the sun once every 560 earth years at an average distance of about 6300 million miles from the sun. Based on its *Position*, how does Eris's *Distance* from the sun (re-expressed to logs) compare with the prediction made by your model of Exercise 21?

**T** 24. **Models and laws: Planets 2006 part 5.** The model you found in Exercise 20 is a relationship noted in the 17th century by Kepler as his Third Law of Planetary Motion. It was subsequently explained as a consequence

---

[6] Eris is the Greek goddess of warfare and strife. She stirs up jealousy and envy to cause fighting and anger among men. At the wedding of Peleus and Thetis, the parents of the Greek hero Achilles, all the gods, with the exception of Eris, were invited. Enraged at her exclusion, Eris spitefully caused a quarrel among the goddesses that led to the Trojan war. In the astronomical world, Eris stirred up trouble in the international astronomical community when the question of its proper designation led to a raucous meeting of the IAU in Prague. At the end of the conference, IAU members voted to demote Pluto and Eris to dwarf-planet status.—http://www.gps.caltech.edu/~mbrown/planetlila/#paper

of Newton's Law of Gravitation. The models for Exercises 21–23 relate to what is sometimes called the Titius-Bode "law," a pattern noticed in the 18th century but lacking any scientific explanation.

Compare how well the re-expressed data are described by their respective linear models. What aspect of the model of Exercise 20 suggests that we have found a physical law? In the future, we may learn enough about a planetary system around another star to tell whether the Titius-Bode pattern applies there. If you discovered that another planetary system followed the same pattern, how would it change your opinion about whether this is a real natural "law"? What would you think if the next system we find does not follow this pattern?

**25. Logs (not logarithms).** The value of a log is based on the number of board feet of lumber the log may contain. (A board foot is the equivalent of a piece of wood 1 inch thick, 12 inches wide, and 1 foot long. For example, a 2″ × 4″ piece that is 12 feet long contains 8 board feet.) To estimate the amount of lumber in a log, buyers measure the diameter inside the bark at the smaller end. Then they look in a table based on the Doyle Log Scale. The table below shows the estimates for logs 16 feet long.

| Diameter of Log | 8″ | 12″ | 16″ | 20″ | 24″ | 28″ |
|---|---|---|---|---|---|---|
| Board Feet | 16 | 64 | 144 | 256 | 400 | 576 |

a) What model does this scale use?
b) How much lumber would you estimate that a log 10 inches in diameter contains?
c) What does this model suggest about logs 36 inches in diameter?

**T 26. Weightlifting 2004.** Listed below are the gold medal–winning men's weight-lifting performances at the 2004 Olympics.

| Weight Class (kg) | Winner (country) | Weight Lifted (kg) |
|---|---|---|
| 56 | Halil Mutlu (Turkey) | 295.0 |
| 62 | Zhiyong Shi (China) | 325.0 |
| 69 | Guozheng Zhang (China) | 347.5 |
| 77 | Taner Sagir (Turkey) | 375.0 |
| 85 | George Asanidze (Georgia) | 382.5 |
| 94 | Milen Dobrev (Bulgaria) | 407.5 |
| 105 | Dmitry Berestov (Russia) | 425.0 |

a) Create a linear model for the *Weight Lifted* in each *Weight Class*.
b) Check the residuals plot. Is your linear model appropriate?
c) Create a better model.
d) Explain why you think your new model is better.
e) Based on your model, which of the medalists turned in the most surprising performance? Explain.

**T 27. Life expectancy.** The data in the next column list the *Life Expectancy* for white males in the United States every

decade during the last century (1 = 1900 to 1910, 2 = 1911 to 1920, etc.). Create a model to predict future increases in life expectancy. (National Vital Statistics Report)

| Decade | 1 | 2 | 3 | 4 | 5 | 6 | 7 | 8 | 9 | 10 |
|---|---|---|---|---|---|---|---|---|---|---|
| Life exp. | 48.6 | 54.4 | 59.7 | 62.1 | 66.5 | 67.4 | 68.0 | 70.7 | 72.7 | 74.9 |

**T 28. Lifting more weight 2004.** In Exercise 26 you examined the winning weight-lifting performances for the 2004 Olympics. One of the competitors turned in a performance that appears not to fit the model you created.
a) Consider that competitor to be an outlier. Eliminate that data point and re-create your model.
b) Using this revised model, how much would you have expected the outlier competitor to lift?
c) Explain the meaning of the residual from your new model for that competitor.

**T 29. Slower is cheaper?** Researchers studying how a car's *Fuel Efficiency* varies with its *Speed* drove a compact car 200 miles at various speeds on a test track. Their data are shown in the table.

| Speed (mph) | 35 | 40 | 45 | 50 | 55 | 60 | 65 | 70 | 75 |
|---|---|---|---|---|---|---|---|---|---|
| Fuel Eff. (mpg) | 25.9 | 27.7 | 28.5 | 29.5 | 29.2 | 27.4 | 26.4 | 24.2 | 22.8 |

Create a linear model for this relationship and report any concerns you may have about the model.

**T 30. Orange production.** The table below shows that as the number of oranges on a tree increases, the fruit tends to get smaller. Create a model for this relationship, and express any concerns you may have.

| Number of Oranges/Tree | Average Weight/Fruit (lb) |
|---|---|
| 50 | 0.60 |
| 100 | 0.58 |
| 150 | 0.56 |
| 200 | 0.55 |
| 250 | 0.53 |
| 300 | 0.52 |
| 350 | 0.50 |
| 400 | 0.49 |
| 450 | 0.48 |
| 500 | 0.46 |
| 600 | 0.44 |
| 700 | 0.42 |
| 800 | 0.40 |
| 900 | 0.38 |

**T 31. Years to live 2003.** Insurance companies and other organizations use actuarial tables to estimate the remaining life-spans of their customers. On the next page are the estimated additional years of life for black males in the United States, according to a 2003 National Vital Statistics Report. (www.cdc.gov/nchs/deaths.htm)

| Age | Years Left |
|-----|-----------|
| 10  | 60.3 |
| 20  | 50.7 |
| 30  | 41.8 |
| 40  | 32.9 |
| 50  | 24.8 |
| 60  | 17.9 |
| 70  | 12.1 |
| 80  | 7.9 |
| 90  | 5.0 |
| 100 | 3.0 |

a) Find a re-expression to create an appropriate model.
b) Predict the lifespan of an 18-year-old black man.
c) Are you satisfied that your model has accounted for the relationship between *Years Left* and *Age*? Explain.

**T** **32. Tree growth.** A 1996 study examined the growth of grapefruit trees in Texas, determining the average trunk *Diameter* (in inches) for trees of varying *Ages*:

| Age (yr)       | 2   | 4   | 6   | 8   | 10  | 12  | 14  | 16  | 18   | 20   |
|----------------|-----|-----|-----|-----|-----|-----|-----|-----|------|------|
| Diameter (in.) | 2.1 | 3.9 | 5.2 | 6.2 | 6.9 | 7.6 | 8.3 | 9.1 | 10.0 | 11.4 |

a) Fit a linear model to these data. What concerns do you have about the model?
b) If data had been given for individual trees instead of averages, would you expect the fit to be stronger, less strong, or about the same? Explain.

**T** **33. Internet.** It's often difficult to find the ideal model for situations in which the data are strongly curved. The table below shows the rapid growth of the number of academic journals published on the Internet during the last decade.

| Year | Number of Journals |
|------|--------------------|
| 1991 | 27 |
| 1992 | 36 |
| 1993 | 45 |
| 1994 | 181 |
| 1995 | 306 |
| 1996 | 1093 |
| 1997 | 2459 |

a) Try to create a good model to describe this growth.
b) Use your model to estimate the number of electronic journals in the year 2000.
c) Comment on your faith in this estimate.

**T** **34. Oil production 2005 (again).** In the next column are the data on U.S. oil production first seen in Exercise 42 of Chapter 7.

How successfully might a model based on these data predict the future of U.S. oil production? Explain.

| Year | Production (in thousands of barrels) | Year | Production (in thousands of barrels) |
|------|-------------------------|------|-------------------------|
| 1949 | 1,841,940 | 1978 | 3,178,216 |
| 1950 | 1,973,574 | 1979 | 3,121,310 |
| 1951 | 2,247,711 | 1980 | 3,146,365 |
| 1952 | 2,289,836 | 1981 | 3,128,624 |
| 1953 | 2,357,082 | 1982 | 3,156,715 |
| 1954 | 2,314,988 | 1983 | 3,170,999 |
| 1955 | 2,484,428 | 1984 | 3,249,696 |
| 1956 | 2,617,283 | 1985 | 3,274,553 |
| 1957 | 2,616,901 | 1986 | 3,168,252 |
| 1958 | 2,448,987 | 1987 | 3,047,377 |
| 1959 | 2,574,590 | 1988 | 2,979,126 |
| 1960 | 2,574,933 | 1989 | 2,778,772 |
| 1961 | 2,621,758 | 1990 | 2,684,689 |
| 1962 | 2,676,189 | 1991 | 2,707,039 |
| 1963 | 2,752,723 | 1992 | 2,624,631 |
| 1964 | 2,786,822 | 1993 | 2,499,033 |
| 1965 | 2,848,514 | 1994 | 2,431,476 |
| 1966 | 3,027,763 | 1995 | 2,394,269 |
| 1967 | 3,215,742 | 1996 | 2,366,016 |
| 1968 | 3,329,042 | 1997 | 2,354,269 |
| 1969 | 3,371,751 | 1998 | 2,281,920 |
| 1970 | 3,517,450 | 1999 | 2,146,732 |
| 1971 | 3,453,914 | 2000 | 2,130,706 |
| 1972 | 3,455,368 | 2001 | 2,117,512 |
| 1973 | 3,360,903 | 2002 | 2,097,124 |
| 1974 | 3,202,585 | 2003 | 2,073,454 |
| 1975 | 3,056,779 | 2004 | 1,983,300 |
| 1976 | 2,976,180 | 2005 | 1,890,107 |
| 1977 | 3,009,265 |      |           |

**T** **35. Human Development Index.** In Exercise 3 of Chapter 9 we saw that the United Nations Development Programme (UNDP) uses the Human Development Index (HDI) in an attempt to summarize the progress in health, education, and economics of a country with one number. The gross domestic product per capita (GDPPC) attempts to summarize the wealth produced by a country in one number. Here is a plot of *GDPPC* against *HDI* for 172 countries throughout the world:

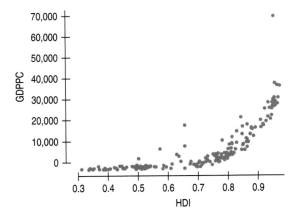

a) *GDPPC* is measured in dollars. Incomes and other economic measures tend to be highly right skewed. Taking logs often makes the distribution more unimodal and symmetric. Compare the histogram of *GDPPC* to the histogram of *log(GDPPC)*.

b) Use the log re-expression to make a scatterplot of *log(GDPPC)* against *HDI*. Comment on the relationship.

c) The HDR report classifies countries into High, Medium, and Low development based in part on their HDI. Looking at the scatterplot in b), why might it be a good idea to separate out the Low-development countries?

d) Look at the scatterplot of *log(GDPPC)* against *HDI* for only the 141 Medium- and High-development countries. Comment.

e) Find the correlation of *log(GDPPC)* with *HDI* for all 172 countries. Find the correlation for only the 141 Medium- and High-development countries. Which is higher? Which relationship is straighter?

**36. Human Development Index revisited.** In Exercise 35 we examined the relationship between *log(GDPPC)* and *HDI* for 172 countries. The number of cell phone subscribers (per 1000 people) is also positively associated with economic progress in a country. Here's a scatterplot of *CellPhones* (subscribers per 1000 people) against *HDI* for 154 countries:

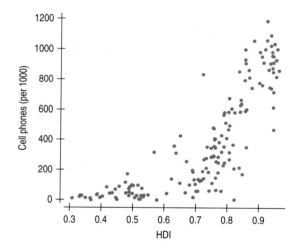

a) *CellPhones* is a count of subscribers (per 1000). What re-expression is often useful for counts? Examine the histogram of *CellPhones* and the histogram of *Cellphones* using the re-expression you suggested. Comment.

b) Use the re-expression in a) for the scatterplot against *HDI*. Comment.

c) Why might you be skeptical of using this relationship to predict the number of cell phone users based on the *HDI*?

## JUST CHECKING
### Answers

1. Counts are often best transformed by using the square root.

2. None. The relationship is already straight.

3. Even though, technically, the population values are counts, you should probably try a stronger transformation like log(population) because populations grow in proportion to their size.

PART
II

# REVIEW OF PART II

## Exploring Relationships Between Variables

### Quick Review

You have now survived your second major unit of Statistics. Here's a brief summary of the key concepts and skills:

▶ We treat data two ways: as categorical and as quantitative.

▶ To explore relationships in categorical data, check out Chapter 3.

▶ To explore relationships in quantitative data:

- Make a picture. Use a scatterplot. Put the explanatory variable on the $x$-axis and the response variable on the $y$-axis.

- Describe the association between two quantitative variables in terms of direction, form, and strength.

- The amount of scatter determines the strength of the association.

- If, as one variable increases so does the other, the association is positive. If one increases as the other decreases, it's negative.

- If the form of the association is linear, calculate a correlation to measure its strength numerically, and do a regression analysis to model it.

- Correlations closer to −1 or +1 indicate stronger linear associations. Correlations near 0 indicate weak linear relationships, but other forms of association may still be present.

- The line of best fit is also called the least squares regression line because it minimizes the sum of the squared residuals.

- The regression line predicts values of the response variable from values of the explanatory variable.

- A residual is the difference between the true value of the response variable and the value predicted by the regression model.

- The slope of the line is a rate of change, best described in "$y$-units" per "$x$-unit."

- $R^2$ gives the fraction of the variation in the response variable that is accounted for by the model.

- The standard deviation of the residuals measures the amount of scatter around the line.

- Outliers and influential points can distort any of our models.

- If you see a pattern (a curve) in the residuals plot, your chosen model is not appropriate; use a different model. You may, for example, straighten the relationship by re-expressing one of the variables.

- To straighten bent relationships, re-express the data using logarithms or a power (squares, square roots, reciprocals, etc.).

- Always remember that an association is not necessarily an indication that one of the variables causes the other.

Need more help with some of this? Try rereading some sections of Chapters 7 through 10. And go on to the next page for more opportunities to review these concepts and skills.

*"One must learn by doing the thing; though you think you know it, you have no certainty until you try."*

—*Sophocles (495–406 B.C.E.)*

# REVIEW EXERCISES

**1. College.** Every year *US News and World Report* publishes a special issue on many U.S. colleges and universities. The scatterplots below have *Student/Faculty Ratio* (number of students per faculty member) for the colleges and universities on the *y*-axes plotted against 4 other variables. The correct correlations for these scatterplots appear in this list. Match them.

$$-0.98 \quad -0.71 \quad -0.51 \quad 0.09 \quad 0.23 \quad 0.69$$

**2. Togetherness.** Are good grades in high school associated with family togetherness? A random sample of 142 high school students was asked how many meals per week their families ate together. Their responses produced a mean of 3.78 meals per week, with a standard deviation of 2.2. Researchers then matched these responses against the students' grade point averages (GPAs). The scatterplot appeared to be reasonably linear, so they created a line of regression. No apparent pattern emerged in the residuals plot. The equation of the line was $\widehat{GPA} = 2.73 + 0.11\,Meals$.

a) Interpret the *y*-intercept in this context.
b) Interpret the slope in this context.
c) What was the mean GPA for the students in this study?
d) If a student in this study had a negative residual, what did that mean?
e) Upon hearing of this study, a counselor recommended that parents who want to improve the grades their children get should get the family to eat together more often. Do you agree with this interpretation? Explain.

**3. Vineyards.** Shown below are the scatterplot and regression analysis for *Case Prices* of 36 wines from vineyards in the Finger Lakes region of New York State and the *Ages* of the vineyards.

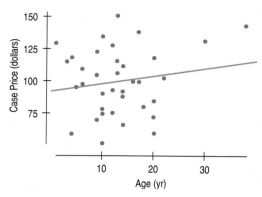

Dependent variable is: Case Price
R-squared = 2.7%

| Variable | Coefficient |
|----------|-------------|
| Constant | 92.7650 |
| Age | 0.567284 |

a) Does it appear that vineyards in business longer get higher prices for their wines? Explain.
b) What does this analysis tell us about vineyards in the rest of the world?
c) Write the regression equation.
d) Explain why that equation is essentially useless.

**4. Vineyards again.** Instead of *Age*, perhaps the *Size* of the vineyard (in acres) is associated with the price of the wines. Look at the scatterplot:

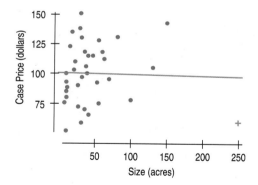

a) Do you see any evidence of an association?
b) What concern do you have about this scatterplot?
c) If the red "+" data point is removed, would you expect the correlation to become stronger or weaker? Explain.
d) If the red "+" data point is removed, would you expect the slope of the line to increase or decrease? Explain.

**5. More twins 2004?** As the table on the next page shows, the number of twins born in the United States has been increasing. (www.cdc.gov/nchs/births.htm)

| Year | Twin Births | Year | Twin Births |
|------|-------------|------|-------------|
| 1980 | 68,339 | 1993 | 96,445 |
| 1981 | 70,049 | 1994 | 97,064 |
| 1982 | 71,631 | 1995 | 96,736 |
| 1983 | 72,287 | 1996 | 100,750 |
| 1984 | 72,949 | 1997 | 104,137 |
| 1985 | 77,102 | 1998 | 110,670 |
| 1986 | 79,485 | 1999 | 114,307 |
| 1987 | 81,778 | 2000 | 118,916 |
| 1988 | 85,315 | 2001 | 121,246 |
| 1989 | 90,118 | 2002 | 125,134 |
| 1990 | 93,865 | 2003 | 128,665 |
| 1991 | 94,779 | 2004 | 132,219 |
| 1992 | 95,372 | | |

a) Find the equation of the regression line for predicting the number of twin births.
b) Explain in this context what the slope of this line means.
c) Predict the number of twin births in the United States for the year 2010. Comment on your faith in that prediction.
d) Comment on the residuals plot.

6. **Dow Jones 2006.**  The Dow Jones stock index measures the performance of the stocks of America's largest companies (http://finance.yahoo.com). A regression of the Dow prices on years 1972–2006 looks like this:

Dependent variable is: Dow Index
R-squared = 83.5%   s = 1577

| Variable | Coefficient |
|----------|-------------|
| Intercept | −2294.01 |
| Year  since 1970 | 341.095 |

a) What is the correlation between the *Dow Index* and the *Year*?
b) Write the regression equation.
c) Explain in this context what the equation says.
d) Here's a scatterplot of the residuals. Which assumption(s) of the regression analysis appear to be violated?

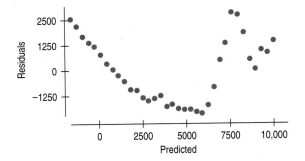

7. **Acid rain.**  Biologists studying the effects of acid rain on wildlife collected data from 163 streams in the Adirondack Mountains. They recorded the *pH* (acidity) of the water and the *BCI*, a measure of biological diversity, and

they calculated $R^2 = 27\%$. Here's a scatterplot of *BCI* against *pH:*

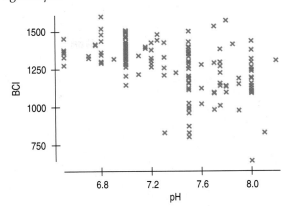

a) What is the correlation between *pH* and *BCI*?
b) Describe the association between these two variables.
c) If a stream has average *pH*, what would you predict about the *BCI*?
d) In a stream where the *pH* is 3 standard deviations above average, what would you predict about the *BCI*?

**T** 8. **Manatees 2005.**  Marine biologists warn that the growing number of powerboats registered in Florida threatens the existence of manatees. The data below come from the Florida Fish and Wildlife Conservation Commission (www.floridamarine.org) and the National Marine Manufacturers Association (www.nmma.org/facts).

| Year | Manatees Killed | Powerboat Registrations (in 1000s) |
|------|-----------------|-------------------------------------|
| 1982 | 13 | 447 |
| 1983 | 21 | 460 |
| 1984 | 24 | 481 |
| 1985 | 16 | 498 |
| 1986 | 24 | 513 |
| 1987 | 20 | 512 |
| 1988 | 15 | 527 |
| 1989 | 34 | 559 |
| 1990 | 33 | 585 |
| 1992 | 33 | 614 |
| 1993 | 39 | 646 |
| 1994 | 43 | 675 |
| 1995 | 50 | 711 |
| 1996 | 47 | 719 |
| 1997 | 53 | 716 |
| 1998 | 38 | 716 |
| 1999 | 35 | 716 |
| 2000 | 49 | 735 |
| 2001 | 81 | 860 |
| 2002 | 95 | 923 |
| 2003 | 73 | 940 |
| 2004 | 69 | 946 |
| 2005 | 79 | 974 |

a) In this context, which do you think is the explanatory variable?

b) Make a scatterplot of these data and describe the association you see.

c) Find the correlation between *Boat Registrations* and *Manatee Deaths*.

d) Interpret the value of $R^2$.

e) Does your analysis prove that powerboats are killing manatees?

**9. A manatee model 2005.** Continue your analysis of the manatee situation from the previous exercise.

a) Create a linear model of the association between *Manatee Deaths* and *Powerboat Registrations*.

b) Interpret the slope of your model.

c) Interpret the *y*-intercept of your model.

d) How accurately did your model predict the high number of manatee deaths in 2005?

e) Which is better for the manatees, positive residuals or negative residuals? Explain.

f) What does your model suggest about the future for the manatee?

**10. Grades.** A Statistics instructor created a linear regression equation to predict students' final exam scores from their midterm exam scores. The regression equation was $\widehat{Fin} = 10 + 0.9\,Mid$.

a) If Susan scored a 70 on the midterm, what did the instructor predict for her score on the final?

b) Susan got an 80 on the final. How big is her residual?

c) Suppose that the standard deviation of the final was 12 points and the standard deviation of the midterm was 10 points. What is the correlation between the two tests?

d) How many points would someone need to score on the midterm to have a predicted final score of 100?

e) Suppose someone scored 100 on the final. Explain why you can't estimate this student's midterm score from the information given.

f) One of the students in the class scored 100 on the midterm but got overconfident, slacked off, and scored only 15 on the final exam. What is the residual for this student?

g) No other student in the class "achieved" such a dramatic turnaround. If the instructor decides not to include this student's scores when constructing a new regression model, will the $R^2$ value of the regression increase, decrease, or remain the same? Explain briefly.

h) Will the slope of the new line increase or decrease?

**11. Traffic.** Highway planners investigated the relationship between traffic *Density* (number of automobiles per mile) and the average *Speed* of the traffic on a moderately large city thoroughfare. The data were collected at the same location at 10 different times over a span of 3 months. They found a mean traffic *Density* of 68.6 cars per mile (cpm) with standard deviation of 27.07 cpm. Overall, the cars' average *Speed* was 26.38 mph, with standard deviation of 9.68 mph. These researchers found the regression line for these data to be $\widehat{Speed} = 50.55 - 0.352\,Density$.

a) What is the value of the correlation coefficient between *Speed* and *Density*?

b) What percent of the variation in average *Speed* is explained by traffic *Density*?

c) Predict the average *Speed* of traffic on the thoroughfare when the traffic *Density* is 50 cpm.

d) What is the value of the residual for a traffic *Density* of 56 cpm with an observed *Speed* of 32.5 mph?

e) The data set initially included the point *Density* = 125 cpm, *Speed* = 55 mph. This point was considered an outlier and was not included in the analysis. Will the slope increase, decrease, or remain the same if we redo the analysis and include this point?

f) Will the correlation become stronger, weaker, or remain the same if we redo the analysis and include this point (125,55)?

g) A European member of the research team measured the *Speed* of the cars in kilometers per hour (1 km ≈ 0.62 miles) and the traffic *Density* in cars per kilometer. Find the value of his calculated correlation between speed and density.

**12. Cramming.** One Thursday, researchers gave students enrolled in a section of basic Spanish a set of 50 new vocabulary words to memorize. On Friday the students took a vocabulary test. When they returned to class the following Monday, they were retested—without advance warning. Both sets of test scores for the 25 students are shown.

| Fri. | Mon. | Fri. | Mon. | Fri. | Mon. |
|------|------|------|------|------|------|
| 42 | 36 | 48 | 37 | 39 | 41 |
| 44 | 44 | 43 | 41 | 46 | 32 |
| 45 | 46 | 45 | 32 | 37 | 36 |
| 48 | 38 | 47 | 44 | 40 | 31 |
| 44 | 40 | 50 | 47 | 41 | 32 |
| 43 | 38 | 34 | 34 | 48 | 39 |
| 41 | 37 | 38 | 31 | 37 | 31 |
| 35 | 31 | 43 | 40 | 36 | 41 |
| 43 | 32 | | | | |

a) What is the correlation between *Friday* and *Monday* scores?

b) What does a scatterplot show about the association between the scores?

c) What does it mean for a student to have a positive residual?

d) What would you predict about a student whose *Friday* score was one standard deviation below average?

e) Write the equation of the regression line.

f) Predict the *Monday* score of a student who earned a 40 on Friday.

**13. Correlations.** What factor most explains differences in *Fuel Efficiency* among cars? On the next page is a correlation matrix exploring that relationship for the car's *Weight, Horsepower,* engine *size* (*Displacement*), and number of *Cylinders*.

|  | MPG | Weight | Horse-power | Displace-ment | Cylinders |
|---|---|---|---|---|---|
| MPG | 1.000 | | | | |
| Weight | −0.903 | 1.000 | | | |
| Horsepower | −0.871 | 0.917 | 1.000 | | |
| Displacement | −0.786 | 0.951 | 0.872 | 1.000 | |
| Cylinders | −0.806 | 0.917 | 0.864 | 0.940 | 1.000 |

a) Which factor seems most strongly associated with *Fuel Efficiency*?

b) What does the negative correlation indicate?

c) Explain the meaning of $R^2$ for that relationship.

**14. Autos revisited.**   Look again at the correlation table for cars in the previous exercise.

a) Which two variables in the table exhibit the strongest association?

b) Is that strong association necessarily cause-and-effect? Offer at least two explanations why that association might be so strong.

c) Engine displacements for U.S.-made cars are often measured in cubic inches. For many foreign cars, the units are either cubic centimeters or liters. How would changing from cubic inches to liters affect the calculated correlations involving *Displacement*?

d) What would you predict about the *Fuel Efficiency* of a car whose engine *Displacement* is one standard deviation above the mean?

**15. Cars, one more time!**   Can we predict the *Horsepower* of the engine that manufacturers will put in a car by knowing the *Weight* of the car? Here are the regression analysis and residuals plot:

Dependent variable is: Horsepower
R-squared = 84.1%

| Variable | Coefficient |
|---|---|
| Intercept | 3.49834 |
| Weight | 34.3144 |

a) Write the equation of the regression line.

b) Do you think the car's *Weight* is measured in pounds or thousands of pounds? Explain.

c) Do you think this linear model is appropriate? Explain.

d) The highest point in the residuals plot, representing a residual of 22.5 horsepower, is for a Chevy weighing 2595 pounds. How much horsepower does this car have?

**16. Colorblind.**   Although some women are colorblind, this condition is found primarily in men. Why is it wrong to say there's a strong correlation between *Sex* and *Colorblindness*?

**17. Old Faithful.**   There is evidence that eruptions of Old Faithful can best be predicted by knowing the duration of the previous eruption.

a) Describe what you see in the scatterplot of *Intervals* between eruptions vs. *Duration* of the previous eruption.

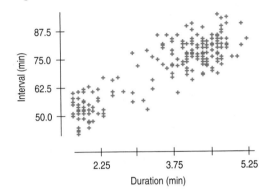

b) Write the equation of the line of best fit. Here's the regression analysis:

Dependent variable is: Interval
R-squared = 77.0%

| Variable | Coefficient |
|---|---|
| Intercept | 33.9668 |
| Duration | 10.3582 |

c) Carefully explain what the slope of the line means in this context.

d) How accurate do you expect predictions based on this model to be? Cite evidence from the regression analysis.

e) If you just witnessed an eruption that lasted 4 minutes, how long do you predict you'll have to wait to see the next eruption?

f) So you waited, and the next eruption came in 79 minutes. Use this as an example to define a residual.

**18. Which croc?**   The ranges inhabited by the Indian gharial crocodile and the Australian saltwater crocodile overlap in Bangladesh. Suppose a very large crocodile skeleton is found there, and we wish to determine the species of the animal. Wildlife scientists have measured the lengths of the heads and the complete bodies of several crocs (in centimeters) of each species, creating the regression analyses below:

| Indian Crocodile | Australian Crocodile |
|---|---|
| Dependent variable is: IBody | Dependent variable is: ABody |
| R-squared = 97.2% | R-squared = 98.0% |

| Variable | Coefficient | Variable | Coefficient |
|---|---|---|---|
| Intercept | −69.3693 | Intercept | −20.2245 |
| IHead | 7.40004 | AHead | 7.71726 |

a) Do the associations between the sizes of the heads and bodies of the two species appear to be strong? Explain.
b) In what ways are the two relationships similar? Explain.
c) What is different about the two models? What does that mean?
d) The crocodile skeleton found had a head length of 62 cm and a body length of 380 cm. Which species do you think it was? Explain why.

**19. How old is that tree?** One can determine how old a tree is by counting its rings, but that requires cutting the tree down. Can we estimate the tree's age simply from its diameter? A forester measured 27 trees of the same species that had been cut down, and counted the rings to determine the ages of the trees.

| Diameter (in.) | Age (yr) | Diameter (in.) | Age (yr) |
|---|---|---|---|
| 1.8 | 4 | 10.3 | 23 |
| 1.8 | 5 | 14.3 | 25 |
| 2.2 | 8 | 13.2 | 28 |
| 4.4 | 8 | 9.9 | 29 |
| 6.6 | 8 | 13.2 | 30 |
| 4.4 | 10 | 15.4 | 30 |
| 7.7 | 10 | 17.6 | 33 |
| 10.8 | 12 | 14.3 | 34 |
| 7.7 | 13 | 15.4 | 35 |
| 5.5 | 14 | 11.0 | 38 |
| 9.9 | 16 | 15.4 | 38 |
| 10.1 | 18 | 16.5 | 40 |
| 12.1 | 20 | 16.5 | 42 |
| 12.8 | 22 | | |

a) Find the correlation between *Diameter* and *Age*. Does this suggest that a linear model may be appropriate? Explain.
b) Create a scatterplot and describe the association.
c) Create the linear model.
d) Check the residuals. Explain why a linear model is probably not appropriate.
e) If you used this model, would it generally overestimate or underestimate the ages of very large trees? Explain.

**20. Improving trees.** In the last exercise you saw that the linear model had some deficiencies. Let's create a better model.
a) Perhaps the cross-sectional area of a tree would be a better predictor of its age. Since area is measured in square units, try re-expressing the data by squaring the diameters. Does the scatterplot look better?
b) Create a model that predicts *Age* from the square of the *Diameter*.
c) Check the residuals plot for this new model. Is this model more appropriate? Why?
d) Estimate the age of a tree 18 inches in diameter.

**21. New homes.** A real estate agent collects data to develop a model that will use the *Size* of a new home (in square feet) to predict its *Sale Price* (in thousands of dollars). Which of these is most likely to be the slope of the regression line: 0.008, 0.08, 0.8, or 8? Explain.

**22. Smoking and pregnancy 2003.** The organization Kids Count monitors issues related to children. The table shows a 50-state average of the percent of expectant mothers who smoked cigarettes during their pregnancies.

| Year | % Smoking While Pregnant | Year | % Smoking While Pregnant |
|---|---|---|---|
| 1990 | 19.2 | 1997 | 14.9 |
| 1991 | 18.7 | 1998 | 14.8 |
| 1992 | 17.9 | 1999 | 14.1 |
| 1993 | 16.8 | 2000 | 14.0 |
| 1994 | 16.0 | 2001 | 13.8 |
| 1995 | 15.4 | 2002 | 13.3 |
| 1996 | 15.3 | 2003 | 12.7 |

a) Create a scatterplot and describe the trend you see.
b) Find the correlation.
c) How is the value of the correlation affected by the fact that the data are averages rather than percentages for each of the 50 states?
d) Write a linear model and interpret the slope in this context.

**23. No smoking?** The downward trend in smoking you saw in the last exercise is good news for the health of babies, but will it ever stop?
a) Explain why you can't use the linear model you created in Exercise 22 to see when smoking during pregnancy will cease altogether.
b) Create a model that could estimate the year in which the level of smoking would be 0%.
c) Comment on the reliability of such a prediction.

**24. Tips.** It's commonly believed that people use tips to reward good service. A researcher for the hospitality industry examined tips and ratings of service quality from 2645 dining parties at 21 different restaurants. The correlation between ratings of service and tip percentages was 0.11. (M. Lynn and M. McCall, "Gratitude and Gratuity." *Journal of Socio-Economics* 29: 203–214)
a) Describe the relationship between *Quality of Service* and *Tip Size*.
b) Find and interpret the value of $R^2$ in this context.

**25. US Cities.** Data from 50 large U.S. cities show the mean *January Temperature* and the *Latitude*. Describe what you see in the scatterplot.

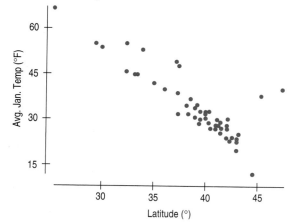

**26. Correlations.** The study of U.S. cities in Exercise 25 found the mean *January Temperature* (degrees Fahrenheit), *Altitude* (feet above sea level), and *Latitude* (degrees north of the equator) for 55 cities. Here's the correlation matrix:

|  | Jan. Temp | Latitude | Altitude |
|---|---|---|---|
| **Jan. Temp** | 1.000 | | |
| **Latitude** | −0.848 | 1.000 | |
| **Altitude** | −0.369 | 0.184 | 1.000 |

a) Which seems to be more useful in predicting *January Temperature*—*Altitude* or *Latitude*? Explain.
b) If the *Temperature* were measured in degrees Celsius, what would be the correlation between *Temperature* and *Latitude*?
c) If the *Temperature* were measured in degrees Celsius and the *Altitude* in meters, what would be the correlation? Explain.
d) What would you predict about the January *Temperatures* in a city whose *Altitude* is two standard deviations higher than the average *Altitude*?

**27. Winter in the city.** Summary statistics for the data relating the latitude and average January temperature for 55 large U.S. cities are given below.

| Variable | Mean | StdDev |
|---|---|---|
| **Latitude** | 39.02 | 5.42 |
| **JanTemp** | 26.44 | 13.49 |

Correlation = −0.848

a) What percent of the variation in January *Temperatures* can be explained by variation in *Latitude*?
b) What is indicated by the fact that the correlation is negative?
c) Write the equation of the line of regression for predicting January *Temperature* from *Latitude*.
d) Explain what the slope of the line means.
e) Do you think the *y*-intercept of the line is meaningful? Explain.
f) The latitude of Denver is 40° N. Predict the mean January temperature there.
g) If the residual for a city is positive, what does that mean?

**28. Depression.** The September 1998 issue of the *American Psychologist* published an article by Kraut et al. that reported on an experiment examining "the social and psychological impact of the Internet on 169 people in 73 households during their first 1 to 2 years online." In the experiment, 73 households were offered free Internet access for 1 or 2 years in return for allowing their time and activity online to be tracked. The members of the households who participated in the study were also given a battery of tests at the beginning and again at the end of the study. The conclusion of the study made news headlines: Those who spent more time online tended to be more depressed at the end of the experiment. Although the paper reports a more complex model, the basic result can be summarized in the following regression of *Depression* (at the end of the study, in "depression scale units") vs. *Internet Use* (in mean hours per week):

Dependent variable is: Depression

R-squared = 4.6%

s = 0.4563

| Variable | Coefficient |
|---|---|
| Intercept | 0.5655 |
| Internet use | 0.0199 |

The news reports about this study clearly concluded that using the Internet causes depression. Discuss whether such a conclusion can be drawn from this regression. If so, discuss the supporting evidence. If not, say why not.

**29. Jumps 2004.** How are Olympic performances in various events related? The plot shows winning long-jump and high-jump distances, in inches, for the Summer Olympics from 1912 through 2004.

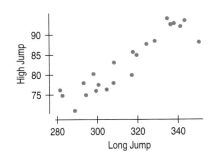

a) Describe the association.
b) Do long-jump performances somehow influence the high-jumpers? How do you account for the relationship you see?
c) The correlation for the given scatterplot is 0.925, but at the Olympics these jumps are actually measured in meters rather than inches. Does that make the actual correlation higher or lower?
d) What would you predict about the long jump in a year when the high-jumper jumped one standard deviation better than the average high jump?

**30. Modeling jumps.** Here are the summary statistics for the Olympic long jumps and high jumps displayed in the scatterplot above:

| Event | Mean | StdDev |
|---|---|---|
| **Long Jump** | 316.04 | 20.85 |
| **High Jump** | 83.85 | 7.46 |

Correlation = 0.925

a) Write the equation of the line of regression for estimating *High Jump* from *Long Jump*.
b) Interpret the slope of the line.
c) In a year when the long jump is 350 inches, what high jump would you predict?
d) Why can't you use this line to estimate the long jump for a year when you know the high jump was 85 inches?
e) Write the equation of the line you need to make that prediction.

**31. French.** Consider the association between a student's score on a French vocabulary test and the weight of the student. What direction and strength of correlation would you expect in each of the following situations? Explain.
a) The students are all in third grade.

b) The students are in third through twelfth grades in the same school district.

c) The students are in tenth grade in France.

d) The students are in third through twelfth grades in France.

**32. Twins.** Twins are often born after a pregnancy that lasts less than 9 months. The graph from the *Journal of the American Medical Association (JAMA)* shows the rate of preterm twin births in the United States over the past 20 years. In this study, *JAMA* categorized mothers by the level of prenatal medical care they received: inadequate, adequate, or intensive.

a) Describe the overall trend in preterm twin births.

b) Describe any differences you see in this trend, depending on the level of prenatal medical care the mother received.

c) Should expectant mothers be advised to cut back on the level of medical care they seek in the hope of avoiding preterm births? Explain.

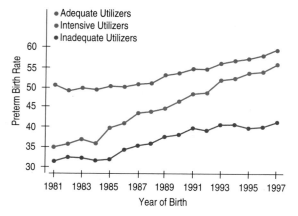

Preterm Birth Rate *per 100 live twin births among U.S. twins by intensive, adequate, and less than adequate prenatal care utilization, 1981–1997. (JAMA 284[2000]: 335–341)*

**T 33. Lunchtime.** Create and interpret a model for the toddlers' lunchtime data presented in Chapter 7. The table and graph show the number of minutes the kids stayed at the table and the number of calories they consumed.

| Calories | Time | Calories | Time |
|----------|------|----------|------|
| 472 | 21.4 | 450 | 42.4 |
| 498 | 30.8 | 410 | 43.1 |
| 465 | 37.7 | 504 | 29.2 |
| 456 | 33.5 | 437 | 31.3 |
| 423 | 32.8 | 489 | 28.6 |
| 437 | 39.5 | 436 | 32.9 |
| 508 | 22.8 | 480 | 30.6 |
| 431 | 34.1 | 439 | 35.1 |
| 479 | 33.9 | 444 | 33.0 |
| 454 | 43.8 | 408 | 43.7 |

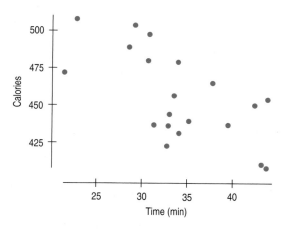

**34. Gasoline.** Since clean-air regulations have dictated the use of unleaded gasoline, the supply of leaded gas in New York state has diminished. The table below was given on the August 2001 New York State Math B exam, a statewide achievement test for high school students.

| Year | 1984 | 1988 | 1992 | 1996 | 2000 |
|------|------|------|------|------|------|
| Gallons (1000's) | 150 | 124 | 104 | 76 | 50 |

a) Create a linear model to predict the number of gallons that will be available in 2005.

b) The exam then asked students to estimate the year when leaded gasoline will first become unavailable, expecting them to use the model from part a to answer the question. Explain why that method is incorrect.

c) Create a model that *would* be appropriate for that task, and make the estimate.

d) The "wrong" answer from the other model is fairly accurate in this case. Why?

**T 35. Tobacco and alcohol.** Are people who use tobacco products more likely to consume alcohol? Here are data on household spending (in pounds) taken by the British Government on 11 regions in Great Britain. Do tobacco and alcohol spending appear to be related? What questions do you have about these data? What conclusions can you draw?

| Region | Alcohol | Tobacco |
|--------|---------|---------|
| North | 6.47 | 4.03 |
| Yorkshire | 6.13 | 3.76 |
| Northeast | 6.19 | 3.77 |
| East Midlands | 4.89 | 3.34 |
| West Midlands | 5.63 | 3.47 |
| East Anglia | 4.52 | 2.92 |
| Southeast | 5.89 | 3.20 |
| Southwest | 4.79 | 2.71 |
| Wales | 5.27 | 3.53 |
| Scotland | 6.08 | 4.51 |
| Northern Ireland | 4.02 | 4.56 |

**36. Football weights.**   The Sears Cup was established in 1993 to honor institutions that maintain a broad-based athletic program, achieving success in many sports, both men's and women's. Since its Division III inception in 1995, the cup has been won by Williams College in every year except one. Their football team has a 85.3% winning record under their current coach. Why does the football team win so much? Is it because they're heavier than their opponents? The table shows the average team weights for selected years from 1973 to 1993.

| Year | Weight (lb) | Year | Weight (lb) |
|------|-------------|------|-------------|
| 1973 | 185.5 | 1983 | 192.0 |
| 1975 | 182.4 | 1987 | 196.9 |
| 1977 | 182.1 | 1989 | 202.9 |
| 1979 | 191.1 | 1991 | 206.0 |
| 1981 | 189.4 | 1993 | 198.7 |

a) Fit a straight line to the relationship between *Weight* and *Year.*
b) Does a straight line seem reasonable?
c) Predict the average weight of the team for the year 2003. Does this seem reasonable?
d) What about the prediction for the year 2103? Explain.
e) What about the prediction for the year 3003? Explain.

**37. Models.**   Find the predicted value of *y*, using each model for $x = 10$.
a) $\hat{y} = 2 + 0.8 \ln x$
b) $\log \hat{y} = 5 - 0.23x$
c) $\frac{1}{\sqrt{\hat{y}}} = 17.1 - 1.66x$

**38. Williams vs. Texas.**   Here are the average weights of the football team for the University of Texas for various years in the 20th century.

| Year | Weight (lb) |
|------|-------------|
| 1905 | 164 |
| 1919 | 163 |
| 1932 | 181 |
| 1945 | 192 |
| 1955 | 195 |
| 1965 | 199 |

a) Fit a straight line to the relationship of *Weight* by *Year* for Texas football players.
b) According to these models, in what year will the predicted weight of the Williams College team from Exercise 36 first be more than the weight of the University of Texas team?
c) Do you believe this? Explain.

**39. Vehicle weights.**   The Minnesota Department of Transportation hoped that they could measure the weights of big trucks without actually stopping the vehicles by using a newly developed "weigh-in-motion" scale. After installation of the scale, a study was conducted to find out whether the scale's readings correspond to the true weights of the trucks being monitored. In Exercise 16 of Chapter 7, you examined the scatterplot for the data they collected, finding the association to be approximately linear with $R^2 = 93\%$. Their regression equation is $\widehat{Wt} = 10.85 + 0.64\ Scale$, where both the scale reading and the predicted weight of the truck are measured in thousands of pounds.
a) Estimate the weight of a truck if this scale read 31,200 pounds.
b) If that truck actually weighed 32,120 pounds, what was the residual?
c) If the scale reads 35,590 pounds, and the truck has a residual of −2440 pounds, how much does it actually weigh?
d) In general, do you expect estimates made using this equation to be reasonably accurate? Explain.
e) If the police plan to use this scale to issue tickets to trucks that appear to be overloaded, will negative or positive residuals be a greater problem? Explain.

**40. Profit.**   How are a company's profits related to its sales? Let's examine data from 71 large U.S. corporations. All amounts are in millions of dollars.
a) Here are histograms of *Profits* and *Sales* and histograms of the logarithms of *Profits* and *Sales*. Why are the re-expressed data better for regression?

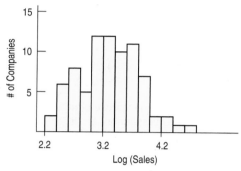

b) Here are the scatterplot and residuals plot for the regression of logarithm of *Profits* vs. log of *Sales*. Do you think this model is appropriate? Explain.

c) Here's the regression analysis. Write the equation.

Dependent variable is: Log Profit
R-squared = 48.1%

| Variable | Coefficient |
| --- | --- |
| Intercept | −0.106259 |
| LogSales | 0.647798 |

d) Use your equation to estimate profits earned by a company with sales of 2.5 billion dollars. (That's 2500 million.)

**41. Down the drain.** Most water tanks have a drain plug so that the tank may be emptied when it's to be moved or repaired. How long it takes a certain size of tank to drain depends on the size of the plug, as shown in the table. Create a model.

| Diameter of Plug (in.) | Drain Time (min.) |
| --- | --- |
| $\frac{3}{8}$ | 140 |
| $\frac{1}{2}$ | 80 |
| $\frac{3}{4}$ | 35 |
| 1 | 20 |
| $1\frac{1}{4}$ | 13 |
| $1\frac{1}{2}$ | 10 |
| 2 | 5 |

**42. Chips.** A start-up company has developed an improved electronic chip for use in laboratory equipment. The company needs to project the manufacturing cost, so it develops a spreadsheet model that takes into account the purchase of production equipment, overhead, raw materials, depreciation, maintenance, and other business costs. The spreadsheet estimates the cost of producing 10,000 to 200,000 chips per year, as seen in the table. Develop a regression model to predict *Costs* based on the *Level* of production.

| Chips Produced (1000s) | Cost per Chip ($) |
| --- | --- |
| 10 | 146.10 |
| 20 | 105.80 |
| 30 | 85.75 |
| 40 | 77.02 |
| 50 | 66.10 |
| 60 | 63.92 |
| 70 | 58.80 |
| 80 | 50.91 |
| 90 | 47.22 |
| 100 | 44.31 |
| 120 | 42.88 |
| 140 | 39.05 |
| 160 | 37.47 |
| 180 | 35.09 |
| 200 | 34.04 |

**43. Least squares.** Consider the four points (12,800), (24,680), (36,740), and (48,660). The line of best fit is $\hat{y} = 810 - 3x$. Use these data to explain what "least squares" means.

# PART
# III

# Gathering Data

**Chapter 11**
Understanding Randomness

**Chapter 12**
Sample Surveys

**Chapter 13**
Experiments and Observational Studies

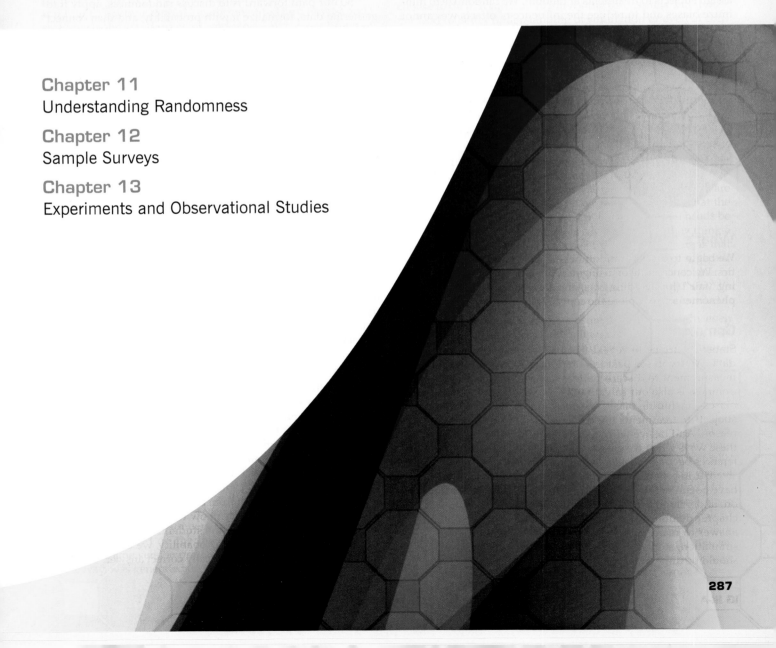

## RESOURCES

### ActivStats

▶ Chapter 13—"Designed Experiments." Note the activity on the last page of this *ActivStats* chapter, where students can experiment on themselves and then look at their own data.

### Web Links

▶ "Randomization and Inference" explores the distinction between sampling and experimentation in the Experimental Design section of notes from the NCSSM Statistics Leadership Institute.

### Printed Test Bank and Resource Guide

The *Printed Test Bank and Resource Guide* provides a chapter quiz, and an Investigative Task in which students design an experiment for themselves. Also, there's a worksheet for a group project in which students collect data with a survey, experiment, or simulation and submit a written report. And it's time for a test on Gathering Data (Chapters 11–13). Three full tests are provided.

# CHAPTER 11

# Understanding Randomness

---

## Where are we going?

Few things in life are certain. But that doesn't mean that we all understand randomness. We'll be formal about it in a few chapters, but for now we'll simulate what we want to understand to see the patterns that emerge.

---

*"The most decisive conceptual event of twentieth century physics has been the discovery that the world is not deterministic. . . . A space was cleared for chance."*

— Ian Hocking
*The Taming of Chance*

W e all know what it means for something to be random. Or do we? Many children's games rely on chance outcomes. Rolling dice, spinning spinners, and shuffling cards all select at random. Adult games use randomness as well, from card games to lotteries to Bingo. What's the most important aspect of the randomness in these games? It must be fair.

What is it about random selection that makes it seem fair? It's really two things. First, nobody can guess the outcome before it happens. Second, when we want things to be fair, usually some underlying set of outcomes will be equally likely (although in many games, some combinations of outcomes are more likely than others).

Randomness is not always what we might think of as "at random." Random outcomes have a lot of structure, especially when viewed in the long run. You can't predict how a fair coin will land on any single toss, but you're pretty confident that if you flipped it thousands of times you'd see about 50% heads. As we will see, randomness is an essential tool of Statistics. Statisticians don't think of randomness as the annoying tendency of things to be unpredictable or haphazard. Statisticians use randomness as a tool. In fact, without deliberately applying randomness, we couldn't do most of Statistics, and this book would stop right about here.

But truly random values are surprisingly hard to get. Just to see how fair humans are at selecting, pick a number at random from the top of the next page. Go ahead. Turn the page, look at the numbers quickly, and pick a number at random.

Ready?

Go.

# 1 2 3 4

## It's Not Easy Being Random

*"The generation of random numbers is too important to be left to chance."*

—Robert R. Coveyou, Oak Ridge National Laboratory

Did you pick 3? If so, you've got company. Almost 75% of all people pick the number 3. About 20% pick either 2 or 4. If you picked 1, well, consider yourself a little different. Only about 5% choose 1. Psychologists have proposed reasons for this phenomenon, but for us, it simply serves as a lesson that we've got to find a better way to choose things at random.

So how should we generate **random numbers?** It's surprisingly difficult to get random values even when they're equally likely. Computers have become a popular way to generate random numbers. Even though they often do much better than humans, computers can't generate truly random numbers either. Computers follow programs. Start a computer from the same place, and it will always follow exactly the same path. So numbers generated by a computer program are not truly random. Technically, "random" numbers generated this way are *pseudorandom* numbers. Pseudorandom values are generated in a fixed sequence, and because computers can represent only a finite number of distinct values, the sequence of pseudorandom numbers must eventually repeat itself. Fortunately, pseudorandom values are good enough for most purposes because they are virtually indistinguishable from truly random numbers.

There *are* ways to generate random numbers so that they are both equally likely and truly random. In the past, entire books of carefully generated random numbers were published. The books never made the best-seller lists and probably didn't make for great reading, but they were quite valuable to those who needed truly random values.[1] Today, we have a choice. We can use these books or find genuinely random digits from several Internet sites. The sites use methods like timing the decay of a radioactive element or even the random changes of lava

---

[1] You'll find a table of random digits of this kind in the back of this book.

lamps to generate truly random digits.[2] In either case, a string of random digits might look like this:

221772630438741009253708627058199762272584979590703282500110896332175358226438002922546449437606423890437665572041073541860245088906427308645681412198226653885873285801699027843110380420067664874052226398245305199020270444649843220009462386785779026390029548887003319933147508331265192321413908608674496383528968974910533694418271316891940602218128130475101932154630387048140767663674060702049165089136328553513613610437942934284869094628814317933607706356513310563210508993624272872250535395513645991015328128202

You probably have more interesting things to download than a few million random digits, but we'll discuss ways to use such random digits to apply randomness to real situations soon. The best ways we know to generate data that give a fair and accurate picture of the world rely on randomness, and the ways in which we draw conclusions from those data depend on the randomness, too.

*An ordinary deck of playing cards, like the ones used in bridge and many other card games, consists of 52 cards. There are numbered cards (2 through 10), and face cards (Jack, Queen, King, Ace) whose value depends on the game you are playing. Each card is also marked by one of four suits (clubs, diamonds, hearts, or spades) whose significance is also game-specific.*

> **Aren't you done shuffling yet?** Even something as common as card shuffling may not be as random as you might think. If you shuffle cards by the usual method in which you split the deck in half and try to let cards fall roughly alternately from each half, you're doing a "riffle shuffle."
>
> How many times should you shuffle cards to make the deck random? A surprising fact was discovered by statisticians Persi Diaconis, Ronald Graham, and W. M. Kantor. It takes seven riffle shuffles. Fewer than seven leaves order in the deck, but after that, more shuffling does little good. Most people, though, don't shuffle that many times.
>
> When computers were first used to generate hands in bridge tournaments, some professional bridge players complained that the computer was making too many "weird" hands—hands with 10 cards of one suit, for example. Suddenly these hands were appearing more often than players were used to when cards were shuffled by hand. The players assumed that the computer was doing something wrong. But it turns out that it's humans who hadn't been shuffling enough to make the decks really random and have those "weird" hands appear as often as they should.

# Practical Randomness

Suppose a cereal manufacturer puts pictures of famous athletes on cards in boxes of cereal in the hope of boosting sales. The manufacturer announces that 20% of the boxes contain a picture of Tiger Woods, 30% a picture of David Beckham, and the rest a picture of Serena Williams. You want all three pictures. How many boxes of cereal do you expect to have to buy in order to get the complete set?

How can we answer questions like this? Well, one way is to buy hundreds of boxes of cereal to see what might happen. But let's not. Instead, we'll consider using a random model. Why random? When we pick a box of cereal off the shelf, we don't know what picture is inside. We'll assume that the pictures are randomly placed in the boxes and that the boxes are distributed randomly to stores around the country. Why a model? Because we won't actually buy the cereal boxes. We can't afford all those boxes and we don't want to waste food. So we need an imitation of the real process that we can manipulate and control. In short, we're going to **simulate** reality.

---

[2] For example, www.random.org or www.randomnumbers.info

# A Simulation

Modern physics has shown that randomness is not just a mathematical game; it is fundamentally the way the universe works.

*Regardless of improvements in data collection or in computer power, the best we can ever do, according to quantum mechanics . . . is predict the probability that an electron, or a proton, or a neutron, or any other of nature's constituents, will be found here or there. Probability reigns supreme in the microcosmos.*
—Brian Greene, *The Fabric of the Cosmos: Space, Time, and the Texture of Reality* (p. 91)

The question we've asked is how many boxes do you expect to buy to get a complete card collection. But we can't answer our question by completing a card collection just once. We want to understand the *typical* number of boxes to open, how that number varies, and, often, the shape of the distribution. So we'll have to do this over and over. We call each time we obtain a simulated answer to our question a **trial.**

For the sports cards, a trial's outcome is the number of boxes. We'll need at least 3 boxes to get one of each card, but with really bad luck, you could empty the shelves of several supermarkets before finding the card you need to get all 3. So, the possible outcomes of a trial are 3, 4, 5, or lots more. But we can't simply pick one of those numbers at random, because they're not equally likely. We'd be surprised if we only needed 3 boxes to get all the cards, but we'd probably be even more surprised to find that it took exactly 7,359 boxes. In fact, the reason we're doing the simulation is that it's hard to guess how many boxes we'd expect to open.

## BUILDING A SIMULATION

We know how to find equally likely random digits. How can we get from there to simulating the trial outcomes? We know the relative frequencies of the cards: 20% Tiger, 30% Beckham, and 50% Serena. So, we can interpret the digits 0 and 1 as finding Tiger; 2, 3, and 4 as finding Beckham; and 5 through 9 as finding Serena to simulate opening one box. Opening one box is the basic building block, called a **component** of our simulation. But the component's outcome isn't the result we want. We need to observe a sequence of components until our card collection is complete. The *trial's* outcome for this simulation is the *number* of components (boxes) in the sequence.

Let's look at the steps for making a simulation:

**Specify how to model a component outcome using equally likely random digits:**

1. **Identify the component to be repeated.** In this case, our component is the opening of a box of cereal.
2. **Explain how you will model the component's outcome.** The digits from 0 to 9 are equally likely to occur. Because 20% of the boxes contain Tiger's picture, we'll use 2 of the 10 digits to represent that outcome. Three of the 10 digits can model the 30% of boxes with David Beckham cards, and the remaining 5 digits can represent the 50% of boxes with Serena. One possible assignment of the digits, then, is

    0, 1 Tiger    2, 3, 4 Beckham    5, 6, 7, 8, 9 Serena.

**Specify how to combine components to simulate trials:**

3. **State clearly what the response variable is.** What are we interested in? We want to find out the number of boxes it might take to get all three pictures.
4. **Explain how you will combine the components into a trial to model the response variable.** We open boxes (repeat components) until the collection is complete. The trial's outcome is the number of boxes (components.)

**Put it all together to run the simulation:**

5. **Run several trials.** For example, consider the third line of random digits shown earlier (p. 291):

    89064273086456814121982266538858732858016990278431103804 20067664.

Let's see what happened.

The first random digit, 8, means you get Serena's picture. So the first component's outcome is Serena. The second digit, 9, means Serena's picture is also in the next box. Continuing to interpret the random digits, we get Tiger's picture (0) in the third, Serena's (6) again in the fourth, and finally Beckham (4) on the fifth box. Since we've now found all three pictures, we've finished one trial of our simulation. This trial's outcome is 5 boxes.

Now we keep going, running more trials by looking at the rest of our line of random digits:

89064 2730 8645681 41219 822665388587328580 169902 78431 1038 042006 7664.

It's best to create a chart to keep track of what happens:

| Trial Number | Component Outcomes | Trial Outcomes: $y$ = Number of boxes |
|---|---|---|
| 1 | 89064 = Serena, Serena, Tiger, Serena, Beckham | 5 |
| 2 | 2730 = Beckham, Serena, Beckham, Tiger | 4 |
| 3 | 8645681 = Serena, Serena, Beckham, . . . , Tiger | 7 |
| 4 | 41219 = Beckham, Tiger, Beckham, Tiger, Serena | 5 |
| 5 | 822665388587328580 = Serena, Beckham, . . . , Tiger | 18 |
| 6 | 169902 = Tiger, Serena, Serena, Serena, Tiger, Beckham | 6 |
| 7 | 78431 = Serena, Serena, Beckham, Beckham, Tiger | 5 |
| 8 | 1038 = Tiger, Tiger, Beckham, Serena | 4 |
| 9 | 042006 = Tiger, Beckham, Beckham, Tiger, Tiger, Serena | 6 |
| 10 | 7664 . . . = Serena, Serena, Serena, Beckham . . . | ? |

**Analyze the response variable:**

6. **Collect and summarize the results of all the trials.** You know how to summarize and display a response variable. You'll certainly want to report the shape, center, and spread, and depending on the question asked, you may want to include more.

7. **State your conclusion.** Be sure to refer to the question you wanted to answer. Based on this simulation, we estimate that customers hoping to complete their card collection will need to open a median of 5 boxes, but it could take a lot more.

If you fear that these may not be accurate estimates because we ran only nine trials, you are absolutely correct. The more trials the better, and nine is woefully inadequate. Twenty trials is probably a reasonable minimum if you are doing this by hand. Even better, use a computer and run a few hundred trials.

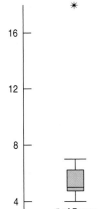

# of Boxes

**A S** *Activity:* **Bigger Samples Are Better.** The random simulation tool can generate lots of outcomes with a single click, so you can see more of the long run with less effort.

**FOR EXAMPLE**    Simulating a dice game

The game of 21 can be played with an ordinary 6-sided die. Competitors each roll the die repeatedly, trying to get the highest total less than or equal to 21. If your total exceeds 21, you lose.

Suppose your opponent has rolled an 18. Your task is to try to beat him by getting more than 18 points without going over 21. How many rolls do you expect to make, and what are your chances of winning?

*(continued)*

**For Example** (*continued*)

**Question:** How will you simulate the components?

A component is one roll of the die. I'll simulate each roll by looking at a random digit from a table or an Internet site. The digits 1 through 6 will represent the results on the die; I'll ignore digits 7–9 and 0.

**Question:** What's the response variable? How will you combine components to obtain a response?

There are two response variables. I'll count the number of times I roll the die, and I'll keep track of whether I win or lose. I'll add components until my total is greater than 18, counting the number of rolls. If my total is greater than 21, it is a loss; if not, it is a win.

**Question:** How would you use these random digits to run trials?

91129 58757 69274 92380 82464 33089

Show your method clearly for two trials.

I've marked the discarded digits in color.

Trial #1:      9 **1 1 2** 9 **5** 8 7 5 **6**

      Total:      1  2  4      9      14  20      Outcomes:  6 rolls, won

Trial #2:      9 **2** 7 **4** 9 **2 3** 8 0 8 **2 4 6**

      Total:      2      6      8  11            13 17 23  Outcomes:  7 rolls, lost

**Question:** Suppose you run 30 trials, getting the outcomes tallied here. What is your conclusion?

| Number of rolls | | Result | |
|---|---|---|---|
| 4 | /// | Won | ⫽〵 ⫽〵 ⫽〵 ⫽〵 / |
| 5 | ⫽〵 ⫽〵 | Lost | ⫽〵 //// |
| 6 | ⫽〵 ⫽〵 / | | |
| 7 | ⫽〵 | | |
| 8 | / | | |

Based on my simulation, when competing against an opponent who has a score of 18, I expect my turn to usually last 5 or 6 rolls, and I should win about 70% of the time.

## JUST CHECKING

The baseball World Series consists of up to seven games. The first team to win four games wins the series. The first two are played at one team's home ballpark, the next three at the other team's park, and the final two (if needed) are played back at the first park. Records over the past century show that there is a home field advantage; the home team has about a 55% chance of winning. Does the current system of alternating ballparks even out the home field advantage? How often will the team that begins at home win the series?

Let's set up the simulation:

1. What is the component to be repeated?

2. How will you model each component from equally likely random digits?

3. What is the response variable?

4. How will you model a trial by combining components? What rule will you use for stopping the collection of components? How will you use components to generate the outcome of each trial?

5. How will you analyze the response variable?

## STEP-BY-STEP EXAMPLE | Simulation

Fifty-seven students participated in a lottery for a particularly desirable dorm room—a triple with a fireplace and private bath in the tower. Twenty of the participants were members of the same varsity team. When all three winners were members of the team, the other students cried foul.

**Question:** Could an all-team outcome reasonably be expected to happen if everyone had a fair shot at the room?

**Plan** State the problem. Identify the important parts of your simulation.

I'll use a simulation to investigate whether it's unlikely that three varsity athletes would get the great room in the dorm if the lottery were fair.

**Components** Identify the components.

A component is the selection of a student.

**Outcomes** State how you will model each component using equally likely random digits. You can't just use the digits from 0 to 9 because the outcomes you are simulating are not multiples of 10%.

I'll look at two-digit random numbers.

Let 00–19 represent the 20 varsity applicants.

Let 20–56 represent the other 37 applicants.

There are 20 and 37 students in the two groups. This time you must use *pairs* of random digits (and ignore some of them) to represent the 57 students.

Skip 57–99. If I get a number in this range, I'll throw it away and go back for another two-digit random number.

**Response Variable** Define your response variable.

The response variable is whether or not all three selected students are on the varsity team.

**Trial** Define a trial. Explain how you will combine the components to simulate each trial's outcome. In each of these trials, you can't choose the same student twice, so you'll need to ignore a random number if it comes up a second or third time. Be sure to mention this in describing your simulation.

Each trial consists of identifying pairs of digits as V (varsity) or N (nonvarsity) until 3 people are chosen, ignoring out-of-range or repeated numbers (X)—I can't put the same person in the room twice.

**Mechanics** Run several trials. Carefully record the random numbers, indicating

1) the corresponding component outcomes (here, Varsity, Nonvarsity, or ignored number) and
2) the resulting trial outcome.

| Trial Number | Component Outcomes | Trial Outcome: All Varsity? |
|---|---|---|
| 1 | 74 02 94 39 02 77 55<br>X  V  X  N  X  X  N | No |
| 2 | 18 63 33 25<br>V  X  N  N | No |
| 3 | 05 45 88 91 56<br>V  N  X  X  N | No |
| 4 | 39 09 07<br>N  V  V | No |
| 5 | 65 39 45 95 43<br>X  N  N  X  N | No |

*(continued)*

| 6 | 98 95 11  68 77 12  17 | |
|---|---|---|
| | X  X  V  X  X  V  V | Yes |
| 7 | 26 19 89 93  77 27 | |
| | N  V  X  X  X  N | No |
| 8 | 23 52 37 | |
| | N  N  N | No |
| 9 | 16  50 83 44 | |
| | V  N  X  N | No |
| 10 | 74  17  46 85 09 | |
| | X  V  N  X  V | No |

**Analyze** Summarize the results across all trials to answer the initial question.

"All varsity" occurred once, or 10% of the time.

 **Conclusion** Describe what the simulation shows, and interpret your results in the context of the real world.

In my simulation of "fair" room draws, the three people chosen were all varsity team members only 10% of the time. While this result could happen by chance, it is not particularly likely. I'm suspicious, but I'd need many more trials and a smaller frequency of the all-varsity outcome before I would make an accusation of unfairness.

# WHAT CAN GO WRONG?

▶ **Don't overstate your case.** Let's face it: In some sense, a simulation is *always* wrong. After all, it's not the real thing. We didn't buy any cereal or run a room draw. So beware of confusing what *really* happens with what a simulation suggests *might* happen. Never forget that future results will not match your simulated results exactly.

▶ **Model outcome chances accurately.** A common mistake in constructing a simulation is to adopt a strategy that may appear to produce the right kind of results, but that does not accurately model the situation. For example, in our room draw, we could have gotten 0, 1, 2, or 3 team members. Why not just see how often these digits occur in random digits from 0 to 9, ignoring the digits 4 and up?

3 2 1 7 9 0 0 5 9 7 3 7 9 2 5 2 4 1 3 8

**3 2 1 x x 0 0 x x x 3 x x 2 x 2 x 1 3 x**

This "simulation" makes it seem fairly likely that three team members would be chosen. There's a big problem with this approach, though: The digits 0, 1, 2, and 3 occur with equal frequency among random digits, making each outcome appear to happen 25% of the time. In fact, the selection of 0, 1, 2, or all 3 team members are not all equally likely outcomes. In our correct simulation, we estimated that all 3 would be chosen only about 10% of the time. If your simulation overlooks important aspects of the real situation, your model will not be accurate.

▶ **Run enough trials.** Simulation is cheap and fairly easy to do. Don't try to draw conclusions based on 5 or 10 trials (even though we did for illustration purposes here). We'll make precise how many trials to use in later chapters. For now, err on the side of large numbers of trials.

**A S** *Activity:* **Estimating Summaries from Random Outcomes.** See how well you can estimate something you can't know just by generating random outcomes.

# CONNECTIONS

Simulations often generate many outcomes of a response variable, and we are often interested in the distribution of these responses. The tools we use to display and summarize the distribution of any real variable are appropriate for displaying and summarizing randomly generated responses as well.

Make histograms, boxplots, and Normal probability plots of the response variables from simulations, and summarize them with measures of center and spread. Be especially careful to report the variation of your response variable.

Don't forget to think about your analyses. Simulations can hide subtle errors. A careful analysis of the responses can save you from erroneous conclusions based on a faulty simulation.

You may be less likely to find an outlier in simulated responses, but if you find one, you should certainly determine how it happened.

# WHAT HAVE WE LEARNED?

We've learned to harness the power of randomness. We've learned that a simulation model can help us investigate a question for which many outcomes are possible, we can't (or don't want to) collect data, and a mathematical answer is hard to calculate. We've learned how to base our simulation on random values generated by a computer, generated by a randomizing device such as a die or spinner, or found on the Internet. Like all models, simulations can provide us with useful insights about the real world.

## Terms

**Random**

290. An outcome is random if we know the possible values it can have, but not which particular value it takes.

**Generating random numbers**

290. Random numbers are hard to generate. Nevertheless, several Internet sites offer an unlimited supply of equally likely random values.

**Simulation**

292. A simulation models a real-world situation by using random-digit outcomes to mimic the uncertainty of a response variable of interest.

**Simulation component**

292. A component uses equally likely random digits to model simple random occurrences whose outcomes may not be equally likely.

**Trial**

292. The sequence of several components representing events that we are pretending will take place.

**Response variable**

292. Values of the response variable record the results of each trial with respect to what we were interested in.

## Skills

▶ Be able to recognize random outcomes in a real-world situation.

▶ Be able to recognize when a simulation might usefully model random behavior in the real world.

▶ Know how to perform a simulation either by generating random numbers on a computer or calculator, or by using some other source of random values, such as dice, a spinner, or a table of random numbers.

▶ Be able to describe a simulation so that others can repeat it.

▶ Be able to discuss the results of a simulation study and draw conclusions about the question being investigated.

# ON THE COMPUTER

## Simulation

Simulations are best done with the help of technology simply because more trials makes a better simulation, and computers are fast. There are special computer programs designed for simulation, but most statistics packages can generate random numbers and support a simulation.

*A S* **Activity: Creating Random Values.** Learn to use your statistics package to generate random outcomes.

All technology-generated random numbers are *pseudorandom.* The random numbers available on the Internet may technically be better, but the differences won't matter for any simulation of modest size. Pseudorandom numbers generate the next random value from the previous one by a specified algorithm. But they have to start somewhere. This starting point is called the "seed." Most programs let you set the seed. There's usually little reason to do this, but if you wish to, go ahead. If you reset the seed to the same value, the programs will generate the same sequence of "random" numbers.

### DATA DESK

Generate random numbers in Data Desk with the **Generate Random Numbers . . .** command in the **Manip** menu.
A dialog guides you in specifying the number of variables to fill, the number of cases, and details about the values. For most simulations, generate random uniform values.

COMMENTS

**Bernoulli Trials** generate random values that are 0 or 1, with a specified chance of a 1.
**Binomial Experiments** automatically generate a specified number of Bernoulli trials and count the number of 1's.

### EXCEL

The **RAND** function generates a random value between 0 and 1. You can multiply to scale it up to any range you like and use the INT function to turn the result into an integer.

COMMENTS

Published tests of Excel's random-number generation have declared it to be inadequate. However, for simple simulations, it should be OK. Don't trust it for important large simulations.

### JMP

In a new column, in the **Cols** menu choose **Column Info . . .** In the dialog, click the **New Property** button, and choose **Formula** from the drop-down menu.

Click the **Edit Formula** button, and in the **Functions(grouped)** window click on **Random. Random Integer (10),** for example, will generate a random integer between 1 and 10.

### MINITAB

In the **Calc** menu, choose **Random Data . . .** In the Random Data submenu, choose **Uniform . . .**

A dialog guides you in specifying details of range and number of columns to generate.

### SPSS

The **RV.UNIFORM(min, max)** function returns a random value that is equally likely between the min and max limits.

## TI-83/84 PLUS

To generate random numbers, use **5:RandInt** from the **Math PRB** menu. This command will produce any number of random integers in a specified range.

### COMMENTS

Some examples:
**RandInt(0,1)** randomly chooses a 0 or a 1. This is an effective simulation of a coin toss.
**RandInt(1,6,2)** randomly returns two integers between 1 and 6. This is a good way to simulate rolling two dice. To run several trials, just hit ENTER repeatedly.
**RandInt(0,57,3)** produces three random integers between 0 and 57—a nice way to simulate the chapter's dorm room lottery.

## TI-89

To generate random numbers, move the cursor to highlight the name of a blank list. Use **5:RandInt** from the [F4] (Calc) Probability menu. This command will produce any number of random integers in the specified range.

### COMMENTS

Some examples:
**RandInt(0,10)** randomly chooses a 0 or a 1. This is an effective simulation of 10 coin tosses.
**RandInt(1,6,2)** randomly returns two integers between 1 and 6. This is a good way to simulate rolling two dice.
**RandInt(0,56,3)** produces three random integers between 0 and 56, a nice way to simulate the chapter's dorm room lottery.

# EXERCISES

1. **Coin toss.** Is a coin flip random? Why or why not, in your opinion?

2. **Casino.** A casino claims that its electronic "video roulette" machine is truly random. What should that claim mean?

3. **The lottery.** Many states run lotteries, giving away millions of dollars if you match a certain set of winning numbers. How are those numbers determined? Do you think this method guarantees randomness? Explain.

4. **Games.** Many kinds of games people play rely on randomness. Cite three different methods commonly used in the attempt to achieve this randomness, and discuss the effectiveness of each.

5. **Birth defects.** The American College of Obstetricians and Gynecologists says that out of every 100 babies born in the United States, 3 have some kind of major birth defect. How would you assign random numbers to conduct a simulation based on this statistic?

6. **Colorblind.** By some estimates, about 10% of all males have some color perception defect, most commonly red–green colorblindness. How would you assign random numbers to conduct a simulation based on this statistic?

7. **Geography.** An elementary school teacher with 25 students plans to have each of them make a poster about two different states. The teacher first numbers the states (in alphabetical order, from 1-Alabama to 50-Wyoming), then uses a random number table to decide which states each kid gets. Here are the random digits:

   45921 01710 22892 37076

   a) Which two state numbers does the first student get?
   b) Which two state numbers go to the second student?

8. **Get rich.** Your state's BigBucks Lottery prize has reached $100,000,000, and you decide to play. You have to pick five numbers between 1 and 60, and you'll win if your numbers match those drawn by the state. You decide to pick your "lucky" numbers using a random number table. Which numbers do you play, based on these random digits?

   43680 98750 13092 76561 58712

9. **Play the lottery.** Some people play state-run lotteries by always playing the same favorite "lucky" number. Assuming that the lottery is truly random, is this strategy better, worse, or the same as choosing different numbers for each play? Explain.

10. **Play it again, Sam.** In Exercise 8 you imagined playing the lottery by using random digits to decide what numbers to play. Is this a particularly good or bad strategy? Explain.

11. **Bad simulations.** Explain why each of the following simulations fails to model the real situation properly:
    a) Use a random integer from 0 through 9 to represent the number of heads that appear when 9 coins are tossed.
    b) A basketball player takes a foul shot. Look at a random digit, using an odd digit to represent a good shot and an even digit to represent a miss.
    c) Use five random digits from 1 through 13 to represent the denominations of the cards in a poker hand.

12. **More bad simulations.** Explain why each of the following simulations fails to model the real situation properly:
    a) Use random numbers 2 through 12 to represent the sum of the faces when two dice are rolled.
    b) Use a random integer from 0 through 5 to represent the number of boys in a family of 5 children.
    c) Simulate a baseball player's performance at bat by letting 0 = an out, 1 = a single, 2 = a double, 3 = a triple, and 4 = a home run.

13. **Wrong conclusion.** A Statistics student properly simulated the length of checkout lines in a grocery store and then reported, "The average length of the line will be 3.2 people." What's wrong with this conclusion?

14. **Another wrong conclusion.** After simulating the spread of a disease, a researcher wrote, "24% of the people contracted the disease." What should the correct conclusion be?

15. **Election.** You're pretty sure that your candidate for class president has about 55% of the votes in the entire school. But you're worried that only 100 students will show up to vote. How often will the underdog (the one with 45% support) win? To find out, you set up a simulation.
    a) Describe how you will simulate a component and its outcomes.
    b) Describe how you will simulate a trial.
    c) Describe the response variable.

16. **Two pair, or three of a kind?** When drawing five cards randomly from a deck, which is more likely, two pairs or three of a kind? A pair is exactly two of the same denomination. Three of a kind is exactly 3 of the same denomination. (Don't count three 8's as a pair—that's 3 of a kind. And don't count 4 of the same kind as two pair— that's 4 of a kind, a very special hand.) How could you simulate 5-card hands? Be careful; once you've picked the 8 of spades for a hand, you can't get it again until the next hand.
    a) Describe how you will simulate a component and its outcomes.
    b) Describe how you will simulate a trial.
    c) Describe the response variable.

17. **Cereal.** In the chapter's example, 20% of the cereal boxes contained a picture of Tiger Woods, 30% David Beckham, and the rest Serena Williams. Suppose you buy five boxes of cereal. Estimate the probability that you end up with a complete set of the pictures. Your simulation should have at least 20 runs.

18. **Cereal, again.** Suppose you really want the Tiger Woods picture. How many boxes of cereal do you need to buy to be pretty sure of getting at least one? Your simulation should use at least 10 runs.

19. **Multiple choice.** You take a quiz with 6 multiple choice questions. After you studied, you estimated that you would have about an 80% chance of getting any individual question right. What are your chances of getting them all right? Your simulation should use at least 20 runs.

20. **Lucky guessing?** A friend of yours who took the multiple choice quiz in Exercise 19 got all 6 questions right, but now claims to have guessed blindly on every question. If each question offered 4 possible answers, do you believe her? Explain, basing your argument on a simulation involving at least 10 runs.

21. **Beat the lottery.** Many states run lotteries to raise money. A Web site advertises that it knows "how to increase YOUR chances of Winning the Lottery." They offer several systems and criticize others as foolish. One system is called *Lucky Numbers*. People who play the *Lucky Numbers* system just pick a "lucky" number to play, but maybe some numbers are luckier than others. Let's use a simulation to see how well this system works.
    To make the situation manageable, simulate a simple lottery in which a single digit from 0 to 9 is selected as the winning number. Pick a single value to bet, such as 1, and keep playing it over and over. You'll want to run at least 100 trials. (If you can program the simulations on a computer or programmable calculator, run several hundred. Or generalize the questions to a lottery that chooses two- or three-digit numbers—for which you'll need thousands of trials.)
    a) What proportion of the time do you expect to win?
    b) Would you expect better results if you picked a "luckier" number, such as 7? (Try it if you don't know.) Explain.

22. **Random is as random does.** The "beat the lottery" Web site discussed in Exercise 21 suggests that because lottery numbers are random, it is better to select your bet randomly. For the same simple lottery in Exercise 21 (random values from 0 to 9), generate each bet by choosing a separate random value between 0 and 9. Play many games. What proportion of the time do you win?

23. **It evens out in the end.** The "beat the lottery" Web site of Exercise 21 notes that in the long run we expect each value to turn up about the same number of times. That leads to their recommended betting strategy. First, watch the lottery for a while, recording all the winners. Then bet the value that has turned up the least, because we expect it will need to turn up more often to even things out. If there is more than one "rarest" value, just take the lowest one (since it doesn't matter). Simulating the simplified lottery described in Exercise 21, play many games with this system. What proportion of the time do you win?

**24. Play the winner?** Another strategy for beating the lottery is the reverse of the system described in Exercise 23. Simulate the simplified lottery described in Exercise 21. Each time, bet the number that just turned up. The Web site suggests that this method should do worse. Does it? Play many games and see.

**25. Driving test.** You are about to take the road test for your driver's license. You hear that only 34% of candidates pass the test the first time, but the percentage rises to 72% on subsequent retests. Estimate the average number of tests drivers take in order to get a license. Your simulation should use at least 20 runs.

**26. Still learning?** As in Exercise 25, assume that your chance of passing the driver's test is 34% the first time and 72% for subsequent retests. Estimate the percentage of those tested who still do not have a driver's license after two attempts.

**27. Basketball strategy.** Late in a basketball game, the team that is behind often fouls someone in an attempt to get the ball back. Usually the opposing player will get to shoot foul shots "one and one," meaning he gets a shot, and then a second shot only if he makes the first one. Suppose the opposing player has made 72% of his foul shots this season. Estimate the number of points he will score in a one-and-one situation.

**28. Blood donors.** A person with type O-positive blood can receive blood only from other type O donors. About 44% of the U.S. population has type O blood. At a blood drive, how many potential donors do you expect to examine in order to get three units of type O blood?

**29. Free groceries.** To attract shoppers, a supermarket runs a weekly contest that involves "scratch-off" cards. With each purchase, customers get a card with a black spot obscuring a message. When the spot is scratched away, most of the cards simply say, "Sorry—please try again." But during the week, 100 customers will get cards that make them eligible for a drawing for free groceries. Ten of the cards say they may be worth $200, 10 others say $100, 20 may be worth $50, and the rest could be worth $20. To register those cards, customers write their names on them and put them in a barrel at the front of the store. At the end of the week the store manager draws cards at random, awarding the lucky customers free groceries in the amount specified on their card. The drawings continue until the store has given away more than $500 of free groceries. Estimate the average number of winners each week.

**30. Find the ace.** A new electronics store holds a contest to attract shoppers. Once an hour someone in the store is chosen at random to play the Music Game. Here's how it works: An ace and four other cards are shuffled and placed face down on a table. The customer gets to turn cards over one at a time, looking for the ace. The person wins $100 worth of free CDs or DVDs if the ace is the first card, $50 if it is the second card, and $20, $10, or $5 if it is the third, fourth, or fifth card chosen. What is the average dollar amount of music the store will give away?

**31. The family.** Many couples want to have both a boy and a girl. If they decide to continue to have children until they have one child of each sex, what would the average family size be? Assume that boys and girls are equally likely.

**32. A bigger family.** Suppose a couple will continue having children until they have at least two children of each sex (two boys *and* two girls). How many children might they expect to have?

**33. Dice game.** You are playing a children's game in which the number of spaces you get to move is determined by the rolling of a die. You must land exactly on the final space in order to win. If you are 10 spaces away, how many turns might it take you to win?

**34. Parcheesi.** You are three spaces from a win in Parcheesi. On each turn, you will roll two dice. To win, you must roll a total of 3 or roll a 3 on one of the dice. How many turns might you expect this to take?

**35. The hot hand.** A basketball player with a 65% shooting percentage has just made 6 shots in a row. The announcer says this player "is hot tonight! She's in the zone!" Assume the player takes about 20 shots per game. Is it unusual for her to make 6 or more shots in a row during a game?

**36. The World Series.** The World Series ends when a team wins 4 games. Suppose that sports analysts consider one team a bit stronger, with a 55% chance to win any individual game. Estimate the likelihood that the underdog wins the series.

**37. Teammates.** Four couples at a dinner party play a board game after the meal. They decide to play as teams of two and to select the teams randomly. All eight people write their names on slips of paper. The slips are thoroughly mixed, then drawn two at a time. How likely is it that every person will be teamed with someone other than the person he or she came to the party with?

**38. Second team.** Suppose the couples in Exercise 37 choose the teams by having one member of each couple write their names on the cards and the other people each pick a card at random. How likely is it that every person will be teamed with someone other than the person he or she came with?

**39. Job discrimination?** A company with a large sales staff announces openings for three positions as regional managers. Twenty-two of the current salespersons apply, 12 men and 10 women. After the interviews, when the company announces the newly appointed managers, all three positions go to women. The men complain of job discrimination. Do they have a case? Simulate a random selection of three people from the applicant pool, and make a decision about the likelihood that a fair process would result in hiring all women.

**40. Cell phones.** A proud legislator claims that your state's new law against talking on a cell phone while driving has reduced cell phone use to less than 12% of all drivers. While waiting for your bus the next morning, you notice that 4 of the 10 people who drive by are using their cell phones. Does this cast doubt on the legislator's figure of 12%? Use a simulation to estimate the likelihood of seeing at least 4 of 10 randomly selected drivers talking on their cell phones if the actual rate of usage is 12%. Explain your conclusion clearly.

41. **Freshmen.** A certain college estimates that the 3-score SAT total for students who apply for admission can be described by a Normal model with a mean of 1570 and a standard deviation of 180. Admissions officers search the pile of envelopes, opening them at random to look for three applicants with SAT totals over 1800. How many envelopes do you think they will need to open?

42. **Tires.** A tire manufacturer believes that the tread life of its snow tires can be described by a Normal model with mean of 32,000 miles and a standard deviation of 2500 miles. You buy four of these tires, hoping to drive them at least 30,000 miles. Estimate the chances that all four last at least that long.

**JUST CHECKING**
*Answers*

1. The component is one game.

2. I'll generate random numbers and assign numbers from 00 to 54 to the home team's winning and from 55 to 99 to the visitors' winning.

3. The response is who wins the series.

4. I'll generate components until one team wins 4 games. I'll record which team wins the series.

5. I'll analyze the response variable by counting up the proportion of wins by the team that starts at home.

# CHAPTER 12

# Sample Surveys

## Where are we going?

We see surveys all the time. How can asking just a thousand people tell us much about a national election? And how *do* they select the respondents? It turns out that there are many ways to select a good sample. But there are just three main ideas to understand.

In 2007, Pew Research conducted a survey to assess Americans' knowledge of current events. They asked a random sample of 1,502 U.S. adults 23 factual questions about topics currently in the news.[1] Pew also asked respondents where they got their news. Those who frequented major newspaper Web sites or who are regular viewers of the *Daily Show* or *Colbert Report* scored best on knowledge of current events.[2] Even among those viewers, only 54% responded correctly to 15 or more of the questions. Pew claimed that this was close to the true percentage responding correctly that they would have found if they had asked all U.S. adults who got their news from those sources. That step from a small sample to the entire population is impossible without understanding Statistics. To make business decisions, to do science, to choose wise investments, or to understand what voters think they'll do the next election, we need to stretch beyond the data at hand to the world at large.

To make that stretch, we need three ideas. You'll find the first one natural. The second may be more surprising. The third is one of the strange but true facts that often confuse those who don't know Statistics.

## Idea 1: Examine a Part of the Whole

The first idea is to draw a sample. We'd like to know about an entire **population** of individuals, but examining all of them is usually impractical, if not impossible.

[1] For example, two of the questions were "Who is the vice-president of the United States?" and "What party controls Congress?"
[2] The lowest scores came from those whose main source of news was network morning shows or *Fox News*.

So we settle for examining a smaller group of individuals—a **sample**—selected from the population.

You do this every day. For example, suppose you wonder how the vegetable soup you're cooking for dinner tonight is going to go over with your friends. To decide whether it meets your standards, you only need to try a small amount. You might taste just a spoonful or two. You certainly don't have to consume the whole pot. You trust that the taste will *represent* the flavor of the entire pot. The idea behind your tasting is that a small sample, if selected properly, can represent the entire population.

It's hard to go a day without hearing about the latest opinion poll. These polls are examples of **sample surveys,** designed to ask questions of a small group of people in the hope of learning something about the entire population. Most likely, you've never been selected to be part of one of these national opinion polls. That's true of most people. So how can the pollsters claim that a sample is representative of the entire population? The answer is that professional pollsters work quite hard to ensure that the "taste"—the sample that they take—represents the population. If not, the sample can give misleading information about the population.

> **The W's and Sampling**
> The population we are interested in is usually determined by the *Why* of our study. The sample we draw will be the *Who*. *When* and *How* we draw the sample may depend on what is practical.

## Bias

*In 1936, a young pollster named George Gallup used a subsample of only 3000 of the 2.4 million responses that the* Literary Digest *received to reproduce the wrong prediction of Landon's victory over Roosevelt. He then used an entirely different sample of 50,000 and predicted that Roosevelt would get 56% of the vote to Landon's 44%. His sample was apparently much more representative of the actual voting populace. The Gallup Organization went on to become one of the leading polling companies.*

Selecting a sample to represent the population fairly is more difficult than it sounds. Polls or surveys most often fail because they use a sampling method that tends to over- or underrepresent parts of the population. The method may overlook subgroups that are harder to find (such as the homeless or those who use only cell phones) or favor others (such as Internet users who like to respond to online surveys). Sampling methods that, by their nature, tend to over- or underemphasize some characteristics of the population are said to be **biased.** Bias is the bane of sampling—the one thing above all to avoid. Conclusions based on samples drawn with biased methods are inherently flawed. There is usually no way to fix bias after the sample is drawn and no way to salvage useful information from it.

What are the basic techniques for making sure that a sample is representative? Sometimes the best way to see how to do something is to study a really dismal failure. Here's a famous one. By the beginning of the 20th century, it was common for newspapers to ask readers to return "straw" ballots on a variety of topics. (Today's Internet surveys are the same idea, gone electronic.) The earliest known example of such a straw vote in the United States dates back to 1824.

During the period from 1916 to 1936, the magazine *Literary Digest* regularly surveyed public opinion and forecast election results correctly. During the 1936 presidential campaign between Alf Landon and Franklin Delano Roosevelt, it mailed more than 10 million ballots and got back an astonishing 2.4 million. (Polls were still a relatively novel idea, and many people thought it was important to send back their opinions.) The results were clear: Alf Landon would be the next president by a landslide, 57% to 43%. You remember President Landon? No? In fact, Landon carried only two states. Roosevelt won, 62% to 37%, and, perhaps coincidentally, the *Digest* went bankrupt soon afterward.

What went wrong? One problem was that the *Digest*'s sample wasn't representative. Where would *you* find 10 million names and addresses to sample? The *Digest* used the phone book, as modern surveys do.[3] But in 1936, at the height of the

---

[3] Actually, today phone numbers are computer-generated to make sure that unlisted numbers are included. But even today, cell phones and VOIP Internet phones are not included.

**A S** *Video:* **The *Literary Digest* Poll and the Election of 1936.** Hear the story of one of the most famous polling failures in history.

Great Depression, telephones were a real luxury, so they sampled more rich than poor voters. The campaign of 1936 focused on the economy, and those who were less well off were more likely to vote for the Democrat. So the *Digest's* sample was hopelessly biased.

How do modern polls get their samples to *represent* the entire population? You might think that they'd handpick individuals to sample with care and precision. But in fact, they do something quite different: They select individuals to sample *at random*. The importance of deliberately using randomness is one of the great insights of Statistics.

# Idea 2: Randomize

Think back to the soup sample. Suppose you add some salt to the pot. If you sample it from the top before stirring, you'll get the misleading idea that the whole pot is salty. If you sample from the bottom, you'll get an equally misleading idea that the whole pot is bland. By stirring, you *randomize* the amount of salt throughout the pot, making each taste more typical of the whole pot.

Not only does randomization protect you against factors that you know are in the data. It can also help protect against factors that you didn't even know were there. Suppose, while you weren't looking, a friend added a handful of peas to the soup. If they're down at the bottom of the pot, and you don't randomize the soup by stirring, your test spoonful won't have any peas. By stirring in the salt, you *also* randomize the peas throughout the pot, making your sample taste more typical of the overall pot *even though you didn't know the peas were there.* So randomizing protects us even in this case.

How do we "stir" people in a survey? We select them at random. **Randomizing** protects us from the influences of *all* the features of our population by making sure that, *on average*, the sample looks like the rest of the population.

> **Why not match the sample to the population?** Rather than randomizing, we could try to design our sample so that the people we choose are typical in terms of every characteristic we can think of. We might want the income levels of those we sample to match the population. How about age? Political affiliation? Marital status? Having children? Living in the suburbs? We can't possibly think of all the things that might be important. Even if we could, we wouldn't be able to match our sample to the population for all these characteristics.

**A S** *Activity:* **Sampling from Some Real Populations.** Draw random samples to see how closely they resemble each other and the population.

### FOR EXAMPLE

Is a random sample representative?

Here are summary statistics comparing two samples of 8000 drawn at random from a company's database of 3.5 million customers:

| Age (yr) | White (%) | Female (%) | # of Children | Income Bracket (1–7) | Wealth Bracket (1–9) | Homeowner? (% Yes) |
|---|---|---|---|---|---|---|
| 61.4 | 85.12 | 56.2 | 1.54 | 3.91 | 5.29 | 71.36 |
| 61.2 | 84.44 | 56.4 | 1.51 | 3.88 | 5.33 | 72.30 |

*(continued)*

For Example (*continued*)

**Question:** Do you think these samples are representative of the population? Explain.

*The two samples look very similar with respect to these seven variables. It appears that randomizing has automatically matched them pretty closely. We can reasonably assume that since the two samples don't differ too much from each other, they don't differ much from the rest of the population either.*

# Idea 3: It's the Sample Size

A friend who knows that you are taking Statistics asks your advice on her study. What can you possibly say that will be helpful? Just say, "If you could just get a larger sample, it would probably improve your study." Even though a larger sample might not be worth the cost, it will almost always make the results more precise.

How large a random sample do we need for the sample to be reasonably representative of the population? Most people think that we need a large percentage, or *fraction,* of the population, but it turns out that what matters is the *number* of individuals in the sample, not the size of the population. A random sample of 100 students in a college represents the student body just about as well as a random sample of 100 voters represents the entire electorate of the United States. This is the *third* idea and probably the most surprising one in designing surveys.

How can it be that only the size of the sample, and not the population, matters? Well, let's return one last time to that pot of soup. If you're cooking for a banquet rather than just for a few people, your pot will be bigger, but do you need a bigger spoon to decide how the soup tastes? Of course not. The same-size spoonful is probably enough to make a decision about the entire pot, no matter how large the pot. The *fraction* of the population that you've sampled doesn't matter. It's the **sample size** itself that's important.

How big a sample do you need? That depends on what you're estimating. To get an idea of what's really in the soup, you'll need a large enough taste to get a *representative* sample from the pot. For a survey that tries to find the proportion of the population falling into a category, you'll usually need several hundred respondents to say anything precise enough to be useful.[4]

**What do the pollsters do?**   How do professional polling agencies do their work? The most common polling method today is to contact respondents by telephone. Computers generate random telephone numbers, so pollsters can even call some people with unlisted phone numbers. The person who answers the phone is invited to respond to the survey—if that person qualifies. (For example, only if it's an adult who lives at that address.) If the person answering doesn't qualify, the caller will ask for an appropriate alternative. In phrasing questions, pollsters often list alternative responses (such as candidates' names) in different orders, to avoid biases that might favor the first name on the list.

Do these methods work? The Pew Research Center for the People and the Press, reporting on one survey, says that

*Across five days of interviewing, surveys today are able to make some kind of contact with the vast majority of households (76%), and there is no decline in this contact rate over the past seven years. But because of busy schedules, skepticism and outright refusals, interviews were completed in just 38% of households that were reached using standard polling procedures.*

Nevertheless, studies indicate that those actually sampled can give a good snapshot of larger populations from which the surveyed households were drawn.

**A S** *Activity: Does the Population Size Matter?* Here's the narrated version of this important idea about sampling.

---

[4] Chapter 19 gives the details behind this statement and shows how to decide on a sample size for a survey.

# Does a Census Make Sense?

**A S** *Video:* **Frito-Lay Sampling for Quality.** How does a potato chip manufacturer make sure to cook only the best potatoes?

Why bother determining the right sample size? Wouldn't it be better to just include everyone and "sample" the entire population? Such a special sample is called a **census**. Although a census would appear to provide the best possible information about the population, there are a number of reasons why it might not.

First, it can be difficult to complete a census. Some individuals in the population will be hard (and expensive) to locate. Or a census might just be impractical. If you were a taste tester for the Hostess™ Company, you probably wouldn't want to census *all* the Twinkies on the production line. Not only might this be life-endangering, but you wouldn't have any left to sell.

Second, populations rarely stand still. In populations of people, babies are born and folks die or leave the country. In opinion surveys, events may cause a shift in opinion during the survey. A census takes longer to complete and the population changes while you work. A sample surveyed in just a few days may give more accurate information.

Third, taking a census can be more complex than sampling. For example, the U.S. Census records too many college students. Many are counted once with their families and are then counted a second time in a report filed by their schools.

> **The undercount.** It's particularly difficult to compile a complete census of a population as large, complex, and spread out as the U.S. population. The U.S. Census is known to miss some residents. On occasion, the undercount has been striking. For example, there have been blocks in inner cities in which the number of residents recorded by the Census was smaller than the number of electric meters for which bills were being paid. What makes the problem particularly important is that some groups have a higher probability of being missed than others—undocumented immigrants, the homeless, the poor. The Census Bureau proposed the use of random sampling to estimate the number of residents missed by the ordinary census. Unfortunately, the resulting debate has become more political than statistical.

# Populations and Parameters

> Any quantity that we calculate from data could be called a "statistic." But in practice, we usually use a statistic to estimate a population parameter.

**A S** *Activity:* **Statistics and Parameters.** Explore the difference between statistics and parameters.

A study found that teens were less likely to "buckle up." The National Center for Chronic Disease Prevention and Health Promotion reports that 21.7% of U.S. teens never or rarely wear seatbelts. We're sure they didn't take a census, so what *does* the 21.7% mean? We can't know what percentage of teenagers wear seatbelts. Reality is just too complex. But we can simplify the question by building a model.

Models use mathematics to represent reality. Parameters are the key numbers in those models. A parameter used in a model for a population is sometimes called (redundantly) a **population parameter**.

But let's not forget about the data. We use summaries of the data to estimate the population parameters. As we know, any summary found from the data is a **statistic.** Sometimes you'll see the (also redundant) term **sample statistic.**[5]

We've already met two parameters in Chapter 6: the mean, $\mu$, and the standard deviation, $\sigma$. We'll try to keep denoting population model parameters with

---

[5] Where else besides a sample *could* a statistic come from?

> Remember: Population model parameters are not just unknown—usually they are *unknowable*. We have to settle for sample statistics.

Greek letters and the corresponding statistics with Latin letters. Usually, but not always, the letter used for the statistic and the parameter correspond in a natural way. So the standard deviation of the data is $s$, and the corresponding parameter is $\sigma$ (Greek for $s$). In Chapter 7, we used $r$ to denote the sample correlation. The corresponding correlation in a model for the population would be called $\rho$ (rho). In Chapter 8, $b_1$ represented the slope of a linear regression estimated from the data. But when we think about a (linear) *model* for the population, we denote the slope parameter $\beta_1$ (beta).

Get the pattern? Good. Now it breaks down. We denote the mean of a population model with $\mu$ (because $\mu$ is the Greek letter for $m$). It might make sense to denote the sample mean with $m$, but long-standing convention is to put a bar over anything when we average it, so we write $\bar{y}$. What about proportions? Suppose we want to talk about the proportion of teens who don't wear seatbelts. If we use $p$ to denote the proportion from the data, what is the corresponding model parameter? By all rights it should be $\pi$. But statements like $\pi = 0.25$ might be confusing because $\pi$ has been equal to $3.1415926\ldots$ for so long, and it's worked so *well*. So, once again we violate the rule. We'll use $p$ for the population model parameter and $\hat{p}$ for the proportion from the data (since, like $\hat{y}$ in regression, it's an estimated value).

Here's a table summarizing the notation:

| Name | Statistic | Parameter |
|---|---|---|
| Mean | $\bar{y}$ | $\mu$ (mu, pronounced "meeoo," not "moo") |
| Standard deviation | $s$ | $\sigma$ (sigma) |
| Correlation | $r$ | $\rho$ (rho) |
| Regression coefficient | $b$ | $\beta$ (beta, pronounced "baytah"[6]) |
| Proportion | $\hat{p}$ | $p$ (pronounced "pee"[7]) |

We draw samples because we can't work with the entire population, but we want the statistics we compute from a sample to reflect the corresponding parameters accurately. A sample that does this is said to be **representative.**

## JUST CHECKING

1. Various claims are often made for surveys. Why is each of the following claims not correct?
   a) It is always better to take a census than to draw a sample.
   b) Stopping students on their way out of the cafeteria is a good way to sample if we want to know about the quality of the food there.
   c) We drew a sample of 100 from the 3000 students in a school. To get the same level of precision for a town of 30,000 residents, we'll need a sample of 1000.
   d) A poll taken at a statistics support Web site garnered 12,357 responses. The majority said they enjoy doing statistics homework. With a sample size that large, we can be pretty sure that most Statistics students feel this way, too.
   e) The true percentage of all Statistics students who enjoy the homework is called a "population statistic."

---

[6] If you're from the United States. If you're British or Canadian, it's "beetah."
[7] Just in case you weren't sure.

# Simple Random Samples

How would you select a representative sample? Most people would say that every individual in the population should have an equal chance to be selected, and certainly that seems fair. But it's not sufficient. There are many ways to give everyone an equal chance that still wouldn't give a representative sample. Consider, for example, a school that has equal numbers of males and females. We could sample like this: Flip a coin. If it comes up heads, select 100 female students at random. If it comes up tails, select 100 males at random. Everyone has an equal chance of selection, but every sample is of only a single sex—hardly representative.

We need to do better. Suppose we insist that every possible *sample* of the size we plan to draw has an equal chance to be selected. This ensures that situations like the one just described are not likely to occur and still guarantees that each person has an equal chance of being selected. What's different is that with this method, each *combination* of people has an equal chance of being selected as well. A sample drawn in this way is called a **Simple Random Sample,** usually abbreviated **SRS.** An SRS is the standard against which we measure other sampling methods, and the sampling method on which the theory of working with sampled data is based.

To select a sample at random, we first need to define where the sample will come from. The **sampling frame** is a list of individuals from which the sample is drawn. For example, to draw a random sample of students at a college, we might obtain a list of all registered full-time students and sample from that list. In defining the sampling frame, we must deal with the details of defining the population. Are part-time students included? How about those who are attending school elsewhere and transferring credits back to the college?

Once we have a sampling frame, the easiest way to choose an SRS is to assign a random number to each individual in the sampling frame. We then select only those whose random numbers satisfy some rule.[8] Let's look at some ways to do this.

---

**FOR EXAMPLE** | Using random numbers to get an SRS

There are 80 students enrolled in an introductory Statistics class; you are to select a sample of 5.

**Question:** How can you select an SRS of 5 students using these random digits found on the Internet?

05166    29305    77482

First I'll number the students from 00 to 79. Taking the random numbers two digits at a time gives me 05, 16, 62, 93, 05, 77, and 48. I'll ignore 93 because the students were numbered only up to 79. And, so as not to pick the same person twice, I'll skip the repeated number 05. My simple random sample consists of students with the numbers 05, 16, 62, 77, and 48.

---

▶ We can be more efficient when we're choosing a larger sample from a sampling frame stored in a data file. First we obtain random numbers with several digits (say, from 0 to 10,000) and assign one to each individual. Then we arrange the random numbers in numerical order, keeping the names along with them. Choosing the first *n* names from this list will give us a random sample of that size.

---

[8] Chapter 11 presented ways of finding and working with random numbers.

▶ Often the sampling frame is so large that it would be too tedious to number everyone consecutively. If our intended sample size is approximately 10% of the sampling frame, we can assign each individual a single random digit 0 to 9. Then we select only those with a specific random digit, say, 5.

Samples drawn at random generally differ one from another. Each draw of random numbers selects *different* people for our sample. These differences lead to different values for the variables we measure. We call these sample-to-sample differences **sampling variability.** Surprisingly, sampling variability isn't a problem; it's an opportunity. In future chapters we'll investigate what the variation in a sample can tell us about its population.

---

**FOR EXAMPLE**    Designing a sample

What do the freshmen at your school think of the food served on campus? Food Services has asked you to design a survey. The registrar is willing to make available an alphabetical list of all freshmen as a computer file.

**Question:** How would you draw a Simple Random Sample?

I would list the names in one column of a spreadsheet (or a variable in a statistics program).

In the next column (or variable), I would generate random numbers between 1 and about 5 or 10 times the number of names on the list. I could get these from a suitable Internet site.

Then I would sort the random numbers into numerical order, "carrying along" the names to randomize the order of the names.

My sample would take names starting at the top of the sorted list.

---

# Stratified Sampling

Simple random sampling is not the only fair way to sample. More complicated designs may save time or money or help avoid sampling problems. All statistical sampling designs have in common the idea that chance, rather than human choice, is used to select the sample.

Designs that are used to sample from large populations—especially populations residing across large areas—are often more complicated than simple random samples. Sometimes the population is first sliced into homogeneous groups, called **strata,** before the sample is selected. Then simple random sampling is used within each stratum before the results are combined. This common sampling design is called **stratified random sampling.**

Why would we want to complicate things? Here's an example. Suppose we want to learn how students feel about funding for the football team at a large university. The campus is 60% men and 40% women, and we suspect that men and women have different views on the funding. If we use simple random sampling to select 100 people for the survey, we could end up with 70 men and 30 women or 35 men and 65 women. Our resulting estimates of the level of support for the football funding could vary widely. To help reduce this sampling variability, we can decide to force a representative balance, selecting 60 men at random and 40 women at random. This would guarantee that the proportions of men and women within our sample match the proportions in the population, and that should make such samples more accurate in representing population opinion.

You can imagine the importance of stratifying by race, income, age, and other characteristics, depending on the questions in the survey. Samples taken within a stratum vary less, so our estimates can be more precise. This reduced sampling variability is the most important benefit of stratifying.

Stratified sampling can also help us notice important differences among groups. As we saw in Chapter 3, if we unthinkingly combine group data, we risk reaching the wrong conclusion, becoming victims of Simpson's paradox.

---

**FOR EXAMPLE**  Stratifying the sample

**Recap:** You're trying to find out what freshmen think of the food served on campus. Food Services believes that men and women typically have different opinions about the importance of the salad bar.

**Question:** How should you adjust your sampling strategy to allow for this difference?

I will stratify my sample by drawing an SRS of men and a separate SRS of women—assuming that the data from the registrar include information about each person's sex.

---

# Cluster and Multistage Sampling

Suppose we wanted to assess the reading level of this textbook based on the length of the sentences. Simple random sampling could be awkward; we'd have to number each sentence, then find, for example, the 576th sentence or the 2482nd sentence, and so on. Doesn't sound like much fun, does it?

It would be much easier to pick a few *pages* at random and count the lengths of the sentences on those pages. That works if we believe that each page is representative of the entire book in terms of reading level. Splitting the population into representative **clusters** can make sampling more practical. Then we could simply select one or a few clusters at random and perform a census within each of them. This sampling design is called **cluster sampling.** If each cluster represents the full population fairly, cluster sampling will give us an unbiased sample.

---

**FOR EXAMPLE**  Cluster sampling

**Recap:** In trying to find out what freshmen think about the food served on campus, you've considered both an SRS and a stratified sample. Now you have run into a problem: It's simply too difficult and time-consuming to track down the individuals whose names were chosen for your sample. Fortunately, freshmen at your school are all housed in 10 freshman dorms.

**Questions:** How could you use this fact to draw a cluster sample? How might that alleviate the problem? What concerns do you have?

To draw a cluster sample, I would select one or two dorms at random and then try to contact everyone in each selected dorm. I could save time by simply knocking on doors on a given evening and interviewing people. I'd have to assume that freshmen were assigned to dorms pretty much at random and that the people I'm able to contact are representative of everyone in the dorm.

---

What's the difference between cluster sampling and stratified sampling? We stratify to ensure that our sample represents different groups in the population, and we sample randomly within each stratum. Strata are homogeneous, but differ from one another. By contrast, clusters are heterogeneous and resemble the overall population. We select clusters to make sampling more practical or affordable.

> **Stratified vs. cluster sampling.**  Boston cream pie consists of a layer of yellow cake, a layer of pastry creme, another cake layer, and then a chocolate frosting. Suppose you are a professional taster (yes, there really are such people) whose job is to check your company's pies for quality. You'd need to eat small samples of randomly selected pies, tasting all three components: the cake, the creme, and the frosting.
>
> One approach is to cut a thin vertical slice out of the pie. Such a slice will be a lot like the entire pie, so by eating that slice, you'll learn about the whole pie. This vertical slice containing all the different ingredients in the pie would be a *cluster* sample.
>
> Another approach is to sample in *strata*: Select some tastes of the cake at random, some tastes of creme at random, and some bits of frosting at random. You'll end up with a reliable judgment of the pie's quality.
>
> Many populations you might want to learn about are like this Boston cream pie. You can think of the subpopulations of interest as horizontal strata, like the layers of pie. Cluster samples slice vertically across the layers to obtain clusters, each of which is representative of the entire population. Stratified samples represent the population by drawing some from each layer, reducing variability in the results that could arise because of the differences among the layers.

> **Strata or Clusters?**
> We may split a population into strata or clusters. What's the difference? We create strata by dividing the population into groups of similar individuals so that each stratum is different from the others. By contrast, since clusters each represent the entire population, they all look pretty much alike.

Sometimes we use a variety of sampling methods together. In trying to assess the reading level of this book, we might worry that it starts out easy and then gets harder as the concepts become more difficult. If so, we'd want to avoid samples that selected heavily from early or from late chapters. To guarantee a fair mix of chapters, we could randomly choose one chapter from each of the seven parts of the book and then randomly select a few pages from each of those chapters. If, altogether, that made too many sentences, we might select a few sentences at random from each of the chosen pages. So, what is our sampling strategy? First we stratify by the part of the book and randomly choose a chapter to represent each stratum. Within each selected chapter, we choose pages as clusters. Finally, we consider an SRS of sentences within each cluster. Sampling schemes that combine several methods are called **multistage samples.** Most surveys conducted by professional polling organizations use some combination of stratified and cluster sampling as well as simple random samples.

---

**FOR EXAMPLE**  Multistage sampling

**Recap:** Having learned that freshmen are housed in separate dorms allowed you to sample their attitudes about the campus food by going to dorms chosen at random, but you're still concerned about possible differences in opinions between men and women. It turns out that these freshmen dorms house the sexes on alternate floors.

**Question:** How can you design a sampling plan that uses this fact to your advantage?

Now I can stratify my sample by sex. I would first choose one or two dorms at random and then select some dorm floors at random from among those that house men and, separately, from among those that house women. I could then treat each floor as a cluster and interview everyone on that floor.

---

# Systematic Samples

Some samples select individuals systematically. For example, you might survey every 10th person on an alphabetical list of students. To make it random, you still must start the systematic selection from a randomly selected individual. When the order of the list is not associated in any way with the responses sought,

**systematic sampling** can give a representative sample. Systematic sampling can be much less expensive than true random sampling. When you use a systematic sample, you should justify the assumption that the systematic method is not associated with any of the measured variables.

Think about the reading-level sampling example again. Suppose we have chosen a chapter of the book at random, then three pages at random from that chapter, and now we want to select a sample of 10 sentences from the 73 sentences found on those pages. Instead of numbering each sentence so we can pick a simple random sample, it would be easier to sample systematically. A quick calculation shows 73/10 = 7.3, so we can get our sample by just picking every seventh sentence on the page. But where should you start? At random, of course. We've accounted for 10 × 7 = 70 of the sentences, so we'll throw the extra 3 into the starting group and choose a sentence at random from the first 10. Then we pick every seventh sentence after that and record its length.

## JUST CHECKING

2. We need to survey a random sample of the 300 passengers on a flight from San Francisco to Tokyo. Name each sampling method described below.
   **a)** Pick every 10th passenger as people board the plane.
   **b)** From the boarding list, randomly choose 5 people flying first class and 25 of the other passengers.
   **c)** Randomly generate 30 seat numbers and survey the passengers who sit there.
   **d)** Randomly select a seat position (right window, right center, right aisle, etc.) and survey all the passengers sitting in those seats.

---

**STEP-BY-STEP EXAMPLE** | Sampling

The assignment says, "Conduct your own sample survey to find out how many hours per week students at your school spend watching TV during the school year." Let's see how we might do this step by step. (Remember, though—actually collecting the data from your sample can be difficult and time consuming.)

**Question:** How would you design this survey?

**Plan** State what you want to know.

I wanted to design a study to find out how many hours of TV students at my school watch.

**Population and Parameter** Identify the W's of the study. The *Why* determines the population and the associated sampling frame. The *What* identifies the parameter of interest and the variables measured. The *Who* is the sample we actually draw. The *How, When,* and *Where* are given by the sampling plan.

The population studied was students at our school. I obtained a list of all students currently enrolled and used it as the sampling frame. The parameter of interest was the number of TV hours watched per week during the school year, which I attempted to measure by asking students how much TV they watched during the previous week.

Often, thinking about the *Why* will help us see whether the sampling frame and plan are adequate to learn about the population.

**Sampling Plan** Specify the sampling method and the sample size, *n*. Specify how the sample was actually drawn. What is the sampling frame?

The description should, if possible, be complete enough to allow someone to replicate the procedure, drawing another sample from the same population in the same manner. A good description of the procedure is essential, even if it could never practically be repeated.

Terms like "simple random sample," "cluster sample," and "stratified sample" often appear in this part of the discussion. Be sure to describe how the randomization was performed.

> I decided against stratifying by class or sex because I didn't think TV watching would differ much between males and females or across classes. I selected a simple random sample of students from the list. I obtained a list of random digits, matched it to an alphabetically arranged list of students, and selected all students who were assigned a "4." This method generated a sample of 212 students from the population of 2133 students.

---

**Sampling Practice** Specify *When*, *Where*, and *How* the sampling was performed. Specify any other details of your survey, such as how respondents were contacted, what incentives were offered to encourage them to respond, how nonrespondents were treated, and so on.

> The survey was taken over the period Oct. 15 to Oct. 25. Surveys were sent to selected students by e-mail, with the request that they respond by e-mail as well. Students who could not be reached by e-mail were handed the survey in person.

---

**Summary and Conclusion** This report should include a discussion of all the elements. In addition, it's good practice to discuss any special circumstances. Professional polling organizations report the *When* of their samples but will also note, for example, any important news that might have changed respondents' opinions during the sampling process. In this survey, perhaps, a major news story or sporting event might change students' TV viewing behavior.

The question you ask also matters. It's better to be specific ("How many hours did you watch TV last week?") than to ask a general question ("How many hours of TV do you usually watch in a week?").

> During the period Oct. 15 to Oct. 25, 212 students were randomly selected, using a simple random sample from a list of all students currently enrolled. The survey they received asked the following question: "How many hours did you spend watching television last week?"
>
> Of the 212 students surveyed, 110 responded. It's possible that the nonrespondents differ in the number of TV hours watched from those who responded, but I was unable to follow up on them due to limited time and funds. The 110 respondents reported an average 3.62 hours of TV watching per week. The median was only 2 hours per week. A histogram of the data shows that the distribution is highly right-skewed, indicating that the median might be a more appropriate summary of the typical TV watching of the students.

The report should show a display of the data, provide and interpret the statistics from the sample, and state the conclusions that you reached about the population.

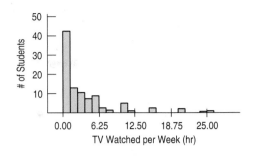

Most of the students (90%) watch between 0 and 10 hours per week, while 30% reported watching less than 1 hour per week. A few watch much more. About 3% reported watching more than 20 hours per week.

# Defining the "Who": You Can't Always Get What You Want

> The population is determined by the *Why* of the study. Unfortunately, the sample is just those we can reach to obtain responses—the *Who* of the study. This difference could undermine even a well-designed study.

Before you start a survey, think first about the population you want to study. You may find that it's not the well-defined group you thought it was. Who, exactly, is a student, for example? Even if the population seems well defined, it may not be a practical group from which to draw a sample. For example, election polls want to sample from all those who will vote in the next election—a population that is impossible to identify before Election Day.

Next, you must specify the sampling frame. (Do you have a list of students to sample from? How about a list of registered voters?) Usually, the sampling frame is not the group you *really* want to know about. (All those registered to vote are not equally likely to show up.) The sampling frame limits what your survey can find out.

Then there's your target sample. These are the individuals for whom you *intend* to measure responses. You're not likely to get responses from all of them. ("I know it's dinnertime, but I'm sure you wouldn't mind answering a few questions. It'll only take 20 minutes or so. Oh, you're busy?") Nonresponse is a problem in many surveys.

Finally, there's your sample—the actual respondents. These are the individuals about whom you *do* get data and can draw conclusions. Unfortunately, they might not be representative of the sampling frame or the population.

CALVIN AND HOBBES © 1993 Watterson. Reprinted with permission of Universal Press Syndicate. All rights reserved.

At each step, the group we can study may be constrained further. The *Who* keeps changing, and each constraint can introduce biases. A careful study should address the question of how well each group matches the population of interest. One of the main benefits of simple random sampling is that it never loses its sense of who's *Who*. The *Who* in an SRS is the population of interest from which we've drawn a representative sample. That's not always true for other kinds of samples.

# The Valid Survey

It isn't sufficient to just draw a sample and start asking questions. We'll want our survey to be *valid*. A valid survey yields the information we are seeking about the population we are interested in. Before setting out to survey, ask yourself:

- ▸ What do I want to know?
- ▸ Am I asking the right respondents?
- ▸ Am I asking the right questions?
- ▸ What would I do with the answers if I had them; would they address the things I want to know?

These questions may sound obvious, but there are a number of pitfalls to avoid.

*Know what you want to know.* Before considering a survey, understand what you hope to learn and about whom you hope to learn it. If you don't know that, you can't even judge whether you have a valid survey. Far too often, people decide to perform a survey without any clear idea of what they hope to learn.

*Use the right frame.* A valid survey obtains responses from the appropriate respondents. Be sure you have a suitable *sampling frame*. Have you identified the population of interest and sampled from it appropriately? A company might survey customers who returned warranty registration cards—after all, that's a readily available sampling frame. But if the company wants to know how to make their product more attractive, they may be missing the most important population—the customers who rejected their product in favor of one from a competitor. Those might be the folks who can tell the company what to improve.

*Tune your instrument.* The survey instrument—the questionnaire itself—can be a source of errors. It is often tempting to ask questions you don't really need, since you're sending out the survey anyway. (Who knows? It might be interesting to find out. . . .) But beware—longer questionnaires yield fewer responses and thus a greater chance of nonresponse bias. So, for each question in your survey instrument, ask yourself, "What would I do with the responses if I had them?" If you don't have a good use for the answer, don't ask the question.

*Ask specific rather than general questions.* Most people can recall what they ate for dinner last night or what TV shows they watched. But two or three days ago is already a hazy blur. (Try it: What did you eat for lunch the day before yesterday? What were you wearing that day?) People are not very good at estimating their typical behavior. So it is better to ask "How many hours did you sleep last night?" than "How much do you usually sleep?" Sure, some responses will include some unusual events (My dog was sick; I was up all night.) but overall, you'll get better data.

*Ask for quantitative results when possible.* "How many magazines did you read last week?" is better than "How much do you read: A lot, A moderate amount, A little, or None at all?"

*Be careful in phrasing questions.* A respondent may not understand the question—or may understand the question differently than the researcher intended it. ("Does anyone in your family belong to a union?" Do you mean just me, my spouse, and my children? Or does "family" include my father, my siblings, and my second cousin once removed? What about my grandfather, who is staying with us? I think he once belonged to the Autoworkers Union.) Respondents are unlikely (or may not have the opportunity) to ask for clarification. A question like "Do you approve of the recent actions of the Secretary of Labor?" is likely not to measure what you want if many respondents don't know who the Secretary of Labor is or what actions he or she recently made.

Respondents may even lie or shade their responses if they feel embarrassed by the question ("Did you have too much to drink last night?"), are intimidated or insulted by the question ("Could you understand our new *Instructions for Dummies* manual, or was it too difficult for you?"), or if they want to avoid offending the interviewer ("Would you hire a man with a tattoo?" asked by a tattooed interviewer). Also, be careful to avoid phrases that have double or regional meanings. "How often do you go to town?" might be interpreted differently by different people and cultures.

*Even subtle differences in phrasing can make a difference.* In January 2006, the *New York Times* asked half of the 1229 U.S. adults in their sample the following question:

> *After 9/11, President Bush authorized government wiretaps on some phone calls in the U.S. without getting court warrants, saying this was necessary to reduce the threat of terrorism. Do you approve or disapprove of this?*

They found that 53% of respondents approved. But, when they asked the other half of their sample a question with only slightly different phrasing,

> *After 9/11, George W. Bush authorized government wiretaps on some phone calls in the U.S. without getting court warrants. Do you approve or disapprove of this?*

only 46% approved.

*Be careful in phrasing answers.* It's often a good idea to offer choices rather than inviting a free response. Open-ended answers can be difficult to analyze. "How did you like the movie?" may start an interesting debate, but it may be better to give a range of possible responses. Be sure to phrase them in a neutral way. When asking "Do you support higher school taxes?" positive responses could be worded "Yes," "Yes, it is important for our children," or "Yes, our future depends on it." But those are not equivalent answers.

THE WIZARD OF ID

parker and hart

The best way to protect a survey from such unanticipated measurement errors is to perform a pilot survey. A **pilot** is a trial run of the survey you eventually plan to give to a larger group, using a draft of your survey questions administered to a small sample drawn from the same sampling frame you intend to use. By analyzing the results from this smaller survey, you can often discover ways to improve your instrument.

# WHAT CAN GO WRONG?—OR, HOW TO SAMPLE BADLY

Bad sample designs yield worthless data. Many of the most convenient forms of sampling can be seriously biased. And there is no way to correct for the bias from a bad sample. So it's wise to pay attention to sample design—and to beware of reports based on poor samples.

## SAMPLE BADLY WITH VOLUNTEERS

One of the most common dangerous sampling methods is a voluntary response sample. In a **voluntary response sample,** a large group of individuals is invited to respond, and all who do respond are counted. This method is used by call-in shows, 900 numbers, Internet polls, and letters written to members of Congress. Voluntary response samples are almost always biased, and so conclusions drawn from them are almost always wrong.

It's often hard to define the sampling frame of a voluntary response study. Practically, the frames are groups such as Internet users who frequent a particular Web site or those who happen to be watching a particular TV show at the moment. But those sampling frames don't correspond to interesting populations.

Even within the sampling frame, voluntary response samples are often biased toward those with strong opinions or those who are strongly motivated. People with very negative opinions tend to respond more often than those with equally strong positive opinions. The sample is not representative, even though every individual in the population may have been offered the chance to respond. The resulting **voluntary response bias** invalidates the survey.

How often do people write to their congressional representative when they're pretty happy about how things are going? People respond when they feel strongly. Which survey would *you* be more likely to respond to—one that asked, "Should the minimum age to drive a car be raised to 25?" or one that asked, "Should shoe sizes be adjusted so women's and men's sizes correspond?"

**A S** *Activity:* **Sources of Sampling Bias.** Here's a narrated exploration of sampling bias.

> **If you had it to do over again, would you have children?** Ann Landers, the advice columnist, asked parents this question. The overwhelming majority—70% of the more than 10,000 people who wrote in—said no, kids weren't worth it. A more carefully designed survey later showed that about 90% of parents actually are happy with their decision to have children. What accounts for the striking difference in these two results? What kind of parents do you think are most likely to respond to the original question?

---

### FOR EXAMPLE    Bias in sampling

**Recap:** You're trying to find out what freshmen think of the food served on campus, and have thought of a variety of sampling methods, all time-consuming. A friend suggests that you set up a "Tell Us What You Think" Web site and invite freshmen to visit the site to complete a questionnaire.

**Question:** What's wrong with this idea?

*Letting each freshman decide whether to participate makes this a voluntary response survey. Students who were dissatisfied might be more likely to go to the Web site to record their complaints, and this could give me a biased view of the opinions of all freshmen.*

## SAMPLE BADLY, BUT CONVENIENTLY

Another sampling method that doesn't work is convenience sampling. As the name suggests, in **convenience sampling** we simply include the individuals who are convenient for us to sample. Unfortunately, this group may not be representative of the population. A recent survey of 437 potential home buyers in Orange County, California, found, among other things, that

> All but 2 percent of the buyers have at least one computer at home, and 62 percent have two or more. Of those with a computer, 99 percent are connected to the Internet (Jennifer Hieger, "Portrait of Homebuyer Household: 2 Kids and a PC," Orange County Register, 27 July 2001).

Later in the article, we learn that the survey was conducted via the Internet! That was a convenient way to collect data and surely easier than drawing a simple random sample, but perhaps home builders shouldn't conclude from this study that *every* family has a computer and an Internet connection.

Many surveys conducted at shopping malls suffer from the same problem. People in shopping malls are not necessarily representative of the population of interest. Mall shoppers tend to be more affluent and include a larger percentage of teenagers and retirees than the population at large. To make matters worse, survey interviewers tend to select individuals who look "safe," or easy to interview.

Do you use the Internet?
Click here ⃝ for yes
Click here ⃝ for no

Internet convenience surveys are worthless. As voluntary response surveys, they have no well-defined sampling frame (all those who use the Internet and visit their site?) and thus report no useful information. Do not believe them.

---

**FOR EXAMPLE**  Bias in sampling

**Recap:** To try to gauge freshman opinion about the food served on campus, Food Services suggests that you just stand outside a school cafeteria at lunchtime and stop people to ask them questions.

**Questions:** What's wrong with this sampling strategy?

This would be a convenience sample, and it's likely to be biased. I would miss people who use the cafeteria for dinner, but not for lunch, and I'd never hear from anyone who hates the food so much that they have stopped coming to the school cafeterias.

---

## SAMPLE FROM A BAD SAMPLING FRAME

An SRS from an incomplete sampling frame introduces bias because the individuals included may differ from the ones not in the frame. People in prison, homeless people, students, and long-term travelers are all likely to be missed. In telephone surveys, people who have only cell phones or who use VOIP Internet phones are missing from the sampling frame.

## UNDERCOVERAGE

Many survey designs suffer from **undercoverage,** in which some portion of the population is not sampled at all or has a smaller representation in the sample than it has in the population. Undercoverage can arise for a number of reasons, but it's always a potential source of bias.

Telephone surveys are usually conducted when you are likely to be home, interrupting your dinner. If you eat out often, you may be less likely to be surveyed, a possible source of undercoverage.

# WHAT *Else* CAN GO WRONG?

▶ **Watch out for nonrespondents.** A common and serious potential source of bias for most surveys is **nonresponse bias.** No survey succeeds in getting responses from everyone. The problem is that those who don't respond may differ from those who do. And they may differ on just the variables we care about. The lack of response will bias the results. Rather than sending out a large number of surveys for which the response rate will be low, it is often better to design a smaller randomized survey for which you have the resources to ensure a high response rate. One of the problems with nonresponse bias is that it's usually impossible to tell what the nonrespondents might have said.

> **Do people like filling out questionnaires?** A business school student wanted to study how people feel about filling out questionnaires. To do this, he designed—you guessed it—a questionnaire and gave it to a sample of all the other students at his business school. He was surprised and happy to learn that nearly all the questionnaires he got back indicated a positive attitude toward answering surveys. From this, he concluded that people in general must not mind filling out questionnaires.

▶ **Don't bore respondents with surveys that go on and on and on and on . . .** Surveys that are too long are more likely to be refused, reducing the response rate and biasing *all* the results. For each question you consider including in the survey, ask yourself, "What would I do if I knew the answer to this question?" If you don't have a use for the answer, then don't ask the question.

▶ **Work hard to avoid influencing responses.** **Response bias** refers to anything in the survey design that influences the responses. Response bias is not the opposite of nonresponse bias. (We don't make these terms up; we just try to explain them.) Response biases include the tendency of respondents to tailor their responses to try to please the interviewer, the ways in which the wording of the questions can change responses, and the natural unwillingness of respondents to reveal personal facts or admit to illegal or unapproved behavior.

▶ **Make sure the question wording is neutral.** Many surveys, especially those conducted by special-interest groups, present one side of an issue before the question itself. For example, asking a question like

> *Given that the threat of nuclear war is higher now than it has ever been in human history, and the fact that a nuclear war poses a threat to the very existence of the human race, would you favor an all-out nuclear test ban?*

will probably result in a higher percentage of people in favor of the ban than the simpler

> *Are you in favor of or opposed to a nuclear test ban?*

**A S** *Video:* **Biased Question Wording.** Watch a hapless interviewer make every mistake in the book.

**A Short Survey**

Given the fact that those who understand Statistics are smarter and better looking than those who don't, don't you think it is important to take a course in Statistics?

> **Remember the *Literary Digest* Survey?** It turns out that they were wrong on two counts. First, their list of 10 million people was not representative. There was a selection bias in their sampling frame. There was also a nonresponse bias. We know this because the *Digest* also surveyed a *systematic* sample in Chicago, sending the same question used in the larger survey to every third registered voter. They *still* got a result in favor of Landon, even though Chicago voted overwhelmingly for Roosevelt in the election. This suggests that the Roosevelt supporters were less likely to respond to the *Digest* survey. There's a modern version of this problem: It's been suggested that those who screen their calls with caller ID or an answering machine, and so might not talk to a pollster, may differ in wealth or political views from those who just answer the phone.

## HOW TO THINK ABOUT BIASES

**A S**  *Activity:* **Can a Large Sample Protect Against Bias?** Explore how we can learn about the population from large or repeated samples.

▶ **Look for biases in any survey you encounter.** If you design one of your own, ask someone else to help look for biases that may not be obvious to you. And do this *before* you collect your data. There's no way to recover from a biased sample or a survey that asks biased questions. Sorry, it just can't be done.

A bigger sample size for a biased study just gives you a bigger useless study. A really big sample gives you a really big useless study. (Think of the 2.4 million *Literary Digest* responses.)

▶ **Spend your time and resources reducing biases.** No other use of resources is as worthwhile as reducing the biases.

▶ **If you can, pilot test your survey.** Administer the survey in the exact form that you intend to use it to a small sample drawn from the population you intend to sample. Look for misunderstandings, misinterpretation, confusion, or other possible biases. Then refine your survey instrument.

A researcher distributed a survey to an organization before some economizing changes were made. She asked how people felt about a proposed cutback in secretarial and administrative support on a seven-point scale from Very Happy to Very Unhappy.

But virtually all respondents were very unhappy about the cutbacks, so the results weren't particularly useful. If she had pretested the question, she might have chosen a scale that ran from Unhappy to Outraged.

▶ **Always report your sampling methods in detail.** Others may be able to detect biases where you did not expect to find them.

# CONNECTIONS

With this chapter, we take our first formal steps to relate our sample data to a larger population. Some of these ideas have been lurking in the background as we sought patterns and summaries for data. Even when we only worked with the data at hand, we often thought about implications for a larger population of individuals.

Notice the ongoing central importance of models. We've seen models in several ways in previous chapters. Here we recognize the value of a model for a population. The parameters of such a model are values we will often want to estimate using statistics such as those we've been calculating. The connections to summary statistics for center, spread, correlation, and slope are obvious.

We now have a specific application for random numbers. The idea of applying randomness deliberately showed up in Chapter 11 for simulation. Now we need randomization to get good-quality data from the real world.

# WHAT HAVE WE LEARNED?

We've learned that a representative sample can offer us important insights about populations. It's the size of the sample—and not its fraction of the larger population—that determines the precision of the statistics it yields.

We've learned several ways to draw samples, all based on the power of randomness to make them representative of the population of interest:

▶ A Simple Random Sample (SRS) is our standard. Every possible group of *n* individuals has an equal chance of being our sample. That's what makes it *simple*.

▶ Stratified samples can reduce sampling variability by identifying homogeneous subgroups and then randomly sampling within each.

▸ Cluster samples randomly select among heterogeneous subgroups that each resemble the population at large, making our sampling tasks more manageable.

▸ Systematic samples can work in some situations and are often the least expensive method of sampling. But we still want to start them randomly.

▸ Multistage samples combine several random sampling methods.

**We've learned that bias can destroy our ability to gain insights from our sample:**

▸ Nonresponse bias can arise when sampled individuals will not or cannot respond.

▸ Response bias arises when respondents' answers might be affected by external influences, such as question wording or interviewer behavior.

**We've learned that bias can also arise from poor sampling methods:**

▸ Voluntary response samples are almost always biased and should be avoided and distrusted.

▸ Convenience samples are likely to be flawed for similar reasons.

▸ Even with a reasonable design, sample frames may not be representative. Undercoverage occurs when individuals from a subgroup of the population are selected less often than they should be.

Finally, we've learned to look for biases in any survey we find and to be sure to report our methods whenever we perform a survey so that others can evaluate the fairness and accuracy of our results.

# Terms

**Population**

303. The entire group of individuals or instances about whom we hope to learn.

**Sample**

304. A (representative) subset of a population, examined in hope of learning about the population.

**Sample survey**

304. A study that asks questions of a sample drawn from some population in the hope of learning something about the entire population. Polls taken to assess voter preferences are common sample surveys.

**Bias**

304. Any systematic failure of a sampling method to represent its population is bias. It is almost impossible to recover from bias, so efforts to avoid it are well spent. Common errors include

▸ relying on voluntary response.
▸ undercoverage of the population.
▸ nonresponse bias.
▸ response bias.

**Randomization**

305. The best defense against bias is randomization, in which each individual is given a fair, random chance of selection.

**Sample size**

306. The number of individuals in a sample. The sample size determines how well the sample represents the population, not the fraction of the population sampled.

**Census**

307. A sample that consists of the entire population is called a census.

**Population parameter**

307. A numerically valued attribute of a model for a population. We rarely expect to know the true value of a population parameter, but we do hope to estimate it from sampled data. For example, the mean income of all employed people in the country is a population parameter.

**Statistic, sample statistic**

307. Statistics are values calculated for sampled data. Those that correspond to, and thus estimate, a population parameter, are of particular interest. For example, the mean income of all employed people in a representative sample can provide a good estimate of the corresponding population parameter. The term "sample statistic" is sometimes used, usually to parallel the corresponding term "population parameter."

**Representative**

308. A sample is said to be representative if the statistics computed from it accurately reflect the corresponding population parameters.

**Simple random sample (SRS)**

309. A simple random sample of sample size $n$ is a sample in which each set of $n$ elements in the population has an equal chance of selection.

**Sampling frame**

309. A list of individuals from whom the sample is drawn is called the sampling frame. Individuals who may be in the population of interest, but who are not in the sampling frame, cannot be included in any sample.

**Sampling variability**

310. The natural tendency of randomly drawn samples to differ, one from another. Sometimes, unfortunately, called *sampling error,* sampling variability is no error at all, but just the natural result of random sampling.

| | |
|---|---|
| **Stratified random sample** | 310. A sampling design in which the population is divided into several subpopulations, or **strata,** and random samples are then drawn from each stratum. If the strata are homogeneous, but are different from each other, a stratified sample may yield more consistent results. |
| **Cluster sample** | 311. A sampling design in which entire groups, or **clusters,** are chosen at random. Cluster sampling is usually selected as a matter of convenience, practicality, or cost. Each cluster should be representative of the population, so all the clusters should be heterogeneous and similar to each other. |
| **Multistage sample** | 312. Sampling schemes that combine several sampling methods are called multistage samples. For example, a national polling service may stratify the country by geographical regions, select a random sample of cities from each region, and then interview a cluster of residents in each city. |
| **Systematic sample** | 312. A sample drawn by selecting individuals systematically from a sampling frame. When there is no relationship between the order of the sampling frame and the variables of interest, a systematic sample can be representative. |
| **Pilot** | 317. A small trial run of a survey to check whether questions are clear. A pilot study can reduce errors due to ambiguous questions. |
| **Voluntary response bias** | 318. Bias introduced to a sample when individuals can choose on their own whether to participate in the sample. Samples based on voluntary response are always invalid and cannot be recovered, no matter how large the sample size. |
| **Convenience sample** | 319. A convenience sample consists of the individuals who are conveniently available. Convenience samples often fail to be representative because every individual in the population is not equally convenient to sample. |
| **Undercoverage** | 319. A sampling scheme that biases the sample in a way that gives a part of the population less representation than it has in the population, suffers from undercoverage. |
| **Nonresponse bias** | 320. Bias introduced when a large fraction of those sampled fails to respond. Those who do respond are likely to not represent the entire population. Voluntary response bias is a form of nonresponse bias, but nonresponse may occur for other reasons. For example, those who are at work during the day won't respond to a telephone survey conducted only during working hours. |
| **Response bias** | 320. Anything in a survey design that influences responses falls under the heading of response bias. One typical response bias arises from the wording of questions, which may suggest a favored response. Voters, for example, are more likely to express support of "the president" than support of the particular person holding that office at the moment. |

## Skills

▶ Know the basic concepts and terminology of sampling (see the preceding list).

▶ Recognize population parameters in descriptions of populations and samples.

▶ Understand the value of randomization as a defense against bias.

▶ Understand the value of sampling to estimate population parameters from statistics calculated on representative samples drawn from the population.

▶ Understand that the size of the sample (not the fraction of the population) determines the precision of estimates.

▶ Know how to draw a simple random sample from a master list of a population, using a computer or a table of random numbers.

▶ Know what to report about a sample as part of your account of a statistical analysis.

▶ Report possible sources of bias in sampling methods. Recognize voluntary response and nonresponse as sources of bias in a sample survey.

# ON THE COMPUTER

## Sampling

Computer-generated pseudorandom numbers are usually quite good enough for drawing random samples. But there is little reason not to use the truly random values available on the Internet.

Here's a convenient way to draw an SRS of a specified size using a computer-based sampling frame. The sampling frame can be a list of names or of identification numbers arrayed, for example, as a column in a spreadsheet, statistics program, or database:

1. Generate random numbers of enough digits so that each exceeds the size of the sampling frame list by several digits. This makes duplication unlikely.
2. Assign the random numbers arbitrarily to individuals in the sampling frame list. For example, put them in an adjacent column.
3. Sort the list of random numbers, *carrying* along the sampling frame list.
4. Now the first *n* values in the sorted sampling frame column are an SRS of *n* values from the entire sampling frame.

# EXERCISES

1. **Roper.** Through their *Roper Reports Worldwide*, GfK Roper conducts a global consumer survey to help multinational companies understand different consumer attitudes throughout the world. Within 30 countries, the researchers interview 1000 people aged 13–65. Their samples are designed so that they get 500 males and 500 females in each country. (www.gfkamerica.com)
   a) Are they using a simple random sample? How do you know?
   b) What kind of design do you think they are using?

2. **Student Center Survey.** For their class project, a group of Statistics students decide to survey the student body to assess opinions about the proposed new student center. Their sample of 200 contained 50 first-year students, 50 sophomores, 50 juniors, and 50 seniors.
   a) Do you think the group was using an SRS? Why?
   b) What kind of sampling design do you think they used?

3. **Emoticons.** The Web site www.gamefaqs.com asked, as their question of the day to which visitors to the site were invited to respond, *"Do you ever use emoticons when you type online?"* Of the 87,262 respondents, 27% said that they did not use emoticons. ;-(
   a) What kind of sample was this?
   b) How much confidence would you place in using 27% as an estimate of the fraction of people who use emoticons?

4. **Drug tests.** Major League Baseball tests players to see whether they are using performance-enhancing drugs. Officials select a team at random, and a drug-testing crew shows up unannounced to test all 40 players on the team. Each testing day can be considered a study of drug use in Major League Baseball.
   a) What kind of sample is this?
   b) Is that choice appropriate?

5. **Gallup.** At its Web site (www.galluppoll.com) the Gallup Poll publishes results of a new survey each day. Scroll down to the end, and you'll find a statement that includes words such as these:

   *Results are based on telephone interviews with 1,008 national adults, aged 18 and older, conducted April 2–5, 2007. . . . In addition to sampling error, question wording and practical difficulties in conducting surveys can introduce error or bias into the findings of public opinion polls.*

   a) For this survey, identify the population of interest.
   b) Gallup performs its surveys by phoning numbers generated at random by a computer program. What is the sampling frame?
   c) What problems, if any, would you be concerned about in matching the sampling frame with the population?

6. **Gallup World.** At its Web site (www.gallupworldpoll .com) the Gallup World Poll reports results of surveys conducted in various places around the world. At the end of one of these reports, they describe their methods, including explanations such as the following:

   *Results are based on face-to-face interviews with randomly selected national samples of approximately 1,000 adults, aged 15 and older, who live permanently in each of the 21 sub-Saharan African nations surveyed. Those countries include Angola (areas where land mines might be expected were excluded), Benin, Botswana, Burkina Faso, Cameroon, Ethiopia, Ghana, Kenya, Madagascar (areas where interviewers had to walk more than 20 kilometers from a road were excluded), Mali, Mozambique, Niger, Nigeria, Senegal, Sierra Leone, South Africa, Tanzania, Togo, Uganda (the area of activity of the Lord's Resistance Army was excluded from the survey), Zambia, and Zimbabwe. . . . In all countries except Angola, Madagascar, and Uganda, the sample is representative of the entire population.*

a) Gallup is interested in sub-Saharan Africa. What kind of survey design are they using?
b) Some of the countries surveyed have large populations. (Nigeria is estimated to have about 130 million people.) Some are quite small. (Togo's population is estimated at 5.4 million.) Nonetheless, Gallup sampled 1000 adults in each country. How does this affect the precision of its estimates for these countries?

*7–16. What did they do? For the following reports about statistical studies, identify the following items (if possible). If you can't tell, then say so—this often happens when we read about a survey.*

a) The population
b) The population parameter of interest
c) The sampling frame
d) The sample
e) The sampling method, including whether or not randomization was employed
f) Any potential sources of bias you can detect and any problems you see in generalizing to the population of interest

7. A business magazine mailed a questionnaire to the human resource directors of all Fortune 500 companies, and received responses from 23% of them. Those responding reported that they did not find that such surveys intruded significantly on their work day.

8. A question posted on the Lycos Web site on 18 June 2000 asked visitors to the site to say whether they thought that marijuana should be legally available for medicinal purposes. (www.lycos.com)

9. Consumers Union asked all subscribers whether they had used alternative medical treatments and, if so, whether they had benefited from them. For almost all of the treatments, approximately 20% of those responding reported cures or substantial improvement in their condition.

10. The Gallup Poll interviewed 1007 randomly selected U.S. adults aged 18 and older, March 23–25, 2007. Gallup reports that when asked when (if ever) the effects of global warming will begin to happen, 60% of respondents said the effects had already begun. Only 11% thought that they would never happen.

11. Researchers waited outside a bar they had randomly selected from a list of such establishments. They stopped every 10th person who came out of the bar and asked whether he or she thought drinking and driving was a serious problem.

12. Hoping to learn what issues may resonate with voters in the coming election, the campaign director for a mayoral candidate selects one block from each of the city's election districts. Staff members go there and interview all the residents they can find.

13. The Environmental Protection Agency took soil samples at 16 locations near a former industrial waste dump and checked each for evidence of toxic chemicals. They found no elevated levels of any harmful substances.

14. State police set up a roadblock to estimate the percentage of cars with up-to-date registration, insurance, and safety inspection stickers. They usually find problems with about 10% of the cars they stop.

15. A company packaging snack foods maintains quality control by randomly selecting 10 cases from each day's production and weighing the bags. Then they open one bag from each case and inspect the contents.

16. Dairy inspectors visit farms unannounced and take samples of the milk to test for contamination. If the milk is found to contain dirt, antibiotics, or other foreign matter, the milk will be destroyed and the farm reinspected until purity is restored.

17. **Mistaken poll.** A local TV station conducted a "PulsePoll" to predict the winner in the upcoming mayoral election. Evening news viewers were invited to phone in their votes, with the results to be announced on the late-night news. Based on the phone calls, the station predicted that Amabo would win the election with 52% of the vote. They were wrong: Amabo lost, getting only 46% of the vote. Do you think the station's faulty prediction is more likely to be a result of bias or sampling error? Explain.

18. **Another mistaken poll.** Prior to the mayoral election discussed in Exercise 17, the newspaper also conducted a poll. The paper surveyed a random sample of registered voters stratified by political party, age, sex, and area of residence. This poll predicted that Amabo would win the election with 52% of the vote. The newspaper was wrong: Amabo lost, getting only 46% of the vote. Do you think the newspaper's faulty prediction is more likely to be a result of bias or sampling error? Explain.

19. **Parent opinion, part 1.** In a large city school system with 20 elementary schools, the school board is considering the adoption of a new policy that would require elementary students to pass a test in order to be promoted to the next grade. The PTA wants to find out whether parents agree with this plan. Listed below are some of the ideas proposed for gathering data. For each, indicate what kind of sampling strategy is involved and what (if any) biases might result.
a) Put a big ad in the newspaper asking people to log their opinions on the PTA Web site.
b) Randomly select one of the elementary schools and contact every parent by phone.
c) Send a survey home with every student, and ask parents to fill it out and return it the next day.
d) Randomly select 20 parents from each elementary school. Send them a survey, and follow up with a phone call if they do not return the survey within a week.

**20. Parent opinion, part 2.** Let's revisit the school system described in Exercise 19. Four new sampling strategies have been proposed to help the PTA determine whether parents favor requiring elementary students to pass a test in order to be promoted to the next grade. For each, indicate what kind of sampling strategy is involved and what (if any) biases might result.

a) Run a poll on the local TV news, asking people to dial one of two phone numbers to indicate whether they favor or oppose the plan.

b) Hold a PTA meeting at each of the 20 elementary schools, and tally the opinions expressed by those who attend the meetings.

c) Randomly select one class at each elementary school and contact each of those parents.

d) Go through the district's enrollment records, selecting every 40th parent. PTA volunteers will go to those homes to interview the people chosen.

**21. Churches.** For your political science class, you'd like to take a survey from a sample of all the Catholic Church members in your city. A list of churches shows 17 Catholic churches within the city limits. Rather than try to obtain a list of all members of all these churches, you decide to pick 3 churches at random. For those churches, you'll ask to get a list of all current members and contact 100 members at random.

a) What kind of design have you used?

b) What could go wrong with the design that you have proposed?

**22. Fish.** The U.S. Fish and Wildlife Service plans to study the kinds of fish being taken out of Saginaw Bay. To do that, they decide to randomly select 5 fishing boats at the end of a randomly chosen fishing day and to count the numbers and types of all the fish on those boats.

a) What kind of design have they used?

b) What could go wrong with the design that they have proposed?

**23. Roller coasters.** An amusement park has opened a new roller coaster. It is so popular that people are waiting for up to 3 hours for a 2-minute ride. Concerned about how patrons (who paid a large amount to enter the park and ride on the rides) feel about this, they survey every 10th person on the line for the roller coaster, starting from a randomly selected individual.

a) What kind of sample is this?

b) Is it likely to be representative?

c) What is the sampling frame?

**24. Playground.** Some people have been complaining that the children's playground at a municipal park is too small and is in need of repair. Managers of the park decide to survey city residents to see if they believe the playground should be rebuilt. They hand out questionnaires to parents who bring children to the park. Describe possible biases in this sample.

**25. Wording the survey.** Two members of the PTA committee in Exercises 19 and 20 have proposed different questions to ask in seeking parents' opinions.

*Question 1: Should elementary school–age children have to pass high-stakes tests in order to remain with their classmates?*

*Question 2: Should schools and students be held accountable for meeting yearly learning goals by testing students before they advance to the next grade?*

a) Do you think responses to these two questions might differ? How? What kind of bias is this?

b) Propose a question with more neutral wording that might better assess parental opinion.

**26. Banning ephedra.** An online poll at a popular Web site asked:

*A nationwide ban of the diet supplement ephedra went into effect recently. The herbal stimulant has been linked to 155 deaths and many more heart attacks and strokes. Ephedra manufacturer NVE Pharmaceuticals, claiming that the FDA lacked proof that ephedra is dangerous if used as directed, was denied a temporary restraining order on the ban yesterday by a federal judge. Do you think that ephedra should continue to be banned nationwide?*

65% of 17,303 respondents said "yes." Comment on each of the following statements about this poll:

a) With a sample size that large, we can be pretty certain we know the true proportion of Americans who think ephedra should be banned.

b) The wording of the question is clearly very biased.

c) The sampling frame is all Internet users.

d) This is a voluntary response survey, so the results can't be reliably generalized to any population of interest.

**27. Another ride.** The survey of patrons waiting in line for the roller coaster in Exercise 23 asks whether they think it is worthwhile to wait a long time for the ride and whether they'd like the amusement park to install still more roller coasters. What biases might cause a problem for this survey?

**28. Playground, act two.** The survey described in Exercise 24 asked,

*Many people believe this playground is too small and in need of repair. Do you think the playground should be repaired and expanded even if that means raising the entrance fee to the park?*

Describe two ways this question may lead to response bias.

**29. Survey questions.** Examine each of the following questions for possible bias. If you think the question is biased, indicate how and propose a better question.

a) Should companies that pollute the environment be compelled to pay the costs of cleanup?

b) Given that 18-year-olds are old enough to vote and to serve in the military, is it fair to set the drinking age at 21?

**30. More survey questions.** Examine each of the following questions for possible bias. If you think the question is biased, indicate how and propose a better question.

a) Do you think high school students should be required to wear uniforms?

b) Given humanity's great tradition of exploration, do you favor continued funding for space flights?

**31. Phone surveys.** Anytime we conduct a survey, we must take care to avoid undercoverage. Suppose we plan

to select 500 names from the city phone book, call their homes between noon and 4 p.m., and interview whoever answers, anticipating contacts with at least 200 people.
a) Why is it difficult to use a simple random sample here?
b) Describe a more convenient, but still random, sampling strategy.
c) What kinds of households are likely to be included in the eventual sample of opinion? Who will be excluded?
d) Suppose, instead, that we continue calling each number, perhaps in the morning or evening, until an adult is contacted and interviewed. How does this improve the sampling design?
e) Random-digit dialing machines can generate the phone calls for us. How would this improve our design? Is anyone still excluded?

32. **Cell phone survey.** What about drawing a random sample only from cell phone exchanges? Discuss the advantages and disadvantages of such a sampling method compared with surveying randomly generated telephone numbers from non–cell phone exchanges. Do you think these advantages and disadvantages have changed over time? How do you expect they'll change in the future?

33. **Arm length.** How long is your arm compared with your hand size? Put your right thumb at your left shoulder bone, stretch your hand open wide, and extend your hand down your arm. Put your thumb at the place where your little finger is, and extend down the arm again. Repeat this a third time. Now your little finger will probably have reached the back of your left hand. If the fourth hand width goes past the end of your middle finger, turn your hand sideways and count finger widths to get there.
a) How many hand and finger widths is your arm?
b) Suppose you repeat your measurement 10 times and average your results. What parameter would this average estimate? What is the population?
c) Suppose you now collect arm lengths measured in this way from 9 friends and average these 10 measurements. What is the population now? What parameter would this average estimate?
d) Do you think these 10 arm lengths are likely to be representative of the population of arm lengths in your community? In the country? Why or why not?

34. **Fuel economy.** Occasionally, when I fill my car with gas, I figure out how many miles per gallon my car got. I wrote down those results after 6 fill-ups in the past few months. Overall, it appears my car gets 28.8 miles per gallon.
a) What statistic have I calculated?
b) What is the parameter I'm trying to estimate?
c) How might my results be biased?
d) When the Environmental Protection Agency (EPA) checks a car like mine to predict its fuel economy, what parameter is it trying to estimate?

35. **Accounting.** Between quarterly audits, a company likes to check on its accounting procedures to address any problems before they become serious. The accounting staff processes payments on about 120 orders each day. The next day, the supervisor rechecks 10 of the transactions to be sure they were processed properly.

a) Propose a sampling strategy for the supervisor.
b) How would you modify that strategy if the company makes both wholesale and retail sales, requiring different bookkeeping procedures?

36. **Happy workers?** A manufacturing company employs 14 project managers, 48 foremen, and 377 laborers. In an effort to keep informed about any possible sources of employee discontent, management wants to conduct job satisfaction interviews with a sample of employees every month.
a) Do you see any danger of bias in the company's plan? Explain.
b) Propose a sampling strategy that uses a simple random sample.
c) Why do you think a simple random sample might not provide the representative opinion the company seeks?
d) Propose a better sampling strategy.
e) Listed below are the last names of the project managers. Use random numbers to select two people to be interviewed. Be sure to explain your method carefully.

| | | |
|---|---|---|
| Barrett | Bowman | Chen |
| DeLara | DeRoos | Grigorov |
| Maceli | Mulvaney | Pagliarulo |
| Rosica | Smithson | Tadros |
| Williams | Yamamoto | |

37. **Quality control.** Sammy's Salsa, a small local company, produces 20 cases of salsa a day. Each case contains 12 jars and is imprinted with a code indicating the date and batch number. To help maintain consistency, at the end of each day, Sammy selects three bottles of salsa, weighs the contents, and tastes the product. Help Sammy select the sample jars. Today's cases are coded 07N61 through 07N80.
a) Carefully explain your sampling strategy.
b) Show how to use random numbers to pick the three jars for testing.
c) Did you use a simple random sample? Explain.

38. **A fish story.** Concerned about reports of discolored scales on fish caught downstream from a newly sited chemical plant, scientists set up a field station in a shore-line public park. For one week they asked fishermen there to bring any fish they caught to the field station for a brief inspection. At the end of the week, the scientists said that 18% of the 234 fish that were submitted for inspection displayed the discoloration. From this information, can the researchers estimate what proportion of fish in the river have discolored scales? Explain.

39. **Sampling methods.** Consider each of these situations. Do you think the proposed sampling method is appropriate? Explain.
a) We want to know what percentage of local doctors accept Medicaid patients. We call the offices of 50 doctors randomly selected from local Yellow Page listings.
b) We want to know what percentage of local businesses anticipate hiring additional employees in the upcoming month. We randomly select a page in the Yellow Pages and call every business listed there.

**40. More sampling methods.** Consider each of these situations. Do you think the proposed sampling method is appropriate? Explain.

a) We want to know if there is neighborhood support to turn a vacant lot into a playground. We spend a Saturday afternoon going door-to-door in the neighborhood, asking people to sign a petition.

b) We want to know if students at our college are satisfied with the selection of food available on campus. We go to the largest cafeteria and interview every 10th person in line.

## JUST CHECKING
## Answers

**1. a)** It can be hard to reach all members of a population, and it can take so long that circumstances change, affecting the responses. A well-designed sample is often a better choice.

**b)** This sample is probably biased—students who didn't like the food at the cafeteria might not choose to eat there.

**c)** No, only the sample size matters, not the fraction of the overall population.

**d)** Students who frequent this Web site might be more enthusiastic about Statistics than the overall population of Statistics students. A large sample cannot compensate for bias.

**e)** It's the population "parameter." "Statistics" describe samples.

**2. a)** systematic
**b)** stratified
**c)** simple
**d)** cluster

# CHAPTER 13

# Experiments and Observational Studies

## Where are we going?

Experiments are the "Gold Standard" of data collection. No drug comes to market without at least one FDA-approved experiment to demonstrate its safety and effectiveness. Much of what we know in science and social science comes from carefully designed experiments.

The Four Principles of Experimental Design (Control what you can, Randomize for the rest, Replicate the trials, and, when appropriate, Block to remove identifiable variation) describe what makes a sound experiment and how to understand the results.

W ho gets good grades? And, more importantly, why? Is there something schools and parents could do to help weaker students improve their grades? Some people think they have an answer: music! No, not your iPod, but an instrument. In a study conducted at Mission Viejo High School, in California, researchers compared the scholastic performance of music students with that of non-music students. Guess what? The music students had a much higher overall grade point average than the non-music students, 3.59 to 2.91. Not only that: A whopping 16% of the music students had all A's compared with only 5% of the non-music students.

As a result of this study and others, many parent groups and educators pressed for expanded music programs in the nation's schools. They argued that the work ethic, discipline, and feeling of accomplishment fostered by learning to play an instrument also enhance a person's ability to succeed in school. They thought that involving more students in music would raise academic performance. What do you think? Does this study provide solid evidence? Or are there other possible explanations for the difference in grades? Is there any way to really prove such a conjecture?

## Observational Studies

This research tried to show an association between music education and grades. But it wasn't a survey. Nor did it assign students to get music education. Instead, it simply observed students "in the wild," recording the choices they made and

**A S** *Video:* **An Industrial Experiment.** Manufacturers often use designed experiments to help them perfect new products. Watch this video about one such experiment.

- identifying "new" risk factors for these and other diseases in women;
- comparing risk factors, presence of disease at the start of the study, and new occurrences of disease during the study across all study components; and
- creating a future resource to identify biological indicators of disease, especially substances and factors found in blood.

That is, the study seeks to identify possible risk factors and assess how serious they might be. It seeks to build up data that might be checked retrospectively as the women in the study continue to be followed. There would be no way to find out these things with an experiment because the task includes identifying new risk factors. If we don't know those risk factors, we could never control them as factors in an experiment.

By contrast, one of the clinical trials (randomized experiments) that received much press attention randomly assigned postmenopausal women to take either hormone replacement therapy or an inactive pill. The results published in 2002 and 2004 concluded that hormone replacement with estrogen carried increased risks of stroke.

**FOR EXAMPLE**    Determining the treatments and response variable

**Recap:** In 2007, deaths of a large number of pet dogs and cats were ultimately traced to contamination of some brands of pet food. The manufacturer now claims that the food is safe, but before it can be released, it must be tested.

**Question:** In an experiment to test whether the food is now safe for dogs to eat,[1] what would be the treatments and what would be the response variable?

*The treatments would be ordinary size portions of two dog foods: the new one from the company (the test food) and one that I was certain was safe (perhaps prepared in my kitchen or laboratory). The response would be a veterinarian's assessment of the health of the test animals.*

# The Four Principles of Experimental Design

1. **Control.** We control sources of variation other than the factors we are testing by making conditions as similar as possible for all treatment groups. For human subjects, we try to treat them alike. However, there is always a question of degree and practicality. Controlling extraneous sources of variation reduces the variability of the responses, making it easier to detect differences among the treatment groups.

   Making generalizations from the experiment to other levels of the controlled factor can be risky. For example, suppose we test two laundry detergents and carefully control the water temperature at 180°F. This would reduce the variation in our results due to water temperature, but what could we say about the detergents' performance in cold water? Not much. It would be hard to justify extrapolating the results to other temperatures.

   Although we control both experimental factors and other sources of variation, we think of them very differently. We control a factor by assigning

---

[1] It may disturb you (as it does us) to think of deliberately putting dogs at risk in this experiment, but in fact that is what is done. The risk is borne by a small number of dogs so that the far larger population of dogs can be kept safe.

*The deep insight that experiments should use random assignment is quite an old one. It can be attributed to the American philosopher and scientist C. S. Peirce in his experiments with J. Jastrow, published in 1885.*

**A S** **Activity: The Three Rules of Experimental Design.** Watch an animated discussion of three rules of design.

**A S** **Activity: Perform an Experiment.** How well can you read pie charts and bar charts? Find out as you serve as the subject in your own experiment.

subjects to different factor levels because we want to see how the response will change at those different levels. We control other sources of variation to *prevent* them from changing and affecting the response variable.

2. **Randomize.** As in sample surveys, **randomization** allows us to equalize the effects of unknown or uncontrollable sources of variation. It does not eliminate the effects of these sources, but it spreads them out across the treatment levels so that we can see past them. If experimental units were not assigned to treatments at random, we would not be able to use the powerful methods of Statistics to draw conclusions from an experiment. Assigning subjects to treatments at random reduces bias due to uncontrolled sources of variation. Randomization protects us even from effects we didn't know about. There's an adage that says "control what you can, and randomize the rest."

3. **Replicate.** Two kinds of replication show up in comparative experiments. First, we should apply each treatment to a number of subjects. Only with such replication can we estimate the variability of responses. If we have not assessed the variation, the experiment is not complete. The outcome of an experiment on a single subject is an anecdote, not data.

A second kind of replication shows up when the experimental units are not a representative sample from the population of interest. We may believe that what is true of the students in Psych 101 who volunteered for the sleep experiment is true of all humans, but we'll feel more confident if our results for the experiment are *replicated* in another part of the country, with people of different ages, and at different times of the year. **Replication** of an entire experiment with the controlled sources of variation at different levels is an essential step in science.

**Replicating cold fusion** In 1989 Stanley Pons and Martin Fleischmann of the University of Utah announced what seemed to be the scientific discovery of the century: cold fusion. They claimed that nuclear fusion, producing usable amounts of heat, could be induced to take place on a table-top by electrolyzing heavy water, using electrodes made of palladium and platinum, two precious metals. If so, the world's energy problems were at an end, to say nothing of the fiscal difficulties of the University of Utah. What followed was a kind of feeding frenzy, science by press conference and e-mail, confirmations and disconfirmations, claims and retractions, ugly charges and obfuscation, science gone berserk. For all practical purposes, it ended a mere 5 weeks after it began, on May 1st, 1989, at a dramatic session of The American Physical Society, in Baltimore. Although there were numerous presentations at this session, only two really counted. Steven Koonin and Nathan Lewis, speaking for himself and Charles Barnes, all three from Caltech, executed between them a perfect slam-dunk that cast Cold Fusion right out of the arena of mainstream science. . . . seasoned experimentalists like Lewis and Barnes refused to believe what they couldn't reproduce in their own laboratories."—David Goodstein, "Whatever Happened to Cold Fusion?" http://physicsweb.org

4. **Block.** The ability of randomizing to equalize variation across treatment groups works best in the long run. For example, if we're allocating players to two 6-player soccer teams from a pool of 12 children, we might do so at random to equalize the talent. But what if there were two 12-year-olds and ten 6–year-olds in the group? Randomizing may place both 12-year-olds on the same team. In the long run, if we did this over and over, it would all equalize. But wouldn't it be better to assign one 12-year-old to each group (at random) and five 6-year-olds to each team (at random)? By doing this, we would improve fairness in the short run. This approach makes the division more fair by recognizing the variation in *age* and allocating the players at random *within* each age level. When we do this, we call the variable *age* a **blocking variable.** The levels of *age* are called blocks.

Sometimes, attributes of the experimental units that we are not studying and that we can't control may nevertheless affect the outcomes of an experiment. If we group similar individuals together and then randomize within each of these **blocks,** we can remove much of the variability due to the difference among the blocks. Blocking is an important compromise between randomization and control. However, unlike the first three principles, blocking is not *required* in an experimental design.

**FOR EXAMPLE**      Control, randomize, and replicate

**Recap:** We're planning an experiment to see whether the new pet food is safe for dogs to eat. We'll feed some animals the new food and others a food known to be safe, comparing their health after a period of time.

**Questions:** In this experiment, how will you implement the principles of control, randomization, and replication?

I'd control the portion sizes eaten by the dogs. To reduce possible variability from factors other than the food, I'd standardize other aspects of their environments—housing the dogs in similar pens and ensuring that each got the same amount of water, exercise, play, and sleep time, for example. I might restrict the experiment to a single breed of dog and to adult dogs to further minimize variation.

To equalize traits, pre-existing conditions, and other unknown influences, I would assign dogs to the two feed treatments randomly.

I would replicate by assigning more than one dog to each treatment to allow for variability among individual dogs. If I had the time and funding, I might replicate the entire experiment using, for example, a different breed of dog.

# Diagrams

An experiment is carried out over time with specific actions occurring in a specified order. A diagram of the procedure can help in thinking about experiments.[2]

---

[2] Diagrams of this sort were introduced by David Moore in his textbooks and are widely used.

The diagram emphasizes the random allocation of subjects to treatment groups, the separate treatments applied to these groups, and the ultimate comparison of results. It's best to specify the responses that will be compared. A good way to start comparing results for the treatment groups is with boxplots.

---

**STEP-BY-STEP EXAMPLE**   |   **Designing an Experiment**

> A **completely randomized experiment** is the ideal simple design, just as a *simple random sample* is the ideal simple sample—and for many of the same reasons.

An ad for OptiGro plant fertilizer claims that with this product you will grow "juicier, tastier" tomatoes. You'd like to test this claim, and wonder whether you might be able to get by with half the specified dose. How can you set up an experiment to check out the claim?

Of course, you'll have to get some tomatoes, try growing some plants with the product and some without, and see what happens. But you'll need a clearer plan than that. How should you design your experiment?

Let's work through the design, step by step. We'll design the simplest kind of experiment, a **completely randomized experiment in one factor**. Since this is a *design* for an experiment, most of the steps are part of the *Think* stage. The statements in the right column are the kinds of things you would need to say in *proposing* an experiment. You'd need to include them in the "methods" section of a report once the experiment is run.

**Question:** How would you design an experiment to test OptiGro fertilizer?

| | |
|---|---|
|  **Plan** State what you want to know. | I want to know whether tomato plants grown with OptiGro yield juicier, tastier tomatoes than plants raised in otherwise similar circumstances but without the fertilizer. |
| **Response** Specify the response variable. | I'll evaluate the juiciness and taste of the tomatoes by asking a panel of judges to rate them on a scale from 1 to 7 in juiciness and in taste. |
| **Treatments** Specify the factor levels and the treatments. | The factor is fertilizer, specifically *OptiGro* fertilizer. I'll grow tomatoes at three different factor levels: some with no fertilizer, some with half the specified amount of *OptiGro*, and some with the full dose of *OptiGro*. These are the three treatments. |
| **Experimental Units** Specify the experimental units. | I'll obtain 24 tomato plants of the same variety from a local garden store. |

**Experimental Design** Observe the principles of design:

**Control** any sources of variability you know of and can control.

I'll locate the farm plots near each other so that the plants get similar amounts of sun and rain and experience similar temperatures. I will weed the plots equally and otherwise treat the plants alike.

**Randomly assign** experimental units to treatments, to equalize the effects of unknown or uncontrollable sources of variation.

Specify how the random numbers needed for randomization will be obtained.

I'll randomly divide the plants into three groups. I will use random numbers from a table to determine the assignment.

**Replicate** results by placing more than one plant in each treatment group.

There are 8 plants in each treatment group.

**Make a Picture** A diagram of your design can help you think about it clearly.

Specify any other experiment details. You must give enough details so that another experimenter could exactly replicate your experiment. It's generally better to include details that might seem irrelevant than to leave out matters that could turn out to make a difference.

Specify how to measure the response.

I will grow the plants until the tomatoes are mature, as judged by reaching a standard color.

I'll harvest the tomatoes when ripe and store them for evaluation.

I'll set up a numerical scale of juiciness and one of tastiness for the taste testers. Several people will taste slices of tomato and rate them.

Once you collect the data, you'll need to display them and compare the results for the three treatment groups.

I will display the results with side-by-side box-plots to compare the three treatment groups.

I will compare the means of the groups.

To answer the initial question, we ask whether the differences we observe in the means of the three groups are meaningful.

Because this is a randomized experiment, we can attribute significant differences to the treatments. To do this properly, we'll need methods from what is called "statistical inference," the subject of the rest of this book.

*If the differences in taste and juiciness among the groups are greater than I would expect by knowing the usual variation among tomatoes, I may be able to conclude that these differences can be attributed to treatment with the fertilizer.*

# Does the Difference Make a Difference?

**A S** *Activity:* **Graph the Data.** Do you think there's a significant difference in your perception of pie charts and bar charts? Explore the data from your plot perception experiment.

If the differences among the treatment groups are big enough, we'll attribute the differences to the treatments, but how can we decide whether the differences are big enough?

Would we expect the group means to be identical? Not really. Even if the treatment made no difference whatever, there would still be some variation. We assigned the plants to treatments at random. But a different random assignment would have led to different results. Even a repeat of the *same* treatment on a different randomly assigned set of plants would lead to a different mean. The real question is whether the differences we observed are about as big as we'd get just from the randomization alone, or whether they're bigger than that. If we decide that they're bigger, we'll attribute the differences to the treatments. In that case we say the differences are **statistically significant.**

How will we decide if something is different enough to be considered statistically significant? Later chapters will offer methods to help answer that question, but to get some intuition, think about deciding whether a coin is fair. If we flip a fair coin 100 times, we expect, *on average,* to get 50 heads. Suppose we get 54 heads out of 100. That doesn't seem very surprising. It's well within the bounds of ordinary random fluctuations. What if we'd seen 94 heads? That's clearly outside the bounds. We'd be pretty sure that the coin flips were not random. But what about 74 heads? Is that far enough from 50% to arouse our suspicions? That's the sort of question we need to ask of our experiment results.

In Statistics terminology, 94 heads would be a statistically significant difference from 50, and 54 heads would not. Whether 74 is *statistically significant* or not would depend on the chance of getting 74 heads in 100 flips of a fair coin and on our tolerance for believing that rare events can happen to us.

Back at the tomato stand, we ask whether the differences we see among the treatment groups are the kind of differences we'd expect from randomization. A good way to get a feeling for that is to look at how much our results vary among plants that get the *same* treatment. Boxplots of our results by treatment group can give us a general idea.

For example, Figure 13.1 shows two pairs of boxplots whose centers differ by exactly the same amount. In the upper set, that difference appears to be larger than we'd expect just by chance. Why? Because the variation is quite small *within* treatment groups, so the larger difference *between* the groups is unlikely to be just from the randomization. In the bottom pair, that same difference between the centers looks less impressive. There the variation *within* each group swamps the difference *between* the two means. We'd say the difference is statistically significant in the upper pair and not statistically significant in the lower pair.

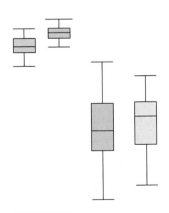

**FIGURE 13.1**

*The boxplots in both pairs have centers the same distance apart, but when the spreads are large, the observed difference may be just from random fluctuation.*

Later we'll see statistical tests that quantify this intuition. For now, the important point is that a difference is statistically significant if we don't believe that it's likely to have occurred only by chance.

## JUST CHECKING

**1.** At one time, a method called "gastric freezing" was used to treat people with peptic ulcers. An inflatable bladder was inserted down the esophagus and into the stomach, and then a cold liquid was pumped into the bladder. Now you can find the following notice on the Internet site of a major insurance company:

*[Our company] does not cover gastric freezing (intragastric hypothermia) for chronic peptic ulcer disease. . . .*

*Gastric freezing for chronic peptic ulcer disease is a non-surgical treatment which was popular about 20 years ago but now is seldom performed. It has been abandoned due to a high complication rate, only temporary improvement experienced by patients, and a lack of effectiveness when tested by double-blind, controlled clinical trials.*

What did that "controlled clinical trial" (experiment) probably look like? (Don't worry about "double-blind"; we'll get to that soon.)
**a)** What was the factor in this experiment?
**b)** What was the response variable?
**c)** What were the treatments?
**d)** How did researchers decide which subjects received which treatment?
**e)** Were the results statistically significant?

# Experiments and Samples

Both experiments and sample surveys use randomization to get unbiased data. But they do so in different ways and for different purposes. Sample surveys try to estimate population parameters, so the sample needs to be as representative of the population as possible. By contrast, experiments try to assess the effects of treatments. Experimental units are not always drawn randomly from a population. For example, a medical experiment may deal only with patients who have the disease under study. The randomization is in the assignment of their therapy. This is appropriate because our focus is on differences in the effects of the treatments.

Unless the experimental units are chosen from the population at random, you should be cautious about generalizing experiment results to larger populations until the experiment has been repeated under different circumstances. Results become more persuasive if they remain the same in completely different settings, such as in a different season, in a different country, or for a different species, to name a few.

Even without choosing experimental units from a population at random, experiments can draw stronger conclusions than surveys. By looking only at the differences across treatment groups, experiments cancel out many sources of bias. For example, the entire pool of subjects may be biased and not representative of the population. (College students may need more sleep, on average, than the general population.) When we assign subjects randomly to treatment groups, all the groups are still biased, but *in the same way*. When we consider the dif-

Experiments are rarely performed on random samples from a population. Don't describe the subjects in an experiment as a random sample unless they really are. More likely, the randomization was in assigning subjects to treatments.

ferences in their responses, these biases cancel out, allowing us to see the *differences* due to treatment effects more clearly.

## Control Treatments

> **A S** Activity: **Control Groups in Experiments.** Is a control group really necessary?

Suppose you wanted to test a $300 piece of software designed to shorten download times. You could just try it on several files and record the download times, but you probably want to *compare* the speed with what would happen *without* the software installed. Such a baseline measurement is called a **control** treatment, and the experimental units to whom it is applied are called a **control group.**

This is a use of the word "control" in an entirely different context. Previously, we controlled extraneous sources of variation by keeping them constant. Here, we use a control treatment as another *level* of the factor in order to compare the treatment results to a situation in which "nothing happens." That's what we did in the tomato experiment when we used no fertilizer on the 8 tomatoes in Group 1.

## Blinding

Humans are notoriously susceptible to errors in judgment.[3] All of us. When we know what treatment was assigned, it's difficult not to let that knowledge influence our assessment of the response, even when we try to be careful.

Suppose you were trying to advise your school on which brand of cola to stock in the school's vending machines. You set up an experiment to see which of the three competing brands students prefer (or whether they can tell the difference at all). But people have brand loyalties. You probably prefer one brand already. So if you knew which brand you were tasting, it might influence your rating. To avoid this bias, it would be better to disguise the brands as much as possible. This strategy is called **blinding** the participants to the treatment.[4]

> **Blinding by Misleading**
> Social science experiments can sometimes blind subjects by misleading them about the purpose of a study. One of the authors participated as an undergraduate volunteer in a (now infamous) psychology experiment using such a blinding method. The subjects were told that the experiment was about three-dimensional spatial perception and were assigned to draw a model of a horse. While they were busy drawing, a loud noise and then groaning were heard coming from the room next door. The *real* purpose of the experiment was to see how people reacted to the apparent disaster. The experimenters wanted to see whether the social pressure of being in groups made people react to the disaster differently. Subjects had been randomly assigned to draw either in groups or alone; that was the treatment. The experimenter had no interest in how well the subjects could draw the horse, but the subjects were blinded to the treatment because they were misled.

But it isn't just the subjects who should be blind. Experimenters themselves often subconsciously behave in ways that favor what they believe. Even technicians may treat plants or test animals differently if, for example, they expect them to die. An animal that starts doing a little better than others by showing an increased appetite may get fed a bit more than the experimental protocol specifies.

People are so good at picking up subtle cues about treatments that the best (in fact, the *only*) defense against such biases in experiments on human subjects is to keep *anyone* who could affect the outcome or the measurement of the response from knowing which subjects have been assigned to which treatments. So, not only should your cola-tasting subjects be blinded, but also *you*, as the experimenter, shouldn't know which drink is which, either—at least until you're ready to analyze the results.

---

[3] For example, here we are in Chapter 13 and you're still reading the footnotes.
[4] C. S. Peirce, in the same 1885 work in which he introduced randomization, also recommended blinding.

There are two main classes of individuals who can affect the outcome of the experiment:

▷ those who could influence the results (the subjects, treatment administrators, or technicians)

▷ those who evaluate the results (judges, treating physicians, etc.)

When all the individuals in either one of these classes are blinded, an experiment is said to be **single-blind**. When everyone in *both* classes is blinded, we call the experiment **double-blind**. Even if several individuals in one class are blinded—for example, both the patients and the technicians who administer the treatment—the study would still be just single-blind. If only some of the individuals in a class are blind—for example, if subjects are not told of their treatment, but the administering technician is not blind—there is a substantial risk that subjects can discern their treatment from subtle cues in the technician's behavior or that the technician might inadvertently treat subjects differently. Such experiments cannot be considered truly blind.

In our tomato experiment, we certainly don't want the people judging the taste to know which tomatoes got the fertilizer. That makes the experiment single-blind. We might also not want the people caring for the tomatoes to know which ones were being fertilized, in case they might treat them differently in other ways, too. We can accomplish this double-blinding by having some fake fertilizer for them to put on the other plants. Read on.

---

### FOR EXAMPLE     Blinding

**Recap:** In our experiment to see if the new pet food is now safe, we're feeding one group of dogs the new food and another group a food we know to be safe. Our response variable is the health of the animals as assessed by a veterinarian.

**Questions:** Should the vet be blinded? Why or why not? How would you do this? (Extra credit: Can this experiment be double-blind? Would that mean that the test animals wouldn't know what they were eating?)

*Whenever the response variable involves judgment, it is a good idea to blind the evaluator to the treatments. The veterinarian should not be told which dogs ate which foods.*

*Extra credit: There is a need for double-blinding. In this case, the workers who care for and feed the animals should not be aware of which dogs are receiving which food. We'll need to make the "safe" food look as much like the "test" food as possible.*

---

## Placebos

> **A S**   *Activity:* **Blinded Experiments.** This narrated account of blinding isn't a placebo!

Often, simply applying *any* treatment can induce an improvement. Every parent knows the medicinal value of a kiss to make a toddler's scrape or bump stop hurting. Some of the improvement seen with a treatment—even an effective treatment—can be due simply to the act of treating. To separate these two effects, we can use a control treatment that mimics the treatment itself.

A "fake" treatment that looks just like the treatments being tested is called a **placebo**. Placebos are the best way to blind subjects from knowing whether they are receiving the treatment or not. One common version of a placebo in drug test-

The placebo effect is stronger when placebo treatments are administered with authority or by a figure who appears to be an authority. "Doctors" in white coats generate a stronger effect than salespeople in polyester suits. But the placebo effect is not reduced much even when subjects know that the effect exists. People often suspect that they've gotten the placebo if nothing at all happens. So, recently, drug manufacturers have gone so far in making placebos realistic that they cause the same side effects as the drug being tested! Such "active placebos" usually induce a stronger placebo effect. When those side effects include loss of appetite or hair, the practice may raise ethical questions.

ing is a "sugar pill." Especially when psychological attitude can affect the results, control group subjects treated with a placebo may show an improvement.

The fact is that subjects treated with a placebo sometimes improve. It's not unusual for 20% or more of subjects given a placebo to report reduction in pain, improved movement, or greater alertness, or even to demonstrate improved health or performance. This **placebo effect** highlights both the importance of effective blinding and the importance of comparing treatments with a control. Placebo controls are so effective that you should use them as an essential tool for blinding whenever possible.

The best experiments are usually
▶ randomized.  ▶ double-blind.
▶ comparative.  ▶ placebo-controlled.

**Does ginkgo biloba improve memory?**  Researchers investigated the purported memory-enhancing effect of ginkgo biloba tree extract (P. R. Solomon, F. Adams, A. Silver, J. Zimmer, R. De Veaux, "Ginkgo for Memory Enhancement. A Randomized Controlled Trial." *JAMA* 288 [2002]: 835–840). In a randomized, comparative, double-blind, placebo-controlled study, they administered treatments to 230 elderly community members. One group received Ginkoba™ according to the manufacturer's instructions. The other received a similar-looking placebo. Thirteen different tests of memory were administered before and after treatment. The placebo group showed greater improvement on 7 of the tests, the treatment group on the other 6. None showed any significant differences. Here are boxplots of one measure.

*By permission of John L. Hart FLP and Creators Syndicate, Inc.*

## Blocking

We wanted to use 18 tomato plants of the same variety for our experiment, but suppose the garden store had only 12 plants left. So we drove down to the nursery and bought 6 more plants of that variety. We worry that the tomato plants from the two stores are different somehow, and, in fact, they don't really look the same.

How can we design the experiment so that the differences between the stores don't mess up our attempts to see differences among fertilizer levels? We can't measure the effect of a store the same way as we can the fertilizer because we can't assign it as we would a factor in the experiment. You can't tell a tomato what store to come from.

Because stores may vary in the care they give plants or in the sources of their seeds, the plants from either store are likely to be more like each other than they are like the plants from the other store. When groups of experimental units are similar, it's often a good idea to gather them together into **blocks.** By blocking, we isolate the variability attributable to the differences between the blocks, so that we can see the differences caused by the treatments more clearly. Here, we would define the plants from each store to be a block. The randomization is introduced when we randomly assign treatments within each block.

In a completely randomized design, each of the 18 plants would have an equal chance to land in each of the three treatment groups. But we realize that the store may have an effect. To isolate the store effect, we block on store by assigning the plants from each store to treatments at random. So we now have six treatment groups, three for each block. Within each block, we'll randomly assign the same number of plants to each of the three treatments. The experiment is still fair because each treatment is still applied (at random) to the same number of plants and to the same proportion from each store: 4 from store A and 2 from store B. Because the randomization occurs only within the blocks (plants from one store cannot be assigned to treatment groups for the other), we call this a **randomized block design.**

In effect, we conduct two parallel experiments, one for tomatoes from each store, and then combine the results. The picture tells the story:

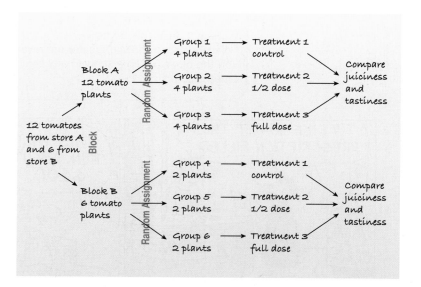

In a retrospective or prospective study, subjects are sometimes paired because they are similar in ways *not* under study. **Matching** subjects in this way can reduce variation in much the same way as blocking. For example, a retrospective study of music education and grades might match each student who studies an instrument with someone of the same sex who is similar in family income but didn't study an instrument. When we compare grades of music students with those of non-music students, the matching would reduce the variation due to income and sex differences.

Blocking is the same idea for experiments as stratifying is for sampling. Both methods group together subjects that are similar and randomize within those groups as a way to remove unwanted variation. (But be careful to keep the terms straight. Don't say that we "stratify" an experiment or "block" a sample.) We use blocks to reduce variability so we can see the effects of the factors; we're not usually interested in studying the effects of the blocks themselves.

**FOR EXAMPLE** Blocking

**Recap:** In 2007, pet food contamination put cats at risk, as well as dogs. Our experiment should probably test the safety of the new food on both animals.

**Questions:** Why shouldn't we randomly assign a mix of cats and dogs to the two treatment groups? What would you recommend instead?

*Dogs and cats might respond differently to the foods, and that variability could obscure my results. Blocking by species can remove that superfluous variation. I'd randomize cats to the two treatments (test food and safe food) separately from the dogs. I'd measure their responses separately and look at the results afterward.*

### JUST CHECKING

2. Recall the experiment about gastric freezing, an old method for treating peptic ulcers that you read about in the first Just Checking. Doctors would insert an inflatable bladder down the patient's esophagus and into the stomach and then pump in a cold liquid. A major insurance company now states that it doesn't cover this treatment because "double-blind, controlled clinical trials" failed to demonstrate that gastric freezing was effective.
   a) What does it mean that the experiment was double-blind?
   b) Why would you recommend a placebo control?
   c) Suppose that researchers suspected that the effectiveness of the gastric freezing treatment might depend on whether a patient had recently developed the peptic ulcer or had been suffering from the condition for a long time. How might the researchers have designed the experiment?

## Adding More Factors

There are two kinds of gardeners. Some water frequently, making sure that the plants are never dry. Others let Mother Nature take her course and leave the watering to her. The makers of OptiGro want to ensure that their product will work under a wide variety of watering conditions. Maybe we should include the amount of watering as part of our experiment. Can we study a second factor at the same time and still learn as much about fertilizer?

We now have two factors (fertilizer at three levels and irrigation at two levels). We combine them in all possible ways to yield six treatments:

|  | No Fertilizer | Half Fertilizer | Full Fertilizer |
|---|---|---|---|
| No Added Water | 1 | 2 | 3 |
| Daily Watering | 4 | 5 | 6 |

If we allocate the original 12 plants, the experiment now assigns 2 plants to each of these six treatments at random. This experiment is a **completely randomized two-factor experiment** because any plant could end up assigned at random to any of the six treatments (and we have two factors).

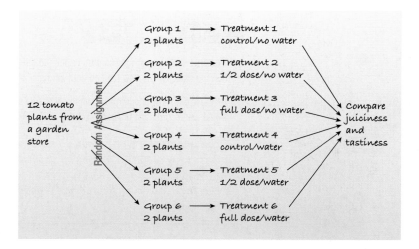

It's often important to include several factors in the same experiment in order to see what happens when the factor levels are applied in different *combinations*. A common misconception is that applying several factors at once makes it difficult to separate the effects of the individual factors. You may hear people say that experiments should always be run "one factor at a time." In fact, just the opposite is true: Experiments with more than one factor are both more efficient and provide more information than one-at-a-time experiments. There are many ways to design efficient multifactor experiments. You can take a whole course on the design and analysis of such experiments.

# Confounding

Professor Stephen Ceci of Cornell University performed an experiment to investigate the effect of a teacher's classroom style on student evaluations. He taught a class in developmental psychology during two successive terms to a total of 472 students in two very similar classes. He kept everything about his teaching identical (same text, same syllabus, same office hours, etc.) and modified only his style in class. During the fall term, he maintained a subdued demeanor. During the spring term, he used expansive gestures and lectured with more enthusiasm, varying his vocal pitch and using more hand gestures. He administered a standard student evaluation form at the end of each term.

The students in the fall term class rated him only an average teacher. Those in the spring term class rated him an excellent teacher, praising his knowledge and accessibility, and even the quality of the textbook. On the question "How much did you learn in the course?" the average response changed from 2.93 to 4.05 on a 5-point scale.[5]

How much of the difference he observed was due to his difference in manner, and how much might have been due to the season of the year? Fall term in Ithaca, NY (home of Cornell University), starts out colorful and pleasantly warm but ends cold and bleak. Spring starts out bitter and snowy and ends with blooming flowers and singing birds. Might students' overall happiness have been affected by the season and reflected in their evaluations?

Unfortunately, there's no way to tell. Nothing in the data enables us to tease apart these two effects, because all the students who experienced the subdued manner did so during the fall term and all who experienced the expansive manner did so during the spring. When the levels of one factor are associated with the levels of another factor, we say that these two factors are **confounded**.

---

[5] But the two classes performed almost identically well on the final exam.

In some experiments, such as this one, it's just not possible to avoid some confounding. Professor Ceci could have randomly assigned students to one of two classes during the same term, but then we might question whether mornings or afternoons were better, or whether he really delivered the same class the second time (after practicing on the first class). Or he could have had another professor deliver the second class, but that would have raised more serious issues about differences in the two professors and concern over more serious confounding.

---

**FOR EXAMPLE**　　Confounding

**Recap:** After many dogs and cats suffered health problems caused by contaminated foods, we're trying to find out whether a newly formulated pet food is safe. Our experiment will feed some animals the new food and others a food known to be safe, and a veterinarian will check the response.

**Question:** Why would it be a bad design to feed the test food to some dogs and the safe food to cats?

*This would create confounding. We would not be able to tell whether any differences in animals' health were attributable to the food they had eaten or to differences in how the two species responded.*

---

**A two-factor example**　 Confounding can also arise from a badly designed multifactor experiment. Here's a classic. A credit card bank wanted to test the sensitivity of the market to two factors: the annual fee charged for a card and the annual percentage rate charged. Not wanting to scrimp on sample size, the bank selected 100,000 people at random from a mailing list. It sent out 50,000 offers with a low rate and no fee, and 50,000 offers with a higher rate and a $50 annual fee. Guess what happened? That's right—people preferred the low-rate, no-fee card. No surprise. In fact, they signed up for that card at over twice the rate as the other offer. And because of the large sample size, the bank was able to estimate the difference precisely. But the question the bank really wanted to answer was "How much of the change was due to the rate, and how much was due to the fee?" Unfortunately, there's simply no way to separate out the two effects. If the bank had sent out all four possible different treatments—low rate with no fee, low rate with $50 fee, high rate with no fee, and high rate with $50 fee—each to 25,000 people, it could have learned about both factors and could have also seen what happens when the two factors occur in combination.

# Lurking or Confounding?

Confounding may remind you of the problem of lurking variables we discussed back in Chapters 7 and 9. Confounding variables and lurking variables are alike in that they interfere with our ability to interpret our analyses simply. Each can mislead us, but there are important differences in both how and where the confusion may arise.

A lurking variable creates an association between two other variables that tempts us to think that one may cause the other. This can happen in a regression analysis or an observational study when a lurking variable influences both the explanatory and response variables. Recall that countries with more TV sets per capita tend to have longer life expectancies. We shouldn't conclude it's the TVs "causing" longer life. We suspect instead that a generally higher standard of living may mean that people can afford more TVs and get better health care, too. Our data revealed an association between TVs and life expectancy, but economic conditions were a likely lurking variable. A lurking variable, then, is usually thought of as a variable associated with both $y$ and $x$ that makes it appear that $x$ may be causing $y$.

Confounding can arise in experiments when some other variable associated with a factor has an effect on the response variable. However, in a designed experiment, the experimenter *assigns* treatments (at random) to subjects rather than just observing them. A confounding variable can't be thought of as causing that assignment. Professor Ceci's choice of teaching styles was not caused by the weather, but because he used one style in the fall and the other in spring, he was unable to tell how much of his students' reactions were attributable to his teaching and how much to the weather. A confounding variable, then, is associated in a noncausal way with a factor and affects the response. Because of the confounding, we find that we can't tell whether any effect we see was caused by our factor or by the confounding variable—or even by both working together.

Both confounding and lurking variables are outside influences that make it harder to understand the relationship we are modeling. However, the nature of the causation is different in the two situations. In regression and observational studies, we can only observe associations between variables. Although we can't demonstrate a causal relationship, we often imagine whether $x$ could cause $y$. We can be misled by a lurking variable that influences both. In a designed experiment, we often hope to show that the factor causes a response. Here we can be misled by a confounding variable that's associated with the factor and causes or contributes to the differences we observe in the response.

## WHAT CAN GO WRONG?

▶ **Don't give up just because you can't run an experiment.** Sometimes we can't run an experiment because we can't identify or control the factors. Sometimes it would simply be unethical to run the experiment. (Consider randomly assigning students to take—and be graded in—a Statistics course deliberately taught to be boring and difficult or one that had an unlimited budget to use multimedia, real-world examples and field trips to make the subject more interesting.) If we can't perform an experiment, often an observational study is a good choice.

▶ **Beware of confounding.** Use randomization whenever possible to ensure that the factors not in your experiment are not confounded with your treatment levels. Be alert to confounding that cannot be avoided, and report it along with your results.

▶ **Bad things can happen even to good experiments.** Protect yourself by recording additional information. An experiment in which the air conditioning failed for 2 weeks, affecting the results, was saved by recording the temperature (although that was not originally one of the factors) and estimating the effect the higher temperature had on the response.[6]

It's generally good practice to collect as much information as possible about your experimental units and the circumstances of the experiment. For example, in the tomato experiment, it would be wise to record details of the weather (temperature, rainfall, sunlight) that might affect the plants and any facts available about their growing situation. (Is one side of the field in shade sooner than the other as the day proceeds? Is one area lower and a bit wetter?) Sometimes we can use this extra information during the analysis to reduce biases.

▶ **Don't spend your entire budget on the first run.** Just as it's a good idea to pretest a survey, it's always wise to try a small pilot experiment before running the full-scale experiment. You may learn, for example, how to choose factor levels more effectively, about effects you forgot to control, and about unanticipated confoundings.

---

[6] R. D. DeVeaux and M. Szelewski, "Optimizing Automatic Splitless Injection Parameters for Gas Chromatographic Environmental Analysis." *Journal of Chromatographic Science* 27, no. 9 (1989): 513–518.

# CONNECTIONS

The fundamental role of randomization in experiments clearly points back to our discussions of randomization, to our experiments with simulations, and to our use of randomization in sampling. The similarities and differences between experiments and samples are important to keep in mind and can make each concept clearer.

If you think that blocking in an experiment resembles stratifying in a sample, you're quite right. Both are ways of removing variation we can identify to help us see past the variation in the data.

Experiments compare groups of subjects that have been treated differently. Graphics such as boxplots that help us compare groups are closely related to these ideas. Think about what we look for in a boxplot to tell whether two groups look really different, and you'll be thinking about the same issues as experiment designers.

Generally, we're going to consider how different the mean responses are for different treatment groups. And we're going to judge whether those differences are large by using standard deviations as rulers. (That's why we needed to replicate results for each treatment; we need to be able to estimate those standard deviations.) The discussion in Chapter 6 introduced this fundamental statistical thought, and it's going to keep coming back over and over again. Statistics is about variation.

We'll see a number of ways to analyze results from experiments in subsequent chapters.

## WHAT HAVE WE LEARNED?

We've learned to recognize sample surveys, observational studies, and randomized comparative experiments. We know that these methods collect data in different ways and lead us to different conclusions.

We've learned to identify retrospective and prospective observational studies and understand the advantages and disadvantages of each.

We've learned that only well-designed experiments can allow us to reach cause-and-effect conclusions. We manipulate levels of treatments to see if the factor we have identified produces changes in our response variable.

We've learned the principles of experimental design:

▶ We want to be sure that variation in the response variable can be attributed to our factor, so we identify and control as many other sources of variability as possible.

▶ Because there are many possible sources of variability that we cannot identify, we try to equalize those by randomly assigning experimental units to treatments.

▶ We replicate the experiment on as many subjects as possible.

▶ We consider blocking to reduce variability from sources we recognize but cannot control.

We've learned the value of having a control group and of using blinding and placebo controls.

Finally, we've learned to recognize the problems posed by confounding variables in experiments and lurking variables in observational studies.

## Terms

**Observational study**  329. A study based on data in which no manipulation of factors has been employed.

**Retrospective study**  330. An observational study in which subjects are selected and then their previous conditions or behaviors are determined. Because retrospective studies are not based on random samples, they usually focus on estimating differences between groups or associations between variables.

**Prospective study**  330. An observational study in which subjects are followed to observe future outcomes. Because no treatments are deliberately applied, a prospective study is not an experiment. Nevertheless, prospective studies typically focus on estimating differences among groups that might appear as the groups are followed during the course of the study.

| | |
|---|---|
| **Experiment** | 331. An experiment *manipulates* factor levels to create treatments, *randomly assigns* subjects to these treatment levels, and then *compares* the responses of the subject groups across treatment levels. |
| **Random assignment** | 331. To be valid, an experiment must assign experimental units to treatment groups at random. This is called random assignment. |
| **Factor** | 331. A variable whose levels are controlled by the experimenter. Experiments attempt to discover the effects that differences in factor levels may have on the responses of the experimental units. |
| **Response** | 331. A variable whose values are compared across different treatments. In a randomized experiment, large response differences can be attributed to the effect of differences in treatment level. |
| **Experimental units** | 331. Individuals on whom an experiment is performed. Usually called **subjects** or **participants** when they are human. |
| **Level** | 331. The specific values that the experimenter chooses for a factor are called the levels of the factor. |
| **Treatment** | 331. The process, intervention, or other controlled circumstance applied to randomly assigned experimental units. Treatments are the different levels of a single factor or are made up of combinations of levels of two or more factors. |
| **Principles of experimental design** | ▸ 332. **Control** aspects of the experiment that we know may have an effect on the response, but that are not the factors being studied. |
| | ▸ 333. **Randomize** subjects to treatments to even out effects that we cannot control. |
| | ▸ 333. **Replicate** over as many subjects as possible. Results for a single subject are just anecdotes. If, as often happens, the subjects of the experiment are not a representative sample from the population of interest, replicate the entire study with a different group of subjects, preferably from a different part of the population. |
| | ▸ 334. **Block** to reduce the effects of identifiable attributes of the subjects that cannot be controlled. |
| **Statistically significant** | 337. When an observed difference is too large for us to believe that it is likely to have occurred naturally, we consider the difference to be statistically significant. Subsequent chapters will show specific calculations and give rules, but the principle remains the same. |
| **Control group** | 339. The experimental units assigned to a baseline treatment level, typically either the default treatment, which is well understood, or a null, placebo treatment. Their responses provide a basis for comparison. |
| **Blinding** | 339. Any individual associated with an experiment who is not aware of how subjects have been allocated to treatment groups is said to be blinded. |
| **Single-blind Double-blind** | 340. There are two main classes of individuals who can affect the outcome of an experiment: <br>▸ those who could *influence the results* (the subjects, treatment administrators, or technicians). <br>▸ those who *evaluate the results* (judges, treating physicians, etc.). <br><br>When every individual in *either* of these classes is blinded, an experiment is said to be single-blind. When everyone in *both* classes is blinded, we call the experiment double-blind. |
| **Placebo** | 340. A treatment known to have no effect, administered so that all groups experience the same conditions. Many subjects respond to such a treatment (a response known as a placebo effect). Only by comparing with a placebo can we be sure that the observed effect of a treatment is not due simply to the placebo effect. |
| **Placebo effect** | 341. The tendency of many human subjects (often 20% or more of experiment subjects) to show a response even when administered a placebo. |
| **Blocking** | 341. When groups of experimental units are similar, it is often a good idea to gather them together into blocks. By blocking, we isolate the variability attributable to the differences between the blocks so that we can see the differences caused by the treatments more clearly. |
| **Matching** | 342. In a retrospective or prospective study, subjects who are similar in ways not under study may be matched and then compared with each other on the variables of interest. Matching, like blocking, reduces unwanted variation. |
| **Designs** | 335, 343. In a **completely randomized design,** all experimental units have an equal chance of receiving any treatment. |
| | 342. In a **randomized block design,** the randomization occurs only within blocks. |

**Confounding**  344. When the levels of one factor are associated with the levels of another factor in such a way that their effects cannot be separated, we say that these two factors are confounded

## Skills

- ▸ Recognize when an observational study would be appropriate.
- ▸ Be able to identify observational studies as retrospective or prospective, and understand the strengths and weaknesses of each method.
- ▸ Know the four basic principles of sound experimental design—control, randomize, replicate, and block—and be able to explain each.
- ▸ Be able to recognize the factors, the treatments, and the response variable in a description of a designed experiment.
- ▸ Understand the essential importance of randomization in assigning treatments to experimental units.
- ▸ Understand the importance of replication to move from anecdotes to general conclusions.
- ▸ Understand the value of blocking so that variability due to differences in attributes of the subjects can be removed.
- ▸ Understand the importance of a control group and the need for a placebo treatment in some studies.
- ▸ Understand the importance of blinding and double-blinding in studies on human subjects, and be able to identify blinding and the need for blinding in experiments.
- ▸ Understand the value of a placebo in experiments with human participants.
- ▸ Be able to design a completely randomized experiment to test the effect of a single factor.
- ▸ Be able to design an experiment in which blocking is used to reduce variation.
- ▸ Know how to use graphical displays to compare responses for different treatment groups. Understand that you should *never* proceed with any other analysis of a designed experiment without first looking at boxplots or other graphical displays.
- ▸ Know how to report the results of an observational study. Identify the subjects, how the data were gathered, and any potential biases or flaws you may be aware of. Identify the factors known and those that might have been revealed by the study.
- ▸ Know how to compare the responses in different treatment groups to assess whether the differences are larger than could be reasonably expected from ordinary sampling variability.
- ▸ Know how to report the results of an experiment. Tell who the subjects are and how their assignment to treatments was determined. Report how and in what measurement units the response variable was measured.
- ▸ Understand that your description of an experiment should be sufficient for another researcher to replicate the study with the same methods.
- ▸ Be able to report on the statistical significance of the result in terms of whether the observed group-to-group differences are larger than could be expected from ordinary sampling variation.

## ON THE COMPUTER

## Experiments

Most experiments are analyzed with a statistics package. You should almost always display the results of a comparative experiment with side-by-side boxplots. You may also want to display the means and standard deviations of the treatment groups in a table.

The analyses offered by statistics packages for comparative randomized experiments fall under the general heading of Analysis of Variance, usually abbreviated ANOVA. These analyses are beyond the scope of this chapter.

# EXERCISES

1. **Standardized test scores.** For his Statistics class experiment, researcher J. Gilbert decided to study how parents' income affects children's performance on standardized tests like the SAT. He proposed to collect information from a random sample of test takers and examine the relationship between parental income and SAT score.
   a) Is this an experiment? If not, what kind of study is it?
   b) If there is relationship between parental income and SAT score, why can't we conclude that differences in score are caused by differences in parental income?

2. **Heart attacks and height.** Researchers who examined health records of thousands of males found that men who died of myocardial infarction (heart attack) tended to be shorter than men who did not.
   a) Is this an experiment? If not, what kind of study is it?
   b) Is it correct to conclude that shorter men are at higher risk for heart attack? Explain.

3. **MS and vitamin D.** Multiple sclerosis (MS) is an autoimmune disease that strikes more often the farther people live from the equator. Could vitamin D—which most people get from the sun's ultraviolet rays—be a factor? Researchers compared vitamin D levels in blood samples from 150 U.S. military personnel who have developed MS with blood samples of nearly 300 who have not. The samples were taken, on average, five years before the disease was diagnosed. Those with the highest blood vitamin D levels had a 62% lower risk of MS than those with the lowest levels. (The link was only in whites, not in blacks or Hispanics.)
   a) What kind of study was this?
   b) Is that an appropriate choice for investigating this problem? Explain.
   c) Who were the subjects?
   d) What were the variables?

4. **Super Bowl commercials.** When spending large amounts to purchase advertising time, companies want to know what audience they'll reach. In January 2007, a poll asked 1008 American adults whether they planned to watch the upcoming Super Bowl. Men and women were asked separately whether they were looking forward more to the football game or to watching the commercials. Among the men, 16% were planning to watch and were looking forward primarily to the commercials. Among women, 30% were looking forward primarily to the commercials.
   a) Was this a stratified sample or a blocked experiment? Explain.
   b) Was the design of the study appropriate for the advertisers' questions?

5. **Menopause.** Researchers studied the herb black cohosh as a treatment for hot flashes caused by menopause. They randomly assigned 351 women aged 45 to 55 who reported at least two hot flashes a day to one of five groups: (1) black cohosh, (2) a multiherb supplement with black cohosh, (3) the multiherb supplement plus advice to consume more soy foods, (4) estrogen replacement therapy, or (5) receive a placebo. After a year, only the women given estrogen replacement therapy had symptoms different from those of the placebo group. [*Annals of Internal Medicine* 145:12, 869–897]
   a) What kind of study was this?
   b) Is that an appropriate choice for this problem?
   c) Who were the subjects?
   d) Identify the treatment and response variables.

6. **Honesty.** Coffee stations in offices often just ask users to leave money in a tray to pay for their coffee, but many people cheat. Researchers at Newcastle University replaced the picture of flowers on the wall behind the coffee station with a picture of staring eyes. They found that the average contribution increased significantly above the well-established standard when people felt they were being watched, even though the eyes were patently not real. (NY *Times* 12/10/06)
   a) Was this a survey, an observational study, or an experiment? How can we tell?
   b) Identify the variables.
   c) What does "increased significantly" mean in a statistical sense?

*7–26. What's the design?* *Read each brief report of statistical research, and identify*
   a) whether it was an observational study or an experiment.

*If it was an observational study, identify (if possible)*
   b) whether it was retrospective or prospective.
   c) the subjects studied and how they were selected.
   d) the parameter of interest.
   e) the nature and scope of the conclusion the study can reach.

*If it was an experiment, identify (if possible)*
   b) the subjects studied.
   c) the factor(s) in the experiment and the number of levels for each.
   d) the number of treatments.
   e) the response variable measured.
   f) the design (completely randomized, blocked, or matched).
   g) whether it was blind (or double-blind).
   h) the nature and scope of the conclusion the experiment can reach.

7. Over a 4-month period, among 30 people with bipolar disorder, patients who were given a high dose (10 g/day) of omega-3 fats from fish oil improved more than those given a placebo. (*Archives of General Psychiatry* 56 [1999]: 407)

8. The leg muscles of men aged 60 to 75 were 50% to 80% stronger after they participated in a 16-week, high-intensity resistance-training program twice a week. (*Journal of Gerontology* 55A [2000]: B336)

9. In a test of roughly 200 men and women, those with moderately high blood pressure (averaging 164/89 mm Hg) did worse on tests of memory and reaction time than those with normal blood pressure. (*Hypertension* 36 [2000]: 1079)

10. Among a group of disabled women aged 65 and older who were tracked for several years, those who had a vitamin $B_{12}$ deficiency were twice as likely to suffer severe depression as those who did not. (*American Journal of Psychiatry* 157 [2000]: 715)

11. An examination of the medical records of more than 360,000 Swedish men showed that those who were overweight or who had high blood pressure had a higher risk of kidney cancer. (*New England Journal of Medicine* 3434 [2000]: 1305)

12. To research the effects of "dietary patterns" on blood pressure in 459 subjects, subjects were randomly assigned to three groups and had their meals prepared by dieticians. Those who were fed a diet low in fat and cholesterol and high in fruits, vegetables, and low-fat dairy foods (known as the DASH diet) lowered their systolic blood pressure by an average of 6.7 points compared with subjects fed a control diet.

13. After menopause, some women take supplemental estrogen. There is some concern that if these women also drink alcohol, their estrogen levels will rise too high. Twelve volunteers who were receiving supplemental estrogen were randomly divided into two groups, as were 12 other volunteers not on estrogen. In each case, one group drank an alcoholic beverage, the other a nonalcoholic beverage. An hour later, everyone's estrogen level was checked. Only those on supplemental estrogen who drank alcohol showed a marked increase.

14. Is diet or exercise effective in combating insomnia? Some believe that cutting out desserts can help alleviate the problem, while others recommend exercise. Forty volunteers suffering from insomnia agreed to participate in a month-long test. Half were randomly assigned to a special no-desserts diet; the others continued desserts as usual. Half of the people in each of these groups were randomly assigned to an exercise program, while the others did not exercise. Those who ate no desserts and engaged in exercise showed the most improvement.

15. Some gardeners prefer to use nonchemical methods to control insect pests in their gardens. Researchers have designed two kinds of traps and want to know which design will be more effective. They randomly choose 10 locations in a large garden and place one of each kind of trap at each location. After a week, they count the number of bugs in each trap.

16. Researchers have linked an increase in the incidence of breast cancer in Italy to dioxin released by an industrial accident in 1976. The study identified 981 women who lived near the site of the industrial explosion and were under age 40 at the time. Fifteen of the women had developed breast cancer at an unusually young average age of 45. Medical records showed that these women had heightened concentrations of dioxin in their blood and that each tenfold increase in dioxin level was associated with a doubling of the risk of breast cancer. (*Science News*, Aug. 3, 2002)

17. In 2002 the journal *Science* reported that a study of women in Finland indicated that having sons shortened the lifespans of mothers by about 34 weeks per son, but that daughters helped to lengthen the mothers' lives. The data came from church records from the period 1640 to 1870.

18. In 2001 a report in the *Journal of the American Cancer Institute* indicated that women who work nights have a 60% greater risk of developing breast cancer. Researchers based these findings on the work histories of 763 women with breast cancer and 741 women without the disease.

19. The May 4, 2000, issue of *Science News* reported that, contrary to popular belief, depressed individuals cry no more often in response to sad situations than nondepressed people. Researchers studied 23 men and 48 women with major depression, and 9 men and 24 women with no depression. They showed the subjects a sad film about a boy whose father has died, noting whether or not the subjects cried. Women cried more often than men, but there were no significant differences between the depressed and nondepressed groups.

20. Scientists at a major pharmaceutical firm investigated the effectiveness of an herbal compound to treat the common cold. They exposed each subject to a cold virus, then gave him or her either the herbal compound or a sugar solution known to have no effect on colds. Several days later they assessed the patient's condition, using a cold severity scale ranging from 0 to 5. They found no evidence of benefits associated with the compound.

21. Scientists examined the glycogen content of rats' brains at the rats' normal bedtimes and after they had been kept awake for an extra 6, 12, or 24 hours. The scientists found that glycogen was 38% lower among rats that had been sleep-deprived for 12 hours or more, and that the levels recovered during subsequent sleep. These researchers speculate that we may need to sleep in order to restore the brain's energy fuel. (*Science News*, July 20, 2002)

22. Some people who race greyhounds give the dogs large doses of vitamin C in the belief that the dogs will run faster. Investigators at the University of Florida tried three different diets in random order on each of five racing greyhounds. They were surprised to find that when the dogs ate high amounts of vitamin C they ran more slowly. (*Science News*, July 20, 2002)

23. Some people claim they can get relief from migraine headache pain by drinking a large glass of ice water. Researchers plan to enlist several people who suffer from migraines in a test. When a participant experiences a migraine headache, he or she will take a pill that may be a

standard pain reliever or a placebo. Half of each group will also drink ice water. Participants will then report the level of pain relief they experience.

24. Weight is an issue for both humans and their pets. A dog food company wants to compare a new lower-calorie food with their standard dog food to see if it's effective in helping inactive dogs maintain a healthy weight. They have found several dog owners willing to participate in the trial. The dogs have been classified as small, medium, or large breeds, and the company will supply some owners of each size of dog with one of the two foods. The owners have agreed not to feed their dogs anything else for a period of 6 months, after which the dogs' weights will be checked.

25. Athletes who had suffered hamstring injuries were randomly assigned to one of two exercise programs. Those who engaged in static stretching returned to sports activity in a mean of 37.4 days (*SD* = 27.6 days). Those assigned to a program of agility and trunk stabilization exercises returned to sports in a mean of 22.2 days (*SD* = 8.3 days). (*Journal of Orthopaedic & Sports Physical Therapy* 34 [March 2004]: 3)

26. Pew Research compared respondents to an ordinary 5-day telephone survey with respondents to a 4-month-long rigorous survey designed to generate the highest possible response rate. They were especially interested in identifying any variables for which those who responded to the ordinary survey were different from those who could be reached only by the rigorous survey.

27. **Omega-3.** Exercise 7 describes an experiment that showed that high doses of omega-3 fats might be of benefit to people with bipolar disorder. The experiment involved a control group of subjects who received a placebo. Why didn't the experimenters just give everyone the omega-3 fats to see if they improved?

28. **Insomnia.** Exercise 14 describes an experiment that showed that getting exercise helped people sleep better. The experiment involved other groups of subjects who didn't exercise. Why didn't the experimenters just have everyone exercise and see if their ability to sleep improved?

29. **Omega-3 revisited.** Exercises 7 and 27 describe an experiment investigating a dietary approach to treating bipolar disorder. Researchers randomly assigned 30 subjects to two treatment groups, one group taking a high dose of omega-3 fats and the other a placebo.
    a) Why was it important to randomize in assigning the subjects to the two groups?
    b) What would be the advantages and disadvantages of using 100 subjects instead of 30?

30. **Insomnia again.** Exercises 14 and 28 describe an experiment investigating the effectiveness of exercise in combating insomnia. Researchers randomly assigned half of the 40 volunteers to an exercise program.
    a) Why was it important to randomize in deciding who would exercise?
    b) What would be the advantages and disadvantages of using 100 subjects instead of 40?

31. **Omega-3, finis.** Exercises 7, 27, and 29 describe an experiment investigating the effectiveness of omega-3 fats in treating bipolar disorder. Suppose some of the 30 subjects were very active people who walked a lot or got vigorous exercise several times a week, while others tended to be more sedentary, working office jobs and watching a lot of TV. Why might researchers choose to block the subjects by activity level before randomly assigning them to the omega-3 and placebo groups?

32. **Insomnia, at last.** Exercises 14, 28, and 30 describe an experiment investigating the effectiveness of exercise in combating insomnia. Suppose some of the 40 subjects had maintained a healthy weight, but others were quite overweight. Why might researchers choose to block the subjects by weight level before randomly assigning some of each group to the exercise program?

33. **Tomatoes.** Describe a strategy to randomly split the 24 tomato plants into the three groups for the chapter's completely randomized single factor test of OptiGro fertilizer.

34. **Tomatoes II.** The chapter also described a completely randomized two-factor experiment testing OptiGro fertilizer in conjunction with two different routines for watering the plants. Describe a strategy to randomly assign the 24 tomato plants to the six treatments.

35. **Shoes.** A running-shoe manufacturer wants to test the effect of its new sprinting shoe on 100-meter dash times. The company sponsors 5 athletes who are running the 100-meter dash in the 2004 Summer Olympic games. To test the shoe, it has all 5 runners run the 100-meter dash with a competitor's shoe and then again with their new shoe. The company uses the difference in times as the response variable.
    a) Suggest some improvements to the design.
    b) Why might the shoe manufacturer not be able to generalize the results they find to all runners?

36. **Swimsuits.** A swimsuit manufacturer wants to test the speed of its newly designed suit. The company designs an experiment by having 6 randomly selected Olympic swimmers swim as fast as they can with their old swimsuit first and then swim the same event again with the new, expensive swimsuit. The company will use the difference in times as the response variable. Criticize the experiment and point out some of the problems with generalizing the results.

37. **Hamstrings.** Exercise 25 discussed an experiment to see if the time it took athletes with hamstring injuries to be able to return to sports was different depending on which of two exercise programs they engaged in.
    a) Explain why it was important to assign the athletes to the two different treatments randomly.
    b) There was no control group consisting of athletes who did not participate in a special exercise program. Explain the advantage of including such a group in this experiment.
    c) How might blinding have been used in this experiment?
    d) One group returned to sports activity in a mean of 37.4 days (*SD* = 27.6 days) and the other in a mean of

22.2 days (*SD* = 8.3 days). Do you think this difference is statistically significant? Explain.

**38. Diet and blood pressure.** Exercise 12 reports on an experiment that showed that subjects fed the DASH diet were able to lower their blood pressure by an average of 6.7 points compared to a group fed a "control diet." All meals were prepared by dieticians.
a) Why were the subjects randomly assigned to the diets instead of letting people pick what they wanted to eat?
b) Why were the meals prepared by dieticians?
c) Why did the researchers need the control group? If the DASH diet group's blood pressure was lower at the end of the experiment than at the beginning, wouldn't that prove the effectiveness of that diet?
d) What additional information would you want to know in order to decide whether an average reduction in blood pressure of 6.7 points was statistically significant?

**39. Mozart.** Will listening to a Mozart piano sonata make you smarter? In a 1995 study published in the journal *Psychological Science,* Rauscher, Shaw, and Ky reported that when students were given a spatial reasoning section of a standard IQ test, those who listened to Mozart for 10 minutes improved their scores more than those who simply sat quietly.
a) These researchers said the differences were statistically significant. Explain what that means in this context.
b) Steele, Bass, and Crook tried to replicate the original study. In their study, also published in *Psychological Science* (1999), the subjects were 125 college students who participated in the experiment for course credit. Subjects first took the test. Then they were assigned to one of three groups: listening to a Mozart piano sonata, listening to music by Philip Glass, and sitting for 10 minutes in silence. Three days after the treatments, they were retested. Draw a diagram displaying the design of this experiment.
c) These boxplots show the differences in score before and after treatment for the three groups. Did the Mozart group show improvement?

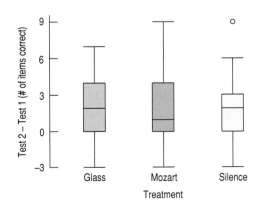

d) Do you think the results prove that listening to Mozart is beneficial? Explain.

**40. More Mozart.** The *NY Times* (Sept. 9, 1991) reported that "A sake brewer [near] Tokyo is marketing a Mozart brand of sake, asserting that Mozart is regularly played at the brewery. 'It seems that the malt grows well especially with Mozart music in the background,' the company director [said]." Suppose, just for the sake (as it were) of discussion, you wished to design an experiment to test whether this is true. Assume you have the full cooperation of the sake brewery. Specify how you would design the experiment. Indicate factors and response and how they would be measured, controlled, or randomized.

**41. Frumpies.** The makers of Frumpies, "the breakfast of rug rats," want to improve their marketing, so they consult you:
a) They first want to know what fraction of children, ages 10 to 13, like their celery-flavored cereal. What kind of study should they perform?
b) They are thinking of introducing a new flavor, maple-marshmallow Frumpies, and want to know whether children will prefer the new flavor to the old one. Design a completely randomized experiment to investigate this question.
c) They suspect that children who regularly watch the Saturday morning cartoon show starring Frump, the flying teenage warrior rabbit who eats Frumpies in every episode, may respond differently to the new flavor. How would you take that into account in your design?

**42. Full moon.** It's a common belief that people behave strangely when there's a full moon and that as a result police and emergency rooms are busier than usual. Design a way you could find out whether there is any merit to this belief. Will you use an observational study or an experiment? Why?

**43. Wine.** A 2001 Danish study published in the *Archives of Internal Medicine* casts significant doubt on suggestions that adults who drink wine have higher levels of "good" cholesterol and fewer heart attacks. These researchers followed a group of individuals born at a Copenhagen hospital between 1959 and 1961 for 40 years. Their study found that in this group the adults who drank wine were richer and better educated than those who did not.
a) What kind of study was this?
b) It is generally true that people with high levels of education and high socioeconomic status are healthier than others. How does this call into question the supposed health benefits of wine?
c) Can studies such as these prove causation (that wine helps prevent heart attacks, that drinking wine makes one richer, that being rich helps prevent heart attacks, etc.)? Explain.

**44. Swimming.** Recently, a group of adults who swim regularly for exercise were evaluated for depression. It turned out that these swimmers were less likely to be depressed than the general population. The researchers said the difference was statistically significant.
a) What does "statistically significant" mean in this context?

b) Is this an experiment or an observational study? Explain.

c) News reports claimed this study proved that swimming can prevent depression. Explain why this conclusion is not justified by the study. Include an example of a possible confounding variable.

d) But perhaps it is true. We wonder if exercise can ward off depression, and whether anaerobic exercise (like weight training) is as effective as aerobic exercise (like swimming). We find 120 volunteers not currently engaged in a regular program of exercise. Design an appropriate experiment.

**45. Dowsing.** A water dowser claims to be able to sense the presence of water using a forked stick. Suppose we wish to set up an experiment to test his ability. We get 20 identical containers, fill some with water, and ask the dowser to tell which ones are full and which empty.

a) How will we randomize this procedure?

b) The dowser correctly identifies the contents of 12 out of 20 containers. Do you think this level of success is statistically significant? Explain.

c) How many correct identifications (out of 20) would the dowser have to make to convince you that the forked-stick trick works? Explain.

**46. Healing.** A medical researcher suspects that giving postsurgical patients large doses of vitamin E will speed their recovery times by helping their incisions heal more quickly. Design an experiment to test this conjecture. Be sure to identify the factors, levels, treatments, response variable, and the role of randomization.

**47. Reading.** Some schools teach reading using phonics (the sounds made by letters) and others using whole language (word recognition). Suppose a school district wants to know which method works better. Suggest a design for an appropriate experiment.

**48. Gas mileage.** Do cars get better gas mileage with premium instead of regular unleaded gasoline? While it might be possible to test some engines in a laboratory setting, we'd rather use real cars and real drivers in real day-to-day driving, so we get 20 volunteers. Design the experiment.

**49. Weekend deaths.** A study published in the *New England Journal of Medicine* (Aug. 2001) suggests that it's dangerous to enter a hospital on a weekend. During a 10-year period, researchers tracked over 4 million emergency admissions to hospitals in Ontario, Canada. Their findings revealed that patients admitted on weekends had a much higher risk of death than those who went to the emergency room on weekdays.

a) The researchers said the difference in death rates was "statistically significant." Explain in this context what that means.

b) What kind of study was this? Explain.

c) If you think you're quite ill on a Saturday, should you wait until Monday to seek medical help? Explain.

d) Suggest some possible explanations for this troubling finding.

**50. Shingles.** A research doctor has discovered a new ointment that she believes will be more effective than the current medication in the treatment of shingles (a painful skin rash). Eight patients have volunteered to participate in the initial trials of this ointment. You are the statistician hired as a consultant to help design a completely randomized experiment.

a) Describe how you will conduct this experiment.

b) Suppose the eight patients' last names start with the letters A to H. Using the random numbers listed below, show which patients you will assign to each treatment. Explain your randomization procedure clearly.

41098 18329 78458 31685 55259

c) Can you make this experiment double-blind? If so, explain how.

d) The initial experiment revealed that males and females may respond differently to the ointment. Further testing of the drug's effectiveness is now planned, and many patients have volunteered. What changes in your first design, if any, would you make for this second stage of testing?

**51. Beetles.** Hoping to learn how to control crop damage by a certain species of beetle, a researcher plans to test two different pesticides in small plots of corn. A few days after application of the chemicals, he'll check the number of beetle larvae found on each plant. The researcher wants to know whether either pesticide works and whether there is a significant difference in effectiveness between them. Design an appropriate experiment.

**52. SAT Prep.** Can special study courses actually help raise SAT scores? One organization says that the 30 students they tutored achieved an average gain of 60 points when they retook the test.

a) Explain why this does not necessarily prove that the special course caused the scores to go up.

b) Propose a design for an experiment that could test the effectiveness of the tutorial course.

c) Suppose you suspect that the tutorial course might be more helpful for students whose initial scores were particularly low. How would this affect your proposed design?

**53. Safety switch.** An industrial machine requires an emergency shutoff switch that must be designed so that it can be easily operated with either hand. Design an experiment to find out whether workers will be able to deactivate the machine as quickly with their left hands as with their right hands. Be sure to explain the role of randomization in your design.

**54. Washing clothes.** A consumer group wants to test the effectiveness of a new "organic" laundry detergent and make recommendations to customers about how to best use the product. They intentionally get grass stains on 30 white T-shirts in order to see how well the detergent will clean them. They want to try the detergent in cold water and in hot water on both the "regular" and "delicates" wash cycles. Design an appropriate experiment, indicating the number of factors, levels, and treatments. Explain the role of randomization in your experiment.

**55. Skydiving, anyone?**   A humor piece published in the *British Medical Journal* ("Parachute use to prevent death and major trauma related to gravitational challenge: systematic review of randomized control trials," Gordon, Smith, and Pell, *BMJ*, 2003:327) notes that we can't tell for sure whether parachutes are safe and effective because there has never been a properly randomized, double-blind, placebo-controlled study of parachute effectiveness in skydiving. (Yes, this is the sort of thing statisticians find funny. . . .) Suppose you were designing such a study:

a) What is the factor in this experiment?
b) What experimental units would you propose?[7]
c) Explain what would serve as a placebo for this study.
d) What would the treatments be?
e) What would be the response variable for such a study?
f) What sources of variability would you control?
g) How would you randomize this "experiment"?
h) How would you make the experiment double-blind?

## JUST CHECKING
### Answers

**1. a)** The factor was type of treatment for peptic ulcer.
   **b)** The response variable could be a measure of relief from gastric ulcer pain or an evaluation by a physician of the state of the disease.
   **c)** Treatments would be gastric freezing and some alternative control treatment.
   **d)** Treatments should be assigned randomly.
   **e)** No. The Web site reports "lack of effectiveness," indicating that no large differences in patient healing were noted.

**2. a)** Neither the patients who received the treatment nor the doctor who evaluated them to see if they had improved knew what treatment they had received.
   **b)** The placebo is needed to accomplish blinding. The best alternative would be using body-temperature liquid rather than the freezing liquid.
   **c)** The researchers should block the subjects by the length of time they had had the ulcer, then randomly assign subjects in each block to the freezing and placebo groups.

---

[7] Don't include your Statistics instructor!

# REVIEW OF PART III

## Gathering Data

### QUICK REVIEW

Before you can make a boxplot, calculate a mean, describe a distribution, or fit a line, you must have meaningful data to work with. Getting good data is essential to any investigation. No amount of clever analysis can make up for badly collected data. Here's a brief summary of the key concepts and skills:

▶ The way you gather data depends both on what you want to discover and on what is practical.

▶ To get some insight into what might happen in a real situation, model it with a **simulation** using random numbers.

▶ To answer questions about a target population, collect information from a sample with a **survey** or poll.

  • Choose the sample randomly. Random sampling designs include simple, stratified, systematic, cluster, and multistage.

  • A simple random sample draws without restriction from the entire target population.

  • When there are subgroups within the population that may respond differently, use a stratified sample.

  • Avoid bias, a systematic distortion of the results. Sample designs that allow undercoverage or response bias and designs such as voluntary response or convenience samples don't faithfully represent the population.

  • Samples will naturally vary one from another. This sample-to-sample variation is called sampling error. Each sample only approximates the target population.

▶ **Observational studies** collect information from a sample drawn from a target population.

  • Retrospective studies examine existing data. Prospective studies identify subjects in advance, then follow them to collect data as the data are created, perhaps over many years.

  • Observational studies can spot associations between variables but cannot establish cause and effect. It's impossible to eliminate the possibility of lurking or confounding variables.

▶ To see how different treatments influence a response variable, design an **experiment.**

  • Assign subjects to treatments randomly. If you don't assign treatments randomly, your experiment is not likely to yield valid results.

  • Control known sources of variation as much as possible. Reduce variation that cannot be controlled by using blocking, if possible.

  • Replicate the experiment, assigning several subjects to each treatment level.

  • If possible, replicate the entire experiment with an entirely different collection of subjects.

  • A well-designed experiment can provide evidence that changes in the factors cause changes in the response variable.

Now for more opportunities to review these concepts and skills . . .

# REVIEW EXERCISES

*1–18. What design?* *Analyze the design of each research example reported. Is it a sample, an observational study, or an experiment? If a sample, what are the population, the parameter of interest, and the sampling procedure? If an observational study, was it retrospective or prospective? If an experiment, describe the factors, treatments, randomization, response variable, and any blocking, matching, or blinding that may be present. In each, what kind of conclusions can be reached?*

1. Researchers identified 242 children in the Cleveland area who had been born prematurely (at about 29 weeks). They examined these children at age 8 and again at age 20, comparing them to another group of 233 children not born prematurely. According to their report, published in the *New England Journal of Medicine*, the "preemies" engaged in significantly less risky behavior than the others. Differences between the groups showed up in the use of alcohol and marijuana, conviction of crimes, and teenage pregnancy.

2. The journal *Circulation* reported that among 1900 people who had heart attacks, those who drank an average of 19 cups of tea a week were 44% more likely than non-drinkers to survive at least 3 years after the attack.

3. Researchers at the Purina Pet Institute studied Labrador retrievers for evidence of a relationship between diet and longevity. At 8 weeks of age, 2 puppies of the same sex and weight were randomly assigned to one of two groups—a total of 48 dogs in all. One group was allowed to eat all they wanted, while the other group was fed a low-calorie diet (about 75% as much as the others). The median lifespan of dogs fed the restricted diet was 22 months longer than that of other dogs. (*Science News* 161, no. 19)

4. The radioactive gas radon, found in some homes, poses a health risk to residents. To assess the level of contamination in their area, a county health department wants to test a few homes. If the risk seems high, they will publicize the results to emphasize the need for home testing. Officials plan to use the local property tax list to randomly choose 25 homes from various areas of the county.

5. Almost 90,000 women participated in a 16-year study of the role of the vitamin folate in preventing colon cancer. Some of the women had family histories of colon cancer in close relatives. In this at-risk group, the incidence of colon cancer was cut in half among those who maintained a high folate intake. No such difference was observed in those with no family-based risk. (*Science News*, Feb. 9, 2002)

6. In a study appearing in the journal *Science*, a research team reports that plants in southern England are flowering earlier in the spring. Records of the first flowering dates for 385 species over a period of 47 years indicate that flowering has advanced an average of 15 days per decade, an indication of climate warming, according to the authors.

7. Fireworks manufacturers face a dilemma. They must be sure that the rockets work properly, but test firing a rocket essentially destroys it. On the other hand, not testing the product leaves open the danger that they sell a bunch of duds, leading to unhappy customers and loss of future sales. The solution, of course, is to test a few of the rockets produced each day, assuming that if those tested work properly, the others are ready for sale.

8. Can makeup damage fetal development? Many cosmetics contain a class of chemicals called phthalates. Studies that exposed some laboratory animals to these chemicals found a heightened incidence of damage to male reproductive systems. Since traces of phthalates are found in the urine of women who use beauty products, there is growing concern that they may present a risk to male fetuses. (*Science News*, July 20, 2002)

9. Can long-term exposure to strong electromagnetic fields cause cancer? Researchers in Italy tracked down 13 years of medical records for people living near Vatican Radio's powerful broadcast antennas. A disproportionate share of the leukemia cases occurred among men and children who lived within 6 kilometers of the antennas. (*Science News*, July 20, 2002)

10. Some doctors have expressed concern that men who have vasectomies seemed more likely to develop prostate cancer. Medical researchers used a national cancer registry to identify 923 men who had had prostate cancer and 1224 men of similar ages who had not. Roughly one quarter of the men in each group had undergone a vasectomy, many more than 25 years before the study. The study's authors concluded that there is strong evidence that having the operation presents no long-term risk for developing prostate cancer. (*Science News*, July 20, 2002)

11. Researchers investigating appetite control as a means of losing weight found that female rats ate less and lost weight after injections of the hormone leptin, while male rats responded better to insulin. (*Science News*, July 20, 2002)

12. An artisan wants to create pottery that has the appearance of age. He prepares several samples of clay with four different glazes and test fires them in a kiln at three different temperature settings.

13. Tests of gene therapy on laboratory rats have raised hopes of stopping the degeneration of tissue that characterizes chronic heart failure. Researchers at the University of California, San Diego, used hamsters with cardiac disease, randomly assigning 30 to receive the gene therapy and leaving the other 28 untreated. Five weeks after treatment the gene therapy group's heart muscles stabilized, while those of the untreated hamsters continued to weaken. (*Science News*, July 27, 2002)

14. Researchers at the University of Bristol (England) investigated reasons why different species of birds begin to sing at different times in the morning. They captured and

examined birds of 57 species at seven different sites. They measured the diameter of the birds' eyes and also recorded the time of day at which each species began to sing. These researchers reported a strong relationship between eye diameter and time of singing, saying that birds with bigger eyes tended to sing earlier. (*Science News*, 161, no. 16 [2002])

15. An orange-juice processing plant will accept a shipment of fruit only after several hundred oranges selected from various locations within the truck are carefully inspected. If too many of those checked show signs of unsuitability for juice (bruised, rotten, unripe, etc.) the whole truckload is rejected.

16. A soft-drink manufacturer must be sure the bottle caps on the soda are fully sealed and will not come off easily. Inspectors pull a few bottles off the production line at regular intervals and test the caps. If they detect any problems, they will stop the bottling process to adjust or repair the machine that caps the bottles.

17. Physically fit people are less likely to die of cancer. A report in the May 2002 issue of *Medicine and Science in Sports and Exercise* followed 25,892 men aged 30 to 87 for 10 years. The most physically fit men had a 55% lower risk of death from cancer than the least fit group.

18. Does the use of computer software in Introductory Statistics classes lead to better understanding of the concepts? A professor teaching two sections of Statistics decides to investigate. She teaches both sections using the same lectures and assignments, but gives one class statistics software to help them with their homework. The classes take the same final exam, and graders do not know which students used computers during the semester. The professor is also concerned that students who have had calculus may perform differently from those who have not, so she plans to compare software vs. no-software scores separately for these two groups of students.

19. **Point spread.** When taking bets on sporting events, bookmakers often include a "point spread" that awards the weaker team extra points. In theory this makes the outcome of the bet a toss-up. Suppose a gambler places a $10 bet and picks the winners of five games. If he's right about fewer than three of the games, he loses. If he gets three, four, or all five correct, he's paid $10, $20, and $50, respectively. Estimate the amount such a bettor might expect to lose over many weeks of gambling.

20. **The lottery.** Many people spend a lot of money trying to win huge jackpots in state lotteries. Let's play a simplified version using only the numbers from 1 to 20. You bet on three numbers. The state picks five winning numbers. If your three are all among the winners, you are rich!
    a. Simulate repeated plays. How long did it take you to win?
    b. In real lotteries, there are many more choices (often 54) and you must match all five winning numbers. Explain how these changes affect your chances of hitting the jackpot.

21. **Everyday randomness.** Aside from casinos, lotteries, and games, there are other situations you encounter in which something is described as "random" in some way.

Give three different examples. Describe how randomness is (or is not) achieved in each.

22. **Cell phone risks.** Researchers at the Washington University School of Medicine randomly placed 480 rats into one of three chambers containing radio antennas. One group was exposed to digital cell phone radio waves, the second to analog cell phone waves, and the third group to no radio waves. Two years later the rats were examined for signs of brain tumors. In June 2002 the scientists said that differences among the three groups were not statistically significant.
    a) Is this a study or an experiment? Explain.
    b) Explain in this context what "statistically significant" means.
    c) Comment on the fact that this research was supported by funding from Motorola, a manufacturer of cell phones.

23. **Tips.** In restaurants, servers rely on tips as a major source of income. Does serving candy after the meal produce larger tips? To find out, two waiters determined randomly whether or not to give candy to 92 dining parties. They recorded the sizes of the tips and reported that guests getting candy tipped an average of 17.8% of the bill, compared with an average tip of only 15.1% from those who got no candy. ("Sweetening the Till: The Use of Candy to Increase Restaurant Tipping." *Journal of Applied Social Psychology* 32, no. 2 [2002]: 300–309)
    a) Was this an experiment or an observational study? Explain.
    b) Is it reasonable to conclude that the candy caused guests to tip more? Explain.
    c) The researchers said the difference was statistically significant. Explain in this context what that means.

24. **Tips, take 2.** In another experiment to see if getting candy after a meal would induce customers to leave a bigger tip, a waitress randomly decided what to do with 80 dining parties. Some parties received no candy, some just one piece, and some two pieces. Others initially got just one piece of candy, and then the waitress suggested that they take another piece. She recorded the tips received, finding that, in general, the more candy, the higher the tip, but the highest tips (23%) came from the parties who got one piece and then were offered more. ("Sweetening the Till: The Use of Candy to Increase Restaurant Tipping." *Journal of Applied Social Psychology* 32, no. 2 [2002]: 300–309)
    a) Diagram this experiment.
    b) How many factors are there? How many levels?
    c) How many treatments are there?
    d) What is the response variable?
    e) Did this experiment involve blinding? Double blinding?
    f) In what way might the waitress, perhaps unintentionally, have biased the results?

25. **Cloning.** In September 1998, *USA Weekend* magazine asked, "Should humans be cloned?" Readers were invited to register a "Yes" or "No" answer by calling one of two different 900 numbers. Based on 38,023 responses, the magazine reported that "9 out of 10 readers oppose cloning."

a) Explain why you think the conclusion is not justified. Describe the types of bias that may be present.

b) Reword the question in a way that you think might create a more positive response.

**26. Laundry.** An experiment to test a new laundry detergent, SparkleKleen, is being conducted by a consumer advocate group. They would like to compare its performance with that of a laboratory standard detergent they have used in previous experiments. They can stain 16 swatches of cloth with 2 tsp of a common staining compound and then use a well-calibrated optical scanner to detect the amount of the stain that is left after washing with detergent. To save time in the experiment, several suggestions have been made. Comment on the possible merits and drawbacks of each one.

a) Since data for the laboratory standard detergent are already available from previous experiments, for this experiment wash all 16 swatches with SparkleKleen, and compare the results with the previous data.

b) Use both detergents with eight separate runs each, but to save time, use only a 10-second wash time with very hot water.

c) To ease bookkeeping, run successively all of the standard detergent washes on eight swatches, then run all of the SparkleKleen washes on the other eight swatches.

d) Rather than run the experiment, use data from the company that produced SparkleKleen, and compare them with past data from the standard detergent.

**27. When to Stop?** You play a game that involves rolling a die. You can roll as many times as you want, and your score is the total for all the rolls. But . . . if you roll a 6 your score is 0 and your turn is over. What might be a good strategy for a game like this?

a) One of your opponents decides to roll 4 times, then stop (hoping not to get the dreaded 6 before then). Use a simulation to estimate his average score.

b) Another opponent decides to roll until she gets at least 12 points, then stop. Use a simulation to estimate her average score.

c) Propose another strategy that you would use to play this game. Using your strategy, simulate several turns. Do you think you would beat the two opponents?

**28. Rivets.** A company that manufactures rivets believes the shear strength of the rivets they manufacture follows a Normal model with a mean breaking strength of 950 pounds and a standard deviation of 40 pounds.

a) What percentage of rivets selected at random will break when tested under a 900-pound load?

b) You're trying to improve the rivets and want to examine some that fail. Use a simulation to estimate how many rivets you might need to test in order to find three that fail at 900 pounds (or below).

**29. Homecoming.** A college Statistics class conducted a survey concerning community attitudes about the college's large homecoming celebration. That survey drew its sample in the following manner: Telephone numbers were generated at random by selecting one of the local telephone exchanges (first three digits) at random and then generating a random four-digit number to follow the exchange. If a person answered the phone and the call was to a residence, then that person was taken to be the subject for interview. (Undergraduate students and those under voting age were excluded, as was anyone who could not speak English.) Calls were placed until a sample of 200 eligible respondents had been reached.

a) Did every telephone number that could occur in that community have an equal chance of being generated?

b) Did this method of generating telephone numbers result in a simple random sample (SRS) of local residences? Explain.

c) Did this method generate an SRS of local voters? Explain.

d) Did this method generate an unbiased sample of households? Explain.

**30. Youthful appearance.** *Readers' Digest* reported results of several surveys that asked graduate students to examine photographs of men and women and try to guess their ages. Researchers compared these guesses with the number of times the people in the pictures reported having sexual intercourse. It turned out that those who had been more sexually active were judged as looking younger, and that the difference was described as "statistically significant." Psychologist David Weeks, who compiled the research, speculated that lovemaking boosts hormones that "reduce fatty tissue and increase lean muscle, giving a more youthful appearance."

a) What does "statistically significant" mean in this context?

b) Explain in statistical terms why you might be skeptical about Dr. Weeks' conclusion. Propose an alternative explanation for these results.

**31. Smoking and Alzheimer's.** Medical studies indicate that smokers are less likely to develop Alzheimer's disease than people who never smoked.

a) Does this prove that smoking may offer some protection against Alzheimer's? Explain.

b) Offer an alternative explanation for this association.

c) How would you conduct a study to investigate this issue?

**32. Antacids.** A researcher wants to compare the performance of three types of antacid in volunteers suffering from acid reflux disease. Because men and women may react differently to this medication, the subjects are split into two groups, by sex. Subjects in each group are randomly assigned to take one of the antacids or to take a sugar pill made to look the same. The subjects will rate their level of discomfort 30 minutes after eating.

a) What kind of design is this?

b) The experiment uses volunteers rather than a random sample of all people suffering from acid reflux disease. Does this make the results invalid? Explain.

c) How may the use of the placebo confound this experiment? Explain.

**33. Sex and violence.** Does the content of a television program affect viewers' memory of the products advertised in commercials? Design an experiment to compare the ability of viewers to recall brand names of items featured in commercials during programs with violent content, sexual content, or neutral content.

**34. Pubs.** In England, a Leeds University researcher said that the local watering hole's welcoming atmosphere helps men get rid of the stresses of modern life and is vital for their psychological well-being. Author of the report, Dr. Colin Gill, said rather than complain, women should encourage men to "pop out for a swift half." "Pub-time allows men to bond with friends and colleagues," he said. "Men need break-out time as much as women and are mentally healthier for it." Gill added that men might feel unfulfilled or empty if they had not been to the pub for a week. The report, commissioned by alcohol-free beer brand Kaliber, surveyed 900 men on their reasons for going to the pub. More than 40% said they went for the conversation, with relaxation and a friendly atmosphere being the other most common reasons. Only 1 in 10 listed alcohol as the overriding reason.

Let's examine this news story from a statistical perspective.
a) What are the W's: *Who, What, When, Where, Why?*
b) What population does the researcher think the study applies to?
c) What is the most important thing about the selection process that the article does *not* tell us?
d) How do *you* think the 900 respondents were selected? (Name a method of drawing a sample that is likely to have been used.)
e) Do you think the report that only 10% of respondents listed alcohol as an important reason for going to the pub might be a biased result? Why?

**35. Age and party.** The Gallup Poll conducted a representative telephone survey during the first quarter of 1999. Among its reported results was the following table concerning the preferred political party affiliation of respondents and their ages:

|  |  | Party | | |
| --- | --- | --- | --- | --- |
| | | Republican | Democratic | Independent | Total |
| **Age** | **18–29** | 241 | 351 | 409 | 1001 |
| | **30–49** | 299 | 330 | 370 | 999 |
| | **50–64** | 282 | 341 | 375 | 998 |
| | **65+** | 279 | 382 | 343 | 1004 |
| | **Total** | 1101 | 1404 | 1497 | **4002** |

a) What sampling strategy do you think the pollsters used? Explain.
b) What percentage of the people surveyed were Democrats?
c) Do you think this is a good estimate of the percentage of voters in the United States who are registered Democrats? Why or why not?
d) In creating this sample design, what question do you think the pollsters were trying to answer?

**36. Bias?** Political analyst Michael Barone has written that "conservatives are more likely than others to refuse to respond to polls, particularly those polls taken by media outlets that conservatives consider biased" (*The Weekly Standard*, March 10, 1997). The Pew Research Foundation tested this assertion by asking the same questions in a national survey run by standard methods and in a more rigorous survey that was a true SRS with careful follow-up to encourage participation. The response rate in the "standard survey" was 42%. The response rate in the "rigorous survey" was 71%.
a) What kind of bias does Barone claim may exist in polls?
b) What is the population for these surveys?
c) On the question of political position, the Pew researchers report the following table:

| | Standard Survey | Rigorous Survey |
| --- | --- | --- |
| **Conservative** | 37% | 35% |
| **Moderate** | 40% | 41% |
| **Liberal** | 19% | 20% |

What makes you think these results are incomplete?
d) The Pew researchers report that differences between opinions expressed on the two surveys were not statistically significant. Explain what "statistically significant" means in this context.

**37. Save the grapes.** Vineyard owners have problems with birds that like to eat the ripening grapes. Grapes damaged by birds cannot be used for winemaking (or much of anything else). Some vineyards use scarecrows to try to keep birds away. Others use netting that covers the plants. Owners really would like to know if either method works and, if so, which one is better. One owner has offered to let you use his vineyard this year for an experiment. Propose a design. Carefully indicate how you would set up the experiment, specifying the factor(s) and response variable.

**38. Bats.** It's generally believed that baseball players can hit the ball farther with aluminum bats than with the traditional wooden ones. Is that true? And, if so, how much farther? Players on your local high school baseball team have agreed to help you find out. Design an appropriate experiment.

**39. Knees.** Research reported in the spring of 2002 cast doubt on the effectiveness of arthroscopic knee surgery for patients with arthritis. Patients suffering from arthritis pain who volunteered to participate in the study were randomly divided into groups. One group received arthroscopic knee surgery. The other group underwent "placebo surgery" during which incisions were made in their knees, but no surgery was actually performed. Follow-up evaluations over a period of 2 years found that differences in the amount of pain relief experienced by the two groups were not statistically significant. (*NEJM* 347:81–88 July 11, 2002)
a) Why did the researchers feel it was necessary to have some of the patients undergo "placebo surgery"?

b) Because patients had to consent to participate in this experiment, the subjects were essentially self-selected—a kind of voluntary response group. Explain why that does not invalidate the findings of the experiment.

c) What does "statistically significant" mean in this context?

**40. NBA draft lottery.** Professional basketball teams hold a "draft" each year in which they get to pick the best available college and high school players. In an effort to promote competition, teams with the worst records get to pick first, theoretically allowing them to add better players. To combat the fear that teams with no chance to make the playoffs might try to get better draft picks by intentionally losing late-season games, the NBA's Board of Governors adopted a weighted lottery system in 1990. Under this system, the 11 teams that did not make the playoffs were eligible for the lottery. The NBA prepared 66 cards, each naming one of the teams. The team with the worst win–loss record was named on 11 of the cards, the second-worst team on 10 cards, and so on, with the team having the best record among the nonplayoff clubs getting only one chance at having the first pick. The cards were mixed, then drawn randomly to determine the order in which the teams could draft players. (Since 1995, 13 teams have been involved in the lottery, using a complicated system with 14 numbered Ping-Pong balls drawn in groups of four.) Suppose there are two exceptional players available in this year's draft and your favorite team had the third-worst record. Use a simulation to find out how likely it is that your team gets to pick first or second. Describe your simulation carefully.

**41. Security.** There are 20 first-class passengers and 120 coach passengers scheduled on a flight. In addition to the usual security screening, 10% of the passengers will be subjected to a more complete search.

a) Describe a sampling strategy to randomly select those to be searched.

b) Here is the first-class passenger list and a set of random digits. Select two passengers to be searched, carefully demonstrating your process.

65436 71127 04879 41516 20451 02227 94769 23593

| | | | |
|---|---|---|---|
| Bergman | Cox | Fontana | Perl |
| Bowman | DeLara | Forester | Rabkin |
| Burkhauser | Delli-Bovi | Frongillo | Roufaiel |
| Castillo | Dugan | Furnas | Swafford |
| Clancy | Febo | LePage | Testut |

c) Explain how you would use a random number table to select the coach passengers to be searched.

**42. Profiling?** Among the 20 first-class passengers on the flight described in Exercise 41, there were four businessmen from the Middle East. Two of them were the two passengers selected to be searched. They complained of profiling, but the airline claims that the selection was random. What do you think? Support your conclusion with a simulation.

**43. Par 4.** In theory, a golfer playing a par-4 hole tees off, hitting the ball in the fairway, then hits an approach shot onto the green. The first putt (usually long) probably won't go in, but the second putt (usually much shorter) should. Sounds simple enough, but how many strokes might it really take? Use a simulation to estimate a pretty good golfer's score based on these assumptions:

a) The tee shot hits the fairway 70% of the time.

b) A first approach shot lands on the green 80% of the time from the fairway, but only 40% of the time otherwise.

c) Subsequent approach shots land on the green 90% of the time.

d) The first putt goes in 20% of the time, and subsequent putts go in 90% of the time.

**44. The back nine.** Use simulations to estimate more golf scores, similar to the procedure in Exercise 43.

a) On a par 3, the golfer hopes the tee shot lands on the green. Assume that the tee shot behaves like the first approach shot described in Exercise 43.

b) On a par 5, the second shot will reach the green 10% of the time and hit the fairway 60% of the time. If it does not hit the green, the golfer must play an approach shot as described in Exercise 43.

c) Create a list of assumptions that describe your golfing ability, and then simulate your score on a few holes. Explain your simulation clearly.

# Randomness and Probability

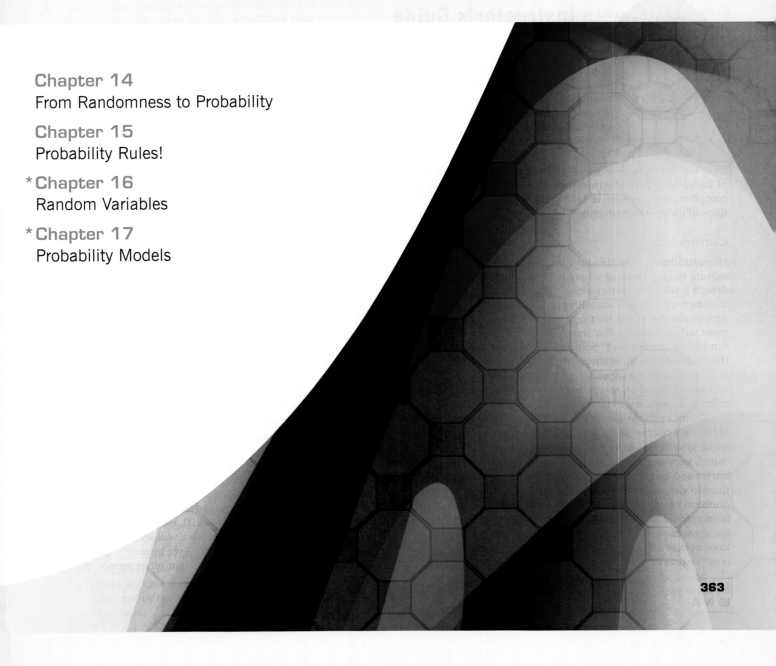

of experience and reflects a sense of what has happened in the past in similar situations. When you hear a probability stated, it's good to try to ascertain what kind of probability is intended.

# The First Three Rules for Working with Probability

1. Make a picture.
2. Make a picture.
3. Make a picture.

We're dealing with probabilities now, not data, but the three rules don't change. The most common kind of picture to make is called a Venn diagram. We'll use Venn diagrams throughout the rest of this chapter. Even experienced statisticians make Venn diagrams to help them think about probabilities of compound and overlapping events. You should, too.

*John Venn (1834–1923) created the Venn diagram. His book on probability,* The Logic of Chance, *was "strikingly original and considerably influenced the development of the theory of Statistics," according to John Maynard Keynes, one of the luminaries of Economics.*

# Formal Probability

For some people, the phrase "50/50" means something vague like "I don't know" or "whatever." But when we discuss probabilities of outcomes, it takes on the precise meaning of *equally likely*. Speaking vaguely about probabilities will get us into trouble, so whenever we talk about probabilities, we'll need to be precise.[10] And to do that, we'll need to develop some formal rules about how probability works.

The simplest way to deal with probabilities is to base the calculations on individual outcomes. But any interesting analysis is likely to combine individual outcomes into events. In a database containing customer information on zip codes, each individual zip code is an outcome. Often we're interested in questions like the probability that the customer is from Illinois, or from the Midwest, rather than in a particular zip code. We could always compute the probability of each individual outcome separately and add them up, but as we've already seen, this might get tedious. Instead, we'll want to develop rules[11] for the probability of events—rules like the following:

1. If the probability is 0, the event can't occur, and likewise if it has probability 1, it *always* occurs. Even if you think an event is very unlikely, its probability

## Surprising Probabilities

We've been careful to discuss probabilities only for situations in which the outcomes were finite, or even countably infinite. But if the outcomes can take on *any* numerical value at all (we say they are *continuous*), things can get surprising. For example, what is the probability that a randomly selected child will be *exactly* 3 feet tall? Well, if we mean 3.00000 . . . feet, the answer is zero. No randomly selected child—even one whose height would be recorded as 3 feet, will be *exactly* 3 feet tall (to an infinite number of decimal places). But, if you've grown taller than 3 feet, there must have been a time in your life when you actually *were* exactly 3 feet tall, even if only for a second. So this is an outcome with probability 0 that not only has happened—it has happened to *you*.

We've seen another example of this already in Chapter 6 when we worked with the Normal model. We said that the probability of any *specific* value—say, $z = 0.5$—is zero. The model gives a probability for any *interval* of values, such as $0.49 < z < 0.51$. The probability is smaller if we ask for $0.499 < z < 0.501$, and smaller still for $0.49999999 < z < 0.50000001$. Well, you get the idea. Continuous probabilities are useful for the mathematics behind much of what we'll do, but it's easier to deal with probabilities for countable outcomes.

---

[10] And to be precise, we will be talking only about sample spaces where we can enumerate all the outcomes. Mathematics call this a countable number of outcomes.

[11] Actually, in mathematical terms, these are axioms—statements that we assume for a probability. We'll derive other rules from these in the next chapter.

can't be negative, and even if you're sure it will happen, its probability can't be greater than 1. So we require that

**A probability is a number between 0 and 1.**

**For any event A, $0 \leq P(A) \leq 1$.**

2. If a random phenomenon has only one possible outcome, it's not very interesting (or very random). So we need to distribute the probabilities among all the outcomes a trial can have. How can we do that so that it makes sense? For example, consider what you're doing as you read this book. The possible outcomes might be

**A:** You read to the end of this chapter before stopping.
**B:** You finish this section but stop reading before the end of the chapter.
**C:** You bail out before the end of this section.

When we assign probabilities to these outcomes, the first thing to be sure of is that we distribute all of the available probability. Something always occurs, so the probability of the entire sample space is 1.

Making this more formal gives the **Probability Assignment Rule.**

**The set of all possible outcomes of a trial must have probability 1.**

**$P(S) = 1$**

3. Suppose the probability that you get to class on time is 0.8. What's the probability that you don't get to class on time? Yes, it's 0.2. The set of outcomes that are *not* in the event **A** is called the **complement** of **A**, and is denoted **A$^C$**. This leads to the **Complement Rule:**

**The probability of an event occurring is 1 minus the probability that it doesn't occur.**

**$P(A) = 1 - P(A^C)$**

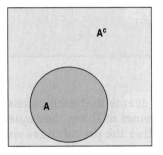

*The set **A** and its complement **A$^C$**. Together, they make up the entire sample space **S**.*

**FOR EXAMPLE**    Applying the Complement Rule

**Recap:** We opened the chapter by looking at the traffic light at the corner of College and Main, observing that when we arrive at that intersection, the light is green about 35% of the time.

**Question:** If $P(green) = 0.35$, what's the probability the light isn't green when you get to College and Main?

"Not green" is the complement of "green," so

$$P(not\ green) = 1 - P(green)$$
$$= 1 - 0.35 = 0.65$$

There's a 65% chance I won't have a green light.

4. Suppose the probability that (**A**) a randomly selected student is a sophomore is 0.20, and the probability that (**B**) he or she is a junior is 0.30. What is the probability that the student is *either* a sophomore *or* a junior, written $P(\textbf{A}\ or\ \textbf{B})$? If you guessed 0.50, you've deduced the **Addition Rule,** which says that you can add the probabilities of events that are disjoint.[12] To see whether two events are

**A S** *Activity:* **Addition Rule for Disjoint Events.** Experiment with disjoint events to explore the Addition Rule.

---

[12] You may see $P(\textbf{A}\ or\ \textbf{B})$ written as $P(\textbf{A} \cup \textbf{B})$. The symbol $\cup$ means "union," representing outcomes that are in event **A** *or* event **B** (or both). The symbol $\cap$ means "intersection," representing outcomes that are in both event **A** *and* event **B**. You may sometimes see $P(\textbf{A}\ and\ \textbf{B})$ written as $P(\textbf{A} \cap \textbf{B})$.

For Example (*continued*)

**Question:** What's the probability that you'll have to stop *at least once* during the week?

Having to stop at least once means that I have to stop for the light either 1, 2, 3, 4, or 5 times next week. It's easier to think about the complement: never having to stop at a red light. Having to stop at least once means that I didn't make it through the week with no red lights.

P(having to stop at the light at least once in 5 days)
= 1 − P(no red lights for 5 days in a row)
= 1 − P(not red AND not red AND not red AND not red AND not red)
= 1 − (0.39)(0.39)(0.39)(0.39)(0.39)
= 1 − 0.0090
= 0.991

I'm not likely to make it through the intersection of College and Main without having to stop sometime this week. There's over a 99% chance I'll hit at least one red light there.

Note that the phrase "at least" is often a tip-off to think about the complement. Something that happens *at least once* <u>does</u> happen. Happening at least once is the complement of not happening at all, and that's easier to find.

## JUST CHECKING

2. Opinion polling organizations contact their respondents by telephone. Random telephone numbers are generated, and interviewers try to contact those households. In the 1990s this method could reach about 69% of U.S. households. According to the Pew Research Center for the People and the Press, by 2003 the contact rate had risen to 76%. We can reasonably assume each household's response to be independent of the others.
   a) What is the probability that the interviewer successfully contacts the next household on her list?
   b) What is the probability that the interviewer successfully contacts both of the next two households on her list?
   c) What is the probability that the interviewer's first successful contact is the third household on the list?
   d) What is the probability the interviewer makes at least one successful contact among the next five households on the list?

> In informal English, you may see "some" used to mean "at least one." "What's the probability that some of the eggs in that cartoon are broken?" means at least one.

**STEP-BY-STEP EXAMPLE** | Probability

The five rules we've seen can be used in a number of different combinations to answer a surprising number of questions. Let's try one to see how we might go about it.

In 2001, Masterfoods, the manufacturers of M&M's® milk chocolate candies, decided to add another color to the standard color lineup of brown, yellow, red, orange, blue, and green. To decide which color to add, they surveyed kids in nearly every country of the world and asked them to vote among purple, pink, and teal. The global winner was purple! In the United States, 42% of those who voted said purple, 37% said teal, and only 19% said pink.

But in Japan the percentages were 38% pink, 36% teal, and only 16% purple. Let's use Japan's percentages to ask some questions:

1. What's the probability that a Japanese M&M's survey respondent selected at random preferred either pink or teal?
2. If we pick two respondents at random, what's the probability that they both selected purple?
3. If we pick three respondents at random, what's the probability that *at least one* preferred purple?

The probability of an event is its long-term relative frequency. It can be determined in several ways: by looking at many replications of an event, by deducing it from equally likely events, or by using some other information. Here, we are told the relative frequencies of the three responses.

Make sure the probabilities are legitimate. Here, they're not. Either there was a mistake, or the other voters must have chosen a color other than the three given. A check of the reports from other countries shows a similar deficit, so probably we're seeing those who had no preference or who wrote in another color.

The M&M's Web site reports the proportions of Japanese votes by color. These give the probability of selecting a voter who preferred each of the colors:

$$P(pink) = 0.38$$
$$P(teal) = 0.36$$
$$P(purple) = 0.16$$

Each is between 0 and 1, but they don't all add up to 1. The remaining 10% of the voters must have not expressed a preference or written in another color. I'll put them together into "no preference" and add $P(no\ preference) = 0.10$.

With this addition, I have a legitimate assignment of probabilities.

**Question 1.** What's the probability that a Japanese M&M's survey respondent selected at random preferred either pink or teal?

**Plan** Decide which rules to use and check the conditions they require.

The events "Pink" and "Teal" are individual outcomes (A respondent can't choose both colors.), so they are disjoint. I can apply the Addition Rule.

**Mechanics** Show your work.

$$P(pink\ or\ teal) = P(pink) + P(teal)$$
$$= 0.38 + 0.36 = 0.74$$

**Conclusion** Interpret your results in the proper context.

The probability that the respondent said pink or teal is 0.74.

**Question 2.** If we pick two respondents at random, what's the probability that they both said purple?

| | | |
|---|---|---|
| **THINK** | **Plan** The word "both" suggests we want $P(\mathbf{A} \text{ and } \mathbf{B})$, which calls for the Multiplication Rule. Think about the assumption. | ✓ **Independence Assumption:** It's unlikely that the choice made by one respondent affected the choice of the other, so the events seem to be independent. I can use the Multiplication Rule. |
| **SHOW** | **Mechanics** Show your work. For both respondents to pick purple, each one has to pick purple. | $P(\text{both purple})$ $= P(\text{first respondent picks purple and second respondent picks purple})$ $= P(\text{first respondent picks purple}) \times P(\text{second respondent picks purple})$ $= 0.16 \times 0.16 = 0.0256$ |
| **TELL** | **Conclusion** Interpret your results in the proper context. | The probability that both respondents pick purple is 0.0256. |

**Question 3.** If we pick three respondents at random, what's the probability that at least one preferred purple?

| | | |
|---|---|---|
| **THINK** | **Plan** The phrase "at least . . ." often flags a question best answered by looking at the complement, and that's the best approach here. The complement of "At least one preferred purple" is "None of them preferred purple." Think about the assumption. | $P(\text{at least one picked purple})$ $= P(\{\text{none picked purple}\}^C)$ $= 1 - P(\text{none picked purple}).$ $P(\text{none picked purple}) = P(\text{not purple and not purple and not purple}).$ ✓ **Independence Assumption:** These are independent events because they are choices by three random respondents. I can use the Multiplication Rule: |
| **SHOW** | **Mechanics** We calculate $P(\text{none purple})$ by using the Multiplication Rule. | $P(\text{none picked purple}) = P(\text{first not purple}) \times P(\text{second not purple}) \times P(\text{third not purple})$ $= [P(\text{not purple})]^3.$ $P(\text{not purple}) = 1 - P(\text{purple})$ $= 1 - 0.16 = 0.84.$ So $P(\text{none picked purple}) = (0.84)^3 = 0.5927.$ |
| | Then we can use the Complement Rule to get the probability we want. | $P(\text{at least 1 picked purple})$ $= 1 - P(\text{none picked purple})$ $= 1 - 0.5927 = 0.4073.$ |

**Conclusion** Interpret your results in the proper context.

> *There's about a 40.7% chance that at least one of the respondents picked purple.*

## WHAT CAN GO WRONG?

▶ **Beware of probabilities that don't add up to 1.** To be a legitimate probability assignment, the sum of the probabilities for all possible outcomes must total 1. If the sum is less than 1, you may need to add another category ("other") and assign the remaining probability to that outcome. If the sum is more than 1, check that the outcomes are disjoint. If they're not, then you can't assign probabilities by just counting relative frequencies.

▶ **Don't add probabilities of events if they're not disjoint.** Events must be disjoint to use the Addition Rule. The probability of being under 80 *or* a female is not the probability of being under 80 *plus* the probability of being female. That sum may be more than 1.

▶ **Don't multiply probabilities of events if they're not independent.** The probability of selecting a student at random who is over 6'10" tall *and* on the basketball team is *not* the probability the student is over 6'10" tall *times* the probability he's on the basketball team. Knowing that the student is over 6'10" changes the probability of his being on the basketball team. You can't multiply these probabilities. The multiplication of probabilities of events that are not independent is one of the most common errors people make in dealing with probabilities.

▶ **Don't confuse disjoint and independent.** Disjoint events *can't* be independent. If **A** = {you get an A in this class} and **B** = {you get a B in this class}, **A** and **B** are disjoint. Are they independent? If you find out that **A** is true, does that change the probability of **B**? You bet it does! So they can't be independent. We'll return to this issue in the next chapter.

# CONNECTIONS

We saw in the previous three chapters that randomness plays a critical role in gathering data. That fact alone makes it important that we understand how random events behave. The rules and concepts of probability give us a language to talk and think about random phenomena. From here on, randomness will be fundamental to how we think about data, and probabilities will show up in every chapter.

We began thinking about independence back in Chapter 3 when we looked at contingency tables and asked whether the distribution of one variable was the same for each category of another. Then, in Chapter 12, we saw that independence was fundamental to drawing a Simple Random Sample. For computing compound probabilities, we again ask about independence. And we'll continue to think about independence throughout the rest of the book.

Our interest in probability extends back to the start of the book. We've talked about "relative frequencies" often. But—let's be honest—that's just a casual term for probability. For example, you can now rephrase the 68–95–99.7 Rule to talk about the *probability* that a random value selected from a Normal model will fall within 1, 2, or 3 standard deviations of the mean.

Why not just say "probability" from the start? Well, we didn't need any of the formal rules of this chapter (or the next one), so there was no point to weighing down the discussion with those rules. And "relative frequency" is the right intuitive way to think about probability in this course, so you've been thinking right all along.

Keep it up.

# WHAT HAVE WE LEARNED?

We've learned that probability is based on long-run relative frequencies. We've thought about the Law of Large Numbers and noted that it speaks only of long-run behavior. Because the long run is a very long time, we need to be careful not to misinterpret the Law of Large Numbers. Even when we've observed a string of heads, we shouldn't expect extra tails in subsequent coin flips.

Also, we've learned some basic rules for combining probabilities of outcomes to find probabilities of more complex events. These include

- ▸ the Probability Assignment Rule,
- ▸ the Complement Rule,
- ▸ the Addition Rule for disjoint events, and
- ▸ the Multiplication Rule for independent events.

## Terms

| | |
|---|---|
| Random phenomenon | 364, 365. A phenomenon is random if we know what outcomes could happen, but not which particular values will happen. |
| Trial | 366. A single attempt or realization of a random phenomenon. |
| Outcome | 366. The outcome of a trial is the value measured, observed, or reported for an individual instance of that trial. |
| Event | 366. A collection of outcomes. Usually, we identify events so that we can attach probabilities to them. We denote events with bold capital letters such as **A, B,** or **C.** |
| Sample Space | 366. The collection of all possible outcome values. The sample space has a probability of 1. |
| Law of Large Numbers | 366. The Law of Large Numbers states that the long-run *relative frequency* of repeated independent events gets closer and closer to the *true* relative frequency as the number of trials increases. |
| Independence (informally) | 366. Two events are *independent* if learning that one event occurs does not change the probability that the other event occurs. |
| Probability | 367. The probability of an event is a number between 0 and 1 that reports the likelihood of that event's occurrence. We write $P(\mathbf{A})$ for the probability of the event **A.** |
| Empirical probability | 367. When the probability comes from the long-run relative frequency of the event's occurrence, it is an **empirical probability.** |
| Theoretical probability | 368. When the probability comes from a model (such as equally likely outcomes), it is called a **theoretical probability.** |
| Personal probability | 369. When the probability is subjective and represents your personal degree of belief, it is called a **personal probability.** |
| The Probability Assignment Rule | 371. The probability of the entire sample space must be 1. $P(\mathbf{S}) = 1$ |
| Complement Rule | 371. The probability of an event occurring is 1 minus the probability that it doesn't occur. $$P(\mathbf{A}) = 1 - P(\mathbf{A}^{\mathbf{C}})$$ |
| Addition Rule | 372. If **A** and **B** are disjoint events, then the probability of **A** *or* **B** is $$P(\mathbf{A}\ or\ \mathbf{B}) = P(\mathbf{A}) + P(\mathbf{B}).$$ |
| Disjoint (Mutually exclusive) | 372. Two events are disjoint if they share no outcomes in common. If **A** and **B** are disjoint, then knowing that **A** occurs tells us that **B** cannot occur. Disjoint events are also called "mutually exclusive." |
| Legitimate probability assignment | 372. An assignment of probabilities to outcomes is legitimate if <br> ▸ each probability is between 0 and 1 (inclusive). <br> ▸ the sum of the probabilities is 1. |
| Multiplication Rule | 373. If **A** and **B** are independent events, then the probability of **A** *and* **B** is $$P(\mathbf{A}\ and\ \mathbf{B}) = P(\mathbf{A}) \times P(\mathbf{B}).$$ |
| Independence Assumption | 373. We often require events to be independent. (So you should think about whether this assumption is reasonable.) |

# Skills

▶ Understand that random phenomena are unpredictable in the short term but show long-run regularity.

▶ Be able to recognize random outcomes in a real-world situation.

▶ Know that the relative frequency of a random event settles down to a value called the (empirical) probability. Know that this is guaranteed for independent events by the Law of Large Numbers.

▶ Know the basic definitions and rules of probability.

▶ Recognize when events are disjoint and when events are independent. Understand the difference and that disjoint events cannot be independent.

▶ Be able to use the facts about probability to determine whether an assignment of probabilities is legitimate. Each probability must be a number between 0 and 1, and the sum of the probabilities assigned to all possible outcomes must be 1.

▶ Know how and when to apply the Addition Rule. Know that events must be disjoint for the Addition Rule to apply.

▶ Know how and when to apply the Multiplication Rule. Know that events must be independent for the Multiplication Rule to apply. Be able to use the Multiplication Rule to find probabilities for combinations of independent events.

▶ Know how to use the Complement Rule to make calculating probabilities simpler. Recognize that probabilities of "at least. . ." are likely to be simplified in this way.

▶ Be able to use statements about probability in describing a random phenomenon. You will need this skill soon for making statements about statistical inference.

▶ Know and be able to use the terms "sample space", "disjoint events", and "independent events" correctly.

# EXERCISES

1. **Sample spaces.** For each of the following, list the sample space and tell whether you think the events are equally likely:
   a) Toss 2 coins; record the order of heads and tails.
   b) A family has 3 children; record the number of boys.
   c) Flip a coin until you get a head or 3 consecutive tails.
   d) Roll two dice; record the larger number.

2. **Sample spaces.** For each of the following, list the sample space and tell whether you think the events are equally likely:
   a) Roll two dice; record the sum of the numbers.
   b) A family has 3 children; record each child's sex in order of birth.
   c) Toss four coins; record the number of tails.
   d) Toss a coin 10 times; record the longest run of heads.

3. **Roulette.** A casino claims that its roulette wheel is truly random. What should that claim mean?

4. **Rain.** The weather reporter on TV makes predictions such as a 25% chance of rain. What do you think is the meaning of such a phrase?

5. **Winter.** Comment on the following quotation:

   *"What I think is our best determination is it will be a colder than normal winter," said Pamela Naber Knox, a Wisconsin state climatologist. "I'm basing that on a couple of different things. First, in looking at the past few winters, there has been a lack of really cold weather. Even though we are not supposed to use the law of averages, we are due."* (Associated Press, fall 1992, quoted by Schaeffer et al.)

6. **Snow.** After an unusually dry autumn, a radio announcer is heard to say, "Watch out! We'll pay for these sunny days later on this winter." Explain what he's trying to say, and comment on the validity of his reasoning.

7. **Cold streak.** A batter who had failed to get a hit in seven consecutive times at bat then hits a game-winning home run. When talking to reporters afterward, he says he was very confident that last time at bat because he knew he was "due for a hit." Comment on his reasoning.

8. **Crash.** Commercial airplanes have an excellent safety record. Nevertheless, there are crashes occasionally, with

the loss of many lives. In the weeks following a crash, airlines often report a drop in the number of passengers, probably because people are afraid to risk flying.
a) A travel agent suggests that, since the law of averages makes it highly unlikely to have two plane crashes within a few weeks of each other, flying soon after a crash is the safest time. What do you think?
b) If the airline industry proudly announces that it has set a new record for the longest period of safe flights, would you be reluctant to fly? Are the airlines due to have a crash?

**9. Fire insurance.** Insurance companies collect annual payments from homeowners in exchange for paying to rebuild houses that burn down.
a) Why should you be reluctant to accept a $300 payment from your neighbor to replace his house should it burn down during the coming year?
b) Why can the insurance company make that offer?

**10. Jackpot.** On January 20, 2000, the International Gaming Technology company issued a press release:

*(LAS VEGAS, Nev.)—Cynthia Jay was smiling ear to ear as she walked into the news conference at The Desert Inn Resort in Las Vegas today, and well she should. Last night, the 37-year-old cocktail waitress won the world's largest slot jackpot—$34,959,458—on a Megabucks machine. She said she had played $27 in the machine when the jackpot hit. Nevada Megabucks has produced 49 major winners in its 14-year history. The top jackpot builds from a base amount of $7 million and can be won with a 3-coin ($3) bet.*

a) How can the Desert Inn afford to give away millions of dollars on a $3 bet?
b) Why did the company issue a press release? Wouldn't most businesses want to keep such a huge loss quiet?

**11. Spinner.** The plastic arrow on a spinner for a child's game stops rotating to point at a color that will determine what happens next. Which of the following probability assignments are possible?

| | Probabilities of . . . | | | |
| | Red | Yellow | Green | Blue |
|---|---|---|---|---|
| a) | 0.25 | 0.25 | 0.25 | 0.25 |
| b) | 0.10 | 0.20 | 0.30 | 0.40 |
| c) | 0.20 | 0.30 | 0.40 | 0.50 |
| d) | 0 | 0 | 1.00 | 0 |
| e) | 0.10 | 0.20 | 1.20 | −1.50 |

**12. Scratch off.** Many stores run "secret sales": Shoppers receive cards that determine how large a discount they get, but the percentage is revealed by scratching off that black stuff (what *is* that?) only after the purchase has been totaled at the cash register. The store is required to reveal (in the fine print) the distribution of discounts available. Which of these probability assignments are plausible?

| | Probabilities of . . . | | | |
| | 10% off | 20% off | 30% off | 50% off |
|---|---|---|---|---|
| a) | 0.20 | 0.20 | 0.20 | 0.20 |
| b) | 0.50 | 0.30 | 0.20 | 0.10 |
| c) | 0.80 | 0.10 | 0.05 | 0.05 |
| d) | 0.75 | 0.25 | 0.25 | −0.25 |
| e) | 1.00 | 0 | 0 | 0 |

**13. Vehicles.** Suppose that 46% of families living in a certain county own a car and 18% own an SUV. The Addition Rule might suggest, then, that 64% of families own either a car or an SUV. What's wrong with that reasoning?

**14. Homes.** Funding for many schools comes from taxes based on assessed values of local properties. People's homes are assessed higher if they have extra features such as garages and swimming pools. Assessment records in a certain school district indicate that 37% of the residential properties have garages and 3% have swimming pools. The Addition Rule might suggest, then, that 40% of residences have a garage or a pool. What's wrong with that reasoning?

**15. Speeders.** Traffic checks on a certain section of highway suggest that 60% of drivers are speeding there. Since $0.6 \times 0.6 = 0.36$, the Multiplication Rule might suggest that there's a 36% chance that two vehicles in a row are both speeding. What's wrong with that reasoning?

**16. Lefties.** Although it's hard to be definitive in classifying people as right or left handed, some studies suggest that about 14% of people are left handed. Since $0.14 \times 0.14 = 0.0196$, the Multiplication Rule might suggest that there's about a 2% chance that a brother and a sister are both lefties. What's wrong with that reasoning?

**17. College admissions.** For high school students graduating in 2007, college admissions to the nation's most selective schools were the most competitive in memory. (*The New York Times*, "A Great Year for Ivy League Schools, but Not So Good for Applicants to Them," April 4, 2007). Harvard accepted about 9% of its applicants, Stanford 10%, and Penn 16%. Jorge has applied to all three. Assuming that he's a typical applicant, he figures that his chances of getting into both Harvard and Stanford must be about 0.09%.
a) How has he arrived at this conclusion?
b) What additional assumption is he making?
c) Do you agree with his conclusion?

**18. College admissions II.** In Exercise 17, we saw that in 2007 Harvard accepted about 9% of its applicants, Stanford 10%, and Penn 16%. Jorge has applied to all three. Assuming that he's a typical applicant, he figures that his chances of getting into at least one of the three must be about 35%.
a) How has he arrived at this conclusion?
b) What assumption is he making?
c) Do you agree with his conclusion?

**19. Car repairs.** A consumer organization estimates that over a 1-year period 17% of cars will need to be repaired once, 7% will need repairs twice, and 4% will require three or more repairs. What is the probability that a car chosen at random will need
a) no repairs?
b) no more than one repair?
c) some repairs?

**20. Stats projects.** In a large Introductory Statistics lecture hall, the professor reports that 55% of the students enrolled have never taken a Calculus course, 32% have taken only one semester of Calculus, and the rest have taken two or more semesters of Calculus. The professor randomly assigns students to groups of three to work on a project for the course. What is the probability that the first groupmate you meet has studied
a) two or more semesters of Calculus?
b) some Calculus?
c) no more than one semester of Calculus?

**21. More repairs.** Consider again the auto repair rates described in Exercise 19. If you own two cars, what is the probability that
a) neither will need repair?
b) both will need repair?
c) at least one car will need repair?

**22. Another project.** You are assigned to be part of a group of three students from the Intro Stats class described in Exercise 20. What is the probability that, of your other two groupmates,
a) neither has studied Calculus?
b) both have studied at least one semester of Calculus?
c) at least one has had more than one semester of Calculus?

**23. Repairs, again.** You used the Multiplication Rule to calculate repair probabilities for your cars in Exercise 21.
a) What must be true about your cars in order to make that approach valid?
b) Do you think this assumption is reasonable? Explain.

**24. Final project.** You used the Multiplication Rule to calculate probabilities about the Calculus background of your Statistics groupmates in Exercise 22.
a) What must be true about the groups in order to make that approach valid?
b) Do you think this assumption is reasonable? Explain.

**25. Energy 2007.** A Gallup poll in March 2007 asked 1005 U.S. adults whether increasing domestic energy production or protecting the environment should be given a higher priority. Here are the results:

| Response | Number |
|---|---|
| Increase production | 342 |
| Protect environment | 583 |
| Equally important | 30 |
| No opinion | 50 |
| Total | **1005** |

If we select a person at random from this sample of 1005 adults,
a) what is the probability that the person responded "Increase production"?
b) what is the probability that the person responded "Equally important" or had no opinion?

**26. Failing fathers?** A Pew Research poll in 2007 asked 2020 U.S. adults whether fathers today were doing as good a job of fathering as fathers of 20–30 years ago. Here's how they responded:

| Response | Number |
|---|---|
| Better | 424 |
| Same | 566 |
| Worse | 950 |
| No Opinion | 80 |
| Total | **2020** |

If we select a respondent at random from this sample of 2020 adults,
a) what is the probability that the selected person responded "Worse"?
b) what is the probability that the person responded the "Same" or "Better"?

**27. More energy.** Exercise 25 shows the results of a Gallup Poll about energy. Suppose we select three people at random from this sample.
a) What is the probability that all three responded "Protect the environment"?
b) What is the probability that none responded "Equally important"?
c) What assumption did you make in computing these probabilities?
d) Explain why you think that assumption is reasonable.

**28. Fathers revisited.** Consider again the results of the poll about fathering discussed in Exercise 26. If we select two people at random from this sample,
a) what is the probability that both think fathers are better today?
b) what is the probability that neither thinks fathers are better today?
c) what is the probability that one person thinks fathers are better today and the other doesn't?
d) What assumption did you make in computing these probabilities?
e) Explain why you think that assumption is reasonable.

**29. Polling.** As mentioned in the chapter, opinion-polling organizations contact their respondents by sampling random telephone numbers. Although interviewers now can reach about 76% of U.S. households, the percentage of those contacted who agree to cooperate with the survey has fallen from 58% in 1997 to only 38% in 2003 (Pew Research Center for the People and the Press). Each household, of course, is independent of the others.
a) What is the probability that the next household on the list will be contacted but will refuse to cooperate?

b) What is the probability (in 2003) of failing to contact a household or of contacting the household but not getting them to agree to the interview?

c) Show another way to calculate the probability in part b.

**30. Polling, part II.** According to Pew Research, the contact rate (probability of contacting a selected household) was 69% in 1997 and 76% in 2003. However, the cooperation rate (probability of someone at the contacted household agreeing to be interviewed) was 58% in 1997 and dropped to 38% in 2003.

a) What is the probability (in 2003) of obtaining an interview with the next household on the sample list? (To obtain an interview, an interviewer must both contact the household and then get agreement for the interview.)

b) Was it more likely to obtain an interview from a randomly selected household in 1997 or in 2003?

**31. M&M's.** The Masterfoods company says that before the introduction of purple, yellow candies made up 20% of their plain M&M's, red another 20%, and orange, blue, and green each made up 10%. The rest were brown.

a) If you pick an M&M at random, what is the probability that
1) it is brown?
2) it is yellow or orange?
3) it is not green?
4) it is striped?

b) If you pick three M&M's in a row, what is the probability that
1) they are all brown?
2) the third one is the first one that's red?
3) none are yellow?
4) at least one is green?

**32. Blood.** The American Red Cross says that about 45% of the U.S. population has Type O blood, 40% Type A, 11% Type B, and the rest Type AB.

a) Someone volunteers to give blood. What is the probability that this donor
1) has Type AB blood?
2) has Type A or Type B?
3) is not Type O?

b) Among four potential donors, what is the probability that
1) all are Type O?
2) no one is Type AB?
3) they are not all Type A?
4) at least one person is Type B?

**33. Disjoint or independent?** In Exercise 31 you calculated probabilities of getting various M&M's. Some of your answers depended on the assumption that the outcomes described were *disjoint*; that is, they could not both happen at the same time. Other answers depended on the assumption that the events were *independent*; that is, the occurrence of one of them doesn't affect the probability of the other. Do you understand the difference between disjoint and independent?

a) If you draw one M&M, are the events of getting a red one and getting an orange one disjoint, independent, or neither?

b) If you draw two M&M's one after the other, are the events of getting a red on the first and a red on the second disjoint, independent, or neither?

c) Can disjoint events ever be independent? Explain.

**34. Disjoint or independent?** In Exercise 32 you calculated probabilities involving various blood types. Some of your answers depended on the assumption that the outcomes described were *disjoint*; that is, they could not both happen at the same time. Other answers depended on the assumption that the events were *independent*; that is, the occurrence of one of them doesn't affect the probability of the other. Do you understand the difference between disjoint and independent?

a) If you examine one person, are the events that the person is Type A and that the person is Type B disjoint, independent, or neither?

b) If you examine two people, are the events that the first is Type A and the second Type B disjoint, independent, or neither?

c) Can disjoint events ever be independent? Explain.

**35. Dice.** You roll a fair die three times. What is the probability that

a) you roll all 6's?
b) you roll all odd numbers?
c) none of your rolls gets a number divisible by 3?
d) you roll at least one 5?
e) the numbers you roll are not all 5's?

**36. Slot machine.** A slot machine has three wheels that spin independently. Each has 10 equally likely symbols: 4 bars, 3 lemons, 2 cherries, and a bell. If you play, what is the probability that

a) you get 3 lemons?
b) you get no fruit symbols?
c) you get 3 bells (the jackpot)?
d) you get no bells?
e) you get at least one bar (an automatic loser)?

**37. Champion bowler.** A certain bowler can bowl a strike 70% of the time. What is the probability that she

a) goes three consecutive frames without a strike?
b) makes her first strike in the third frame?
c) has at least one strike in the first three frames?
d) bowls a perfect game (12 consecutive strikes)?

**38. The train.** To get to work, a commuter must cross train tracks. The time the train arrives varies slightly from day to day, but the commuter estimates he'll get stopped on about 15% of work days. During a certain 5-day work week, what is the probability that he

a) gets stopped on Monday and again on Tuesday?
b) gets stopped for the first time on Thursday?
c) gets stopped every day?
d) gets stopped at least once during the week?

**39. Voters.** Suppose that in your city 37% of the voters are registered as Democrats, 29% as Republicans, and 11% as members of other parties (Liberal, Right to Life, Green, etc.). Voters not aligned with any official party are termed "Independent." You are conducting a poll by calling

registered voters at random. In your first three calls, what is the probability you talk to
a) all Republicans?
b) no Democrats?
c) at least one Independent?

40. **Religion.** Census reports for a city indicate that 62% of residents classify themselves as Christian, 12% as Jewish, and 16% as members of other religions (Muslims, Buddhists, etc.). The remaining residents classify themselves as nonreligious. A polling organization seeking information about public opinions wants to be sure to talk with people holding a variety of religious views, and makes random phone calls. Among the first four people they call, what is the probability they reach
a) all Christians?
b) no Jews?
c) at least one person who is nonreligious?

41. **Tires.** You bought a new set of four tires from a manufacturer who just announced a recall because 2% of those tires are defective. What is the probability that at least one of yours is defective?

42. **Pepsi.** For a sales promotion, the manufacturer places winning symbols under the caps of 10% of all Pepsi bottles. You buy a six-pack. What is the probability that you win something?

43. **9/11?** On September 11, 2002, the first anniversary of the terrorist attack on the World Trade Center, the New York State Lottery's daily number came up 9–1–1. An interesting coincidence or a cosmic sign?

a) What is the probability that the winning three numbers match the date on any given day?
b) What is the probability that a whole year passes without this happening?
c) What is the probability that the date and winning lottery number match at least once during any year?
d) If every one of the 50 states has a three-digit lottery, what is the probability that at least one of them will come up 9–1–1 on September 11?

44. **Red cards.** You shuffle a deck of cards and then start turning them over one at a time. The first one is red. So is the second. And the third. In fact, you are surprised to get 10 red cards in a row. You start thinking, "The next one is due to be black!"
a) Are you correct in thinking that there's a higher probability that the next card will be black than red? Explain.
b) Is this an example of the Law of Large Numbers? Explain.

**JUST CHECKING**
**Answers**

1. The LLN works only in the long run, not in the short run. The random methods for selecting lottery numbers have no memory of previous picks, so there is no change in the probability that a certain number will come up.

2. **a)** 0.76
   **b)** $0.76(0.76) = 0.5776$
   **c)** $(1 - 0.76)^2(0.76) = 0.043776$
   **d)** $1 - (1 - 0.76)^5 = 0.9992$

# Probability Rules!

## Where are we going?

Is the probability of a car accident the same for all age groups? Insurance companies want to know, so they can set their rates. Is everyone at equal risk for getting the flu next winter? Medical researchers use factors like age, sex, lifestyle, and family history to estimate the probability for each individual. These are examples of **conditional** probabilities. We'll see how the probability of an event can change when we learn more about the situation at hand. Sometimes the results are surprising.

ull a bill from your wallet or pocket without looking at it. An outcome of this trial is the bill you select. The sample space is all the bills in circulation: **S** = {$1 bill, $2 bill, $5 bill, $10 bill, $20 bill, $50 bill, $100 bill}.[1] These are *all* the possible outcomes. (In spite of what you may have seen in bank robbery movies, there are no $500 or $1000 bills.)

We can combine the outcomes in different ways to make many different events. For example, the event **A** = {$1, $5, $10} represents selecting a $1, $5, or $10 bill. The event **B** = {a bill that does not have a president on it} is the collection of outcomes (Don't look! Can you name them?): {$10 (Hamilton), $100 (Franklin)}. The event **C** = {enough money to pay for a $12 meal with one bill} is the set of outcomes {$20, $50, $100}.

Notice that these outcomes are not equally likely. You'd no doubt be more surprised (and pleased) to pull out a $100 bill than a $1 bill—it's not very likely, though. You probably carry many more $1 than $100 bills, but without information about the probability of each outcome, we can't calculate the probability of an event.

---

[1] Well, technically, the sample space is all the bills in your pocket. You may be quite sure there isn't a $100 bill in there, but *we* don't know that, so humor us that it's at least *possible* that any legal bill could be there.

The probability of the event **C** (getting a bill worth more than $12) is *not* 3/7. There are 7 possible outcomes, and 3 of them exceed $12, but they are *not equally* likely. (Remember the probability that your lottery ticket will win rather than lose still isn't 1/2.)

# The General Addition Rule

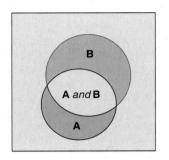

*Events **A** and **B** and their intersection.*

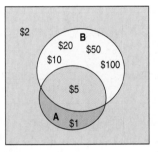

*Denominations of bills that are odd (**A**) or that have a building on the reverse side (**B**). The two sets both include the $5 bill, and both exclude the $2 bill.*

Now look at the bill in your hand. There are images of famous buildings in the center of the backs of all but two bills in circulation. The $1 bill has the word ONE in the center, and the $2 bill shows the signing of the Declaration of Independence.

What's the probability of randomly selecting **A** = {a bill with an odd-numbered value} *or* **B** = {a bill with a building on the reverse}? We know **A** = {$1, $5} and **B** = {$5, $10, $20, $50, $100}. But $P(\mathbf{A}\ or\ \mathbf{B})$ is not simply the sum $P(\mathbf{A}) + P(\mathbf{B})$, because the events **A** and **B** are not disjoint. The $5 bill is in both sets. So what can we do? We'll need a new probability rule.

As the diagrams show, we can't use the Addition Rule and add the two probabilities because the events are not disjoint; they overlap. There's an outcome (the $5 bill) in the *intersection* of **A** and **B**. The Venn diagram represents the sample space. Notice that the $2 bill has neither a building nor an odd denomination, so it sits outside both circles.

The $5 bill plays a crucial role here because it is both odd *and* has a building on the reverse. It's in both **A** and **B**, which places it in the *intersection* of the two circles. The reason we can't simply add the probabilities of **A** and **B** is that we'd count the $5 bill twice.

If we did add the two probabilities, we could compensate by *subtracting* out the probability of that $5 bill. So,

$P$(odd number value or building)
$= P$(odd number value) $+ P$(building) $- P$(odd number value *and* building)
$= P(\$1, \$5) + P(\$5, \$10, \$20, \$50, \$100) - P(\$5)$.

This method works in general. We add the probabilities of two events and then subtract out the probability of their intersection. This approach gives us the **General Addition Rule,** which does not require disjoint events:

$$P(\mathbf{A}\ or\ \mathbf{B}) = P(\mathbf{A}) + P(\mathbf{B}) - P(\mathbf{A}\ and\ \mathbf{B}).$$

---

**FOR EXAMPLE** | Using the General Addition Rule

A survey of college students found that 56% live in a campus residence hall, 62% participate in a campus meal program, and 42% do both.

**Question:** What's the probability that a randomly selected student either lives or eats on campus?

Let **L** = {student lives on campus} and **M** = {student has a campus mean plan}.

$P$(a student either lives or eats on campus) $= P(\mathbf{L}\ or\ \mathbf{M})$
$= P(\mathbf{L}) + P(\mathbf{M}) - P(\mathbf{L}\ and\ \mathbf{M})$
$= 0.56 + 0.62 - 0.42$
$= 0.76$

There's a 76% chance that a randomly selected college student either lives or eats on campus.

**Would you like dessert or coffee?** Natural language can be ambiguous. In this question, is the answer one of the two alternatives, or simply "yes"? Must you decide between them, or may you have both? That kind of ambiguity can confuse our probabilities.

Suppose we had been asked a different question: What is the probability that the bill we draw has *either* an odd value *or* a building but *not both*? Which bills are we talking about now? The set we're interested in would be {$1, $10, $20, $50, $100}. We don't include the $5 bill in the set because it has both characteristics.

Why isn't this the same answer as before? The problem is that when we say the word "or," we usually mean *either* one *or* both. We don't usually mean the *exclusive* version of "or" as in, "Would you like the steak *or* the vegetarian entrée?" Ordinarily when we ask for the probability that **A** *or* **B** occurs, we mean **A** *or* **B** or both. And we know *that* probability is $P(A) + P(B) - P(A \text{ and } B)$. The General Addition Rule subtracts the probability of the outcomes in **A** *and* **B** because we've counted those outcomes *twice*. But they're still there.

If we really mean **A** *or* **B**, but NOT both, we have to get rid of the outcomes in {**A** *and* **B**}. So $P(A \text{ or } B, \text{ but } not \text{ both}) = P(A \text{ or } B) - P(A \text{ and } B) = P(A) + P(B) - 2 \times P(A \text{ and } B)$. Now we've subtracted $P(A \text{ and } B)$ twice—once because we don't want to double-count these events and a second time because we really didn't want to count them at all. At this point, it would be a good idea to make a picture to be sure you see how this works!

---

**FOR EXAMPLE**     Using Venn diagrams

**Recap:** We return to our survey of college students: 56% live on campus, 62% have a campus meal program, and 42% do both.

**Questions:** Based on a Venn diagram, what is the probability that a randomly selected student

   a) lives off campus and doesn't have a meal program?
   b) lives in a residence hall but doesn't have a meal program?

Let **L** = {student lives on campus} and **M** = {student has a campus mean plan}. In the Venn diagram, the intersection of the circles is $P(L \text{ and } M) = 0.42$. Since $P(L) = 0.56$, $P(L \text{ and } M^c) = 0.56 - 0.42 = 0.14$. Also, $P(L^c \text{ and } M) = 0.62 - 0.42 = 0.20$. Now, $0.14 + 0.42 + 0.20 = 0.76$, leaving $1 - 0.76 = 0.24$ for the region outside both circles.

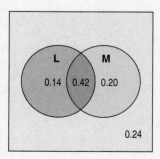

$P(\text{off campus and no meal program}) = P(L^c \text{ and } M^c) = 0.24$

$P(\text{on campus and no meal program}) = P(L \text{ and } M^c) = 0.14$

## JUST CHECKING

**1.** Back in Chapter 1 we suggested that you sample some pages of this book at random to see whether they held a graph or other data display. We actually did just that. We drew a representative sample and found the following:

*48% of pages had some kind of data display,*

*27% of pages had an equation, and*

*7% of pages had both a data display and an equation.*

**a)** Display these results in a Venn diagram.
**b)** What is the probability that a randomly selected sample page had neither a data display nor an equation?
**c)** What is the probability that a randomly selected sample page had a data display but no equation?

---

**STEP-BY-STEP EXAMPLE** | **Using the General Addition Rule**

Police report that 78% of drivers stopped on suspicion of drunk driving are given a breath test, 36% a blood test, and 22% both tests.

**Question:** What is the probability that a randomly selected DWI suspect is given
1. a test?
2. a blood test or a breath test, but not both?
3. neither test?

**Plan** Define the events we're interested in. There are no conditions to check; the General Addition Rule works for any events!

**Plot** Make a picture, and use the given probabilities to find the probability for each region.

The blue region represents **A** but not **B**. The green intersection region represents **A** *and* **B**. Note that since $P(\mathbf{A}) = 0.78$ and $P(\mathbf{A} \text{ and } \mathbf{B}) = 0.22$, the probability of **A** but not **B** must be $0.78 - 0.22 = 0.56$.

The yellow region is **B** but not **A**.

The gray region outside both circles represents the outcome neither **A** nor **B**. All the probabilities must total 1, so you can determine the probability of that region by subtraction.

Then, figure out what you want to know. The probabilities can come from the diagram or a formula. Sometimes translating the words to equations is the trickiest step.

Let **A** = {suspect is given a breath test}.
Let **B** = {suspect is given a blood test}.

I know that
$$P(\mathbf{A}) = 0.78$$
$$P(\mathbf{B}) = 0.36$$
$$P(\mathbf{A} \text{ and } \mathbf{B}) = 0.22$$

So
$$P(\mathbf{A} \text{ and } \mathbf{B}^C) = 0.78 - 0.22 = 0.56$$
$$P(\mathbf{B} \text{ and } \mathbf{A}^C) = 0.36 - 0.22 = 0.14$$
$$P(\mathbf{A}^C \text{ and } \mathbf{B}^C) = 1 - (0.56 + 0.22 + 0.14)$$
$$= 0.08$$

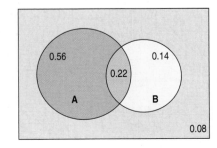

**Question 1.** What is the probability that the suspect is given a test?

| SHOW | **Mechanics** The probability the suspect is given a test is $P(\textbf{A or B})$. We can use the General Addition Rule, or we can add the probabilities seen in the diagram. | $P(\textbf{A or B}) = P(\textbf{A}) + P(\textbf{B}) - P(\textbf{A and B})$<br>$\qquad\quad = 0.78 + 0.36 - 0.22$<br>$\qquad\quad = 0.92$<br><br>OR<br><br>$P(\textbf{A or B}) = 0.56 + 0.22 + 0.14 = 0.92$ |
|---|---|---|
| TELL | **Conclusion** Don't forget to interpret your result in context. | 92% of all suspects are given a test. |

**Question 2.** What is the probability that the suspect gets either a blood test or a breath test but NOT both?

| SHOW | **Mechanics** We can use the rule, or just add the appropriate probabilities seen in the Venn diagram. | $P(\textbf{A or B but NOT both}) = P(\textbf{A or B}) - P(\textbf{A and B})$<br>$\qquad\qquad\qquad\qquad = 0.92 - 0.22 = 0.70$<br><br>OR<br><br>$P(\textbf{A or B but NOT both})$<br>$\qquad\qquad = P(\textbf{A and B}^C) + P(\textbf{B and A}^C)$<br>$\qquad\qquad = 0.56 + 0.14 = 0.70$ |
|---|---|---|
| TELL | **Conclusion** Interpret your result in context. | 70% of the suspects get exactly one of the tests. |

**Question 3.** What is the probability that the suspect gets neither test?

| SHOW | **Mechanics** Getting neither test is the complement of getting one or the other. Use the Complement Rule or just notice that "neither test" is represented by the region outside both circles. | $P(\text{neither test}) = 1 - P(\text{either test})$<br>$\qquad\qquad\qquad = 1 - P(\textbf{A or B})$<br>$\qquad\qquad\qquad = 1 - 0.92 = 0.08$<br>OR<br>$P(\textbf{A}^C \textbf{ and B}^C) = 0.08$ |
|---|---|---|
| TELL | **Conclusion** Interpret your result in context. | Only 8% of the suspects get no test. |

# It Depends . . .

Two psychologists surveyed 478 children in grades 4, 5, and 6 in elementary schools in Michigan. They stratified their sample, drawing roughly 1/3 from rural, 1/3 from suburban, and 1/3 from urban schools. Among other questions, they asked the students whether their primary goal was to get good grades, to be popular, or to be good at sports. One question of interest was whether boys and girls at this age had similar goals.

Here's a *contingency table* giving counts of the students by their goals and sex:

|  |  | Grades | Popular | Sports | Total |
|---|---|---|---|---|---|
|  |  |  | Goals |  |  |
| Sex | **Boy** | 117 | 50 | 60 | **227** |
|  | **Girl** | 130 | 91 | 30 | **251** |
|  | Total | **247** | **141** | **90** | **478** |

**Table 15.1**

The distribution of goals for boys and girls.

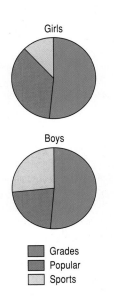

Girls

Boys

- Grades
- Popular
- Sports

**FIGURE 15.1**

*The distribution of goals for boys and girls.*

**A S** *Activity:* **Birthweights and Smoking.** Does smoking increase the chance of having a baby with low birth weight?

We looked at contingency tables and graphed *conditional distributions* back in Chapter 3. The graphs show the *relative frequencies* with which boys and girls named the three goals. It's only a short step from these relative frequencies to probabilities.

Let's focus on this study and make the sample space just the set of these 478 students. If we select a student at random from this study, the probability we select a girl is just the corresponding relative frequency (since we're equally likely to select any of the 478 students). There are 251 girls in the data out of a total of 478, giving a probability of

$$P(\text{girl}) = 251/478 = 0.525$$

The same method works for more complicated events like intersections. For example, what's the probability of selecting a girl whose goal is to be popular? Well, 91 girls named popularity as their goal, so the probability is

$$P(\text{girl and popular}) = 91/478 = 0.190$$

The probability of selecting a student whose goal is to excel at sports is

$$P(\text{sports}) = 90/478 = 0.188$$

We can now build on what we did in Chapter 3. Now that we've defined the sample space as these 478 students, we can recognize the relative frequencies as probabilities.

What if we are given the information that the selected student is a girl? Would that change the probability that the selected student's goal is sports? You bet it would! The pie charts show that girls are much less likely to say their goal is to excel at sports than are boys. When we restrict our focus to girls, we look only at the girls' row of the table, which gives the conditional distribution of goals given "girl." Of the 251 girls, only 30 of them said their goal was to excel at sports.

We write the probability that a selected student wants to excel at sports *given that we have selected a girl* as

$$P(\text{sports} \mid \text{girl}) = 30/251 = 0.120$$

For boys, we look at the conditional distribution of goals given "boy" shown in the top row of the table. There, of the 227 boys, 60 said their goal was to excel at sports. So, $P(\text{sports} \mid \text{boy}) = 60/227 = 0.264$, more than twice the girls' probability.

In general, when we want the probability of an event from a *conditional* distribution, we write $P(\mathbf{B}|\mathbf{A})$ and pronounce it "the probability of **B** *given* **A**." A probability that takes into account a given *condition* such as this is called a **conditional probability.**

Let's look at what we did. We worked with the counts, but we could work with the probabilities just as well. There were 30 students who both were girls and had sports as their goal, and there are 251 girls. So we found the probability to be 30/251. To find the probability of the event **B** *given* the event **A**, we restrict our attention to the outcomes in **A**. We then find in what fraction of *those* outcomes **B** also occurred. Formally, we write:

$P(\mathbf{B}|\mathbf{A})$ is the conditional probability of **B** *given* **A**.

$$P(\mathbf{B}|\mathbf{A}) = \frac{P(\mathbf{A} \text{ and } \mathbf{B})}{P(\mathbf{A})}.$$

Thinking this through, we can see that it's just what we've been doing, but with probabilities rather than with counts. Look back at the girls for whom sports was the goal. How did we calculate $P(\text{sports}|\text{girl})$?

The rule says to use probabilities. It says to find $P(\mathbf{A} \text{ and } \mathbf{B})/P(\mathbf{A})$. The result is the same whether we use counts or probabilities because the total number in the sample cancels out:

$$\frac{P(\text{sports } and \text{ girl})}{P(\text{girl})} = \frac{30/478}{251/478} = \frac{30}{251}.$$

**A S** *Activity:* **Conditional Probability.** Simulation is great for seeing conditional probabilities at work.

To use the formula for conditional probability, we're supposed to insist on one restriction. The formula doesn't work if $P(\mathbf{A})$ is 0. That would mean that we were "given" the fact that **A** was true even though the probability of **A** is 0, which would be a contradiction. The formula works only when the event that's given has probability greater than 0.

Let's take our rule out for a spin. What's the probability that we have selected a girl *given* that the selected student's goal is popularity? Applying the rule, we get

$$P(\text{girl}|\text{popular}) = \frac{P(\text{girl } and \text{ popular})}{P(\text{popular})}$$

$$= \frac{91/478}{141/478} = \frac{91}{141}.$$

---

**FOR EXAMPLE**  Finding a conditional probability

**Recap:** Our survey found that 56% of college students live on campus, 62% have a campus meal program, and 42% do both.

**Question:** While dining in a campus facility open only to students with meal plans, you meet someone interesting. What is the probability that your new acquaintance lives on campus?

Let **L** = {student lives on campus} and **M** = {student has a campus meal plan}.

P(student lives on campus given that the student has a meal plan) =

$$P(L|M) = \frac{P(L \text{ and } M)}{P(M)}$$

$$= \frac{0.42}{0.62}$$

$$\approx 0.677$$

There's a probability of about 0.677 that a student with a meal plan lives on campus.

# The General Multiplication Rule

Remember the Multiplication Rule for the probability of **A** *and* **B**? It said

$$P(\mathbf{A}\ and\ \mathbf{B}) = P(\mathbf{A}) \times P(\mathbf{B}) \text{ when } \mathbf{A} \text{ and } \mathbf{B} \text{ are independent.}$$

Now we can write a more general rule that doesn't require independence. In fact, we've *already* written it down. We just need to rearrange the equation a bit.

The equation in the definition for conditional probability contains the probability of **A** *and* **B**. Rearranging the equation gives

$$P(\mathbf{A}\ and\ \mathbf{B}) = P(\mathbf{A}) \times P(\mathbf{B}|\mathbf{A}).$$

**A S**  *Activity:* **The General Multiplication Rule.** The best way to understand the General Multiplication Rule is with an experiment.

This is a **General Multiplication Rule** for compound events that does not require the events to be independent. Better than that, it even makes sense. The probability that two events, **A** and **B**, *both* occur is the probability that event **A** occurs multiplied by the probability that event **B** *also* occurs—that is, by the probability that event **B** occurs *given* that event **A** occurs.

Of course, there's nothing special about which set we call **A** and which one we call **B**. We should be able to state this the other way around. And indeed we can. It is equally true that

$$P(\mathbf{A}\ and\ \mathbf{B}) = P(\mathbf{B}) \times P(\mathbf{A}|\mathbf{B}).$$

# Independence

If we had to pick one idea in this chapter that you should understand and remember, it's the definition and meaning of independence. We'll need this idea in every one of the chapters that follow.

Let's return to the question of just what it means for events to be independent. We've said informally that what we mean by independence is that the outcome of one event does not influence the probability of the other. With our new notation for conditional probabilities, we can write a formal definition: Events **A** and **B** are **independent** whenever

$$P(\mathbf{B}|\mathbf{A}) = P(\mathbf{B}).$$

Now we can see that the Multiplication Rule for independent events we saw in Chapter 14 is just a special case of the General Multiplication Rule. The general rule says

$$P(\mathbf{A}\ and\ \mathbf{B}) = P(\mathbf{A}) \times P(\mathbf{B}|\mathbf{A}).$$

**A S**  *Activity:* **Independence.** Are *Smoking* and *Low Birthweight* independent?

whether the events are independent or not. But when events **A** and **B** are independent, we can write $P(\mathbf{B})$ for $P(\mathbf{B}|\mathbf{A})$ and we get back our simple rule:

$$P(\mathbf{A}\ and\ \mathbf{B}) = P(\mathbf{A}) \times P(\mathbf{B}).$$

Sometimes people use this statement as the definition of independent events, but we find the other definition more intuitive. Either way, the idea is that for independent events, the probability of one doesn't change when the other occurs.

In earlier chapters we said informally that two events were independent if learning that one occurred didn't change what you thought about the other occurring. Now we can be more formal. Events A and B are independent if (and only if) the probability of **A** is the same when we are given that **B** has occurred. That is, $P(\mathbf{A}) = P(\mathbf{A}|\mathbf{B})$.

Although sometimes your intuition is enough, now that we have the formal rule, use it whenever you can.

Is the probability of having good grades as a goal independent of the sex of the responding student? Looks like it might be. We need to check whether

$$P(\text{grades}|\text{girl}) = P(\text{grades})$$

$$\frac{130}{251} = 0.52 \overset{?}{=} \frac{247}{478} = 0.52$$

To two decimal place accuracy, it looks like we can consider choosing good grades as a goal to be independent of sex.

On the other hand, $P(\text{sports})$ is 90/478, or about 18.8%, but $P(\text{sports}|\text{boy})$ is 60/227 = 26.4%. Because these probabilities aren't equal, we can be pretty sure that choosing success in sports as a goal is not independent of the student's sex.

---

**FOR EXAMPLE** | Checking for independence

**Recap:** Our survey told us that 56% of college students live on campus, 62% have a campus meal program, and 42% do both.

**Question:** Are living on campus and having a meal plan independent? Are they disjoint?

Let **L** = {student lives on campus} and **M** = {student has a campus meal plan}. If these events are independent, then knowing that a student lives on campus doesn't affect the probability that he or she has a meal plan. I'll check to see if $P(M|L) = P(M)$:

$$P(M|L) = \frac{P(L \text{ and } M)}{P(L)}$$

$$= \frac{0.42}{0.56}$$

$$= 0.75, \quad \text{but } P(M) = 0.62.$$

Because $0.75 \neq 0.62$, the events are not independent; students who live on campus are more likely to have meal plans. Living on campus and having a meal plan are not disjoint either; in fact, 42% of college students do both.

---

# Independent ≠ Disjoint

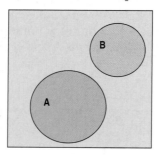

**FIGURE 15.2**

*Disjoint events **A** and **B**. Because these events are mutually exclusive, learning that **A** happened tells us that **B** didn't. The probability of **B** has changed from whatever it was to zero. So **A** and **B** are not independent.*

Are disjoint events independent? Both concepts seem to have similar ideas of separation and distinctness about them, but in fact disjoint events *cannot* be independent.[2] Let's see why. Consider the two disjoint events {you get an A in this course} and {you get a B in this course}. They're disjoint because they have no outcomes in common. Suppose you learn that you *did* get an A in the course. Now what is the probability that you got a B? You can't get both grades, so it must be 0.

Think about what that means. Knowing that the first event (getting an A) occurred changed your probability for the second event (down to 0). So these events aren't independent.

Mutually exclusive events can't be independent. They have no outcomes in common, so if one occurs, the other doesn't. A common error is to treat disjoint events as if they were independent, and apply the Multiplication Rule for independent events. Don't make that mistake.

## JUST CHECKING

**2.** The American Association for Public Opinion Research (AAPOR) is an association of about 1600 individuals who share an interest in public opinion and survey research. They report that typically as few as 10% of random phone calls result in a completed interview. Reasons are varied, but some of the most common include no answer, refusal to cooperate, and failure to complete the call.

---

[2] Well, technically two disjoint events *can* be independent, but only if the probability of one of the events is 0. For practical purposes, though, we can ignore this case. After all, as statisticians we don't anticipate having data about things that don't happen.

Which of the following events are independent, which are disjoint, and which are neither independent nor disjoint?

a) **A** = Your telephone number is randomly selected. **B** = You're not at home at dinnertime when they call.

b) **A** = As a selected subject, you complete the interview. **B** = As a selected subject, you refuse to cooperate.

c) **A** = You are not at home when they call at 11 a.m. **B** = You are employed full time.

# Depending on Independence

It's much easier to think about independent events than to deal with conditional probabilities. It seems that most people's natural intuition for probabilities breaks down when it comes to conditional probabilities. Someone may estimate the probability of a compound event by multiplying the probabilities of its component events together without asking seriously whether those probabilities are independent.

For example, experts have assured us that the probability of a major commercial nuclear plant failure is so small that we should not expect such a failure to occur even in a span of hundreds of years. After only a few decades of commercial nuclear power, however, the world has seen two failures (Chernobyl and Three Mile Island). How could the estimates have been so wrong?

One simple part of the failure calculation is to test a particular valve and determine that valves such as this one fail only once in, say, 100 years of normal use. For a coolant failure to occur, several valves must fail. So we need the compound probability, *P*(valve 1 fails *and* valve 2 fails *and* . . .). A simple risk assessment might multiply the small probability of one valve failure together as many times as needed.

But if the valves all came from the same manufacturer, a flaw in one might be found in the others. And maybe when the first fails, it puts additional pressure on the next one in line. In either case, the events aren't independent and so we can't simply multiply the probabilities together.

Whenever you see probabilities multiplied together, stop and ask whether you think they are really independent.

# Tables and Conditional Probability

One of the easiest ways to think about conditional probabilities is with contingency tables. We did that earlier in the chapter when we began our discussion. But sometimes we're given probabilities without a table. You can often construct a simple table to correspond to the probabilities.

For example, in the drunk driving data, we are told that 78% of suspect drivers get a breath test, 36% a blood test, and 22% both. That's enough information. Translating percentages to probabilities, what we know looks like this:

| | | Breath Test | | |
|---|---|---|---|---|
| | | **Yes** | **No** | Total |
| **Blood Test** | **Yes** | 0.22 | | 0.36 |
| | **No** | | | |
| | Total | 0.78 | | 1.00 |

Notice that the 0.78 and 0.36 are *marginal* probabilities and so they go into the *margins*. The 0.22 is the probability of getting both tests—a breath test *and* a blood test—so that's a *joint* probability. Those belong in the interior of the table.

Because the cells of the table show disjoint events, the probabilities always add to the marginal totals going across rows or down columns. So, filling in the rest of the table is quick:

|  | | Breath Test | | |
|---|---|---|---|---|
| | | **Yes** | **No** | Total |
| **Blood Test** | **Yes** | 0.22 | 0.14 | **0.36** |
| | **No** | 0.56 | 0.08 | **0.64** |
| | Total | **0.78** | **0.22** | **1.00** |

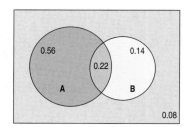

Compare this with the Venn diagram. Notice which entries in the table match up with the sets in this diagram. Whether a Venn diagram or a table is better to use will depend on what you are given and the questions you're being asked. Try both.

---

## STEP-BY-STEP EXAMPLE    Are the Events Disjoint? Independent?

Let's take another look at the drunk driving situation. Police report that 78% of drivers are given a breath test, 36% a blood test, and 22% both tests.

Questions: 1. Are giving a DWI suspect a blood test and a breath test mutually exclusive?
         2. Are giving the two tests independent?

| THINK | **Plan** Define the events we're interested in. | Let **A** = {suspect is given a breath test}. |
|---|---|---|
| | | Let **B** = {suspect is given a blood test}. |
| | State the given probabilities. | I know that |
| | | $$P(\mathbf{A}) = 0.78$$ $$P(\mathbf{B}) = 0.36$$ $$P(\mathbf{A} \text{ and } \mathbf{B}) = 0.22$$ |

**Question 1.** Are giving a DWI suspect a blood test and a breath test mutually exclusive?

| SHOW | **Mechanics** Disjoint events cannot *both* happen at the same time, so check to see if $P(\mathbf{A} \text{ and } \mathbf{B}) = 0$. | $P(\mathbf{A} \text{ and } \mathbf{B}) = 0.22$. Since some suspects are given both tests, $P(\mathbf{A} \text{ and } \mathbf{B}) \neq 0$. The events are *not* mutually exclusive. |
|---|---|---|
| TELL | **Conclusion** State your conclusion in context. | 22% of all suspects get both tests, so a breath test and a blood test are *not* disjoint events. |

**Question 2.** Are the two tests independent?

**Plan** Make a table.

|  |  | Breath Test | | |
|---|---|---|---|---|
|  |  | Yes | No | Total |
| Blood Test | Yes | 0.22 | 0.14 | 0.36 |
|  | No | 0.56 | 0.08 | 0.64 |
|  | Total | 0.78 | 0.22 | 1.00 |

**Mechanics** Does getting a breath test change the probability of getting a blood test? That is, does $P(\mathbf{B}|\mathbf{A}) = P(\mathbf{B})$?

Because the two probabilities are *not* the same, the events are not independent.

$$P(\mathbf{B}|\mathbf{A}) = \frac{P(\mathbf{A} \text{ and } \mathbf{B})}{P(\mathbf{A})} = \frac{0.22}{0.78} \approx 0.28$$
$$P(\mathbf{B}) = 0.36$$
$$P(\mathbf{B}|\mathbf{A}) \neq P(\mathbf{B})$$

**Conclusion** Interpret your results in context.

Overall, 36% of the drivers get blood tests, but only 28% of those who get a breath test do. Since suspects who get a breath test are less likely to have a blood test, the two events are not independent.

### JUST CHECKING

3. Remember our sample of pages in this book from this chapter's first Just Checking . . . ? We found that

    *48% of pages had a data display.*

    *27% of pages had an equation, and*

    *7% of pages had both a data display and an equation.*

    **a)** Make a contingency table for the variables *display* and *equation*.
    **b)** What is the probability that a randomly selected sample page with an equation also had a data display?
    **c)** Are having an equation and having a data display disjoint events?
    **d)** Are having an equation and having a data display independent events?

## Drawing Without Replacement

Room draw is a process for assigning dormitory rooms to students who live on campus. Sometimes, when students have equal priority, they are randomly assigned to the currently available dorm rooms. When it's time for you and your friend to draw, there are 12 rooms left. Three are in Gold Hall, a very desirable dorm with spacious wood-paneled rooms. Four are in Silver Hall, centrally located, but not quite as desirable. And five are in Wood Hall, a new dorm with cramped rooms, located half a mile from the center of campus on the edge of the woods.

You get to draw first, and then your friend will draw. Naturally, you would both like to score rooms in Gold. What are your chances? In particular, what's the chance that you *both* can get rooms in Gold?

When you go first, the chance that *you* will draw one of the Gold rooms is 3/12. Suppose you do. Now, with you clutching your prized room assignment, what chance does your friend have? At this point there are only 11 rooms left and just 2 left in Gold, so your friend's chance is now 2/11.

Using our notation, we write

$$P(\text{friend draws Gold} \mid \text{you draw Gold}) = 2/11.$$

The reason the denominator changes is that we draw these rooms *without replacement*. That is, once one is drawn, it doesn't go back into the pool.

We often sample without replacement. When we draw from a very large population, the change in the denominator is too small to worry about. But when there's a small population to draw from, as in this case, we need to take note and adjust the probabilities.

What are the chances that *both* of you will luck out? Well, now we've calculated the two probabilities we need for the General Multiplication Rule, so we can write:

$$P(\text{you draw Gold } and \text{ friend draws Gold})$$
$$= P(\text{you draw Gold}) \times P(\text{friend draws Gold} \mid \text{you draw Gold})$$
$$= 3/12 \times 2/11 = 1/22 = 0.045$$

In this instance, it doesn't matter who went first, or even if the rooms were drawn simultaneously. Even if the room draw was accomplished by shuffling cards containing the names of the dormitories and then dealing them out to 12 applicants (rather than by each student drawing a room in turn) we can still *think* of the calculation as having taken place in two steps:

That is, one of you has a probability of 3/12 of drawing a Gold room and the other then has a probability of 2/11 of also drawing a Gold room. It doesn't matter whose draw we think of first. The probability changes for the second person nonetheless. The diagram shows this ordering of our thoughts.

Diagramming conditional probabilities leads to a more general way of helping us think with pictures—one that works for calculating conditional probabilities even when they involve different variables.

## Tree Diagrams

For men, binge drinking is defined as having five or more drinks in a row, and for women as having four or more drinks in a row. (The difference is because of the average difference in weight.) According to a study by the Harvard School of Public Health (H. Wechsler, G. W. Dowdall, A. Davenport, and W. DeJong, "Binge Drinking on Campus: Results of a National Study"), 44% of college students engage in binge drinking, 37% drink moderately, and 19% abstain entirely. Another study, published in the *American Journal of Health Behavior*, finds that among binge drinkers aged 21 to 34, 17% have been involved in an alcohol-related automobile accident, while among non-bingers of the same age, only 9% have been involved in such accidents.

What's the probability that a randomly selected college student will be a binge drinker who has had an alcohol-related car accident?

To start, we see that the probability of selecting a binge drinker is about 44%. To find the probability of selecting someone who is both a binge drinker and a driver with an alcohol-related accident, we would need to pull out the General Multiplication Rule and multiply the probability of one of the events by the conditional probability of the other given the first.

Or we *could* make a picture. Which would you prefer?

We thought so.

The kind of picture that helps us think through this kind of reasoning is called a **tree diagram**, because it shows sequences of events, like those we had in room draw, as paths that look like branches of a tree. It is a good idea to make a tree diagram almost any time you plan to use the General Multiplication Rule. The number of different paths we can take can get large, so we usually draw the tree starting from the left and growing vine-like across the page, although sometimes you'll see them drawn from the bottom up or top down.

The first branch of our tree separates students according to their drinking habits. We label each branch of the tree with a possible outcome and its corresponding probability.

> *"Why," said the Dodo, "the best way to explain it is to do it."*
> —Lewis Carroll

**FIGURE 15.3**

*We can diagram the three outcomes of drinking and indicate their respective probabilities with a simple tree diagram.*

Notice that we cover all possible outcomes with the branches. The probabilities add up to one. But we're also interested in car accidents. The probability of having an alcohol-related accident *depends* on one's drinking behavior. Because the probabilities are *conditional,* we draw the alternatives separately on each branch of the tree:

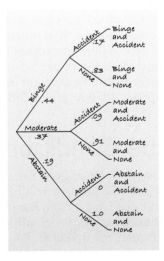

**FIGURE 15.4**

*Extending the tree diagram, we can show both drinking and accident outcomes. The accident probabilities are conditional on the drinking outcomes, and they change depending on which branch we follow. Because we are concerned only with alcohol-related accidents, the conditional probability P(accident|abstinence) must be 0.*

On each of the second set of branches, we write the possible outcomes associated with having an alcohol-related car accident (having an accident or not) and the associated probability. These probabilities are different because they are *conditional* depending on the student's drinking behavior. (It shouldn't be too surprising that those who binge drink have a higher probability of alcohol-related accidents.) The probabilities add up to one, because given the outcome on the first branch, these outcomes cover all the possibilities. Looking back at the General Multiplication Rule, we can see how the tree depicts the calculation. To find the probability that a randomly selected student will be a binge drinker who has had an alcohol-related car accident, we follow the top branches. The probability of selecting a binger is 0.44. The conditional probability of an accident *given* binge drinking is 0.17. The General Multiplication Rule tells us that to find the *joint* probability of being a binge drinker and having an accident, we multiply these two probabilities together:

$$P(\text{binge } and \text{ accident}) = P(\text{binge}) \times P(\text{accident} | \text{binge})$$
$$= 0.44 \times 0.17 = 0.075$$

And we can do the same for each combination of outcomes:

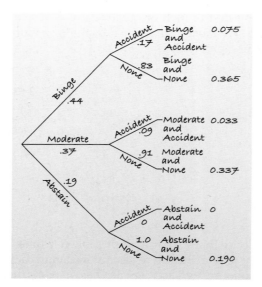

**FIGURE 15.5**

*We can find the probabilities of compound events by multiplying the probabilities along the branch of the tree that leads to the event, just the way the General Multiplication Rule specifies.*

*The probability of abstaining and having an alcohol-related accident is, of course, zero.*

All the outcomes at the far right are disjoint because at each branch of the tree we chose between disjoint alternatives. And they are *all* the possibilities, so the probabilities on the far right must add up to one.

Because the final outcomes are disjoint, we can add up their probabilities to get probabilities for compound events. For example, what's the probability that a selected student has had an alcohol-related car accident? We simply find *all* the outcomes on the far right in which an accident has happened. There are three and we can add their probabilities: 0.075 + 0.033 + 0 = 0.108—almost an 11% chance.

## Reversing the Conditioning

If we know a student has had an alcohol-related accident, what's the probability that the student is a binge drinker? That's an interesting question, but we can't just read it from the tree. The tree gives us $P(\text{accident} | \text{binge})$, but we want $P(\text{binge} | \text{accident})$—conditioning in the other direction. The two probabilities are definitely *not* the same. We have reversed the conditioning.

We may not have the conditional probability we want, but we do know everything we need to know to find it. To find a conditional probability, we need the probability that both events happen divided by the probability that the given event occurs. We have already found the probability of an alcohol-related accident: 0.075 + 0.033 + 0 = 0.108.

The joint probability that a student is both a binge drinker and someone who's had an alcohol-related accident is found at the top branch: 0.075. We've restricted the *Who* of the problem to the students with alcohol-related accidents, so we divide the two to find the conditional probability:

$$P(\text{binge} \mid \text{accident}) = \frac{P(\text{binge } and \text{ accident})}{P(\text{accident})}$$

$$= \frac{0.075}{0.108} = 0.694$$

The chance that a student who has an alcohol-related car accident is a binge drinker is more than 69%! As we said, reversing the conditioning is rarely intuitive, but tree diagrams help us keep track of the calculation when there aren't too many alternatives to consider.

---

**STEP-BY-STEP EXAMPLE** | **Reversing the Conditioning**

When the authors were in college, there were only three requirements for graduation that were the same for all students: You had to be able to tread water for 2 minutes, you had to learn a foreign language, and you had to be free of tuberculosis. For the last requirement, all freshmen had to take a TB screening test that consisted of a nurse jabbing what looked like a corncob holder into your forearm. You were then expected to report back in 48 hours to have it checked. If you were healthy and TB-free, your arm was supposed to look as though you'd never had the test.

Sometime during the 48 hours, one of us had a reaction. When he finally saw the nurse, his arm was about 50% bigger than normal and a very unhealthy red. Did he have TB? The nurse had said that the test was about 99% effective, so it seemed that the chances must be pretty high that he had TB. How high do you think the chances were? Go ahead and guess. Guess low.

We'll call **TB** the event of actually having TB and + the event of testing positive. To start a tree, we need to know $P(\textbf{TB})$, the probability of having TB.[3] We also need to know the conditional probabilities $P(+ \mid \textbf{TB})$ and $P(+ \mid \textbf{TB}^C)$. Diagnostic tests can make two kinds of errors. They can give a positive result for a healthy person (a *false positive*) or a negative result for a sick person (a *false negative*). Being 99% accurate usually means a false-positive rate of 1%. That is, someone who doesn't have the disease has a 1% chance of testing positive anyway. We can write $P(+ \mid \textbf{TB}^C) = 0.01$.

Since a false negative is more serious (because a sick person might not get treatment), tests are usually constructed to have a lower false-negative rate. We don't know exactly, but let's assume a 0.1% false-negative rate. So only 0.1% of sick people test negative. We can write $P(- \mid \textbf{TB}) = 0.001$.

| | |
|---|---|
|  **Plan** Define the events we're interested in and their probabilities. | Let **TB** = {having TB} and **TB**$^C$ = {no TB}<br>　　+ = {testing positive} and<br>　　− = {testing negative}<br><br>I know that $P(+ \mid \textbf{TB}^C) = 0.01$ and $P(- \mid \textbf{TB}) = 0.001$. I also know that $P(\textbf{TB}) = 0.00005$. |
| Figure out what you want to know in terms of the events. Use the notation of conditional probability to write the event whose probability you want to find. | I'm interested in the probability that the author had TB given that he tested positive: $P(\textbf{TB} \mid +)$. |

---

[3] This isn't given, so we looked it up. Although TB is a matter of serious concern to public health officials, it is a fairly uncommon disease, with an incidence of about 5 cases per 100,000 in the United States (see *http://www.cdc.gov/tb/default.htm*).

**Plot** Draw the tree diagram. When probabilities are very small like these are, be careful to keep all the significant digits.

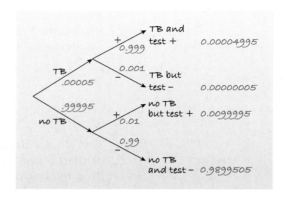

To finish the tree we need $P(\textbf{TB}^C)$, $P(-|\textbf{TB}^C)$, and $P(-|\textbf{TB})$. We can find each of these from the Complement Rule:

$$P(\textbf{TB}^C) = 1 - P(\textbf{TB}) = 0.99995$$
$$P(-|\textbf{TB}^C) = 1 - P(+|\textbf{TB}^C)$$
$$= 1 - 0.01 = 0.99 \text{ and}$$
$$P(+|\textbf{TB}) = 1 - P(-|\textbf{TB})$$
$$= 1 - 0.001 = 0.999$$

**Mechanics** Multiply along the branches to find the probabilities of the four possible outcomes. It's a good idea to check your work by seeing if they total 1.

(Check: 0.00004995 + 0.00000005 + 0.0099995 + 0.98995050 = 1)

Add up the probabilities corresponding to the condition of interest—in this case, testing positive. We can add the probabilities from the tree twigs that correspond to testing positive because the tree shows disjoint events.

$P(+) = P(\textbf{TB} \text{ and } +) + P(\textbf{TB}^C \text{and } +)$
$P(+) = 0.00004995 + 0.0099995$
$\quad = 0.01004945$

Divide the probability of both events occuring (here, having TB and a positive test) by the probability (or frequency) of satisfying the condition (testing positive).

$$P(\textbf{TB}|+) = \frac{P(\textbf{TB} \text{ and } +)}{P(+)}$$
$$= \frac{0.00004995}{0.01004945}$$
$$= 0.00497$$

 **Conclusion** Interpret your result in context.

The chance of having TB after you test positive is less than 0.5%.

When we reverse the order of conditioning, we change the *Who* we are concerned with. With events of low probability, the result can be surprising. That's the reason patients who test positive for HIV, for example, are always told to seek medical counseling. They may have only a small chance of actually being infected. That's why global drug or disease testing can have unexpected consequences if people interpret *testing* positive as *being* positive.

# Bayes's Rule

When we have $P(\textbf{A}|\textbf{B})$ but want the *reverse* probability $P(\textbf{B}|\textbf{A})$, we need to find $P(\textbf{A} \text{ and } \textbf{B})$ and $P(\textbf{A})$. A tree is often a convenient way of finding these probabilities. It can work even when we have more than two possible events, as we saw in

*The Reverend Thomas Bayes is credited posthumously with the rule that is the foundation of Bayesian Statistics.*

the binge drinking example. Instead of using the tree, we *could* write the calculation algebraically, showing exactly how we found the quantities that we needed: $P(\mathbf{A}\ and\ \mathbf{B})$ and $P(\mathbf{A})$. The result is a formula known as Bayes's Rule, after the Reverend Thomas Bayes (1702?–1761), who was credited with the rule after his death, when he could no longer defend himself. Bayes's Rule is quite important in Statistics and is the foundation of an approach to Statistical analysis known as Bayesian Statistics. Although the simple rule deals with two alternative outcomes, the rule can be extended to the situation in which there are more than two branches to the first split of the tree. The principle remains the same (although the math gets more difficult). Bayes's Rule is just a formula for reversing the probability from the conditional probability that you're originally given. Bayes's Rule for two events says that $P(\mathbf{B}|\mathbf{A}) = \dfrac{P(\mathbf{A}|\mathbf{B})P(\mathbf{B})}{P(\mathbf{A}|\mathbf{B})P(\mathbf{B}) + P(\mathbf{A}|\mathbf{B^C})P(\mathbf{B^C})}$. Try it with the TB testing probabilities. (It's easier to just draw the tree, isn't it?)

---

**FOR EXAMPLE**    Reversing the conditioning

A recent Maryland highway safety study found that in 77% of all accidents the driver was wearing a seatbelt. Accident reports indicated that 92% of those drivers escaped serious injury (defined as hospitalization or death), but only 63% of the non-belted drivers were so fortunate.

**Question:** What's the probability that a driver who was seriously injured wasn't wearing a seatbelt?

Let B = the driver was wearing a seatbelt, and NB = no belt.

Let I = serious injury or death, and OK = not seriously injured.

I know P(B) = 0.77, so P(NB) = 1 − 0.77 = 0.23.

Also, P(OK|B) = 0.92, so P(I|B) = 0.08
and P(OK|NB) = 0.63, so P(I|NB) = 0.37

$$P(NB|I) = \frac{P(NB\ and\ I)}{P(I)} = \frac{0.0851}{0.0616 + 0.0851} = 0.58$$

Even though only 23% of drivers weren't wearing seatbelts, they accounted for 58% of all the deaths and serious injuries.

Just some advice from your friends, the authors: *Please buckle up!* (We want you to finish this course.)

*Nicholas Saunderson (1682–1739) was a blind English mathematician who invented a tactile board to help other blind people do mathematics. And he may have been the true originator of "Bayes's Rule."*

**Who discovered Bayes's Rule?** Stigler's "Law of Eponymy" states that discoveries named for someone (eponyms) are usually named for the wrong person. Steven Stigler, who admits he didn't originate the law, is an expert on the history of Statistics, and he suspected that the law might apply to Bayes's Rule. He looked at the possibility that another candidate—one Nicholas Saunderson—was the real discoverer, not the Reverend Bayes. He assembled historical evidence and compared probabilities that the historical events would have happened *given* that Bayes was the discoverer of the rule, with the corresponding probabilities *given* that Saunderson was the discoverer. Of course, what he really wanted to know were the probabilities that Bayes or Saunderson was the discoverer *given* the historical events. How did he *reverse* the conditional probabilities? He used Bayes's Rule and concluded that, actually, it's more likely that Saunderson is the real originator of the rule.

But that doesn't change our tradition of naming the rule for Bayes and calling the branch of Statistics arising from this approach Bayesian Statistics.

## WHAT CAN GO WRONG?

▶ **Don't use a simple probability rule where a general rule is appropriate.** Don't assume independence without reason to believe it. Don't assume that outcomes are disjoint without checking that they are. Remember that the general rules always apply, even when outcomes are in fact independent or disjoint.

▶ **Don't find probabilities for samples drawn without replacement as if they had been drawn with replacement.** Remember to adjust the denominator of your probabilities. This warning applies only when we draw from small populations or draw a large fraction of a finite population. When the population is very large relative to the sample size, the adjustments make very little difference, and we ignore them.

▶ **Don't reverse conditioning naively.** As we have seen, the probability of **A** *given* **B** may not, and, in general does not, resemble the probability of **B** *given* **A**. The true probability may be counterintuitive.

▶ **Don't confuse "disjoint" with "independent."** Disjoint events *cannot* happen at the same time. When one happens, you know the other did not, so $P(\mathbf{B}|\mathbf{A}) = 0$. Independent events *must* be able to happen at the same time. When one happens, you know it has no effect on the other, so $P(\mathbf{B}|\mathbf{A}) = P(\mathbf{B})$.

# CONNECTIONS

This chapter shows the unintuitive side of probability. If you've been thinking, "My mind doesn't work this way," you're probably right. Humans don't seem to find conditional and compound probabilities natural and often have trouble with them. Even statisticians make mistakes with conditional probability.

Our central connection is to the guiding principle that Statistics is about understanding the world. The events discussed in this chapter are close to the kinds of real-world situations in which understanding probabilities matters. The methods and concepts of this chapter are the tools you need to understand the part of the real world that deals with the outcomes of complex, uncertain events.

# WHAT HAVE WE LEARNED?

The last chapter's basic rules of probability are important, but they work only in special cases—when events are disjoint or independent. Now we've learned the more versatile General Addition Rule and General Multiplication Rule. We've also learned about conditional probabilities, and seen that reversing the conditioning can give surprising results.

We've learned the value of Venn diagrams, tables, and tree diagrams to help organize our thinking about probabilities.

Most important, we've learned to think clearly about independence. We've seen how to use conditional probability to determine whether two events are independent and to work with events that are not independent. A sound understanding of independence will be important throughout the rest of this book.

## Terms

**General Addition Rule** 385. For any two events, **A** and **B,** the probability of **A** *or* **B** is

$$P(\textbf{A } or \textbf{ B}) = P(\textbf{A}) + P(\textbf{B}) - P(\textbf{A } and \textbf{ B}).$$

**Conditional probability** 390. $P(\textbf{B}|\textbf{A}) = \dfrac{P(\textbf{A } and \textbf{ B})}{P(\textbf{A})}$

$P(\textbf{B}|\textbf{A})$ is read "the probability of **B** *given* **A**."

**General Multiplication Rule** 391. For any two events, **A** and **B,** the probability of **A** and **B** is

$$P(\textbf{A } and \textbf{ B}) = P(\textbf{A}) \times P(\textbf{B}|\textbf{A}).$$

**Independence (used formally)** 391. Events **A** and **B** are independent when $P(\textbf{B}|\textbf{A}) = P(\textbf{B})$.

**Tree diagram** 396. A display of conditional events or probabilities that is helpful in thinking through conditioning.

## Skills

▸ Understand the concept of conditional probability as redefining the *Who* of concern, according to the information about the event that is *given.*

▸ Understand the concept of independence.

▸ Know how and when to apply the General Addition Rule.

▸ Know how to find probabilities for compound events as fractions of counts of occurrences in a two-way table.

▸ Know how and when to apply the General Multiplication Rule.

▸ Know how to make and use a tree diagram to understand conditional probabilities and reverse conditioning.

▸ Be able to make a clear statement about a conditional probability that makes clear how the condition affects the probability.

▸ Avoid making statements that assume independence of events when there is no clear evidence that they are in fact independent.

# EXERCISES

1. **Homes.** Real estate ads suggest that 64% of homes for sale have garages, 21% have swimming pools, and 17% have both features. What is the probability that a home for sale has
   a) a pool or a garage?
   b) neither a pool nor a garage?
   c) a pool but no garage?

2. **Travel.** Suppose the probability that a U.S. resident has traveled to Canada is 0.18, to Mexico is 0.09, and to both countries is 0.04. What's the probability that an American chosen at random has
   a) traveled to Canada but not Mexico?
   b) traveled to either Canada or Mexico?
   c) not traveled to either country?

3. **Amenities.** A check of dorm rooms on a large college campus revealed that 38% had refrigerators, 52% had TVs, and 21% had both a TV and a refrigerator. What's the probability that a randomly selected dorm room has
   a) a TV but no refrigerator?
   b) a TV or a refrigerator, but not both?
   c) neither a TV nor a refrigerator?

4. **Workers.** Employment data at a large company reveal that 72% of the workers are married, that 44% are college graduates, and that half of the college grads are married. What's the probability that a randomly chosen worker
   a) is neither married nor a college graduate?
   b) is married but not a college graduate?
   c) is married or a college graduate?

5. **Global survey.** The marketing research organization GfK NOP Roper conducts a yearly survey on consumer attitudes worldwide. They collect demographic information on the roughly 1500 respondents from each country that they survey. Here is a table showing the number of people with various levels of education in five countries:

| | Post-graduate | College | Some high school | Primary or less | No answer | Total |
|---|---|---|---|---|---|---|
| **Educational Level by Country** | | | | | | |
| China | 7 | 315 | 671 | 506 | 3 | 1502 |
| France | 69 | 388 | 766 | 309 | 7 | 1539 |
| India | 161 | 514 | 622 | 227 | 11 | 1535 |
| U.K. | 58 | 207 | 1240 | 32 | 20 | 1557 |
| USA | 84 | 486 | 896 | 87 | 4 | 1557 |
| Total | 379 | 1910 | 4195 | 1161 | 45 | 7690 |

If we select someone at random from this survey,
   a) What is the probability that the person is from the United States?
   b) What is the probability that the person completed his or her education before college?
   c) What is the probability that the person is from France *or* did some post-graduate study?
   d) What is the probability that the person is from France *and* finished only primary school or less?

6. **Birth order.** A survey of students in a large Introductory Statistics class asked about their birth order (1 = oldest or only child) and which college of the university they were enrolled in. Here are the data:

| | Birth Order | | |
|---|---|---|---|
| College | **1 or only** | **2 or more** | **Total** |
| **Arts & Sciences** | 34 | 23 | 57 |
| **Agriculture** | 52 | 41 | 93 |
| **Human Ecology** | 15 | 28 | 43 |
| **Other** | 12 | 18 | 30 |
| Total | **113** | **110** | **223** |

Suppose we select a student at random from this class.
   a) What is the probability we select a Human Ecology student?
   b) What is the probability that we select a firstborn student?
   c) What is the probability that the person is firstborn *and* a Human Ecology student?
   d) What is the probability that the person is firstborn *or* a Human Ecology student?

7. **Cards.** You draw a card at random from a standard deck of 52 cards. Find each of the following conditional probabilities:
   a) The card is a heart, given that it is red.
   b) The card is red, given that it is a heart.
   c) The card is an ace, given that it is red.
   d) The card is a queen, given that it is a face card.

8. **Pets.** In its monthly report, the local animal shelter states that it currently has 24 dogs and 18 cats available for adoption. Eight of the dogs and 6 of the cats are male. Find each of the following conditional probabilities if an animal is selected at random:
   a) The pet is male, given that it is a cat.
   b) The pet is a cat, given that it is female.
   c) The pet is female, given that it is a dog.

9. **Health.** The probabilities that an adult American man has high blood pressure and/or high cholesterol are shown in the table.

| | Blood Pressure | |
|---|---|---|
| Cholesterol | **High** | **OK** |
| **High** | 0.11 | 0.21 |
| **OK** | 0.16 | 0.52 |

   a) What's the probability that a man has both conditions?
   b) What's the probability that he has high blood pressure?

c) What's the probability that a man with high blood pressure has high cholesterol?

d) What's the probability that a man has high blood pressure if it's known that he has high cholesterol?

**10. Death penalty.**   The table shows the political affiliations of American voters and their positions on the death penalty.

|  |  | Death Penalty | |
|---|---|---|---|
|  |  | **Favor** | **Oppose** |
| *Party* | **Republican** | 0.26 | 0.04 |
|  | **Democrat** | 0.12 | 0.24 |
|  | **Other** | 0.24 | 0.10 |

a) What's the probability that a randomly chosen voter favors the death penalty?

b) What's the probability that a Republican favors the death penalty?

c) What's the probability that a voter who favors the death penalty is a Democrat?

d) A candidate thinks she has a good chance of gaining the votes of anyone who is a Republican or in favor of the death penalty. What portion of the voters is that?

**11. Global survey, take 2.**   Look again at the table summarizing the Roper survey in Exercise 5.

a) If we select a respondent at random, what's the probability we choose a person from the United States who has done post-graduate study?

b) Among the respondents who have done post-graduate study, what's the probability the person is from the United States?

c) What's the probability that a respondent from the United States has done post-graduate study?

d) What's the probability that a respondent from China has only a primary-level education?

e) What's the probability that a respondent with only a primary-level education is from China?

**12. Birth order, take 2.**   Look again at the data about birth order of Intro Stats students and their choices of colleges shown in Exercise 6.

a) If we select a student at random, what's the probability the person is an Arts and Sciences student who is a second child (or more)?

b) Among the Arts and Sciences students, what's the probability a student was a second child (or more)?

c) Among second children (or more), what's the probability the student is enrolled in Arts and Sciences?

d) What's the probability that a first or only child is enrolled in the Agriculture College?

e) What is the probability that an Agriculture student is a first or only child?

**13. Sick kids.**   Seventy percent of kids who visit a doctor have a fever, and 30% of kids with a fever have sore throats. What's the probability that a kid who goes to the doctor has a fever and a sore throat?

**14. Sick cars.**   Twenty percent of cars that are inspected have faulty pollution control systems. The cost of repairing a pollution control system exceeds $100 about 40% of the time. When a driver takes her car in for inspection, what's the probability that she will end up paying more than $100 to repair the pollution control system?

**15. Cards.**   You are dealt a hand of three cards, one at a time. Find the probability of each of the following.

a) The first heart you get is the third card dealt.

b) Your cards are all red (that is, all diamonds or hearts).

c) You get no spades.

d) You have at least one ace.

**16. Another hand.**   You pick three cards at random from a deck. Find the probability of each event described below.

a) You get no aces.

b) You get all hearts.

c) The third card is your first red card.

d) You have at least one diamond.

**17. Batteries.**   A junk box in your room contains a dozen old batteries, five of which are totally dead. You start picking batteries one at a time and testing them. Find the probability of each outcome.

a) The first two you choose are both good.

b) At least one of the first three works.

c) The first four you pick all work.

d) You have to pick 5 batteries in order to find one that works.

**18. Shirts.**   The soccer team's shirts have arrived in a big box, and people just start grabbing them, looking for the right size. The box contains 4 medium, 10 large, and 6 extra-large shirts. You want a medium for you and one for your sister. Find the probability of each event described.

a) The first two you grab are the wrong sizes.

b) The first medium shirt you find is the third one you check.

c) The first four shirts you pick are all extra-large.

d) At least one of the first four shirts you check is a medium.

**19. Eligibility.**   A university requires its biology majors to take a course called BioResearch. The prerequisite for this course is that students must have taken either a Statistics course or a computer course. By the time they are juniors, 52% of the Biology majors have taken Statistics, 23% have had a computer course, and 7% have done both.

a) What percent of the junior Biology majors are ineligible for BioResearch?

b) What's the probability that a junior Biology major who has taken Statistics has also taken a computer course?

c) Are taking these two courses disjoint events? Explain.

d) Are taking these two courses independent events? Explain.

**20. Benefits.**   Fifty-six percent of all American workers have a workplace retirement plan, 68% have health insurance, and 49% have both benefits. We select a worker at random.

a) What's the probability he has neither employer-sponsored health insurance nor a retirement plan?

b) What's the probability he has health insurance if he has a retirement plan?

c) Are having health insurance and a retirement plan independent events? Explain.

d) Are having these two benefits mutually exclusive? Explain.

**21. For sale.** In the real-estate ads described in Exercise 1, 64% of homes for sale have garages, 21% have swimming pools, and 17% have both features.

a) If a home for sale has a garage, what's the probability that it has a pool, too?

b) Are having a garage and a pool independent events? Explain.

c) Are having a garage and a pool mutually exclusive? Explain.

**22. On the road again.** According to Exercise 2, the probability that a U.S. resident has traveled to Canada is 0.18, to Mexico is 0.09, and to both countries is 0.04.

a) What's the probability that someone who has traveled to Mexico has visited Canada, too?

b) Are traveling to Mexico and to Canada disjoint events? Explain.

c) Are traveling to Mexico and to Canada independent events? Explain.

**23. Cards.** If you draw a card at random from a well-shuffled deck, is getting an ace independent of the suit? Explain.

**24. Pets again.** The local animal shelter in Exercise 8 reported that it currently has 24 dogs and 18 cats available for adoption; 8 of the dogs and 6 of the cats are male. Are the species and sex of the animals independent? Explain.

**25. Unsafe food.** Early in 2007 *Consumer Reports* published the results of an extensive investigation of broiler chickens purchased from food stores in 23 states. Tests for bacteria in the meat showed that 81% of the chickens were contaminated with campylobacter, 15% with salmonella, and 13% with both.

a) What's the probability that a tested chicken was not contaminated with either kind of bacteria?

b) Are contamination with the two kinds of bacteria disjoint? Explain.

c) Are contamination with the two kinds of bacteria independent? Explain.

**26. Birth order, finis.** In Exercises 6 and 12 we looked at the birth orders and college choices of some Intro Stats students. For these students:

a) Are enrolling in Agriculture and Human Ecology disjoint? Explain.

b) Are enrolling in Agriculture and Human Ecology independent? Explain.

c) Are being firstborn and enrolling in Human Ecology disjoint? Explain.

d) Are being firstborn and enrolling in Human Ecology independent? Explain.

**27. Men's health, again.** Given the table of probabilities from Exercise 9, are high blood pressure and high cholesterol independent? Explain.

|  |  | Blood Pressure | |
|---|---|---|---|
|  |  | **High** | **OK** |
| Cholesterol | **High** | 0.11 | 0.21 |
|  | **OK** | 0.16 | 0.52 |

**28. Politics.** Given the table of probabilities from Exercise 10, are party affiliation and position on the death penalty independent? Explain.

|  |  | Death Penalty | |
|---|---|---|---|
|  |  | **Favor** | **Oppose** |
| Party | **Republican** | 0.26 | 0.04 |
|  | **Democrat** | 0.12 | 0.24 |
|  | **Other** | 0.24 | 0.10 |

**29. Phone service.** According to estimates from the federal government's 2003 National Health Interview Survey, based on face-to-face interviews in 16,677 households, approximately 58.2% of U.S. adults have both a landline in their residence and a cell phone, 2.8% have only cell phone service but no landline, and 1.6% have no telephone service at all.

a) Polling agencies won't phone cell phone numbers because customers object to paying for such calls. What proportion of U.S. households can be reached by a landline call?

b) Are having a cell phone and having a landline independent? Explain.

**30. Snoring.** After surveying 995 adults, 81.5% of whom were over 30, the National Sleep Foundation reported that 36.8% of all the adults snored. 32% of the respondents were snorers over the age of 30.

a) What percent of the respondents were under 30 and did not snore?

b) Is snoring independent of age? Explain.

**31. Montana.** A 1992 poll conducted by the University of Montana classified respondents by sex and political party, as shown in the table. Is party affiliation independent of the respondents' sex? Explain.

|  | **Democrat** | **Republican** | **Independent** |
|---|---|---|---|
| **Male** | 36 | 45 | 24 |
| **Female** | 48 | 33 | 16 |

**32. Cars.** A random survey of autos parked in student and staff lots at a large university classified the brands by country of origin, as seen in the table on the next page. Is country of origin independent of type of driver?

| | | Driver | |
|---|---|---|---|
| | | **Student** | **Staff** |
| Origin | **American** | 107 | 105 |
| | **European** | 33 | 12 |
| | **Asian** | 55 | 47 |

**33. Luggage.** Leah is flying from Boston to Denver with a connection in Chicago. The probability her first flight leaves on time is 0.15. If the flight is on time, the probability that her luggage will make the connecting flight in Chicago is 0.95, but if the first flight is delayed, the probability that the luggage will make it is only 0.65.
a) Are the first flight leaving on time and the luggage making the connection independent events? Explain.
b) What is the probability that her luggage arrives in Denver with her?

**34. Graduation.** A private college report contains these statistics:

*70% of incoming freshmen attended public schools.*

*75% of public school students who enroll as freshmen eventually graduate.*

*90% of other freshmen eventually graduate.*

a) Is there any evidence that a freshman's chances to graduate may depend upon what kind of high school the student attended? Explain.
b) What percent of freshmen eventually graduate?

**35. Late luggage.** Remember Leah (Exercise 33)? Suppose you pick her up at the Denver airport, and her luggage is not there. What is the probability that Leah's first flight was delayed?

**36. Graduation, part II.** What percent of students who graduate from the college in Exercise 34 attended a public high school?

**37. Absenteeism.** A company's records indicate that on any given day about 1% of their day-shift employees and 2% of the night-shift employees will miss work. Sixty percent of the employees work the day shift.
a) Is absenteeism independent of shift worked? Explain.
b) What percent of employees are absent on any given day?

**38. Lungs and smoke.** Suppose that 23% of adults smoke cigarettes. It's known that 57% of smokers and 13% of nonsmokers develop a certain lung condition by age 60.
a) Explain how these statistics indicate that lung condition and smoking are not independent.
b) What's the probability that a randomly selected 60-year-old has this lung condition?

**39. Absenteeism, part II.** At the company described in Exercise 37, what percent of the absent employees are on the night shift?

**40. Lungs and smoke, again.** Based on the statistics in Exercise 38, what's the probability that someone with the lung condition was a smoker?

**41. Drunks.** Police often set up sobriety checkpoints—roadblocks where drivers are asked a few brief questions to allow the officer to judge whether or not the person may have been drinking. If the officer does not suspect a problem, drivers are released to go on their way. Otherwise, drivers are detained for a Breathalyzer test that will determine whether or not they will be arrested. The police say that based on the brief initial stop, trained officers can make the right decision 80% of the time. Suppose the police operate a sobriety checkpoint after 9 p.m. on a Saturday night, a time when national traffic safety experts suspect that about 12% of drivers have been drinking.
a) You are stopped at the checkpoint and, of course, have not been drinking. What's the probability that you are detained for further testing?
b) What's the probability that any given driver will be detained?
c) What's the probability that a driver who is detained has actually been drinking?
d) What's the probability that a driver who was released had actually been drinking?

**42. No-shows.** An airline offers discounted "advance-purchase" fares to customers who buy tickets more than 30 days before travel and charges "regular" fares for tickets purchased during those last 30 days. The company has noticed that 60% of its customers take advantage of the advance-purchase fares. The "no-show" rate among people who paid regular fares is 30%, but only 5% of customers with advance-purchase tickets are no-shows.
a) What percent of all ticket holders are no-shows?
b) What's the probability that a customer who didn't show had an advance-purchase ticket?
c) Is being a no-show independent of the type of ticket a passenger holds? Explain.

**43. Dishwashers.** Dan's Diner employs three dishwashers. Al washes 40% of the dishes and breaks only 1% of those he handles. Betty and Chuck each wash 30% of the dishes, and Betty breaks only 1% of hers, but Chuck breaks 3% of the dishes he washes. (He, of course, will need a new job soon. . . .) You go to Dan's for supper one night and hear a dish break at the sink. What's the probability that Chuck is on the job?

**44. Parts.** A company manufacturing electronic components for home entertainment systems buys electrical connectors from three suppliers. The company prefers to use supplier A because only 1% of those connectors prove to be defective, but supplier A can deliver only 70% of the connectors needed. The company also must purchase connectors from two other suppliers, 20% from supplier B and the rest from supplier C. The rates of defective connectors from B and C are 2% and 4%, respectively. You buy one of these components, and when you try to use it you find that the connector is defective. What's the probability that your component came from supplier A?

**45. HIV testing.** In July 2005 the journal *Annals of Internal Medicine* published a report on the reliability of HIV testing. Results of a large study suggested that among people with HIV, 99.7% of tests conducted were (correctly) positive, while for people without HIV 98.5% of the tests were (correctly) negative. A clinic serving an at-risk population offers free HIV testing, believing that 15% of the patients may actually carry HIV. What's the probability that a patient testing negative is truly free of HIV?

**46. Polygraphs.** Lie detectors are controversial instruments, barred from use as evidence in many courts. Nonetheless, many employers use lie detector screening as part of their hiring process in the hope that they can avoid hiring people who might be dishonest. There has been some research, but no agreement, about the reliability of polygraph tests. Based on this research, suppose that a polygraph can detect 65% of lies, but incorrectly identifies 15% of true statements as lies.

A certain company believes that 95% of its job applicants are trustworthy. The company gives everyone a polygraph test, asking, "Have you ever stolen anything from your place of work?" Naturally, all the applicants answer "No," but the polygraph identifies some of those answers as lies, making the person ineligible for a job. What's the probability that a job applicant rejected under suspicion of dishonesty was actually trustworthy?

## JUST CHECKING
## Answers

**1. a)**

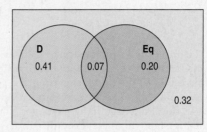

**b)** 0.32
**c)** 0.41

**2. a)** Independent
**b)** Disjoint
**c)** Neither

**3. a)**

|         | Equation |       |       |
|         | Yes  | No   | Total |
|---------|------|------|-------|
| **Yes** | 0.07 | 0.41 | **0.48** |
| **No**  | 0.20 | 0.32 | **0.52** |
| Total   | **0.27** | **0.73** | **1.00** |

(Display is the row label on the left side.)

**b)** $P(\mathbf{D}\,|\,\mathbf{Eq}) = P(\mathbf{D}\ and\ \mathbf{Eq})/P(\mathbf{Eq}) = 0.07/0.27 = 0.259$
**c)** No, pages can (and 7% do) have both.
**d)** To be independent, we'd need $P(\mathbf{D}\,|\,\mathbf{Eq}) = P(\mathbf{D})$. $P(\mathbf{D}\,|\,\mathbf{Eq}) = 0.259$, but $P(\mathbf{D}) = 0.48$. Overall, 48% of pages have data displays, but only about 26% of pages with equations do. They do not appear to be independent.

# Random Variables

## Where are we going?

How long do products last? Should you expect your computer to die just after the warranty runs out? How can you reduce your risk for developing hepatitis? Businesses, medical researchers, and other scientists all use probability to determine risk factors to help answer questions like these. To do that, they model the probability of outcomes using a special kind of variable—a *random* variable. Using random variables can help us talk about and predict random behavior.

### What Is an Actuary?

Actuaries are the daring people who put a price on risk, estimating the likelihood and costs of rare events, so they can be insured. That takes financial, statistical, and business skills. It also makes them invaluable to many businesses. Actuaries are rather rare themselves; only about 19,000 work in North America. Perhaps because of this, they are well paid. If you're enjoying this course, you may want to look into a career as an actuary. Contact the Society of Actuaries or the Casualty Actuarial Society (who, despite what you may think, did not pay for this blurb).

Insurance companies make bets. They bet that you're going to live a long life. You bet that you're going to die sooner. Both you and the insurance company want the company to stay in business, so it's important to find a "fair price" for your bet. Of course, the right price for *you* depends on many factors, and nobody can predict exactly how long you'll live. But when the company averages over enough customers, it can make reasonably accurate estimates of the amount it can expect to collect on a policy before it has to pay its benefit.

Here's a simple example. An insurance company offers a "death and disability" policy that pays $10,000 when you die or $5000 if you are permanently disabled. It charges a premium of only $50 a year for this benefit. Is the company likely to make a profit selling such a plan? To answer this question, the company needs to know the *probability* that its clients will die or be disabled in any year. From actuarial information like this, the company can calculate the expected value of this policy.

## Expected Value: Center

We'll want to build a probability model in order to answer the questions about the insurance company's risk. First we need to define a few terms. The amount the company pays out on an individual policy is called a **random variable** because its

**A S** *Activity:* **Random Variables.** Learn more about random variables from this animated tour.

numeric value is based on the outcome of a random event. We use a capital letter, like $X$, to denote a random variable. We'll denote a particular value that it can have by the corresponding lower-case letter, in this case $x$. For the insurance company, $x$ can be $10,000 (if you die that year), $5000 (if you are disabled), or $0 (if neither occurs). Because we can list all the outcomes, we might formally call this random variable a **discrete** random variable. Otherwise, we'd call it a **continuous** random variable. The collection of all the possible values and the probabilities that they occur is called the **probability model** for the random variable.

Suppose, for example, that the death rate in any year is 1 out of every 1000 people, and that another 2 out of 1000 suffer some kind of disability. Then we can display the probability model for this insurance policy in a table like this:

| Policyholder Outcome | Payout $x$ | Probability $P(X = x)$ |
|---|---|---|
| Death | 10,000 | $\dfrac{1}{1000}$ |
| Disability | 5000 | $\dfrac{2}{1000}$ |
| Neither | 0 | $\dfrac{997}{1000}$ |

To see what the insurance company can expect, imagine that it insures exactly 1000 people. Further imagine that, in perfect accordance with the probabilities, 1 of the policyholders dies, 2 are disabled, and the remaining 997 survive the year unscathed. The company would pay $10,000 to one client and $5000 to each of 2 clients. That's a total of $20,000, or an average of 20000/1000 = $20 per policy. Since it is charging people $50 for the policy, the company expects to make a profit of $30 per customer. Not bad!

We can't predict what *will* happen during any given year, but we can say what we *expect* to happen. To do this, we (or, rather, the insurance company) need the probability model. The expected value of a policy is a parameter of this model. In fact, it's the mean. We'll signify this with the notation $\mu$ (for population mean) or $E(X)$ for expected value. This isn't an average of some data values, so we won't estimate it. Instead, we assume that the probabilities are known and simply calculate the expected value from them.

How did we come up with $20 as the expected value of a policy payout? Here's the calculation. As we've seen, it often simplifies probability calculations to think about some (convenient) number of outcomes. For example, we could imagine that we have exactly 1000 clients. Of those, exactly 1 died and 2 were disabled, corresponding to what the probabilities would say.

$$\mu = E(X) = \frac{10,000(1) + 5000(2) + 0(997)}{1000}$$

So our total payout comes to $20,000, or $20 per policy.

Instead of writing the expected value as one big fraction, we can rewrite it as separate terms each divided by 1000.

$$\mu = E(X)$$
$$= \$10,000\left(\frac{1}{1000}\right) + \$5000\left(\frac{2}{1000}\right) + \$0\left(\frac{997}{1000}\right)$$
$$= \$20.$$

How convenient! See the probabilities? For each policy, there's a 1/1000 chance that we'll have to pay $10,000 for a death and a 2/1000 chance that we'll have to pay $5000 for a disability. Of course, there's a 997/1000 chance that we won't have to pay anything.

Take a good look at the expression now. It's easy to calculate the **expected value** of a (discrete) random variable—just multiply each possible value by the probability that it occurs, and find the sum:

$$\mu = E(X) = \sum xP(x).$$

Be sure that every possible outcome is included in the sum. And verify that you have a valid probability model to start with—the probabilities should each be between 0 and 1 and should sum to one.

---

**FOR EXAMPLE** | Love and expected values

On Valentine's Day the *Quiet Nook* restaurant offers a *Lucky Lovers Special* that could save couples money on their romantic dinners. When the waiter brings the check, he'll also bring the four aces from a deck of cards. He'll shuffle them and lay them out face down on the table. The couple will then get to turn one card over. If it's a black ace, they'll owe the full amount, but if it's the ace of hearts, the waiter will give them a $20 Lucky Lovers discount. If they first turn over the ace of diamonds (hey—at least it's red!), they'll then get to turn over one of the remaining cards, earning a $10 discount for finding the ace of hearts this time.

**Question:** Based on a probability model for the size of the Lucky Lovers discounts the restaurant will award, what's the expected discount for a couple?

Let $X$ = the Lucky Lovers discount. The probabilities of the three outcomes are:

$$P(X = 20) = P(A\heartsuit) = \frac{1}{4}$$

$$P(X = 10) = P(A\diamondsuit, \text{then } A\heartsuit) = P(A\diamondsuit) \cdot P(A\heartsuit | A\diamondsuit) = \frac{1}{4} \cdot \frac{1}{3} = \frac{1}{12}$$

$$P(X = 0) = P(X \neq 20 \text{ or } 10) = 1 - \left(\frac{1}{4} + \frac{1}{12}\right) = \frac{2}{3}.$$

My probability model is:

| Outcome | $A\heartsuit$ | $A\diamondsuit$, then $A\heartsuit$ | Black Ace |
|---|---|---|---|
| $x$ | 20 | 10 | 0 |
| $P(X = x)$ | $\frac{1}{4}$ | $\frac{1}{12}$ | $\frac{2}{3}$ |

$$E(X) = 20 \cdot \frac{1}{4} + 10 \cdot \frac{1}{12} + 0 \cdot \frac{2}{3} = \frac{70}{12} \approx 5.83$$

Couples dining at the Quiet Nook can expect an average discount of $5.83.

---

### JUST CHECKING

**1.** One of the authors took his minivan in for repair recently because the air conditioner was cutting out intermittently. The mechanic identified the problem as dirt in a control unit. He said that in about 75% of such cases, drawing down and then recharging the coolant a couple of times cleans up the problem—and costs only $60. If that fails, then the control unit must be replaced at an additional cost of $100 for parts and $40 for labor.

> **a)** Define the random variable and construct the probability model.
> **b)** What is the expected value of the cost of this repair?
> **c)** What does that mean in this context?
>
> Oh—in case you were wondering—the $60 fix worked!

# First Center, Now Spread . . .

Of course, this expected value (or mean) is not what actually happens to any *particular* policyholder. No individual policy actually costs the company $20. We are dealing with random events, so some policyholders receive big payouts, others nothing. Because the insurance company must anticipate this variability, it needs to know the *standard deviation* of the random variable.

For data, we calculated the **standard deviation** by first computing the deviation from the mean and squaring it. We do that with (discrete) random variables as well. First, we find the deviation of each payout from the mean (expected value):

| Policyholder Outcome | Payout $x$ | Probability $P(X = x)$ | Deviation $(x - \mu)$ |
|---|---|---|---|
| Death | 10,000 | $\frac{1}{1000}$ | $(10{,}000 - 20) = 9980$ |
| Disability | 5000 | $\frac{2}{1000}$ | $(5000 - 20) = 4980$ |
| Neither | 0 | $\frac{997}{1000}$ | $(0 - 20) = -20$ |

Next, we square each deviation. The **variance** is the expected value of those squared deviations, so we multiply each by the appropriate probability and sum those products. That gives us the variance of $X$. Here's what it looks like:

$$Var(X) = 9980^2\left(\frac{1}{1000}\right) + 4980^2\left(\frac{2}{1000}\right) + (-20)^2\left(\frac{997}{1000}\right) = 149{,}600.$$

Finally, we take the square root to get the standard deviation:

$$SD(X) = \sqrt{149{,}600} \approx \$386.78.$$

The insurance company can expect an average payout of $20 per policy, with a standard deviation of $386.78.

Think about that. The company charges $50 for each policy and expects to pay out $20 per policy. Sounds like an easy way to make $30. In fact, most of the time (probability 997/1000) the company pockets the entire $50. But would you consider selling your roommate such a policy? The problem is that occasionally the company loses big. With probability 1/1000, it will pay out $10,000, and with probability 2/1000, it will pay out $5000. That may be more risk than you're willing to take on. The standard deviation of $386.78 gives an indication that it's no sure thing. That's a pretty big spread (and risk) for an average profit of $30.

Here are the formulas for what we just did. Because these are parameters of our probability model, the variance and standard deviation can also be written as $\sigma^2$ and $\sigma$. You should recognize both kinds of notation.

$$\sigma^2 = Var(X) = \sum(x - \mu)^2 P(x)$$
$$\sigma = SD(X) = \sqrt{Var(X)}$$

**FOR EXAMPLE**    Finding the standard deviation

**Recap:** The probability model for the Lucky Lovers restaurant discount is

| Outcome | A♥ | A♦, then A♥ | Black Ace |
|---------|-----|-------------|-----------|
| $x$ | 20 | 10 | 0 |
| $P(X = x)$ | $\dfrac{1}{4}$ | $\dfrac{1}{12}$ | $\dfrac{2}{3}$ |

We found that couples can expect an average discount of $\mu = \$5.83$.

**Question:** What's the standard deviation of the discounts?

First find the variance:

$$Var(X) = \sum (x - \mu)^2 \cdot P(x)$$

$$= (20 - 5.83)^2 \cdot \frac{1}{4} + (10 - 5.83)^2 \cdot \frac{1}{12} + (0 - 5.83)^2 \cdot \frac{2}{3}$$

$$\approx 74.306$$

So, $SD(X) = \sqrt{74.306} \approx \$8.62$

Couples can expect the Lucky Lovers discounts to average $5.83, with a standard deviation of $8.62.

---

**STEP-BY-STEP EXAMPLE**    **Expected Values and Standard Deviations for Discrete Random Variables**

As the head of inventory for Knowway computer company, you were thrilled that you had managed to ship 2 computers to your biggest client the day the order arrived. You are horrified, though, to find out that someone had restocked refurbished computers in with the new computers in your storeroom. The shipped computers were selected randomly from the 15 computers in stock, but 4 of those were actually refurbished.

If your client gets 2 new computers, things are fine. If the client gets one refurbished computer, it will be sent back at your expense—$100—and you can replace it. However, if both computers are refurbished, the client will cancel the order this month and you'll lose a total of $1000.

**Question:** What's the expected value and the standard deviation of the company's loss?

**Plan** State the problem.

*I want to find the company's expected loss for shipping refurbished computers and the standard deviation.*

**Variable** Define the random variable.

*Let $X$ = amount of loss.*

**Plot** Make a picture. This is another job for tree diagrams.

If you prefer calculation to drawing, find $P(\mathbf{NN})$ and $P(\mathbf{RR})$, then use the Complement Rule to find $P(\mathbf{NR}\ or\ \mathbf{RN})$.

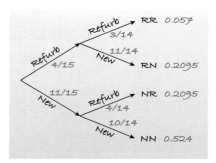

**Model** List the possible values of the random variable, and determine the probability model.

| Outcome | x | $P(X = x)$ |
|---|---|---|
| Two refurbs | 1000 | $P(\mathbf{RR}) = 0.057$ |
| One refurb | 100 | $P(\mathbf{NR}\ or\ \mathbf{RN}) = 0.2095$ $+\ 0.2095 = 0.419$ |
| New/new | 0 | $P(\mathbf{NN}) = 0.524$ |

**Mechanics** Find the expected value.

$$E(X) = 0(0.524) + 100(0.419) + 1000(0.057)$$
$$= \$98.90$$

Find the variance.

$$Var(X) = (0 - 98.90)^2\,(0.524)$$
$$+\ (100 - 98.90)^2\,(0.419)$$
$$+\ (1000 - 98.90)^2\,(0.057)$$
$$= 51,408.79$$

Find the standard deviation.

$$SD(X) = \sqrt{51,408.79} = \$226.735$$

**Conclusion** Interpret your results in context.

**REALITY CHECK** Both numbers seem reasonable. The expected value of $98.90 is between the extremes of $0 and $1000, and there's great variability in the outcome values.

I expect this mistake to cost the firm $98.90, with a standard deviation of $226.74. The large standard deviation reflects the fact that there's a pretty large range of possible losses.

## More About Means and Variances

Our insurance company expected to pay out an average of $20 per policy, with a standard deviation of about $387. If we take the $50 premium into account, we see the company makes a profit of $50 - 20 = \$30$ per policy. Suppose the company lowers the premium by $5 to $45. It's pretty clear that the expected profit also drops an average of $5 per policy, to $45 - 20 = \$25$.

What about the standard deviation? We know that adding or subtracting a constant from data shifts the mean but doesn't change the variance or standard deviation. The same is true of random variables.[1]

$$E(X \pm c) = E(X) \pm c \qquad Var(X \pm c) = Var(X).$$

---

[1] The rules in this section are true for both discrete *and* continuous random variables.

---

**FOR EXAMPLE**    Adding a constant

**Recap:** We've determined that couples dining at the *Quiet Nook* can expect Lucky Lovers discounts averaging $5.83 with a standard deviation of $8.62. Suppose that for several weeks the restaurant has also been distributing coupons worth $5 off any one meal (one discount per table).

**Question:** If every couple dining there on Valentine's Day brings a coupon, what will be the mean and standard deviation of the total discounts they'll receive?

Let $D$ = total discount (Lucky Lovers plus the coupon); then $D = X + 5$.

$$E(D) = E(X + 5) = E(X) + 5 = 5.83 + 5 = \$10.83$$
$$Var(D) = Var(X + 5) = Var(X) = 8.62^2$$
$$SD(D) = \sqrt{Var(X)} = \$8.62$$

Couples with the coupon can expect total discounts averaging $10.83. The standard deviation is still $8.62.

---

Back to insurance . . . What if the company decides to double all the payouts—that is, pay $20,000 for death and $10,000 for disability? This would double the average payout per policy and also increase the variability in payouts. We have seen that multiplying or dividing all data values by a constant changes both the mean and the standard deviation by the same factor. Variance, being the square of standard deviation, changes by the square of the constant. The same is true of random variables. In general, multiplying each value of a random variable by a constant multiplies the mean by that constant and the variance by the *square* of the constant.

$$E(aX) = aE(X) \qquad Var(aX) = a^2Var(X)$$

---

**FOR EXAMPLE**    Double the love

**Recap:** On Valentine's Day at the *Quiet Nook*, couples may get a Lucky Lovers discount averaging $5.83 with a standard deviation of $8.62. When two couples dine together on a single check, the restaurant doubles the discount offer—$40 for the ace of hearts on the first card and $20 on the second.

**Question:** What are the mean and standard deviation of discounts for such foursomes?

$$E(2X) = 2E(X) = 2(5.83) = \$11.66$$

$$Var(2x) = 2^2Var(x) = 2^2 \cdot 8.62^2 = 297.2176, \text{ so } SD(2X) = \sqrt{297.2176} = \$17.24$$

If the restaurant doubles the discount offer, two couples dining together can expect to save an average of $11.66 with a standard deviation of $17.24.

---

This insurance company sells policies to more than just one person. How can we figure means and variances for a collection of customers? For example, how can the company find the total expected value (and standard deviation) of policies taken over all policyholders? Consider a simple case: just two customers, Mr. Ecks and Ms. Wye. With an expected payout of $20 on each policy, we might predict a total of $20 + $20 = $40 to be paid out on the two policies. Nothing surprising there. The expected value of the sum is the sum of the expected values.

$$E(X + Y) = E(X) + E(Y).$$

The variability is another matter. Is the risk of insuring two people the same as the risk of insuring one person for twice as much? We wouldn't expect both clients to die or become disabled in the same year. Because we've spread the risk, the standard deviation should be smaller. Indeed, this is the fundamental principle behind insurance. By spreading the risk among many policies, a company can keep the standard deviation quite small and predict costs more accurately.

But how much smaller is the standard deviation of the sum? It turns out that, if the random variables are independent, there is a simple Addition Rule for variances: *The variance of the sum of two independent random variables is the sum of their individual variances.*

For Mr. Ecks and Ms. Wye, the insurance company can expect their outcomes to be independent, so (using $X$ for Mr. Ecks's payout and $Y$ for Ms. Wye's)

$$
\begin{aligned}
Var(X + Y) &= Var(X) + Var(Y) \\
&= 149{,}600 + 149{,}600 \\
&= 299{,}200.
\end{aligned}
$$

If they had insured only Mr. Ecks for twice as much, there would only be one outcome rather than two *independent* outcomes, so the variance would have been

$$
Var(2X) = 2^2 Var(X) = 4 \times 149{,}600 = 598{,}400, \text{or}
$$

twice as big as with two independent policies.

Of course, variances are in squared units. The company would prefer to know standard deviations, which are in dollars. The standard deviation of the payout for two independent policies is $\sqrt{299{,}200} = \$546.99$. But the standard deviation of the payout for a single policy of twice the size is $\sqrt{598{,}400} = \$773.56$, or about 40% more.

If the company has two customers, then, it will have an expected annual total payout of \$40 with a standard deviation of about \$547.

---

**FOR EXAMPLE**   Adding the discounts

**Recap:** The Valentine's Day Lucky Lovers discount for couples averages \$5.83 with a standard deviation of \$8.62. We've seen that if the restaurant doubles the discount offer for two couples dining together on a single check, they can expect to save \$11.66 with a standard deviation of \$17.24. Some couples decide instead to get separate checks and pool their two discounts.

**Question:** You and your amour go to this restaurant with another couple and agree to share any benefit from this promotion. Does it matter whether you play separately or together?

Let $X_1$ and $X_2$ represent the two separate discounts, and $T$ the total; then $T = X_1 + X_2$.

$$
E(T) = E(X_1 + X_2) = E(X_1) + E(X_2) = 5.83 + 5.83 = \$11.66,
$$

so the expected saving is the same either way.

The cards are reshuffled for each couple's turn, so the discounts couples receive are independent. It's okay to add the variances:

$$
Var(T) = Var(X_1 + X_2) = Var(X_1) + Var(X_2) = 8.62^2 + 8.62^2 = 148.6088
$$
$$
SD(T) = \sqrt{148.6088} = \$12.19
$$

When two couples get separate checks, there's less variation in their total discount. The standard deviation is \$12.19, compared to \$17.24 for couples who play for the double discount on a single check.

## Pythagorean Theorem of Statistics

We often use the standard deviation to measure variability, but when we add independent random variables, we use their variances. Think of the Pythagorean Theorem. In a right triangle (only), the *square* of the length of the hypotenuse is the sum of the *squares* of the lengths of the other two sides:

$$c^2 = a^2 + b^2.$$

For independent random variables (only), the *square* of the standard deviation of their sum is the sum of the *squares* of their standard deviations:

$$SD^2(X + Y) = SD^2(X) + SD^2(Y).$$

It's simpler to write this with *variances*:

For independent random variables, $X$ and $Y$,
$Var(X + Y) = Var(X) + Var(Y)$.

In general,

▸ *The mean of the sum of two random variables is the sum of the means.*

▸ *The mean of the difference of two random variables is the difference of the means.*

▸ *If the random variables are independent, the variance of their sum or difference is always the sum of the variances.*

$$E(X \pm Y) = E(X) \pm E(Y) \quad Var(X \pm Y) = Var(X) + Var(Y)$$

Wait a minute! Is that third part correct? Do we always *add* variances? Yes. Think about the two insurance policies. Suppose we want to know the mean and standard deviation of the *difference* in payouts to the two clients. Since each policy has an expected payout of $20, the expected difference is $20 - 20 = \$0$. If we also subtract variances, we get $0, too, and that surely doesn't make sense. Note that if the outcomes for the two clients are independent, the difference in payouts could range from $\$10,000 - \$0 = \$10,000$ to $\$0 - \$10,000 = -\$10,000$, a spread of $20,000. The variability in differences increases as much as the variability in sums. If the company has two customers, the difference in payouts has a mean of $0 and a standard deviation of about $547 (again).

---

**FOR EXAMPLE**   Working with differences

**Recap:** The Lucky Lovers discount at the *Quiet Nook* averages $5.83 with a standard deviation of $8.62. Just up the street, the *Wise Fool* restaurant has a competing Lottery of Love promotion. There a couple can select a specially prepared chocolate from a large bowl and unwrap it to learn the size of their discount. The restaurant's manager says the discounts vary with an average of $10.00 and a standard deviation of $15.00.

**Question:** How much more can you expect to save at the *Wise Fool*? With what standard deviation?

Let $W =$ *discount at the Wise Fool*, $X =$ *the discount at the Quiet Nook*, and $D =$ *the difference:* $D = W - X$. These are different promotions at separate restaurants, so the outcomes are independent.

$$E(W - X) = E(W) - E(X) = 10.00 - 5.83 = \$4.17$$
$$\begin{aligned} SD(W - X) &= \sqrt{Var(W - X)} \\ &= \sqrt{Var(W) + Var(X)} \\ &= \sqrt{15^2 + 8.62^2} \\ &\approx \$17.30 \end{aligned}$$

Discounts at the Wise Fool will average $4.17 more than at the Quiet Nook, with a standard deviation of $17.30.

---

**For random variables, does $X + X + X = 3X$?**   Maybe, but be careful. As we've just seen, insuring one person for $30,000 is not the same risk as insuring three people for $10,000 each. When each instance represents a different outcome for the same random variable, it's easy to fall into the trap of writing all of them with the same symbol. Don't make this common mistake. Make sure you write each instance as a *different* random variable. Just because each random variable describes a similar situation doesn't mean that each random outcome will be the same.

These are *random* variables, not the variables you saw in Algebra. Being random, they take on different values each time they're evaluated. So what you really mean is $X_1 + X_2 + X_3$. Written this way, it's clear that the sum shouldn't necessarily equal 3 times *anything*.

**FOR EXAMPLE** Summing a series of outcomes

**Recap:** The *Quiet Nook*'s Lucky Lovers promotion offers couples discounts averaging $5.83 with a standard deviation of $8.62. The restaurant owner is planning on serving 40 couples on Valentine's Day.

**Question:** What's the expected total of the discounts the owner will give? With what standard deviation?

Let $X_1, X_2, X_3, \ldots, X_{40}$ represent the discounts to the 40 couples, and $T$ the total of all the discounts. Then:

$$T = X_1 + X_2 + X_3 + \cdots + X_{40}$$
$$E(T) = E(X_1 + X_2 + X_3 + \cdots + X_{40})$$
$$= E(X_1) + E(X_2) + E(X_3) + \cdots + E(X_{40})$$
$$= 5.83 + 5.83 + 5.83 + \cdots + 5.83$$
$$= \$233.20$$

Reshuffling cards between couples makes the discounts independent, so:

$$SD(T) = \sqrt{Var(X_1 + X_2 + X_3 + \cdots + X_{40})}$$
$$= \sqrt{Var(X_1) + Var(X_2) + Var(X_3) + \cdots + Var(X_{40})}$$
$$= \sqrt{8.62^2 + 8.62^2 + 8.62^2 + \cdots + 8.62^2}$$
$$\approx 54.52$$

The restaurant owner can expect the 40 couples to win discounts totaling $233.20, with a standard deviation of $54.52.

## JUST CHECKING

2. Suppose the time it takes a customer to get and pay for seats at the ticket window of a baseball park is a random variable with a mean of 100 seconds and a standard deviation of 50 seconds. When you get there, you find only two people in line in front of you.
   a) How long do you expect to wait for your turn to get tickets?
   b) What's the standard deviation of your wait time?
   c) What assumption did you make about the two customers in finding the standard deviation?

# Combining Random Variables (The Bad News)

Although we know how to find the expected value and the variance for the sum of two independent random variables, that's not all we'd like to know. It would be nice if we could go directly from models of each random variable to a model for their sum. But the probability model for the sum of two random variables is *not* necessarily the same as the model we started with *even when the variables are independent.*

That's easy to see for discrete random variables because we can just think about their possible values. When we looked at insuring one person, either we paid out $0, $5000, or $10,000. Suppose we insure three people. The possibilities are not just $0, $15,000, or $30,000. We might have to pay out $5000, or $20,000, or other possible values. Even though the expected values add, the probability model is different. The probability model for $3X$ is not the same as the model for $X_1 + X_2 + X_3$. That's another reason to use the subscripted form rather than write $X + X + X$.

| STEP-BY-STEP EXAMPLE | **Hitting the Road: Means and Variances** |

You're planning to spend next year wandering through the mountains of Kyrgyzstan. You plan to sell your used SUV so you can purchase an off-road Honda motor scooter when you get there. Used SUVs of the year and mileage of yours are selling for a mean of $6940 with a standard deviation of $250. Your research shows that scooters in Kyrgyzstan are going for about 65,000 Kyrgyzstan som with a standard deviation of 500 som. One U.S. dollar is worth about 38.5 Kyrgyzstan som (38 som and 50 tylyn).

**Question:** How much cash can you expect to pocket after you sell your SUV and buy the scooter?

| THINK | **Plan** State the problem. | I want to model how much money I'd have (in som) after selling my SUV and buying the scooter. |
| | **Variables** Define the random variables. | Let A = sale price of my SUV (in dollars), <br> B = price of a scooter (in som), and <br> D = profit (in som) |
| | Write an appropriate equation. <br> Think about the assumptions. | $D = 38.5A - B$ <br><br> ✔ **Independence Assumption:** The prices are independent. |

| SHOW | **Mechanics** Find the expected value, using the appropriate rules. | $E(D) = E(38.5A - B)$ <br> $\qquad = 38.5E(A) - E(B)$ <br> $\qquad = 38.5(6{,}940) - (65{,}000)$ <br> $E(D) = 202{,}190$ som |
| | Find the variance, using the appropriate rules. Be sure to check the assumptions first! | Since sale and purchase prices are independent, <br> $Var(D) = Var(38.5A - B)$ <br> $\qquad = Var(38.5A) + Var(B)$ <br> $\qquad = (38.5)^2 Var(A) + Var(B)$ <br> $\qquad = 1482.25(250)^2 + (500)^2$ <br> $Var(D) = 92{,}890{,}625$ |
| | Find the standard deviation. | $SD(D) = \sqrt{92{,}890{,}625} = 9637.98$ som |

**Conclusion** Interpret your results in context. (Here that means talking about dollars.)

**REALITY CHECK** Given the initial cost estimates, the mean and standard deviation seem reasonable.

*I can expect to clear about 202,190 som ($5252) with a standard deviation of 9,638 som ($250).*

# Continuous Random Variables

> **A S** **Activity: Numeric Outcomes.** You've seen how to simulate discrete random outcomes. There's a tool for simulating continuous outcomes, too.

A company manufactures small stereo systems. At the end of the production line, the stereos are packaged and prepared for shipping. Stage 1 of this process is called "packing." Workers must collect all the system components (a main unit, two speakers, a power cord, an antenna, and some wires), put each in plastic bags, and then place everything inside a protective styrofoam form. The packed form then moves on to Stage 2, called "boxing." There, workers place the form and a packet of instructions in a cardboard box, close it, then seal and label the box for shipping.

The company says that times required for the packing stage can be described by a Normal model with a mean of 9 minutes and standard deviation of 1.5 minutes. The times for the boxing stage can also be modeled as Normal, with a mean of 6 minutes and standard deviation of 1 minute.

This is a common way to model events. Do our rules for random variables apply here? What's different? We no longer have a list of discrete outcomes, with their associated probabilities. Instead, we have **continuous random variables** that can take on any value. Now any single value won't have a probability. We saw this back in Chapter 6 when we first saw the Normal model (although we didn't talk then about "random variables" or "probability"). We know that the probability that $z = 1.5$ doesn't make sense, but we *can* talk about the probability that $z$ lies *between* 0.5 and 1.5. For a Normal random variable, the probability that it falls within an interval is just the area under the Normal curve over that interval.

> **A S** **Activity: Means of Random Variables.** Experiment with continuous random variables to learn how their expected values behave.

Some continuous random variables have Normal models; others may be skewed, uniform, or bimodal. Regardless of shape, all continuous random variables have means (which we also call *expected values*) and variances. In this book we won't worry about how to calculate them, but we can still work with models for continuous random variables when we're given these parameters.

# Combining Random Variables (The Good News)

We know that when we add two random variables together, the sum generally has a different probability model than the one we started with. Amazingly, independent Normal random variables behave better. The probability model for the sum of any number of independent Normal random variables is still Normal. And we already know what the mean and variance of that sum will be because those both add.

This is just one of the things that is special about the Normal. However, if this mathematical good behavior alone doesn't impress you, here's more real-world example of how we can use this fact.

**STEP-BY-STEP EXAMPLE** | **Packaging Stereos**

Consider the company that manufactures and ships small stereo systems that we just discussed.

Recall that times required to pack the stereos can be described by a Normal model with a mean of 9 minutes and standard deviation of 1.5 minutes. The times for the boxing stage can also be modeled as Normal, with a mean of 6 minutes and standard deviation of 1 minute.

Questions:
1. What is the probability that packing two consecutive systems takes over 20 minutes?
2. What percentage of the stereo systems take longer to pack than to box?

---

**Question 1:** What is the probability that packing two consecutive systems takes over 20 minutes?

---

**THINK**

**Plan** State the problem.

I want to estimate the probability that packing two consecutive systems takes over 20 minutes.

Let $P_1$ = time for packing the first system
$P_2$ = time for packing the second
$T$ = total time to pack two systems

**Variables** Define your random variables.

Write an appropriate equation.

$T = P_1 + P_2$

Think about the assumptions. Sums of independent Normal random variables follow a Normal model. Such simplicity isn't true in general.

✔ **Normal Model Assumption:** We are told that both random variables follow Normal models.

✔ **Independence Assumption:** We can reasonably assume that the two packing times are independent.

---

**SHOW**

**Mechanics** Find the expected value.

$$E(T) = E(P_1 + P_2)$$
$$= E(P_1) + E(P_2)$$
$$= 9 + 9 = 18 \text{ minutes}$$

For sums of independent random variables, variances add. (We don't need the variables to be Normal for this to be true—just independent.)

Since the times are independent,
$$Var(T) = Var(P_1 + P_2)$$
$$= Var(P_1) + Var(P_2)$$
$$= 1.5^2 + 1.5^2$$
$$Var(T) = 4.50$$

Find the standard deviation.

$$SD(T) = \sqrt{4.50} \approx 2.12 \text{ minutes}$$

Now we use the fact that both random variables follow Normal models to say that their sum is also Normal.

I'll model $T$ with $N(18, 2.12)$.

Sketch a picture of the Normal model for the total time, shading the region representing over 20 minutes.

Find the z-score for 20 minutes.

Use technology or Table Z to find the probability.

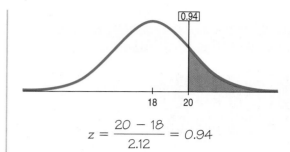

$$z = \frac{20 - 18}{2.12} = 0.94$$

$$P(T > 20) = P(z > 0.94) = 0.1736$$

**Conclusion** Interpret your result in context.

There's a little more than a 17% chance that it will take a total of over 20 minutes to pack two consecutive stereo systems.

---

**Question 2: What percentage of the stereo systems take longer to pack than to box?**

---

**Plan** State the question.

I want to estimate the percentage of the stereo systems that take longer to pack than to box.

**Variables** Define your random variables.

Let $P$ = time for packing a system
$B$ = time for boxing a system
$D$ = difference in times to pack and box a system

Write an appropriate equation.

$D = P - B$

What are we trying to find? Notice that we can tell which of two quantities is greater by subtracting and asking whether the difference is positive or negative.

The probability that it takes longer to pack than to box a system is the probability that the difference $P - B$ is greater than zero.

Don't forget to think about the assumptions.

✔ **Normal Model Assumption:** We are told that both random variables follow Normal models.

✔ **Independence Assumption:** We can assume that the times it takes to pack and to box a system are independent.

**Mechanics** Find the expected value.

$$E(D) = E(P - B)$$
$$= E(P) - E(B)$$
$$= 9 - 6 = 3 \text{ minutes}$$

For the difference of independent random variables, variances add.

Since the times are independent,
$$Var(D) = Var(P - B)$$
$$= Var(P) + Var(B)$$

| | |
|---|---|
| | $= 1.5^2 + 1^2$ <br> $Var(D) = 3.25$ |
| Find the standard deviation. | $SD(D) = \sqrt{3.25} \approx 1.80$ minutes |
| State what model you will use. | I'll model $D$ with $N$ (3, 1.80) |
| Sketch a picture of the Normal model for the difference in times, and shade the region representing a difference greater than zero. | 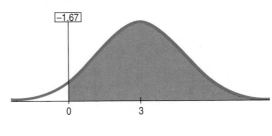 |
| Find the $z$-score for 0 minutes, then use Table Z or technology to find the probability. | $z = \dfrac{0 - 3}{1.80} = -1.67$ <br><br> $P(D > 0) = P(z > -1.67) = 0.9525$ |

| | | |
|---|---|---|
|  | **Conclusion** Interpret your result in context. | About 95% of all the stereo systems will require more time for packing than for boxing. |

## *Correlation and Covariance

In Chapter 7 we saw that the association of two variables could be measured with their correlation. What about random variables? We can talk about the correlation between random variables, too. But it's easier to start with a related concept called covariance.

If $X$ is a random variable with expected value $E(X) = \mu$ and $Y$ is a random variable with expected value $E(Y) = \nu$, then the **covariance** of $X$ and $Y$ is defined as

$$Cov(X,Y) = E((X - \mu)(Y - \nu)).$$

The covariance, like the correlation, measures how $X$ and $Y$ vary together (*co-* = *together*). Think about a scatterplot of two highly correlated variables. When $X$ is above its mean, $Y$ tends to be, too. And when $X$ is below its mean, $Y$ tends to be below its mean. So the product in the covariance formula is positive. Covariance has a few properties worth remembering:

▶ $Cov(X, Y) = Cov(Y, X)$
▶ $Cov(X, X) = Var(X)$
▶ $Cov(cX, dY) = cdCov(X, Y)$, for any constants $c$ and $d$
▶ $Cov(XY) = E(XY) - \mu\nu$
▶ If $X$ and $Y$ are independent, then $Cov(X, Y) = 0$—but be careful not to assume that the converse is true; it is possible for two variables to have zero covariance yet not be independent.

The covariance gives us the extra information we need to find the variance of the sum or difference of two random variables when they are not independent:

$$Var(X \pm Y) = Var(X) + Var(Y) \pm 2Cov(X, Y).$$

When $X$ and $Y$ are independent, their covariance is zero, so we have the Pythagorean theorem of statistics, as we saw earlier.[2]

Covariance, unlike correlation, doesn't have to be between $-1$ and 1. If $X$ and $Y$ have large values, the covariance will be large as well. And that's its problem. If we know the covariance between $X$ and $Y$ is $-64.5$, it doesn't give us a real sense of how negatively related they are. To fix the "problem," we can divide the covariance by each of the standard deviations to get the **correlation**:

$$Corr(X, Y) = \frac{Cov(X, Y)}{\sigma_X \sigma_Y}.$$

Correlation of random variables is usually denoted as $\rho$. Correlation of random variables has many of the properties we saw in Chapter 7 for the correlation coefficient, $r$.

▷ The sign of a correlation coefficient gives the direction of the association between random variables.

▷ Correlation is always between $-1$ and $+1$.

▷ Correlation treats $X$ and $Y$ symmetrically. The correlation of $X$ with $Y$ is the same as the correlation of $Y$ with $X$.

▷ Unlike covariance, correlation has no units.

▷ Correlation is not affected by changes in the center or scale of either variable.

## WHAT CAN GO WRONG?

▷ **Probability models are still just models.** Models can be useful, but they are not reality. Think about the assumptions behind your models. Are your dice really perfectly fair? (They are probably pretty close.) But when you hear that the probability of a nuclear accident is 1/10,000,000 per year, is that likely to be a precise value? Question probabilities as you would data.

▷ **If the model is wrong, so is everything else.** Before you try to find the mean or standard deviation of a random variable, check to make sure the probability model is reasonable. As a start, the probabilities in your model should add up to 1. If not, you may have calculated a probability incorrectly or left out a value of the random variable. For instance, in the insurance example, the description mentions only death and disability. Good health is by far the most likely outcome, not to mention the best for both you and the insurance company (who gets to keep your money). Don't overlook that.

▷ **Don't assume everything's Normal.** Just because a random variable is continuous or you happen to know a mean and standard deviation doesn't mean that a Normal model will be useful. You must *Think* about whether the **Normality Assumption** is justified. Using a Normal model when it really does not apply will lead to wrong answers and misleading conclusions.

To find the expected value of the sum or difference of random variables, we simply add or subtract means. Center is easy; spread is trickier. Watch out for some common traps.

▷ **Watch out for variables that aren't independent.** You can add expected values of *any* two random variables, but you can only add variances of independent random variables. Suppose a survey includes questions about the number of hours of sleep people get

---

[2] If you want to follow the geometry one step further, the more general form for correlated variables is related to the Law of Cosines.

each night and also the number of hours they are awake each day. From their answers, we find the mean and standard deviation of hours asleep and hours awake. The expected total must be 24 hours; after all, people are either asleep or awake.[3] The means still add just fine. Since all the totals are exactly 24 hours, however, the standard deviation of the total will be 0. We can't add variances here because the number of hours you're awake depends on the number of hours you're asleep. Be sure to check for independence before adding variances.

▸ **Don't forget: Variances of independent random variables add. Standard deviations don't.**

▸ **Don't forget: Variances of independent random variables add, even when you're looking at the difference between them.**

▸ **Don't write independent instances of a random variable with notation that looks like they are the same variables.** Make sure you write each instance as a different random variable. Just because each random variable describes a similar situation doesn't mean that each random outcome will be the same. These are *random* variables, not the variables you saw in Algebra. Write $X_1 + X_2 + X_3$ rather than $X + X + X$.

# CONNECTIONS

We've seen means, variances, and standard deviations of data. We know that they estimate parameters of models for these data. Now we're looking at the probability models directly. We have only parameters because there are no data to summarize.

It should be no surprise that expected values and standard deviations adjust to shifts and changes of units in the same way as the corresponding data summaries. The fact that we can add variances of independent random quantities is fundamental and will explain why a number of statistical methods work the way they do.

# WHAT HAVE WE LEARNED?

We've learned to work with random variables. We can use the probability model for a discrete random variable to find its expected value and its standard deviation.

We've learned that the mean of the sum or difference of two random variables, discrete or continuous, is just the sum or difference of their means. And we've learned the Pythagorean Theorem of Statistics: *For independent random variables*, the variance of their sum or difference is always the *sum* of their variances.

Finally, we've learned that Normal models are once again special. Sums or differences of Normally distributed random variables also follow Normal models.

## Terms

Random variable

409. A random variable assumes any of several different numeric values as a result of some random event. Random variables are denoted by a capital letter such as $X$.

Discrete random variable

410. A random variable that can take one of a finite number[4] of distinct outcomes is called a discrete random variable.

---

[3]Although some students do manage to attain a state of consciousness somewhere between sleeping and wakefulness during Statistics class.

[4] Technically, there could be an infinite number of outcomes, as long as they're *countable*. Essentially that means we can imagine listing them all in order, like the counting numbers 1, 2, 3, 4, 5, . . .

| | |
|---|---|
| **Continuous random variable** | 410, 420. A random variable that can take any numeric value within a range of values is called a continuous random variable. The range may be infinite or bounded at either or both ends. |
| **Probability model** | 410. The probability model is a function that associates a probability $P$ with each value of a discrete random variable $X$, denoted $P(X = x)$, or with any interval of values of a continuous random variable. |
| **Expected value** | 410. The expected value of a random variable is its theoretical long-run average value, the center of its model. Denoted $\mu$ or $E(X)$, it is found (if the random variable is discrete) by summing the products of variable values and probabilities: $$\mu = E(X) = \sum xP(x).$$ |
| **Variance** | 412. The variance of a random variable is the expected value of the squared deviation from the mean. For discrete random variables, it can be calculated as: $$\sigma^2 = Var(X) = \sum (x - \mu)^2 P(x).$$ |
| **Standard deviation** | 412. The standard deviation of a random variable describes the spread in the model, and is the square root of the variance: $$\sigma = SD(X) = \sqrt{Var(X)}.$$ |
| **Changing a random variable by a constant:** | 414. $\qquad E(X \pm c) = E(X) \pm c \qquad Var(X \pm c) = Var(X)$ <br> 415. $\qquad E(aX) = aE(X) \qquad\qquad Var(aX) = a^2 Var(X)$ |
| **Adding or subtracting random variables:** | 415. $\qquad E(X \pm Y) = E(X) \pm E(Y).$ <br> 416. *If X and Y are independent,* $Var(X \pm Y) = Var(X) + Var(Y)$ <br> 417. (The Pythagorean Theorem of Statistics). |
| **\*Covariance** | 423. The covariance of random variables $X$ and $Y$ is $Cov(X,Y) = E((X - \mu)(Y - \nu))$ where $\mu = E(X)$ and $\nu = E(Y)$. In general (no need to assume independence) <br> $Var(X \pm Y) = Var(X) + Var(Y) \pm 2Cov(X,Y)$ |

## Skills

▸ Be able to recognize random variables.

▸ Understand that random variables must be independent in order to determine the variability of their sum or difference by adding variances.

▸ Be able to find the probability model for a discrete random variable.

▸ Know how to find the mean (expected value) and the variance of a random variable.

▸ Always use the proper notation for these population parameters, $\mu$ or $E(X)$ for the mean, and $\sigma$, $SD(X)$, $\sigma^2$, or $Var(X)$ when discussing variability.

▸ Know how to determine the new mean and standard deviation after adding a constant, multiplying by a constant, or adding or subtracting two independent random variables.

▸ Be able to interpret the meaning of the expected value and standard deviation of a random variable in the proper context.

# ON THE COMPUTER

## Random Variables

Statistics packages deal with data, not with random variables. Nevertheless, the calculations needed to find means and standard deviations of random variables are little more than weighted means. Most packages can manage that, but then they are just being overblown calculators. For technological assistance with these calculations, we recommend you pull out your calculator.

**TI-83/84 PLUS**

To calculate the mean and standard deviation of a discrete random variable, enter the probability model in two lists:

▸ In one list (say, L1) enter the x-values of the variable.
▸ In a second list (say, L2) enter the associated probabilities $P(X = x)$.
▸ From the **STAT CALC** menu select **1-VarStats** and specify the two lists. You'll see the mean and standard deviation.

COMMENTS

You can enter the probabilities as fractions; the calculator will change them to decimals for you.
Notice that the calculator knows enough to call the standard deviation $\sigma$, but mistakenly uses $\bar{x}$ when it should say $\mu$. Make sure you don't make that mistake!

**TI-89**

To calculate the mean and standard deviation of a discrete random variable, enter the probability model in two lists:

▸ In one list (say, list1) enter the x-values of the variable.
▸ In a second list (say, list2) enter the associated probabilities $P(X = x)$.
▸ From the **STAT CALC** (F4) menu select **1-VarStats**. Use VAR-LINK to enter the list name list1 in the List box and list2 in the Freq box.

COMMENTS

You can enter the probabilities as fractions; the calculator will change them to decimals for you.
Notice that the calculator knows enough to compute only the standard deviation $\sigma$, but mistakenly uses $\bar{x}$ when it should say $\mu$. Make sure you don't make that mistake!

# EXERCISES

1. **Expected value.** Find the expected value of each random variable:

a)

| x | 10 | 20 | 30 |
|---|---|---|---|
| P(X=x) | 0.3 | 0.5 | 0.2 |

b)

| x | 2 | 4 | 6 | 8 |
|---|---|---|---|---|
| P(X=x) | 0.3 | 0.4 | 0.2 | 0.1 |

2. **Expected value.** Find the expected value of each random variable:

a)

| x | 0 | 1 | 2 |
|---|---|---|---|
| P(X=x) | 0.2 | 0.4 | 0.4 |

b)

| x | 100 | 200 | 300 | 400 |
|---|---|---|---|---|
| P(X=x) | 0.1 | 0.2 | 0.5 | 0.2 |

3. **Spinning the wheel.** A wheel comes up green 50% of the time and red 50% of the time. If it comes up green, you win $100. If it comes up red, you win nothing.
   a) Intuitively, how much do you expect to win on one spin, on average?
   b) Calculate the expected value of the game.

4. **Stock market.** A day trader buys an option on a stock that will return $100 profit if the stock goes up today and loses $200 if it goes down. If the trader thinks there is a 75% chance that the stock will go up, what is his expected value of the option?

5. **Pick a card, any card.** You draw a card from a deck. If you get a red card, you win nothing. If you get a spade, you win $5. For any club, you win $10 plus an extra $20 for the ace of clubs.
   a) Create a probability model for the amount you win at this game.
   b) Find the expected amount you'll win.
   c) How much would you be willing to pay to play this game?

6. **You bet!** You roll a die. If it comes up a 6, you win $100. If not, you get to roll again. If you get a 6 the second time, you win $50. If not, you lose.
   a) Create a probability model for the amount you win at this game.
   b) Find the expected amount you'll win.
   c) How much would you be willing to pay to play this game?

7. **Kids.** A couple plans to have children until they get a girl, but they agree that they will not have more than three children even if all are boys. (Assume boys and girls are equally likely.)
   a) Create a probability model for the number of children they'll have.
   b) Find the expected number of children.
   c) Find the expected number of boys they'll have.

8. **Carnival.** A carnival game offers a $100 cash prize for anyone who can break a balloon by throwing a dart at it. It costs $5 to play, and you're willing to spend up to

$20 trying to win. You estimate that you have about a 10% chance of hitting the balloon on any throw.
a) Create a probability model for this carnival game.
b) Find the expected number of darts you'll throw.
c) Find your expected winnings.

9. **Software.** A small software company bids on two contracts. It anticipates a profit of $50,000 if it gets the larger contract and a profit of $20,000 on the smaller contract. The company estimates there's a 30% chance it will get the larger contract and a 60% chance it will get the smaller contract. Assuming the contracts will be awarded independently, what's the expected profit?

10. **Racehorse.** A man buys a racehorse for $20,000 and enters it in two races. He plans to sell the horse afterward, hoping to make a profit. If the horse wins both races, its value will jump to $100,000. If it wins one of the races, it will be worth $50,000. If it loses both races, it will be worth only $10,000. The man believes there's a 20% chance that the horse will win the first race and a 30% chance it will win the second one. Assuming that the two races are independent events, find the man's expected profit.

11. **Variation 1.** Find the standard deviations of the random variables in Exercise 1.

12. **Variation 2.** Find the standard deviations of the random variables in Exercise 2.

13. **Pick another card.** Find the standard deviation of the amount you might win drawing a card in Exercise 5.

14. **The die.** Find the standard deviation of the amount you might win rolling a die in Exercise 6.

15. **Kids again.** Find the standard deviation of the number of children the couple in Exercise 7 may have.

16. **Darts.** Find the standard deviation of your winnings throwing darts in Exercise 8.

17. **Repairs.** The probability model below describes the number of repair calls that an appliance repair shop may receive during an hour.

| Repair Calls | 0 | 1 | 2 | 3 |
|---|---|---|---|---|
| Probability | 0.1 | 0.3 | 0.4 | 0.2 |

a) How many calls should the shop expect per hour?
b) What is the standard deviation?

18. **Red lights.** A commuter must pass through five traffic lights on her way to work and will have to stop at each one that is red. She estimates the probability model for the number of red lights she hits, as shown below.

| $X =$ # of red | 0 | 1 | 2 | 3 | 4 | 5 |
|---|---|---|---|---|---|---|
| $P(X = x)$ | 0.05 | 0.25 | 0.35 | 0.15 | 0.15 | 0.05 |

a) How many red lights should she expect to hit each day?
b) What's the standard deviation?

19. **Defects.** A consumer organization inspecting new cars found that many had appearance defects (dents, scratches, paint chips, etc.). While none had more than three of these defects, 7% had three, 11% two, and 21% one defect. Find the expected number of appearance defects in a new car, and the standard deviation.

20. **Insurance.** An insurance policy costs $100 and will pay policyholders $10,000 if they suffer a major injury (resulting in hospitalization) or $3000 if they suffer a minor injury (resulting in lost time from work). The company estimates that each year 1 in every 2000 policyholders may have a major injury, and 1 in 500 a minor injury.
a) Create a probability model for the profit on a policy.
b) What's the company's expected profit on this policy?
c) What's the standard deviation?

21. **Cancelled flights.** Mary is deciding whether to book the cheaper flight home from college after her final exams, but she's unsure when her last exam will be. She thinks there is only a 20% chance that the exam will be scheduled after the last day she can get a seat on the cheaper flight. If it is and she has to cancel the flight, she will lose $150. If she can take the cheaper flight, she will save $100.
a) If she books the cheaper flight, what can she expect to gain, on average?
b) What is the standard deviation?

22. **Day trading again.** An option to buy a stock is priced at $200. If the stock closes above 30 on May 15, the option will be worth $1000. If it closes below 20, the option will be worth nothing, and if it closes between 20 and 30 (inclusively), the option will be worth $200. A trader thinks there is a 50% chance that the stock will close in the 20–30 range, a 20% chance that it will close above 30, and a 30% chance that it will fall below 20 on May 15.
a) Should she buy the stock option?
b) How much does she expect to gain?
c) What is the standard deviation of her gain?

23. **Contest.** You play two games against the same opponent. The probability you win the first game is 0.4. If you win the first game, the probability you also win the second is 0.2. If you lose the first game, the probability that you win the second is 0.3.
a) Are the two games independent? Explain your answer.
b) What's the probability you lose both games?
c) What's the probability you win both games?
d) Let random variable $X$ be the number of games you win. Find the probability model for $X$.
e) What are the expected value and standard deviation of $X$?

24. **Contracts.** Your company bids for two contracts. You believe the probability you get contract #1 is 0.8. If you get contract #1, the probability you also get contract #2 will be 0.2, and if you do not get #1, the probability you get #2 will be 0.3.
a) Are the two contracts independent? Explain.
b) Find the probability you get both contracts.
c) Find the probability you get no contract.
d) Let $X$ be the number of contracts you get. Find the probability model for $X$.
e) Find the expected value and standard deviation of $X$.

**25. Batteries.** In a group of 10 batteries, 3 are dead. You choose 2 batteries at random.
a) Create a probability model for the number of good batteries you get.
b) What's the expected number of good ones you get?
c) What's the standard deviation?

**26. Kittens.** In a litter of seven kittens, three are female. You pick two kittens at random.
a) Create a probability model for the number of male kittens you get.
b) What's the expected number of males?
c) What's the standard deviation?

**27. Random variables.** Given independent random variables with means and standard deviations as shown, find the mean and standard deviation of each of these variables:
a) $3X$
b) $Y + 6$
c) $X + Y$
d) $X - Y$
e) $X_1 + X_2$

| | Mean | SD |
|---|---|---|
| $X$ | 10 | 2 |
| $Y$ | 20 | 5 |

**28. Random variables.** Given independent random variables with means and standard deviations as shown, find the mean and standard deviation of each of these variables:
a) $X - 20$
b) $0.5Y$
c) $X + Y$
d) $X - Y$
e) $Y_1 + Y_2$

| | Mean | SD |
|---|---|---|
| $X$ | 80 | 12 |
| $Y$ | 12 | 3 |

**29. Random variables.** Given independent random variables with means and standard deviations as shown, find the mean and standard deviation of each of these variables:
a) $0.8Y$
b) $2X - 100$
c) $X + 2Y$
d) $3X - Y$
e) $Y_1 + Y_2$

| | Mean | SD |
|---|---|---|
| $X$ | 120 | 12 |
| $Y$ | 300 | 16 |

**30. Random variables.** Given independent random variables with means and standard deviations as shown, find the mean and standard deviation of each of these variables:
a) $2Y + 20$
b) $3X$
c) $0.25X + Y$
d) $X - 5Y$
e) $X_1 + X_2 + X_3$

| | Mean | SD |
|---|---|---|
| $X$ | 80 | 12 |
| $Y$ | 12 | 3 |

**31. Eggs.** A grocery supplier believes that in a dozen eggs, the mean number of broken ones is 0.6 with a standard deviation of 0.5 eggs. You buy 3 dozen eggs without checking them.
a) How many broken eggs do you expect to get?
b) What's the standard deviation?
c) What assumptions did you have to make about the eggs in order to answer this question?

**32. Garden.** A company selling vegetable seeds in packets of 20 estimates that the mean number of seeds that will

actually grow is 18, with a standard deviation of 1.2 seeds. You buy 5 different seed packets.
a) How many bad seeds do you expect to get?
b) What's the standard deviation?
c) What assumptions did you make about the seeds? Do you think that assumption is warranted? Explain.

**33. Repair calls.** Find the mean and standard deviation of the number of repair calls the appliance shop in Exercise 17 should expect during an 8-hour day.

**34. Stop!** Find the mean and standard deviation of the number of red lights the commuter in Exercise 18 should expect to hit on her way to work during a 5-day work week.

**35. Tickets.** A delivery company's trucks occasionally get parking tickets, and based on past experience, the company plans that the trucks will average 1.3 tickets a month, with a standard deviation of 0.7 tickets.
a) If they have 18 trucks, what are the mean and standard deviation of the total number of parking tickets the company will have to pay this month?
b) What assumption did you make in answering this question?

**36. Donations.** Organizers of a televised fund raiser know from past experience that most people donate small amounts ($10–$25), some donate larger amounts ($50–$100), and a few people make very generous donations of $250, $500, or more. Historically, pledges average about $32 with a standard deviation of $54.
a) If 120 people call in pledges, what are the mean and standard deviation of the total amount raised?
b) What assumption did you make in answering this question?

**37. Fire!** An insurance company estimates that it should make an annual profit of $150 on each homeowner's policy written, with a standard deviation of $6000.
a) Why is the standard deviation so large?
b) If it writes only two of these policies, what are the mean and standard deviation of the annual profit?
c) If it writes 10,000 of these policies, what are the mean and standard deviation of the annual profit?
d) Do you think the company is likely to be profitable? Explain.
e) What assumptions underlie your analysis? Can you think of circumstances under which those assumptions might be violated? Explain.

**38. Casino.** A casino knows that people play the slot machines in hopes of hitting the jackpot, but that most of them lose their dollar. Suppose a certain machine pays out an average of $0.92, with a standard deviation of $120.
a) Why is the standard deviation so large?
b) If you play 5 times, what are the mean and standard deviation of the casino's profit?
c) If gamblers play this machine 1000 times in a day, what are the mean and standard deviation of the casino's profit?
d) Do you think the casino is likely to be profitable? Explain.

39. **Cereal.** The amount of cereal that can be poured into a small bowl varies with a mean of 1.5 ounces and a standard deviation of 0.3 ounces. A large bowl holds a mean of 2.5 ounces with a standard deviation of 0.4 ounces. You open a new box of cereal and pour one large and one small bowl.
    a) How much more cereal do you expect to be in the large bowl?
    b) What's the standard deviation of this difference?
    c) If the difference follows a Normal model, what's the probability the small bowl contains more cereal than the large one?
    d) What are the mean and standard deviation of the total amount of cereal in the two bowls?
    e) If the total follows a Normal model, what's the probability you poured out more than 4.5 ounces of cereal in the two bowls together?
    f) The amount of cereal the manufacturer puts in the boxes is a random variable with a mean of 16.3 ounces and a standard deviation of 0.2 ounces. Find the expected amount of cereal left in the box, and the standard deviation.

40. **Pets.** The American Veterinary Association claims that the annual cost of medical care for dogs averages $100, with a standard deviation of $30, and for cats averages $120, with a standard deviation of $35.
    a) What's the expected difference in the cost of medical care for dogs and cats?
    b) What's the standard deviation of that difference?
    c) If the difference in costs can be described by a Normal model, what's the probability that medical expenses are higher for someone's dog than for her cat?

41. **More cereal.** In Exercise 39 we poured a large and a small bowl of cereal from a box. Suppose the amount of cereal that the manufacturer puts in the boxes is a random variable with mean 16.2 ounces, and standard deviation 0.1 ounces.
    a) Find the expected amount of cereal left in the box.
    b) What's the standard deviation?
    c) If the weight of the remaining cereal can be described by a Normal model, what's the probability that the box still contains more than 13 ounces?

42. **More pets.** You're thinking about getting two dogs and a cat. Assume that annual veterinary expenses are independent and have a Normal model with the means and standard deviations described in Exercise 40.
    a) Define appropriate variables and express the total annual veterinary costs you may have.
    b) Describe the model for this total cost. Be sure to specify its name, expected value, and standard deviation.
    c) What's the probability that your total expenses will exceed $400?

43. **Medley.** In the 4 × 100 medley relay event, four swimmers swim 100 yards, each using a different stroke. A college team preparing for the conference championship looks at the times their swimmers have posted and creates a model based on the following assumptions:

- The swimmers' performances are independent.
- Each swimmer's times follow a Normal model.
- The means and standard deviations of the times (in seconds) are as shown:

| Swimmer | Mean | SD |
|---|---|---|
| 1 (backstroke) | 50.72 | 0.24 |
| 2 (breaststroke) | 55.51 | 0.22 |
| 3 (butterfly) | 49.43 | 0.25 |
| 4 (freestyle) | 44.91 | 0.21 |

a) What are the mean and standard deviation for the relay team's total time in this event?
b) The team's best time so far this season was 3:19.48. (That's 199.48 seconds.) Do you think the team is likely to swim faster than this at the conference championship? Explain.

44. **Bikes.** Bicycles arrive at a bike shop in boxes. Before they can be sold, they must be unpacked, assembled, and tuned (lubricated, adjusted, etc.). Based on past experience, the shop manager makes the following assumptions about how long this may take:
- The times for each setup phase are independent.
- The times for each phase follow a Normal model.
- The means and standard deviations of the times (in minutes) are as shown:

| Phase | Mean | SD |
|---|---|---|
| Unpacking | 3.5 | 0.7 |
| Assembly | 21.8 | 2.4 |
| Tuning | 12.3 | 2.7 |

a) What are the mean and standard deviation for the total bicycle setup time?
b) A customer decides to buy a bike like one of the display models but wants a different color. The shop has one, still in the box. The manager says they can have it ready in half an hour. Do you think the bike will be set up and ready to go as promised? Explain.

45. **Farmers' market.** A farmer has 100 lb of apples and 50 lb of potatoes for sale. The market price for apples (per pound) each day is a random variable with a mean of 0.5 dollars and a standard deviation of 0.2 dollars. Similarly, for a pound of potatoes, the mean price is 0.3 dollars and the standard deviation is 0.1 dollars. It also costs him 2 dollars to bring all the apples and potatoes to the market. The market is busy with eager shoppers, so we can assume that he'll be able to sell all of each type of produce at that day's price.
    a) Define your random variables, and use them to express the farmer's net income.
    b) Find the mean.
    c) Find the standard deviation of the net income.
    d) Do you need to make any assumptions in calculating the mean? How about the standard deviation?

**46. Bike sale.** The bicycle shop in Exercise 44 will be offering 2 specially priced children's models at a sidewalk sale. The basic model will sell for $120 and the deluxe model for $150. Past experience indicates that sales of the basic model will have a mean of 5.4 bikes with a standard deviation of 1.2, and sales of the deluxe model will have a mean of 3.2 bikes with a standard deviation of 0.8 bikes. The cost of setting up for the sidewalk sale is $200.
  a) Define random variables and use them to express the bicycle shop's net income.
  b) What's the mean of the net income?
  c) What's the standard deviation of the net income?
  d) Do you need to make any assumptions in calculating the mean? How about the standard deviation?

**47. Coffee and doughnuts.** At a certain coffee shop, all the customers buy a cup of coffee; some also buy a doughnut. The shop owner believes that the number of cups he sells each day is normally distributed with a mean of 320 cups and a standard deviation of 20 cups. He also believes that the number of doughnuts he sells each day is independent of the coffee sales and is normally distributed with a mean of 150 doughnuts and a standard deviation of 12.
  a) The shop is open every day but Sunday. Assuming day-to-day sales are independent, what's the probability he'll sell over 2000 cups of coffee in a week?
  b) If he makes a profit of 50 cents on each cup of coffee and 40 cents on each doughnut, can he reasonably expect to have a day's profit of over $300? Explain.
  c) What's the probability that on any given day he'll sell a doughnut to more than half of his coffee customers?

**48. Weightlifting.** The Atlas BodyBuilding Company (ABC) sells "starter sets" of barbells that consist of one bar, two 20-pound weights, and four 5-pound weights. The bars weigh an average of 10 pounds with a standard deviation of 0.25 pounds. The weights average the specified amounts, but the standard deviations are 0.2 pounds for the 20-pounders and 0.1 pounds for the 5-pounders. We can assume that all the weights are normally distributed.

  a) ABC ships these starter sets to customers in two boxes: The bar goes in one box and the six weights go in another. What's the probability that the total weight in that second box exceeds 60.5 pounds? Define your variables clearly and state any assumptions you make.
  b) It costs ABC $0.40 per pound to ship the box containing the weights. Because it's an odd-shaped package, though, shipping the bar costs $0.50 a pound plus a $6.00 surcharge. Find the mean and standard deviation of the company's total cost for shipping a starter set.
  c) Suppose a customer puts a 20-pound weight at one end of the bar and the four 5-pound weights at the other end. Although he expects the two ends to weigh the same, they might differ slightly. What's the probability the difference is more than a quarter of a pound?

**JUST CHECKING**
**Answers**

**1. a)**

| Outcome | $X = $ cost | Probability |
|---|---|---|
| Recharging works | $60 | 0.75 |
| Replace control unit | $200 | 0.25 |

  **b)** $60(0.75) + 200(0.25) = \$95$
  **c)** Car owners with this problem will spend an average of $95 to get it fixed.

**2. a)** $100 + 100 = 200$ seconds
  **b)** $\sqrt{50^2 + 50^2} = 70.7$ seconds
  **c)** The times for the two customers are independent.

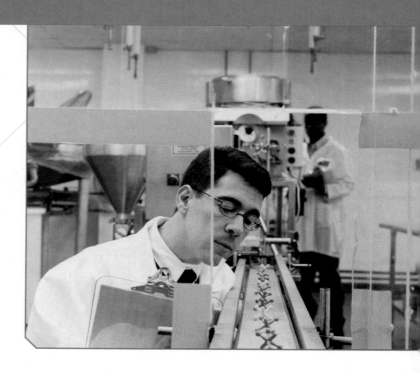

# *CHAPTER 17

# Probability Models

## Where are we going?

How many frogs do you have to kiss before you meet Prince Charming? Is finding 10 leukemia cases in a neighborhood adjacent to an EPA superfund site grounds for a lawsuit? We could simulate to answer almost any question involving probabilities. But in some situations, we can do better with a simple probability model. We'll meet a few of the most common models in this chapter.

S uppose a cereal manufacturer puts pictures of famous athletes on cards in boxes of cereal, in the hope of increasing sales. The manufacturer announces that 20% of the boxes contain a picture of Tiger Woods, 30% a picture of David Beckham, and the rest a picture of Serena Williams.

Sound familiar? In Chapter 11 we simulated to find the number of boxes we'd need to open to get one of each card. That's a fairly complex question and one well suited for simulation. But many important questions can be answered more directly by using simple probability models.

## Searching for Tiger

You're a huge Tiger Woods fan. You don't care about completing the whole sports card collection, but you've just *got* to have the Tiger Woods picture. How many boxes do you expect you'll have to open before you find him? This isn't the same question that we asked before, but this situation is simple enough for a probability model.

We'll keep the assumption that pictures are distributed at random and we'll trust the manufacturer's claim that 20% of the cards are Tiger. So, when you open the box, the probability that you succeed in finding Tiger is 0.20. Now we'll call the act of opening *each* box a trial, and note that:

> There are only two possible outcomes (called *success* and *failure*) on each trial. Either you get Tiger's picture (success), or you don't (failure).

> The probability of success, denoted $p$, is the same on every trial. Here $p = 0.20$.

> The trials are independent. Finding Tiger in the first box does not change what might happen when you reach for the next box.

Situations like this occur often, and are called **Bernoulli trials.** Common examples of Bernoulli trials include tossing a coin, looking for defective products rolling off an assembly line, or even shooting free throws in a basketball game. Just as we found equally likely random digits to be the building blocks for our simulation, we can use Bernoulli trials to build a wide variety of useful probability models.

*Daniel Bernoulli (1700–1782) was the nephew of Jacob, whom you saw in Chapter 14. He was the first to work out the mathematics for what we now call Bernoulli trials.*

**A S** Activity: **Bernoulli Trials.**
Guess what! We've been generating Bernoulli trials all along. Look at the Random Simulation Tool in a new way.

Back to Tiger. We want to know how many boxes we'll need to open to find his card. Let's call this random variable $Y = \#$ boxes, and build a probability model for it. What's the probability you find his picture in the first box of cereal? It's 20%, of course. We could write $P(Y = 1) = 0.20$.

How about the probability that you don't find Tiger until the second box? Well, that means you fail on the first trial and then succeed on the second. With the probability of success 20%, the probability of failure, denoted $q$, is $1 - 0.2 = 80\%$. Since the trials are independent, the probability of getting your first success on the second trial is $P(Y = 2) = (0.8)(0.2) = 0.16$.

Of course, you could have a run of bad luck. Maybe you won't find Tiger until the fifth box of cereal. What are the chances of that? You'd have to fail 4 straight times and then succeed, so $P(Y = 5) = (0.8)^4(0.2) = 0.08192$.

How many boxes might you expect to have to open? We could reason that since Tiger's picture is in 20% of the boxes, or 1 in 5, we expect to find his picture, on average, in the fifth box; that is, $E(Y) = \frac{1}{0.2} = 5$ boxes. That's correct, but not easy to prove.

# The Geometric Model

We want to model how long it will take to achieve the first success in a series of Bernoulli trials. The model that tells us this probability is called the **Geometric probability model.** Geometric models are completely specified by one parameter, $p$, the probability of success, and are denoted Geom($p$). Since achieving the first success on trial number $x$ requires first experiencing $x - 1$ failures, the probabilities are easily expressed by a formula.

---

**GEOMETRIC PROBABILITY MODEL FOR BERNOULLI TRIALS: Geom($p$)**

$p$ = probability of success (and $q = 1 - p$ = probability of failure)

$X$ = number of trials until the first success occurs

$$P(X = x) = q^{x-1} p$$

Expected value: $E(X) = \mu = \dfrac{1}{p}$

Standard deviation: $\sigma = \sqrt{\dfrac{q}{p^2}}$

---

**FOR EXAMPLE**   Spam and the Geometric model

*Postini* is a global company specializing in communications security. The company monitors over 1 billion Internet messages per day and recently reported that 91% of e-mails are spam!

Let's assume that your e-mail is typical—91% spam. We'll also assume you aren't using a spam filter, so every message gets dumped in your inbox. And, since spam comes from many different sources, we'll consider your messages to be independent.

**Questions:** Overnight your inbox collects e-mail. When you first check your e-mail in the morning, about how many spam e-mails should you expect to have to wade through and discard before you find a real message? What's the probability that the 4th message in your inbox is the first one that isn't spam?

There are two outcomes: a real message (success) and spam (failure). Since 91% of e-mails are spam, the probability of success $p = 1 - 0.91 = 0.09$.

Let $X$ = the number of e-mails I'll check until I find a real message. I assume that the messages arrive independently and in a random order. I can use the model Geom(0.09).

$$E(X) = \frac{1}{p} = \frac{1}{0.09} = 11.1$$

$$P(X = 4) = (0.91)^3 (0.09) = 0.0678$$

On average, I expect to have to check just over 11 e-mails before I find a real message. There's slightly less than a 7% chance that my first real message will be the 4th one I check.

Note that the probability calculation isn't new. It's simply Chapter 14's Multiplication Rule used to find $P$(spam *and* spam *and* spam *and* real).

## Independence

One of the important requirements for Bernoulli trials is that the trials be independent. Sometimes that's a reasonable assumption. Is it true for our example? We said that whether we find a Tiger Woods card in one box has no effect on the probabilities in other boxes. This is *almost* true. Technically, if exactly 20% of the boxes have Tiger Woods cards, then when you find one, you've reduced the number of remaining Tiger Woods cards. With a few million boxes of cereal, though, the difference is hardly worth mentioning.

But if you knew there were 2 Tiger Woods cards hiding in the 10 boxes of cereal on the market shelf, then finding one in the first box you try would clearly change your chances of finding Tiger in the next box.

If we had an infinite number of boxes, there wouldn't be a problem. It's selecting from a finite population that causes the probabilities to change, making the trials not independent. Obviously, taking 2 out of 10 boxes changes the probability. Taking even a few hundred out of millions, though, makes very little difference. Fortunately, we have a rule of thumb for the in-between cases. It turns out that if we look at less than 10% of the population, we can pretend that the trials are independent and still calculate probabilities that are quite accurate.

> **The 10% Condition:** Bernoulli trials must be independent. If that assumption is violated, it is still okay to proceed as long as the sample is smaller than 10% of the population.

---

**STEP-BY-STEP EXAMPLE** | **Working with a Geometric Model**

People with O-negative blood are called "universal donors" because O-negative blood can be given to anyone else, regardless of the recipient's blood type. Only about 6% of people have O-negative blood.

**Questions:**
1. If donors line up at random for a blood drive, how many do you expect to examine before you find someone who has O-negative blood?
2. What's the probability that the first O-negative donor found is one of the first four people in line?

| | | |
|---|---|---|
|  | **Plan** State the questions. | I want to estimate how many people I'll need to check to find an O-negative donor, and the probability that 1 of the first 4 people is O-negative. |
| | Check to see that these are Bernoulli trials. | ✔ There are two outcomes:<br>  success = O-negative<br>  failure = other blood types<br>✔ The probability of success for each person is $p = 0.06$, because they lined up randomly.<br>✔ **10% Condition:** Trials aren't independent because the population is finite, but the donors lined up are fewer than 10% of all possible donors. |
| | **Variable** Define the random variable. | Let $X$ = number of donors until one is O-negative. |
| | **Model** Specify the model. | I can model $X$ with Geom(0.06). |

**Mechanics** Find the mean.

Calculate the probability of success on one of the first four trials. That's the probability that $X = 1, 2, 3,$ or $4$.

$$E(X) = \frac{1}{0.06} \approx 16.7$$

$$P(X \leq 4) = P(X = 1) + P(X = 2) + \\ P(X = 3) + P(X = 4)$$
$$= (0.06) + (0.94)(0.06) + \\ (0.94)^2(0.06) + (0.94)^3(0.06)$$
$$\approx 0.2193$$

**Conclusion** Interpret your results in context.

Blood drives such as this one expect to examine an average of 16.7 people to find a universal donor. About 22% of the time there will be one within the first 4 people in line.

# The Binomial Model

We can use the Bernoulli trials to answer other questions. Suppose you buy 5 boxes of cereal. What's the probability you get *exactly* 2 pictures of Tiger Woods? Before, we asked how long it would take until our first success. Now we want to find the probability of getting 2 successes among the 5 trials. We are still talking about Bernoulli trials, but we're asking a different question.

This time we're interested in the *number of successes* in the 5 trials, so we'll call it $X$ = number of successes. We want to find $P(X = 2)$. This is an example of a **Binomial probability.** It takes two parameters to define this **Binomial model:** the number of trials, $n$, and the probability of success, $p$. We denote this model Binom($n, p$). Here, $n = 5$ trials, and $p = 0.2$, the probability of finding a Tiger Woods card in any trial.

Exactly 2 successes in 5 trials means 2 successes and 3 failures. It seems logical that the probability should be $(0.2)^2(0.8)^3$. Too bad! It's not that easy. That calculation would give you the probability of finding Tiger in the first 2 boxes and not in the next 3—*in that order.* But you could find Tiger in the third and fifth boxes and still have 2 successes. The probability of those outcomes in that particular order is $(0.8)(0.8)(0.2)(0.8)(0.2)$. That's also $(0.2)^2(0.8)^3$. In fact, the probability will always be the same, no matter what order the successes and failures occur in. Anytime we get 2 successes in 5 trials, no matter what the order, the probability will be $(0.2)^2(0.8)^3$. We just need to take account of all the possible orders in which the outcomes can occur.

Fortunately, these possible orders are *disjoint.* (For example, if your two successes came on the first two trials, they couldn't come on the last two.) So we can use the Addition Rule and add up the probabilities for all the possible orderings. Since the probabilities are all the same, we only need to know how many orders are possible. For small numbers, we can just make a tree diagram and count the branches. For larger numbers this isn't practical, so we let the computer or calculator do the work.

Each different order in which we can have $k$ successes in $n$ trials is called a "combination." The total number of ways that can happen is written $\binom{n}{k}$ or $_nC_k$ and pronounced "$n$ choose $k$."

**NOTATION ALERT:**

Now punctuation! Throughout mathematics $n!$, pronounced "$n$ factorial," is the product of all the integers from 1 to $n$.

$$_nC_k = \frac{n!}{k!(n-k)!}$$ where $n!$ (pronounced "$n$ factorial") $= n \times (n-1) \times \cdots \times 1$

For 2 successes in 5 trials,

$$_5C_2 = \frac{5!}{2!(5-2)!} = \frac{5 \times 4 \times 3 \times 2 \times 1}{2 \times 1 \times 3 \times 2 \times 1} = \frac{5 \times 4}{2 \times 1} = 10.$$

So there are 10 ways to get 2 Tiger pictures in 5 boxes, and the probability of each is $(0.2)^2(0.8)^3$. Now we can find what we wanted:

$$P(\#\text{success} = 2) = 10(0.2)^2(0.8)^3 = 0.2048$$

In general, the probability of exactly $k$ successes in $n$ trials is $_nC_k p^k q^{n-k}$.

Using this formula, we could find the expected value by adding up $xP(X = x)$ for all values, but it would be a long, hard way to get an answer that you already know intuitively. What's the expected value? If we have 5 boxes, and Tiger's picture is in 20% of them, then we would expect to have $5(0.2) = 1$ success. If we had 100 trials with probability of success 0.2, how many successes would you expect? Can you think of any reason not to say 20? It seems so simple that most people wouldn't even stop to think about it. You just multiply the probability of success by $n$. In other words, $E(X) = np$.[1]

The standard deviation is less obvious; you can't just rely on your intuition. Fortunately, the formula for the standard deviation also boils down to something simple: $SD(X) = \sqrt{npq}$. In 100 boxes of cereal, we expect to find 20 Tiger Woods cards, with a standard deviation of $\sqrt{100 \times 0.8 \times 0.2} = 4$ pictures.

Time to summarize. A Binomial probability model describes the number of successes in a specified number of trials. It takes two parameters to specify this model: the number of trials $n$ and the probability of success $p$.

---

**BINOMIAL PROBABILITY MODEL FOR BERNOULLI TRIALS: Binom($n$, $p$)**

$n$ = number of trials

$p$ = probability of success (and $q = 1 - p$ = probability of failure)

$X$ = number of successes in $n$ trials

$$P(X = x) = {}_nC_x\, p^x q^{n-x}, \text{ where } {}_nC_x = \frac{n!}{x!(n-x)!}$$

Mean: $\mu = np$

Standard deviation: $\sigma = \sqrt{npq}$

---

**FOR EXAMPLE**  Spam and the Binomial model

**Recap:** The communications monitoring company *Postini* has reported that 91% of e-mail messages are spam. Suppose your inbox contains 25 messages.

**Questions:** What are the mean and standard deviation of the number of real messages you should expect to find in your inbox? What's the probability that you'll find only 1 or 2 real messages?

*I assume that messages arrive independently and at random, with the probability of success (a real message) $p = 1 - 0.91 = 0.09$. Let $X =$ the number of real messages among 25. I can use the model Binom(25, 0.09).*

$$E(X) = np = 25(0.09) = 2.25$$

$$SD(X) = \sqrt{npq} = \sqrt{25(0.09)(0.91)} = 1.43$$

$$P(X = 1 \text{ or } 2) = P(X = 1) + P(X = 2)$$
$$= {}_{25}C_1(0.09)^1(0.91)^{24} + {}_{25}C_2(0.09)^2(0.91)^{23}$$
$$= 0.2340 + 0.2777$$
$$= 0.5117$$

*(continued)*

---

[1] It's an amazing fact that this does work out the long way. That is, $\sum_{x=0}^{n} x \cdot {}_nC_x p^x q^{n-x} = np$, something that is not obvious.

For Example (*continued*)

Among 25 e-mail messages, I expect to find an average of 2.25 that aren't spam, with a standard deviation of 1.43 messages. There's just over a 50% chance that 1 or 2 of my 25 e-mails will be real messages.

---

**STEP-BY-STEP EXAMPLE**   **Working with a Binomial Model**

Suppose 20 donors come to a blood drive. Recall that 6% of people are "universal donors."

Questions:
1. What are the mean and standard deviation of the number of universal donors among them?
2. What is the probability that there are 2 or 3 universal donors?

| | | |
|---|---|---|
|  | **Plan**  State the question. | I want to know the mean and standard deviation of the number of universal donors among 20 people, and the probability that there are 2 or 3 of them. |
| | Check to see that these are Bernoulli trials. | ✔  There are two outcomes: success = O-negative failure = other blood types <br> ✔  $p = 0.06$, because people have lined up at random. <br> ✔  **10% Condition:** Trials are not independent, because the population is finite, but fewer than 10% of all possible donors are lined up. |
| | **Variable**  Define the random variable. | Let $X$ = number of O-negative donors among $n = 20$ people. |
| | **Model**  Specify the model. | I can model $X$ with Binom(20, 0.06). |
|  | **Mechanics**  Find the expected value and standard deviation. | $E(X) = np = 20(0.06) = 1.2$ <br> $SD(X) = \sqrt{npq} = \sqrt{20(0.06)(0.94)} \approx 1.06$ <br> $P(X = 2 \text{ or } 3) = P(X = 2) + P(X = 3)$ <br> $\qquad = {}_{20}C_2(0.06)^2(0.94)^{18}$ <br> $\qquad \quad + {}_{20}C_3(0.06)^3(0.94)^{17}$ <br> $\qquad \approx 0.2246 + 0.0860$ <br> $\qquad = 0.3106$ |
|  | **Conclusion**  Interpret your results in context. | In groups of 20 randomly selected blood donors, I expect to find an average of 1.2 universal donors, with a standard deviation of 1.06. About 31% of the time, I'd find 2 or 3 universal donors among the 20 people. |

# The Normal Model to the Rescue!

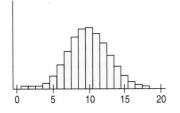

Suppose the Tennessee Red Cross anticipates the need for at least 1850 units of O-negative blood this year. It estimates that it will collect blood from 32,000 donors. How great is the risk that the Tennessee Red Cross will fall short of meeting its need? We've just learned how to calculate such probabilities. We can use the Binomial model with $n = 32,000$ and $p = 0.06$. The probability of getting *exactly* 1850 units of O-negative blood from 32,000 donors is $_{32000}C_{1850} \times 0.06^{1850} \times 0.94^{30150}$. No calculator on earth can calculate that first term (it has more than 100,000 digits).[2] And that's just the beginning. The problem said *at least* 1850, so we have to do it again for 1851, for 1852, and all the way up to 32,000. No thanks.

When we're dealing with a large number of trials like this, making direct calculations of the probabilities becomes tedious (or outright impossible). Here an old friend—the Normal model—comes to the rescue.

The Binomial model has mean $np = 1920$ and standard deviation $\sqrt{npq} \approx 42.48$. We could try approximating its distribution with a Normal model, using the same mean and standard deviation. Remarkably enough, that turns out to be a very good approximation. (We'll see why in the next chapter.) With that approximation, we can find the *probability:*

$$P(X < 1850) = P\left(z < \frac{1850 - 1920}{42.28}\right) \approx P(z < -1.65) \approx 0.05$$

There seems to be about a 5% chance that this Red Cross chapter will run short of O-negative blood.

Can we always use a Normal model to make estimates of Binomial probabilities? No. Consider the Tiger Woods situation—pictures in 20% of the cereal boxes. If we buy five boxes, the actual Binomial probabilities that we get 0, 1, 2, 3, 4, or 5 pictures of Tiger are 33%, 41%, 20%, 5%, 1%, and 0.03%, respectively. The first histogram shows that this probability model is skewed. That makes it clear that we should not try to estimate these probabilities by using a Normal model.

Now suppose we open 50 boxes of this cereal and count the number of Tiger Woods pictures we find. The second histogram shows this probability model. It is centered at $np = 50(0.2) = 10$ pictures, as expected, and it appears to be fairly symmetric around that center. Let's have a closer look.

The third histogram again shows Binom(50, 0.2), this time magnified somewhat and centered at the expected value of 10 pictures of Tiger. It looks close to Normal, for sure. With this larger sample size, it appears that a Normal model might be a useful approximation.

A Normal model, then, is a close enough approximation only for a large enough number of trials. And what we mean by "large enough" depends on the probability of success. We'd need a larger sample if the probability of success were very low (or very high). It turns out that a Normal model works pretty well if we expect to see at least 10 successes and 10 failures. That is, we check the **Success/Failure Condition.**

> **The Success/Failure Condition:** A Binomial model is approximately Normal if we expect at least 10 successes and 10 failures:
>
> $$np \geq 10 \text{ and } nq \geq 10.$$

---

[2] If your calculator *can* find Binom(32000,0.06), then it's smart enough to use an approximation. Read on to see how you can, too.

# *Why 10? (Well, Actually 9)

It's easy to see where the magic number 10 comes from. You just need to remember how Normal models work. The problem is that a Normal model extends infinitely in both directions. But a Binomial model must have between 0 and $n$ successes, so if we use a Normal to approximate a Binomial, we have to cut off its tails. That's not very important if the center of the Normal model is so far from 0 and $n$ that the lost tails have only a negligible area. More than three standard deviations should do it, because a Normal model has little probability past that.

So the mean needs to be at least 3 standard deviations from 0 and at least 3 standard deviations from $n$. Let's look at the 0 end.

| We require: | $\mu - 3\sigma > 0$ |
| --- | --- |
| Or, in other words: | $\mu > 3\sigma$ |
| For a Binomial, that's: | $np > 3\sqrt{npq}$ |
| Squaring yields: | $n^2p^2 > 9npq$ |
| Now simplify: | $np > 9q$ |
| Since $q \leq 1$, we can require: | $np > 9$ |

For simplicity, we usually require that $np$ (and $nq$ for the other tail) be at least 10 to use the Normal approximation, the Success/Failure Condition.[3]

---

**FOR EXAMPLE**     Spam and the Normal approximation to the Binomial

**Recap:** The communications monitoring company *Postini* has reported that 91% of e-mail messages are spam. Recently, you installed a spam filter. You observe that over the past week it okayed only 151 of 1422 e-mails you received, classifying the rest as junk. Should you worry that the filtering is too aggressive?

**Question:** What's the probability that no more than 151 of 1422 e-mails is a real message?

I assume that messages arrive randomly and independently, with a probability of success (a real message) $p = 0.09$. The model Binom(1422, 0.09) applies, but will be hard to work with. Checking conditions for the Normal approximation, I see that:

✔ These messages represent less than 10% of all e-mail traffic.
✔ I expect $np = (1422)(0.09) = 127.98$ real messages and $nq = (1422)(0.91) = 1294.02$ spam messages, both far greater than 10.

It's okay to approximate this binomial probability by using a Normal model.

$\mu = np = 1422(0.09) = 127.98$

$\sigma = \sqrt{npq} = \sqrt{1422(0.09)(0.91)} \approx 10.79$

$P(x \leq 151) = P\left(z \leq \dfrac{151 - 127.98}{10.79}\right)$

$= P(z \leq 2.13)$

$= 0.9834$

Among my 1422 e-mails, there's over a 98% chance that no more than 151 of them were real messages, so the filter may be working properly.

---

[3] Looking at the final step, we see that we need $np > 9$ in the worst case, when $q$ (or $p$) is near 1, making the Binomial model quite skewed. When $q$ and $p$ are near 0.5—say between 0.4 and 0.6—the Binomial model is nearly symmetric and $np > 5$ ought to be safe enough. Although we'll always check for 10 expected successes and failures, keep in mind that for values of $p$ near 0.5, we can be somewhat more forgiving.

# Continuous Random Variables

There's a problem with approximating a Binomial model with a Normal model. The Binomial is discrete, giving probabilities for specific counts, but the Normal models a **continuous** random variable that can take on *any value*. For continuous random variables, we can no longer list all the possible outcomes and their probabilities, as we could for discrete random variables.[4]

As we saw in the previous chapter, models for continuous random variables give probabilities for *intervals* of values. So, when we use the Normal model, we no longer calculate the probability that the random variable equals a *particular* value, but only that it lies *between* two values. We won't calculate the probability of getting exactly 1850 units of blood, but we have no problem approximating the probability of getting 1850 *or more*, which was, after all, what we really wanted.[5]

# The Poisson Model

In the early 1990s, a leukemia cluster was identified in the Massachusetts town of Woburn. Many more cases of leukemia, a cancer that originates in a cell in the marrow of bone, appeared in this small town than would be predicted. Was it evidence of a problem in the town, or was it chance? That question led to a famous trial in which the families of eight leukemia victims sued, and became grist for the book and movie *A Civil Action*. Following an 80-day trial, the judge called for a re-trial after dismissing the jury's contradictory and confusing findings. Shortly thereafter, the chemical companies and the families settled.

When rare events occur together or in clusters, people often want to know if that happened just by chance or whether something else is going on. If we assume that the events occur independently, we can use a Binomial model to find the probability that a cluster of events like this occurs. For rare events, $p$ will be quite small, and when $n$ is large, it may be difficult to compute the exact probability that a certain size cluster occurs. To see why, let's try to compute the probability that a cluster of cases of size $x$ occurs in Woburn. We'll use the *national average* of leukemia incidence to get a value for $p$, and the population of Woburn as our value for $n$. In the United States in the early 1990s, there were about 30,800 new cases of leukemia each year and about 280,000,000 people, giving a value for $p$ of about 0.00011. The population of Woburn was about $n = 35,000$. We'd expect $np = 3.85$ new cases of leukemia in Woburn. How unlikely would 8 or more cases be? To answer that, we'll need to calculate the complement, adding the probabilities of no cases, exactly 1 case, etc., up to 7 cases. Each of those probabilities would have the form $_{35000}C_x p^x q^{35000-x}$. To find $_{35000}C_x$, we'll need 35,000!—a daunting number even for computers. In the 18th century, when people first were interested in computing such probabilities, it was impossible. We can easily go beyond the capabilities of today's computers by making $n$ large enough and $p$ small enough. We could use the Normal model to help us approximate the probabilities as long as $np$ is at least 10, but for rare events such as leukemia in Woburn, when $np$ falls much below 10, the Normal probabilities won't be accurate.

Simeon Denis Poisson[6] was a French mathematician interested in events with very small probability. He originally derived his model to approximate the Binomial model when the probability of a success, $p$, is very small and the number of

---

[4] In fact, some people use an adjustment called the "continuity correction" to help with this problem. It's related to the suggestion we make in the next footnote, and discussed in more advanced textbooks.

[5] If we really had been interested in a single value, we might have approximated it by finding the probability of getting between 1849.5 and 1850.5 units of blood.

[6] *Poisson* is a French name (meaning "fish"), properly pronounced "pwa sohn" and not with an "oy" sound as in poison.

trials, *n*, is very large. Poisson's contribution was providing a simple approximation to find that probability. When you see the formula, however, you won't necessarily see the connection to the Binomial. The Poisson's parameter is often denoted by $\lambda$, the mean of the distribution. To use the **Poisson model** to approximate the Binomial, we'll make their means match, so we set $\lambda = np$.

---

**POISSON PROBABILITY MODEL FOR SUCCESSES:** *Poisson* ($\lambda$)

$\lambda =$ mean number of successes.

$X =$ number of successes.

$$P(X = x) = \frac{e^{-\lambda}\lambda^x}{x!}$$

Expected value: $\qquad E(X) = \lambda$

Standard deviation: $\qquad SD(X) = \sqrt{\lambda}$

The Poisson model is a reasonably good approximation of the Binomial when $n \geq 20$ with $p \leq 0.05$ or $n \geq 100$ with $p \leq 0.10$.

---

Using Poisson's model, we can easily find the probabilities of a given size cluster of leukemia cases. Using $\lambda = np = 35000 \times 0.00011 = 3.85$ new cases a year, we find that the probability of seeing exactly *x* cases in a year is $P(X = x) = \frac{e^{-3.85}3.85^x}{x!}$. By adding up these probabilities for $x = 0, 1, \ldots 7$, we'd find that the probability of 8 or more cases with $\lambda = 3.85$ is about 0.043. That's small but not terribly unusual.

---

**Where does *e* come from?** You might know that $e = 2.7182818 \ldots$ (to 7 decimal places), but does it have any real meaning? Yes! In fact, one of the places *e* originally turned up was in calculating how much more money you'd earn if you could get interest compounded more often. Suppose you receive an offer to earn 100% per year simple interest. (Take it!) At the end of the year, you'd have twice as much money as when you started. But suppose that you have the option of having the interest calculated and paid at the end of every month instead. Then each month you'll earn (100/12)% interest. At the end of the year, you'll wind up with $(1 + 1/12)^{12} = 2.613$ times as much instead of 2. If you could get the interest paid every day, you'd get $(1 + 1/365)^{365} = 2.714$ times as much. If you could convince the bank to compound and pay the interest every second, you'd get $(1 + 1/31536000)^{31536000} = 2.7182818$ times as much at year's end. This is where *e* shows up. In the limit, if you could get the interest compounded continually, you'd get *e* times as much. In other words, as *n* gets large, the limit of $(1 + 1/n)^n = e$. Who discovered this fact? Jacob Bernoulli, in 1683!

---

In spite of its origins as an approximation to the Binomial, the Poisson model is also used directly to model the probability of the occurrence of events for a variety of phenomena. It's a good model to consider whenever your data consist of counts of occurrences. It requires only that the events be independent and that the mean number of occurrences stay constant for the duration of the data collection (and beyond, if we hope to make predictions).

One nice feature of the Poisson model is that it scales according to the sample size.[7] For example, if we know that the average number of occurrences in a town

---

[7] Because *Poisson* means "fish" in French, you can remember this fact by the bilingual pun "*Poisson* scales!"

**Poisson in History**
In his book *Gravity's Rainbow*, Thomas Pynchon describes using the Poisson to model the bombs dropping over London during World War II. "The rockets *are* distributing about London just as Poisson's equation in the textbook predicts. As the data keep coming in, Roger looks more and more like a prophet . . . all I'm doing is plugging numbers into a well-known equation, you can look it up in the book and do it yourself. . . ."

the size of Woburn, with 35,000 people, is 3.85, we know that the average number of occurrences in a town of only 3500 residents is 0.385. We can use that new value of $\lambda$ to calculate the probabilities for the smaller town. Using the Poisson formula, we'd find that the probability of 0 occurrences for a town of 3500 is about 0.68.

One of the consequences of the Poisson model is that, as long as the mean rate of occurrences stays constant, the occurrence of past events doesn't change the probability of future events. That is, even though events that occur according to the Poisson model *appear* to cluster, the probability of *another* event occurring is still the same. This is counterintuitive and may be one reason why so many people believe in the form of the "Law of Averages" that we argued against in Chapter 14. When the Poisson model was used to model bombs dropping over London in World War II, the model said that even though several bombs had hit a particular sector, the probability of *another* hit was still the same. So, there was no point in moving people from one sector to another, even after several hits. You can imagine how difficult it must have been trying to convince people of that! This same phenomenon leads many people to think they see patterns in which an athlete, slot machine, or financial market gets "hot." But the occurrence of several successes in a row is not unusual and is rarely evidence that the mean has changed. Careful studies have been made of "hot streaks," but none has ever demonstrated that they actually exist.

## JUST CHECKING

As we noted a few chapters ago, the Pew Research Center (www.pewresearch.org) reports that they are actually able to contact only 76% of the randomly selected households drawn for a telephone survey.

**1.** Explain why these phone calls can be considered Bernoulli trials.

**2.** Which of the models of this chapter (Geometric, Binomial, Normal) would you use to model the number of successful contacts from a list of 1000 sampled households? Explain.

**3.** Pew further reports that even after they contacted a household, only 38% agree to be interviewed, so the probability of getting a completed interview for a randomly selected household is only 0.29. Which of the models of this chapter would you use to model the number of households Pew has to call before they get the first completed interview?

**4.** Suppose that in the course of a year, legitimate survey organizations (not folks pretending to take a survey but actually trying to sell you something or change your vote) sample 70,000 of the approximately 107,000,000 households in the United States. You wonder if people from your school are represented in these polls. Counting all the living alumni from your school, there are 10,000 households. How would you model the number of these alumni households you'd expect will be contacted next year by a legitimate poll?

# WHAT CAN GO WRONG?

▶ **Be sure you have Bernoulli trials.** Be sure to check the requirements first: two possible outcomes per trial ("success" and "failure"), a constant probability of success, and independence. Remember to check the 10% Condition when sampling without replacement.

▶ **Don't confuse Geometric and Binomial models.** Both involve Bernoulli trials, but the issues are different. If you are repeating trials until your first success, that's a

*(continued)*

Geometric probability. You don't know in advance how many trials you'll need—theoretically, it could take forever. If you are counting the number of successes in a specified number of trials, that's a Binomial probability.

▶ **Don't use the Normal approximation with small *n*.** To use a Normal approximation in place of a Binomial model, there must be at least 10 expected successes and 10 expected failures.

# CONNECTIONS

This chapter builds on what we know about random variables. We now have two more probability models to join the Normal model.

There are a number of "forward" connections from this chapter. We'll see the **10% Condition** and the **Success/Failure Condition** often. And the facts about the Binomial distribution can help explain how proportions behave, as we'll see in the next chapter.

# WHAT HAVE WE LEARNED?

We've learned that Bernoulli trials show up in lots of places. Depending on the random variable of interest, we can use one of three models to estimate probabilities for Bernoulli trials:

▶ a Geometric model when we're interested in the number of Bernoulli trials until the next success;
▶ a Binomial model when we're interested in the number of successes in a certain number of Bernoulli trials;
▶ a Normal model to approximate a Binomial model when we expect at least 10 successes and 10 failures;
▶ a Poisson model to approximate a Binomial model when the probability of success, *p*, is very small and the number of trials, *n*, is very large.

## Terms

**Bernoulli trials, if . . .**
433. 1. there are two possible outcomes.
  2. the probability of success is constant.
  3. the trials are independent.

**Geometric probability model**
433. A Geometric model is appropriate for a random variable that counts the number of Bernoulli trials until the first success.

**Binomial probability model**
436. A Binomial model is appropriate for a random variable that counts the number of successes in a fixed number of Bernoulli trials.

**Success/Failure Condition**
439. For a Normal model to be a good approximation of a Binomial model, we must expect at least 10 successes and 10 failures. That is, $np \geq 10$ and $nq \geq 10$.

**Poisson probability model**
441. A Poisson model can be used to approximate a Binomial model when *p* is small and *n* is large. Use $\lambda = np$ as the mean for the Poisson. The Poisson can also be used to model counts of a wide variety of phenomena.

# Skills

▸ Know how to tell if a situation involves Bernoulli trials.

▸ Be able to choose whether to use a Geometric or a Binomial model for a random variable involving Bernoulli trials.

▸ Know the appropriate conditions for using a Geometric, Binomial, or Normal model.

▸ Know how to find the expected value of a Geometric model.

▸ Be able to calculate Geometric probabilities.

▸ Know how to find the mean and standard deviation of a Binomial model.

▸ Be able to calculate Binomial probabilities, perhaps approximating with a Normal or Poisson model.

▸ Be able to interpret means, standard deviations, and probabilities in the Bernoulli trial context.

# ON THE COMPUTER

## The Binomial, the Geometric, and the Poisson

Most statistics packages offer functions that compute Binomial probabilities, and many offer functions for Geometric and Poisson probabilities as well. Some technology solutions automatically use the Normal approximation for the Binomial when the exact calculations become unmanageable.

The only important differences among these functions are in what they are named and the order of their arguments. In these functions, pdf stands for "probability density function"—what we've been calling a probability model. The letters cdf stand for "cumulative distribution function," the technical term when we want to accumulate probabilities over a range of values. These technical terms show up in many of the function names. The term "cumulative" in a function name says that it corresponds to a cdf.

Generically, the four functions are as follows:

| | | |
|---|---|---|
| Geometric pdf (*prob, x*) | Finds the individual geometric probability of getting the first success on trial *x* when the probability of success is *prob*. | For example, the probability of finding the first Tiger Woods picture in the fifth cereal box is Geometric pdf(0.2, 5) |
| Geometric cdf (*prob, x*) | Finds the cumulative probability of getting the first success on or before trial *x*, when the probability of success is *prob*. | For example, the total probability of finding Tiger's picture in one of the first 4 boxes is Geometric cdf(0.2, 4) |
| Binomial pdf (*n, prob, x*) | Finds the probability of getting *x* successes in *n* trials when the probability of success is *prob*. | For example, Binomial pdf(5, 0.2, 2) is the probability of finding Tiger's picture exactly twice among 5 boxes of cereal. |
| Poisson pdf ($\lambda, x$) | Finds the probability of *x* successes when the mean number of successes is $\lambda = np$. | Best for large *n* and small probability of success. |

### DATA DESK

**BinomDistr(*x, n, prob*)** (pdf)
**CumBinomDistr(*x, n, prob*)** (cdf)
**PoisDistr(*x, mean*)** (pdf)
**CumPoisDistr(*x, mean*)** (cdf)

### COMMENTS

Data Desk does not compute Geometric probabilities.
These functions work in derived variables or in scratchpads.

## EXCEL

Binomdist(*x, n, prob, cumulative*)

**COMMENTS**

Set cumulative = *true* for cdf, *false* for pdf.
Excel's function fails when *x* or *n* is large.
Possibly, it does not use the Normal approximation.
Excel does not compute Geometric or Poisson probabilities.

## JMP

Binomial Probability (*prob, n, x*) (pdf)
Binomial Distribution (*prob, n, x*) (cdf)
Poisson Probability (*mean, k*) (pdf)
Poisson Distribution (*mean, k*) (cdf)

**COMMENTS**

JMP does not compute Geometric probabilities.

## MINITAB

Choose **Probability Distributions** from the **Calc** menu.
Choose **Binomial** from the Probability Distributions submenu.
To calculate the probability of getting *x* successes in *n* trials, choose **Probability.**
To calculate the probability of getting *x* or fewer successes among *n* trials, choose **Cumulative Probability.**
For Poisson, choose **Poisson** from the Probability Distribution submenu.

For Geometric, choose **Geometric** from the Probability Distribution submenu.

## SPSS

PDF.GEOM(*x, prob*)
CDF.GEOM(*x, prob*)
PDF.Poisson(*x, mean*)

CDF.Poisson(*x, mean*)
PDF.BINOM(*x, n, prob*)
CDF.BINOM(*x, n, prob*)

## TI-83/84 PLUS

geometpdf(*prob, x*)
geometcdf(*prob, x*)
binompdf(*n, prob, x*)
binomcdf(*n, prob, x*)
poissonpdf(*mean, x*)
poissoncdf(*mean, x*)

**COMMENTS**

Find these commands in the **2nd DISTR** menu (the calculator refers to models as "distributions").

## TI-89

Find the commands under the F5 (Distributions) menu.
▶ F: **Geometric Pdf** will ask for *p* and *x*. It returns the probability of the first success occurring on the *x*th trial.
▶ G: **Geometric Cdf** will ask for *p* and the upper and lower values of interest, say *a* and *b*. It returns $P(a \leq X \leq b)$, the probability the first success occurs between the *a*th and *b*th trials, inclusive.
▶ A: **Binomial Pdf** asks for *n*, *p*, and *x*.
▶ B: **Binomial Cdf** asks for *n*, *p*, and the lower and upper values of interest.
▶ D: **Poisson Pdf** asks for mean and *x*.
▶ E: **Poisson Cdf** asks for mean, *x*, and the lower and upper values of interest.

**COMMENTS**

For Geometric variables, when finding $P(X \geq a)$ specify an upper value of infinity, 1 EE 99, or a very large number.
For Binomial variables, when finding $P(X \geq a)$ the upper value is *n*.

# EXERCISES

1. **Bernoulli.** Can we use probability models based on Bernoulli trials to investigate the following situations? Explain.
   a) We roll 50 dice to find the distribution of the number of spots on the faces.
   b) How likely is it that in a group of 120 the majority may have Type A blood, given that Type A is found in 43% of the population?
   c) We deal 5 cards from a deck and get all hearts. How likely is that?
   d) We wish to predict the outcome of a vote on the school budget, and poll 500 of the 3000 likely voters to see how many favor the proposed budget.
   e) A company realizes that about 10% of its packages are not being sealed properly. In a case of 24, is it likely that more than 3 are unsealed?

2. **Bernoulli 2.** Can we use probability models based on Bernoulli trials to investigate the following situations? Explain.
   a) You are rolling 5 dice and need to get at least two 6's to win the game.
   b) We record the eye colors found in a group of 500 people.
   c) A manufacturer recalls a doll because about 3% have buttons that are not properly attached. Customers return 37 of these dolls to the local toy store. Is the manufacturer likely to find any dangerous buttons?
   d) A city council of 11 Republicans and 8 Democrats picks a committee of 4 at random. What's the probability they choose all Democrats?
   e) A 2002 Rutgers University study found that 74% of high-school students have cheated on a test at least once. Your local high-school principal conducts a survey in homerooms and gets responses that admit to cheating from 322 of the 481 students.

3. **Simulating the model.** Think about the Tiger Woods picture search again. You are opening boxes of cereal one at a time looking for his picture, which is in 20% of the boxes. You want to know how many boxes you might have to open in order to find Tiger.
   a) Describe how you would simulate the search for Tiger using random numbers.
   b) Run at least 30 trials.
   c) Based on your simulation, estimate the probabilities that you might find your first picture of Tiger in the first box, the second, etc.
   d) Calculate the actual probability model.
   e) Compare the distribution of outcomes in your simulation to the probability model.

4. **Simulation II.** You are one space short of winning a child's board game and must roll a 1 on a die to claim victory. You want to know how many rolls it might take.
   a) Describe how you would simulate rolling the die until you get a 1.
   b) Run at least 30 trials.

   c) Based on your simulation, estimate the probabilities that you might win on the first roll, the second, the third, etc.
   d) Calculate the actual probability model.
   e) Compare the distribution of outcomes in your simulation to the probability model.

5. **Tiger again.** Let's take one last look at the Tiger Woods picture search. You know his picture is in 20% of the cereal boxes. You buy five boxes to see how many pictures of Tiger you might get.
   a) Describe how you would simulate the number of pictures of Tiger you might find in five boxes of cereal.
   b) Run at least 30 trials.
   c) Based on your simulation, estimate the probabilities that you get no pictures of Tiger, 1 picture, 2 pictures, etc.
   d) Calculate the actual probability model.
   e) Compare the distribution of outcomes in your simulation to the probability model.

6. **Seatbelts.** Suppose 75% of all drivers always wear their seatbelts. Let's investigate how many of the drivers might be belted among five cars waiting at a traffic light.
   a) Describe how you would simulate the number of seatbelt-wearing drivers among the five cars.
   b) Run at least 30 trials.
   c) Based on your simulation, estimate the probabilities there are no belted drivers, exactly one, two, etc.
   d) Calculate the actual probability model.
   e) Compare the distribution of outcomes in your simulation to the probability model.

7. **On time.** A Department of Transportation report about air travel found that, nationwide, 76% of all flights are on time. Suppose you are at the airport and your flight is one of 50 scheduled to take off in the next two hours. Can you consider these departures to be Bernoulli trials? Explain.

8. **Lost luggage.** A Department of Transportation report about air travel found that airlines misplace about 5 bags per 1000 passengers. Suppose you are traveling with a group of people who have checked 22 pieces of luggage on your flight. Can you consider the fate of these bags to be Bernoulli trials? Explain.

9. **Hoops.** A basketball player has made 80% of his foul shots during the season. Assuming the shots are independent, find the probability that in tonight's game he
   a) misses for the first time on his fifth attempt.
   b) makes his first basket on his fourth shot.
   c) makes his first basket on one of his first 3 shots.

10. **Chips.** Suppose a computer chip manufacturer rejects 2% of the chips produced because they fail presale testing.
    a) What's the probability that the fifth chip you test is the first bad one you find?
    b) What's the probability you find a bad one within the first 10 you examine?

11. **More hoops.** For the basketball player in Exercise 9, what's the expected number of shots until he misses?

12. **Chips ahoy.** For the computer chips described in Exercise 10, how many do you expect to test before finding a bad one?

13. **Customer center operator.** Raaj works at the customer service call center of a major credit card bank. Cardholders call for a variety of reasons, but regardless of their reason for calling, if they hold a platinum card, Raaj is instructed to offer them a double-miles promotion. About 10% of all cardholders hold platinum cards, and about 50% of those will take the double-miles promotion. On average, how many calls will Raaj have to take before finding the first cardholder to take the double-miles promotion?

14. **Cold calls.** Justine works for an organization committed to raising money for Alzheimer's research. From past experience, the organization knows that about 20% of all potential donors will agree to give something if contacted by phone. They also know that of all people donating, about 5% will give $100 or more. On average, how many potential donors will she have to contact until she gets her first $100 donor?

15. **Blood.** Only 4% of people have Type AB blood.
    a) On average, how many donors must be checked to find someone with Type AB blood?
    b) What's the probability that there is a Type AB donor among the first 5 people checked?
    c) What's the probability that the first Type AB donor will be found among the first 6 people?
    d) What's the probability that we won't find a Type AB donor before the 10th person?

16. **Colorblindness.** About 8% of males are colorblind. A researcher needs some colorblind subjects for an experiment and begins checking potential subjects.
    a) On average, how many men should the researcher expect to check to find one who is colorblind?
    b) What's the probability that she won't find anyone colorblind among the first 4 men she checks?
    c) What's the probability that the first colorblind man found will be the sixth person checked?
    d) What's the probability that she finds someone who is colorblind before checking the 10th man?

17. **Coins and intuition.** If you spin a fair coin 100 times,
    a) Intuitively, how many heads do you expect?
    b) Use the formula for expected value to verify your intuition.

18. **Roulette and intuition.** An American roulette wheel has 38 slots, of which 18 are red, 18 are black, and 2 are green (0 and 00). If you spin the wheel 38 times,
    a) Intuitively, how many times would you expect the ball to wind up in a green slot?
    b) Use the formula for expected value to verify your intuition.

19. **Lefties.** Assume that 13% of people are left-handed. If we select 5 people at random, find the probability of each outcome described below.
    a) The first lefty is the fifth person chosen.
    b) There are some lefties among the 5 people.

    c) The first lefty is the second or third person.
    d) There are exactly 3 lefties in the group.
    e) There are at least 3 lefties in the group.
    f) There are no more than 3 lefties in the group.

20. **Arrows.** An Olympic archer is able to hit the bull's-eye 80% of the time. Assume each shot is independent of the others. If she shoots 6 arrows, what's the probability of each of the following results?
    a) Her first bull's-eye comes on the third arrow.
    b) She misses the bull's-eye at least once.
    c) Her first bull's-eye comes on the fourth or fifth arrow.
    d) She gets exactly 4 bull's-eyes.
    e) She gets at least 4 bull's-eyes.
    f) She gets at most 4 bull's-eyes.

21. **Lefties redux.** Consider our group of 5 people from Exercise 19.
    a) How many lefties do you expect?
    b) With what standard deviation?
    c) If we keep picking people until we find a lefty, how long do you expect it will take?

22. **More arrows.** Consider our archer from Exercise 20.
    a) How many bull's-eyes do you expect her to get?
    b) With what standard deviation?
    c) If she keeps shooting arrows until she hits the bull's-eye, how long do you expect it will take?

23. **Still more lefties.** Suppose we choose 12 people instead of the 5 chosen in Exercise 19.
    a) Find the mean and standard deviation of the number of right-handers in the group.
    b) What's the probability that they're not all right-handed?
    c) What's the probability that there are no more than 10 righties?
    d) What's the probability that there are exactly 6 of each?
    e) What's the probability that the majority is right-handed?

24. **Still more arrows.** Suppose our archer from Exercise 20 shoots 10 arrows.
    a) Find the mean and standard deviation of the number of bull's-eyes she may get.
    b) What's the probability that she never misses?
    c) What's the probability that there are no more than 8 bull's-eyes?
    d) What's the probability that there are exactly 8 bull's-eyes?
    e) What's the probability that she hits the bull's-eye more often than she misses?

25. **Vision.** It is generally believed that nearsightedness affects about 12% of all children. A school district tests the vision of 169 incoming kindergarten children. How many would you expect to be nearsighted? With what standard deviation?

26. **International students.** At a certain college, 6% of all students come from outside the United States. Incoming students there are assigned at random to freshman dorms, where students live in residential clusters of 40 freshmen sharing a common lounge area. How many international students would you expect to find in a typical cluster? With what standard deviation?

**27. Tennis, anyone?** A certain tennis player makes a successful first serve 70% of the time. Assume that each serve is independent of the others. If she serves 6 times, what's the probability she gets
a) all 6 serves in?
b) exactly 4 serves in?
c) at least 4 serves in?
d) no more than 4 serves in?

**28. Frogs.** A wildlife biologist examines frogs for a genetic trait he suspects may be linked to sensitivity to industrial toxins in the environment. Previous research had established that this trait is usually found in 1 of every 8 frogs. He collects and examines a dozen frogs. If the frequency of the trait has not changed, what's the probability he finds the trait in
a) none of the 12 frogs?
b) at least 2 frogs?
c) 3 or 4 frogs?
d) no more than 4 frogs?

**29. And more tennis.** Suppose the tennis player in Exercise 27 serves 80 times in a match.
a) What are the mean and standard deviation of the number of good first serves expected?
b) Verify that you can use a Normal model to approximate the distribution of the number of good first serves.
c) Use the 68–95–99.7 Rule to describe this distribution.
d) What's the probability she makes at least 65 first serves?

**30. More arrows.** The archer in Exercise 20 will be shooting 200 arrows in a large competition.
a) What are the mean and standard deviation of the number of bull's-eyes she might get?
b) Is a Normal model appropriate here? Explain.
c) Use the 68–95–99.7 Rule to describe the distribution of the number of bull's-eyes she may get.
d) Would you be surprised if she made only 140 bull's-eyes? Explain.

**31. Apples.** An orchard owner knows that he'll have to use about 6% of the apples he harvests for cider because they will have bruises or blemishes. He expects a tree to produce about 300 apples.
a) Describe an appropriate model for the number of cider apples that may come from that tree. Justify your model.
b) Find the probability there will be no more than a dozen cider apples.
c) Is it likely there will be more than 50 cider apples? Explain.

**32. Frogs, part II.** Based on concerns raised by his preliminary research, the biologist in Exercise 28 decides to collect and examine 150 frogs.
a) Assuming the frequency of the trait is still 1 in 8, determine the mean and standard deviation of the number of frogs with the trait he should expect to find in his sample.
b) Verify that he can use a Normal model to approximate the distribution of the number of frogs with the trait.
c) He found the trait in 22 of his frogs. Do you think this proves that the trait has become more common? Explain.

**33. Lefties again.** A lecture hall has 200 seats with folding arm tablets, 30 of which are designed for left-handers. The average size of classes that meet there is 188, and we can assume that about 13% of students are left-handed. What's the probability that a right-handed student in one of these classes is forced to use a lefty arm tablet?

**34. No-shows.** An airline, believing that 5% of passengers fail to show up for flights, overbooks (sells more tickets than there are seats). Suppose a plane will hold 265 passengers, and the airline sells 275 tickets. What's the probability the airline will not have enough seats, so someone gets bumped?

**35. Annoying phone calls.** A newly hired telemarketer is told he will probably make a sale on about 12% of his phone calls. The first week he called 200 people, but only made 10 sales. Should he suspect he was misled about the true success rate? Explain.

**36. The euro.** Shortly after the introduction of the euro coin in Belgium, newspapers around the world published articles claiming the coin is biased. The stories were based on reports that someone had spun the coin 250 times and gotten 140 heads—that's 56% heads. Do you think this is evidence that spinning a euro is unfair? Explain.

**37. Hurricanes, redux.** We first looked at the occurrences of hurricanes in Chapter 4 (Exercise 41) and found that they arrive with a mean of 2.45 per year. Suppose the number of hurricanes can be modeled by a Poisson distribution with this mean.
a) What's the probability of no hurricanes next year?
b) What's the probability that during the next two years, there's exactly 1 hurricane?

**38. Bank tellers.** I am the only bank teller on duty at my local bank. I need to run out for 10 minutes, but I don't want to miss any customers. Suppose the arrival of customers can be modeled by a Poisson distribution with mean 2 customers per hour.
a) What's the probability that no one will arrive in the next 10 minutes?
b) What's the probability that 2 or more people arrive in the next 10 minutes?
c) You've just served 2 customers who came in one after the other. Is this a better time to run out?

**39. TB again.** In Chapter 15 we saw that the probability of contracting TB is small, with $p$ about 0.0005 for a new case in a given year. In a town of 8000 people
a) What's the expected number of new cases?
b) Use the Poisson model to approximate the probability that there will be at least one new case of TB next year.

**40. Earthquakes.** Suppose the probability of a major earthquake on a given day is 1 out of 10,000.
a) What's the expected number of major earthquakes in the next 1000 days?
b) Use the Poisson model to approximate the probability that there will be at least one major earthquake in the next 1000 days.

**41. Seatbelts II.** Police estimate that 80% of drivers now wear their seatbelts. They set up a safety roadblock, stopping cars to check for seatbelt use.

a) How many cars do they expect to stop before finding a driver whose seatbelt is not buckled?

b) What's the probability that the first unbelted driver is in the 6th car stopped?

c) What's the probability that the first 10 drivers are all wearing their seatbelts?

d) If they stop 30 cars during the first hour, find the mean and standard deviation of the number of drivers expected to be wearing seatbelts.

e) If they stop 120 cars during this safety check, what's the probability they find at least 20 drivers not wearing their seatbelts?

**42. Rickets.** Vitamin D is essential for strong, healthy bones. Our bodies produce vitamin D naturally when sunlight falls upon the skin, or it can be taken as a dietary supplement. Although the bone disease rickets was largely eliminated in England during the 1950s, some people there are concerned that this generation of children is at increased risk because they are more likely to watch TV or play computer games than spend time outdoors. Recent research indicated that about 20% of British children are deficient in vitamin D. Suppose doctors test a group of elementary school children.

a) What's the probability that the first vitamin D–deficient child is the 8th one tested?

b) What's the probability that the first 10 children tested are all okay?

c) How many kids do they expect to test before finding one who has this vitamin deficiency?

d) They will test 50 students at the third-grade level. Find the mean and standard deviation of the number who may be deficient in vitamin D.

e) If they test 320 children at this school, what's the probability that no more than 50 of them have the vitamin deficiency?

**43. ESP.** Scientists wish to test the mind-reading ability of a person who claims to "have ESP." They use five cards with different and distinctive symbols (square, circle, triangle, line, squiggle). Someone picks a card at random and thinks about the symbol. The "mind reader" must correctly identify which symbol was on the card. If the test consists of 100 trials, how many would this person need to get right in order to convince you that ESP may actually exist? Explain.

**44. True–False.** A true–false test consists of 50 questions. How many does a student have to get right to convince you that he is not merely guessing? Explain.

**45. Hot hand.** A basketball player who ordinarily makes about 55% of his free throw shots has made 4 in a row. Is this evidence that he has a "hot hand" tonight? That is, is this streak so unusual that it means the probability he makes a shot must have changed? Explain.

**46. New bow.** Our archer in Exercise 20 purchases a new bow, hoping that it will improve her success rate to more than 80% bull's-eyes. She is delighted when she first tests her new bow and hits 6 consecutive bull's-eyes. Do you think this is compelling evidence that the new bow is better? In other words, is a streak like this unusual for her? Explain.

**47. Hotter hand.** Our basketball player in Exercise 45 has new sneakers, which he thinks improve his game. Over his past 40 shots, he's made 32—much better than the 55% he usually shoots. Do you think his chances of making a shot really increased? In other words, is making at least 32 of 40 shots really unusual for him? (Do you think it's his sneakers?)

**48. New bow, again.** The archer in Exercise 46 continues shooting arrows, ending up with 45 bull's-eyes in 50 shots. Now are you convinced that the new bow is better? Explain.

### JUST CHECKING
### Answers

1. There are two outcomes (contact, no contact), the probability of contact is 0.76, and random calls should be independent.

2. Binomial, with $n = 1000$ and $p = 0.76$. For actual calculations, we could approximate using a Normal model with $\mu = np = 1000(0.76) = 760$ and $\sigma = \sqrt{npq} = \sqrt{1000(0.76)(0.24)} \approx 13.5$.

3. Geometric, with $p = 0.29$.

4. Poisson, with $\lambda = np = 10000\left(\dfrac{70000}{107000000}\right) = 6.54$.

# REVIEW OF PART IV

## Randomness and Probability

### Quick Review

Here's a brief summary of the key concepts and skills in probability and probability modeling:

▶ The Law of Large Numbers says that the more times we try something, the closer the results will come to theoretical perfection.

- Don't mistakenly misinterpret the Law of Large Numbers as the "Law of Averages." There's no such thing.

▶ Basic rules of probability can handle most situations:

- To find the probability that an event OR another event happens, add their probabilities and subtract the probability that both happen.
- To find the probability that an event AND another independent event both happen, multiply probabilities.
- Conditional probabilities tell you how likely one event is to happen, knowing that another event has happened.
- Mutually exclusive events (also called "disjoint") cannot both happen at the same time.
- Two events are independent if the occurrence of one doesn't change the probability that the other happens.

▶ A probability model for a random variable describes the theoretical distribution of outcomes.

- The mean of a random variable is its expected value.
- For sums or differences of independent random variables, variances add.
- To estimate probabilities involving quantitative variables, you may be able to use a Normal model—but only if the distribution of the variable is unimodal and symmetric.
- To estimate the probability you'll get your first success on a certain trial, use a Geometric model.
- To estimate the probability you'll get a certain number of successes in a specified number of independent trials, use a Binomial model.
- To estimate the probability of the number of occurrences of a relatively rare phenomenon, consider using a Poisson model.

Ready? Here are some opportunities to check your understanding of these ideas.

# REVIEW EXERCISES

1. **Quality control.** A consumer organization estimates that 29% of new cars have a cosmetic defect, such as a scratch or a dent, when they are delivered to car dealers. This same organization believes that 7% have a functional defect—something that does not work properly—and that 2% of new cars have both kinds of problems.
   a) If you buy a new car, what's the probability that it has some kind of defect?
   b) What's the probability it has a cosmetic defect but no functional defect?
   c) If you notice a dent on a new car, what's the probability it has a functional defect?
   d) Are the two kinds of defects disjoint events? Explain.
   e) Do you think the two kinds of defects are independent events? Explain.

2. **Workers.** A company's human resources officer reports a breakdown of employees by job type and sex shown in the table.

|  |  | Sex | |
|---|---|---|---|
|  |  | Male | Female |
| Job Type | Management | 7 | 6 |
|  | Supervision | 8 | 12 |
|  | Production | 45 | 72 |

   a) What's the probability that a worker selected at random is
   i) female?
   ii) female or a production worker?
   iii) female, if the person works in production?
   iv) a production worker, if the person is female?
   b) Do these data suggest that job type is independent of being male or female? Explain.

3. **Airfares.** Each year a company must send 3 officials to a meeting in China and 5 officials to a meeting in France. Airline ticket prices vary from time to time, but the company purchases all tickets for a country at the same price. Past experience has shown that tickets to China have a mean price of $1000, with a standard deviation of $150, while the mean airfare to France is $500, with a standard deviation of $100.
   a) Define random variables and use them to express the total amount the company will have to spend to send these delegations to the two meetings.
   b) Find the mean and standard deviation of this total cost.
   c) Find the mean and standard deviation of the difference in price of a ticket to China and a ticket to France.
   d) Do you need to make any assumptions in calculating these means? How about the standard deviations?

4. **Bipolar.** Psychiatrists estimate that about 1 in 100 adults suffers from bipolar disorder. What's the probability that in a city of 10,000 there are more than 200 people with this condition? Be sure to verify that a Normal model can be used here.

5. **A game.** To play a game, you must pay $5 for each play. There is a 10% chance you will win $5, a 40% chance you will win $7, and a 50% chance you will win only $3.
   a) What are the mean and standard deviation of your net winnings?
   b) You play twice. Assuming the plays are independent events, what are the mean and standard deviation of your total winnings?

6. **Emergency switch.** Safety engineers must determine whether industrial workers can operate a machine's emergency shutoff device. Among a group of test subjects, 66% were successful with their left hands, 82% with their right hands, and 51% with both hands.
   a) What percent of these workers could not operate the switch with either hand?
   b) Are success with right and left hands independent events? Explain.
   c) Are success with right and left hands mutually exclusive? Explain.

7. **Twins.** In the United States, the probability of having twins (usually about 1 in 90 births) rises to about 1 in 10 for women who have been taking the fertility drug Clomid. Among a group of 10 pregnant women, what's the probability that
   a) at least one will have twins if none were taking a fertility drug?
   b) at least one will have twins if all were taking Clomid?
   c) at least one will have twins if half were taking Clomid?

8. **Deductible.** A car owner may buy insurance that will pay the full price of repairing the car after an at-fault accident, or save $12 a year by getting a policy with a $500 deductible. Her insurance company says that about 0.5% of drivers in her area have an at-fault auto accident during any given year. Based on this information, should she buy the policy with the deductible or not? How does the value of her car influence this decision?

9. **More twins.** A group of 5 women became pregnant while undergoing fertility treatments with the drug Clomid, discussed in Exercise 7. What's the probability that
   a) none will have twins?
   b) exactly 1 will have twins?
   c) at least 3 will have twins?

10. **At fault.** The car insurance company in Exercise 8 believes that about 0.5% of drivers have an at-fault accident during a given year. Suppose the company insures 1355 drivers in that city.
    a) What are the mean and standard deviation of the number who may have at-fault accidents?
    b) Can you describe the distribution of these accidents with a Normal model? Explain.

11. **Twins, part III.** At a large fertility clinic, 152 women became pregnant while taking Clomid. (See Exercise 7.)

a) What are the mean and standard deviation of the number of twin births we might expect?
b) Can we use a Normal model in this situation? Explain.
c) What's the probability that no more than 10 of the women have twins?

**12. Child's play.**   In a board game you determine the number of spaces you may move by spinning a spinner and rolling a die. The spinner has three regions: Half of the spinner is marked "5," and the other half is equally divided between "10"and "20." The six faces of the die show 0, 0, 1, 2, 3, and 4 spots. When it's your turn, you spin and roll, adding the numbers together to determine how far you may move.
a) Create a probability model for the outcome on the spinner.
b) Find the mean and standard deviation of the spinner results.
c) Create a probability model for the outcome on the die.
d) Find the mean and standard deviation of the die results.
e) Find the mean and standard deviation of the number of spaces you get to move.

**13. Language.**   Neurological research has shown that in about 80% of people, language abilities reside in the brain's left side. Another 10% display right-brain language centers, and the remaining 10% have two-sided language control. (The latter two groups are mainly left-handers; *Science News*, 161 no. 24 [2002].)
a) Assume that a freshman composition class contains 25 randomly selected people. What's the probability that no more than 15 of them have left-brain language control?
b) In a randomly assigned group of 5 of these students, what's the probability that no one has two-sided language control?
c) In the entire freshman class of 1200 students, how many would you expect to find of each type?
d) What are the mean and standard deviation of the number of these freshmen who might be right-brained in language abilities?
e) If an assumption of Normality is justified, use the 68–95–99.7 Rule to describe how many students in the freshman class might have right-brain language control.

**14. Play again.**   If you land in a "penalty zone" on the game board described in Exercise 12, your move will be determined by subtracting the roll of the die from the result on the spinner. Now what are the mean and standard deviation of the number of spots you may move?

**15. Beanstalks.**   In some cities tall people who want to meet and socialize with other tall people can join Beanstalk Clubs. To qualify, a man must be over 6'2" tall, and a woman over 5'10". According to the National Health Survey, heights of adults may have a Normal model with mean heights of 69.1" for men and 64.0" for women. The respective standard deviations are 2.8" and 2.5".
a) You're probably not surprised to learn that men are generally taller than women, but what does the greater standard deviation for men's heights indicate?

b) Are men or women more likely to qualify for Beanstalk membership?
c) Beanstalk members believe that height is an important factor when people select their spouses. To investigate, we select at random a married man and, independently, a married woman. Define two random variables, and use them to express how many inches taller the man is than the woman.
d) What's the mean of this difference?
e) What's the standard deviation of this difference?
f) What's the probability that the man is taller than the woman (that the difference in heights is greater than 0)?
g) Suppose a survey of married couples reveals that 92% of the husbands were taller than their wives. Based on your answer to part f, do you believe that people's choice of spouses is independent of height? Explain.

**16. Stocks.**   Since the stock market began in 1872, stock prices have risen in about 73% of the years. Assuming that market performance is independent from year to year, what's the probability that
a) the market will rise for 3 consecutive years?
b) the market will rise 3 years out of the next 5?
c) the market will fall during at least 1 of the next 5 years?
d) the market will rise during a majority of years over the next decade?

**17. Multiple choice.**   A multiple choice test has 50 questions, with 4 answer choices each. You must get at least 30 correct to pass the test, and the questions are very difficult.
a) Are you likely to be able to pass by guessing on every question? Explain.
b) Suppose, after studying for a while, you believe you have raised your chances of getting each question right to 70%. How likely are you to pass now?
c) Assuming you are operating at the 70% level and the instructor arranges questions randomly, what's the probability that the third question is the first one you get right?

**18. Stock strategy.**   Many investment advisors argue that after stocks have declined in value for 2 consecutive years, people should invest heavily because the market rarely declines 3 years in a row.
a) Since the stock market began in 1872, there have been two consecutive losing years eight times. In six of those cases, the market rose during the following year. Does this confirm the advice?
b) Overall, stocks have risen in value during 95 of the 130 years since the market began in 1872. How is this fact relevant in assessing the statistical reasoning of the advisors?

**19. Insurance.**   A 65-year-old woman takes out a $100,000 term life insurance policy. The company charges an annual premium of $520. Estimate the company's expected profit on such policies if mortality tables indicate that only 2.6% of women age 65 die within a year.

**20. Teen smoking.**   The Centers for Disease Control say that about 30% of high-school students smoke tobacco (down from a high of 38% in 1997). Suppose you randomly select high-school students to survey them on

their attitudes toward scenes of smoking in the movies. What's the probability that
a) none of the first 4 students you interview is a smoker?
b) the first smoker is the sixth person you choose?
c) there are no more than 2 smokers among 10 people you choose?

21. **Passing stats.** Molly's college offers two sections of Statistics 101. From what she has heard about the two professors listed, Molly estimates that her chances of passing the course are 0.80 if she gets Professor Scedastic and 0.60 if she gets Professor Kurtosis. The registrar uses a lottery to randomly assign the 120 enrolled students based on the number of available seats in each class. There are 70 seats in Professor Scedastic's class and 50 in Professor Kurtosis's class.
a) What's the probability that Molly will pass Statistics?
b) At the end of the semester, we find out that Molly failed. What's the probability that she got Professor Kurtosis?

22. **Teen smoking II.** Suppose that, as reported by the Centers for Disease Control, about 30% of high school students smoke tobacco. You randomly select 120 high school students to survey them on their attitudes toward scenes of smoking in the movies.
a) What's the expected number of smokers?
b) What's the standard deviation of the number of smokers?
c) The number of smokers among 120 randomly selected students will vary from group to group. Explain why that number can be described with a Normal model.
d) Using the 68–95–99.7 Rule, create and interpret a model for the number of smokers among your group of 120 students.

23. **Random variables.** Given independent random variables with means and standard deviations as shown, find the mean and standard deviation of each of these variables:
a) $X + 50$
b) $10Y$
c) $X + 0.5Y$
d) $X - Y$
e) $X_1 + X_2$

| | Mean | SD |
|---|---|---|
| $X$ | 50 | 8 |
| $Y$ | 100 | 6 |

24. **Merger.** Explain why the facts you know about variances of independent random variables might encourage two small insurance companies to merge. (*Hint:* Think about the expected amount and potential variability in payouts for the separate and the merged companies.)

25. **Youth survey.** According to a recent Gallup survey, 93% of teens use the Internet, but there are differences in how teen boys and girls say they use computers. The telephone poll found that 77% of boys had played computer games in the past week, compared with 65% of girls. On the other hand, 76% of girls said they had e-mailed friends in the past week, compared with only 65% of boys.
a) For boys, the cited percentages are 77% playing computer games and 65% using e-mail. That total is 142%, so there is obviously a mistake in the report. No? Explain.

b) Based on these results, do you think playing games and using e-mail are mutually exclusive? Explain.
c) Do you think whether a child e-mails friends is independent of being a boy or a girl? Explain.
d) Suppose that in fact 93% of the teens in your area do use the Internet. You want to interview a few who do not, so you start contacting teenagers at random. What is the probability that it takes you 5 interviews until you find the first person who does not use the Internet?

26. **Meals.** A college student on a seven-day meal plan reports that the amount of money he spends daily on food varies with a mean of $13.50 and a standard deviation of $7.
a) What are the mean and standard deviation of the amount he might spend in two consecutive days?
b) What assumption did you make in order to find that standard deviation? Are there any reasons you might question that assumption?
c) Estimate his average weekly food costs, and the standard deviation.
d) Do you think it likely he might spend less than $50 in a week? Explain, including any assumptions you make in your analysis.

27. **Travel to Kyrgyzstan.** Your pocket copy of *Kyrgyzstan on 4237 ± 360 Som a Day* claims that you can expect to spend about 4237 som each day with a standard deviation of 360 som. How well can you estimate your expenses for the trip?
a) Your budget allows you to spend 90,000 som. To the nearest day, how long can you afford to stay in Kyrgyzstan, on average?
b) What's the standard deviation of your expenses for a trip of that duration?
c) You doubt that your total expenses will exceed your expectations by more than two standard deviations. How much extra money should you bring? On average, how much of a "cushion" will you have per day?

28. **Picking melons.** Two stores sell watermelons. At the first store the melons weigh an average of 22 pounds, with a standard deviation of 2.5 pounds. At the second store the melons are smaller, with a mean of 18 pounds and a standard deviation of 2 pounds. You select a melon at random at each store.
a) What's the mean difference in weights of the melons?
b) What's the standard deviation of the difference in weights?
c) If a Normal model can be used to describe the difference in weights, what's the probability that the melon you got at the first store is heavier?

29. **Home, sweet home.** According to the 2000 Census, 66% of U.S. households own the home they live in. A mayoral candidate conducts a survey of 820 randomly selected homes in your city and finds only 523 owned by the current residents. The candidate then attacks the incumbent mayor, saying that there is an unusually low level of homeownership in the city. Do you agree? Explain.

**30. Buying melons.** The first store in Exercise 28 sells watermelons for 32 cents a pound. The second store is having a sale on watermelons—only 25 cents a pound. Find the mean and standard deviation of the difference in the price you may pay for melons randomly selected at each store.

**31. Who's the boss?** The 2000 Census revealed that 26% of all firms in the United States are owned by women. You call some firms doing business locally, assuming that the national percentage is true in your area.
a) What's the probability that the first 3 you call are all owned by women?
b) What's the probability that none of your first 4 calls finds a firm that is owned by a woman?
c) Suppose none of your first 5 calls found a firm owned by a woman. What's the probability that your next call does?

**32. Jerseys.** A Statistics professor comes home to find that all four of his children got white team shirts from soccer camp this year. He concludes that this year, unlike other years, the camp must not be using a variety of colors. But then he finds out that in each child's age group there are 4 teams, only 1 of which wears white shirts. Each child just happened to get on the white team at random.
a) Why was he so surprised? If each age group uses the same 4 colors, what's the probability that all four kids would get the same-color shirt?
b) What's the probability that all 4 would get white shirts?
c) We lied. Actually, in the oldest child's group there are 6 teams instead of the 4 teams in each of the other three groups. How does this change the probability you calculated in part b?

**33. When to stop?** In Exercise 27 of the Review Exercises for Part III, we posed this question:

*You play a game that involves rolling a die. You can roll as many times as you want, and your score is the total for all the rolls. But . . . if you roll a 6, your score is 0 and your turn is over. What might be a good strategy for a game like this?*

You attempted to devise a good strategy by simulating several plays to see what might happen. Let's try calculating a strategy.
a) On what roll would you expect to get a 6 for the first time?
b) So, roll *one time less* than that. Assuming all those rolls were not 6's, what's your expected score?

c) What's the probability that you can roll that many times without getting a 6?

**34. Plan B.** Here's another attempt at developing a good strategy for the dice game in Exercise 33. Instead of stopping after a certain number of rolls, you could decide to stop when your score reaches a certain number of points.
a) How many points would you expect a roll to *add* to your score?
b) In terms of your current score, how many points would you expect a roll to *subtract* from your score?
c) Based on your answers in parts a and b, at what score will another roll "break even"?
d) Describe the strategy this result suggests.

**35. Technology on campus.** Every 5 years the Conference Board of the Mathematical Sciences surveys college math departments. In 2000 the board reported that 51% of all undergraduates taking Calculus I were in classes that used graphing calculators and 31% were in classes that used computer assignments. Suppose that 16% used both calculators and computers.
a) What percent used neither kind of technology?
b) What percent used calculators but not computers?
c) What percent of the calculator users had computer assignments?
d) Based on this survey, do calculator and computer use appear to be independent events? Explain.

**36. Dogs.** A census by the county dog control officer found that 18% of homes kept one dog as a pet, 4% had two dogs, and 1% had three or more. If a salesman visits two homes selected at random, what's the probability he encounters
a) no dogs?
b) some dogs?
c) dogs in each home?
d) more than one dog in each home?

**37. O-rings.** Failures of O-rings on the space shuttle are fairly rare, but often disastrous, events. If we are testing O-rings, suppose that the probability of a failure of any one O-ring is 0.01. Let $X$ be the number of failures in the next 10 O-rings tested.
a) What model might you use to model $X$?
b) What is the mean number of failures in the next 10 O-rings?
c) What is the probability that there is exactly one failure in the next 10 O-rings?
d) What is the probability that there is at least one failure in the next 10 O-rings?

**38. Volcanoes.** Almost every year, there is some incidence of volcanic activity on the island of Japan. In 2005 there were 5 volcanic episodes, defined as either eruptions or sizable seismic activity. Suppose the mean number of episodes is 2.4 per year. Let $X$ be the number of episodes in the 2-year period 2008–2009.
a) What model might you use to model $X$?
b) What is the mean number of episodes in this period?
c) What is the probability that there will be no episodes in this period?
d) What is the probability that there are more than three episodes in this period?

**39. Socks.** In your sock drawer you have 4 blue socks, 5 grey socks, and 3 black ones. Half asleep one morning, you grab 2 socks at random and put them on. Find the probability you end up wearing
   a) 2 blue socks.
   b) no grey socks.
   c) at least 1 black sock.
   d) a green sock.
   e) matching socks.

**40. Coins.** A coin is to be tossed 36 times.
   a) What are the mean and standard deviation of the number of heads?
   b) Suppose the resulting number of heads is unusual, two standard deviations above the mean. How many "extra" heads were observed?
   c) If the coin were tossed 100 times, would you still consider the same number of extra heads unusual? Explain.
   d) In the 100 tosses, how many extra heads would you need to observe in order to say the results were unusual?
   e) Explain how these results refute the "Law of Averages" but confirm the Law of Large Numbers.

**41. The Drake equation.** In 1961 astronomer Frank Drake developed an equation to try to estimate the number of extraterrestrial civilizations in our galaxy that might be able to communicate with us via radio transmissions. Now largely accepted by the scientific community, the Drake equation has helped spur efforts by radio astronomers to search for extraterrestrial intelligence.

Here is the equation:

$$N_C = N \cdot f_p \cdot n_e \cdot f_l \cdot f_i \cdot f_c \cdot f_L$$

OK, it looks a little messy, but here's what it means:

| Factor | What It Represents | Possible Value |
|---|---|---|
| $N$ | Number of stars in the Milky Way Galaxy | 200–400 billion |
| $f_p$ | Probability that a star has planets | 20%–50% |
| $n_e$ | Number of planets in a solar system capable of sustaining earth-type life | 1? 2? |
| $f_l$ | Probability that life develops on a planet with a suitable environment | 1%–100% |
| $f_i$ | Probability that life evolves intelligence | 50%? |
| $f_c$ | Probability that intelligent life develops radio communication | 10%–20% |
| $f_L$ | Fraction of the planet's life for which the civilization survives | $\frac{1}{1,000,000}$? |
| $N_c$ | Number of extraterrestrial civilizations in our galaxy with which we could communicate | ? |

So, how many ETs are out there? That depends; values chosen for the many factors in the equation depend on ever-evolving scientific knowledge and one's personal guesses. But now, some questions.
   a) What quantity is calculated by the first product, $N \cdot f_p$?
   b) What quantity is calculated by the product, $N \cdot f_p \cdot n_e \cdot f_l$?
   c) What probability is calculated by the product $f_l \cdot f_i$?
   d) Which of the factors in the formula are conditional probabilities? Restate each in a way that makes the condition clear.

*Note:* A quick Internet search will find you a site where you can play with the Drake equation yourself.

**42. Recalls.** In a car rental company's fleet, 70% of the cars are American brands, 20% are Japanese, and the rest are German. The company notes that manufacturers' recalls seem to affect 2% of the American cars, but only 1% of the others.
   a) What's the probability that a randomly chosen car is recalled?
   b) What's the probability that a recalled car is American?

**43. Pregnant?** Suppose that 70% of the women who suspect they may be pregnant and purchase an in-home pregnancy test are actually pregnant. Further suppose that the test is 98% accurate. What's the probability that a woman whose test indicates that she is pregnant actually is?

**44. Door prize.** You are among 100 people attending a charity fundraiser at which a large-screen TV will be given away as a door prize. To determine who wins, 99 white balls and 1 red ball have been placed in a box and thoroughly mixed. The guests will line up and, one at a time, pick a ball from the box. Whoever gets the red ball wins the TV, but if the ball is white, it is returned to the box. If none of the 100 guests gets the red ball, the TV will be auctioned off for additional benefit of the charity.
   a. What's the probability that the first person in line wins the TV?
   b. You are the third person in line. What's the probability that you win the TV?
   c. What's the probability that the charity gets to sell the TV because no one wins?
   d. Suppose you get to pick your spot in line. Where would you want to be in order to maximize your chances of winning?
   e. After hearing some protest about the plan, the organizers decide to award the prize by not returning the white balls to the box, thus ensuring that 1 of the 100 people will draw the red ball and win the TV. Now what position in line would you choose in order to maximize your chances?

PART

V

# From the Data at Hand to the World at Large

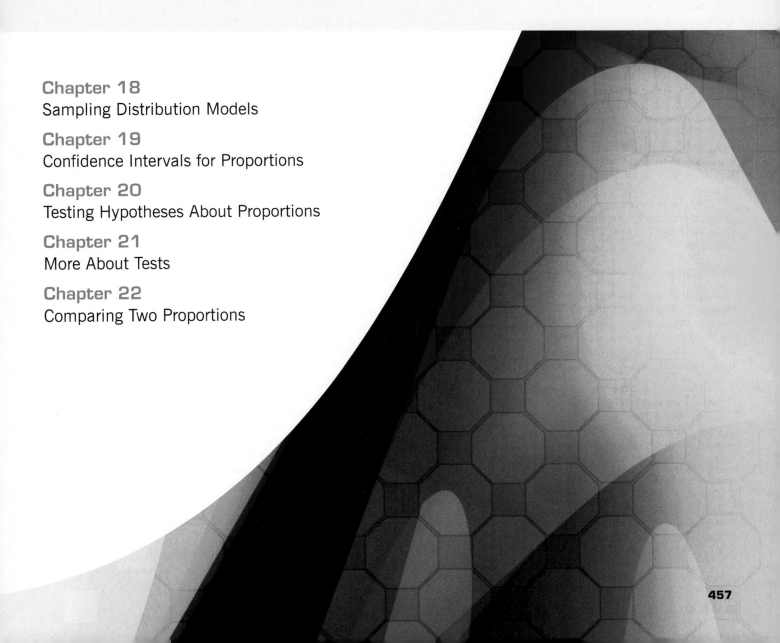

We've (finally!) come to statistical inference. If your students have been thinking about the questions raised in earlier parts of the book, they'll be ready to think about inference. Our approach has been carefully planned, so we ask that you read this section . . .

# Before You Start Teaching Inference . . .

## Making Inference Make Sense

Teaching statistical inference is a challenge.

That's certainly not news. Many students find the reasoning unfamiliar, the mix of populations and samples confusing, the formulas intimidating, and the requirement that they interpret the results clearly and correctly daunting.

And now that challenge is upon us.

In writing this textbook we spent a long time thinking about our own classroom experiences, the kinds of difficulties we have seen our students face, and the sources of their confusion. We concluded that the primary source of trouble was that too many important issues were dumped on students all at once. People learn best when they encounter one new issue at a time and can tie new ideas into frameworks of concepts and skills they already understand. So our goal, as we sought a way to present inference clearly, logically, and understandably, became just that: *one new idea at a time*.

That goal forced us to think about the key concepts and skills, about how to prepare students to deal with it all, and especially about the best order in which to travel through the landscape of inference.

## The Pieces Are in Place

Though we begin our formal treatment of inference now, our strategy is already well under way. We have been foreshadowing this moment throughout the textbook. From the beginning we have tried to promote the kind of statistical thinking that students will need now, and we have already put in place, at least informally, many of the key components.

▶ *Communication.* Students know that doing Statistics is much more than just finding numerical answers. In following the *Think–Show–Tell* approach, students have come to understand that both choosing the right methods and stating well-justified conclusions are at the heart of Statistics.

▶ *Models.* Students recognize the difference between results observed in samples or experiments and theoretical models that may provide useful ways of seeking underlying truths. Inference is, after all, about models. A hypothesis proposes a model, and the test asks whether observed results are consistent with that model. A confidence interval offers a range of plausible values for a model's parameter.

▶ *Assumptions and Conditions.* Students already know that before they can use a statistical method they need to check the conditions necessary to be sure that the underlying mathematical assumptions are met.

▶ *Statistical Significance.* Students already understand that sampling error is always present and, hence, that they need a way to distinguish such random variability from results that are truly unusual. They have confronted this issue while working with simulations, probability, and, most recently, sampling models.

## A Logical Route Through the Inference Jungle

With this informal yet solid groundwork in place, what now remains is our more formal tour of statistical inference. We're sure you have noticed by now that this is not just another statistics text, so it won't surprise you that our approach may not be the way you have taught inference before. We honed this approach for several years in our own classrooms, with great success, and now instructors who adopted the first edition have reported similar successes in their enthusiastic reviews. Starting with proportions may seem odd to you if you've always taught inference with means first, but we encourage you to adopt our approach.

Our chapters are carefully designed to lead students through the inference jungle one easy step at a time. Here's a brief tour:

**Chapter 18:** Sampling Distribution Models
**One New Idea:** Sampling distribution models

Our emphasis on models has laid important groundwork. These are sampling distribution *models*—useful idealized descriptions. Because our emphasis is on the concept of a sampling distribution model rather than on details (after all, we'll see a number of sampling distribution models before the end of the course), we illustrate the concept with both proportions and means. The principal result is the Central Limit Theorem, which we dub the *Fundamental Theorem of Statistics*.

**Chapter 19:** Confidence Intervals for Proportions
**One New Idea:** Confidence intervals

Students know about political polls. They have heard on TV or read in the newspaper that a poll predicts so-and-so would get 42% of the vote, with a margin of error of ±3%. We use

Chapter 18's look at sampling models for a proportion together with the 68–95–99.7 Rule, to produce an interval that we think probably (with 95% confidence) contains the parameter. We formalize the process with assumptions and conditions, with other critical values of $z$, and with careful attention to what students should say (and should not say) about confidence intervals.

**Chapter 20:**   Testing Hypotheses About Proportions
**One New Idea:**   Hypothesis tests

Students already have an informal understanding of the idea of statistical significance. Now we examine the formal process for deciding whether a result seems to be unusual or is reasonably attributable to sampling error. We teach students to write hypotheses, to check assumptions and conditions in deciding what test to perform, to complete the mechanics of finding a P-value, and then to use that P-value in making a decision about the viability of the original hypothesis. Since the assumptions, conditions, and formulas are essentially the same as those they just used in creating confidence intervals, the only new issues here are the formal structure and language of hypothesis testing.

**Chapter 21:**   More About Tests
**One New Idea:**   What can go wrong?

We explore more thoroughly many issues surrounding hypothesis testing. We help students better understand what a P-value is. We look at Type I and Type II errors, and the concept of power. In doing more hypothesis tests, students solidify their understanding of the basic concepts and procedures of Chapter 20 while developing an understanding of the interconnections among power and the two kinds of errors.

**Chapter 22:**   Comparing Two Proportions
**One New Idea:**   Inference when there are two groups

By now students understand confidence intervals and hypothesis tests for a single proportion. We ask them to compare proportions observed in two groups. Nothing else has changed. Confidence intervals still involve an estimate plus or minus a margin of error, now proposing a range of possible differences in the two proportions. A hypothesis supposes that groups do not differ, and then the P-value reveals how unlikely the observed results would be. The assumptions and conditions are basically the same as for one proportion. The calculations differ only in the need to estimate the standard deviation of the difference between two proportions. There's the new issue, easily resolved when students recall that for independent random quantities variances add.

**Chapter 23:**   Inferences About Means
**One New Idea:**   The $t$-models

With inference for proportions behind us, we turn to means. Students can already do it all—almost. They know how to check assumptions and conditions, create and interpret confidence intervals, write hypotheses, and reach conclusions based on P-values. There's just one problem: The sampling model for sample means is based on the Central Limit Theorem, which requires that we know the standard deviation of the population, *and we never do*. Gossett solved this problem with a family of models that account for the increased uncertainty introduced when we

(logically) use the sample's standard deviation instead. And that's the one new idea our students need: Gossett's (Student's) $t$.

**Chapter 24:**   Comparing Means
**One New Idea:**   Two independent groups

No, that's not really new. Students have already dealt with two independent groups when comparing proportions. Can they handle it for means? You bet. Variances add. Again.

**Chapter 25:**   Paired Samples and Blocks
**One New Idea:**   Matched pairs

If the two groups are matched in some way, the Independence Assumption central to Chapter 24 fails, so we cannot add the variances. Here students see that the 2-sample $t$ procedures are inappropriate, and learn paired $t$ procedures for testing hypotheses and creating confidence intervals. Since these are essentially the same one-sample $t$ methods they learned in Chapter 23, there is little new there. Students see that the "choice" of whether to use 2-sample $t$ or paired $t$ procedures is not a choice at all. They learn that they must think about the design of the study that produced the data to see whether the two groups are independent or matched. Design determines the correct approach to inference—the new idea here.

**Chapter 26:**   Comparing Counts
**One New Idea:**   Chi-square models and procedures

With the concepts of inference firmly established, we return to categorical data, looking at tests of goodness-of-fit, homogeneity, and independence. We need to see how to calculate a new test statistic and look at the associated models to generate P-values. The mechanics and the models for chi-square tests are the one new idea here.

**Chapter 27:**   Inferences for Regression
**One New Idea:**   The regression model

This is the culmination of our look at inference. Chapter 26 examined associations between two categorical variables. We now turn to associations between two quantitative variables. We begin with a look at the assumptions and conditions for the regression model that underlies the sampling model for slopes of regression lines—a $t$-model again. In the process, we review our understanding of linear models and how to interpret slopes.

## One More Pitch . . .

We know this is not (yet) the standard sequence of inference topics, but we are convinced that students benefit from this approach. In case we haven't fully convinced you yet, here are some of our reasons for not starting with inference for means based on the Normal model:

▸ How could you know $\sigma$ when you don't know $\mu$? Such assumptions are preposterous, and students recognize that. Suddenly the whole structure of inference you're trying to build rests on quicksand.

▸ Students get really confused later on when you try to convert them to use $t$ instead of $z$. Some never fully recover, finding themselves unsure of when to use $t$ and when $z$. For us, it's easy: $z$ is for proportions, $t$ is for means. Always. No confusion there.

▶ Don't waste valuable classroom time. Why teach the same thing twice—or, more accurately, why teach an unrealistic method, unteach it, and then teach it again the right way? No practicing statistician uses z-methods for inference about means. Only introductory Statistics students do that. Well, only those in other courses. . . .

We hope we've now convinced you to give our approach a try. We're confident that you will find your students moving through inference more smoothly, more quickly, and with better understanding.

## Instructor's Guide

**CHAPTER 18**

# Sampling Distribution Models

## What's It About?

We develop the concept of a sampling distribution. We see that for sample proportions, this sampling distribution can be approximated by a Normal model, and we examine the assumptions and conditions that support its use. We then turn our attention to means and the Central Limit Theorem.

## Comments

Our terminology is a bit different here, consistent with the distinction we have made between models and distributions. We think this helps students understand the very powerful but potentially confusing concepts in this chapter. The confusion arises from the fact that there are many "distributions" in play. When we look at proportions, we must think about the true proportion in the population ($p$) and the proportion we might actually see in any sample ($\hat{p}$). That proportion ($\hat{p}$) will vary from sample to sample. We draw (or imagine that we draw) many samples and see that the distribution of sample proportions centers around the true population value but shows some variability—so-called sampling error. You can do this in class by using bags of M&M's, for example, with each student reporting their proportion of blue M&M's. We note that the distribution of sample proportions appears to be roughly unimodal and symmetric, and see that under certain conditions a Normal model is useful. That Normal model is the sampling distribution model for sample proportions.

When we look at sample means, the plot thickens. First, we draw a sample from a distribution with some underlying shape—uniform, unimodal, bimodal, skewed, or whatever—but we may not know what the correct model for that is. We can make a histogram to examine the distribution of the data in this sample. We find the sample mean ($\bar{y}$), and wonder how it differs from the population mean ($\mu$). If we imagine drawing repeated samples, we could make a histogram showing the distribution of the various means. Again, surprisingly, this histogram appears to be roughly unimodal and symmetric. Again, under certain conditions a Normal model proves to be useful. That Normal model is the sampling distribution model for sample means. By calling it a "sampling model" we help students distinguish it from a model for the sample and the histogram of the sample.

## Looking Ahead

The rest of this book depends on the ideas in this chapter. If sampling models for proportions and means did not turn out to be easily describable (indeed, Normal) then statistical inference as we know it would not exist.

The sampling model for sample proportions leads us directly to inference for proportions, found in Chapters 19 through 22.

The sampling model for sample means supports (with minor adjustment) inference for means, coming in Chapters 23, 24, and 25.

The idea of a sampling model returns in Chapter 27, where we examine the variability in slopes of regression lines based on different samples drawn from the same population. That sampling model will allow us to do inference for regression.

## Class Do's

Help students understand the transition we are making here. We have talked about samples and created descriptive statistics like the sample proportion (for categorical variables) and the sample mean (for quantitative variables). We understand that such statistics vary from sample to sample and that each is an estimate of a population model parameter. We have discussed the notion of sampling error and understand that it is unavoidable. The truly remarkable thing is that sampling error is understandable and predictable. We hope it is small, but, remarkably enough, we *can* know how large it is likely to be. Armed with that knowledge, we can look at sample results and reach important decisions. We may decide that the results are within a reasonable margin of variation from what we expected. Or we may deem our results to be so unlikely that we don't believe they could simply be sampling error. Then we call the outcome "statistically significant." We are about to learn how to make that distinction.

This transition involves stepping back a level in our analysis. We used to focus on the data and derive a statistic from it. Now we focus on the statistic itself. The sample proportion (or mean) becomes our datum, and in our imaginations we compare it to all the other values we might have obtained from all the other samples we might have taken. (Or we might pretend that we're about to draw many more random samples or perform many more randomized trials, but we're just procrastinating and thinking about what's likely to happen when we finally get around to it—if ever.)

Remind students repeatedly that the population is whatever the population is—it remains constant. Only the samples vary. This key insight returns again and again in the chapters ahead.

Take time to construct sampling distributions in class to be sure students know what is happening here. The differences among the population, the sample distribution, a distribution of sample statistics from several samples, and the sampling model that describes such a distribution are potentially confusing, yet profound.

Help students to appreciate the stunning results in this chapter. It is not obvious that Normal models would prove to be so useful. This is one of the most startling and powerful insights in mathematics. We present the Central Limit Theorem as the Fundamental Theorem of Statistics. No one is surprised to think that larger samples look more like the population, or that the means of large samples probably vary less from the mean of the population. But who would guess that the variability among sample means would have a Normal model *even when the population does not*? WOW!

## The Importance of What You Don't Say

***Sampling Distribution of Sample Means (or Proportions).*** Students have a hard time discerning whether you are talking about the actual distribution of data in the sample or the theoretical variability in means from sample to sample. The distinction is critical, and made clearer by talking about "sample distributions" and "sampling models."

***Density.*** We still don't need this term. These are sampling models.

## Class Examples

1. As a classroom activity, have students toss thumbtacks to determine the probability a tack lands with the point up. Tacks work better than coins because students don't have a preconceived notion of what the results should be. Note that the probability depends on the type of tack: Tacks with big heads and a short point may behave much like coins, while small heads and a long point make it unlikely that the tack lands point up. Have students work in teams of two (tosser and counter). Since the tacks bounce easily off desks, have them do it right on the floor. Run at least three stages:

   - Each group tosses the tack five times and computes the sample proportion of the number of "ups." Quickly sketch a histogram (or dotplot) of the results. Describe the distribution. Note that this is a distribution of sample proportions—the proportions are now the data.

   - Each group tosses the tack 20 more times and recomputes the sample proportion (out of 25). Make a new histogram (on the same scale, of course.) Describe the new histogram, and compare it to the first one. Students should see that the centers look about the same. What does that center represent? They should also see that the variability is smaller. Why? Someone should recall the Law of Large Numbers.

   - Now toss an additional 25 (or better, 75) times. Find the sample proportions out of 50 (or 100) tosses. Do another histogram. Discuss center and spread again. And now the shape should also be getting clear. You should be able to go back to the Normal as approximation to the Binomial and derive the shape, center, and spread of the sampling model for sample proportions. Be sure to remind students of the assumptions and conditions that allow use of this model.

2. Draw some Normal models for sample proportions based on the 68–95–99.7 Rule. Always check the conditions first!

   - Of all cars on the interstate, 80% exceed the speed limit. What proportion of speeders might we see among the next 50 cars?

   - We don't know it, but 52% of voters plan to vote "Yes" on the upcoming school budget. We poll a random sample of 300 voters. What might the percentage of yes-voters appear to be in our poll?

3. Use the sampling model to calculate some probabilities.

   - "Groovy" M&M's are supposed to make up 30% of the candies sold. In a large bag of 250 M&M's, what is the probability that we get at least 25% groovy candies?

4. You can discover the Central Limit Theorem using *ActivStats* in class. The simulation uses the tools students have been working with for several chapters already. Alternatively, if you have time, draw random samples from some manageable population and create a sampling distribution of the sample means for various sample sizes. You can also find Web applets and downloadable programs that do this simulation in a variety of ways.

5. As you did with the sampling model for proportions, use the Central Limit Theorem together with the 68–95–99.7 Rule and Normal percentiles to see what samples drawn from various populations might look like.

   - SAT scores should have mean 500 and standard deviation 100. What about the mean of random samples of 20 students? (Note that the small sample is okay because we believe a Normal model applies to the population.)

   - Speeds of cars on a highway have mean 52 mph and standard deviation 6 mph, and are likely to be skewed to the right (a few very fast drivers). Describe what we might see in random samples of 50 cars.

   - At birth, babies average 7.8 pounds, with a standard deviation of 2.1 pounds. A random sample of 34 babies born to mothers living near a large factory that may be polluting the air and water shows a mean birth weight of only 7.2 pounds. Is that unusually low?

   - There are several other good examples in exercises in the text.

## RESOURCES

### ActivStats

▸ Chapter 18 contains activities regarding sampling distributions for proportions and means, and presents the Central Limit Theorem. It is a great idea to assign the simulations *before* covering this material in class. Students can discover the Central Limit Theorem for themselves experimentally, which makes it much easier to believe and to remember. These simulations also make excellent classroom demonstrations, if you have suitable computer projection technology.

### Web Links

▸ There are several Web sites and applets that explore the Central Limit Theorem. For the latest links, see the text's Web site at www.aw-bc.com/dvb.

*Printed Test Bank and Resource Guide*

The *Printed Test Bank and Resource Guide* starts off with a simulation-based Investigative Task. There are three chapter quizzes.

## Instructor's Guide

# Confidence Intervals for Proportions

### What's It About?

Chapter 19 uses the familiar setting of opinion polls to develop the concept of a confidence interval for a proportion, and then explore wider applications. We pay careful attention to helping students understand what a confidence interval means and how to interpret it correctly. We explore the interconnections among interval width, level of confidence, margin of error, and sample size, and see how to calculate the size of sample required to achieve a desired margin of error at a specified level of confidence.

### Comments

The order in which we present the various types of inference differs from that found in many other texts. We hope you'll follow the order of our textbook; we are confident you will discover many benefits in this approach. We explained our rationale and the pedagogical advantages offered by this path through inference in a special commentary at the beginning of this Part of the Instructor's Guide. Please have a look if you skipped that.

### Looking Ahead

We'll apply the concepts of the form and meaning of confidence intervals again to the difference in two proportions (Chapter 22), means (Chapter 23), the difference in means (Chapter 24), paired differences (Chapter 25), and regression slopes (Chapter 27).

### Class Do's

Build your first confidence intervals without a messy formula or a critical value for *z*. You can base the discussion on the sampling model for proportions from the last chapter and the 68–95–99.7 Rule. It seems quite natural to use the sample proportion as an estimate of the unknown *p* in creating the standard error, and by now students easily associate two standard deviations with 95%. After they grasp the general idea, you can deal with the finer points—like a critical value of 1.96 rather than 2.

Open the discussion with a current poll. For example, Gallup (www.galluppoll.com) has a new poll every day, and other polling organizations are almost as prolific. Look at the bottom of the poll report for information on the sample size and margin of error. (Most professional pollsters can be counted on to report these correctly.) Students have all seen these margins of error. Ask what they mean and where they came from. (*Caution:* If you try to reproduce the reported value, you will find that it is almost always computed for an estimated proportion of 0.5, not for each particular observed proportion.)

Concentrate on getting the interpretation right. While students usually get the general idea that they have an estimate plus or minus a margin of error, it's quite common that they will misunderstand some of the nuances of meaning.

▸ Students will think 95% is a probability. It's better to use the term confidence. Strictly speaking, the probability is *not* 95% that that parameter is in our interval. This is based on the misconception that our interval is special in some way, and sometimes the parameter is in there. Remind them that it's the parameter that's special. It's fixed. It's our target—it does not move. We shoot at the target by forming this interval—like throwing a horseshoe at a stake we can't see. Sometimes (usually), we catch the stake somewhere within the horseshoe. Sometimes we miss. The probability that we found the stake is 100% when the horseshoe spans it and 0% when it does not. We just don't know which. So, we prefer to say we have 95% confidence that we've captured the parameter. The 95% reflects our own uncertainty about the interval.

▸ Students will think that other sample results should fall in our interval. Different samples produce different intervals; 95% of those intervals contain the actual proportion we wish we knew. Maybe ours is one of those intervals. Or maybe it's one of the other 5% that miss the target. We don't know. We never will. The other horseshoes need not land near ours—they are aiming at the stake, not at our horseshoe.

▸ Some students will think they're 95% sure they know the sample proportion. Actually, we're 100% sure of *that*. $\hat{p}$'s not just in the interval, it is (by construction) smack-dab in the very center of the interval. Imagine that! Remind them that sample results are known, but populations are not. We're trying to catch a glimpse of the unknown, and that's what we'll write conclusions about. We care about the stake, not the horseshoe.

Spend time thinking about how our level of confidence is related to margin of error, interval width, and sample size. Let students ponder and discuss these connections based on common sense. Messing with the formulas won't be nearly as convincing.

▸ It's common sense that very precise statements are risky. That's why the weatherman predicts that we'll get between 4" and 8" of snow. A prediction of 5" to 6" would be more helpful perhaps, but it's far less reliable.

▸ It's common sense that the more slack you cut yourself, the more faith you can have that you're right. We're very sure that between 1% and 50% of all cars are red.

▸ It's common sense that estimates based on larger samples are usually better. And better means that you get higher precision in your estimate (a narrower interval), or higher confidence, or both.

It is, however, remarkable and fortunate that with sample sizes that are small enough to obtain we can usually make statements that are precise enough to be useful with sufficient confidence. There is no obvious reason why this should be so—and if it weren't, inference would be impractical.

When you do the calculations that determine the sample size necessary to achieve a desired level of accuracy and confidence, make two important points.

▸ These calculations are actually part of the process of designing a study. We just didn't know how to do it when we discussed design issues in Part III.

▸ We did say back then that the size of the sample needed depended on the level of accuracy desired, not on the size of the population. It was hard for some to imagine that then, but now we see that the calculation rests only on level of confidence and margin of error, not on the size of the population. The calculation finds the minimal sample size that will work.

## Class Examples

1. Your local newspaper polls a random sample of 330 voters, finding 144 who say they will vote "yes" on the upcoming school budget. Create a confidence interval for actual sentiment of all voters. Just use 2 SDs and concentrate on the conditions and the interpretation.

2. An experiment finds that 27% of 53 subjects report improvement after using a new medicine. Create a 95% confidence interval for the actual cure rate. Use $z = 1.96$. Why is this in-

terval so wide? Make it narrower—90% confidence. What are the advantages and disadvantages? What sample size would we need in a follow-up study if we want a margin of error of ±5% with 98% confidence?

3. What sample size does it take to estimate the outcome of an election with a margin of error of 3%? Note that we'll do what polling organizations usually do and choose the most cautious proportion, 50%.

4. Have students simulate (or perform) 50 tosses of a fair coin. Each student should calculate his or her own observed sample proportion and find a 90% confidence interval for the true proportion of heads. Ask how many had confidence intervals that missed the target—that is, confidence intervals that did not contain the expected value of 50%. Ask what those students did wrong. (Trick question.) Make sure that everyone understands that you don't have to do anything wrong to have a confidence interval that misses the truth. And since we never actually know the truth, we never know whether any confidence interval worked. We just know they usually do—and "usually" means 90% sure in this case.

5. Try the coin simulation again with 200 tosses. Note that the 90% success rate holds true, but the estimates are more precise.

6. You'll find plenty of other examples among the exercises.

## RESOURCES

### ActivStats

▸ Chapter 19—"Inference for Proportions." Simulations in this chapter give students hands-on experimental experience with confidence intervals. Here again, it is a good idea to let students discover how confidence intervals work for themselves before you tell them about it.

### Web Links

▸ There are several Web applets that explore confidence intervals. Unfortunately, many deal with confidence intervals for means, but they are still useful for demonstrating the key ideas that the population parameter is fixed while confidence intervals vary from sample to sample, capturing the population value most—but not all—of the time. You can find links at www.aw-bc.com/dvb.

▸ Polling firms publish current polls online. The Gallup poll (www.galluppoll.com) posts a daily poll. Pew Research (http://pewresearch.org/) has a different focus on society and culture. www.pollster.com gathers political polls and demonstrates how they differ from one another even when attempting to estimate the same quantity (such as the President's popularity).

### Printed Test Bank and Resource Guide

The *Printed Test Bank and Resource Guide* provides three chapter quizzes.

# Testing Hypotheses About Proportions

## What's It About?

Chapter 20 introduces the formal inference process for testing a hypothesis. As we look specifically at the one-proportion $z$-test, we emphasize the general strategy and logic of hypotheses tests by comparing the process to a jury trial. We lay out a four-step process—hypotheses, model, mechanics, and conclusion—and demonstrate its implementation with step-by-step examples. We discuss the meaning and proper interpretation of P-values and pay careful attention to writing conclusions.

## Comments

Students already know how to use Normal models, and they understand the sampling model for sample proportions that lies at the heart of the mechanics of finding the P-value. We have already introduced the idea of statistical significance. What's new here is the formal structure of a hypothesis test.

You may be familiar with traditional hypothesis testing procedures that make decisions based on prespecified alpha values or critical values of $z$. We have opted for the more modern P-value approach. We think P-values encourage students to think more and, as a result, they understand the reasoning better. We explain that reasoning in the text, and amplify it below.

## Looking Ahead

We stick to the basics in this chapter, then devote all of Chapter 21 to the nuances and the What Can Go Wrong? issues.

The four-step process we introduce here will be the template for all the tests of hypotheses we'll encounter for proportions (Chapter 22), means (Chapters 23, 24, and 25), distributions (Chapter 26), and association (Chapters 26 and 27). Once they are comfortable with this template, students can adapt more easily to each of the tests as they encounter them.

## Class Do's

Each of the four steps of our hypothesis-testing rubric has several requirements. When students organize their hypothesis tests according to these steps, they will be less likely to omit some key component in their answers.

1. *Hypotheses*
   - Write the null hypothesis. A hypothesis is a claim about an unknown population model parameter, so be sure that students use the proper statistical notation: for example, $p = 0.50$—not $\hat{p}$. Students may also write the null hypothesis *in words*; here again it is important to talk about the model, not the observed results: "The proportion of all voters who favor the amendment is 50%." Also, make it clear that the null hypothesis specifies a value for the parameter.

- Write the alternative hypothesis. At this stage we must decide whether we are doing a two-tailed or a one-tailed test, and if one-tailed whether we are interested in the upper tail or lower tail. We base this decision on what we are initially interested in learning about the situation (the *Why* of the study), not on what we think the observed results might show. If we care about whether the percentage of teen smokers may have *changed* in the past 10 years, then we are equally interested in spotting an increase or a decrease and we do a two-tailed test. If we wonder whether a costly anti-smoking ad campaign has had an impact, then we only want to know if the percentage has gone down. That calls for a one-tailed lower tail test. Note that in either case the null hypothesis is that nothing has changed; that is, the percentage of teen smokers is the same as before.

- Remind students that the null hypothesis proposes a *model* for the population. As with all models, we know this one is wrong—the parameter probably does not *exactly* equal the hypothesized value. Unlike previous models, now we ask if it's wrong enough to reject. A null hypothesis is "null" because it is skeptical about the world. It generally asserts that nothing interesting or unusual is happening, not that the parameter value is necessarily 0 (or, for proportions, 50%).

2. *Model*
   - Decide what inference procedure is called for. Right now this is easy—we're just looking at one-proportion $z$-tests. But as our repertoire of inference procedures expands, this will become a key issue. Means or proportions? One group or two? Independent or matched? We'll work hard later on helping students make this decision.

   - List the assumptions and check the conditions. We can never invoke any statistical procedure without being sure it properly fits the circumstances, and inference methods are based on sampling distribution models that assume specific things about the population. Some assumptions are checked by just thinking about the way the data were collected. (If randomization was correctly applied, then the individual responses should be independent.) Some come with associated conditions that we can check with the data. This is one of the most frequently overlooked steps in student responses on exams. Note also that it is not enough to merely state the condition $np \geq 10$. Students should be expected to show that they have actually *checked* that the condition is satisfied: $np = 120(0.2) = 24 \geq 10$.

- Name the test. Indicate that because the conditions are satisfied it is okay to use a Normal model, and that we'll perform (for now) a *one-proportion z-test*. Each of the inference methods in the book comes with a clear name. Encourage students to learn and use them. These names are not universal throughout Statistics, but they are clear and unambiguous.

3. *Mechanics*

- Write down the statistics, emphasizing use of proper notation. Here, those are the sample size, the observed number of successes, and the sample proportion. Later on, the statistics may involve more than one group, means and standard deviations, distributions, tables, slopes, and so on. Often they come from technology—for example, from a summary table displayed by a statistics package.

- Draw a curve depicting the sampling model. Mark the hypothesized parameter and the observed statistic, and shade the appropriate tail (or tails) to show the region corresponding to the P-value. We mean this seriously. Even professional statisticians make this sketch.

- Calculate the value of the test statistic—here $z$, later on $t$, $\chi^2$, or (in the DVD chapters) $F$. Show the formula, substitute all the proper values, and give the final result. Although technology will do this and it's fine to copy the results without actually doing the calculations, it's a good idea for students to show the formula and values that produce that result. (If nothing else, it lets you award partial credit—a reason students can readily accept.)

- Find the P-value. Most often we'll just copy the result from a statistics package or calculator. When we must, we can use tables, a calculator's density functions, or a statistics package's calculations functions.

4. *Conclusion*

- Link the P-value to the decision. We need to be clear how the calculated P-value led to our decision. These statements may take many forms, such as "Because the P-value is so low . . .", "Since P > 0.05, . . .", or "This P-value of ?? means that the observed results are unlikely to be just sampling error, so . . ."

- State the decision about the null hypothesis—either we reject it or we fail to reject it.

- Interpret that decision in the proper context. The final conclusion we write must clearly explain what we have learned about the original question under investigation. A complete conclusion might look like one of these:

  "Because P = 0.003 is very low, I reject the null hypothesis. There is strong evidence that more than 50% of all voters favor the amendment."

  "The high P-value indicated that these results could be reasonably explained by sampling error, so I fail to reject the null hypothesis. We do not have evidence of a change in the percentage of teens who smoke."

Students need practice writing hypotheses. Remind them that "null" means "nothing." In other words, the null hypothesis is that nothing interesting is happening, nothing has changed, or there's nothing unusual about the results. In practice, that usually means that we posit the defendant is innocent, the medicine does not work, the water is not polluted, and the rivets can't withstand the necessary stress. The alternative hypothesis represents the change or difference that we are interested in or concerned about. It is the position we will have to take if the results are so unlikely (were the null hypothesis true) as to make the null hypothesis untenable.

Keep emphasizing that hypotheses are about parameters, not statistics. We'll never see a $\hat{p}$ (or a $\bar{y}$) in a hypothesis. We *know* those values—we calculated them from the data we collected. There's no need to hypothesize about them. Hypotheses are about the unknown (unknowable). That is, they are about models. The null hypothesis proposes a parameter for a model—$p$ (or, later, $\mu$ or $\beta_1$). The test checks to see if the results we observed cast doubt on the viability of that model. Those results can never confirm that the model is correct, but they can convince us (beyond a reasonable doubt) that it is wrong.

Be sure students understand the P-value. It is *not* the probability that the null hypothesis is true. It is not even the probability that the null hypothesis is true given that these results were observed. In fact, it's the other way around. Either the hypothesis is true or it's not; we just don't happen to know which. We *assume* that the null hypothesis is true—that the model behaves as we think it does. We realize that we'll never collect data in perfect agreement with our model. We know that observed results will vary, and have called that variability sampling error. By now we understand how much variability we should reasonably expect. We look at the statistics from the observed data and assess whether they are consistent with the sampling model or so bizarre that it is not reasonable to continue to believe in the model. We ask how likely we'd be to see results like these if our model were correct. That's the P-value: the conditional probability of observing results at least as extreme as ours if the null hypothesis were true. A very low P-value means our results are very unusual, and we then reject the null model.

How low a P-value do we need? That's a personal decision, based on the situation, the belief in the null hypothesis, and the costs of being wrong. Traditionally, statisticians have adopted "alphas," or "levels of significance," of 5%, or maybe 10%, 1%, or 0.1%. These are good rules of thumb, but remember that they are general guidelines, not ironclad laws. The modern P-value approach asks a statistician (a.k.a. student) to look at the P-value, think about what it says about the situation under consideration, and then make a decision. If we are checking on a sociological phenomenon of interest—say, a change in teen smoking—and we find a P-value of 0.08, we might very well say that we have found some evidence of a change. If we are testing the strength of the rivets that hold sheet metal panels in place on the wings of the airplane we're about to board, most of us would want a very strong evidence that those rivets surpass safety specifications, and thus an extremely small P-value. There's nothing magical about 0.05.

Landy Godbold, a contributor on the AP Stats listserve, nicely summarizes these issues in statistical inference by posing three questions when looking at data:

1. Am I surprised? (Should I reject the null hypothesis?)
2. How surprised am I? (What's the P-value?)
3. What would not surprise me? (Write a confidence interval for the parameter.)

Landy's last question is important. A hypothesis poses a single value for a parameter. We can be almost 100% sure that value is incorrect (though perhaps only slightly). A confidence interval proposes a range of plausible values for that parameter, and should almost always accompany a hypothesis test.

## The Importance of What You Don't Say

*"Accept" the Null Hypothesis.*   We can *never* accept the null hypothesis. For one thing, it's probably never true precisely. Is the probability that a coin lands heads exactly 50%? Isn't it possible that the slight bulge of Washington's head makes the bounce of a quarter ever so slightly biased, and that the probability of heads might therefore be 49.997%? We cannot accept the null hypothesis just because we don't find compelling evidence against it. The best we can do is to not reject the hypothesis. This is exactly what happens when a jury fails to convict. Their verdict is "not guilty." In other words, the jury says that they did not see evidence of guilt "beyond a reasonable doubt." Some jurors may still suspect that the defendant is indeed guilty. The jury does not proclaim that the defendant has been proven innocent. We never *"prove"* the null hypothesis—or even the alternative for that matter.

*Type I Error, Type II Error, Beta, Power, etc.*   Not yet. These are important concepts, and we'll deal with them in the next chapter. Right now it's sufficient to concentrate on the fundamentals of hypothesis tests.

*Standard Error.*   This is a subtle, but important point. In this book we reserve the term *standard error* for sample-based estimates of the standard deviation of the sampling distribution model. Some books have used the term more generally for that standard deviation, whether estimated or specified. Proportions have the special property that the value of the proportion determines the value of the standard deviation of its sampling distribution model. A null hypothesis that specifies a population model proportion value has automatically also specified its standard deviation. That then is not a standard error in our terminology, and we'll write $SD(\hat{p})$ rather than $SE(\hat{p})$. Keeping the terminology separate helps students remember this difference.

## Class Examples

1. Propose an example of a hypothesis to test, and build your discussion of the four-step format around it. Here's a possibility:

    A 1996 report from the U.S. Consumer Product Safety Commission claimed that at least 90% of all American homes have at least one smoke detector. A city's fire department has been running a public safety campaign about smoke detectors consisting of posters, billboards, and ads on radio and TV and in the newspaper. The city

wonders if this concerted effort has raised the local level above the 90% national rate. Building inspectors visit 400 randomly selected homes and find that 376 have smoke detectors. Is this strong evidence that the local rate is higher than the national rate?

*Hypotheses.*   The null hypothesis is that this city is no different than anywhere else. The alternative is that the public safety campaign has had a positive effect, so the rate of compliance is higher. The hypotheses deal with the actual percentage of all homes that have smoke detectors in that city.

$$H_0: p = 0.90, H_A: p > 0.90$$

*Model.*   We have a simple random sample of 400 homes, and assume that's less than 10% of all homes in this city, making them essentially independent. We expect $np = 400(0.9) = 360$ successes and $nq = 40$ failures, so the sample is large enough to use a Normal model. We'll do a one-proportion z-test.

*Mechanics.*   $n = 400, x = 376, \hat{p} = 0.94$

$$z = \frac{0.94 - 0.90}{\sqrt{\dfrac{(0.9)(0.1)}{400}}} = 2.67$$

$$P = P(z > 2.67) = 0.004$$

*Conclusion.*   The P-value is very low, making it unlikely that the observed results can be explained by sampling error. We reject the null hypothesis. There is strong evidence that in this city more than 90% of homes have smoke detectors.

*Further Comments.*   Interpret the P-value carefully. If in fact the rate in this city is 90%—the same as anywhere else—then only 0.4% of samples (about 1 in every 250) would find (as ours did) a proportion of 94% or more. While that could be what happened here, it's not the most logical explanation. In fact, we are 95% confident that between 91.7% and 96.3% of the city's homes have smoke detectors.

2. Do a second example where we don't reject the null. There are supposed to be 20% orange M&M's. Suppose a bag of 122 has only 21 orange ones. Does this contradict the company's 20% claim? Note that this is a two-tailed test. Even though the observed result looks as though there were not enough orange ones, *before we had the sample* we'd have been equally interested to discover that there were too many. Now the P-value is $2 \times P(z < -0.77) = 0.44$. That means that even if the company is correct about the 20% orange claim, 44% of all bags this size will differ from perfection by at least as much as this one did. It does

not seem that this result is unusual, so we fail to reject the null hypothesis. We don't have convincing evidence that the 20% figure is wrong. (On the other hand, we certainly didn't prove it was right, so we cannot *accept* the null hypothesis.)

3. It's instructive to try the M&M's example again, this time assuming that the rate is 22%. You won't reject that hypothesis either. Or 15%. Try having different groups of students test hypotheses ranging from 5% to 30%. Some will be rejected, others not. Some models are clearly inconsistent with the facts, but many remain plausible. What would not surprise me? The 95% confidence interval says that *p* could probably be anywhere from about 11% to 23%. That's still more justification for not "accepting" any particular null hypothesis; we just can't reject some.

4. You'll get plenty of opportunity to discuss all the issues as you go over the many questions on the homework exercises. If you still need more in-class examples, there are always unassigned exercises in the text or on the *ActivStats* disk.

## RESOURCES

### *ActivStats*

▸ Chapter 20—"Testing Hypotheses." A simulation exercise in this chapter asks students to test whether the proportion of a striped bar that is red is 50%. Students gather data and draw their own conclusions. In the process, they develop the reasoning of hypothesis testing for themselves. Let them do this before you present it in class, and you'll find they have a much deeper appreciation for the reasoning. Remind them to record the number of trials they needed before they rejected the null and the true proportion (which they will be told). With these, they can compute their own personal critical value. How unlikely did the data have to be before they threw in the towel and rejected the null?

### *Printed Test Bank and Resource Guide*

The *Printed Test Bank and Resource Guide* offers three chapter quizzes.

# Instructor's Guide

**CHAPTER 21**

# More About Tests

## What's It About?

Chapter 20 introduced hypothesis tests. Following our habit of exploring important concepts in greater depth (as we did in Chapters 4 and 5, and again in 8 and 9), Chapter 21 examines several important aspects of statistical inference in more detail. We look again at P-values, introduce alpha levels, and discuss the relationship between them. We discuss the important distinction between statistical significance and practical significance. We clarify the connection between confidence intervals and hypothesis tests. We talk about Type I and Type II errors, and examine the interconnections among these errors, alpha levels, and the power of a test.

## Comments

We don't spend any time here actually *calculating* power or the probability of making a Type II error. Such calculations can be difficult and confusing, and are of limited usefulness to students in an introductory course. At best the calculations are distracting. We think it's less important for students to worry about how to find the power of a test than to understand what power *is*. We want them to know what kinds of errors they should be concerned about and the impact of each. We want them to know how their choice of alpha level may offer greater protection against one error while increasing the risk of the other, and how both relate to sample size and power.

Although we do talk about alpha levels in more detail here, we want these to continue to provide general guidelines rather than firm decision rules. We'll stick to the P-value approach to decision making.

## Looking Ahead

We'll continue to use confidence intervals in conjunction with hypothesis tests as we look at inference for the difference in proportions (Chapter 22) and inference about means (Chapters 23, 24, and 25). And throughout all the chapters on inference we'll ask students to think about power and the two kinds of errors.

## Class Do's

Because this chapter expands on the central issue of hypothesis testing, you can discuss the major ideas by building on the same examples you used before. Start with careful discussion of how we formulate null and alternative hypotheses. Emphasize the meaning of P-values, and refer to alpha levels as you help students make decisions.

Several times in this course we have encountered words that don't quite mean the same thing in Statistics as they do in everyday usage. Here's another: "significant." When we say that a result is statistically significant we mean that it's unusual—so unusual that we have to reassess our underlying assumptions. That may or may not make the result important, and usually that's what we mean when we call some news event significant. With enough data, we might be able to detect even a minute change in the percentage of teenagers who smoke, but we might not think that change is of any practical importance.

Students learned to create confidence intervals in Chapter 19 and to test hypotheses in Chapter 20. These two kinds of statistical inference are not unrelated, and students should see two connections and an important distinction.

▸ *Use a confidence interval to expand your conclusion following a hypothesis test.* After saying that there's strong evidence that a lower percentage of current teenagers are smokers, it's nice to add that we're pretty sure that the rate is between 12% and 16%.

▸ *Instead of finding a P-value, use a confidence interval as the mechanics of the hypothesis test.* Based on the observed data create a confidence interval with confidence level $(100 - \alpha)$%. That interval represents the range of plausible values for the parameter. If the hypothesized value is included, we cannot reject it. If the hypothesized value of the parameter is not in the interval, then the observed results cast doubt on the model, and we must reject it.

▸ *Be clear about standard errors and standard deviations.* The relationship between confidence intervals and hypothesis tests discussed above is not perfect for proportions. We estimate a standard error to find a confidence interval, but—because we pretend to believe the null hypothesis in order to find a P-value—we use the standard deviation of the sampling distribution model based on the null value for the proportion. That value will usually differ a little from the observed value, and will generally differ more for null hypothesis values farther from the observed value (and thus with smaller associated P-values).

Define Type I and Type II errors and power, then, using examples from familiar homework exercises, ask students to explain them in the proper context. Develop clear understanding of these basic ideas before trying to explore the relationships among them.

The "For Example" examples in the chapter follow a debate from the news about the safety of a widely used drug. These illustrations of how the terms and concepts of this chapter give a deeper understanding of current real-world issues can help to bring home the importance of what might otherwise seem esoteric ideas.

It may be worthwhile to pause for a notation discussion. Students may be feeling "P'd" on. They need to keep the following concepts straight: $p$, the population proportion; $\hat{p}$, the sample proportion; the P-value associated with the hypothesis test; and the use of P() to denote a probability.

## Class Examples

1. Almost any homework exercise or earlier example can serve as a setting for expanding the discussion on hypothesis testing. After showing the P-value approach, find a confidence interval and examine how you could have used that to make your decision. Be sure to point out how your (informal) choice of alpha is related to the level of confidence.

2. Similarly, you can use homework exercises or earlier examples as the setting for your discussion of errors and power. Students should be able to explain in context both what the errors are and the consequences of making them. Note that

usually Type I error is more serious, though there's no guarantee that will always be true. We get to control the risk of Type I error by the level of proof we demand ($\alpha$).

3. Use a very obvious example to start the power discussion. Imagine testing a new type of running shoe to see if it's worth the money. If the new shoe made you 5% faster (which may very well be *practically* important), how easy would it be to tell? It would take a lot of runs to make that difference clear. On the other hand, if the new shoe made you *twice as fast*, it should be clear from a very small sample size. Use that intuition to bolster the students' understanding of power. The interaction of *sample size* and *effect size* are the key elements of power.

4. There are lots of ways to create visual demos of the two overlapping curves that show both errors and power, from a blackboard and colored chalk to Internet applets. (Two overhead transparencies that you can slide around work well.) Most important, though, is having a context for the discussion. Use the running shoe example, or consider a test of a sensor that might be able to detect the presence of hidden explosives in one of four identical boxes. Pure guesswork would make the sensor correct about 25% of the time. Somewhere above that there is a level of experimental performance that would convince us that the sensor works, giving us a decision rule (say 20 out of 50). Even someone operating an ineffective sensor might get lucky and make correct identifications enough times to pass this test, in which case we'd start using a worthless device. Thinking we're safer when in fact we are not is the consequence of Type I error here.

Now suppose the sensor actually does work—that it can detect explosives some of the time (say 50%). It still might fail the test by not quite reaching the level of proof we demand. Overlooking the usefulness of the device would be a Type II error. The power of our test is its ability to spot the fact that the sensor does actually work. Note that the better the sensor is at spotting the explosives (imagine a true 80% success rate) the more likely we are to notice, so power increases with the size of the effect.

How can we avoid putting our faith in a bogus sensor (Type I error)? We demand a higher standard of proof—a smaller $\alpha$, in other words. But making the test harder to pass makes it more likely that even an effective sensor will fail to impress us—increasing Type II error and reducing the power of the test.

Want increased power? We could relax the standard of proof, but that increases the likelihood of Type I error. Increasing the number of trials can allow us to reduce the possibility of committing either error.

## RESOURCES

### ActivStats

▸ Chapter 21 offers several interactive demonstrations of these inference concepts.

### Printed Test Bank and Resource Guide

The *Printed Test Bank and Resource Guide* provides an Investigative Task and three chapter quizzes.

## What's It About?

Armed with a basic understanding of confidence intervals and hypothesis tests, we turn here to the specific case of inference for the difference between two proportions. The approach, logic, and interpretations are the same. Only the standard deviation changes, and it's not hard to find once students learn (or recall) that for the difference of independent random variables, variances add. That allows us to create a confidence interval for the difference of two proportions. Add one more idea—pooling samples to better estimate the population proportion—and we can test a hypothesis about the two proportions.

## Comments

This is the chapter where you should begin to see the benefits of the approach we have taken to inference. All the pieces are in place. We've been working with proportions for three chapters now. Students can create and interpret a confidence interval. They understand the reasoning involved in testing hypotheses, and can do the mechanics and write their conclusions. It's quite logical to turn from looking at one proportion to comparing two proportions. Toss in adding variances to describe the variability in the difference between independent random variables, and these pieces go together easily. Students see they can handle inference for two proportions quite well. You'll find this chapter is as much about reviewing and solidifying what students already know about inference as it is about learning two-sample procedures.

## Looking Ahead

In the next chapter we move on to look at inference for means. Fundamental understandings about confidence intervals and hypothesis tests carry us through Chapter 23, and the two-sample issue resurfaces in Chapter 24.

## Class Do's

Using proper notation, always important, becomes even more vital now that there are two groups. Insist that students clearly identify what their notation means. They need to use subscripts to distinguish between the two groups. If they choose something obvious, like "M" and "F" for male and female, then the meanings of $n_F$, $x_M$, $\hat{p}_M$, and $p_F$ are reasonably clear. If students choose the more generic numerical subscripts, then they need to identify which group is "1" and which is "2". Don't accept answers written only in generic notation (as if copied from the formulas in the book). Insist that the groups be clearly identified and that conclusions drawn in the Tell step correctly identify the groups in context.

Start right in with a hypothesis-testing example. Use one in which the difference in proportions is statistically significant, such as the stop smoking experiment described in our Class Examples. You don't even need to suggest that you are now going to do something new and different—because it really isn't. Let students formulate hypotheses and check conditions. Even though there are now two groups, they'll mostly know what to do. Throughout the entire discussion, point out to them that it's really all the same stuff, proving that once they understand the concepts and process of inference, they can handle new situations with just a bit of careful thought.

▸ **Hypotheses.** Point out that we wonder if the true proportions are the same in the two populations from which our samples are drawn. As always, a null hypothesis means nothing unusual is afoot—in other words, the two proportions are really the same and any difference that showed up in the samples can be explained by sampling error. Students will probably propose that you make the null hypothesis about equal proportions ($p_1 = p_2$). There's nothing wrong with that, and you should write it down. But also point out and write down the alternative way of saying "no difference": $p_1 - p_2 = 0$. The fact that we are talking about the difference of two proportions will be important when we need to find the standard deviation of the sampling model for $\hat{p}_1 - \hat{p}_2$.

▸ **Model.** Let the students list the conditions—they know them. They need to check the usual conditions for inference about proportions *for both groups*: randomness, less than 10% of the respective populations, and enough successes and failures. There's another condition, but don't write that yet. When the need to add variances arises, we'll see that the two groups must be independent. You can return to the conditions and add that assumption to the list. At that point, students will understand why it's important.

▸ **Mechanics, part I.** Let the students proceed as they usually would: writing down the observed statistics, drawing the Normal curve, shading the region representing the P-value, and starting to find $z$. The numerator is easy: the observed difference in sample proportions minus the hypothesized difference of 0. The denominator presents the first place they'll hesitate. The problem is in knowing what standard deviation to use. (As an aside, you can point out that standard deviations are always the problem. Once we know how to find the appropriate standard deviation, inference is usually pretty straightforward.) Let them stumble around a few minutes right here. If you covered Chapter 16, one of your students is likely to remember the "variances add" mantra. If not, a brief discussion will suffice (see our commentary on Chapter 16 for suggestions.) Then you can derive (or show) the formula you need in the denominator and add the independence requirement to the list of conditions.

▶ *Mechanics, part II.* The formula for standard deviation of the difference of two independent proportions requires that we know both population proportions, $p_1$ and $p_2$. We don't. In the earlier one-proportion case, we had a hypothesized value to use, but not now. Students will suggest that we simply find a standard error by substituting our best sample-based estimates, $p_1$ and $p_2$. Great idea—this shows they have caught on to our basic tactics. But we can make a slight conceptual improvement here. The null hypothesis is that there is *no difference* in the two population proportions. In other words, we are currently operating under the assumption that $p_1 = p_2$. This means that there is one common population proportion (call it $p$), and *that* is the value we should be substituting for both $p_1$ and $p_2$. (It makes some sense to use two *different* estimates for the same value, and substitute different numbers into the formula where we have hypothesized the values are the same, but it would be better to use one common value.) We don't know this magical value of $p$. We need to come up with the best possible estimate. Chances are someone will suggest using the total number of successes and total number of trials in both samples lumped together. That's called "pooling" and is the right approach when we are testing the hypothesis that two proportions are the same.

▶ *Conclusion.* Students can do this. They know what the P-value means and how to link it to their decision. They will be able to write a good conclusion in the proper context.

▶ *And now the confidence interval . . .* We just decided that the difference was significant. So how big might it be? We need a confidence interval. Students can do this. They have already checked the conditions. The interval is (as always) an estimate plus or minus a margin of error. Here, that's the observed difference in proportions plus or minus 1.96 times the standard error of the difference. We already have the formula for that standard error, but now we no longer believe the two proportions are the same. Now there's no justification for pooling. Because we believe proportions $p_1$ and $p_2$ could be different, we should use the two different estimates $p_1$ and $p_2$ to find the standard error. They'll need to think carefully to write a clear statement that correctly interprets that confidence interval.

Continue to clarify the pooling issue. A short explanation should make sense. When finding a confidence interval for the difference there is an implied assumption that the two proportions could well be different. So use different estimates—don't pool. When testing the hypothesis that the two proportions are equal, we pretend they are, so we use the same value—the pooled estimate—for each. This latter point should be seen for what it is—a technical improvement. The difference between the two SDs isn't great, but when we assume from the null hypothesis that the two proportions are equal, we should use that information.

## Class Examples

1. Would being part of a support group that meets regularly help people who are wearing the nicotine patch actually quit smoking? A county health department tries an experi-

ment using several hundred volunteers who were planning to use the patch to help them quit smoking. The subjects were randomly divided into two groups. People in Group 1 were given the patch and attended a weekly discussion meeting with counselors and others trying to quit. People in Group 2 also used the patch but did not participate in the counseling groups. After six months 46 of the 143 smokers in Group 1 and 30 of 151 smokers in Group 2 had successfully stopped smoking. Do these results suggest that such support groups could be an effective way to help people stop smoking?

**Hypotheses.** $H_0: p_1 - p_2 = 0, H_A: p_1 - p_2 > 0$

**Model.** Smokers were randomly assigned to the groups; Group 1 had 46 successes and 97 failures, and Group 2 had 30 and 121—all greater than 10. It's reasonable to assume the two groups were independent. It's okay to use a Normal model for the difference in two proportions.

**Mechanics.** $n_1 = 143 \quad y_1 = 46 \quad \hat{p}_1 = 0.322$
$$n_2 = 151 \quad y_2 = 30 \quad \hat{p}_2 = 0.199$$

$$\text{pooled } \hat{p} = \frac{46 + 30}{143 + 151} = 0.259$$

$$z = \frac{(0.322 - 0.199) - 0}{\sqrt{\dfrac{(0.259)(0.741)}{143} + \dfrac{(0.259)(0.741)}{151}}} = 2.41$$

$$P = P(z > 2.41) = 0.008$$

$$\hat{p}_1 - \hat{p}_2 = 0.123$$

**Conclusion.** The very low P-value indicates the observed difference is unlikely to be just sampling error, so we reject the null hypothesis. There is strong evidence that being part of a support group can help nicotine patch wearers stop smoking.

**Follow-up.** Now that we've concluded the support program is beneficial, can we convince the government to fund it? That might depend on *how* effective it is. We check a 95% confidence interval, knowing that the assumptions and conditions are okay.

$$(0.322 - 0.199) \pm 1.96\sqrt{\frac{(0.322)(0.678)}{143} + \frac{(0.199)(0.801)}{151}}$$
$$= (0.023, 0.223)$$

We're 95% confident that the support group program could raise the proportion of smokers who manage to quit by using the patch by between 2 and 22 percentage points. Will that get the legislators to vote for it? Some will probably look at the 2% end and oppose the program because they don't think it's cost effective. Others will look at the possibility of a 22% improvement and offer enthusiastic support. Have the students explain why there is so little precision in this confidence interval and what we might do to improve that.

2. In the December 2002 issue of *Consumer Reports*, Consumers Union reported on their investigation of the presence of bacteria in packages of chicken sold in supermarkets.

   • They purchased both name brand (*Perdue*) and store-brand chicken in 25 U.S. cities. Laboratory tests found campylobacter contamination in 33% of the 75 Perdue packages, and in 45% of the 75 store brand packages. Does this indicate that shoppers would be safer buying the name brand product?

   • They also found campylobacter in 56% of *Tyson* brand packages. Create a 90% confidence interval for the difference in contamination levels between *Tyson* and *Perdue* chicken.

## RESOURCES

### *ActivStats*

▸ Chapter 22—"Inference for Two Proportions."

### Web Links

▸ Many of the usual Web sites have data sets that involve two proportions.

▸ Almost any news report of a poll or medical research will contain information about opinions, risk factors, or treatment outcomes suitable for adaptation.

### *Printed Test Bank and Resource Guide*

The *Printed Test Bank and Resource Guide* has two chapter quizzes. This is the end of Part V, so the Test Bank provides three Part Tests on inference for proportions (Chapters 18–22).

# CHAPTER

# 18

# Sampling Distribution Models

## Where are we going?

A poll based on a random sample of U.S. adults reports that 29% of those asked admit that they don't always drive as safely as they should because they are on their cell phone. How much can we trust this statistic? After all, they didn't ask *everyone*. Maybe the true proportion is 33% or 25%? How reliable *are* proportions based on random samples? We'll see that we can be surprisingly precise about how much we expect proportions from random samples to vary. This will enable us to start generalizing from samples we have at hand to the population at large.

| WHO | U.S. adults |
|---|---|
| **WHAT** | Belief in ghosts |
| **WHEN** | November 2005 |
| **WHERE** | United States |
| **WHY** | Public attitudes |

In November 2005 the Harris Poll asked 889 U.S. adults, "Do you believe in ghosts?" 40% said they did. At almost the same time, CBS News polled 808 U.S. adults and asked the same question. 48% of their respondents professed a belief in ghosts. Why the difference? This seems like a simple enough question. Should we be surprised to find that we could get proportions this different from properly selected random samples drawn from the same population? You're probably used to seeing that observations vary, but how much variability among polls should we expect to see?

Why do sample proportions vary at all? How can surveys conducted at essentially the same time by organizations asking the same questions get different results? The answer is at the heart of Statistics. The proportions vary from sample to sample because the samples are composed of different people.

It's actually pretty easy to predict how much a proportion will vary under circumstances like this. Understanding the variability of our estimates will let us actually use that variability to better understand the world.

## The Central Limit Theorem for Sample Proportions

We've talked about *Think*, *Show*, and *Tell*. Now we have to add *Imagine*. In order to understand the CBS poll, we want to imagine the results from all the random samples of size 808 that CBS News didn't take. What would the histogram of all the sample proportions look like?

For people's belief in ghosts, where do you expect the center of that histogram to be? Of course, we don't *know* the answer to that (and probably never will). But we know that it will be at the true proportion in the population, and we can call that $p$. (See the Notation Alert.) For the sake of discussion here, let's suppose that 45% of all American adults believe in ghosts, so we'll use $p = 0.45$.

How about the *shape* of the histogram? We don't have to just imagine. We can simulate. We want to simulate a bunch of random samples that we didn't really draw. To do that, we'll simulate many independent random samples of size 808, keeping the same probability of success. We chose 0.45 for $p$ as a reasonable value. Here's a histogram of the proportions saying they believe in ghosts for 2000 independent samples of 808 adults when the true proportion is $p = 0.45$.

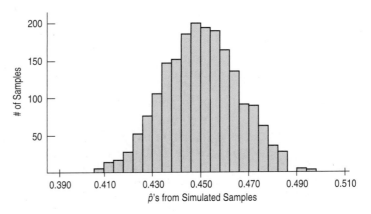

**FIGURE 18.1**

*A histogram of sample proportions for 2000 simulated samples of 808 adults drawn from a population with p = 0.45. The sample proportions vary, but their distribution is centered at the true proportion, p.*

It should be no surprise that we don't get the same proportion for each sample we draw, even though the underlying true value is the same for the population. Each $\hat{p}$ comes from a different simulated sample. The histogram above is a simulation of what we'd get if we could see *all the proportions from all possible samples.* That distribution has a special name. It is called the **sampling distribution** of the proportions.[1]

Does it surprise you that the histogram is unimodal? Symmetric? That it is centered at $p$? You probably don't find any of this shocking. Does the shape remind you of any model that we've discussed? It's an amazing and fortunate fact that a Normal model is just the right one for the histogram of sample proportions.

As we'll see in a few pages, this fact was proved in 1810 by the great French mathematician Pierre-Simon Laplace as part of a more general result. There is no reason you should guess that the Normal model would be the one we need here,[2]

---

[1] A word of caution. Until now we've been plotting the *distribution of the sample*, a display of the actual data that were collected in that one sample. But now we've plotted the *sampling distribution*; a display of summary statistics ($\hat{p}$'s, for example) for many different samples. "Sample distribution" and "sampling distribution" sound a lot alike, but they refer to very different things. (Sorry about that—we didn't make up the terms. It's just the way it is.) And the distinction is critical. Whenever you read or write something about one of these, think very carefully about what the words signify.

[2] Well, the fact that we spent most of Chapter 6 on the Normal model might have been a hint.

*Pierre-Simon Laplace, 1749–1827.*

and, indeed, the importance of Laplace's result was not immediately understood by his contemporaries. But (unlike Laplace's contemporaries in 1810) we know how useful the Normal model can be.

Modeling how sample proportions vary from sample to sample is one of the most powerful ideas we'll see in this course. A **sampling distribution model** for how a sample proportion varies from sample to sample allows us to quantify that variation and to talk about how likely it is that we'd observe a sample proportion in any particular interval.

To use a Normal model, we need to specify two parameters: its mean and standard deviation. The center of the histogram is naturally at $p$, so we'll put $\mu$, the mean of the Normal, at $p$.

What about the standard deviation? Usually the mean gives us no information about the standard deviation. Suppose we told you that a batch of bike helmets had a mean diameter of 26 centimeters and asked what the standard deviation was. If you said, "I have no idea," you'd be exactly right. There's no information about $\sigma$ from knowing the value of $\mu$.

But there's a special fact about proportions. With proportions we get something for free. Once we know the mean, $p$, we automatically also know the standard deviation for $\hat{p}$, the proportion of successes:

$$\sigma(\hat{p}) = SD(\hat{p}) = \sqrt{\frac{p(1-p)}{n}} = \sqrt{\frac{pq}{n}}.$$

When we draw simple random samples of $n$ individuals, the proportions we find will vary from sample to sample. As long as $n$ is reasonably large,[3] we can model the distribution of these sample proportions with a probability model that is

$$N\left(p, \sqrt{\frac{pq}{n}}\right).$$

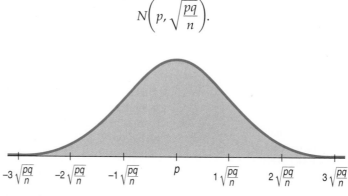

**FIGURE 18.2**

*A Normal model centered at p with a standard deviation of $\sqrt{\frac{pq}{n}}$ is a good model for a collection of proportions found for many random samples of size n from a population with success probability p.*

**A S**   *Simulation:* **Simulating Sampling Distributions.** Watch the Normal model appear from random proportions.

**NOTATION ALERT:**

In Chapter 8 we introduced $\hat{y}$ as the predicted value for $y$. The "hat" here plays a similar role. It indicates that $\hat{p}$—the observed proportion in our data—is our *estimate* of the parameter $p$.

Although we'll never know the true proportion of adults who believe in ghosts, we're supposing it to be 45%. Once we put the center at $p = 0.45$, the standard deviation for the CBS poll is

$$SD(\hat{p}) = \sqrt{\frac{pq}{n}} = \sqrt{\frac{(0.45)(0.55)}{808}} = 0.0175, \text{ or } 1.75\%.$$

---

[3] For smaller $n$, we can just use a Binomial model, which we saw in Chapter 17.

Here's a picture of the Normal model for our simulation histogram:

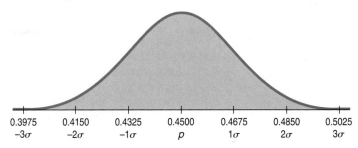

**FIGURE 18.3**

*Using 0.45 for p gives this Normal model for Figure 18.1's histogram of the sample proportions of adults believing in ghosts (n = 808).*

*A S*   **Simulation: The Standard Deviation of a Proportion.** Do you believe this formula for standard deviation? Don't just take our word for it—convince yourself with an experiment.

Because we have a Normal model, we can use the 68–95–99.7 Rule or look up other probabilities using a table or technology. For example, we know that 95% of Normally distributed values are within two standard deviations of the mean, so we should not be surprised if 95% of various polls gave results that were near 45% but varied above and below that by no more than two standard deviations. Since $2 \times 1.75\% = 3.5\%$,[4] we see that the CBS poll estimating belief in ghosts at 48% is *consistent* with our guess of 45%. This is what we mean by **sampling error.** It's not really an *error* at all, but just *variability* you'd expect to see from one sample to another. A better term would be **sampling variability.**

# How Good Is the Normal Model?

Stop and think for a minute about what we've just said. It's a remarkable claim. We've said that if we draw repeated random samples of the same size, $n$, from some population and measure the proportion, $\hat{p}$, we see in each sample, then the collection of these proportions will pile up around the underlying population proportion, $p$, and that a histogram of the sample proportions can be modeled well by a Normal model.

There must be a catch. Suppose the samples were of size 2, for example. Then the only possible proportion values would be 0, 0.5, and 1. There's no way the histogram could ever look like a Normal model with only three possible values for the variable.

Well, there *is* a catch. The claim is only approximately true. (But, that's OK. After all, models are only supposed to be approximately true.) And the model becomes a better and better representation of the distribution of the sample proportions as the sample size gets bigger.[5] Samples of size 1 or 2 just aren't going to work very well. But the distributions of proportions of many larger samples do have histograms that are remarkably close to a Normal model.

**FIGURE 18.4**

*Proportions from samples of size 2 can take on only three possible values. A Normal model does not work well.*

# Assumptions and Conditions

To use a model, we usually must make some assumptions. To use the sampling distribution model for sample proportions, we need two assumptions:

---

[4] The standard deviation is 1.75%. Remember that the standard deviation always has the same units as the data. Here our units are %. But that can be confusing, because the standard deviation is not 1.75% of anything. It is 1.75 percentage points. If that's confusing, try writing the units as "percentage points" instead of %.

[5] Formally, we say the claim is true in the limit as $n$ grows.

**The Independence Assumption:** The sampled values must be independent of each other.

**The Sample Size Assumption:** The sample size, $n$, must be large enough.

Of course, assumptions are hard—often impossible—to check. That's why we *assume* them. But, as we saw in Chapter 8, we should check to see whether the assumptions are reasonable. To think about the Independence Assumption, we often wonder whether there is any reason to think that the data values might affect each other. Fortunately, we can often check *conditions* that provide information about the assumptions. Check these conditions before using the Normal to model the distribution of sample proportions:

**Randomization Condition:** If your data come from an experiment, subjects should have been randomly assigned to treatments. If you have a survey, your sample should be a simple random sample of the population. If some other sampling design was used, be sure the sampling method was not biased and that the data are representative of the population.

**10% Condition:** The sample size, $n$, must be no larger than 10% of the population. For national polls, the total population is usually very large, so the sample is a small fraction of the population.

**Success/Failure Condition:** The sample size has to be big enough so that we expect at least 10 successes and at least 10 failures. When $np$ and $nq$ are at least 10, we have enough data for sound conclusions. For the CBS survey, a "success" might be believing in ghosts. With $p = 0.45$, we expect $808 \times 0.45 = 364$ successes and $808 \times 0.55 = 444$ failures. Both are at least 10, so we certainly expect enough successes and enough failures for the condition to be satisfied.

> The terms "success" and "failure" for the outcomes that have probability $p$ and $q$ are common in Statistics. But they are completely arbitrary labels. When we say that a disease occurs with probability $p$, we certainly don't mean that getting sick is a "success" in the ordinary sense of the word.

These last two conditions seem to conflict with each other. The **Success/Failure Condition** wants sufficient data. How much depends on $p$. If $p$ is near 0.5, we need a sample of only 20 or so. If $p$ is only 0.01, however, we'd need 1000. But the **10% Condition** says that a sample can be no larger than 10% of the population. If the sample were more than 10% of the population, we'd need to use different methods to analyze the data. Fortunately, this isn't usually a problem in practice. Often, as in polls that sample from all U.S. adults or industrial samples from a day's production, the populations are much larger than 10 times the sample size.

# A Sampling Distribution Model for a Proportion

We've simulated repeated samples and looked at a histogram of the sample proportions. We modeled that histogram with a Normal model. Why do we bother to model it? Because this model will give us insight into how much the sample proportion will vary from sample to sample. We've simulated many of the other random samples we might have gotten. The model is an attempt to show the distribution from *all* the random samples. But how do we know that a Normal model will really work? Is this just an observation based on some simulations that *might* be approximately true some of the time?

It turns out that this model can be justified theoretically and that the larger the sample size, the better the model works. That's the result Laplace proved. We won't bother you with the math because, in this instance, it really wouldn't help your understanding.[6] Nevertheless, the fact that we can think of proportions from random samples as random quantities and then say something this specific about their distribution is a fundamental insight—one that we will use in each of the next four chapters.

> **A S** *Simulation:* **Simulate the Sampling Distribution Model of a Proportion.** You probably don't want to work through the formal mathematical proof; a simulation is far more convincing!

---

[6] The proof is pretty technical. We're not sure it helps *our* understanding all that much either.

We have changed our point of view in a very important way. No longer is a proportion something we just compute for a set of data. We now see it as a random quantity that has a distribution, and thanks to Laplace we have a model for that distribution. We call that the **sampling distribution model** for the proportion, and we'll make good use of it.

Without the sampling distribution model, the rest of Statistics just wouldn't exist. Sampling models are what makes Statistics work. They inform us about the amount of variation we should expect when we sample. Suppose we spin a coin 100 times in order to decide whether it's fair or not. If we get 52 heads, we're probably not surprised. Although we'd expect 50 heads, 52 doesn't seem particularly unusual for a fair coin. But we would be surprised to see 90 heads; that might really make us doubt that the coin is fair. How about 64 heads? Harder to say. That's a case where we need the sampling distribution model. The sampling model quantifies the variability, telling us how surprising any sample proportion is. And it enables us to make informed decisions about how precise our estimate of the true proportion might be. That's exactly what we'll be doing for the rest of this book.

These sampling distributions are strange because even though we depend on them, we never actually get to see them. We could take repeated samples to develop the theory and our own intuition about sampling distribution models. But, in practice, we only imagine (or simulate) them. They're important because they act as a bridge from the real world of data to the imaginary model of the statistic and enable us to say something about the population when all we have is data from the real world. This is the huge leap of Statistics. Rather than thinking about the sample proportion as a fixed quantity calculated from our data, we now think of it as a random quantity—just one of many values we might have seen had we chosen a different random sample. By imagining what *might* happen if we were to draw many, many samples from the same population, we can learn a lot about how statistics computed from our one particular sample are related to the corresponding population parameters.

> We have now answered the question raised at the start of the chapter. To know how variable a sample proportion is, we need to know the proportion and the size of the sample. That's all.

---

### THE SAMPLING DISTRIBUTION MODEL FOR A PROPORTION

Provided that the sampled values are independent and the sample size is large enough, the sampling distribution of $\hat{p}$ is modeled by a Normal model with mean $\mu(\hat{p}) = p$ and standard deviation $SD(\hat{p}) = \sqrt{\dfrac{pq}{n}}$.

---

**FOR EXAMPLE**　　Using the sampling distribution model for proportions

The Centers for Disease Control and Prevention report that 22% of 18-year-old women in the United States have a body mass index (BMI)[7] of 25 or more—a value considered by the National Heart Lung and Blood Institute to be associated with increased health risk.

As part of a routine health check at a large college, the physical education department usually requires students to come in to be measured and weighed. This year, the department decided to try out a self-report system. It asked 200 randomly selected female students to report their heights and weights (from which their BMIs could be calculated). Only 31 of these students had BMIs greater than 25.

**Question:** Is this proportion of high-BMI students unusually small?

*(continued)*

---

[7] BMI = weight in kg/(height in m)$^2$.

For Example (*continued*)

First, check the conditions:

✔ **Randomization Condition:** The department drew a random sample, so the respondents should be independent and randomly selected from the population.

✔ **10% Condition:** 200 respondents is less than 10% of all the female students at a "large college."

✔ **Success/Failure Condition:** The department expected $np = 200(0.22) = 44$ "successes" and $nq = 200(0.78) = 156$ "failures," both at least 10.

It's okay to use a Normal model to describe the sampling distribution of the proportion of respondents with BMIs above 25.

The phys ed department observed $\hat{p} = \dfrac{31}{200} = 0.155$.

The department expected $E(\hat{p}) = p = 0.22$, with $SD(\hat{p}) = \sqrt{\dfrac{pq}{n}} = \sqrt{\dfrac{(0.22)(0.78)}{200}}$

$= 0.029$, so $z = \dfrac{\hat{p} - p}{SD(\hat{p})} = \dfrac{0.155 - 0.22}{0.029} = -2.24$.

By the 68–95–99.7 Rule, I know that values more than 2 standard deviations below the mean of a Normal model show up less than 2.5% of the time. Perhaps women at this college differ from the general population, or self-reporting may not provide accurate heights and weights.

---

Sampling distribution models tame the variation in statistics enough to allow us to measure how close our computed statistic values are likely to be to the underlying parameters they estimate. That's the path to the *margin of error* you hear about in polls and surveys. We'll see how to do that in the next chapter.

Once we think of the idea of a sampling distribution, it should be clear that we can find a sampling distribution model for any statistic we can compute on sampled data. What isn't at all clear is whether these sampling distribution models will always be simple probability models like the Normal model. The Normal is a good model for proportions, and we'll soon see that it works for means as well. But it won't work for every statistic. Fortunately, many of the statistics we work with do have simple sampling distribution models. Usually we need only a parameter or two to describe them.

Why do we really care about these distributions that we can never see? The answer is that once we have estimates for those parameters, we can use the model to help us understand how the statistic would have been distributed if we had drawn all those samples—but without the work and expense of actually drawing them. This will help us generalize from our data to the world at large.

## JUST CHECKING

1. You want to poll a random sample of 100 students on campus to see if they are in favor of the proposed location for the new student center. Of course, you'll get just one number, your sample proportion, $\hat{p}$. But if you imagined all the possible samples of 100 students you could draw and imagined the histogram of all the sample proportions from these samples, what shape would it have?

2. Where would the center of that histogram be?

3. If you think that about half the students are in favor of the plan, what would the standard deviation of the sample proportions be?

| STEP-BY-STEP EXAMPLE | Working with Sampling Distribution Models for Proportions |
|---|---|

Suppose that about 13% of the population is left-handed.[8] A 200-seat school auditorium has been built with 15 "lefty seats," seats that have the built-in desk on the left rather than the right arm of the chair. (For the right-handed readers among you, have you ever tried to take notes in a chair with the desk on the left side?)

**Question:** In a class of 90 students, what's the probability that there will not be enough seats for the left-handed students?

**Plan** State what we want to know.

I want to find the probability that in a group of 90 students, more than 15 will be left-handed. Since 15 out of 90 is 16.7%, I need the probability of finding more than 16.7% left-handed students out of a sample of 90 if the proportion of lefties is 13%.

**Model** Think about the assumptions and check the conditions.

You might be able to think of cases where the **Independence Assumption** is not plausible—for example, if the students are all related, or if they were selected for being left- or right-handed. But for a random sample, the assumption of independence seems reasonable.

✔ **Independence Assumption:** It is reasonable to assume that the probability that one student is left-handed is not changed by the fact that another student is right- or left-handed.

✔ **Randomization Condition:** The 90 students in the class can be thought of as a random sample of students.

✔ **10% Condition:** 90 is surely less than 10% of the population of all students. (Even if the school itself is small, I'm thinking of the population of all *possible* students who could have gone to the school.)

✔ **Success/Failure Condition:**

$$np = 90\,(0.13) = 11.7 \geq 10$$

$$nq = 90(0.87) = 78.3 \geq 10$$

State the parameters and the sampling distribution model.

The population proportion is $p = 0.13$. The conditions are satisfied, so I'll model the sampling distribution of $\hat{p}$ with a Normal model with mean 0.13 and a standard deviation of

$$SD\,(\hat{p}) = \sqrt{\frac{pq}{n}} = \sqrt{\frac{(0.13)(0.87)}{90}} \approx 0.035$$

My model for $\hat{p}$ is $N\,(0.13, 0.035\,)$.

---

[8] Actually, it's quite difficult to get an accurate estimate of the proportion of lefties in the population. Estimates range from 8% to 15%.

**Plot** Make a picture. Sketch the model and shade the area we're interested in, in this case the area to the right of 16.7%.

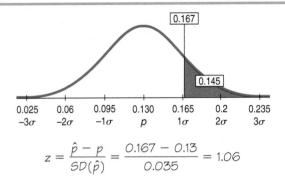

**Mechanics** Use the standard deviation as a ruler to find the z-score of the cutoff proportion. We see that 16.7% lefties would be just over one standard deviation above the mean.

$$z = \frac{\hat{p} - p}{SD(\hat{p})} = \frac{0.167 - 0.13}{0.035} = 1.06$$

Find the resulting probability from a table of Normal probabilities, a computer program, or a calculator.

$$P(\hat{p} > 0.167) = P(z > 1.06) = 0.1446$$

**Conclusion** Interpret the probability in the context of the question.

There is about a 14.5% chance that there will not be enough seats for the left-handed students in the class.

## What About Quantitative Data?

Proportions summarize categorical variables. And the Normal sampling distribution model looks like it is going to be very useful. But can we do something similar with quantitative data?

Of course we can (or we wouldn't have asked). Even more remarkable, not only can we use all of the same concepts, but almost the same model, too.

What are the concepts? We know that when we sample at random or randomize an experiment, the results we get will vary from sample-to-sample and from experiment-to-experiment. The Normal model seems an incredibly simple way to summarize all that variation. Could something that simple work for means? We won't keep you in suspense. It turns out that means also have a sampling distribution that we can model with a Normal model. And it turns out that Laplace's theoretical result applies to means, too. As we did with proportions, we can get some insight from a simulation.

## Simulating the Sampling Distribution of a Mean

Here's a simple simulation. Let's start with one fair die. If we toss this die 10,000 times, what should the histogram of the numbers on the face of the die look like? Here are the results of a simulated 10,000 tosses:

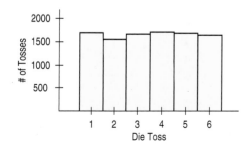

Now let's toss a *pair* of dice and record the average of the two. If we repeat this (or at least simulate repeating it) 10,000 times, recording the average of each pair, what will the histogram of these 10,000 averages look like? Before you look, think a minute. Is getting an average of 1 on *two* dice as likely as getting an average of 3 or 3.5?

Let's see:

We're much more likely to get an average near 3.5 than we are to get one near 1 or 6. Without calculating those probabilities exactly, it's fairly easy to see that the *only* way to get an average of 1 is to get two 1's. To get a total of 7 (for an average of 3.5), though, there are many more possibilities. This distribution even has a name: the *triangular* distribution.

What if we average 3 dice? We'll simulate 10,000 tosses of 3 dice and take their average:

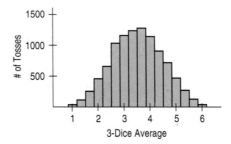

What's happening? First notice that it's getting harder to have averages near the ends. Getting an average of 1 or 6 with 3 dice requires all three to come up 1 or 6, respectively. That's less likely than for 2 dice to come up both 1 or both 6. The distribution is being pushed toward the middle. But what's happening to the shape? (This distribution doesn't have a name, as far as we know.)

Let's continue this simulation to see what happens with larger samples. Here's a histogram of the averages for 10,000 tosses of 5 dice:

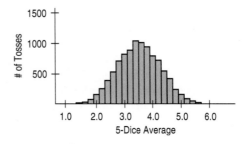

The pattern is becoming clearer. Two things continue to happen. The first fact we knew already from the Law of Large Numbers. It says that as the sample size (number of dice) gets larger, each sample average is more likely to be closer to the population mean. So, we see the shape continuing to tighten around 3.5. But the shape of the distribution is the surprising part. It's becoming bell-shaped. And not just bell-shaped; it's approaching the Normal model.

Are you convinced? Let's skip ahead and try 20 dice. The histogram of averages for 10,000 throws of 20 dice looks like this:

Now we see the Normal shape again (and notice how much smaller the spread is). But can we count on this happening for situations other than dice throws? What kinds of sample means have sampling distributions that we can model with a Normal model? It turns out that Normal models work well amazingly often.

# The Central Limit Theorem: The Fundamental Theorem of Statistics

The dice simulation may look like a special situation. But it turns out that what we saw with dice is true for means of repeated samples for almost every situation. When we looked at the sampling distribution of a proportion, we had to check only a few conditions. For means, the result is even more remarkable. *There are almost no conditions at all.*

Let's say that again: The sampling distribution of *any* mean becomes more nearly Normal as the sample size grows. All we need is for the observations to be independent and collected with randomization. We don't even care about the shape of the population distribution![9] This surprising fact is the result Laplace proved in a fairly general form in 1810. At the time, Laplace's theorem caused quite a stir (at least in mathematics circles) because it is so unintuitive. Laplace's result is called the **Central Limit Theorem**[10] (CLT).

Why should the Normal model show up again for the sampling distribution of means as well as proportions? We're not going to try to persuade you that it is obvious, clear, simple, or straightforward. In fact, the CLT is surprising and a bit weird. Not only does the distribution of means of many random samples get closer and closer to a Normal model as the sample size grows, *this is true regardless of the shape of the population distribution!* Even if we sample from a skewed or bimodal population, the Central Limit Theorem tells us that means of repeated random samples will tend to follow a Normal model as the sample size grows. Of course, you won't be surprised to learn that it works better and faster the closer the population distribution is to a Normal model. And it works better for larger samples. If the data come from a population that's exactly Normal to start with, then the observations themselves are Normal. If we take samples of size 1,

> *"The theory of probabilities is at bottom nothing but common sense reduced to calculus."*
> —Laplace, in *Théorie analytique des probabilités,* 1812.

---

[9] OK, one technical condition. The data must come from a population with a finite variance. You probably can't imagine a population with an infinite variance, but statisticians can construct such things, so we have to discuss them in footnotes like this. It really makes no difference in how you think about the important stuff, so you can just forget we mentioned it.

[10] The word "central" in the name of the theorem means "fundamental." It doesn't refer to the center of a distribution, so the title of this section is actually redundant.

Laplace was one of the greatest scientists and mathematicians of his time. In addition to his contributions to probability and statistics, he published many new results in mathematics, physics, and astronomy (where his nebular theory was one of the first to describe the formation of the solar system in much the way it is understood today). He also played a leading role in establishing the metric system of measurement.

His brilliance, though, sometimes got him into trouble. A visitor to the Académie des Sciences in Paris reported that Laplace let it be known widely that he considered himself the best mathematician in France. The effect of this on his colleagues was not eased by the fact that Laplace was right.

their "means" are just the observations—so, of course, they have Normal sampling distribution. But now suppose the population distribution is very skewed (like the CEO data from Chapter 5, for example). The CLT works, although it may take a sample size of dozens or even hundreds of observations for the Normal model to work well.

For example, think about a really bimodal population, one that consists of only 0's and 1's. The CLT says that even means of samples from this population will follow a Normal sampling distribution model. But wait. Suppose we have a categorical variable and we assign a 1 to each individual in the category and a 0 to each individual not in the category. And then we find the mean of these 0's and 1's. That's the same as counting the number of individuals who are in the category and dividing by $n$. That mean will be . . . the *sample proportion*, $\hat{p}$, of individuals who are in the category (a "success"). So maybe it wasn't so surprising after all that proportions, like means, have Normal sampling distribution models; they are actually just a special case of Laplace's remarkable theorem. Of course, for such an extremely bimodal population, we'll need a reasonably large sample size—and that's where the special conditions for proportions come in.

> **THE CENTRAL LIMIT THEOREM (CLT)**
> The mean of a random sample has a sampling distribution whose shape can be approximated by a Normal model. The larger the sample, the better the approximation will be.

## Assumptions and Conditions

**A S**  *Activity:* **The Central Limit Theorem.** Does it really work for samples from non-Normal populations?

The CLT requires essentially the same assumptions as we saw for modelling proportions:

**Independence Assumption:** The sampled values must be independent of each other.

**Sample Size Assumption:** The sample size must be sufficiently large.

We can't check these directly, but we can think about whether the **Independence Assumption** is plausible. We can also check some related conditions:

**Randomization Condition:** The data values must be sampled randomly, or the concept of a sampling distribution makes no sense.

**10% Condition:** When the sample is drawn without replacement (as is usually the case), the sample size, $n$, should be no more than 10% of the population.

**Large Enough Sample Condition:** Although the CLT tells us that a Normal model is useful in thinking about the behavior of sample means when the sample size is large enough, it doesn't tell us how large a sample we need. The truth is, it depends; there's no one-size-fits-all rule. If the population is unimodal and symmetric, even a fairly small sample is okay. If the population is strongly skewed, like the compensation for CEOs we looked at in Chapter 5, it can take a pretty large sample to allow use of a Normal model to describe the distribution of sample means. For now you'll just need to think about your sample size in the context of what you know about the population, and then tell whether you believe the **Large Enough Sample Condition** has been met.

# But Which Normal?

**A S** *Activity:* **The Standard Deviation of Means.** Experiment to see how the variability of the mean changes with the sample size.

The CLT says that the sampling distribution of any mean or proportion is approximately Normal. But which Normal model? We know that any Normal is specified by its mean and standard deviation. For proportions, the sampling distribution is centered at the population proportion. For means, it's centered at the population mean. What else would we expect?

What about the standard deviations, though? We noticed in our dice simulation that the histograms got narrower as we averaged more and more dice together. This shouldn't be surprising. Means vary less than the individual observations. Think about it for a minute. Which would be more surprising, having *one* person in your Statistics class who is over 6'9" tall or having the *mean* of 100 students taking the course be over 6'9"? The first event is fairly rare.[11] You may have seen somebody this tall in one of your classes sometime. But finding a class of 100 whose mean height is over 6'9" tall just won't happen. Why? Because *means have smaller standard deviations than individuals.*

How much smaller? Well, we have good news and bad news. The good news is that the standard deviation of $y$ falls as the sample size grows. The bad news is that it doesn't drop as fast as we might like. It only goes down by the *square root* of the sample size. The Normal model for the sampling distribution of the mean has a standard deviation equal to

$$SD(\bar{y}) = \frac{\sigma}{\sqrt{n}}$$

where $\sigma$ is the standard deviation of the population. To emphasize that this is a standard deviation *parameter* of the sampling distribution model for the sample mean, $\bar{y}$, we write $SD(\bar{y})$ or $\sigma(\bar{y})$.

**A S** *Activity:* **The Sampling Distribution of the Mean.** The CLT tells us what to expect. In this activity you can work with the CLT or simulate it if you prefer.

> **THE SAMPLING DISTRIBUTION MODEL FOR A MEAN**
>
> When a random sample is drawn from any population with mean $\mu$ and standard deviation $\sigma$, its sample mean, $\bar{y}$, has a sampling distribution with the same *mean $\mu$* but whose *standard deviation* is $\frac{\sigma}{\sqrt{n}}$ (and we write $\sigma(\bar{y}) = SD(\bar{y}) = \frac{\sigma}{\sqrt{n}}$). No matter what population the random sample comes from, the *shape* of the sampling distribution is approximately Normal as long as the sample size is large enough. The larger the sample used, the more closely the Normal approximates the sampling distribution for the mean.

We now have two closely related sampling distribution models that we can use when the appropriate assumptions and conditions are met. Which one we use depends on which kind of data we have:

▶ When we have categorical data, we calculate a sample proportion, $\hat{p}$; its sampling distribution has a Normal model with a mean at the true proportion ("Greek letter") $p$, and a standard deviation of $SD(\hat{p}) = \sqrt{\frac{pq}{n}} = \frac{\sqrt{pq}}{\sqrt{n}}$. We'll use this model in Chapters 19 through 22.

---

[11] If students are a random sample of adults, fewer than 1 out of 10,000 should be taller than 6'9". Why might college students not really be a random sample with respect to height? Even if they're not a perfectly random sample, a college student over 6'9" tall is still rare.

▶ When we have quantitative data, we calculate a sample mean, $\bar{y}$; its sampling distribution has a Normal model with a mean at the true mean, $\mu$, and a standard deviation of $SD(\bar{y}) = \dfrac{\sigma}{\sqrt{n}}$. We'll use this model in Chapters 23, 24, and 25.

The means of these models are easy to remember, so all you need to be careful about is the standard deviations. Remember that these are standard deviations of the *statistics* $\hat{p}$ and $\bar{y}$. They both have a square root of $n$ in the denominator. That tells us that the larger the sample, the less either statistic will vary. The only difference is in the numerator. If you just start by writing $SD(\bar{y})$ for quantitative data and $SD(\hat{p})$ for categorical data, you'll be able to remember which formula to use.

---

**FOR EXAMPLE**          Using the CLT for means

**Recap:** A college physical education department asked a random sample of 200 female students to self-report their heights and weights, but the percentage of students with body mass indexes over 25 seemed suspiciously low. One possible explanation may be that the respondents "shaded" their weights down a bit. The CDC reports that the mean weight of 18-year-old women is 143.74 lb, with a standard deviation of 51.54 lb, but these 200 randomly selected women reported a mean weight of only 140 lb.

**Question:** Based on the Central Limit Theorem and the 68–95–99.7 Rule, does the mean weight in this sample seem exceptionally low, or might this just be random sample-to-sample variation?

The conditions check out okay:

✔ Randomization Condition: The women were a random sample and their weights can be assumed to be independent.

✔ 10% Condition: They sampled fewer than 10% of all women at the college.

✔ Large Enough Sample Condition: The distribution of college women's weights is likely to be unimodal and reasonably symmetric, so the CLT applies to means of even small samples; 200 values is plenty.

The sampling model for sample means is approximately Normal with $E(\bar{y}) = 143.7$ and

$$SD(\bar{y}) = \frac{\sigma}{\sqrt{n}} = \frac{51.54}{\sqrt{200}} = 3.64.$$ The expected distribution of sample means is

The 68–95–99.7 Rule suggests that although the reported mean weight of 140 pounds is somewhat lower than expected, it does not appear to be unusual. Such variability is not all that extraordinary for samples of this size.

**STEP-BY-STEP EXAMPLE**     **Working with the Sampling Distribution Model for the Mean**

The Centers for Disease Control and Prevention reports that the mean weight of adult men in the United States is 190 lb with a standard deviation of 59 lb.[12]

**Question:** An elevator in our building has a weight limit of 10 persons or 2500 lb. What's the probability that if 10 men get on the elevator, they will overload its weight limit?

| | |
|---|---|
| **THINK** **Plan** State what we want to know. | Asking the probability that the total weight of a sample of 10 men exceeds 2500 pounds is equivalent to asking the probability that their mean weight is greater than 250 pounds. |
| **Model** Think about the assumptions and check the conditions. | ✔ **Independence Assumption:** It's reasonable to think that the weights of 10 randomly sampled men will be independent of each other. (But there could be exceptions—for example, if they were all from the same family or if the elevator were in a building with a diet clinic!) |
| | ✔ **Randomization Condition:** I'll assume that the 10 men getting on the elevator are a random sample from the population. |
| | ✔ **10% Condition:** 10 men is surely less than 10% of the population of possible elevator riders. |
| Note that if the sample were larger we'd be less concerned about the shape of the distribution of all weights. | ✔ **Large Enough Sample Condition:** I believe the distribution of population weights is roughly unimodal and symmetric, so my sample of 10 men seems large enough. |
| State the parameters and the sampling model. | The mean for all weights is $\mu = 190$ and the standard deviation is $\sigma = 59$ pounds. Since the conditions are satisfied, the CLT says that the sampling distribution of $\bar{y}$ has a Normal model with mean 190 and standard deviation $$SD(\bar{y}) = \frac{\sigma}{\sqrt{n}} = \frac{59}{\sqrt{10}} \approx 18.66$$ |

**SHOW** **Plot** Make a picture. Sketch the model and shade the area we're interested in. Here the mean weight of 250 pounds appears to be far out on the right tail of the curve.

---

[12] Cynthia L. Ogden, Cheryl D. Fryar, Margaret D. Carroll, and Katherine M. Flegal, *Mean Body Weight, Height, and Body Mass Index, United States 1960–2002, Advance Data from Vital and Health Statistics Number 347*, Oct. 27, 2004. https//www.cdc.gov/nchs

| | |
|---|---|
| **Mechanics** Use the standard deviation as a ruler to find the z-score of the cutoff mean weight. We see that an average of 250 pounds is more than 3 standard deviations above the mean.<br><br>Find the resulting probability from a table of Normal probabilities such as Table Z, a computer program, or a calculator. | $$z = \frac{\bar{y} - \mu}{SD(\bar{y})} = \frac{250 - 190}{18.66} = 3.21$$ $$P(\bar{y} > 250) = P(z > 3.21) = 0.0007$$ |

| | | |
|---|---|---|
|  | **Conclusion** Interpret your result in the proper context, being careful to relate it to the original question. | The chance that a random collection of 10 men will exceed the elevator's weight limit is only 0.0007. So, if they are a random sample, it is quite unlikely that 10 people will exceed the total weight allowed on the elevator. |

# About Variation

*"The n's justify the means."*
—Apocryphal
statistical saying

Means vary less than individual data values. That makes sense. If the same test is given to many sections of a large course and the class average is, say, 80%, some students may score 95% because individual scores vary a lot. But we'd be shocked (and pleased!) if the *average* score of the students in any section was 95%. Averages are much less variable. Not only do group averages vary less than individual values, but common sense suggests that averages should be more consistent for larger groups. The Central Limit Theorem confirms this hunch; the fact that $SD(\bar{y}) = \frac{\sigma}{\sqrt{n}}$ has $n$ in the denominator shows that the variability of sample means decreases as the sample size increases. There's a catch, though. The standard deviation of the sampling distribution declines only with the square root of the sample size and not, for example, with $1/n$.

The mean of a random sample of 4 has half $\left( \frac{1}{\sqrt{4}} = \frac{1}{2} \right)$ the standard deviation of an individual data value. To cut the standard deviation in half again, we'd need a sample of 16, and a sample of 64 to halve it once more.

If only we had a much larger sample, we could get the standard deviation of the sampling distribution *really* under control so that the sample mean could tell us still more about the unknown population mean, but larger samples cost more and take longer to survey. And while we're gathering all that extra data, the population itself may change, or a news story may alter opinions. There are practical limits to most sample sizes. As we shall see, that nasty square root limits how much we can make a sample tell about the population. This is an example of something that's known as the Law of Diminishing Returns.

> **A Billion Dollar Misunderstanding?** In the late 1990s the Bill and Melinda Gates Foundation began funding an effort to encourage the breakup of large schools into smaller schools. Why? It had been noticed that smaller schools were more common among the best-performing schools than one would expect. In time, the Annenberg Foundation, the Carnegie Corporation, the Center for Collaborative Education, the Center for School Change, Harvard's Change Leadership Group, the

Open Society Institute, Pew Charitable Trusts, and the U.S. Department of Education's Smaller Learning Communities Program all supported the effort. Well over a billion dollars was spent to make schools smaller.

But was it all based on a misunderstanding of sampling distributions? Statisticians Howard Wainer and Harris Zwerling[13] looked at the mean test scores of schools in Pennsylvania. They found that indeed 12% of the top-scoring 50 schools were from the smallest 3% of Pennsylvania schools—substantially more than the 3% we'd naively expect. But then they looked at the *bottom* 50. There they found that 18% were small schools! The explanation? Mean test scores are, well, means. We are looking at a rough real-world simulation in which each school is a trial. Even if all Pennsylvania schools were equivalent, we'd expect their mean scores to vary. How much? The CLT tells us that means of test scores vary according to $\frac{\sigma}{\sqrt{n}}$. Smaller schools have (by definition) smaller $n$'s, so the sampling distributions of their mean scores naturally have larger standard deviations. It's natural, then, that small schools have both higher and lower mean scores.

On October 26, 2005, *The Seattle Times* reported:

> [T]he Gates Foundation announced last week it is moving away from its emphasis on converting large high schools into smaller ones and instead giving grants to specially selected school districts with a track record of academic improvement and effective leadership. Education leaders at the Foundation said they concluded that improving classroom instruction and mobilizing the resources of an entire district were more important first steps to improving high schools than breaking down the size.

## The Real World and the Model World

Be careful. We have been slipping smoothly between the real world, in which we draw random samples of data, and a magical mathematical model world, in which we describe how the sample means and proportions we observe in the real world might behave if we could see the results from every random sample that we might have drawn. Now we have *two* distributions to deal with. The first is the real world distribution of the sample, which we might display with a histogram (for quantitative data) or with a bar chart or table (for categorical data). The second is the math world *sampling distribution* of the statistic, which we model with a Normal model based on the Central Limit Theorem. Don't confuse the two.

For example, don't mistakenly think the CLT says that the *data* are Normally distributed as long as the sample is large enough. In fact, as samples get larger, we expect the distribution of the data to look more and more like the population from which they are drawn—skewed, bimodal, whatever—but not necessarily Normal. You can collect a sample of CEO salaries for the next 1000 years,[14] but the histogram will never look Normal. It will be skewed to the right. The Central Limit Theorem doesn't talk about the distribution of the data from the sample. It talks about the sample *means* and sample *proportions* of many different random samples drawn from the same population. Of course, we never actually draw all those samples, so the CLT is talking about an imaginary distribution—the sampling distribution model.

And the CLT does require that the sample be big enough when the population shape is not unimodal and symmetric. But it is still a very surprising and powerful result.

---

[13] Wainer, H. and Zwerling, H., "Legal and empirical evidence that smaller schools do not improve student achievement," *The Phi Delta Kappan* 2006 87:300–303. Discussed in Howard Wainer, "The Most Dangerous Equation," *American Scientist*, May–June 2007, pp. 249–256; also at www.Americanscientist.org.
[14] Don't forget to adjust for inflation.

## JUST CHECKING

**4.** Human gestation times have a mean of about 266 days, with a standard deviation of about 16 days. If we record the gestation times of a sample of 100 women, do we know that a histogram of the times will be well modeled by a Normal model?

**5.** Suppose we look at the *average* gestation times for a sample of 100 women. If we imagined all the possible random samples of 100 women we could take and looked at the histogram of all the sample means, what shape would it have?

**6.** Where would the center of that histogram be?

**7.** What would be the standard deviation of that histogram?

# Sampling Distribution Models

Let's summarize what we've learned about sampling distributions. At the heart is the idea that *the statistic itself is a random quantity*. We can't know what our statistic will be because it comes from a random sample. It's just one instance of something that happened for our particular random sample. A different random sample would have given a different result. This sample-to-sample variability is what generates the sampling distribution. The sampling distribution shows us the distribution of possible values that the statistic could have had.

We could simulate that distribution by pretending to take lots of samples. Fortunately, for the mean and the proportion, the CLT tells us that we can model their sampling distribution directly with a Normal model.

The two basic truths about sampling distributions are:

**A S** *Simulation:* **The CLT for Real Data.** Why settle for a picture when you can see it in action?

1. Sampling distributions arise because samples vary. Each random sample will contain different cases and so, a different value of the statistic.
2. Although we can always simulate a sampling distribution, the Central Limit Theorem saves us the trouble for means and proportions.

Here's a picture showing the process going into the sampling distribution model:

**FIGURE 18.5**

*We start with a population model, which can have any shape. It can even be bimodal or skewed (as this one is). We label the mean of this model $\mu$ and its standard deviation, $\sigma$.*

*We draw one real sample (solid line) of size n and show its histogram and summary statistics. We imagine (or simulate) drawing many other samples (dotted lines), which have their own histograms and summary statistics.*

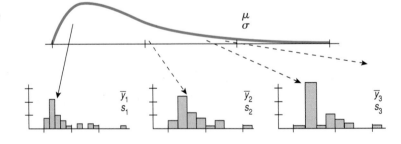

*We (imagine) gathering all the means into a histogram.*

*The CLT tells us we can model the shape of this histogram with a Normal model. The mean of this Normal is $\mu$, and the standard deviation is $SD(\bar{y}) = \dfrac{\sigma}{\sqrt{n}}$.*

## The View from Here . . .

We've just encountered the Central Limit Theorem, the most important insight in Statistics. Let's take a moment to appreciate how we got here and where we're going. We began this journey by exploring data. We saw that sometimes we look at data as categorical and other times as quantitative information. Either way, we're interested in the story the data have to tell. We've learned how to design studies so that the data we collect are as meaningful as possible.

We've seen that when it comes to understanding the data's story, our biggest nemesis is variability. Whether we're looking at information collected in a survey or the results of an experiment, we have only a narrow glimpse of the larger world we wish we knew about. That glimpse is subject to error, the variability that naturally arises from sample to sample and group to group. What we've now learned—and a powerful and stunning insight it is—is that this unavoidable variability is predictable and quantifiable. The Central Limit Theorem quantifies sampling error. That sounds simple, but it's quite profound.

For categorical data, the CLT reveals how proportions observed in many samples drawn from the same population will behave. For quantitative data, the CLT reveals the behavior of means observed in many samples. In each case, we now know what value to expect, how much variability there may be, and (what luck!) that Normal models apply. We may not have fully conquered variability, but we've got it cornered.

So what's left to do? We have to turn theory into practical tools. In this chapter our discussion has been purely theoretical. We've imagined that we know the population parameters—proportions, means, and standard deviations—and we've learned to describe the behavior of statistics observed in many, many samples. But that's not the way the real world works. In practice, we'll never know the population parameters, and we'll have data from just a single study.

In the real world of Statistics we'll collect some information, but we'll really want to know something else. We poll 1000 voters, but we want to know whom the entire electorate will choose. We've seen a new medicine lower blood pressure more than a placebo, but we need to know whether that difference is statistically significant.[15] We now must combine our ability to design studies and summarize the data with the CLT's insights about sampling variability in order to use the sample statistics we observe to make inferences about the population parameters we wish we knew.

That's the path that lies ahead. In Chapters 19–22 we'll learn how to make inferences about proportions. In Chapters 23–25 we'll turn our attention to means. The Central Limit Theorem will be with us all the way.

## WHAT CAN GO WRONG?

▶ **Don't confuse the sampling distribution with the distribution of the sample.** When you take a sample, you always look at the distribution of the values, usually with a histogram, and you may calculate summary statistics. Examining the distribution of the sample like this is wise. But that's not the sampling distribution. The sampling distribution is an imaginary collection of the values that a statistic *might* have taken for all the random samples—the one you got and the ones that you didn't get. We use the sampling distribution model to make statements about how the statistic varies.

---

[15] We first encountered "Statistically significant" in Chapter 13. The term refers to results so unusual that they're probably not merely sample-to-sample variation. You'll be seeing—and saying—those words a lot from here on.

▶ **Beware of observations that are not independent.** The CLT depends crucially on the assumption of independence. If our elevator riders are related, are all from the same school (for example, an elementary school), or in some other way aren't a random sample, then the statements we try to make about the mean are going to be wrong. Unfortunately, this isn't something you can check in your data. You have to think about how the data were gathered. Good sampling practice and well-designed randomized experiments ensure independence.

▶ **Watch out for small samples from skewed populations.** The CLT assures us that the sampling distribution model is Normal if $n$ is large enough. If the population is nearly Normal, even small samples (like our 10 elevator riders) work. If the population is very skewed, then $n$ will have to be large before the Normal model will work well. If we sampled 15 or even 20 CEOs and used $\bar{y}$ to make a statement about the mean of all CEOs' compensation, we'd likely get into trouble because the underlying data distribution is so skewed. Unfortunately, there's no good rule of thumb.[16] It just depends on how skewed the data distribution is. Always plot the data to check.

# CONNECTIONS

The concept of a sampling distribution connects to almost everything we have done. The fundamental connection is to the deliberate application of randomness in random sampling and randomized comparative experiments. If we didn't employ randomness to generate unbiased data, then repeating the data collection would just get the same data values again (with perhaps a few new measurement or recording errors). The distribution of statistic values arises directly because different random samples and randomized experiments would generate different statistic values.

The connection to the Normal distribution is obvious. We first introduced the Normal model before because it was "nice." As a unimodal, symmetric distribution with 99.7% of its area within three standard deviations of the mean, the Normal model is easy to work with. Now we see that the Normal holds a special place among distributions because we can use it to model the sampling distributions of the mean and the proportion.

We use simulation to understand sampling distributions. In fact, some important sampling distributions were discovered first by simulation.

# WHAT HAVE WE LEARNED?

Way back in Chapter 1 we said that Statistics is about variation. We know that no sample fully and exactly describes the population; sample proportions and means will vary from sample to sample. That's sampling error (or, better, sampling variability). We know it will always be present—indeed, the world would be a boring place if variability didn't exist. You might think that sampling variability would prevent us from learning anything reliable about a population by looking at a sample, but that's just not so. The fortunate fact is that sampling variability is not just unavoidable—it's predictable!

We've learned how the Central Limit Theorem describes the behavior of sample proportions—shape, center, and spread—as long as certain assumptions and conditions are met. The sample must be independent, random, and large enough that we expect at least 10 successes and failures. Then:

▶ The sampling distribution (the imagined histogram of the proportions from all possible samples) is shaped like a Normal model.

---

[16] For proportions, of course, there is a rule: the **Success/Failure Condition.** That works for proportions because the standard deviation of a proportion is linked to its mean.

▸ The mean of the sampling model is the true proportion in the population.

▸ The standard deviation of the sample proportions is $\sqrt{\dfrac{pq}{n}}$.

And we've learned to describe the behavior of sample means as well, based on this amazing result known as the Central Limit Theorem—the Fundamental Theorem of Statistics. Again the sample must be independent and random—no surprise there—and needs to be larger if our data come from a population that's not roughly unimodal and symmetric. Then:

▸ Regardless of the shape of the original population, the shape of the distribution of the means of all possible samples can be described by a Normal model, provided the samples are large enough.

▸ The center of the sampling model will be the true mean of the population from which we took the sample.

▸ The standard deviation of the sample means is the population's standard deviation divided by the square root of the sample size, $\dfrac{\sigma}{\sqrt{n}}$.

## Terms

| | |
|---|---|
| **Sampling distribution model** | 460. Different random samples give different values for a statistic. The sampling distribution model shows the behavior of the statistic over all the possible samples for the same size $n$. |
| **Sampling variability** <br> **Sampling error** | 461. The variability we expect to see from one random sample to another. It is sometimes called sampling error, but sampling variability is the better term. |
| **Sampling distribution model for a proportion** | 462. If assumptions of independence and random sampling are met, and we expect at least 10 successes and 10 failures, then the sampling distribution of a proportion is modeled by a Normal model with a mean equal to the true proportion value, $p$, and a standard deviation equal to $\sqrt{\dfrac{pq}{n}}$. |
| **Central Limit Theorem** | 468. The Central Limit Theorem (CLT) states that the sampling distribution model of the sample mean (and proportion) from a random sample is approximately Normal for large $n$, *regardless of the distribution of the population, as long as the observations are independent.* |
| **Sampling distribution model for a mean** | 470. If assumptions of independence and random sampling are met, and the sample size is large enough, the sampling distribution of the sample mean is modeled by a Normal model with a mean equal to the population mean, $\mu$, and a standard deviation equal to $\dfrac{\sigma}{\sqrt{n}}$. |

## Skills

THINK

▸ Understand that the variability of a statistic (as measured by the standard deviation of its sampling distribution) depends on the size of the sample. Statistics based on larger samples are less variable.

▸ Understand that the Central Limit Theorem gives the sampling distribution model of the mean for sufficiently large samples regardless of the underlying population.

SHOW

▸ Be able to demonstrate a sampling distribution by simulation.

▸ Be able to use a sampling distribution model to make simple statements about the distribution of a proportion or mean under repeated sampling.

TELL

▸ Be able to interpret a sampling distribution model as describing the values taken by a statistic in all possible realizations of a sample or randomized experiment under the same conditions.

# EXERCISES

**1. Send money.** When they send out their fundraising letter, a philanthropic organization typically gets a return from about 5% of the people on their mailing list. To see what the response rate might be for future appeals, they did a simulation using samples of size 20, 50, 100, and 200. For each sample size, they simulated 1000 mailings with success rate $p = 0.05$ and constructed the histogram of the 1000 sample proportions, shown below. Explain how these histograms demonstrate what the Central Limit Theorem says about the sampling distribution model for sample proportions. Be sure to talk about shape, center, and spread.

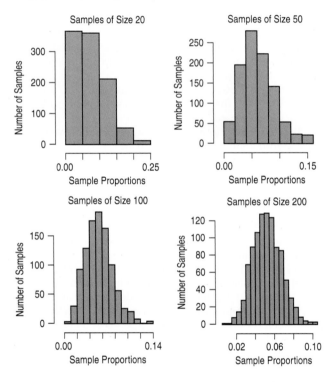

**2. Character recognition.** An automatic character recognition device can successfully read about 85% of handwritten credit card applications. To estimate what might happen when this device reads a stack of applications, the company did a simulation using samples of size 20, 50, 75, and 100. For each sample size, they simulated 1000 samples with success rate $p = 0.85$ and constructed the histogram of the 1000 sample proportions, shown here. Explain how these histograms demonstrate what the Central Limit Theorem says about the sampling distribution model for sample proportions. Be sure to talk about shape, center, and spread.

**3. Send money, again.** The philanthropic organization in Exercise 1 expects about a 5% success rate when they send fundraising letters to the people on their mailing list. In Exercise 1 you looked at the histograms showing distributions of sample proportions from 1000 simulated mailings for samples of size 20, 50, 100, and 200. The sample statistics from each simulation were as follows:

| n | mean | st. dev. |
|-----|--------|----------|
| 20 | 0.0497 | 0.0479 |
| 50 | 0.0516 | 0.0309 |
| 100 | 0.0497 | 0.0215 |
| 200 | 0.0501 | 0.0152 |

a) According to the Central Limit Theorem, what should the theoretical mean and standard deviations be for these sample sizes?
b) How close are those theoretical values to what was observed in these simulations?
c) Looking at the histograms in Exercise 1, at what sample size would you be comfortable using the Normal model as an approximation for the sampling distribution?
d) What does the Success/Failure Condition say about the choice you made in part c?

**4. Character recognition, again.** The automatic character recognition device discussed in Exercise 2 successfully reads about 85% of handwritten credit card applications. In Exercise 2 you looked at the histograms showing distributions of sample proportions from 1000 simulated samples of size 20, 50, 75, and 100. The sample statistics from each simulation were as follows:

| n | mean | st. dev. |
|-----|--------|----------|
| 20 | 0.8481 | 0.0803 |
| 50 | 0.8507 | 0.0509 |
| 75 | 0.8481 | 0.0406 |
| 100 | 0.8488 | 0.0354 |

a) According to the Central Limit Theorem, what should the theoretical mean and standard deviations be for these sample sizes?

b) How close are those theoretical values to what was observed in these simulations?

c) Looking at the histograms in Exercise 2, at what sample size would you be comfortable using the Normal model as an approximation for the sampling distribution?

d) What does the Success/Failure Condition say about the choice you made in part c?

**5. Coin tosses.** In a large class of introductory Statistics students, the professor has each person toss a coin 16 times and calculate the proportion of his or her tosses that were heads. The students then report their results, and the professor plots a histogram of these several proportions.

a) What shape would you expect this histogram to be? Why?

b) Where do you expect the histogram to be centered?

c) How much variability would you expect among these proportions?

d) Explain why a Normal model should not be used here.

**6. M&M's.** The candy company claims that 10% of the M&M's it produces are green. Suppose that the candies are packaged at random in small bags containing about 50 M&M's. A class of elementary school students learning about percents opens several bags, counts the various colors of the candies, and calculates the proportion that are green.

a) If we plot a histogram showing the proportions of green candies in the various bags, what shape would you expect it to have?

b) Can that histogram be approximated by a Normal model? Explain.

c) Where should the center of the histogram be?

d) What should the standard deviation of the proportion be?

**7. More coins.** Suppose the class in Exercise 5 repeats the coin-tossing experiment.

a) The students toss the coins 25 times each. Use the 68–95–99.7 Rule to describe the sampling distribution model.

b) Confirm that you can use a Normal model here.

c) They increase the number of tosses to 64 each. Draw and label the appropriate sampling distribution model. Check the appropriate conditions to justify your model.

d) Explain how the sampling distribution model changes as the number of tosses increases.

**8. Bigger bag.** Suppose the class in Exercise 6 buys bigger bags of candy, with 200 M&M's each. Again the students calculate the proportion of green candies they find.

a) Explain why it's appropriate to use a Normal model to describe the distribution of the proportion of green M&M's they might expect.

b) Use the 68–95–99.7 Rule to describe how this proportion might vary from bag to bag.

c) How would this model change if the bags contained even more candies?

**9. Just (un)lucky?** One of the students in the introductory Statistics class in Exercise 7 claims to have tossed her coin 200 times and found only 42% heads. What do you think of this claim? Explain.

**10. Too many green ones?** In a really large bag of M&M's, the students in Exercise 8 found 500 candies, and 12% of them were green. Is this an unusually large proportion of green M&M's? Explain.

**11. Speeding.** State police believe that 70% of the drivers traveling on a major interstate highway exceed the speed limit. They plan to set up a radar trap and check the speeds of 80 cars.

a) Using the 68–95–99.7 Rule, draw and label the distribution of the proportion of these cars the police will observe speeding.

b) Do you think the appropriate conditions necessary for your analysis are met? Explain.

**12. Smoking.** Public health statistics indicate that 26.4% of American adults smoke cigarettes. Using the 68–95–99.7 Rule, describe the sampling distribution model for the proportion of smokers among a randomly selected group of 50 adults. Be sure to discuss your assumptions and conditions.

**13. Vision.** It is generally believed that nearsightedness affects about 12% of all children. A school district has registered 170 incoming kindergarten children.

a) Can you apply the Central Limit Theorem to describe the sampling distribution model for the sample proportion of children who are nearsighted? Check the conditions and discuss any assumptions you need to make.

b) Sketch and clearly label the sampling model, based on the 68–95–99.7 Rule.

c) How many of the incoming students might the school expect to be nearsighted? Explain.

**14. Mortgages.** In early 2007 the Mortgage Lenders Association reported that homeowners, hit hard by rising interest rates on adjustable-rate mortgages, were defaulting in record numbers. The foreclosure rate of 1.6% meant that millions of families were in jeopardy of losing their homes. Suppose a large bank holds 1731 adjustable-rate mortgages.

a) Can you apply the Central Limit Theorem to describe the sampling distribution model for the sample proportion of foreclosures? Check the conditions and discuss any assumptions you need to make.

b) Sketch and clearly label the sampling model, based on the 68–95–99.7 Rule.

c) How many of these homeowners might the bank expect will default on their mortgages? Explain.

**15. Loans.** Based on past experience, a bank believes that 7% of the people who receive loans will not make payments on time. The bank has recently approved 200 loans.
  a) What are the mean and standard deviation of the proportion of clients in this group who may not make timely payments?
  b) What assumptions underlie your model? Are the conditions met? Explain.
  c) What's the probability that over 10% of these clients will not make timely payments?

**16. Contacts.** Assume that 30% of students at a university wear contact lenses.
  a) We randomly pick 100 students. Let $\hat{p}$ represent the proportion of students in this sample who wear contacts. What's the appropriate model for the distribution of $\hat{p}$? Specify the name of the distribution, the mean, and the standard deviation. Be sure to verify that the conditions are met.
  b) What's the approximate probability that more than one third of this sample wear contacts?

**17. Back to school?** Best known for its testing program, ACT, Inc., also compiles data on a variety of issues in education. In 2004 the company reported that the national college freshman-to-sophomore retention rate held steady at 74% over the previous four years. Consider colleges with freshman classes of 400 students. Use the 68–95–99.7 Rule to describe the sampling distribution model for the percentage of those students we expect to return to that school for their sophomore years. Do you think the appropriate conditions are met?

**18. Binge drinking.** As we learned in Chapter 15, a national study found that 44% of college students engage in binge drinking (5 drinks at a sitting for men, 4 for women). Use the 68–95–99.7 Rule to describe the sampling distribution model for the proportion of students in a randomly selected group of 200 college students who engage in binge drinking. Do you think the appropriate conditions are met?

**19. Back to school, again.** Based on the 74% national retention rate described in Exercise 17, does a college where 522 of the 603 freshman returned the next year as sophomores have a right to brag that it has an unusually high retention rate? Explain.

**20. Binge sample.** After hearing of the national result that 44% of students engage in binge drinking (5 drinks at a sitting for men, 4 for women), a professor surveyed a random sample of 244 students at his college and found that 96 of them admitted to binge drinking in the past week. Should he be surprised at this result? Explain.

**21. Polling.** Just before a referendum on a school budget, a local newspaper polls 400 voters in an attempt to predict whether the budget will pass. Suppose that the budget actually has the support of 52% of the voters. What's the probability the newspaper's sample will lead them to predict defeat? Be sure to verify that the assumptions and conditions necessary for your analysis are met.

**22. Seeds.** Information on a packet of seeds claims that the germination rate is 92%. What's the probability that more than 95% of the 160 seeds in the packet will germinate? Be sure to discuss your assumptions and check the conditions that support your model.

**23. Apples.** When a truckload of apples arrives at a packing plant, a random sample of 150 is selected and examined for bruises, discoloration, and other defects. The whole truckload will be rejected if more than 5% of the sample is unsatisfactory. Suppose that in fact 8% of the apples on the truck do not meet the desired standard. What's the probability that the shipment will be accepted anyway?

**24. Genetic defect.** It's believed that 4% of children have a gene that may be linked to juvenile diabetes. Researchers hoping to track 20 of these children for several years test 732 newborns for the presence of this gene. What's the probability that they find enough subjects for their study?

**25. Nonsmokers.** While some nonsmokers do not mind being seated in a smoking section of a restaurant, about 60% of the customers demand a smoke-free area. A new restaurant with 120 seats is being planned. How many seats should be in the nonsmoking area in order to be very sure of having enough seating there? Comment on the assumptions and conditions that support your model, and explain what "very sure" means to you.

**26. Meals.** A restauranteur anticipates serving about 180 people on a Friday evening, and believes that about 20% of the patrons will order the chef's steak special. How many of those meals should he plan on serving in order to be pretty sure of having enough steaks on hand to meet customer demand? Justify your answer, including an explanation of what "pretty sure" means to you.

**27. Sampling.** A sample is chosen randomly from a population that can be described by a Normal model.
  a) What's the sampling distribution model for the sample mean? Describe shape, center, and spread.
  b) If we choose a larger sample, what's the effect on this sampling distribution model?

**28. Sampling, part II.** A sample is chosen randomly from a population that was strongly skewed to the left.
  a) Describe the sampling distribution model for the sample mean if the sample size is small.
  b) If we make the sample larger, what happens to the sampling distribution model's shape, center, and spread?
  c) As we make the sample larger, what happens to the expected distribution of the data in the sample?

**29. Waist size.** A study measured the *Waist Size* of 250 men, finding a mean of 36.33 inches and a standard deviation of 4.02 inches. Here is a histogram of these measurements

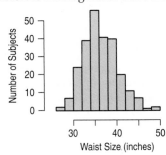

a) Describe the histogram of *Waist Size*.
b) To explore how the mean might vary from sample to sample, they simulated by drawing many samples of size 2, 5, 10, and 20, with replacement, from the 250 measurements. Here are histograms of the sample means for each simulation. Explain how these histograms demonstrate what the Central Limit Theorem says about the sampling distribution model for sample means.

30. **CEO compensation.** In Chapter 4 we saw the distribution of the total compensation of the chief executive officers (CEOs) of the 800 largest U.S. companies (the Fortune 800). The average compensation (in thousands of dollars) is 10,307.31 and the standard deviation is 17,964.62. Here is a histogram of their annual compensations (in $1000):

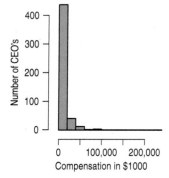

a) Describe the histogram of *Total Compensation*.
A research organization simulated sample means by drawing samples of 30, 50, 100, and 200, with replacement, from the 800 CEOs. The histograms show the distributions of means for many samples of each size.

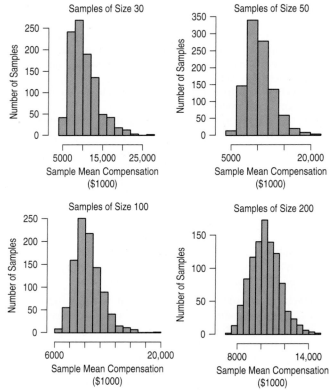

b) Explain how these histograms demonstrate what the Central Limit Theorem says about the sampling distribution model for sample means. Be sure to talk about shape, center, and spread.
c) Comment on the "rule of thumb" that "With a sample size of at least 30, the sampling distribution of the mean is Normal"?

31. **Waist size revisited.** Researchers measured the *Waist Sizes* of 250 men in a study on body fat. The true mean and standard deviation of the *Waist Sizes* for the 250 men are 36.33 in and 4.019 inches, respectively. In Exercise 29 you looked at the histograms of simulations that drew samples of sizes 2, 5, 10, and 20 (with replacement). The summary statistics for these simulations were as follows:

| $n$ | mean | st. dev. |
|---|---|---|
| 2 | 36.314 | 2.855 |
| 5 | 36.314 | 1.805 |
| 10 | 36.341 | 1.276 |
| 20 | 36.339 | 0.895 |

a) According to the Central Limit Theorem, what should the theoretical mean and standard deviation be for each of these sample sizes?
b) How close are the theoretical values to what was observed in the simulation?
c) Looking at the histograms in Exercise 29, at what sample size would you be comfortable using the Normal model as an approximation for the sampling distribution?
d) What about the shape of the distribution of *Waist Size* explains your choice of sample size in part c?

**32. CEOs revisited.** In Exercise 30 you looked at the annual compensation for 800 CEOs, for which the true mean and standard deviation were (in thousands of dollars) 10,307.31 and 17,964.62, respectively. A simulation drew samples of sizes 30, 50, 100, and 200 (with replacement) from the total annual compensations of the Fortune 800 CEOs. The summary statistics for these simulations were as follows:

| n | mean | st. dev. |
|---|---|---|
| 30 | 10,251.73 | 3359.64 |
| 50 | 10,343.93 | 2483.84 |
| 100 | 10,329.94 | 1779.18 |
| 200 | 10,340.37 | 1230.79 |

a) According to the Central Limit Theorem, what should the theoretical mean and standard deviation be for each of these sample sizes?
b) How close are the theoretical values to what was observed from the simulation?
c) Looking at the histograms in Exercise 30, at what sample size would you be comfortable using the Normal model as an approximation for the sampling distribution?
d) What about the shape of the distribution of *Total Compensation* explains your answer in part c?

**33. GPAs.** A college's data about the incoming freshmen indicates that the mean of their high school GPAs was 3.4, with a standard deviation of 0.35; the distribution was roughly mound-shaped and only slightly skewed. The students are randomly assigned to freshman writing seminars in groups of 25. What might the mean GPA of one of these seminar groups be? Describe the appropriate sampling distribution model—shape, center, and spread—with attention to assumptions and conditions. Make a sketch using the 68–95–99.7 Rule.

**34. Home values.** Assessment records indicate that the value of homes in a small city is skewed right, with a mean of $140,000 and standard deviation of $60,000. To check the accuracy of the assessment data, officials plan to conduct a detailed appraisal of 100 homes selected at random. Using the 68–95–99.7 Rule, draw and label an appropriate sampling model for the mean value of the homes selected.

**35. The trial of the pyx.** In 1150, it was recognized in England that coins should have a standard weight of precious metal as the basis for their value. A guinea, for example, was supposed to contain 128 grains of gold. (There are 360 grains in an ounce.) In the "trial of the pyx," coins minted under contract to the crown were weighed and compared to standard coins (which were kept in a wooden box called the pyx). Coins were allowed to deviate by no more than 0.28 grains—roughly equivalent to specifying that the standard deviation should be no greater than 0.09 grains (although they didn't know what a standard deviation was in 1150). In fact, the trial was performed by weighing 100 coins at a time and requiring the *sum* to deviate by no more than $100 \times 0.28 = 28$ or 28 grains—equivalent to the sum having a standard deviation of about 9 grains.

a) In effect, the trial of the pyx required that the mean weight of the sample of 100 coins have a standard deviation of 0.09 grains. Explain what was wrong with performing the trial in this manner.
b) What should the limit have been on the standard deviation of the mean?

*Note:* Because of this error, the crown was exposed to being cheated by private mints that could mint coins with greater variation and then, after their coins passed the trial, select out the heaviest ones and recast them at the proper weight, retaining the excess gold for themselves. The error persisted for over 600 years, until sampling distributions became better understood.

**36. Safe cities.** Allstate Insurance Company identified the 10 safest and 10 least-safe U.S. cities from among the 200 largest cities in the United States, based on the mean number of years drivers went between automobile accidents. The cities on both lists were all smaller than the 10 largest cities. Using facts about the sampling distribution model of the mean, explain why this is not surprising.

*Exercises 37–54 require the use of Normal tables or technology*

**37. Pregnancy.** Assume that the duration of human pregnancies can be described by a Normal model with mean 266 days and standard deviation 16 days.
a) What percentage of pregnancies should last between 270 and 280 days?
b) At least how many days should the longest 25% of all pregnancies last?
c) Suppose a certain obstetrician is currently providing prenatal care to 60 pregnant women. Let $\bar{y}$ represent the mean length of their pregnancies. According to the Central Limit Theorem, what's the distribution of this sample mean, $\bar{y}$? Specify the model, mean, and standard deviation.
d) What's the probability that the mean duration of these patients' pregnancies will be less than 260 days?

**38. Rainfall.** Statistics from Cornell's Northeast Regional Climate Center indicate that Ithaca, NY, gets an average of 35.4" of rain each year, with a standard deviation of 4.2". Assume that a Normal model applies.
a) During what percentage of years does Ithaca get more than 40" of rain?
b) Less than how much rain falls in the driest 20% of all years?
c) A Cornell University student is in Ithaca for 4 years. Let $\bar{y}$ represent the mean amount of rain for those 4 years. Describe the sampling distribution model of this sample mean, $\bar{y}$.
d) What's the probability that those 4 years average less than 30" of rain?

**39. Pregnant again.** The duration of human pregnancies may not actually follow a Normal model, as described in Exercise 37.
a) Explain why it may be somewhat skewed to the left.
b) If the correct model is in fact skewed, does that change your answers to parts a, b, and c of Exercise 37? Explain why or why not for each.

**40. At work.** Some business analysts estimate that the length of time people work at a job has a mean of 6.2 years and a standard deviation of 4.5 years.
a) Explain why you suspect this distribution may be skewed to the right.
b) Explain why you could estimate the probability that 100 people selected at random had worked for their employers an average of 10 years or more, but you could not estimate the probability that an individual had done so.

**41. Dice and dollars.** You roll a die, winning nothing if the number of spots is odd, $1 for a 2 or a 4, and $10 for a 6.
a) Find the expected value and standard deviation of your prospective winnings.
b) You play twice. Find the mean and standard deviation of your total winnings.
c) You play 40 times. What's the probability that you win at least $100?

**42. New game.** You pay $10 and roll a die. If you get a 6, you win $50. If not, you get to roll again. If you get a 6 this time, you get your $10 back.
a) Create a probability model for this game.
b) Find the expected value and standard deviation of your prospective winnings.
c) You play this game five times. Find the expected value and standard deviation of your average winnings.
d) 100 people play this game. What's the probability the person running the game makes a profit?

**43. AP Stats 2006.** The College Board reported the score distribution shown in the table for all students who took the 2006 AP Statistics exam.

| Score | Percent of Students |
|-------|---------------------|
| 5 | 12.6 |
| 4 | 22.2 |
| 3 | 25.3 |
| 2 | 18.3 |
| 1 | 21.6 |

a) Find the mean and standard deviation of the scores.
b) If we select a random sample of 40 AP Statistics students, would you expect their scores to follow a Normal model? Explain.
c) Consider the mean scores of random samples of 40 AP Statistics students. Describe the sampling model for these means (shape, center, and spread).

**44. Museum membership.** A museum offers several levels of membership, as shown in the table.

| Member Category | Amount of Donation ($) | Percent of Members |
|-----------------|------------------------|--------------------|
| Individual | 50 | 41 |
| Family | 100 | 37 |
| Sponsor | 250 | 14 |
| Patron | 500 | 7 |
| Benefactor | 1000 | 1 |

a) Find the mean and standard deviation of the donations.
b) During their annual membership drive, they hope to sign up 50 new members each day. Would you expect the distribution of the donations for a day to follow a Normal model? Explain.
c) Consider the mean donation of the 50 new members each day. Describe the sampling model for these means (shape, center, and spread).

**45. AP Stats 2006, again.** An AP Statistics teacher had 63 students preparing to take the AP exam discussed in Exercise 43. Though they were obviously not a random sample, he considered his students to be "typical" of all the national students. What's the probability that his students will achieve an average score of at least 3?

**46. Joining the museum.** One of the museum's phone volunteers sets a personal goal of getting an average donation of at least $100 from the new members she enrolls during the membership drive. If she gets 80 new members and they can be considered a random sample of all the museum's members, what is the probability that she can achieve her goal?

**47. Pollution.** Carbon monoxide (CO) emissions for a certain kind of car vary with mean 2.9 g/mi and standard deviation 0.4 g/mi. A company has 80 of these cars in its fleet. Let $\bar{y}$ represent the mean CO level for the company's fleet.
a) What's the approximate model for the distribution of $\bar{y}$? Explain.
b) Estimate the probability that $\bar{y}$ is between 3.0 and 3.1 g/mi.
c) There is only a 5% chance that the fleet's mean CO level is greater than what value?

**48. Potato chips.** The weight of potato chips in a medium-size bag is stated to be 10 ounces. The amount that the packaging machine puts in these bags is believed to have a Normal model with mean 10.2 ounces and standard deviation 0.12 ounces.
a) What fraction of all bags sold are underweight?
b) Some of the chips are sold in "bargain packs" of 3 bags. What's the probability that none of the 3 is underweight?
c) What's the probability that the mean weight of the 3 bags is below the stated amount?
d) What's the probability that the mean weight of a 24-bag case of potato chips is below 10 ounces?

**49. Tips.** A waiter believes the distribution of his tips has a model that is slightly skewed to the right, with a mean of $9.60 and a standard deviation of $5.40.
a) Explain why you cannot determine the probability that a given party will tip him at least $20.
b) Can you estimate the probability that the next 4 parties will tip an average of at least $15? Explain.
c) Is it likely that his 10 parties today will tip an average of at least $15? Explain.

**50. Groceries.** Grocery store receipts show that customer purchases have a skewed distribution with a mean of $32 and a standard deviation of $20.
a) Explain why you cannot determine the probability that the next customer will spend at least $40.

b) Can you estimate the probability that the next 10 customers will spend an average of at least $40? Explain.

c) Is it likely that the next 50 customers will spend an average of at least $40? Explain.

**51. More tips.** The waiter in Exercise 49 usually waits on about 40 parties over a weekend of work.

a) Estimate the probability that he will earn at least $500 in tips.

b) How much does he earn on the best 10% of such weekends?

**52. More groceries.** Suppose the store in Exercise 50 had 312 customers today.

a) Estimate the probability that the store's revenues were at least $10,000.

b) If, in a typical day, the store serves 312 customers, how much does the store take in on the worst 10% of such days?

**53. IQs.** Suppose that IQs of East State University's students can be described by a Normal model with mean 130 and standard deviation 8 points. Also suppose that IQs of students from West State University can be described by a Normal model with mean 120 and standard deviation 10.

a) We select a student at random from East State. Find the probability that this student's IQ is at least 125 points.

b) We select a student at random from each school. Find the probability that the East State student's IQ is at least 5 points higher than the West State student's IQ.

c) We select 3 West State students at random. Find the probability that this group's average IQ is at least 125 points.

d) We also select 3 East State students at random. What's the probability that their average IQ is at least 5 points higher than the average for the 3 West Staters?

**54. Milk.** Although most of us buy milk by the quart or gallon, farmers measure daily production in pounds. Ayrshire cows average 47 pounds of milk a day, with a standard deviation of 6 pounds. For Jersey cows, the mean daily production is 43 pounds, with a standard deviation of 5 pounds. Assume that Normal models describe milk production for these breeds.

a) We select an Ayrshire at random. What's the probability that she averages more than 50 pounds of milk a day?

b) What's the probability that a randomly selected Ayrshire gives more milk than a randomly selected Jersey?

c) A farmer has 20 Jerseys. What's the probability that the average production for this small herd exceeds 45 pounds of milk a day?

d) A neighboring farmer has 10 Ayrshires. What's the probability that his herd average is at least 5 pounds higher than the average for the Jersey herd?

**JUST CHECKING**
**Answers**

1. A Normal model (approximately).

2. At the actual proportion of all students who are in favor.

3. $SD(\hat{p}) = \sqrt{\dfrac{(0.5)(0.5)}{100}} = 0.05$

4. No, this is a histogram of individuals. It may or may not be Normal, but we can't tell from the information provided.

5. A Normal model (approximately).

6. 266 days

7. $\dfrac{16}{\sqrt{100}} = 1.6$ days

# Confidence Intervals for Proportions

## Where are we going?

In March of 2006, the Pew Research Center surveyed 1286 cell phone users.[1] They found that, overall, 22% admitted that "When I'm on my cell phone I'm not always truthful about exactly where I am." Pew reports that there is a "3% margin of error" for this result. Among younger respondents, those 18 to 29 years old, the percentage increased to 39%, and Pew warns that the margin of error for this group is larger, too. What does that mean? Are 18- to 29-year-olds less reliable (as well as, apparently, less honest)? What exactly is a margin of error, how do we find one, and how should we interpret them? We'll see what they are all about in this chapter.

| | |
|---|---|
| **WHO** | Sea fans |
| **WHAT** | Percent infected |
| **WHEN** | June 2000 |
| **WHERE** | Las Redes Reef, Akumal, Mexico, 40 feet deep |
| **WHY** | Research |

Coral reef communities are home to one quarter of all marine plants and animals worldwide. These reefs support large fisheries by providing breeding grounds and safe havens for young fish of many species. Coral reefs are seawalls that protect shorelines against tides, storm surges, and hurricanes, and are sand "factories" that produce the limestone and sand of which beaches are made. Beyond the beach, these reefs are major tourist attractions for snorkelers and divers, driving a tourist industry worth tens of billions of dollars.

But marine scientists say that 10% of the world's reef systems have been destroyed in recent times. At current rates of loss, 70% of the reefs could be gone in 40 years. Pollution, global warming, outright destruction of reefs, and increasing acidification of the oceans are all likely factors in this loss.

Dr. Drew Harvell's lab studies corals and the diseases that affect them. They sampled sea fans[2] at 19 randomly selected reefs along the Yucatan peninsula and diagnosed whether the animals were affected by the disease *aspergillosis*.[3] In

---

[1] www.pewinternet.org
[2] That's a sea fan in the picture. Although they look like trees, they are actually colonies of genetically identical animals.
[3] K. M. Mullen, C. D. Harvell, A. P. Alker, D. Dube, E. Jordán-Dahlgren, J. R. Ward, and L. E. Petes, "Host range and resistance to aspergillosis in three sea fan species from the Yucatan," *Marine Biology* (2006), Springer-Verlag.

specimens collected at a depth of 40 feet at the Las Redes Reef in Akumal, Mexico, these scientists found that 54 of 104 sea fans sampled were infected with that disease.

Of course, we care about much more than these particular 104 sea fans. We care about the health of coral reef communities throughout the Caribbean. What can this study tell us about the prevalence of the disease among sea fans?

We have a sample proportion, which we write as $\hat{p}$, of 54/104, or 51.9%. Our first guess might be that this observed proportion is close to the population proportion, $p$. But we also know that because of natural sampling variability, if the researchers had drawn a second sample of 104 sea fans at roughly the same time, the proportion infected from that sample probably wouldn't have been exactly 51.9%.

What *can* we say about the population proportion, $p$? To start to answer this question, think about how different the sample proportion might have been if we'd taken another random sample from the same population. But wait. Remember—we aren't actually going to take more samples. We just want to *imagine* how the sample proportions might vary from sample to sample. In other words, we want to know about the *sampling distribution* of the sample proportion of infected sea fans.

## A Confidence Interval

Let's look at our model for the sampling distribution. What do we know about it? We know it's approximately Normal (under certain assumptions, which we should be careful to check) and that its mean is the proportion of all infected sea fans on the Las Redes Reef. Is the infected proportion of *all* sea fans 51.9%? No, that's just $\hat{p}$, our estimate. We don't know the proportion, $p$, of all the infected sea fans; that's what we're trying to find out. We do know, though, that the sampling distribution model of $\hat{p}$ is centered at $p$, and we know that the standard deviation of the sampling distribution is $\sqrt{\dfrac{pq}{n}}$.

Since we don't know $p$, we can't find the true standard deviation of the sampling distribution model. Instead we'll use $\hat{p}$ and find the standard error,

$$SE(\hat{p}) = \sqrt{\frac{\hat{p}\hat{q}}{n}} = \sqrt{\frac{(0.519)(0.481)}{104}} = 0.049 = 4.9\%.$$

Now we know that the sampling model for $\hat{p}$ should look like this:

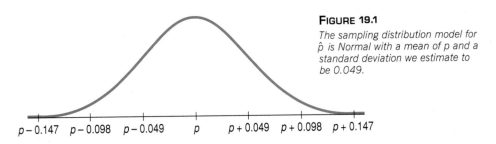

**FIGURE 19.1**

*The sampling distribution model for $\hat{p}$ is Normal with a mean of p and a standard deviation we estimate to be 0.049.*

$p-0.147$   $p-0.098$   $p-0.049$   $p$   $p+0.049$   $p+0.098$   $p+0.147$

Great. What does that tell us? Well, because it's Normal, it says that about 68% of all samples of 104 sea fans will have $\hat{p}$'s within 1 $SE$, 0.049, of $p$. And about 95% of all these samples will be within $p \pm 2$ $SE$s. But where is *our* sample proportion in this picture? And what value does $p$ have? We still don't know!

We do know that for 95% of random samples, $\hat{p}$ will be no more than 2 $SE$s away from $p$. So let's look at this from $\hat{p}$'s point of view. If I'm $\hat{p}$, there's a 95% chance that $p$ is no more than 2 $SE$s away from me. If I reach out 2 $SE$s, or $2 \times 0.049$, away from me on both sides, I'm 95% sure that $p$ will be within my grasp. Now, I've got him! Probably. Of course, even if my interval does catch $p$, I still don't know its true value. The best I can do is an interval, and even then I can't be positive it contains $p$.

**FIGURE 19.2**

*Reaching out 2 SEs on either side of $\hat{p}$ makes us 95% confident that we'll trap the true proportion, $p$.*

So what can we really say about $p$? Here's a list of things we'd like to be able to say, in order of strongest to weakest and the reasons we can't say most of them:

**A S**   *Activity:* **Can We Estimate a Parameter?** Consider these four interpretations of a confidence interval by simulating to see whether they could be right.

1. **"51.9% of *all* sea fans on the Las Redes Reef are infected."** It would be nice to be able to make absolute statements about population values with certainty, but we just don't have enough information to do that. There's no way to be sure that the population proportion is the same as the sample proportion; in fact, it almost certainly isn't. Observations vary. Another sample would yield a different sample proportion.
2. **"It is *probably* true that 51.9% of all sea fans on the Las Redes Reef are infected."** No. In fact, we can be pretty sure that whatever the true proportion is, it's not exactly 51.900%. So the statement is not true.
3. **"We don't know exactly what proportion of sea fans on the Las Redes Reef is infected but we *know* that it's within the interval 51.9% $\pm$ 2 $\times$ 4.9%. That is, it's between 42.1% and 61.7%."** This is getting closer, but we still can't be certain. We can't know *for sure* that the true proportion is in this interval—or in any particular interval.
4. **"We don't know exactly what proportion of sea fans on the Las Redes Reef is infected, but the interval from 42.1% to 61.7% *probably* contains the true proportion."** We've now fudged twice—first by giving an interval and second by admitting that we only think the interval "probably" contains the true value. And this statement is true.

*"Far better an approximate answer to the right question, . . . than an exact answer to the wrong question."*

—John W. Tukey

That last statement may be true, but it's a bit wishy-washy. We can tighten it up a bit by quantifying what we mean by "probably." We saw that 95% of the time when we reach out 2 *SE*s from $\hat{p}$ we capture $p$, *so we can be 95% confident that this is one of those times.* After putting a number on the probability that this interval covers the true proportion, we've given our best guess of where the parameter is and how certain we are that it's within some range.

5. **"We are 95% confident that between 42.1% and 61.7% of Las Redes sea fans are infected."** Statements like these are called **confidence intervals.** They're the best we can do.

Each confidence interval discussed in the book has a name. You'll see many different kinds of confidence intervals in the following chapters. Some will be about more than *one* sample, some will be about statistics other than *proportions*, and some will use models other than the Normal. The interval calculated and interpreted here is sometimes called a **one-proportion z-interval**.[4]

### JUST CHECKING

A Pew Research study regarding cell phones asked other questions about cell phone experience. One growing concern is unsolicited advertising in the form of text messages. Pew asked cell phone owners, "Have you ever received unsolicited text messages on your cell phone from advertisers?" and 17% reported that they had. Pew estimates a 95% confidence interval to be 0.17 ± 0.04, or between 13% and 21%.

Are the following statements about people who have cell phones correct? Explain.

**1.** In Pew's sample, somewhere between 13% and 21% of respondents reported that they had received unsolicited advertising text messages.

**2.** We can be 95% confident that 17% of U.S. cell phone owners have received unsolicited advertising text messages.

**3.** We are 95% confident that between 13% and 21% of all U.S. cell phone owners have received unsolicited advertising text messages.

**4.** We know that between 13% and 21% of all U.S. cell phone owners have received unsolicited advertising text messages.

**5.** 95% of all U.S. cell phone owners have received unsolicited advertising text messages.

# What Does "95% Confidence" Really Mean?

**A S**   *Activity:* **Confidence Intervals for Proportions.** This new interactive tool makes it easy to construct and experiment with confidence intervals. We'll use this tool for the rest of the course—sure beats calculating by hand!

What do we mean when we say we have 95% confidence that our interval contains the true proportion? Formally, what we mean is that "95% of samples of this size will produce confidence intervals that capture the true proportion." This is correct, but a little long winded, so we sometimes say, "we are 95% confident that the true proportion lies in our interval." Our uncertainty is about whether the particular sample we have at hand is one of the successful ones or one of the 5% that fail to produce an interval that captures the true value.

Back in Chapter 18 we saw that proportions vary from sample to sample. If other researchers select their own samples of sea fans, they'll also find some infected by the disease, but each person's sample proportion will almost certainly differ from ours. When they each try to estimate the true rate of infection in the entire population, they'll center *their* confidence intervals at the proportions they observed in their own samples. Each of us will end up with a different interval.

Our interval guessed the true proportion of infected sea fans to be between about 42% and 62%. Another researcher whose sample contained more infected fans than ours did might guess between 46% and 66%. Still another who happened to collect fewer infected fans might estimate the true proportion to be between 23% and 43%. And so on. Every possible sample would produce yet another confidence interval. Although wide intervals like these can't pin down the actual rate of infection very precisely, we expect that most of them should be

---

[4] In fact, this confidence interval is so standard for a single proportion that you may see it simply called a "confidence interval for the proportion."

winners, capturing the true value. Nonetheless, some will be duds, missing the population proportion entirely.

The figure below shows the confidence intervals produced by simulating 20 different random samples. The red dots are the proportions of infected fans in each sample, and the blue segments show the confidence intervals found for each. The green line represents the true rate of infection in the population, so you can see that most of the intervals caught it—but a few missed. (And notice again that it is the *intervals* that vary from sample to sample; the green line doesn't move.)

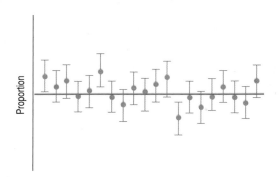

*The horizontal green line shows the true percentage of all sea fans that are infected. Most of the 20 simulated samples produced confidence intervals that captured the true value, but a few missed.*

Of course, there's a huge number of possible samples that *could* be drawn, each with its own sample proportion. These are just some of them. Each sample proportion can be used to make a confidence interval. That's a large pile of possible confidence intervals, and ours is just one of those in the pile. Did *our* confidence interval "work"? We can never be sure, because we'll never know the true proportion of all the sea fans that are infected. However, the Central Limit Theorem assures us that 95% of the intervals in the pile are winners, covering the true value, and only 5% are duds. *That's* why we're 95% confident that our interval is a winner!

---

**FOR EXAMPLE** | Polls and margin of error

On January 30–31, 2007, Fox News/Opinion Dynamics polled 900 registered voters nationwide.[5] When asked, "Do you believe global warming exists?" 82% said "Yes". Fox reported their margin of error to be ±3%.

**Question:** It is standard among pollsters to use a 95% confidence level unless otherwise stated. Given that, what does Fox News mean by claiming a margin of error of ±3% in this context?

If this polling were done repeatedly, 95% of all random samples would yield estimates that come within ±3% of the true proportion of all registered voters who believe that global warming exists.

---

# Margin of Error: Certainty vs. Precision

We've just claimed that with a certain confidence we've captured the true proportion of all infected sea fans. Our confidence interval had the form

$$\hat{p} \pm 2\, SE(\hat{p}).$$

---

[5] www.foxnews.com, "Fox News Poll: Most Americans Believe in Global Warming," Feb 7, 2007.

The extent of the interval on either side of $\hat{p}$ is called the **margin of error** (*ME*). We'll want to use the same approach for many other situations besides estimating proportions. In general, confidence intervals look like this:

*Estimate* $\pm$ *ME.*

The margin of error for our 95% confidence interval was 2 *SE*. What if we wanted to be more confident? To be more confident, we'll need to capture *p* more often, and to do that we'll need to make the interval wider. For example, if we want to be 99.7% confident, the margin of error will have to be 3 *SE*.

**FIGURE 19.3**

*Reaching out 3 SEs on either side of $\hat{p}$ makes us 99.7% confident we'll trap the true proportion p. Compare with Figure 19.2.*

$\hat{p} - 3\ SE$        $\hat{p}$        $\hat{p} + 3\ SE$

*A S*    **Activity: Balancing Precision and Certainty.** What percent of parents expect their kids to pay for college with a student loan? Investigate the balance between the precision and the certainty of a confidence interval.

The more confident we want to be, the larger the margin of error must be. We can be 100% confident that the proportion of infected sea fans is between 0% and 100%, but this isn't likely to be very useful. On the other hand, we could give a confidence interval from 51.8% to 52.0%, but we can't be very confident about a precise statement like this. Every confidence interval is a balance between certainty and precision.

The tension between certainty and precision is always there. Fortunately, in most cases we can be both sufficiently certain and sufficiently precise to make useful statements. There is no simple answer to the conflict. You must choose a confidence level yourself. The data can't do it for you. The choice of confidence level is somewhat arbitrary. The most commonly chosen confidence levels are 90%, 95%, and 99%, but any percentage can be used. (In practice, though, using something like 92.9% or 97.2% is likely to make people think you're up to something.)

**FOR EXAMPLE**    Finding the margin of error (Take 1)

**Recap:** A January 2007 Fox poll of 900 registered voters reported a margin of error of $\pm 3\%$. It is a convention among pollsters to use a 95% confidence level and to report the "worst case" margin of error, based on $p = 0.5$.

*(continued)*

For Example (*continued*)

**Question:** How did Fox calculate their margin of error?

Assuming $p = 0.5$, for random samples of $n = 900$,

$$SD(\hat{p}) = \sqrt{\frac{pq}{n}} = \sqrt{\frac{(0.5)(0.5)}{900}} = 0.0167$$

For a 95% confidence level, $ME = 2(0.0167) = 0.033$.
Fox's margin of error is just a bit over ±3%.

## Critical Values

**NOTATION ALERT:**

We'll put an asterisk on a letter to indicate a critical value, so $z^*$ is always a critical value from a Normal model.

In our sea fans example we used $2\ SE$ to give us a 95% confidence interval. To change the confidence level, we'd need to change the *number* of SEs so that the size of the margin of error corresponds to the new level. This number of SEs is called the **critical value.** Here it's based on the Normal model, so we denote it $z^*$. For any confidence level, we can find the corresponding critical value from a computer, a calculator, or a Normal probability table, such as Table Z.

For a 95% confidence interval, you'll find the precise critical value is $z^* = 1.96$. That is, 95% of a Normal model is found within ±1.96 standard deviations of the mean. We've been using $z^* = 2$ from the 68–95–99.7 Rule because it's easy to remember.

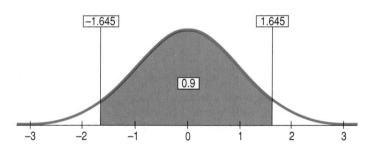

**FIGURE 19.4**
*For a 90% confidence interval, the critical value is 1.645, because, for a Normal model, 90% of the values are within 1.645 standard deviations from the mean.*

**FOR EXAMPLE**   Finding the margin of error (Take 2)

**Recap:** In January 2007 a Fox News poll of 900 registered voters found that 82% of the respondents believed that global warming exists. Fox reported a 95% confidence interval with a margin of error of ±3%.

**Questions:** Using the critical value of $z$ and the standard error based on the observed proportion, what would be the margin of error for a 90% confidence interval? What's good and bad about this change?

With $n = 900$ and $\hat{p} = 0.82$,

$$SE(\hat{p}) = \sqrt{\frac{\hat{p}\hat{q}}{n}} = \sqrt{\frac{(0.82)(0.18)}{900}} = 0.0128$$

For a 90% confidence level, $z^* = 1.645$, so

$$ME = 1.645(0.0128) = 0.021$$

Now the margin of error is only about ±2%, producing a narrower interval. That makes for a more precise estimate of voter belief, but provides less certainty that the interval actually contains the true proportion of voters believing in global warming.

# Assumptions and Conditions

We've just made some pretty sweeping statements about sea fans. Those statements were possible because we used a Normal model for the sampling distribution. But is that model appropriate?

As we've seen, all statistical models make assumptions. Different models make different assumptions. If those assumptions are not true, the model might be inappropriate and our conclusions based on it may be wrong. Because the confidence interval is built on the Normal model for the sampling distribution, the assumptions and conditions are the same as those we discussed in Chapter 18. But, because they are so important, we'll go over them again.

We can never be certain that an assumption is true, but we can decide intelligently whether it is reasonable. When we have data, we can often decide whether an assumption is plausible by checking a related condition. However, we want to make a statement about the world at large, not just about the data we collected. So the assumptions we make are not just about how our data look, but about how representative they are.

### INDEPENDENCE ASSUMPTION

**Independence Assumption:** We first need to *Think* about whether the independence assumption is plausible. We often look for reasons to suspect that it fails. We wonder whether there is any reason to believe that the data values somehow affect each other. (For example, might the disease in sea fans be contagious?) Whether you decide that the **Independence Assumption** is plausible depends on your knowledge of the situation. It's not one you can check by looking at the data.

However, now that we have data, there are two conditions that we can check:

**Randomization Condition:** Were the data sampled at random or generated from a properly randomized experiment? Proper randomization can help ensure independence.

**10% Condition:** Samples are almost always drawn without replacement. Usually, of course, we'd like to have as large a sample as we can. But when the population itself is small we have another concern. When we sample from small populations, the probability of success may be different for the last few individuals we draw than it was for the first few. For example, if most of the women have already been sampled, the chance of drawing a woman from the remaining population is lower. If the sample exceeds 10% of the population, the probability of a success changes so much during the sampling that our Normal model may no longer be appropriate. But if less than 10% of the population is sampled, the effect on independence is negligible.

### SAMPLE SIZE ASSUMPTION

The model we use for inference is based on the Central Limit Theorem. The **Sample Size Assumption** addresses the question of whether the sample is large enough to make the sampling model for the sample proportions approximately Normal. It turns out that we need more data as the proportion gets closer and closer to either extreme (0 or 1). We can check this assumption with the:

**Success/Failure Condition:** We must expect at least 10 "successes" and at least 10 "failures." Recall that by tradition we arbitrarily label one alternative (usually the outcome being counted) as a "success" even if it's something bad (like a sick sea fan). The other alternative is, of course, then a "failure."

**A S**  **_Activity:_ A Confidence Interval for _p._** View the video story of pollution in Chesapeake Bay, and make a confidence interval for the analysis with the interactive tool.

ONE-PROPORTION z-INTERVAL

When the conditions are met, we are ready to find the confidence interval for the population proportion, $p$. The confidence interval is $\hat{p} \pm z^* \times SE(\hat{p})$ where the standard deviation of the proportion is estimated by $SE(\hat{p}) = \sqrt{\dfrac{\hat{p}\hat{q}}{n}}$.

---

**STEP-BY-STEP EXAMPLE**       **A Confidence Interval for a Proportion**

| | |
|---|---|
| **WHO** | Adults in the United States |
| **WHAT** | Response to a question about the death penalty |
| **WHEN** | May 2006 |
| **WHERE** | United States |
| **HOW** | 510 adults were randomly sampled and asked by the Gallup Poll |
| **WHY** | Public opinion research |

In May 2006, the Gallup Poll[6] asked 510 randomly sampled adults the question "Generally speaking, do you believe the death penalty is applied fairly or unfairly in this country today?" Of these, 60% answered "Fairly," 35% said "Unfairly," and 4% said they didn't know.

- Fairly
- Unfairly
- Don't Know

**Question:** From this survey, what can we conclude about the opinions of _all_ adults?

To answer this question, we'll build a confidence interval for the proportion of all U.S. adults who believe the death penalty is applied fairly. There are four steps to building a confidence interval for proportions: Plan, Model, Mechanics, and Conclusion.

---

**Plan** State the problem and the W's.

Identify the _parameter_ you wish to estimate.

Identify the _population_ about which you wish to make statements.

Choose and state a confidence level.

**Model** Think about the assumptions and check the conditions.

I want to find an interval that is likely with 95% confidence to contain the true proportion, $p$, of U.S. adults who think the death penalty is applied fairly. I have a random sample of 510 U.S. adults.

✔ **Independence Assumption:** Gallup phoned a random sample of U.S. adults. It is very unlikely that any of their respondents influenced each other.

✔ **Randomization Condition:** Gallup drew a random sample from all U.S. adults. I don't have details of their randomization but assume that I can trust it.

✔ **10% Condition:** Although sampling was necessarily without replacement, there are many more U.S. adults than were sampled.

---

[6] www.galluppoll.com

The sample is certainly less than 10% of the population.

✓ **Success/Failure Condition:**
$n\hat{p} = 510(60\%) = 306 \geq 10$ and
$n\hat{q} = 510(40\%) = 204 \geq 10$,
so the sample appears to be large enough to use the Normal model.

State the sampling distribution model for the statistic.

Choose your method.

The conditions are satisfied, so I can use a Normal model to find a **one-proportion z-interval.**

---

 **Mechanics** Construct the confidence interval.

First find the standard error. (Remember: It's called the "standard error" because we don't know $p$ and have to use $\hat{p}$ instead.)

Next find the margin of error. We could informally use 2 for our critical value, but 1.96 is more accurate.

Write the confidence interval (CI).

 The CI is centered at the sample proportion and about as wide as we might expect for a sample of 500.

$n = 510$, $\hat{p} = 0.60$, so

$$SE(\hat{p}) = \sqrt{\frac{\hat{p}\hat{q}}{n}} = \sqrt{\frac{(0.60)(0.40)}{510}} = 0.022$$

Because the sampling model is Normal, for a 95% confidence interval, the critical value $z^* = 1.96$.

The margin of error is

$$ME = z^* \times SE(\hat{p}) = 1.96(0.022) = 0.043$$

So the 95% confidence interval is

$$0.60 \pm 0.043 \text{ or } (0.557, 0.643)$$

---

**TELL** **Conclusion** Interpret the confidence interval in the proper context. We're 95% confident that our interval captured the true proportion.

I am 95% confident that between 55.7% and 64.3% of all U.S. adults think that the death penalty is applied fairly.

---

## JUST CHECKING

Think some more about the 95% confidence interval we just created for the proportion of U.S. adults who think the death penalty is applied fairly.

**6.** If we wanted to be 98% confident, would our confidence interval need to be wider or narrower?

**7.** Our margin of error was about ±4%. If we wanted to reduce it to ±3%, would our level of confidence be higher or lower?

**8.** If the Gallup organization had polled more people, would the interval's margin of error have been larger or smaller?

## CHOOSING YOUR SAMPLE SIZE

The question of how large a sample to take is an important step in planning any study. We weren't ready to make that calculation when we first looked at study design in Chapter 12, but now we can—and we always should.

Suppose a candidate is planning a poll and wants to estimate voter support within 3% with 95% confidence. How large a sample does she need?

Let's look at the margin of error:

$$ME = z^* \sqrt{\frac{\hat{p}\hat{q}}{n}}$$

$$0.03 = 1.96 \sqrt{\frac{\hat{p}\hat{q}}{n}}.$$

We want to find $n$, the sample size. To find $n$ we need a value for $\hat{p}$. We don't know $\hat{p}$ because we don't have a sample yet, but we can probably guess a value. The worst case—the value that makes $\hat{p}\hat{q}$ (and therefore $n$) largest—is 0.50, so if we use that value for $\hat{p}$, we'll certainly be safe. Our candidate probably expects to be near 50% anyway.

Our equation, then, is

$$0.03 = 1.96 \sqrt{\frac{(0.5)(0.5)}{n}}.$$

To solve for $n$, we first multiply both sides of the equation by $\sqrt{n}$ and then divide by 0.03:

$$0.03\sqrt{n} = 1.96\sqrt{(0.5)(0.5)}$$

$$\sqrt{n} = \frac{1.96\sqrt{(0.5)(0.5)}}{0.03} \approx 32.67$$

Notice that evaluating this expression tells us the *square root* of the sample size. We need to square that result to find $n$:

$$n \approx (32.67)^2 \approx 1067.1$$

To be safe, we round up and conclude that we need at least 1068 respondents to keep the margin of error as small as 3% with a confidence level of 95%.

> **What do I use instead of $\hat{p}$?**
> Often we have an estimate of the population proportion based on experience or perhaps a previous study. If so, use that value as $\hat{p}$ in calculating what size sample you need. If not, the cautious approach is to use $p = 0.5$ in the sample size calculation; that will determine the largest sample necessary regardless of the true proportion.

---

**FOR EXAMPLE**    Choosing a sample size

**Recap:** The Fox News poll which estimated that 82% of all voters believed global warming exists had a margin of error of $\pm 3\%$. Suppose an environmental group planning a follow-up survey of voters' opinions on global warming wants to determine a 95% confidence interval with a margin of error of no more than $\pm 2\%$.

**Question:** How large a sample do they need? Use the Fox News estimate as the basis for your calculation.

$$ME = z^* \sqrt{\frac{\hat{p}\hat{q}}{n}}$$

$$0.02 = 1.96 \sqrt{\frac{(0.82)(0.18)}{n}}$$

$$\sqrt{n} = \frac{1.96\sqrt{(0.82)(0.18)}}{0.02} \approx 37.65$$

$$n = 37.65^2 = 1{,}417.55$$

The environmental group's survey will need about 1,418 respondents.

Public opinion polls often sample 1000 people, which gives an ME of 3% when $p = 0.5$. But businesses and nonprofit organizations typically use much larger samples to estimate the proportion who will accept a direct mail offer. Why? Because that proportion is very low—often far below 5%. An ME of 3% wouldn't be precise enough. An ME like 0.1% would be more useful, and that requires a very large sample size.

Unfortunately, bigger samples cost more money and more effort. Because the standard error declines only with the *square root* of the sample size, to cut the standard error (and thus the ME) in half, we must *quadruple* the sample size.

Generally a margin of error of 5% or less is acceptable, but different circumstances call for different standards. For a pilot study, a margin of error of 10% may be fine, so a sample of 100 will do quite well. In a close election, a polling organization might want to get the margin of error down to 2%. Drawing a large sample to get a smaller ME, however, can run into trouble. It takes time to survey 2400 people, and a survey that extends over a week or more may be trying to hit a target that moves during the time of the survey. An important event can change public opinion in the middle of the survey process.

Keep in mind that the sample size for a survey is the number of respondents, not the number of people to whom questionnaires were sent or whose phone numbers were dialed. And keep in mind that a low response *rate* turns any study essentially into a voluntary response study, which is of little value for inferring population values. It's almost always better to spend resources on increasing the response rate than on surveying a larger group. A full or nearly full response by a modest-size sample can yield useful results.

Surveys are not the only place where proportions pop up. Banks sample huge mailing lists to estimate what proportion of people will accept a credit card offer. Even pilot studies may mail offers to over 50,000 customers. Most don't respond; that doesn't make the sample smaller—they simply said "No thanks". Those who do respond want the card. To the bank, the response rate[7] is $\hat{p}$. With a typical success rate around 0.5%, the bank needs a very small margin of error—often as low as 0.1%—to make a sound business decision. That calls for a large sample, and the bank must take care in estimating the size needed. For our election poll calculation we used $p = 0.5$, both because it's safe and because we honestly believed $p$ to be near 0.5. If the bank used 0.5, they'd get an absurd answer. Instead, they base their calculation on a proportion closer to the one they expect to find.

---

### HOW MUCH OF A DIFFERENCE CAN IT MAKE?

A credit card company is about to send out a mailing to test the market for a new credit card. From that sample, they want to estimate the true proportion of people who will sign up for the card nationwide. To be within a tenth of a percentage point, or 0.001 of the true rate with 95% confidence, how big does the test mailing have to be? A pilot study suggests that about 0.5% of the people receiving the offer will accept it. Using that estimate the company finds:

$$ME = 0.001 = z^* \sqrt{\frac{\hat{p}\hat{q}}{n}} = 1.96 \sqrt{\frac{(0.005)(0.995)}{n}}$$

$$(0.001)^2 = 1.96^2 \frac{(0.005)(0.995)}{n} \Rightarrow n = \frac{1.96^2 (0.005)(0.995)}{(0.001)^2}$$

$$= 19{,}111.96 \ or \ 19{,}112$$

---

[7] In marketing studies every mailing yields a response— "yes" or "no" —and "response rate" means the proportion of customers who accept an offer. That's not the way we use the term for survey response.

That's a perfectly reasonable size for a trial mailing. But if they had assumed 0.50 for the value of $p$, they would have found

$$ME = 0.001 = z^*\sqrt{\frac{pq}{n}} = 1.96\sqrt{\frac{(0.5)(0.5)}{n}}$$

$$(0.001)^2 = 1.96^2\frac{(0.5)(0.5)}{n} \Rightarrow n = \frac{1.96^2(0.5)(0.5)}{(0.001)^2} = 960,400.$$

Quite a different result.

# *A Confidence Interval for Small Samples

When the **Success/Failure Condition** fails, all is not lost. A simple adjustment to the calculation lets us make a confidence interval anyway.

All we do is add four *phony* observations—two to the successes, two to the failures. So instead of the proportion $\hat{p} = \frac{y}{n}$, we use the adjusted proportion $\tilde{p} = \frac{y+2}{n+4}$ and, for convenience, we write $\tilde{n} = n + 4$. We modify the interval by using these adjusted values for both the center of the interval *and* the margin of error. Now the adjusted interval is

$$\tilde{p} \pm z^*\sqrt{\frac{\tilde{p}(1-\tilde{p})}{\tilde{n}}}.$$

This adjusted form gives better performance overall[8] and works much better for proportions near 0 or 1. It has the additional advantage that we no longer need to check the **Success/Failure Condition** that $n\hat{p}$ and $n\hat{q}$ are greater than 10.

### FOR EXAMPLE    An Agresti–Coull interval

Surgeons examined their results to compare two methods for a surgical procedure used to alleviate pain on the outside of the wrist. A new method was compared with the traditional "freehand" method for the procedure. Of 45 operations using the "freehand" method, three were unsuccessful, for a failure rate of 6.7%. With only 3 failures, the data don't satisfy the **Success/Failure Condition,** so we can't use a standard confidence interval.

Question:  What's the confidence interval using the Agresti–Coull method?

There were 42 successes and 3 failures. Adding 2 "pseudo-successes" and 2 "pseudo-failures," we find

$$\tilde{p} = \frac{3+2}{45+4} = 0.102$$

[8] By "better performance," we mean that a 95% confidence interval has more nearly a 95% chance of covering the true population proportion. Simulation studies have shown that our original, simpler confidence interval in fact is less likely than 95% to cover the true population proportion when the sample size is small or the proportion very close to 0 or 1. The original idea for this method can be attributed to E. B. Wilson. The simpler approach discussed here was proposed by Agresti and Coull (A. Agresti and B. A. Coull, "Approximate Is Better Than 'Exact' for Interval Estimation of Binomial Proportions," *The American Statistician*, 52[1998]: 119–129).

A 95% confidence interval is then

$$0.102 \pm 1.96\sqrt{\frac{0.102(1 - 0.102)}{49}} = 0.102 \pm 0.085$$

or (0.017, 0.187).

Notice that although the observed failure rate of 0.067 is contained in the interval, it is not at the center of the interval—something we haven't seen with any of the other confidence intervals we've considered.

# WHAT CAN GO WRONG?

Confidence intervals are powerful tools. Not only do they tell what we know about the parameter value, but—more important—they also tell what we *don't* know. In order to use confidence intervals effectively, you must be clear about what you say about them.

### What *Can* I Say?

Confidence intervals are based on random samples, so the interval is random, too. The CLT tells us that 95% of the random samples will yield intervals that capture the true value. That's what we mean by being 95% confident.

Technically, we should say, "I am 95% confident that the interval from 42.1% to 61.7% captures the true proportion of infected sea fans." That formal phrasing emphasizes that *our confidence (and our uncertainty) is about the interval, not the true proportion.* But you may choose a more casual phrasing like "I am 95% confident that between 42.1% and 61.7% of the Las Redes fans are infected." Because you've made it clear that the uncertainty is yours and you didn't suggest that the randomness is in the true proportion, this is OK. Keep in mind that it's the interval that's random and is the focus of both our confidence and doubt.

## DON'T MISSTATE WHAT THE INTERVAL MEANS

▶ **Don't suggest that the parameter varies.** A statement like "There is a 95% chance that the true proportion is between 42.7% and 51.3%" sounds as though you think the population proportion wanders around and sometimes happens to fall between 42.7% and 51.3%. When you interpret a confidence interval, make it clear that *you* know that the population parameter is fixed and that it is the interval that varies from sample to sample.

▶ **Don't claim that other samples will agree with yours.** Keep in mind that the confidence interval makes a statement about the true population proportion. An interpretation such as "In 95% of samples of U.S. adults, the proportion who think marijuana should be decriminalized will be between 42.7% and 51.3%" is just wrong. The interval isn't about sample proportions but about the population proportion.

▶ **Don't be certain about the parameter.** Saying "Between 42.1% and 61.7% of sea fans are infected" asserts that the population proportion cannot be outside that interval. Of course, we can't be absolutely certain of that. (Just pretty sure.)

▶ **Don't forget: It's about the parameter.** Don't say, "I'm 95% confident that $\hat{p}$ is between 42.1% and 61.7%." Of course you are—in fact, we calculated that $\hat{p} = 51.9\%$ of the fans in our sample were infected. So we already *know* the sample proportion. The confidence interval is about the (unknown) population parameter, $p$.

▶ **Don't claim to know too much.** Don't say, "I'm 95% confident that between 42.1% and 61.7% of all the sea fans in the world are infected." You didn't sample from all 500 species of sea fans found in coral reefs around the world. Just those of this type on the Las Redes Reef.

▶ **Do take responsibility.** Confidence intervals are about *uncertainty*. *You* are the one who is uncertain, not the parameter. You have to accept the responsibility and consequences of the fact that not all the intervals you compute will capture the true value.

*(continued)*

In fact, about 5% of the 95% confidence intervals you find will fail to capture the true value of the parameter. You *can* say, "I am 95% confident that between 42.1% and 61.7% of the sea fans on the Las Redes Reef are infected."[9]

▶ **Do treat the whole interval equally.** Although a confidence interval is a set of plausible values for the parameter, don't think that the values in the middle of a confidence interval are somehow "more plausible" than the values near the edges. Your interval provides no information about where in your current interval (if at all) the parameter value is most likely to be hiding.

## MARGIN OF ERROR TOO LARGE TO BE USEFUL

We know we can't be exact, but how precise do we need to be? A confidence interval that says that the percentage of infected sea fans is between 10% and 90% wouldn't be of much use. Most likely, you have some sense of how large a margin of error you can tolerate. What can you do?

One way to make the margin of error smaller is to reduce your level of confidence. But that may not be a useful solution. It's a rare study that reports confidence levels lower than 80%. Levels of 95% or 99% are more common.

The time to think about whether your margin of error is small enough to be useful is when you design your study. Don't wait until you compute your confidence interval. To get a narrower interval without giving up confidence, you need to have less variability in your sample proportion. How can you do that? Choose a larger sample.

## VIOLATIONS OF ASSUMPTIONS

Confidence intervals and margins of error are often reported along with poll results and other analyses. But it's easy to misuse them and wise to be aware of the ways things can go wrong.

▶ **Watch out for biased sampling.** Don't forget about the potential sources of bias in surveys that we discussed in Chapter 12. Just because we have more statistical machinery now doesn't mean we can forget what we've already learned. A questionnaire that finds that 85% of people enjoy filling out surveys still suffers from nonresponse bias even though now we're able to put confidence intervals around this (biased) estimate.

▶ **Think about independence.** The assumption that the values in our sample are mutually independent is one that we usually cannot check. It always pays to think about it, though. For example, the disease affecting the sea fans might be contagious, so that fans growing near a diseased fan are more likely themselves to be diseased. Such contagion would violate the Independence Assumption and could severely affect our sample proportion. It could be that the proportion of infected sea fans on the entire reef is actually quite small, and the researchers just happened to find an infected area. To avoid this, the researchers should be careful to sample sites far enough apart to make contagion unlikely.

# CONNECTIONS

Now we can see a practical application of sampling distributions. To find a confidence interval, we lay out an interval measured in standard deviations. We're using the standard deviation as a ruler again. But now the standard deviation we need is the standard deviation of the sampling distribution. That's the one that tells how much the proportion varies. (And when we estimate it from the data, we call it a standard error.)

---

[9] When we are being very careful we say, "95% of samples of this size will produce confidence intervals that capture the true proportion of infected sea fans on the Las Redes Reef."

# WHAT HAVE WE LEARNED?

The first 10 chapters of the book explored graphical and numerical ways of summarizing and presenting sample data. We've learned (at last!) to use the sample we have at hand to say something about the *world at large*. This process, called statistical inference, is based on our understanding of sampling models and will be our focus for the rest of the book.

As our first step in statistical inference, we've learned to use our sample to make a *confidence interval* that estimates what proportion of a population has a certain characteristic.

We've learned that:

▶ Our best estimate of the true population proportion is the proportion we observed in the sample, so we center our confidence interval there.

▶ Samples don't represent the population perfectly, so we create our interval with a *margin of error*.

▶ This method successfully captures the true population proportion most of the time, providing us with a level of confidence in our interval.

▶ The higher the level of confidence we want, the *wider* our confidence interval becomes.

▶ The larger the sample size we have, the *narrower* our confidence interval can be.

▶ When designing a study, we can calculate the sample size we'll need to be able to reach conclusions that have a desired degree of precision and level of confidence.

▶ There are important assumptions and conditions we must check before using this (or any) statistical inference procedure.

We've learned to interpret a confidence interval by *Telling* what we believe is true in the entire population from which we took our random sample. Of course, we can't be *certain*. We've learned not to overstate or misinterpret what the confidence interval says.

## Terms

**Confidence interval**

487. A level C confidence interval for a model parameter is an interval of values usually of the form

$$estimate \pm margin\ of\ error$$

found from data in such a way that C% of all random samples will yield intervals that capture the true parameter value.

**One-proportion *z*-interval**

487–489. A confidence interval for the true value of a proportion. The confidence interval is

$$\hat{p} \pm z^*SE(\hat{p}),$$

where $z^*$ is a critical value from the Standard Normal model corresponding to the specified confidence level.

**Margin of error**

490. In a confidence interval, the extent of the interval on either side of the observed statistic value is called the margin of error. A margin of error is typically the product of a critical value from the sampling distribution and a standard error from the data. A small margin of error corresponds to a confidence interval that pins down the parameter precisely. A large margin of error corresponds to a confidence interval that gives relatively little information about the estimated parameter. For a proportion,

$$ME = z^*\sqrt{\frac{\hat{p}\hat{q}}{n}}$$

**Critical value**

494. The number of standard errors to move away from the mean of the sampling distribution to correspond to the specified level of confidence. The critical value, denoted $z^*$, is usually found from a table or with technology.

## Skills

▶ Understand confidence intervals as a balance between the precision and the certainty of a statement about a model parameter.

▶ Understand that the margin of error of a confidence interval for a proportion changes with the sample size and the level of confidence.

▸ Know how to examine your data for violations of conditions that would make inference about a population proportion unwise or invalid.

▸ Be able to construct a one-proportion $z$-interval.

▸ Be able to interpret a one-proportion $z$-interval in a simple sentence or two. Write such an interpretation so that it does not state or suggest that the parameter of interest is itself random, but rather that the bounds of the confidence interval are the random quantities about which we state our degree of confidence.

# ON THE COMPUTER

## Confidence Intervals for Proportions

Confidence intervals for proportions are so easy and natural that many statistics packages don't offer special commands for them. Most statistics programs want the "raw data" for computations. For proportions, the raw data are the "success" and "failure" status for each case. Usually, these are given as 1 or 0, but they might be category names like "yes" and "no." Often we just know the proportion of successes, $\hat{p}$, and the total count, $n$. Computer packages don't usually deal with summary data like this easily, but the statistics routines found on many graphing calculators allow you to create confidence intervals from summaries of the data—usually all you need to enter are the number of successes and the sample size.

In some programs you can reconstruct variables of 0's and 1's with the given proportions. But even when you have (or can reconstruct) the raw data values, you may not get *exactly* the same margin of error from a computer package as you would find working by hand. The reason is that some packages make approximations or use other methods. The result is very close but not exactly the same. Fortunately, Statistics means never having to say you're certain, so the approximate result is good enough.

### DATA DESK

Data Desk does not offer built-in methods for inference with proportions.

COMMENTS

For summarized data, open a Scratchpad to compute the standard deviation and margin of error by typing the calculation. Then use **z-interval for individual $\mu$s**.

### EXCEL

Inference methods for proportions are not part of the standard Excel tool set.

COMMENTS

For summarized data, type the calculation into any cell and evaluate it.

### JMP

For a **categorical** variable that holds category labels, the **Distribution** platform includes tests and intervals for proportions. For summarized data, put the category names in one variable and the frequencies in an adjacent variable. Designate the frequency column to have the **role** of **frequency.** Then use the **Distribution** platform.

COMMENTS

JMP uses slightly different methods for proportion inferences than those discussed in this text. Your answers are likely to be slightly different, especially for small samples.

## MINITAB

Choose **Basic Statistics** from the **Stat** menu.

▸ Choose **1Proportion** from the Basic Statistics submenu.
▸ If the data are category names in a variable, assign the variable from the variable list box to the **Samples in columns** box. If you have summarized data, click the **Summarized Data** button and fill in the number of trials and the number of successes.
▸ Click the **Options** button and specify the remaining details.
▸ If you have a large sample, check **Use test and interval based on normal distribution.** Click the **OK** button.

### COMMENTS

When working from a variable that names categories, MINITAB treats the last category as the "success" category. You can specify how the categories should be ordered.

## SPSS

SPSS does not find confidence intervals for proportions.

## TI-83/84 PLUS

To calculate a confidence interval for a population proportion:

▸ Go to the **STATS TESTS** menu and select **A:1-PropZInt.**
▸ Enter the number of successes observed and the sample size.
▸ Specify a confidence level.
▸ Calculate the interval.

### COMMENTS

*Beware:* When you enter the value of $x$, you need the count, not the percentage. The count must be a whole number. If the number of successes are given as a percentage, you must first multiply $np$ and round the result.

## TI-89

To calculate a confidence interval for a population proportion:

▸ Go to the **Ints** menu (2nd F2) and select **5:1-PropZInt.**
▸ Enter the number of successes observed and the sample size.
▸ Specify a confidence level.
▸ Calculate the interval.

### COMMENTS

*Beware:* When you enter the value of $x$, you need the count, not the percentage. The count must be a whole number. If the number of successes are given as a percentage, you must first multiply $np$ and round the result.

# EXERCISES

1. **Margin of error.** A TV newscaster reports the results of a poll of voters, and then says, "The margin of error is plus or minus 4%." Explain carefully what that means.

2. **Margin of error.** A medical researcher estimates the percentage of children who are exposed to lead-base paint, adding that he believes his estimate has a margin of error of about 3%. Explain what the margin of error means.

3. **Conditions.** Consider each situation described below. Identify the population and the sample, explain what $p$ and $\hat{p}$ represent, and tell whether the methods of this chapter can be used to create a confidence interval.

a) Police set up an auto checkpoint at which drivers are stopped and their cars inspected for safety problems. They find that 14 of the 134 cars stopped have at least one safety violation. They want to estimate the percentage of all cars that may be unsafe.

b) A TV talk show asks viewers to register their opinions on prayer in schools by logging on to a Web site. Of the 602 people who voted, 488 favored prayer in schools. We want to estimate the level of support among the general public.

c) A school is considering requiring students to wear uniforms. The PTA surveys parent opinion by sending a questionnaire home with all 1245 students; 380 surveys are returned, with 228 families in favor of the change.

d) A college admits 1632 freshmen one year, and four years later 1388 of them graduate on time. The college wants to estimate the percentage of all their freshman enrollees who graduate on time.

**4. More conditions.** Consider each situation described. Identify the population and the sample, explain what $p$ and $\hat{p}$ represent, and tell whether the methods of this chapter can be used to create a confidence interval.
a) A consumer group hoping to assess customer experiences with auto dealers surveys 167 people who recently bought new cars; 3% of them expressed dissatisfaction with the salesperson.
b) What percent of college students have cell phones? 2883 students were asked as they entered a football stadium, and 243 indicated they had phones with them.
c) 240 potato plants in a field in Maine are randomly checked, and only 7 show signs of blight. How severe is the blight problem for the U.S. potato industry?
d) 12 of the 309 employees of a small company suffered an injury on the job last year. What can the company expect in future years?

**5. Conclusions.** A catalog sales company promises to deliver orders placed on the Internet within 3 days. Follow-up calls to a few randomly selected customers show that a 95% confidence interval for the proportion of all orders that arrive on time is 88% ± 6%. What does this mean? Are these conclusions correct? Explain.
a) Between 82% and 94% of all orders arrive on time.
b) 95% of all random samples of customers will show that 88% of orders arrive on time.
c) 95% of all random samples of customers will show that 82% to 94% of orders arrive on time.
d) We are 95% sure that between 82% and 94% of the orders placed by the customers in this sample arrived on time.
e) On 95% of the days, between 82% and 94% of the orders will arrive on time.

**6. More conclusions.** In January 2002, two students made worldwide headlines by spinning a Belgian euro 250 times and getting 140 heads—that's 56%. That makes the 90% confidence interval (51%, 61%). What does this mean? Are these conclusions correct? Explain.
a) Between 51% and 61% of all euros are unfair.
b) We are 90% sure that in this experiment this euro landed heads on between 51% and 61% of the spins.
c) We are 90% sure that spun euros will land heads between 51% and 61% of the time.
d) If you spin a euro many times, you can be 90% sure of getting between 51% and 61% heads.
e) 90% of all spun euros will land heads between 51% and 61% of the time.

**7. Confidence intervals.** Several factors are involved in the creation of a confidence interval. Among them are the sample size, the level of confidence, and the margin of error. Which statements are true?
a) For a given sample size, higher confidence means a smaller margin of error.
b) For a specified confidence level, larger samples provide smaller margins of error.

c) For a fixed margin of error, larger samples provide greater confidence.
d) For a given confidence level, halving the margin of error requires a sample twice as large.

**8. Confidence intervals, again.** Several factors are involved in the creation of a confidence interval. Among them are the sample size, the level of confidence, and the margin of error. Which statements are true?
a) For a given sample size, reducing the margin of error will mean lower confidence.
b) For a certain confidence level, you can get a smaller margin of error by selecting a bigger sample.
c) For a fixed margin of error, smaller samples will mean lower confidence.
d) For a given confidence level, a sample 9 times as large will make a margin of error one third as big.

**9. Cars.** What fraction of cars is made in Japan? The computer output below summarizes the results of a random sample of 50 autos. Explain carefully what it tells you.

z-Interval for proportion
With 90.00% confidence,
0.29938661 < p(japan) < 0.46984416

**10. Parole.** A study of 902 decisions made by the Nebraska Board of Parole produced the following computer output. Assuming these cases are representative of all cases that may come before the Board, what can you conclude?

z-Interval for proportion
With 95.00% confidence,
0.56100658 < p(parole) < 0.62524619

**11. Contaminated chicken.** In January 2007 *Consumer Reports* published their study of bacterial contamination of chicken sold in the United States. They purchased 525 broiler chickens from various kinds of food stores in 23 states and tested them for types of bacteria that cause food-borne illnesses. Laboratory results indicated that 83% of these chickens were infected with *Campylobacter*.
a) Construct a 95% confidence interval.
b) Explain what your confidence interval says about chicken sold in the United States.
c) A spokesperson for the U.S. Department of Agriculture dismissed the *Consumer Reports* finding, saying, "That's 500 samples out of 9 billion chickens slaughtered a year. . . . With the small numbers they [tested], I don't know that one would want to change one's buying habits." Is this criticism valid? Explain.

**12. Contaminated chicken, second course.** The January 2007 *Consumer Reports* study described in Exercise 11 also found that 15% of the 525 broiler chickens tested were infected with *Salmonella*.
a) Are the conditions for creating a confidence interval satisfied? Explain.
b) Construct a 95% confidence interval.
c) Explain what your confidence interval says about chicken sold in the United States.

**13. Baseball fans.** In a poll taken in March of 2007, Gallup asked 1006 national adults whether they were baseball fans. 36% said they were. A year previously,

37% of a similar-size sample had reported being baseball fans.
a) Find the margin of error for the 2007 poll if we want 90% confidence in our estimate of the percent of national adults who are baseball fans.
b) Explain what that margin of error means.
c) If we wanted to be 99% confident, would the margin of error be larger or smaller? Explain.
d) Find that margin of error.
e) In general, if all other aspects of the situation remain the same, will smaller margins of error produce greater or less confidence in the interval?
f) Do you think there's been a change from 2006 to 2007 in the real proportion of national adults who are baseball fans? Explain.

**14. Cloning 2007.** A May 2007 Gallup Poll found that only 11% of a random sample of 1003 adults approved of attempts to clone a human.
a) Find the margin of error for this poll if we want 95% confidence in our estimate of the percent of American adults who approve of cloning humans.
b) Explain what that margin of error means.
c) If we only need to be 90% confident, will the margin of error be larger or smaller? Explain.
d) Find that margin of error.
e) In general, if all other aspects of the situation remain the same, would smaller samples produce smaller or larger margins of error?

**15. Contributions, please.** The Paralyzed Veterans of America is a philanthropic organization that relies on contributions. They send free mailing labels and greeting cards to potential donors on their list and ask for a voluntary contribution. To test a new campaign, they recently sent letters to a random sample of 100,000 potential donors and received 4781 donations.
a) Give a 95% confidence interval for the true proportion of those from their entire mailing list who may donate.
b) A staff member thinks that the true rate is 5%. Given the confidence interval you found, do you find that percentage plausible?

**16. Take the offer.** First USA, a major credit card company, is planning a new offer for their current cardholders. The offer will give double airline miles on purchases for the next 6 months if the cardholder goes online and registers for the offer. To test the effectiveness of the campaign, First USA recently sent out offers to a random sample of 50,000 cardholders. Of those, 1184 registered.
a) Give a 95% confidence interval for the true proportion of those cardholders who will register for the offer.
b) If the acceptance rate is only 2% or less, the campaign won't be worth the expense. Given the confidence interval you found, what would you say?

**17. Teenage drivers.** An insurance company checks police records on 582 accidents selected at random and notes that teenagers were at the wheel in 91 of them.
a) Create a 95% confidence interval for the percentage of all auto accidents that involve teenage drivers.
b) Explain what your interval means.

c) Explain what "95% confidence" means.
d) A politician urging tighter restrictions on drivers' licenses issued to teens says, "In one of every five auto accidents, a teenager is behind the wheel." Does your confidence interval support or contradict this statement? Explain.

**18. Junk mail.** Direct mail advertisers send solicitations (a.k.a. "junk mail") to thousands of potential customers in the hope that some will buy the company's product. The acceptance rate is usually quite low. Suppose a company wants to test the response to a new flyer, and sends it to 1000 people randomly selected from their mailing list of over 200,000 people. They get orders from 123 of the recipients.
a) Create a 90% confidence interval for the percentage of people the company contacts who may buy something.
b) Explain what this interval means.
c) Explain what "90% confidence" means.
d) The company must decide whether to now do a mass mailing. The mailing won't be cost-effective unless it produces at least a 5% return. What does your confidence interval suggest? Explain.

**19. Safe food.** Some food retailers propose subjecting food to a low level of radiation in order to improve safety, but sale of such "irradiated" food is opposed by many people. Suppose a grocer wants to find out what his customers think. He has cashiers distribute surveys at checkout and ask customers to fill them out and drop them in a box near the front door. He gets responses from 122 customers, of whom 78 oppose the radiation treatments. What can the grocer conclude about the opinions of all his customers?

**20. Local news.** The mayor of a small city has suggested that the state locate a new prison there, arguing that the construction project and resulting jobs will be good for the local economy. A total of 183 residents show up for a public hearing on the proposal, and a show of hands finds only 31 in favor of the prison project. What can the city council conclude about public support for the mayor's initiative?

**21. Death penalty, again.** In the survey on the death penalty you read about in the chapter, the Gallup Poll actually split the sample at random, asking 510 respondents the question quoted earlier, "Generally speaking, do you believe the death penalty is applied fairly or unfairly in this country today?" The other 510 were asked "Generally speaking, do you believe the death penalty is applied unfairly or fairly in this country today?" Seems like the same question, but sometimes the order of the choices matters. Suppose that for the second way of phrasing it, only 54% said they thought the death penalty was fairly applied.
a) Construct a 95% confidence interval for the true proportion of adults who approve of the way the death penalty is currently applied, according to the responses for this second question.
b) Recall that 60% of the respondents in the other random half of the study said that the death penalty is applied fairly. Does a proportion of 0.60 fall inside the confidence interval you just found?

**22. Drinking.** A national health organization warns that 30% of middle school students nationwide have been drunk. Concerned, a local health agency randomly and anonymously surveys 110 of the 1212 middle school students in its city. Only 21 of them report having been drunk.
a) What proportion of the sample reported having been drunk?
b) Does this mean that this city's youth are not drinking as much as the national data would indicate? Explain.
c) Create a 95% confidence interval for the proportion of the city's middle school students who have been drunk.
d) Is there any reason to believe that the national level of 30% is not true of the middle school students in this city?

**23. Death penalty poll, part III.** In the chapter's example and again in Exercise 21 we looked at a Gallup Poll investigating the public's attitude toward the death penalty. In response to one question, 60% thought it was fair, but when the question was phrased differently, the proportion in favor dropped to 54%.
a) What kind of bias may be present here?
b) Each group consisted of 510 respondents. If we combine them, considering the overall group to be one larger random sample, what is a 95% confidence interval for the proportion of the general public that thinks the death penalty is being fairly applied?
c) How does the margin of error based on this pooled sample compare with the margins of error from the separate groups? Why?

**24. Gambling.** A city ballot includes a local initiative that would legalize gambling. The issue is hotly contested, and two groups decide to conduct polls to predict the outcome. The local newspaper finds that 53% of 1200 randomly selected voters plan to vote "yes," while a college Statistics class finds 54% of 450 randomly selected voters in support. Both groups will create 95% confidence intervals.
a) Without finding the confidence intervals, explain which one will have the larger margin of error.
b) Find both confidence intervals.
c) Which group concludes that the outcome is too close to call? Why?

**25. Rickets.** Vitamin D, whether ingested as a dietary supplement or produced naturally when sunlight falls on the skin, is essential for strong, healthy bones. The bone disease rickets was largely eliminated in England during the 1950s, but now there is concern that a generation of children more likely to watch TV or play computer games than spend time outdoors is at increased risk. A recent study of 2700 children randomly selected from all parts of England found 20% of them deficient in vitamin D.
a) Find a 98% confidence interval.
b) Explain carefully what your interval means.
c) Explain what "98% confidence" means.

**26. Pregnancy.** In 1998 a San Diego reproductive clinic reported 49 live births to 207 women under the age of 40 who had previously been unable to conceive.
a) Find a 90% confidence interval for the success rate at this clinic.

b) Interpret your interval in this context.
c) Explain what "90% confidence" means.
d) Do these data refute the clinic's claim of a 25% success rate? Explain.

**27. Only child.** In a random survey of 226 college students, 20 reported being "only" children (with no siblings). Estimate the proportion of students nationwide who are only children.
a) Check the conditions (to the extent you can) for constructing a confidence interval.
b) Construct a 95% confidence interval.
c) Interpret your interval.
d) Explain what "95% confidence" means in this context.

**28. Back to campus.** In 2004 ACT, Inc., reported that 74% of 1644 randomly selected college freshmen returned to college the next year. Estimate the national freshman-to-sophomore retention rate.
a) Verify that the conditions are met.
b) Construct a 98% confidence interval.
c) Interpret your interval.
d) Explain what "98% confidence" means in this context.

**29. Payments.** In a May 2007 Experian/Gallup Personal Credit Index poll of 1008 U.S. adults aged 18 and over, 8% of respondents said they were very uncomfortable with their ability to make their monthly payments on their current debt during the next three months. Find a 95% confidence interval for the proportion of the adult population that feels this way. Be sure to check the appropriate conditions and interpret your interval correctly.

**30. Back to campus again.** The ACT, Inc., study described in Exercise 28 was actually stratified by type of college—public or private. The retention rates were 71.9% among 505 students enrolled in public colleges and 74.9% among 1139 students enrolled in private colleges.
a) Will the 95% confidence interval for the true national retention rate in private colleges be wider or narrower than the 95% confidence interval for the retention rate in public colleges? Explain.
b) Find the 95% confidence interval for the public college retention rate.
c) Should a public college whose retention rate is 75% proclaim that they do a better job than other public colleges of keeping freshmen in school? Explain.

**31. Another payment.** Exercise 29 described an Experian/Gallup poll of 1008 adults which found that 8% of them were worried about their ability to make their monthly payments. A more detailed poll surveyed 1288 adults, reporting similar overall results and also noting differences among four age groups: 18–29, 30–49, 50–64, and 65+.
a) Do you expect the 95% confidence interval for the true proportion of all 18- to 29-year-olds who are worried to be wider or narrower than the 95% confidence interval for the true proportion of all U.S. consumers? Explain.
b) Do you expect this second poll's overall margin of error to be larger or smaller than the Experian/Gallup poll's? Explain.

**32. Legal Music.** A random sample of 168 students were asked how many songs were in their digital music library

and what fraction of them were legally purchased. Overall, they reported having a total of 117,079 songs, of which 23.1% were legal. The music industry would like a good estimate of the fraction of songs in students' digital music libraries that are legal.
a) Think carefully. What is the parameter being estimated? What is the population? What is the sample size?
b) Check the conditions for making a confidence interval.
c) Construct a 95% confidence interval for the fraction of legal digital music.
d) Explain what this interval means. Do you believe that you can be this confident about your result? Why or why not?

33. **Deer ticks.**   Wildlife biologists inspect 153 deer taken by hunters and find 32 of them carrying ticks that test positive for Lyme disease.
a) Create a 90% confidence interval for the percentage of deer that may carry such ticks.
b) If the scientists want to cut the margin of error in half, how many deer must they inspect?
c) What concerns do you have about this sample?

34. **Pregnancy, II.**   The San Diego reproductive clinic in Exercise 26 wants to publish updated information on its success rate.
a) The clinic wants to cut the stated margin of error in half. How many patients' results must be used?
b) Do you have any concerns about this sample? Explain.

35. **Graduation.**   It's believed that as many as 25% of adults over 50 never graduated from high school. We wish to see if this percentage is the same among the 25 to 30 age group.
a) How many of this younger age group must we survey in order to estimate the proportion of non-grads to within 6% with 90% confidence?
b) Suppose we want to cut the margin of error to 4%. What's the necessary sample size?
c) What sample size would produce a margin of error of 3%?

36. **Hiring.**   In preparing a report on the economy, we need to estimate the percentage of businesses that plan to hire additional employees in the next 60 days.
a) How many randomly selected employers must we contact in order to create an estimate in which we are 98% confident with a margin of error of 5%?
b) Suppose we want to reduce the margin of error to 3%. What sample size will suffice?
c) Why might it not be worth the effort to try to get an interval with a margin of error of only 1%?

37. **Graduation, again.**   As in Exercise 35, we hope to estimate the percentage of adults aged 25 to 30 who never graduated from high school. What sample size would allow us to increase our confidence level to 95% while reducing the margin of error to only 2%?

38. **Better hiring info.**   Editors of the business report in Exercise 36 are willing to accept a margin of error of 4% but want 99% confidence. How many randomly selected employers will they need to contact?

39. **Pilot study.**   A state's environmental agency worries that many cars may be violating clean air emissions standards. The agency hopes to check a sample of vehicles in order to estimate that percentage with a margin of error of 3% and 90% confidence. To gauge the size of the problem, the agency first picks 60 cars and finds 9 with faulty emissions systems. How many should be sampled for a full investigation?

40. **Another pilot study.**   During routine screening, a doctor notices that 22% of her adult patients show higher than normal levels of glucose in their blood—a possible warning signal for diabetes. Hearing this, some medical researchers decide to conduct a large-scale study, hoping to estimate the proportion to within 4% with 98% confidence. How many randomly selected adults must they test?

41. **Approval rating.**   A newspaper reports that the governor's approval rating stands at 65%. The article adds that the poll is based on a random sample of 972 adults and has a margin of error of 2.5%. What level of confidence did the pollsters use?

42. **Amendment.**   A TV news reporter says that a proposed constitutional amendment is likely to win approval in the upcoming election because a poll of 1505 likely voters indicated that 52% would vote in favor. The reporter goes on to say that the margin of error for this poll was 3%.
a) Explain why the poll is actually inconclusive.
b) What confidence level did the pollsters use?

**JUST CHECKING**
*Answers*

1. No. We know that in the sample 17% said "yes"; there's no need for a margin of error.

2. No, we are 95% confident that the percentage falls in some interval, not exactly on a particular value.

3. Yes. That's what the confidence interval means.

4. No. We don't know for sure that's true; we are only 95% confident.

5. No. That's our level of confidence, not the proportion of voters. The sample suggests the proportion is much lower.

6. Wider.

7. Lower.

8. Smaller.

# CHAPTER 20

# Testing Hypotheses About Proportions

## Where are we going?

Do people 18 to 24 really prefer Pepsi to Coke? Does this new allergy medication really reduce symptoms more than a placebo? There are times when we want to make a *decision*. To do that, we'll propose a model for the situation at hand and test a hypothesis about that model. The result will help us answer the real-world question.

**A S**    *Activity:* **Testing a Claim.** Can we really draw a reasonable conclusion from a random sample? Run this simulation before you read the chapter, and you'll gain a solid sense of what we're doing here.

*"Half the money I spend on advertising is wasted; the trouble is I don't know which half."*

—John Wanamaker (attributed)

Ingots are huge pieces of metal, often weighing more than 20,000 pounds, made in a giant mold. They must be cast in one large piece for use in fabricating large structural parts for cars and planes. If they crack while being made, the crack can propagate into the zone required for the part, compromising its integrity. Airplane manufacturers insist that metal for their planes be defect-free, so the ingot must be made over if any cracking is detected.

Even though the metal from the cracked ingot is recycled, the scrap cost runs into the tens of thousands of dollars. Metal manufacturers would like to avoid cracking if at all possible. But the casting process is complicated and not everything is completely under control. In one plant, only about 80% of the ingots have been free of cracks. In an attempt to reduce the cracking proportion, the plant engineers and chemists recently tried out some changes in the casting process. Since then, 400 ingots have been cast and only 17% of them have cracked. Should management declare victory? Has the cracking rate really decreased, or was 17% just due to luck?

We can treat the 400 ingots cast with the new method as a random sample. We know that each random sample will have a somewhat different proportion of cracked ingots. Is the 17% we observe merely a result of natural sampling variability, or is this lower cracking rate strong enough evidence to assure management that the true cracking rate now is really below 20%?

People want answers to questions like these all the time. Has the president's approval rating changed since last month? Has teenage smoking decreased in the past five years? Is the global temperature increasing? Did the Super Bowl ad we bought actually increase sales? To answer such questions, we test *hypotheses* about models.

# Hypotheses

Hypothesis n.;
pl. {Hypotheses}.
   A supposition; a proposition or principle which is supposed or taken for granted, in order to draw a conclusion or inference for proof of the point in question; something not proved, but assumed for the purpose of argument.
—*Webster's Unabridged Dictionary*, 1913

**NOTATION ALERT:**

Capital H is the standard letter for hypotheses, and $H_0$ always labels the null hypothesis.

Every child knows that he (or she) is at the "center of the universe," so it's natural to suppose that the sun revolves around the earth. The fact that the sun appears to rise in the east every morning and set in the west every evening is *consistent* with this hypothesis and *seems* to lend support to it, but it certainly doesn't prove it, as we all eventually come to understand.

**A S** *Activity:* **The Reasoning of Hypothesis Testing.** Our reasoning is based on a rule of logic that dates back to ancient scholars. Here's a modern discussion of it.

To remind us that the parameter value comes from the null hypothesis, it is sometimes written as $p_0$ and the standard deviation as

$$SD(\hat{p}) = \sqrt{\frac{p_0 q_0}{n}}.$$

How can we state and test a hypothesis about ingot cracking? Hypotheses are working models that we adopt temporarily. To test whether the changes made by the engineers have *improved* the cracking rate, we assume that they have in fact made no difference and that any apparent improvement is just random fluctuation. So, our starting hypothesis, called the **null hypothesis,** is that the proportion of cracks is still 20%.

The null hypothesis, which we denote $H_0$, specifies a population model parameter of interest and proposes a value for that parameter. We usually write down the null hypothesis in the form $H_0$: *parameter = hypothesized value*. This is a concise way to specify the two things we need most: the identity of the parameter we hope to learn about and a specific hypothesized value for that parameter. (We need a hypothesized value so we can compare our observed statistic value to it.)

Which value to take is often obvious from the *Who* and *What* of the data. But sometimes it takes a bit of thinking to translate the question we hope to answer into a hypothesis about a parameter. For the ingots we can write $H_0$: $p = 0.20$.

The alternative hypothesis, which we denote $H_A$, contains the values of the parameter that we consider plausible if we reject the null hypothesis. In the ingots example, our null hypothesis is that $p = 0.20$. What's the alternative? Management is interested in *reducing* the cracking rate, so their alternative is $H_A$: $p < 0.20$.

What would convince you that the cracking rate had actually gone down? If you observed a cracking rate *much lower* than 20% in your sample, you'd likely be convinced. If only 3 out of the next 400 ingots crack (for a rate of 0.75%), most folks would conclude that the changes helped. But if the sample cracking rate is only slightly lower than 20%, you should be skeptical. After all, observations do vary, so we wouldn't be surprised to see some difference. How much smaller must the cracking rate be before we *are* convinced that it has changed? Whenever we ask about the size of a statistical difference, we naturally think of the standard deviation. So let's start by finding the standard deviation of the sample cracking rate.

Since the change in process, 400 new ingots have been cast. The sample size of 400 is big enough to satisfy the **Success/Failure Condition.** (We expect $0.20 \times 400 = 80$ ingots to crack.) We have no reason to think the ingots are not independent, so the Normal sampling distribution model should work well. The standard deviation of the sampling model is

$$SD(\hat{p}) = \sqrt{\frac{pq}{n}} = \sqrt{\frac{(0.20)(0.80)}{400}} = 0.02$$

**Why is this a standard deviation and not a standard error?** Because we haven't estimated anything. When we assume that the null hypothesis is true, it gives us a value for the model parameter $p$. With proportions, if we know $p$, then we also automatically know its standard deviation. And because we find the standard deviation from the model parameter, this is a standard deviation and not a standard error. When we found a confidence interval for $p$, we could not assume that we knew its value, so we estimated the standard deviation from the sample value $\hat{p}$.

Now we know both parameters of the Normal sampling distribution model: $p = 0.20$ and $SD(\hat{p}) = 0.02$, so we can find out how likely it would be to see the observed value of $\hat{p} = 17\%$. Since we are using a Normal model, we find the *z*-score:

$$z = \frac{0.17 - 0.20}{0.02} = -1.5$$

Then we ask, "How likely is it to observe a value at least 1.5 standard deviations below the mean of a Normal model?" The answer (from a calculator, computer program, or the Normal table) is about 0.067. This is the probability of observing a cracking rate of 17% or less in a sample of 400 if the null hypothesis is true. Management now must decide whether an event that would happen 6.7% of the time by chance is strong enough evidence to conclude that the true cracking proportion has decreased.

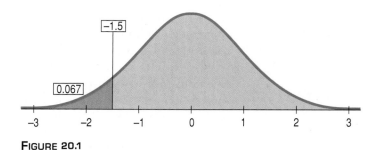

**FIGURE 20.1**

*How likely is a z-score of −1.5 (or lower)? This is what it looks like. The red area is 0.067 of the total area under the curve.*

## A Trial as a Hypothesis Test

Does the reasoning of hypothesis tests seem backwards? That could be because we usually prefer to think about getting things right rather than getting them wrong. You have seen this reasoning before in a different context. This is the logic of jury trials.

Let's suppose a defendant has been accused of robbery. In British common law and those systems derived from it (including U.S. law), the null hypothesis is that the defendant is innocent. Instructions to juries are quite explicit about this.

The evidence takes the form of facts that seem to contradict the presumption of innocence. For us, this means collecting data. In the trial, the prosecutor presents evidence. ("If the defendant were innocent, wouldn't it be remarkable that the police found him at the scene of the crime with a bag full of money in his hand, a mask on his face, and a getaway car parked outside?")

The next step is to judge the evidence. Evaluating the evidence is the responsibility of the jury in a trial, but it falls on your shoulders in hypothesis testing. The jury considers the evidence in light of the *presumption* of innocence and judges whether the evidence against the defendant would be plausible *if the defendant were in fact innocent.*

Like the jury, we ask, "Could these data plausibly have happened by chance if the null hypothesis were true?" If they are very unlikely to have occurred, then the evidence raises a reasonable doubt about the null hypothesis.

Ultimately, you must make a decision. The standard of "beyond a reasonable doubt" is wonderfully ambiguous because it leaves the jury to decide the degree to which the evidence contradicts the hypothesis of innocence. Juries don't explicitly use probability to help them decide whether to reject that hypothesis. But when you ask the same question of your null hypothesis, you have the advantage of being able to quantify exactly how surprising the evidence would be were the null hypothesis true.

How unlikely is unlikely? Some people set rigid standards, like 1 time out of 20 (0.05) or 1 time out of 100 (0.01). But if *you* have to make the decision, you must judge for yourself in each situation whether the probability of observing your data is small enough to constitute "reasonable doubt."

# P-Values

**Beyond a Reasonable Doubt**
We ask whether the data
were unlikely beyond a
reasonable doubt. We've just
calculated that probability.
The probability that the
observed statistic value (or
an even more extreme value)
could occur if the null model
were true—in this case,
0.067—is the P-value.

---

**NOTATION ALERT:**

We have many P's to keep
straight. We use an uppercase P
for probabilities, as in $P(\mathbf{A})$, and
for the special probability we
care about in hypothesis testing, the P-value.

We use lowercase $p$ to denote our model's underlying
proportion parameter and $\hat{p}$ to
denote our observed proportion
statistic.

The fundamental step in our reasoning is the question "Are the data surprising,
given the null hypothesis?" And the key calculation is to determine exactly how
likely the data we observed would be were the null hypothesis a true model of the
world. So we need a *probability*. Specifically, we want to find the probability of seeing data like these (or something even less likely) *given* the null hypothesis. Statisticians are so thrilled with their ability to measure precisely how surprised they
are that they give this probability a special name. It's called a **P-value.**[1]

When the P-value is high, we haven't seen anything unlikely or surprising at
all. Events that have a high probability of happening happen all the time. The
data are consistent with the model from the null hypothesis, and we have no reason to reject the null hypothesis. But we realize that many other similar hypotheses could also account for the data we've seen, so we haven't proven that the null
hypothesis is true. The most we can say is that it doesn't appear to be false. Formally, we "fail to reject" the null hypothesis. That's a pretty weak conclusion, but
it's all we're entitled to.

When the P-value *is* low enough, it says that the data we have observed
would be very unlikely if our null hypothesis were true. We started with a model.
Now that model tells us that the data we have are unlikely to have happened. The
model and data are at odds with each other, so we have to make a choice. Either
the null hypothesis is correct and we've just seen something remarkable, or the
null hypothesis is wrong, and we were wrong to use it as the basis for computing
our P-value. Perhaps another model is correct, and the data really aren't that
remarkable after all. If you believe in data more than in assumptions, then,
given that choice, you should reject the null hypothesis.

# What to Do with an "Innocent" Defendant

*"If the People fail to satisfy their
burden of proof, you must find
the defendant not guilty."*

—NY state jury
instructions

If the evidence is not strong enough to reject the defendant's presumption of
innocence, what verdict does the jury return? They say "not guilty." Notice that
they do not say that the defendant is innocent. Nor do they employ a standard of
"reasonable certainty" of guilt in place of the standard of "reasonable doubt" of
innocence. All they say is that they have not seen sufficient evidence to convict, to
reject innocence. The defendant may, in fact, be innocent, but the jury has no way
to be sure.

Said statistically, the jury's null hypothesis is $H_0$: innocent defendant. If the
evidence is too unlikely given this assumption, the jury rejects the null hypothesis
and finds the defendant guilty. But—and this is an important distinction—if there
is *insufficient evidence* to convict the defendant, the jury does not decide that $H_0$ is
true and declare the defendant innocent. Juries can only *fail to reject* the null hypothesis and declare the defendant "not guilty."

In the same way, if the data are not particularly unlikely under the assumption that the null hypothesis is true, then the most we can do is to "fail to reject"
our null hypothesis. We never declare the null hypothesis to be true, because we
simply do not know whether it's true or not. (After all, more evidence may come
along later.)

In the trial, the burden of proof is on the prosecution. In a hypothesis test, the
burden of proof is on the unusual claim. The null hypothesis is the ordinary state

---

[1] You'd think if they were so excited, they'd give it a better name, but "P-value" is about as
excited as statisticians get.

**Don't We Want to Reject the Null?**

Often the folks who collect the data or perform the experiment hope to reject the null. They hope the new drug is better than the placebo; they hope the new ad campaign is better than the old one; they hope their candidate is ahead of her opponent. But when we practice Statistics, we can't allow that hope to affect our decision. The essential attitude for a hypothesis tester is skepticism. Until we become convinced otherwise, we cling to the null's assertion that there's nothing unusual, nothing unexpected, no effect, no difference, etc. As in a jury trial, the burden of proof rests with the alternative hypothesis—innocent until proven guilty. When you test a hypothesis, you must act as judge and jury, but you are not the prosecutor.

of affairs, so it's the alternative to the null hypothesis that we consider unusual and for which we must marshal evidence.

Imagine a clinical trial testing the effectiveness of a new headache remedy. In Chapter 13 we saw the value of comparing such treatments to a placebo. The null hypothesis, then, is that the new treatment is no more effective than the placebo. This is important, because some patients will improve even when administered the placebo treatment. If we use only six people to test the drug, the results are likely *not to be clear* and we'll be unable to reject the hypothesis. Does this mean the drug doesn't work? Of course not. It simply means that we don't have enough evidence to reject our assumption. That's why we don't start by assuming that the drug *is more effective*. If we were to do that, then we could test just a few people, find that the results aren't clear, and claim that since we've been unable to reject our original assumption the drug must be effective. The FDA is unlikely to be impressed by that argument.

## JUST CHECKING

1. A research team wants to know if aspirin helps to thin blood. The null hypothesis says that it doesn't. They test 12 patients, observe the proportion with thinner blood, and get a P-value of 0.32. They proclaim that aspirin doesn't work. What would you say?

2. An allergy drug has been tested and found to give relief to 75% of the patients in a large clinical trial. Now the scientists want to see if the new, improved version works even better. What would the null hypothesis be?

3. The new drug is tested and the P-value is 0.0001. What would you conclude about the new drug?

# The Reasoning of Hypothesis Testing

*"The null hypothesis is never proved or established, but is possibly disproved, in the course of experimentation. Every experiment may be said to exist only in order to give the facts a chance of disproving the null hypothesis."*

—Sir Ronald Fisher, *The Design of Experiments*

**NOTATION ALERT:**

$H_A$ always labels the alternative hypothesis.

Hypothesis tests follow a carefully structured path. To avoid getting lost as we navigate down it, we divide that path into four distinct sections.

## 1. HYPOTHESES

First we state the null hypothesis. That's usually the skeptical claim that nothing's different. Are we considering a (New! Improved!) possibly better method? The null hypothesis says, "Oh yeah? Convince me!" To convert a skeptic, we must pile up enough evidence against the null hypothesis that we can reasonably reject it.

In statistical hypothesis testing, hypotheses are almost always about model parameters. To assess how unlikely our data may be, we need a null model. The null hypothesis specifies a particular parameter value to use in our model. In the usual shorthand, we write $H_0$: *parameter = hypothesized value*. The **alternative hypothesis**, $H_A$, contains the values of the parameter we consider plausible when we reject the null.

**FOR EXAMPLE** | Writing hypotheses

A large city's Department of Motor Vehicles claimed that 80% of candidates pass driving tests, but a newspaper reporter's survey of 90 randomly selected local teens who had taken the test found only 61 who passed.

**Question:** Does this finding suggest that the passing rate for teenagers is lower than the DMV reported? Write appropriate hypotheses.

*I'll assume that the passing rate for teenagers is the same as the DMV's overall rate of 80%, unless there's strong evidence that it's lower.*

$$H_O: p = 0.80$$
$$H_A: p < 0.80$$

## 2. MODEL

> Some folks pronounce the hypothesis labels "Ho!" and "Ha!" (but it makes them seem overexcitable). Others pronounce $H_0$ "H naught" (as in "all is for naught"). Nobody, it seems, says "H zero" or "H-Oh," so you probably shouldn't either.

To plan a statistical hypothesis test, specify the *model* you will use to test the null hypothesis and the parameter of interest. Of course, all models require assumptions, so you will need to state them and check any corresponding conditions.

Your Model step should end with a statement such as

*Because the conditions are satisfied, I can model the sampling distribution of the proportion with a Normal model.*

Watch out, though. Your Model step could end with

*Because the conditions are not satisfied, I can't proceed with the test.* (If that's the case, stop and reconsider.)

> **When the Conditions Fail . . .**
> You might proceed with caution, explicitly stating your concerns. Or you may need to do the analysis with and without an outlier, or on different subgroups, or after re-expressing the response variable. Or you may not be able to proceed at all.

Each test in the book has a name that you should include in your report. We'll see many tests in the chapters that follow. Some will be about more than one sample, some will involve statistics other than proportions, and some will use models other than the Normal (and so will not use $z$-scores). The test about proportions is called a **one-proportion $z$-test**.[2]

> **A** **S** *Activity:* **Was the Observed Outcome Unlikely?** Complete the test you started in the first activity for this chapter. The narration explains the steps of the hypothesis test.

> **ONE-PROPORTION $z$-TEST**
> The conditions for the one-proportion $z$-test are the same as for the one-proportion $z$-interval. We test the hypothesis $H_0: p = p_0$ using the statistic $z = \dfrac{(\hat{p} - p_0)}{SD(\hat{p})}$. We use the hypothesized proportion to find the standard deviation, $SD(\hat{p}) = \sqrt{\dfrac{p_0 q_0}{n}}$.
>
> When the conditions are met and the null hypothesis is true, this statistic follows the standard Normal model, so we can use that model to obtain a P-value.

---

[2] It's also called the "one-sample test for a proportion."

---

**FOR EXAMPLE** Checking the conditions

**Recap:** A large city's DMV claimed that 80% of candidates pass driving tests. A reporter has results from a survey of 90 randomly selected local teens who had taken the test.

**Question:** Are the conditions for inference satisfied?

✔ The 90 teens surveyed were a random sample of local teenage driving candidates.

✔ 90 is fewer than 10% of the teenagers who take driving tests in a large city.

✔ We expect $np_O = 90(0.80) = 72$ successes and $nq_O = 90(0.20) = 18$ failures. Both are at least 10.

The conditions are satisfied, so it's okay to use a Normal model and perform a one-proportion z-test.

---

> **Conditional Probability**
>
> Did you notice that a P-value is a conditional probability? It's the probability that the observed results could have happened *if the null hypothesis is true.*

## 3. MECHANICS

Under "Mechanics," we place the actual calculation of our test statistic from the data. Different tests we encounter will have different formulas and different test statistics. Usually, the mechanics are handled by a statistics program or calculator, but it's good to have the formulas recorded for reference and to know what's being computed. The ultimate goal of the calculation is to obtain a P-value—the probability that the observed statistic value (or an even more extreme value) occur if the null model is correct. If the P-value is small enough, we'll reject the null hypothesis.

---

**FOR EXAMPLE** Finding a P-value

**Recap:** A large city's DMV claimed that 80% of candidates pass driving tests, but a survey of 90 randomly selected local teens who had taken the test found only 61 who passed.

**Question:** What's the P-value for the one-proportion z-test?

I have $n = 90$, $x = 61$, and a hypothesized $p = 0.80$.

$$\hat{p} = \frac{61}{90} \approx 0.678$$

$$SD(\hat{p}) = \sqrt{\frac{p_O q_O}{n}} = \sqrt{\frac{(0.8)(0.2)}{90}} \approx 0.042$$

$$z = \frac{\hat{p} - p_O}{SD(\hat{p})} = \frac{0.678 - 0.800}{0.042} \approx -2.90$$

$$\text{P-value} = P(z < -2.90) = 0.002$$

### 4. CONCLUSION

The conclusion in a hypothesis test is always a statement about the null hypothesis. The conclusion must state either that we reject or that we fail to reject the null hypothesis. And, as always, the conclusion should be stated in context.

---

**FOR EXAMPLE** | Stating the conclusion

**Recap:** A large city's DMV claimed that 80% of candidates pass driving tests. Data from a reporter's survey of randomly selected local teens who had taken the test produced a P-value of 0.002.

**Questions:** What can the reporter conclude? And how might the reporter explain what the P-value means for the newspaper story?

Because the P-value of 0.002 is very low, I reject the null hypothesis. These survey data provide strong evidence that the passing rate for teenagers taking the driving test is lower than 80%.

If the passing rate for teenage driving candidates were actually 80%, we'd expect to see success rates this low in only about 1 in 500 samples (0.2%). This seems quite unlikely, casting doubt that the DMV's stated success rate applies to teens.

---

*". . . They make things admirably plain, But one hard question will remain: If one hypothesis you lose, Another in its place you choose . . ."*

—James Russell Lowell, *Credidimus Jovem Regnare*

Your conclusion about the null hypothesis should never be the end of a testing procedure. Often there are actions to take or policies to change. In our ingot example, management must decide whether to continue the changes proposed by the engineers. The decision always includes the practical consideration of whether the new method is worth the cost. Suppose management decides to reject the null hypothesis of 20% cracking in favor of the alternative that the percentage has been reduced. They must still evaluate how much the cracking rate has been reduced and how much it cost to accomplish the reduction. The *size of the effect* is always a concern when we test hypotheses. A good way to look at the effect size is to examine a confidence interval.

---

**How much does it cost?** Formal tests of a null hypothesis base the decision of whether to reject the null hypothesis solely on the size of the P-value. But in real life, we want to evaluate the costs of our decisions as well. How much would you be willing to pay for a faster computer? Shouldn't your decision depend on how much faster? And on how much more it costs? Costs are not just monetary, either. Would you use the same standard of proof for testing the safety of an airplane as for the speed of your new computer?

---

## Alternative Alternatives

Tests on the ingot data can be viewed in two different ways. We know the old cracking rate is 20%, so the null hypothesis is

$$H_0: p = 0.20$$

**A S** *Activity:* **Practice with Testing Hypotheses About Proportions.** Here's an interactive tool that makes it easy to see what's going on in a hypothesis test.

But we have a choice of alternative hypotheses. A metallurgist working for the company might be interested in *any* change in the cracking rate due to the new process. Even if the rate got worse, she might learn something useful from it. She's interested in possible changes on both sides of the null hypothesis. So she would write her alternative hypothesis as

$$H_A: p \neq 0.20$$

An alternative hypothesis such as this is known as a **two-sided alternative**,[3] because we are equally interested in deviations on either side of the null hypothesis value. For two-sided alternatives, the P-value is the probability of deviating in *either* direction from the null hypothesis value.

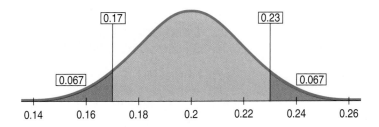

But management is really interested only in *lowering* the cracking rate below 20%. The scientific value of knowing how to *increase* the cracking rate may not appeal to them. The only alternative of interest to them is that the cracking rate *decreases*. They would write their alternative hypothesis as

$$H_A: p < 0.20$$

An alternative hypothesis that focuses on deviations from the null hypothesis value in only one direction is called a **one-sided alternative.**

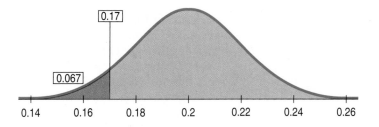

For a hypothesis test with a one-sided alternative, the P-value is the probability of deviating *only in the direction of the alternative* away from the null hypothesis value. For the same data, the one-sided P-value is half the two-sided P-value. So, a one-sided test will reject the null hypothesis more often. If you aren't sure which to use, a two-sided test is always more conservative. Be sure you can justify the choice of a one-sided test from the *Why* of the situation.

**STEP-BY-STEP EXAMPLE**     Testing a Hypothesis

Advances in medical care such as prenatal ultrasound examination now make it possible to determine a child's sex early in a pregnancy. There is a fear that in some cultures some parents may use this technology to select the sex of their children. A study from Punjab, India (E. E. Booth, M. Verma, and R. S. Beri, "Fetal Sex Determination in Infants in Punjab, India: Correlations and Implications," *BMJ* 309 [12 November 1994]: 1259–1261), reports that, in 1993, in one hospital, 56.9% of

---

[3] It is also called a **two-tailed alternative,** because the probabilities we care about are found in both tails of the sampling distribution.

the 550 live births that year were boys. It's a medical fact that male babies are slightly more common than female babies. The study's authors report a baseline for this region of 51.7% male live births.

**Question:** Is there evidence that the proportion of male births has changed?

---

**THINK**

**Plan** State what we want to know.

Define the variables and discuss the W's.

**Hypotheses** The null hypothesis makes the claim of no difference from the baseline.

Before seeing the data, we were interested in any change in male births, so the alternative hypothesis is two-sided.

**Model** Think about the assumptions and check the appropriate conditions.

For testing proportions, the conditions are the same ones we had for making confidence intervals, except that we check the **Success/Failure Condition** with the *hypothesized* proportions rather than with the *observed* proportions.

I want to know whether the proportion of male births has changed from the established baseline of 51.7%. The data are the recorded sexes of the 550 live births from a hospital in Punjab, India, in 1993, collected for a study on fetal sex determination. The parameter of interest, $p$, is the proportion of male births:

$$H_0: p = 0.517$$

$$H_A: p \neq 0.517$$

✔ **Independence Assumption:** There is no reason to think that the sex of one baby can affect the sex of other babies, so births can reasonably be assumed to be independent with regard to the sex of the child.

✔ **Randomization Condition:** The 550 live births are not a random sample, so I must be cautious about any general conclusions. I hope that this is a representative year, and I think that the births at this hospital may be typical of this area of India.

✔ **10% Condition:** I would like to be able to make statements about births at similar hospitals in India. These 550 births are fewer than 10% of all of those births.

✔ **Success/Failure Condition:** Both $np_0 = 550(0.517) = 284.35$ and $nq_0 = 550(0.483) = 265.65$ are greater than 10; I expect the births of at least 10 boys and at least 10 girls, so the sample is large enough.

Specify the sampling distribution model.

Tell what test you plan to use.

The conditions are satisfied, so I can use a Normal model and perform a **one-proportion z-test.**

---

**SHOW**

**Mechanics** The null model gives us the mean, and (because we are working with proportions) the mean gives us the standard deviation.

We find the $z$-score for the observed proportion to find out how many standard deviations it is from the hypothesized proportion.

The null model is a Normal distribution with a mean of 0.517 and a standard deviation of

$$SD(\hat{p}) = \sqrt{\frac{p_0 q_0}{n}} = \sqrt{\frac{(0.517)(1 - 0.517)}{550}}.$$

$$= 0.0213$$

The observed proportion, $\hat{p}$, is 0.569, so

$$z = \frac{\hat{p} - p_0}{SD(\hat{p})} = \frac{0.569 - 0.517}{0.0213} = 2.44$$

Make a picture. Sketch a Normal model centered at $p_0 = 0.517$. Shade the region to the right of the observed proportion, and because this is a two-tail test, also shade the corresponding region in the other tail.

The sample proportion lies 2.44 standard deviations above the mean.

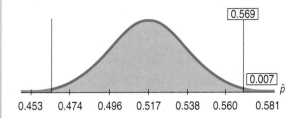

0.453   0.474   0.496   0.517   0.538   0.560   0.581

From the $z$-score, we can find the P-value, which tells us the probability of observing a value that extreme (or more). Use technology or a table (see below).

$$P = 2P(z > 2.44) = 2(0.0073) = 0.0146$$

Because this is a two-tail test, the P-value is the probability of observing an outcome more than 2.44 standard deviations from the mean of a Normal model *in either direction*. We must therefore *double* the probability we find in the upper tail.

**Conclusion** State your conclusion in context.

This P-value is roughly 1 time in 70. That's clearly significant, but don't jump to other conclusions. We can't be sure how this deviation came about. For instance, we don't know whether this hospital is typical, or whether the time period studied was selected at random.

The P-value of 0.0146 says that if the true proportion of male babies were still at 51.7%, then an observed proportion as different as 56.9% male babies would occur at random only about 15 times in 1000. With a P-value this small, I reject $H_0$. This is strong evidence that the birth ratio of boys to girls is not equal to its natural level. It appears that the proportion of boys may have increased.

Here's a portion of a Normal table that gives the probability we needed for the hypothesis test. At $z = 2.44$, the table gives the percentile as 0.9927. The upper-tail probability (shaded red) is, therefore, $1 - 0.9927 = 0.0073$; so, for our two-sided test, the P-value is $2(0.0073) = 0.0146$.

-3σ   -2σ   -1σ   0   1σ   2σ   3σ
*z* (hundredths)

**FIGURE 20.2**

*A portion of a Normal table with the look-up for z = 2.44 indicated. Since 1 − 0.9927 = 0.0073, the P-value we want is 2(0.0073) = 0.0146.*

| z | 0.00 | 0.01 | 0.02 | 0.03 | 0.04 | 0.05 |
|-----|--------|--------|--------|--------|--------|--------|
| 1.9 | 0.9713 | 0.9719 | 0.9726 | 0.9732 | 0.9738 | 0.9744 |
| 2.0 | 0.9772 | 0.9778 | 0.9783 | 0.9788 | 0.9793 | 0.9798 |
| 2.1 | 0.9821 | 0.9826 | 0.9830 | 0.9834 | 0.9838 | 0.9842 |
| 2.2 | 0.9861 | 0.9864 | 0.9868 | 0.9871 | 0.9875 | 0.9878 |
| 2.3 | 0.9893 | 0.9896 | 0.9898 | 0.9901 | 0.9904 | 0.9906 |
| 2.4 | 0.9918 | 0.9920 | 0.9922 | 0.9925 | 0.9927 | 0.9929 |
| 2.5 | 0.9938 | 0.9940 | 0.9941 | 0.9943 | 0.9945 | 0.9946 |
| 2.6 | 0.9953 | 0.9955 | 0.9956 | 0.9957 | 0.9959 | 0.9960 |

# P-Values and Decisions: What to Tell About a Hypothesis Test

Hypothesis tests are particularly useful when we must make a decision. Is the defendant guilty or not? Should we choose print advertising or television? Questions like these cannot always be answered with the margins of error of confidence intervals. The absolute nature of the hypothesis test decision, however, makes some people (including the authors) uneasy. If possible, it's often a good idea to report a confidence interval for the parameter of interest as well.

How small should the P-value be in order for you to reject the null hypothesis? A jury needs enough evidence to show the defendant guilty "beyond a reasonable doubt." How does that translate to P-values? The answer is that it's highly context-dependent. When we're screening for a disease and want to be sure we treat all those who are sick, we may be willing to reject the null hypothesis of no disease with a P-value as large as 0.10. We would rather treat the occasional healthy person than fail to treat someone who was really sick. But a long-standing hypothesis, believed by many to be true, needs stronger evidence (and a correspondingly small P-value) to reject it.

See if you require the same P-value to reject each of the following null hypotheses:

▷ A renowned musicologist claims that she can distinguish between the works of Mozart and Haydn simply by hearing a randomly selected 20 seconds of music from any work by either composer. What's the null hypothesis? If she's just guessing, she'll get 50% of the pieces correct, on average. So our null hypothesis is that $p$ is 50%. If she's for real, she'll get more than 50% correct. Now, we present her with 10 pieces of Mozart or Haydn chosen at random. She gets 9 out of 10 correct. It turns out that the P-value associated with that result is 0.011. (In other words, if you tried to just guess, you'd get at least 9 out of 10 correct only about 1% of the time.) What would *you* conclude? Most people would probably reject the null hypothesis and be convinced that she has some ability to do as she claims. Why? Because the P-value is small and we don't have any particular reason to doubt the alternative.

*"Extraordinary claims require extraordinary proof."*
—Carl Sagan

▷ On the other hand, imagine a student who bets that he can make a flipped coin land the way he wants just by thinking hard. To test him, we flip a fair coin 10 times. Suppose he gets 9 out of 10 right. This also has a P-value of 0.011. Are you willing now to reject this null hypothesis? Are you convinced that he's not just lucky? What amount of evidence *would* convince you? We require more evidence if rejecting the null hypothesis would contradict long-standing beliefs or other scientific results. Of course, with sufficient evidence we would revise our opinions (and scientific theories). That's how science makes progress.

Another factor in choosing a P-value is the importance of the issue being tested. Consider the following two tests:

▷ A researcher claims that the proportion of college students who hold part-time jobs now is higher than the proportion known to hold such jobs a decade ago. You might be willing to believe the claim (and reject the null hypothesis of no change) with a P-value of 10%.

▷ An engineer claims that the proportion of rivets holding the wing on an airplane that are likely to fail is below the proportion at which the wing would fall off. What P-value would be small enough to get you to fly on that plane?

Your conclusion about any null hypothesis should be accompanied by the P-value of the test. When you have the actual data, you should also include a confidence interval for the parameter of interest, to report the size of the effect. Don't just declare the null hypothesis rejected or not rejected. Report the P-value

**A S** **Activity: Hypothesis Tests for Proportions.** You've probably noticed that the tools for confidence intervals and for hypothesis tests are similar. See how tests and intervals for proportions are related—and an important way in which they differ.

to show the strength of the evidence against the hypothesis and the effect size. This will let each reader decide whether or not to reject the null hypothesis and whether or not to consider the result important if it is statistically significant.

---

**FOR EXAMPLE** | A confidence interval for the teen drivers

**Recap:** In a large city, only 61 of 90 randomly selected teenagers passed their driving tests, leading the investigating newspaper reporter to reject the DMV's claim of an 80% passing rate.

**Question:** Based on this sample, what might the reporter say about the true passing rate for teenage driving candidates?

With $x = 61$ and $n = 90$, $\hat{p} = 0.678$. I'll find a 95% confidence interval for $p$:

$$\hat{p} \pm z^*SE(\hat{p}) = 0.678 \pm 1.96\sqrt{\frac{(0.678)(0.322)}{90}}$$

$$= 0.678 \pm 0.097 = (0.581, 0.775)$$

Based on this investigation, it's unlikely that the true passing rate for teenagers is any higher than 77.5%, and it may be as low as 58%.

---

## JUST CHECKING

**4.** A bank is testing a new method for getting delinquent customers to pay their past-due credit card bills. The standard way was to send a letter (costing about $0.40) asking the customer to pay. That worked 30% of the time. They want to test a new method that involves sending a DVD to customers encouraging them to contact the bank and set up a payment plan. Developing and sending the video costs about $10.00 per customer. What is the parameter of interest? What are the null and alternative hypotheses?

**5.** The bank sets up an experiment to test the effectiveness of the DVD. They mail it out to several randomly selected delinquent customers and keep track of how many actually do contact the bank to arrange payments. The bank's statistician calculates a P-value of 0.003. What does this P-value suggest about the DVD?

**6.** The statistician tells the bank's management that the results are clear and that they should switch to the DVD method. Do you agree? What else might you want to know?

---

**STEP-BY-STEP EXAMPLE** | **Tests and Intervals**

Anyone who plays or watches sports has heard of the "home field advantage." Teams tend to win more often when they play at home. Or do they?

If there were no home field advantage, the home teams would win about half of all games played. In the 2006 Major League Baseball season, there were 2429 regular-season games. (One rained-out game was never made up.) It turns out that the home team won 1327 of the 2429 games, or 54.63% of the time.

**Question:** Could this deviation from 50% be explained just from natural sampling variability, or is it evidence to suggest that there really is a home field advantage, at least in professional baseball?

**Plan** State what we want to know.

Define the variables and discuss the W's.

**Hypotheses** The null hypothesis makes the claim of no difference from the base-line. Here, that means no home field advantage.

We are interested only in a home field *advantage*, so the alternative hypothesis is one-sided.

**Model** Think about the assumptions and check the appropriate conditions.

I want to know whether the home team in pro-fessional baseball is more likely to win. The data are all 2429 games from the 2006 Major League Baseball season. The variable is whether or not the home team won. The parameter of interest is the proportion of home team wins. If there's no advantage, I'd expect that propor-tion to be 0.50.

$$H_O: p = 0.50$$
$$H_A: p > 0.50$$

✔ **Independence Assumption:** Generally, the outcome of one game has no effect on the outcome of another game. But this may not be strictly true. For example, if a key player is injured, the probability that the team will win in the next couple of games may decrease slightly, but independence is still roughly true. The data come from one entire season, but I expect other seasons to be similar.

✔ **Randomization Condition:** I have results for all 2429 games of the 2006 season. But I'm not just interested in 2006, and those games, while not randomly selected, should be a reasonable representative sample of all recent Major League Baseball games.

✔ **10% Condition:** We are interested in home field advantage for Major League Baseball for all seasons. While not a random sample, these 2429 games are fewer than 10% of all games played over the years.

✔ **Success/Failure Condition:** Both $np_O = 2429(0.50) = 1214.5$ and $nq_O = 2429(0.50) = 1214.5$ are at least 10.

Specify the sampling distribution model.

State what test you plan to use.

Because the conditions are satisfied, I'll use a Normal model for the sampling distribution of the proportion and do a **one-proportion z-test**.

**Mechanics** The null model gives us the mean, and (because we are working with proportions) the mean gives us the standard deviation.

The null model is a Normal distribution with a mean of 0.50 and a standard deviation of

$$SD(\hat{p}) = \sqrt{\frac{p_0 q_0}{n}} = \sqrt{\frac{(0.5)(1-0.5)}{2429}}.$$

$$= 0.01015$$

Next, we find the z-score for the observed proportion, to find out how many standard deviations it is from the hypothesized proportion.

The observed proportion, $\hat{p}$, is 0.5463.

So the z-value is

$$z = \frac{0.5463 - 0.5}{0.01015} = 4.56$$

From the z-score, we can find the P-value, which tells us the probability of observing a value that extreme (or more).

The sample proportion lies 4.56 standard deviations above the mean.

The probability of observing a value 4.78 or more standard deviations above the mean of a Normal model can be found by computer, calculator, or table to be < 0.001.

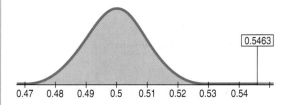

The corresponding P-value is < 0.001.

**Conclusion** State your conclusion about the parameter—in context, of course!

The P-value of < 0.001 says that if the true proportion of home team wins were 0.50, then the observed value of 0.5463 (or larger) would occur less than 1 out of 1000 times. With a P-value that small, I reject $H_0$. I conclude that the true proportion of home team wins is not 50% and that there is a home field advantage.

---

**Question: How big a difference are we talking about? Let's find a confidence interval for the home field advantage.**

---

**Model** Think about the assumptions and check the conditions.

The conditions are identical to those for the hypothesis test, with one difference: Now we are not given a hypothesized proportion, $p_0$, so we must instead work with the observed results.

✔ **Success/Failure Condition:** There were 1327 home team wins and 1102 losses, both at least 10.

Specify the sampling distribution model.

Tell what method you plan to use.

The conditions are satisfied, so I can model the sampling distribution of the proportion with a Normal model and find a **one-proportion z-interval**.

**Mechanics** We can't find the sampling model standard deviation from the null model proportion. (In fact, we've just rejected it.) Instead, we find the standard error of $\hat{p}$ from the *observed* proportions. Other than that substitution, the calculation looks the same as for the hypothesis test.

With this large a sample size, the difference is negligible, but in smaller samples, it could make a bigger difference.

$$SE(\hat{p}) = \sqrt{\frac{\hat{p}\hat{q}}{n}} = \sqrt{\frac{(0.5463)(1 - 0.5463)}{2429}}$$
$$= 0.0101$$

The sampling model is Normal, so for a 95% confidence interval, the critical value $z^* = 1.96$.

The margin of error is

$ME = z^* \times SE(\hat{p}) = 1.96 \times 0.0101 = 0.0198$

So the 95% confidence interval is

$0.5463 \pm 0.0198$ or $(0.5265, 0.5661)$.

**Conclusion** Confidence intervals help us think about the size of the effect. Here we can see that the home field advantage may affect enough games to make a real difference.

I am 95% confident that, in professional baseball, home teams win between 52.7% and 56.6% of the games.

In a season of 162 games, the low end of this interval, 52.7% of the 81 home games, is about 2 extra home victories, on average. The upper end, 56.6%, is a bit over 5 extra wins.

# WHAT CAN GO WRONG?

Hypothesis tests are so widely used—and so widely misused—that we've devoted all of the next chapter to discussing the pitfalls involved, but there are a few issues that we can talk about already.

▶ **Don't base your null hypotheses on what you see in the data.** You are not allowed to look at the data first and then adjust your null hypothesis so that it will be rejected. When your sample value turns out to be $\hat{p} = 51.8\%$, with a standard deviation of 1%, don't form a null hypothesis like $H_0$: $p = 49.8\%$, knowing that you can reject it. You should always *Think* about the situation you are investigating and make your null hypothesis describe the "nothing interesting" or "nothing has changed" scenario. No peeking at the data!

▶ **Don't base your alternative hypothesis on the data, either.** Again, you need to *Think* about the situation. Are you interested only in knowing whether something has *increased*? Then write a one-sided (upper-tail) alternative. Or would you be equally interested in a change in either direction? Then you want a two-sided alternative. You should decide whether to do a one- or two-sided test based on what results would be of interest to you, not what you see in the data.

▶ **Don't make your null hypothesis what you want to show to be true.** Remember, the null hypothesis is the status quo, the nothing-is-strange-here position a skeptic would take. You wonder whether the data cast doubt on that. You can reject the null hypothesis, but you can never "accept" or "prove" the null.

▶ **Don't forget to check the conditions.** The reasoning of inference depends on randomization. No amount of care in calculating a test result can recover from a biased sample. The probabilities we compute depend on the independence assumption. And our sample must be large enough to justify our use of a Normal model.

*(continued)*

*Activity:* **The Alternative Hypotheses.** This interactive tool provides easy ways to visualize how one- and two-tailed alternative hypotheses work.

▶ **If you fail to reject the null hypothesis, don't think that a bigger sample would be more likely to lead to rejection.** If the results you looked at were "almost" significant, it's enticing to think that because you would have rejected the null had these same observations come from a larger sample, then a larger sample would surely lead to rejection. Don't be misled. Remember, each sample is different, and a larger sample won't necessarily duplicate your current observations. Indeed, the Central Limit Theorem tells us that statistics will vary *less* in larger samples. We should therefore expect such results to be less extreme. Maybe they'd be statistically significant, but maybe (perhaps even probably) not. Even if you fail to reject the null hypothesis, it's a good idea to examine a confidence interval. If none of the plausible parameter values in the interval would matter to you (for example, because none would be *practically* significant), then even a larger study with a correspondingly smaller standard error is unlikely to be worthwhile.

# CONNECTIONS

Hypothesis tests and confidence intervals share many of the same concepts. Both rely on sampling distribution models, and because the models are the same and require the same assumptions, both check the same conditions. They also calculate many of the same statistics. Like confidence intervals, hypothesis tests use the standard deviation of the sampling distribution as a ruler, as we first saw in Chapter 6.

For testing, we find ourselves looking once again at z-scores, and we compute the P-value by finding the distance of our test statistic from the center of the null model. P-values are conditional probabilities. They give the probability of observing the result we have seen (or one even more extreme) *given* that the null hypothesis is true.

The Standard Normal model is here again as our connection between z-score values and probabilities.

## WHAT HAVE WE LEARNED?

We've learned to use what we see in a random sample to test a particular hypothesis about the world. This is our second step in statistical inference, complementing our use of confidence intervals.

We've learned that testing a hypothesis involves proposing a model, then seeing whether the data we observe are consistent with that model or are so unusual that we must reject it. We do this by finding a P-value—the probability that data like ours could have occurred if the model is correct.

We've learned that

- ▶ We start with a null hypothesis specifying the parameter of a model we'll test using our data.
- ▶ Our alternative hypothesis can be one- or two-sided, depending on what we want to learn.
- ▶ We must check the appropriate assumptions and conditions before proceeding with our test.
- ▶ If the data are out of line with the null hypothesis model, the P-value will be small and we will reject the null hypothesis.
- ▶ If the data are consistent with the null hypothesis model, the P-value will be large and we will not reject the null hypothesis.
- ▶ We must always state our conclusion in the context of the original question.

And we've learned that confidence intervals and hypothesis tests go hand in hand in helping us think about models. A hypothesis test makes a yes/no decision about the plausibility of a parameter value. The confidence interval shows us the range of plausible values for the parameter.

## Terms

**Null hypothesis**

509. The claim being assessed in a hypothesis test is called the null hypothesis. Usually, the null hypothesis is a statement of "no change from the traditional value," "no effect," "no difference," or "no relationship." For a claim to be a testable null hypothesis, it must specify a value for some population parameter that can form the basis for assuming a sampling distribution for a test statistic.

**Alternative hypothesis**

509. The alternative hypothesis proposes what we should conclude if we find the null hypothesis to be unlikely.

**Two-sided alternative (Two-tailed alternative)**

516. An alternative hypothesis is two-sided ($H_A: p \neq p_0$) when we are interested in deviations in *either* direction away from the hypothesized parameter value.

**One-sided alternative (One-tailed alternative)**

516. An alternative hypothesis is one-sided (e.g., $H_A: p > p_0$ or $H_A: p < p_0$) when we are interested in deviations in *only one* direction away from the hypothesized parameter value.

**P-value**

511. The probability of observing a value for a test statistic at least as far from the hypothesized value as the statistic value actually observed if the null hypothesis is true. A small P-value indicates either that the observation is improbable or that the probability calculation was based on incorrect assumptions. The assumed truth of the null hypothesis is the assumption under suspicion.

**One-proportion z-test**

513. A test of the null hypothesis that the proportion of a single sample equals a specified value ($H_0: p = p_0$) by referring the statistic $z = \dfrac{\hat{p} - p_0}{SD(\hat{p})}$ to a Standard Normal model.

## Skills

▸ Be able to state the null and alternative hypotheses for a one-proportion z-test.

▸ Know the conditions that must be true for a one-proportion z-test to be appropriate, and know how to examine your data for violations of those conditions.

▸ Be able to identify and use the alternative hypothesis when testing hypotheses. Understand how to choose between a one-sided and two-sided alternative hypothesis, and be able to explain your choice.

▸ Be able to perform a one-proportion z-test.

▸ Be able to write a sentence interpreting the results of a one-proportion z-test.

▸ Know how to interpret the meaning of a P-value in nontechnical language, making clear that the probability claim is made about computed values under the assumption that the null model is true and not about the population parameter of interest.

## ON THE COMPUTER

# Hypothesis Tests for Proportions

Hypothesis tests for proportions are so easy and natural that many statistics packages don't offer special commands for them. Most statistics programs want to know the "success" and "failure" status for each case. Usually these are given as 1 or 0, but they might be category names like "yes" and "no." Often we just know the proportion of successes, $\hat{p}$, and the total count, $n$. Computer packages don't usually deal naturally with summary data like this, but the statistics routines found on many graphing calculators do. These calculators allow you to test hypotheses from summaries of the data—usually, all you need to enter are the number of successes and the sample size.

In some programs you can reconstruct the original values. But even when you have reconstructed (or can reconstruct) the raw data values, often you won't get *exactly* the same test statistic from a computer package as you would find working by hand. The reason is that when the packages treat the proportion as a mean, they make some approximations. The result is very close, but not exactly the same.

## DATA DESK

Data Desk does not offer built-in methods for inference with proportions. The **Replicate Y by X** command in the **Manip** menu will "reconstruct" summarized count data so that you can display it.

### COMMENTS

For summarized data, open a Scratchpad to compute the standard deviation and margin of error by typing the calculation. Then perform the test with the **z-test for individual $\mu$s** found in the Test command.

## EXCEL

Inference methods for proportions are not part of the standard Excel tool set.

### COMMENTS

For summarized data, type the calculation into any cell and evaluate it.

## JMP

For a **categorical** variable that holds category labels, the **Distribution** platform includes tests and intervals of proportions. For summarized data, put the category names in one variable and the frequencies in an adjacent variable. Designate the frequency column to have the **role** of **frequency.** Then use the **Distribution** platform.

### COMMENTS

JMP uses slightly different methods for proportion inferences than those discussed in this text. Your answers are likely to be slightly different.

## MINITAB

Choose **Basic Statistics** from the **Stat** menu.
▸ Choose **1Proportion** from the Basic Statistics submenu.
▸ If the data are category names in a variable, assign the variable from the variable list box to the **Samples in columns** box.
▸ If you have summarized data, click the **Summarized Data** button and fill in the number of trials and the number of successes.
▸ Click the **Options** button and specify the remaining details.
▸ If you have a large sample, check **Use test and interval based on Normal distribution.**
▸ Click the **OK** button.

### COMMENTS

When working from a variable that names categories, MINITAB treats the last category as the "success" category. You can specify how the categories should be ordered.

## SPSS

SPSS does not find hypothesis tests for proportions.

## TI-83/84 PLUS

To do the mechanics of a hypothesis test for a proportion,
▸ Select **5:1-PropZTest** from the **STAT TESTS** menu.
▸ Specify the hypothesized proportion.
▸ Enter the observed value of *x.*
▸ Specify the sample size.
▸ Indicate what kind of test you want: one-tail lower tail, two-tail, or one-tail upper tail.
▸ Calculate the result.

### COMMENTS

*Beware:* When you enter the value of *x,* you need the *count,* not the percentage. The count must be a whole number. If the number of successes is given as a percent, you must first multiply *np* and round the result to obtain *x.*

## TI-89

To do the mechanics of a hypothesis test for a proportion,

▸ Select **5:1-PropZTest** from the **STAT TESTS** 2nd F1 menu.
▸ Specify the hypothesized proportion.
▸ Enter the observed value of *x*.
▸ Specify the sample size.
▸ Indicate what kind of test you want: one-tail lower tail, two-tail, or one-tail upper tail.
▸ Specify whether to calculate the result or draw the result (a normal curve with *p*-value area shaded.)

## COMMENTS

*Beware:* When you enter the value of *x*, you need the *count*, not the percentage. The count must be a whole number. If the number of successes is given as a percent, you must first multiply *np* and round the result to obtain *x*.

# EXERCISES

1. **Hypotheses.** Write the null and alternative hypotheses you would use to test each of the following situations:
   a) A governor is concerned about his "negatives"—the percentage of state residents who express disapproval of his job performance. His political committee pays for a series of TV ads, hoping that they can keep the negatives below 30%. They will use follow-up polling to assess the ads' effectiveness.
   b) Is a coin fair?
   c) Only about 20% of people who try to quit smoking succeed. Sellers of a motivational tape claim that listening to the recorded messages can help people quit.

2. **More hypotheses.** Write the null and alternative hypotheses you would use to test each of the following situations.
   a) In the 1950s only about 40% of high school graduates went on to college. Has the percentage changed?
   b) 20% of cars of a certain model have needed costly transmission work after being driven between 50,000 and 100,000 miles. The manufacturer hopes that a redesign of a transmission component has solved this problem.
   c) We field-test a new-flavor soft drink, planning to market it only if we are sure that over 60% of the people like the flavor.

3. **Negatives.** After the political ad campaign described in Exercise 1a, pollsters check the governor's negatives. They test the hypothesis that the ads produced no change against the alternative that the negatives are now below 30% and find a P-value of 0.22. Which conclusion is appropriate? Explain.
   a) There's a 22% chance that the ads worked.
   b) There's a 78% chance that the ads worked.
   c) There's a 22% chance that the poll they conducted is correct.
   d) There's a 22% chance that natural sampling variation could produce poll results like these if there's really no change in public opinion.

4. **Dice.** The seller of a loaded die claims that it will favor the outcome 6. We don't believe that claim, and roll the die 200 times to test an appropriate hypothesis. Our

P-value turns out to be 0.03. Which conclusion is appropriate? Explain.
   a) There's a 3% chance that the die is fair.
   b) There's a 97% chance that the die is fair.
   c) There's a 3% chance that a loaded die could randomly produce the results we observed, so it's reasonable to conclude that the die is fair.
   d) There's a 3% chance that a fair die could randomly produce the results we observed, so it's reasonable to conclude that the die is loaded.

5. **Relief.** A company's old antacid formula provided relief for 70% of the people who used it. The company tests a new formula to see if it is better and gets a P-value of 0.27. Is it reasonable to conclude that the new formula and the old one are equally effective? Explain.

6. **Origins.** In a 1993 Gallup poll, 47% of the respondents agreed with the statement "*God created human beings pretty much in their present form at one time within the last 10,000 years or so.*" When Gallup asked the same question in 2001, only 45% of those respondents agreed. Is it reasonable to conclude that there was a change in public opinion given that the P-value is 0.37? Explain.

7. **Name recognition.** A political candidate runs a week-long series of TV ads designed to attract public attention to his campaign. Polls taken before and after the ad campaign show some increase in the proportion of voters who now recognize this candidate's name, with a P-value of 0.033. Is it reasonable to believe the ads may be effective?

8. **Cars.** A survey investigating whether the proportion of today's high school seniors who own their own cars is higher than it was a decade ago finds a P-value of 0.017. Is it reasonable to conclude that more high-schoolers have cars? Explain.

9. **He cheats!** A friend of yours claims that when he tosses a coin he can control the outcome. You are skeptical and want him to prove it. He tosses the coin, and you call heads; it's tails. You try again and lose again.
   a) Do two losses in a row convince you that he really can control the toss? Explain.

b) You try a third time, and again you lose. What's the probability of losing three tosses in a row if the process is fair?

c) Would three losses in a row convince you that your friend cheats? Explain.

d) How many times in a row would you have to lose in order to be pretty sure that this friend really can control the toss? Justify your answer by calculating a probability and explaining what it means.

10. **Candy.** Someone hands you a box of a dozen chocolate-covered candies, telling you that half are vanilla creams and the other half peanut butter. You pick candies at random and discover that the first three you eat are all vanilla.

a) If there really were 6 vanilla and 6 peanut butter candies in the box, what is the probability that you would have picked three vanillas in a row?

b) Do you think there really might have been 6 of each? Explain.

c) Would you continue to believe that half are vanilla if the fourth one you try is also vanilla? Explain.

11. **Cell phones.** Many people have trouble setting up all the features of their cell phones, so a company has developed what it hopes will be easier instructions. The goal is to have at least 96% of customers succeed. The company tests the new system on 200 people, of whom 188 were successful. Is this strong evidence that the new system fails to meet the company's goal? A student's test of this hypothesis is shown. How many mistakes can you find?

$H_0: \hat{p} = 0.96$

$H_A: \hat{p} \neq 0.96$

SRS, $0.96(200) > 10$

$\dfrac{188}{200} = 0.94;$ $SD(\hat{p}) = \sqrt{\dfrac{(0.94)(0.06)}{200}} = 0.017$

$z = \dfrac{0.96 - 0.94}{0.017} = 1.18$

$P = P(z > 1.18) = 0.12$

There is strong evidence that the new instructions do not work.

12. **Got milk?** In November 2001, the *Ag Globe Trotter* newsletter reported that 90% of adults drink milk. A regional farmers' organization planning a new marketing campaign across its multicounty area polls a random sample of 750 adults living there. In this sample, 657 people said that they drink milk. Do these responses provide strong evidence that the 90% figure is not accurate for this region? Correct the mistakes you find in a student's attempt to test an appropriate hypothesis.

$H_0: \hat{p} = 0.9$

$H_A: \hat{p} < 0.9$

SRS, $750 > 10$

$\dfrac{657}{750} = 0.876;$ $SD(\hat{p}) = \sqrt{\dfrac{(0.88)(0.12)}{750}} = 0.012$

$z = \dfrac{0.876 - 0.90}{0.012} = -2$

$P = P(z > -2) = 0.977$

There is more than a 97% chance that the stated percentage is correct for this region.

13. **Dowsing.** In a rural area, only about 30% of the wells that are drilled find adequate water at a depth of 100 feet or less. A local man claims to be able to find water by "dowsing"—using a forked stick to indicate where the well should be drilled. You check with 80 of his customers and find that 27 have wells less than 100 feet deep. What do you conclude about his claim?

a) Write appropriate hypotheses.

b) Check the necessary assumptions.

c) Perform the mechanics of the test. What is the P-value?

d) Explain carefully what the P-value means in this context.

e) What's your conclusion?

14. **Abnormalities.** In the 1980s it was generally believed that congenital abnormalities affected about 5% of the nation's children. Some people believe that the increase in the number of chemicals in the environment has led to an increase in the incidence of abnormalities. A recent study examined 384 children and found that 46 of them showed signs of an abnormality. Is this strong evidence that the risk has increased?

a) Write appropriate hypotheses.

b) Check the necessary assumptions.

c) Perform the mechanics of the test. What is the P-value?

d) Explain carefully what the P-value means in this context.

e) What's your conclusion?

f) Do environmental chemicals cause congenital abnormalities?

15. **Absentees.** The National Center for Education Statistics monitors many aspects of elementary and secondary education nationwide. Their 1996 numbers are often used as a baseline to assess changes. In 1996 34% of students had not been absent from school even once during the previous month. In the 2000 survey, responses from 8302 students showed that this figure had slipped to 33%. Officials would, of course, be concerned if student attendance were declining. Do these figures give evidence of a change in student attendance?

a) Write appropriate hypotheses.

b) Check the assumptions and conditions.

c) Perform the test and find the P-value.

d) State your conclusion.

e) Do you think this difference is meaningful? Explain.

16. **Educated mothers.** The National Center for Education Statistics monitors many aspects of elementary and secondary education nationwide. Their 1996 numbers are often used as a baseline to assess changes. In 1996, 31% of students reported that their mothers had graduated from college. In 2000, responses from 8368 students found that this figure had grown to 32%. Is this evidence of a change in education level among mothers?

a) Write appropriate hypotheses.

b) Check the assumptions and conditions.

c) Perform the test and find the P-value.

d) State your conclusion.

e) Do you think this difference is meaningful? Explain.

17. **Contributions, please, part II.** In Exercise 19.15 you learned that the Paralyzed Veterans of America is a philanthropic organization that relies on contributions.

They send free mailing labels and greeting cards to potential donors on their list and ask for a voluntary contribution. To test a new campaign, the organization recently sent letters to a random sample of 100,000 potential donors and received 4781 donations. They've had a contribution rate of 5% in past campaigns, but a staff member worries that the rate will be lower if they run this campaign as currently designed.
a) What are the hypotheses?
b) Are the assumptions and conditions for inference met?
c) Do you think the rate would drop? Explain.

18. **Take the offer, part II.** In Exercise 19.16 you learned that First USA, a major credit card company, is planning a new offer for their current cardholders. First USA will give double airline miles on purchases for the next 6 months if the cardholder goes online and registers for this offer. To test the effectiveness of this campaign, the company recently sent out offers to a random sample of 50,000 cardholders. Of those, 1184 registered. A staff member suspects that the success rate for the full campaign will be comparable to the standard 2% rate that they are used to seeing in similar campaigns. What do you predict?
a) What are the hypotheses?
b) Are the assumptions and conditions for inference met?
c) Do you think the rate would change if they use this fundraising campaign? Explain.

19. **Smoking 2004.** National data in the 1960s showed that about 44% of the adult population had never smoked cigarettes. In 2004 a national health survey interviewed a random sample of 881 adults and found that 54.6% had never been smokers.
a) Create a 95% confidence interval for the proportion of adults (in 2004) who had never been smokers.
b) Does this provide evidence of a change in behavior among Americans? Using your confidence interval, test an appropriate hypothesis and state your conclusion.

20. **Satisfaction.** A company hopes to improve customer satisfaction, setting as a goal no more than 5% negative comments. A random survey of 350 customers found only 10 with complaints.
a) Create a 95% confidence interval for the true level of dissatisfaction among customers.
b) Does this provide evidence that the company has reached its goal? Using your confidence interval, test an appropriate hypothesis and state your conclusion.

21. **Law School.** According to the Law School Admission Council, in the fall of 2006, 63% of law school applicants were accepted to some law school.[4] The training program *LSATisfaction* claims that 163 of the 240 students trained in 2006 were admitted to law school. You can safely consider these trainees to be representative of the population of law school applicants. Has *LSATisfaction* demonstrated a real improvement over the national average?
a) What are the hypotheses?

b) Verify that the conditions are satisfied and find the P-value.
c) Would you recommend this program based on what you see here? Explain.

22. **Med School.** According to the Association of American Medical Colleges, only 46% of medical school applicants were admitted to a medical school in the fall of 2006.[5] Upon hearing this, the trustees of Striving College expressed concern that only 77 of the 180 students in their class of 2006 who applied to medical school were admitted. The college president assured the trustees that this was just the kind of year-to-year fluctuation in fortunes that is to be expected and that, in fact, the school's success rate was consistent with the national average. Who is right?
a) What are the hypotheses?
b) Verify that the conditions are satisfied and find the P-value.
c) Are the trustees right to be concerned, or is the president correct? Explain.

23. **Pollution.** A company with a fleet of 150 cars found that the emissions systems of 7 out of the 22 they tested failed to meet pollution control guidelines. Is this strong evidence that more than 20% of the fleet might be out of compliance? Test an appropriate hypothesis and state your conclusion. Be sure the appropriate assumptions and conditions are satisfied before you proceed.

24. **Scratch and dent.** An appliance manufacturer stockpiles washers and dryers in a large warehouse for shipment to retail stores. Sometimes in handling them the appliances get damaged. Even though the damage may be minor, the company must sell those machines at drastically reduced prices. The company goal is to keep the level of damaged machines below 2%. One day an inspector randomly checks 60 washers and finds that 5 of them have scratches or dents. Is this strong evidence that the warehouse is failing to meet the company goal? Test an appropriate hypothesis and state your conclusion. Be sure the appropriate assumptions and conditions are satisfied before you proceed.

25. **Twins.** In 2001 a national vital statistics report indicated that about 3% of all births produced twins. Is the rate of twin births the same among very young mothers? Data from a large city hospital found that only 7 sets of twins were born to 469 teenage girls. Test an appropriate hypothesis and state your conclusion. Be sure the appropriate assumptions and conditions are satisfied before you proceed.

26. **Football 2006.** During the 2006 season, the home team won 136 of the 240 regular-season National Football League games. Is this strong evidence of a home field advantage in professional football? Test an appropriate hypothesis and state your conclusion. Be sure the appropriate assumptions and conditions are satisfied before you proceed.

27. **WebZine.** A magazine is considering the launch of an online edition. The magazine plans to go ahead only if it's convinced that more than 25% of current readers would subscribe. The magazine contacted a simple random

---

[4] As reported by the Cornell office of career services in their *Class of 2006 Postgraduate Report*.

[5] *Ibid.*

sample of 500 current subscribers, and 137 of those surveyed expressed interest. What should the company do? Test an appropriate hypothesis and state your conclusion. Be sure the appropriate assumptions and conditions are satisfied before you proceed.

**28. Seeds.** A garden center wants to store leftover packets of vegetable seeds for sale the following spring, but the center is concerned that the seeds may not germinate at the same rate a year later. The manager finds a packet of last year's green bean seeds and plants them as a test. Although the packet claims a germination rate of 92%, only 171 of 200 test seeds sprout. Is this evidence that the seeds have lost viability during a year in storage? Test an appropriate hypothesis and state your conclusion. Be sure the appropriate assumptions and conditions are satisfied before you proceed.

**29. Women executives.** A company is criticized because only 13 of 43 people in executive-level positions are women. The company explains that although this proportion is lower than it might wish, it's not surprising given that only 40% of all its employees are women. What do you think? Test an appropriate hypothesis and state your conclusion. Be sure the appropriate assumptions and conditions are satisfied before you proceed.

**30. Jury.** Census data for a certain county show that 19% of the adult residents are Hispanic. Suppose 72 people are called for jury duty and only 9 of them are Hispanic. Does this apparent underrepresentation of Hispanics call into question the fairness of the jury selection system? Explain.

**31. Dropouts.** Some people are concerned that new tougher standards and high-stakes tests adopted in many states may drive up the high-school dropout rate. The National Center for Education Statistics reported that the high school dropout rate for the year 2004 was 10.3%. One school district whose dropout rate has always been very close to the national average reports that 210 of their 1782 high-school students dropped out last year. Is their experience evidence that the dropout rate may be increasing? Explain.

**32. Acid rain.** A study of the effects of acid rain on trees in the Hopkins Forest shows that 25 of 100 trees sampled exhibited some sort of damage from acid rain. This rate seemed to be higher than the 15% quoted in a recent *Environmetrics* article on the average proportion of damaged trees in the Northeast. Does the sample suggest that trees in the Hopkins Forest are more susceptible than trees from the rest of the region? Comment, and write up your own conclusions based on an appropriate confidence interval as well as a hypothesis test. Include any assumptions you made about the data.

**33. Lost luggage.** An airline's public relations department says that the airline rarely loses passengers' luggage. It further claims that on those occasions when luggage is lost, 90% is recovered and delivered to its owner within 24 hours. A consumer group that surveyed a large number of air travelers found that only 103 of 122 people who lost luggage on that airline were reunited with the missing items by the next day. Does this cast doubt on the airline's claim? Explain.

**34. TV ads.** A start-up company is about to market a new computer printer. It decides to gamble by running commercials during the Super Bowl. The company hopes that name recognition will be worth the high cost of the ads. The goal of the company is that over 40% of the public recognize its brand name and associate it with computer equipment. The day after the game, a pollster contacts 420 randomly chosen adults and finds that 181 of them know that this company manufactures printers. Would you recommend that the company continue to advertise during Super Bowls? Explain.

**35. John Wayne.** Like a lot of other Americans, John Wayne died of cancer. But is there more to this story? In 1955 Wayne was in Utah shooting the film *The Conqueror*. Across the state line, in Nevada, the United States military was testing atomic bombs. Radioactive fallout from those tests drifted across the filming location. A total of 46 of the 220 people working on the film eventually died of cancer. Cancer experts estimate that one would expect only about 30 cancer deaths in a group this size.
a) Is the death rate observed in the movie crew unusually high?
b) Does this prove that exposure to radiation increases the risk of cancer?

**36. AP Stats.** The College Board reported that 60% of all students who took the 2006 AP Statistics exam earned scores of 3 or higher. One teacher wondered if the performance of her school was different. She believed that year's students to be typical of those who will take AP Stats at that school and was pleased when 65% of her 54 students achieved scores of 3 or better. Can she claim that her school is different? Explain.

## JUST CHECKING
### Answers

**1.** You can't conclude that the null hypothesis is true. You can conclude only that the experiment was unable to reject the null hypothesis. They were unable, on the basis of 12 patients, to show that aspirin was effective.

**2.** The null hypothesis is $H_0$: $p = 0.75$.

**3.** With a P-value of 0.0001, this is very strong evidence against the null hypothesis. We can reject $H_0$ and conclude that the improved version of the drug gives relief to a higher proportion of patients.

**4.** The parameter of interest is the proportion, $p$, of all delinquent customers who will pay their bills. $H_0$: $p = 0.30$ and $H_A$: $p > 0.30$.

**5.** The very low P-value leads us to reject the null hypothesis. There is strong evidence that the DVD is more effective in getting people to start paying their debts than just sending a letter had been.

**6.** All we know is that there is strong evidence to suggest that $p > 0.30$. We don't know how much higher than 30% the new proportion is. We'd like to see a confidence interval to see if the new method is worth the cost.

## CHAPTER 21

# More About Tests

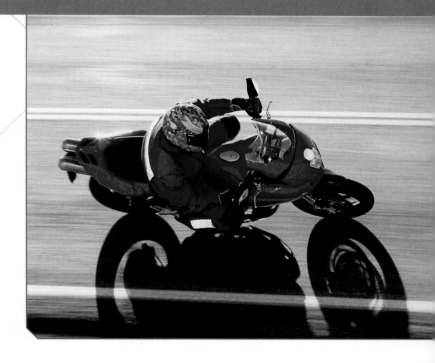

## Where are we going?

A news headline reports a "statistically significant" increase in global temperatures. Another says that studies have found no "statistically significant" benefits of taking vitamin C to prevent colds. What does significance really mean? Can failing to reject the null hypothesis sometimes be as important as rejecting it? Knowing what the hypotheses were and how the researchers arrived at their conclusion can help you decide whether you agree with the findings of their studies. We'll look at hypothesis testing in more depth in this chapter.

| | |
|---|---|
| **WHO** | Florida motorcycle riders aged 20 and less involved in motorcycle accidents |
| **WHAT** | % wearing helmets |
| **WHEN** | 2001–2003 |
| **WHERE** | Florida |
| **WHY** | Assessment of injury rates commissioned by the National Highway Traffic Safety Administration (NHTSA) |

In 2000 Florida changed its motorcycle helmet law. No longer were riders 21 and older required to wear helmets. Under the new law, those under 21 still must wear helmets. But did helmet use change among the younger riders after the change in the law? A report by the Preusser Group (www .preussergroup.com) suggests that helmet use may have declined in this group, too.

It isn't practical to survey young motorcycle riders. (For example, how can you construct a sampling frame? If you contacted licensed riders, would they admit to riding illegally without a helmet?) The Preusser Group adopted a different strategy. Police reports of motorcycle accidents record whether the rider wore a helmet and give the rider's age. Before the change in the helmet law, 60% of youths involved in a motorcycle accident had been wearing their helmets.[1] The Preusser study looked at accident reports during 2001–2003, the three years following the law change, considering these riders to be a representative sample of the larger population. They observed 781 young riders who were involved in accidents. Of these, 396 (or 50.7%) were wearing helmets. Is this evidence of a decline in helmet-wearing, or just the natural fluctuation of such statistics?

---

[1] Preusser based this on two sources. The Center for Urban Transportation Research found that 60% of all motorcycle riders in Florida complied with the helmet law before 1998. Preusser's own study confirmed this figure for riders under 21 with a methodology that matched their post-law change methods.

# Zero In on the Null

Null hypotheses have special requirements. In order to perform a statistical test of the hypothesis, the null must be a statement about the value of a parameter for a model. We use this value to compute the probability that the observed sample statistic—or something even farther from the null value—will occur.

How do we choose the null hypothesis? The appropriate null arises directly from the context of the problem. It is dictated, not by the data, but by the situation.

One good way to identify both the null and alternative hypotheses is to think about the *Why* of the situation. A pharmaceutical company wanting to develop and market a new drug needs to show that the new drug is effective. The Food and Drug Administration (FDA) will not allow a new drug to be sold in the United States that has not been proved effective in a double-blind, randomized clinical trial. (Most countries have similar restrictions on the introduction of new medications.) Typical null hypotheses for such cases might be that the proportion of patients recovering after receiving a new drug is the same as we would expect of patients receiving a placebo or that the mean strength attained by athletes training with new equipment is the same as with the old equipment. The alternative hypotheses would be that the new drug cures a higher proportion of patients or that the new equipment results in a greater mean strength.

To write a null hypothesis, you can't just choose any parameter value you like. The null must relate to the question at hand. Even though the null usually means no difference or no change, you can't automatically interpret "null" to mean zero. A claim that "nobody" wears a motorcycle helmet would be absurd. The null hypothesis for the Florida study could be that the true rate of helmet use remained the same among young riders after the law changed. You need to find the value for the parameter in the null hypothesis from the context of the problem.

---

**FOR EXAMPLE**   Writing hypotheses

---

The diabetes drug Avandia® was approved to treat Type 2 diabetes in 1999. But in 2007 an article in the *New England Journal of Medicine* (*NEJM*)[2] raised concerns that the drug might carry an increased risk of heart attack. This study combined results from a number of other separate studies to obtain an overall sample of 4485 diabetes patients taking Avandia. People with Type 2 diabetes are known to have about a 20.2% chance of suffering a heart attack within a seven-year period. According to the article's author, Dr. Steven E. Nissen,[3] the risk found in the *NEJM* study was equivalent to a 28.9% chance of heart attack over seven years. The FDA is the government agency responsible for relabeling Avandia to warn of the risk if it is judged to be unsafe. Although the statistical methods they use are more sophisticated, we can get an idea of their reasoning with the tools we have learned.

**Question:** What null hypothesis and alternative hypothesis about seven-year heart attack risk would you test? Explain.

$$H_0: p = 0.202$$
$$H_A: p > 0.202$$

*The parameter of interest is the proportion of diabetes patients suffering a heart attack in seven years. The FDA is concerned only with whether Avandia increases the seven-year risk of heart attacks above the baseline value of 20.2%, so a one-sided upper-tail test is appropriate.*

---

[2] Steven E. Nissen, M.D., and Kathy Wolski, M.P.H., "Effect of Rosiglitazone on the Risk of Myocardial Infarction and Death from Cardiovascular Causes," *NEJM* 2007; 356.
[3] Interview reported in the *New York Times* [May 26, 2007].

**One-sided or two?**   In the 1930s, a series of experiments was performed at Duke University in an attempt to see whether humans were capable of extrasensory perception, or ESP. Psychologist Karl Zener designed a set of cards with 5 symbols, later made infamous in the movie *Ghostbusters*:

In the experiment, the "sender" selects one of the 5 cards at random from a deck and then concentrates on it. The "receiver" tries to determine which card it is. If we let $p$ be the proportion of correct responses, what's the null hypothesis? The null hypothesis is that ESP makes no difference. Without ESP, the receiver would just be guessing, and since there are 5 possible responses, there would be a 20% chance of guessing each card correctly. So, $H_0$ is $p = 0.20$. What's the alternative? It seems that it should be $p > 0.20$, a one-sided alternative. But some ESP researchers have expressed the claim that if the proportion guessed were much *lower* than expected, that would show an "interference" and should be considered evidence for ESP as well. So they argue for a two-sided alternative.

There is a temptation to state your *claim* as the null hypothesis. As we have seen, however, you cannot prove a null hypothesis true any more than you can prove a defendant innocent. So, it makes more sense to use what you want to show as the *alternative*. This way, when you reject the null, you are left with what you want to show.

---

**STEP-BY-STEP EXAMPLE**   |   **Another One-Proportion $z$-Test**

Let's try to answer the question raised at the start of the chapter.

**Question: Has helmet use in Florida changed among riders under the age of 21 subsequent to the change in the helmet laws?**

**Plan** State the problem and discuss the variables and the W's.

**Hypotheses** The null hypothesis is established by the rate set before the change in the law. The study was commissioned by the NHTSA, who are concerned with safety. They'll want to know of any decline in helmet use.

> I want to know whether the rate of helmet wearing among Florida's motorcycle riders under the age of 21 remained at 60% after the law changed to allow older riders to go without helmets. I have data from accident records showing 396 of 781 young riders were wearing helmets.
>
> $H_0$: $p = 0.60$
> $H_A$: $p < 0.60$

**Model** Check the conditions.

The Risky Behavior Surveillance survey is in fact a complex, multistage sample, but it is randomized and great effort is taken to make it representative. It is safe to treat it as though it were a random sample.

> ✔  **Independence Assumption**: The data are for riders involved in accidents during a three-year period. Individuals are independent of one another.

✘ **Randomization Condition:** No randomization was applied, but we are considering these riders involved in accidents to be a representative sample of all riders. We should take care in generalizing our conclusions.

✔ **10% Condition:** These 781 riders are a small sample of a larger population of all young motorcycle riders.

✔ **Success/Failure Condition:** We'd expect $np = 781(0.6) = 468.6$ helmeted riders and $nq = 781(0.4) = 312.4$ non-helmeted. Both are at least 10.

Specify the sampling distribution model and name the test.

The conditions are satisfied, so I can use a Normal model and perform a **one-proportion z-test.**

---

**Mechanics** Find the standard deviation of the sampling model using the hypothesized proportion.

There were 396 helmet wearers among the 781 accident victims.

$$\hat{p} = \frac{396}{781} = 0.507$$

$$SD(\hat{p}) = \sqrt{\frac{p_0 q_0}{n}} = \sqrt{\frac{(0.60)(0.40)}{781}} = 0.0175$$

Find the z-score for the observed proportion.

$$z = \frac{\hat{p} - p_0}{SD(\hat{p})} = \frac{0.507 - 0.60}{0.0175} = -5.31$$

Make a picture. Sketch a Normal model centered at the hypothesized helmet rate of 60%. This is a lower tail test, so shade the region to the left of the observed rate.

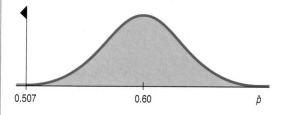

Given this z-score, the P-value is obviously very low.

The observed helmet rate is 5.31 standard deviations below the former rate. The corresponding P-value is less than 0.001.

---

**Conclusion** Link the P-value to your decision about the null hypothesis, and then state your conclusion in context.

The very small P-value says that if the true rate of helmet-wearing among riders under 21 were still 60%, the probability of observing a rate no higher than 50.7% in a sample like this is less than 1 chance in 1000, so I reject the null hypothesis. There is strong evidence that there has been a decline in helmet use among riders under 21.

| If possible, propose a course of action. | It looks like programs to encourage motorcycle helmet use among young riders are needed. Possibly, Florida legislators should re-consider the change in the law. |

# How to Think About P-values

A P-value actually is a conditional probability. It tells us the probability of getting results at least as unusual as the observed statistic, *given* that the null hypothesis is true. We can write P-value $= P(\text{observed statistic value [or even more extreme]} \mid H_0)$.

Writing the P-value this way helps to make clear that the P-value is *not* the probability that the null hypothesis is true. It is a probability about the data. Let's say that again:

*The P-value is not the probability that the null hypothesis is true.*

The P-value is not even the conditional probability that the null hypothesis is true given the data. We would write that probability as $P(H_0 \mid \text{observed statistic value})$. This is the conditional probability for the P-value, in reverse. It would be nice to know this, but it's impossible to calculate without making additional assumptions. As we saw in Chapter 15, reversing the order in a conditional probability is difficult, and the results can be counterintuitive.

> **How guilty is the suspect?**   We might like to know $P(H_0 \mid \text{data})$, but when you think about it, we can't talk about the probability that the null hypothesis is true. The null is not a random event, so either it is true or it isn't. The data, however, are random in the sense that if we were to repeat a randomized experiment or draw another random sample, we'd get different data and expect to find a different statistic value. So we can talk about the probability of the data given the null hypothesis, and that's the P-value.
>
> But it does make sense that the smaller the P-value, the more confident we can be in declaring that we doubt the null hypothesis. Think again about the jury trial. Our null hypothesis is that the defendant is innocent. Then the evidence starts rolling in. A car the same color as his was parked in front of the bank. Well, there are lots of cars that color. The probability of that happening (given his innocence) is pretty high, so we're not persuaded that he's guilty. The bank's security camera showed the robber was male and about the dependant's height and weight. Hmmm. Could that be a coincidence? If he's innocent, then it's a little less likely that the car and description would *both* match, so our P-value goes down. We're starting to question his innocence a little. Witnesses said the robber wore a blue jacket just like the one the police found in a garbage can behind the defendant's house. Well, if he's innocent, then that doesn't seem very likely, does it? If he's really innocent, the probability that all of these could have happened is getting pretty low. Now our P-value may be small enough to be called "beyond a reasonable doubt" and lead to a conviction. Each new piece of evidence strains our skepticism a bit more. The more compelling the evidence—the more *unlikely* it would be were he innocent—the more convinced we become that he's guilty.
>
> But even though it may make *us* more confident in declaring him guilty, additional evidence does not make *him* any guiltier. Either he robbed the bank or he didn't. Additional evidence (like the teller picking him out of a police lineup) just makes us more confident that we did the right thing when we convicted him. The lower the P-value, the more comfortable we feel about our decision to reject the null hypothesis, but the null hypothesis doesn't get any more false.

*"The wise man proportions his belief to the evidence."*
—David Hume, "Enquiry Concerning Human Understanding," 1748

*"You're so guilty now."*
—Rearview Mirror

We can find the P-value, $P(\text{observed statistic value} \mid H_0)$, because $H_0$ gives the parameter values that we need to find the required probability. But there's no direct way to find $P(H_0 \mid \text{observed statistic value})$.[4] As tempting as it may be to say that a P-value of 0.03 means there's a 3% chance that the null hypothesis is true, that just isn't right. All we can say is that, given the null hypothesis, there's a 3% chance of observing the statistic value that we have actually observed (or one more unlike the null value).

---

**FOR EXAMPLE**     Thinking about the P-value

**Recap:** A *New England Journal of Medicine* paper reported that the seven-year risk of heart attack in diabetes patients taking the drug Avandia was increased from the baseline of 20.2% to an estimated risk of 28.9% and said the P-value was 0.03.

**Question:** How should the P-value be interpreted in this context?

The P-value $= P(\hat{p} \geq 28.9\% \mid p = 20.2\%)$. That is, it's the probability of seeing such a high heart attack rate among the people studied if, in fact, taking Avandia really didn't increase the risk at all.

---

# What to Do with a High P-value

**A S** *Video:* **Is There Evidence for Therapeutic Touch?** This video shows the experiment and tells the story.

**A S** *Activity:* **Testing Therapeutic Touch.** Perform the one-proportion z-test using *ActivStats* technology. The test in *ActivStats* is two-sided. Do you think this is the appropriate choice?

Therapeutic touch (TT), taught in many schools of nursing, is a therapy in which the practitioner moves her hands near, but does not touch, a patient in an attempt to manipulate a "human energy field." Therapeutic touch practitioners believe that by adjusting this field they can promote healing. However, no instrument has ever detected a human energy field, and no experiment has ever shown that TT practitioners can detect such a field.

In 1998, the *Journal of the American Medical Association* published a paper reporting work by a then nine-year-old girl.[5] She had performed a simple experiment in which she challenged 15 TT practitioners to detect whether her unseen hand was hovering over their left or right hand (selected by the flip of a coin).

The practitioners "warmed up" with a period during which they could see the experimenter's hand, and each said that they could detect the girl's human energy field. Then a screen was placed so that the practitioners could not see the girl's hand, and they attempted 10 trials each. Overall, of 150 trials, the TT practitioners were successful 70 times, for a success proportion of 46.7%. Is there evidence from this experiment that TT practitioners can successfully detect a "human energy field"?

When we see a small P-value, we could continue to believe the null hypothesis and conclude that we just witnessed a rare event. But instead, we trust the data and use it as evidence to reject the null hypothesis.

In the therapeutic touch example, the null hypothesis is that the practitioners are guessing, so we expect them to be right about half the time by chance. That's why we say $H_0: p = 0.5$. They claim that they can detect a "human energy field" and that their success rate should be well above chance, so our alternative is that they would do *better* than guessing. That's a one-sided alternative

---

[4] The approach to statistical inference known as Bayesian Statistics addresses the question in just this way, but it requires more advanced mathematics and more assumptions. See p. 401 for more about the founding father of this approach.

[5] L. Rosa, E. Rosa, L. Sarner, and S. Barrett, "A Close Look at Therapeutic Touch," *JAMA* 279(13) [1 April 1998]:1005–1010.

hypothesis: $H_A: p > 0.5$. With a one-sided hypothesis, our P-value is the probability the practitioners could achieve the observed number of successes or *more* even if they were just guessing.

If the practitioners had been highly successful, that would have been unusually lucky for guessing, so we would have seen a correspondingly low P-value. Since we don't believe in rare events, we would then have concluded that they weren't guessing.

Under our null hypothesis, the practitioners would usually get close to half their guesses right, and we'd observe a proportion of successes close to 50%. Sometimes they'd do a bit better than 50%, sometimes a bit worse. But we still define the P-value as the probability of seeing whatever success rate we do see *or better*. What we actually observed was that they did slightly *worse* than 50%, with a $\hat{p} = 0.467$ success rate.

As the figure shows, the probability of a success rate of 0.467 *or more* is even bigger than 0.5. In this case, it turns out to be 0.788. Obviously, we won't be rejecting the null hypothesis; for us to reject it, the P-value would have to be quite small. But a P-value of 0.788 seems so big it is almost awkward.

Because the observed success rate was on the opposite side of 0.5 from the alternative, we could have seen immediately that the P-value had to be greater than 0.5, so we could have concluded right away that we have no evidence for rejecting $H_0$.

Big P-values just mean that what we've observed isn't surprising. That is, the results are in line with our assumption that the null hypothesis models the world, so we have no reason to reject it. A big P-value doesn't prove that the null hypothesis is true, but it certainly offers no evidence that it's *not* true. When we see a large P-value, all we can say is that we "don't reject the null hypothesis."

---

**FOR EXAMPLE**    More about P-values

**Recap:** The question of whether the diabetes drug Avandia increased the risk of heart attack was raised by a study in the *New England Journal of Medicine*. This study estimated the seven-year risk of heart attack to be 28.9% and reported a P-value of 0.03 for a test of whether this risk was higher than the baseline seven-year risk of 20.2%. An earlier study (the ADOPT study) had estimated the seven-year risk to be 26.9% and reported a P-value of 0.27.

*(continued)*

> **For Example** (*continued*)
>
> **Question:** Why did the researchers in the ADOPT study not express alarm about the increased risk they had seen?
>
> A P-value of 0.27 means that a heart attack rate at least as high as the one they observed could be expected in 27% of similar experiments even if, in fact, there were no increased risk from taking Avandia. That's not remarkable enough to reject the null hypothesis. In other words, the ADOPT study wasn't convincing.

# Alpha Levels

> **A S** **Activity: Rejecting the Null Hypothesis.** See alpha levels at work in the animated hypothesis-testing tool.

*Sir Ronald Fisher (1890–1962) was one of the founders of modern Statistics.*

Sometimes we need to make a firm decision about whether or not to reject the null hypothesis. A jury must *decide* whether the evidence reaches the level of "beyond a reasonable doubt." A business must *select* a Web design. You need to decide which section of Statistics to enroll in.

When the P-value is small, it tells us that our data are rare, *given the null hypothesis*. As humans, we are suspicious of rare events. If the data are "rare enough," we just don't think that could have happened due to chance. Since the data *did* happen, something must be wrong. All we can do now is to reject the null hypothesis.

But how rare is "rare"?

We can define "rare event" arbitrarily by setting a threshold for our P-value. If our P-value falls below that point, we'll reject the null hypothesis. We call such results **statistically significant.** The threshold is called an **alpha level.** Not surprisingly, it's labeled with the Greek letter $\alpha$. Common $\alpha$ levels are 0.10, 0.05, and 0.01. You have the option—almost the *obligation*—to consider your alpha level carefully and choose an appropriate one for the situation. If you're assessing the safety of air bags, you'll want a low alpha level; even 0.01 might not be low enough. If you're just wondering whether folks prefer their pizza with or without pepperoni, you might be happy with $\alpha = 0.10$. It can be hard to justify your choice of $\alpha$, though, so often we arbitrarily choose 0.05.

> **Where did the value 0.05 come from?** In 1931, in a famous book called *The Design of Experiments*, Sir Ronald Fisher discussed the amount of evidence needed to reject a null hypothesis. He said that it was *situation dependent*, but remarked, somewhat casually, that for many scientific applications, 1 out of 20 *might be* a reasonable value. Since then, some people—indeed some entire disciplines—have treated the number 0.05 as sacrosanct.

> **NOTATION ALERT:**
>
> The first Greek letter, $\alpha$, is used in Statistics for the threshold value of a hypothesis test. You'll hear it referred to as the alpha level. Common values are 0.10, 0.05, 0.01, and 0.001.

The alpha level is also called the **significance level.** When we reject the null hypothesis, we say that the test is "significant at that level." For example, we might say that we reject the null hypothesis "at the 5% level of significance." You must select the alpha level *before* you look at the data. Otherwise you can be accused of cheating by tuning your alpha level to suit the data.

What can you say if the P-value does not fall below $\alpha$?

When you have not found sufficient evidence to reject the null according to the standard you have established, you should say that "The data have failed to provide sufficient evidence to reject the null hypothesis." Don't say that you "accept the null hypothesis." You certainly haven't proven or established it; it was assumed to begin with. Say that you've failed to reject it.

Think again about the therapeutic touch example. The P-value was 0.788. This is so much larger than any reasonable alpha level that we can't reject $H_0$. For this

**It Could Happen to You!**
Of course, if the null hypothesis *is* true, no matter what alpha level you choose, you still have a probability $\alpha$ of rejecting the null hypothesis by mistake. This is the rare event we want to protect ourselves against. When we do reject the null hypothesis, no one ever thinks that *this* is one of those rare times. As statistician Stu Hunter notes, "*The statistician says 'rare events do happen—but not to me!'*"

test, we'd conclude, "We fail to reject the null hypothesis. There is insufficient evidence to conclude that the practitioners are performing better than they would if they were just guessing."

The automatic nature of the reject/fail-to-reject decision when we use an alpha level may make you uncomfortable. If your P-value falls just slightly above your alpha level, you're not allowed to reject the null. Yet a P-value just barely below the alpha level leads to rejection. If this bothers you, you're in good company. Many statisticians think it better to report the P-value than to choose an alpha level and carry the decision through to a final reject/fail-to-reject verdict. So when you decide to declare a verdict, it's always a good idea to report the P-value as an indication of the strength of the evidence.

> **It's in the stars**   Some disciplines carry the idea further and code P-values by their size. In this scheme, a P-value between 0.05 and 0.01 gets highlighted by *. A P-value between 0.01 and 0.001 gets **, and a P-value less than 0.001 gets ***. This can be a convenient summary of the weight of evidence against the null hypothesis if it's not taken too literally. But we warn you against taking the distinctions too seriously and against making a black-and-white decision near the boundaries. The boundaries are a matter of tradition, not science; there is nothing special about 0.05. A P-value of 0.051 should be looked at very seriously and not casually thrown away just because it's larger than 0.05, and one that's 0.009 is not very different from one that's 0.011.

Sometimes it's best to report that the conclusion is not yet clear and to suggest that more data be gathered. (In a trial, a jury may "hang" and be unable to return a verdict.) In these cases, it's an especially good idea to report the P-value, since it's the best summary we have of what the data say or fail to say about the null hypothesis.

# What Not to Say About Significance

**Practical vs. Statistical Significance**
A large insurance company mined its data and found a statistically significant ($P = 0.04$) difference between the mean value of policies sold in 2001 and 2002. The difference in the mean values was $9.83. Even though it was statistically significant, management did not see this as an important difference when a typical policy sold for more than $1000. On the other hand, even a clinically important improvement of 10% in cure rate with a new treatment is not likely to be statistically significant in a study of fewer than 225 patients. A small clinical trial would probably not be conclusive.

What do we mean when we say that a test is statistically significant? All we mean is that the test statistic had a P-value lower than our alpha level. Don't be lulled into thinking that statistical significance carries with it any sense of practical importance or impact.

For large samples, even small, unimportant ("insignificant") deviations from the null hypothesis can be statistically significant. On the other hand, if the sample is not large enough, even large, financially or scientifically "significant" differences may not be statistically significant.

It's good practice to report the magnitude of the difference between the observed statistic value and the null hypothesis value (in the data units) along with the P-value on which we base statistical significance.

# Critical Values Again

When making a confidence interval, we've found a **critical value,** $z^*$, to correspond to our selected confidence level. Critical values can also be used as a shortcut for hypothesis tests. Before computers and calculators were common, P-values were hard to find. It was easier to select a few common alpha levels (0.05, 0.01, 0.001, for example) and learn the corresponding critical values for the Normal model (that is, the critical values corresponding to confidence levels 0.95, 0.99, and 0.999, respectively). Rather than looking up the probability corresponding to your $z$-score in the table, you'd just check your $z$-score directly against these $z^*$ values. Any $z$-score larger in magnitude (that is, more extreme) than a particular critical value has to be less likely, so it will have a P-value smaller than the corresponding alpha. If we are willing to settle for a flat reject/fail-to-reject decision, comparing an observed $z$-score with the critical value for a specified alpha level gives a shortcut path to that decision. For the motorcycle helmet example, if we choose $\alpha = 0.05$, then, in order to reject $H_0$, our $z$-score has to be larger than the one-sided critical value of 1.645. Our calculated $z$-score is $-5.31$, so clearly we can reject the null hypothesis. This is perfectly correct and does give us a yes/no decision, but it gives us less information about the hypothesis because we don't have the P-value to think about. With technology, P-values are easy to find. And since they give more information about the strength of the evidence, you should always report them.

Here are the traditional critical values from the Normal model:[6]

| $\alpha$ | 1-sided | 2-sided |
|---|---|---|
| 0.05 | 1.645 | 1.96 |
| 0.01 | 2.33 | 2.576 |
| 0.001 | 3.09 | 3.29 |

**FIGURE 21.1**
*When the alternative is one-sided, the critical value puts all of $\alpha$ on one side.*

**FIGURE 21.2**
*When the alternative is two-sided, the critical value splits $\alpha$ equally into two tails.*

# Confidence Intervals and Hypothesis Tests

For the motorcycle helmet example, a 95% confidence interval would give $0.507 \pm 1.96 \times 0.0175 = (0.472, 0.542)$, or 47.2% to 54.2%. If the previous rate of helmet compliance had been, say, 50%, we would not have been able to reject the null hypothesis because 50% is in the interval, so it's a plausible value. Indeed, *any* hypothesized value for the true proportion of helmet wearers in this interval is consistent with the data. Any value outside the confidence interval would make a null hypothesis that we would reject, but we'd feel more strongly about values far outside the interval.

---

[6] In a sense, these are the flip side of the 68–95–99.7 Rule. When we studied that rule, we chose simple statistical distances from the mean and recalled the areas of the tails. Now we select convenient tail areas (0.05, 0.01, and 0.001, either on one side or adding both together) and record the corresponding statistical distances.

Confidence intervals and hypothesis tests are built from the same calculations.[7] They have the same assumptions and conditions. As we have just seen, you can approximate a hypothesis test by examining the confidence interval. Just ask whether the null hypothesis value is consistent with a confidence interval for the parameter at the corresponding confidence level. Because confidence intervals are naturally two-sided, they correspond to two-sided tests. For example, a 95% confidence interval corresponds to a two-sided hypothesis test at $\alpha = 5\%$. In general, a confidence interval with a confidence level of $C\%$ corresponds to a two-sided hypothesis test with an $\alpha$ level of $100 - C\%$.

The relationship between confidence intervals and one-sided hypothesis tests is a little more complicated. For a one-sided test with $\alpha = 5\%$, the corresponding confidence interval has a confidence level of 90%—that's 5% in each tail. In general, a confidence interval with a confidence level of $C\%$ corresponds to a one-sided hypothesis test with an $\alpha$ level of $\frac{1}{2}(100 - C)\%$.

---

**FOR EXAMPLE** | Making a decision based on a confidence interval

**Recap:** The baseline seven-year risk of heart attacks for diabetics is 20.2%. In 2007 a *NEJM* study reported a 95% confidence interval equivalent to 20.8% to 40.0% for the risk among patients taking the diabetes drug Avandia.

**Question:** What did this confidence interval suggest to the FDA about the safety of the drug?

*The FDA could be 95% confident that the interval from 20.8% to 40.0% included the true risk of heart attack for diabetes patients taking Avandia. Because the lower limit of this interval was higher than the baseline risk of 20.2%, there was evidence of an increased risk.*

---

## JUST CHECKING

1. An experiment to test the fairness of a roulette wheel gives a z-score of 0.62. What would you conclude?

2. In the last chapter we encountered a bank that wondered if it could get more customers to make payments on delinquent balances by sending them a DVD urging them to set up a payment plan. Well, the bank just got back the results on their test of this strategy. A 90% confidence interval for the success rate is (0.29, 0.45). Their old send-a-letter method had worked 30% of the time. Can you reject the null hypothesis that the proportion is still 30% at $\alpha = 0.05$? Explain.

3. Given the confidence interval the bank found in their trial of DVDs, what would you recommend that they do? Should they scrap the DVD strategy?

---

[7] As we saw in Chapter 20, this is not *exactly* true for proportions. For a confidence interval, we estimate the standard deviation of $\hat{p}$ from $\hat{p}$ itself. Because we estimate it from the data, we have a *standard error*. For the corresponding hypothesis test, we use the model's standard deviation for $\hat{p}$, based on the null hypothesis value $p_0$. When $\hat{p}$ and $p_0$ are close, these calculations give similar results. When they differ, you're likely to reject $H_0$ (because the observed proportion is far from your hypothesized value). In that case, you're better off building your confidence interval with a standard error estimated from the data.

**STEP-BY-STEP EXAMPLE** | **Wear that Seat Belt!**

Teens are at the greatest risk of being killed or injured in traffic crashes. According to the National Highway Traffic Safety Administration, 65% of young people killed were not wearing a safety belt. In 2001, a total of 3322 teens were killed in motor vehicle crashes, an average of 9 teenagers a day. Because many of these deaths could easily be prevented by the use of safety belts, several states have begun "Click It or Ticket" campaigns in which increased enforcement and publicity have resulted in significantly higher seat belt use. Overall use in Massachusetts quickly increased from 51% in 2002 to 64.8% in 2006, with a goal of surpassing the national average of 82%. Recently, a local newspaper reported that a roadblock resulted in 23 tickets to drivers who were unbelted out of 134 stopped for inspection.

**Question:** Does this provide evidence that the goal of over 82% compliance was met?

Let's use a confidence interval to test this hypothesis.

**Plan** State the problem and discuss the variables and the W's.

**Hypotheses** The null hypothesis is that the compliance rate is only 82%. The alternative is that it is now higher. It's clearly a one-sided test, so if we use a confidence interval, we'll have to be careful about what level we use.

**Model** Think about the assumptions and check the conditions.

We are finding a confidence interval, so we work from the data rather than the null model.

State your method.

---

The data come from a local newspaper report that tells the number of tickets issued and number of drivers stopped at a recent road-block. I want to know whether the rate of compliance with the seat-belt law is greater than 82%.

$$H_0: p = 0.82$$
$$H_A: p > 0.82$$

✓ **Independence Assumption:** Drivers are not likely to influence one another when it comes to wearing a seat belt.

✓ **Randomization Condition:** This wasn't a random sample, but I assume these drivers are representative of the driving public.

✓ **10% Condition:** The police stopped fewer than 10% of all drivers.

✓ **Success/Failure Condition:** There were 111 successes and 23 failures, both at least 10. The sample is large enough.

Under these conditions, the sampling model is Normal. I'll create a **one-proportion z-interval.**

---

**Mechanics** Write down the given information, and determine the sample proportion.

To use a confidence interval, we need a confidence level that corresponds to the alpha level of the test. If we use $\alpha = 0.05$, we should construct a 90% confidence interval, because this is a one-sided test.

---

$n = 134$, so

$$\hat{p} = \frac{111}{134} = 0.828 \text{ and}$$

$$SE(\hat{p}) = \sqrt{\frac{\hat{p}\hat{q}}{n}} = \sqrt{\frac{(0.828)(0.172)}{134}} = 0.033$$

| That will leave 5% on *each* side of the observed proportion. Determine the standard error of the sample proportion and the margin of error. The critical value is $z^* = 1.645$. | $ME = z^* \times SE(\hat{p})$ <br> $\quad = 1.645(0.033) = 0.054$ |
|---|---|
| The confidence interval is <br><br> $\qquad$ estimate $\pm$ margin of error. | The 90% confidence interval is <br><br> $\quad 0.828 \pm 0.054$ or <br> $\quad (0.774, 0.882).$ |

|  **Conclusion** Link the confidence interval to your decision about the null hypothesis, and then state your conclusion in context. | I am 90% confident that between 77.4% and 88.2% of all drivers wear their seat belts. Because the hypothesized rate of 82% is within this interval, I do not reject the null hypothesis. There is insufficient evidence to conclude that the campaign was truly effective and now more than 82% of all drivers are wearing seat belts. <br><br> The upper limit of the confidence interval shows it's possible that the campaign is quite successful, but the small sample size makes the interval too wide to be very specific. |

# Making Errors

Nobody's perfect. Even with lots of evidence, we can still make the wrong decision. In fact, when we perform a hypothesis test, we can make mistakes in *two* ways:

  **I.** The null hypothesis is true, but we mistakenly reject it.
  **II.** The null hypothesis is false, but we fail to reject it.

These two types of errors are known as **Type I** and **Type II errors.** One way to keep the names straight is to remember that we start by assuming the null hypothesis is true, so a Type I error is the first kind of error we could make.

In medical disease testing, the null hypothesis is usually the assumption that a person is healthy. The alternative is that he or she has the disease we're testing for. So a Type I error is a *false positive:* A healthy person is diagnosed with the disease. A Type II error, in which an infected person is diagnosed as disease free, is a *false negative.* These errors have other names, depending on the particular discipline and context.

Some false-positive results mean no more than an unnecessary chest X-ray. But for a drug test or a disease like AIDS, a false-positive result that is not kept confidential could have serious consequences.

Which type of error is more serious depends on the situation. In the jury trial, a Type I error occurs if the jury convicts an innocent person. A Type II error occurs if the jury fails to convict a guilty person. Which seems more serious? In medical diagnosis, a false negative could mean that a sick patient goes untreated. A false positive might mean that the person must undergo further tests. In a Statistics final exam (with $H_0$: the student has learned only 60% of the material), a Type I error would be passing a student who in fact learned less than 60% of the material, while a Type II error would be failing a student who knew enough to pass. Which of these errors seems more serious? It depends on the situation, the cost, and your point of view.

Here's an illustration of the situations:

How often will a Type I error occur? It happens when the null hypothesis is true but we've had the bad luck to draw an unusual sample. To reject $H_0$, the P-value must fall below $\alpha$. When $H_0$ is true, that happens *exactly* with probability $\alpha$. So when you choose level $\alpha$, you're setting the probability of a Type I error to $\alpha$.

What if $H_0$ is not true? Then we can't possibly make a Type I error. You can't get a false positive from a sick person. A Type I error can happen only when $H_0$ is true.

When $H_0$ is false and we reject it, we have done the right thing. A test's ability to detect a false null hypothesis is called the **power** of the test. In a jury trial, power is the ability of the criminal justice system to convict people who are guilty—a good thing! We'll have a lot more to say about power soon.

When $H_0$ is false, but we fail to reject it, we have made a Type II error. We assign the letter $\beta$ to the probability of this mistake. What's the value of $\beta$? That's harder to assess than $\alpha$ because we don't know what the value of the parameter really is. When $H_0$ is true, it specifies a single parameter value. But when $H_0$ is false, we don't have a specific one; we have many possible values. We can compute the probability $\beta$ for any parameter value in $H_A$. But which one should we choose?

There is no single value for $\beta$. In fact, we can think of a whole collection of $\beta$'s, one for each incorrect parameter value. Then we can display them as a curve, plotting each $\beta$ against the corresponding parameter value in $H_A$. One way to focus our attention is by thinking about the *effect size*. That is, we ask *"How big a difference would matter?"* Suppose a charity wants to test whether placing personalized address labels in the envelope along with a request for a donation increases the response rate above the baseline of 5%. If the minimum response that would pay for the address labels is 6%, they would calculate $\beta$ for the alternative $p = 0.06$.

Of course, we could reduce $\beta$ for *all* alternative parameter values by increasing $\alpha$. By making it easier to reject the null, we'd be more likely to reject it whether it's true or not. So we'd reduce $\beta$, the chance that we fail to reject a false null—but we'd make more Type I errors. This tension between Type I and Type II errors is inevitable. In the political arena, think of the ongoing debate between those who favor provisions to reduce Type I errors in the courts (supporting Miranda rights, requiring warrants for wiretaps, providing legal representation for those who can't afford it) and those who advocate changes to reduce Type II errors (admitting into evidence confessions made when no lawyer is present, eavesdropping on conferences with lawyers, restricting paths of appeal, etc.).

The only way to reduce *both* types of error is to collect more evidence or, in statistical terms, to collect more data. Otherwise, we just wind up trading off one kind of error against the other. Whenever you design a survey or experiment, it's a good idea to calculate $\beta$ (for a reasonable $\alpha$ level). Use a parameter value in the alternative that corresponds to an effect size that you want to be able to detect. Too often, studies fail because their sample sizes are too small to detect the change they are looking for.

**NOTATION ALERT:**

In Statistics, $\alpha$ is almost always saved for the alpha level. But $\beta$ has already been used for the parameters of a linear model. Fortunately, it's usually clear whether we're talking about a Type II error probability or the slope or intercept of a regression model.

> The null hypothesis specifies a single value for the parameter. So it's easy to calculate the probability of a Type I error. But the alternative gives a whole range of possible values, and we may want to find a $\beta$ for several of them.

> We have seen ways to find a sample size by specifying the margin of error. Choosing the sample size to achieve a specified $\beta$ (for a particular alternative value) is sometimes more appropriate, but the calculation is more complex and lies beyond the scope of this book.

**Thinking about errors**

**Recap:** A published study found the risk of heart attack to be increased in patients taking the diabetes drug Avandia. The issue of the *New England Journal of Medicine* (*NEJM*) in which that study appeared also included an editorial that said, in part, "A few events either way might have changed the findings for myocardial infarction[8] or for death from cardiovascular causes. In this setting, the possibility that the findings were due to chance cannot be excluded."

**Question:** What kind of error would the researchers have made if, in fact, their findings were due to chance? What could be the consequences of this error?

The null hypothesis said the risk didn't change, but the researchers rejected that model and claimed evidence of a higher risk. If these findings were just due to chance, they rejected a true null hypothesis—a Type I error.

If, in fact, Avandia carried no extra risk, then patients might be deprived of its benefits for no good reason.

# Power

When we failed to reject the null hypothesis about TT practitioners, did we prove that they were just guessing? No, it could be that they actually *can* discern a human energy field but we just couldn't tell. For example, suppose they really have the ability to get 53% of the trials right but just happened to get only 47% in our experiment. Our confidence interval shows that with these data we wouldn't have rejected the null. And if we retained the null even though the true proportion was actually greater than 50%, we would have made a Type II error because we failed to detect their ability.

Remember, we can never prove a null hypothesis true. We can only fail to reject it. But when we fail to reject a null hypothesis, it's natural to wonder whether we looked hard enough. Might the null hypothesis actually be false and our test too weak to tell?

When the null hypothesis actually *is* false, we hope our test is strong enough to reject it. We'd like to know how likely we are to succeed. The power of the test gives us a way to think about that. The **power** of a test is the probability that it correctly rejects a false null hypothesis. When the power is high, we can be confident that we've looked hard enough. We know that $\beta$ is the probability that a test *fails* to reject a false null hypothesis, so the power of the test is the probability that it *does* reject: $1 - \beta$. We might have just written $1 - \beta$, but power is such an important concept that it gets its own name.

Whenever a study fails to reject its null hypothesis, the test's power comes into question. Was the sample size big enough to detect an effect had there been one? Might we have missed an effect large enough to be interesting just because we failed to gather sufficient data or because there was too much variability in the data we could gather? The therapeutic touch experiment failed to reject the null hypothesis that the TT practitioners were just guessing. Might the problem be that the experiment simply lacked adequate power to detect their ability?

**Errors and power**

**Recap:** The study of Avandia published in the *NEJM* combined results from 47 different trials—a method called *meta-analysis*. The drug's manufacturer, GlaxoSmithKline (GSK) issued a statement that pointed out,

*(continued)*

---

[8] Doctorese for "heart attack."

For Example *(continued)*

"Each study is designed differently and looks at unique questions: For example, individual studies vary in size and length, in the type of patients who participated, and in the outcomes they investigate." Nevertheless, by combining data from many studies, meta-analyses can achieve a much larger sample size.

**Question:** How could this larger sample size help?

*If Avandia really did increase the seven-year heart attack rate, doctors needed to know. To overlook that would have been a Type II error (failing to detect a false null hypothesis), resulting in patients being put at greater risk. Increasing the sample size could increase the power of the analysis, making it more likely that researchers will detect the danger if there is one.*

When we calculate power, we imagine that the null hypothesis is false. The value of the power depends on how far the truth lies from the null hypothesis value. We call the distance between the null hypothesis value, $p_0$, and the truth, $p$, the **effect size.** The power depends directly on the effect size. It's easier to see larger effects, so the farther $p_0$ is from $p$, the greater the power. If the therapeutic touch practitioners were in fact able to detect human energy fields 90% of the time, it should be easy to see that they aren't guessing. With an effect size this large, we'd have a powerful test. If their true success rate were only 53%, however, we'd need a larger sample size to have a good chance of noticing that (and rejecting $H_0$).

How can we decide what power we need? Choice of power is more a financial or scientific decision than a statistical one because, to calculate the power, we need to specify the "true" parameter value we're interested in. In other words, power is calculated for a particular effect size, and it changes depending on the size of the effect we want to detect. For example, do you think that health insurance companies should pay for therapeutic touch if practitioners could detect a human energy field only 53% of the time—just slightly better than chance? That doesn't seem clinically useful.[9] How about 75% of the time? No therapy works all the time, and insurers might be quite willing to pay for such a success rate. Let's take 75% as a reasonably interesting effect size (keeping in mind that 50% is the level of guessing). With 150 trials, the TT experiment would have been able to detect such an ability with a power of 99.99%. So power was not an issue in this study. There is only a very small chance that the study would have failed to detect a practitioner's ability, had it existed. The sample size was clearly big enough.

## JUST CHECKING

**4.** Remember our bank that's sending out DVDs to try to get customers to make payments on delinquent loans? It is looking for evidence that the costlier DVD strategy produces a higher success rate than the letters it has been sending. Explain what a Type I error is in this context and what the consequences would be to the bank.

**5.** What's a Type II error in the bank experiment context, and what would the consequences be?

**6.** For the bank, which situation has higher power: a strategy that works really well, actually getting 60% of people to pay off their balances, or a strategy that barely increases the payoff rate to 32%? Explain briefly.

---

[9] On the other hand, a scientist might be interested in anything clearly different from the 50% guessing rate because that might suggest an entirely new Physics at work. In fact, it could lead to a Nobel prize.

---

*A S*    **Activity: The Power of a Test.** Power is a concept that's much easier to understand when you can visualize what's happening.

# A Picture Worth $\dfrac{1}{P(z > 3.09)}$ Words

It makes intuitive sense that the larger the effect size, the easier it should be to see it. Obtaining a larger sample size decreases the probability of a Type II error, so it increases the power. It also makes sense that the more we're willing to accept a Type I error, the less likely we will be to make a Type II error.

**NOTATION ALERT:**

We've attached symbols to many of the $p$'s. Let's keep them straight. $p$ is a true proportion parameter. $p_0$ is a hypothesized value of $p$. $\hat{p}$ is an observed proportion. $p^*$ is a critical value of a proportion corresponding to a specified $\alpha$.

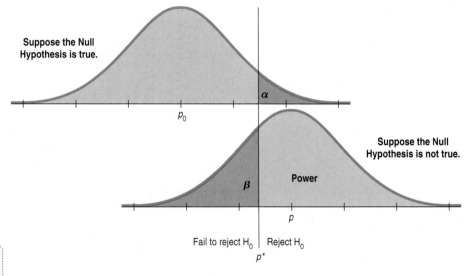

**FIGURE 21.3**

*The power of a test is the probability that it rejects a false null hypothesis. The upper figure shows the null hypothesis model. We'd reject the null in a one-sided test if we observed a value of $\hat{p}$ in the red region to the right of the critical value, $p^*$. The lower figure shows the true model. If the true value of $p$ is greater than $p_0$, then we're more likely to observe a value that exceeds the critical value and make the correct decision to reject the null hypothesis. The power of the test is the purple region on the right of the lower figure. Of course, even drawing samples whose observed proportions are distributed around $p$, we'll sometimes get a value in the red region on the left and make a Type II error of failing to reject the null.*

**Sensitivity and Specificity**

The terms *sensitivity* and *specificity* often appear in medical studies. Both are conditional probabilities that a diagnostic test works the way we want it to.

In testing for a disease, the usual null hypothesis is that you are not sick. The *sensitivity* of a test is P(Reject | $H_0$ is false)—it tells how likely the test is to (correctly) detect that you are sick when in fact you are.

The *specificity* is P(Fail to Reject | $H_0$ is true). This is the flip-side—the probability the test will *not* claim you are sick when you are healthy.

So these are the probabilities that the test diagnoses your condition correctly—sensitivity if you are sick, specificity if you are healthy. Because it is important to diagnose an illness so it can be treated, diagnostic tests are often designed to maximize sensitivity, but the best tests have both high sensitivity and high specificity.

Figure 21.3 shows a good way to visualize the relationships among these concepts. Suppose we are testing $H_0$: $p = p_0$ against the alternative $H_A$: $p > p_0$. We'll reject the null if the observed proportion, $\hat{p}$, is big enough. By big enough, we mean $\hat{p} > p^*$ for some critical value, $p^*$ (shown as the red region in the right tail of the upper curve). For example, we might be willing to believe the ability of therapeutic touch practitioners if they were successful in 65% of our trials. This is what the upper model shows. It's a picture of the sampling distribution model for the proportion when the null hypothesis is true. If the null were true, then this would be a picture of that truth. We'd make a Type I error whenever the sample gave us $\hat{p} > p^*$, because we would reject the (true) null hypothesis. And unusual samples like that would happen only with probability $\alpha$.

In reality, though, the null hypothesis is rarely *exactly* true. The lower probability model supposes that $H_0$ is not true. In particular, it supposes that the true value is $p$, not $p_0$. (Perhaps the TT practitioner really can detect the human energy field 72% of the time.) It shows a distribution of possible observed $\hat{p}$ values around this true value. Because of sampling variability, sometimes $\hat{p} < p^*$ and we fail to reject the (false) null hypothesis. Suppose a TT practitioner with a true ability level of 72% is actually successful on fewer than 65% of our tests. Then we'd make a Type II error. The area under the curve to the left of $p^*$ in the bottom model represents how often this happens. The probability is $\beta$. In this picture, $\beta$ is less than half, so most of the time we *do* make the right decision. The *power* of the test—the probability that we make the right decision—is shown as the region to the right of $p^*$. It's $1 - \beta$.

We calculate $p^*$ based on the upper model because $p^*$ depends only on the null model and the alpha level. No matter what the true proportion, no matter whether the practitioners can detect a human energy field 90%, 53%, or 2% of the time, $p^*$ doesn't change. After all, we don't *know* the truth, so we can't use it to determine the critical value. But we always reject $H_0$ when $\hat{p} > p^*$.

How often we are able to reject $H_0$ when it's *false* depends on the effect size. We can see from the picture that if the effect size were larger (the true proportion were farther from the hypothesized value), the bottom curve would shift to the right, making the power greater.

We can see several important relationships from this figure:

▶ Power = $1 - \beta$.

▶ Reducing $\alpha$ to lower the chance of committing a Type I error will move the critical value, $p^*$, to the right (in this example). This will have the effect of increasing $\beta$, the probability of a Type II error, and correspondingly reducing the power.

▶ The larger the real difference between the hypothesized value, $p_0$, and the true population value, $p$, the smaller is the chance of making a Type II error and the greater is the power of the test. If the two proportions are very far apart, the two models will barely overlap, and we will not be likely to make any Type II errors at all—but then, we are unlikely to really need a formal hypothesis-testing procedure to see such an obvious difference. If the TT practitioners were successful almost all the time, we'd be able to see that with even a small experiment.

# Reducing Both Type I and Type II Errors

Figure 21.3 seems to show that if we reduce Type I error, we automatically must increase Type II error. But there is a way to reduce both. Can you think of it?

If we can make both curves narrower, as shown in Figure 21.4, then both the probability of Type I errors and the probability of Type II errors will decrease, and the power of the test will increase.

**A S** **Activity: Power and Sample Size.** Investigate how the power of a test changes with the sample size. The interactive tool is really the only way you can see this easily.

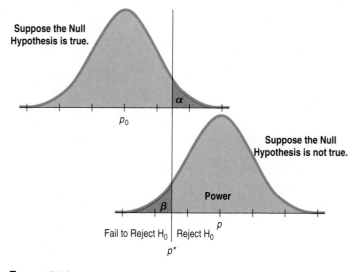

**FIGURE 21.4**

*Making the standard deviations smaller increases the power without changing the alpha level or corresponding critical value. The means are just as far apart as in Figure 21.3, but the error rates are reduced.*

Why did Sir Ronald Fisher suggest 0.05 as a criterion for testing hypotheses? It turns out that he had in mind small initial studies. Small studies have relatively little power. Fisher was concerned that they might make too many Type II errors—failing to discover an important effect—if too strict a criterion were used. Once a test failed to reject a null hypothesis, it was unlikely that researchers would return to that hypothesis to try again.

On the other hand, the increased risk of Type I errors arising from a generous criterion didn't concern him as much for exploratory studies because these are ordinarily followed by a replication or a larger study. The probability of a Type I error is $\alpha$—in this case, 0.05. The probability that two independent studies would both make Type I errors is $0.05 \times 0.05 = 0.0025$, so Fisher was confident that Type I errors in initial studies were not a major concern.

The widespread use of the relatively generous 0.05 criterion even in large studies is most likely not what Fisher had in mind.

How can we accomplish that? The only way is to reduce the standard deviations by increasing the sample size. (Remember, these are pictures of sampling distribution models, not of data.) Increasing the sample size works regardless of the true population parameters. But recall the curse of diminishing returns. The standard deviation of the sampling distribution model decreases only as the *square root* of the sample size, so to halve the standard deviations we must *quadruple* the sample size.

---

**FOR EXAMPLE**  |  Sample size, errors, and power

**Recap:** The meta-analysis of the risks of heart attacks in patients taking the diabetes drug Avandia combined results from 47 smaller studies. As GlaxoSmithKline (GSK), the drug's manufacturer, pointed out in their rebuttal, "Data from the ADOPT clinical trial did show a small increase in reports of myocardial infarction among the *Avandia*-treated group . . . however, the number of events is too small to reach a reliable conclusion about the role any of the medicines may have played in this finding."

**Question:** Why would this smaller study have been less likely to detect the difference in risk? What are the appropriate statistical concepts for comparing the smaller studies?

Smaller studies are subject to greater sampling variability; that is, the sampling distributions they estimate have a larger standard deviation for the sample proportion. That gives small studies less power: They'd be less able to discern whether an apparently higher risk was merely the result of chance variation or evidence of real danger. The FDA doesn't want to restrict the use of a drug that's safe and effective (Type I error), nor do they want patients to continue taking a medication that puts them at risk (Type II error). Larger sample sizes can reduce the risk of both kinds of error. Greater power (the probability of rejecting a false null hypothesis) means a better chance of spotting a genuinely higher risk of heart attacks.

---

## WHAT CAN GO WRONG?

▶ **Don't interpret the P-value as the probability that $H_0$ is true.** The P-value is about the data, not the hypothesis. It's the probability of the data, *given* that $H_0$ is true, not the other way around.

▶ **Don't believe too strongly in arbitrary alpha levels.** There's not really much difference between a P-value of 0.051 and a P-value of 0.049, but sometimes it's regarded as the difference between night (having to retain $H_0$) and day (being able to shout to the world that your results are "statistically significant"). It may just be better to report the P-value and a confidence interval and let the world decide along with you.

▶ **Don't confuse practical and statistical significance.** A large sample size can make it easy to discern even a trivial change from the null hypothesis value. On the other hand, an important difference can be missed if your test lacks sufficient power.

▶ **Don't forget that in spite of all your care, you might make a wrong decision.** We can never reduce the probability of a Type I error ($\alpha$) or of a Type II error ($\beta$) to zero (but increasing the sample size helps).

# CONNECTIONS

All of the hypothesis tests we'll see boil down to the same question: "Is the difference between two quantities large?" We always measure "how large" by finding a ratio of this difference to the standard deviation of the sampling distribution of the statistic. Using the standard deviation as our ruler for inference is one of the core ideas of statistical thinking.

We've discussed the close relationship between hypothesis tests and confidence intervals. They are two sides of the same coin.

This chapter also has natural links to the discussion of probability, to the Normal model, and to the two previous chapters on inference.

# WHAT HAVE WE LEARNED?

We've learned that there's a lot more to hypothesis testing than a simple yes/no decision.

► We've learned that the P-value can indicate evidence against the null hypothesis when it's small, but it does not tell us the probability that the null hypothesis is true.

► We've learned that the alpha level of the test establishes the level of proof we'll require. That determines the critical value of z that will lead us to reject the null hypothesis.

► We've also learned more about the connection between hypothesis tests and confidence intervals; they're really two ways of looking at the same question. The hypothesis test gives us the answer to a decision about a parameter; the confidence interval tells us the plausible values of that parameter.

We've learned about the two kinds of errors we might make, and we've seen why in the end we're never sure we've made the right decision.

► If the null hypothesis is really true and we reject it, that's a Type I error; the alpha level of the test is the probability that this happens.

► If the null hypothesis is really false, but we fail to reject it, that's a Type II error.

► The power of the test is the probability that we reject the null hypothesis when it's false. The larger the size of the effect we're testing for, the greater the power of the test to detect it.

► We've seen that tests with a greater likelihood of Type I error have more power and less chance of a Type II error. We can increase power while reducing the chances of both kinds of error by increasing the sample size.

## Terms

**Alpha level**
538. The threshold P-value that determines when we reject a null hypothesis. If we observe a statistic whose P-value based on the null hypothesis is less than $\alpha$, we reject that null hypothesis.

**Statistically significant**
538. When the P-value falls below the alpha level, we say that the test is "statistically significant" at that alpha level.

**Significance level**
538. The alpha level is also called the significance level, most often in a phrase such as a conclusion that a particular test is "significant at the 5% significance level."

**Critical value**
539. The value in the sampling distribution model of the statistic whose P-value is equal to the alpha level. Any statistic value farther from the null hypothesis value than the critical value will have a smaller P-value than $\alpha$ and will lead to rejecting the null hypothesis. The critical value is often denoted with an asterisk, as $z^*$, for example.

**Type I error**
543. The error of rejecting a null hypothesis when in fact it is true (also called a "false positive"). The probability of a Type I error is $\alpha$.

| Type II error | 543. The error of failing to reject a null hypothesis when in fact it is false (also called a "false negative"). The probability of a Type II error is commonly denoted $\beta$ and depends on the effect size. |
|---|---|
| Power | 544, 545. The probability that a hypothesis test will correctly reject a false null hypothesis is the power of the test. To find power, we must specify a particular alternative parameter value as the "true" value. For any specific value in the alternative, the power is $1 - \beta$. |
| Effect size | 546. The difference between the null hypothesis value and true value of a model parameter is called the effect size. |

## Skills

▶ Understand that statistical significance does not measure the importance or magnitude of an effect. Recognize when others misinterpret statistical significance as proof of practical importance.

▶ Understand the close relationship between hypothesis tests and confidence intervals.

▶ Be able to identify and use the alternative hypothesis when testing hypotheses. Understand how to choose between a one-sided and two-sided alternative hypothesis, and know how to defend the choice of a one-sided alternative.

▶ Understand how the critical value for a test is related to the specified alpha level.

▶ Understand that the power of a test gives the probability that it correctly rejects a false null hypothesis when a specified alternative is true.

▶ Understand that the power of a test depends in part on the sample size. Large sample sizes lead to greater power (and thus fewer Type II errors).

▶ Know how to complete a hypothesis test for a population proportion.

▶ Be able to interpret the meaning of a P-value in nontechnical language.

▶ Understand that the P-value of a test does not give the probability that the null hypothesis is correct.

▶ Know that we do not "accept" a null hypothesis if we cannot reject it, but rather that we can only "fail to reject" the hypothesis for lack of evidence against it.

## ON THE COMPUTER

# Hypothesis Tests

Reports about hypothesis tests generated by technologies don't follow a standard form. Most will name the test, provide the test statistic value, its standard deviation, and the P-value. But these elements may not be labeled clearly. For example, the expression "Prob > |z|" means the probability (the "Prob") of observing a test statistic whose magnitude (the absolute value tells us this) is larger than that of the one (the "z") found in the data (which, because it is written as "z," we know follows a Normal model). That is a fancy (and not very clear) way of saying P-value. In some packages, you can specify that the test be one-sided. Others might report three P-values, covering the ground for both one-sided tests and the two-sided test.

Sometimes a confidence interval and hypothesis test are automatically given together. The CI ought to be for the corresponding confidence level: $1 - \alpha$.

Often, the standard deviation of the statistic is called the "standard error," and usually that's appropriate because we've had to estimate its value from the data. That's not the case for proportions, however: We get the standard deviation for a proportion from the null hypothesis value. Nevertheless, you may see the standard deviation called a "standard error" even for tests with proportions.

It's common for statistics packages and calculators to report more digits of "precision" than could possibly have been found from the data. You can safely ignore them. Round values such as the standard deviation to one digit more than the number of digits reported in your data.

Here are the kind of results you might see. This is not from any program or calculator we know of, but it shows some of the things you might see in typical computer output.

*usually, the test is named*

$\hat{p}$

```
Test of p = 0.5
                   Value   Test Stat   Prob > |z|
   Estimate        0.467   -0.825      0.42
   Std Err         0.04073
   Upper 95%       0.547
   Lower 95%       0.387
```

*Actually, a standard deviation because this is a test*

*Might offer a CI as well. These are bounds for the 95% CI because α = 0.05—a fact not clearly stated*

*test statistic value*

*P-value*

*2-sided alternative*

For information on hypothesis testing with particular statistics packages, see the **On the Computer** section in Chapter 20 on pages 525–527.

# EXERCISES

**1. One sided or two?** In each of the following situations, is the alternative hypothesis one-sided or two-sided? What are the hypotheses?
a) A business student conducts a taste test to see whether students prefer Diet Coke or Diet Pepsi.
b) PepsiCo recently reformulated Diet Pepsi in an attempt to appeal to teenagers. They run a taste test to see if the new formula appeals to teenagers more than the standard formula.
c) A budget override in a small town requires a two-thirds majority to pass. A local newspaper conducts a poll to see if there's evidence it will pass.
d) One financial theory states that the stock market will go up or down with equal probability. A student collects data over several years to test the theory.

**2. Which alternative?** In each of the following situations, is the alternative hypothesis one-sided or two-sided? What are the hypotheses?
a) A college dining service wants to know if students prefer plastic or metal cutlery. They conduct a survey to find out.
b) In recent years, 10% of college juniors have applied for study abroad. The dean's office conducts a survey to see if that's changed this year.
c) A pharmaceutical company conducts a clinical trial to see if more patients who take a new drug experience headache relief than the 22% who claimed relief after taking the placebo.
d) At a small computer peripherals company, only 60% of the hard drives produced passed all their performance

tests the first time. Management recently invested a lot of resources into the production system and now conducts a test to see if it helped.

**3. P-value.** A medical researcher has tested a new treatment for poison ivy against the traditional ointment. He concludes that the new treatment, with a P-value of 0.047, is more effective. Explain what the P-value means in this context.

**4. Another P-value.** Have harsher penalties and ad campaigns increased seat-belt use among drivers and passengers? Observations of commuter traffic failed to find evidence of a significant change compared with three years ago. Explain what the study's P-value of 0.17 means in this context.

**5. Alpha.** A researcher developing scanners to search for hidden weapons at airports has concluded that a new device is significantly better than the current scanner. He made this decision based on a test using $\alpha = 0.05$. Would he have made the same decision at $\alpha = 0.10$? How about $\alpha = 0.01$? Explain.

**6. Alpha again.** Environmentalists concerned about the impact of high-frequency radio transmissions on birds found that there was no evidence of a higher mortality rate among hatchlings in nests near cell towers. They based this conclusion on a test using $\alpha = 0.05$. Would they have made the same decision at $\alpha = 0.10$? How about $\alpha = 0.01$? Explain.

**7. Significant?** Public health officials believe that 90% of children have been vaccinated against measles. A random

survey of medical records at many schools across the country found that, among more than 13,000 children, only 89.4% had been vaccinated. A statistician would reject the 90% hypothesis with a P-value of $P = 0.011$.
a) Explain what the P-value means in this context.
b) The result is statistically significant, but is it important? Comment.

8. **Significant again?** A new reading program may reduce the number of elementary school students who read below grade level. The company that developed this program supplied materials and teacher training for a large-scale test involving nearly 8500 children in several different school districts. Statistical analysis of the results showed that the percentage of students who did not attain the grade-level standard was reduced from 15.9% to 15.1%. The hypothesis that the new reading program produced no improvement was rejected with a P-value of 0.023.
a) Explain what the P-value means in this context.
b) Even though this reading method has been shown to be significantly better, why might you not recommend that your local school adopt it?

9. **Success.** In August 2004, *Time* magazine reported the results of a random telephone poll commissioned by the Spike network. Of the 1302 men who responded, only 39 said that their most important measure of success was their work.
a) Estimate the percentage of all American males who measure success primarily from their work. Use a 98% confidence interval. Don't forget to check the conditions first.
b) Some believe that few contemporary men judge their success primarily by their work. Suppose we wished to conduct a hypothesis test to see if the fraction has fallen below the 5% mark. What does your confidence interval indicate? Explain.
c) What is the level of significance of this test? Explain.

10. **Is the Euro fair?** Soon after the Euro was introduced as currency in Europe, it was widely reported that someone had spun a Euro coin 250 times and gotten heads 140 times. We wish to test a hypothesis about the fairness of spinning the coin.
a) Estimate the true proportion of heads. Use a 95% confidence interval. Don't forget to check the conditions first.
b) Does your confidence interval provide evidence that the coin is unfair when spun? Explain.
c) What is the significance level of this test? Explain.

11. **Approval 2007.** In May 2007, George W. Bush's approval rating stood at 30% according to a CBS News/*New York Times* national survey of 1125 randomly selected adults.
a) Make a 95% confidence interval for his approval rating by all U.S. adults.
b) Based on the confidence interval, test the null hypothesis that Bush's approval rating was no better than the 27% level established by Richard Nixon during the Watergate scandal.

12. **Superdads.** The Spike network commissioned a telephone poll of randomly sampled U.S. men. Of the 712 respondents who had children, 22% said "yes" to the question "Are you a stay-at-home dad?" (*Time*, August 23, 2004)
a) To help market commercial time, Spike wants an accurate estimate of the true percentage of stay-at-home dads. Construct a 95% confidence interval.
b) An advertiser of baby-carrying slings for dads will buy commercial time if at least 25% of men are stay-at-home dads. Use your confidence interval to test an appropriate hypothesis, and make a recommendation to the advertiser.
c) Could Spike claim to the advertiser that it is possible that 25% of men with young children are stay-at-home dads? What is wrong with the reasoning?

13. **Loans.** Before lending someone money, banks must decide whether they believe the applicant will repay the loan. One strategy used is a point system. Loan officers assess information about the applicant, totaling points they award for the person's income level, credit history, current debt burden, and so on. The higher the point total, the more convinced the bank is that it's safe to make the loan. Any applicant with a lower point total than a certain cutoff score is denied a loan.
We can think of this decision as a hypothesis test. Since the bank makes its profit from the interest collected on repaid loans, their null hypothesis is that the applicant will repay the loan and therefore should get the money. Only if the person's score falls below the minimum cutoff will the bank reject the null and deny the loan. This system is reasonably reliable, but, of course, sometimes there are mistakes.
a) When a person defaults on a loan, which type of error did the bank make?
b) Which kind of error is it when the bank misses an opportunity to make a loan to someone who would have repaid it?
c) Suppose the bank decides to lower the cutoff score from 250 points to 200. Is that analogous to choosing a higher or lower value of $\alpha$ for a hypothesis test? Explain.
d) What impact does this change in the cutoff value have on the chance of each type of error?

14. **Spam.** Spam filters try to sort your e-mails, deciding which are real messages and which are unwanted. One method used is a point system. The filter reads each incoming e-mail and assigns points to the sender, the subject, key words in the message, and so on. The higher the point total, the more likely it is that the message is unwanted. The filter has a cutoff value for the point total; any message rated lower than that cutoff passes through to your inbox, and the rest, suspected to be spam, are diverted to the junk mailbox.
We can think of the filter's decision as a hypothesis test. The null hypothesis is that the e-mail is a real message and should go to your inbox. A higher point total provides evidence that the message may be spam; when there's sufficient evidence, the filter rejects the null, classifying the message as junk. This usually works pretty well, but, of course, sometimes the filter makes a mistake.
a) When the filter allows spam to slip through into your inbox, which kind of error is that?

b) Which kind of error is it when a real message gets classified as junk?

c) Some filters allow the user (that's you) to adjust the cutoff. Suppose your filter has a default cutoff of 50 points, but you reset it to 60. Is that analogous to choosing a higher or lower value of $\alpha$ for a hypothesis test? Explain.

d) What impact does this change in the cutoff value have on the chance of each type of error?

**15. Second loan.** Exercise 13 describes the loan score method a bank uses to decide which applicants it will lend money. Only if the total points awarded for various aspects of an applicant's financial condition fail to add up to a minimum cutoff score set by the bank will the loan be denied.

a) In this context, explain what is meant by the power of the test.

b) What could the bank do to increase the power?

c) What's the disadvantage of doing that?

**16. More spam.** Consider again the points-based spam filter described in Exercise 14. When the points assigned to various components of an e-mail exceed the cutoff value you've set, the filter rejects its null hypothesis (that the message is real) and diverts that e-mail to a junk mailbox.

a) In this context, explain what is meant by the power of the test.

b) What could you do to increase the filter's power?

c) What's the disadvantage of doing that?

**17. Homeowners 2005.** In 2005 the U.S. Census Bureau reported that 68.9% of American families owned their homes. Census data reveal that the ownership rate in one small city is much lower. The city council is debating a plan to offer tax breaks to first-time home buyers in order to encourage people to become homeowners. They decide to adopt the plan on a 2-year trial basis and use the data they collect to make a decision about continuing the tax breaks. Since this plan costs the city tax revenues, they will continue to use it only if there is strong evidence that the rate of home ownership is increasing.

a) In words, what will their hypotheses be?

b) What would a Type I error be?

c) What would a Type II error be?

d) For each type of error, tell who would be harmed.

e) What would the power of the test represent in this context?

**18. Alzheimer's.** Testing for Alzheimer's disease can be a long and expensive process, consisting of lengthy tests and medical diagnosis. Recently, a group of researchers (Solomon *et al.*, 1998) devised a 7-minute test to serve as a quick screen for the disease for use in the general population of senior citizens. A patient who tested positive would then go through the more expensive battery of tests and medical diagnosis. The authors reported a false positive rate of 4% and a false negative rate of 8%.

a) Put this in the context of a hypothesis test. What are the null and alternative hypotheses?

b) What would a Type I error mean?

c) What would a Type II error mean?

d) Which is worse here, a Type I or Type II error? Explain.

e) What is the power of this test?

**19. Testing cars.** A clean air standard requires that vehicle exhaust emissions not exceed specified limits for various pollutants. Many states require that cars be tested annually to be sure they meet these standards. Suppose state regulators double-check a random sample of cars that a suspect repair shop has certified as okay. They will revoke the shop's license if they find significant evidence that the shop is certifying vehicles that do not meet standards.

a) In this context, what is a Type I error?

b) In this context, what is a Type II error?

c) Which type of error would the shop's owner consider more serious?

d) Which type of error might environmentalists consider more serious?

**20. Quality control.** Production managers on an assembly line must monitor the output to be sure that the level of defective products remains small. They periodically inspect a random sample of the items produced. If they find a significant increase in the proportion of items that must be rejected, they will halt the assembly process until the problem can be identified and repaired.

a) In this context, what is a Type I error?

b) In this context, what is a Type II error?

c) Which type of error would the factory owner consider more serious?

d) Which type of error might customers consider more serious?

**21. Cars again.** As in Exercise 19, state regulators are checking up on repair shops to see if they are certifying vehicles that do not meet pollution standards.

a) In this context, what is meant by the power of the test the regulators are conducting?

b) Will the power be greater if they test 20 or 40 cars? Why?

c) Will the power be greater if they use a 5% or a 10% level of significance? Why?

d) Will the power be greater if the repair shop's inspectors are only a little out of compliance or a lot? Why?

**22. Production.** Consider again the task of the quality control inspectors in Exercise 20.

a) In this context, what is meant by the power of the test the inspectors conduct?

b) They are currently testing 5 items each hour. Someone has proposed that they test 10 each hour instead. What are the advantages and disadvantages of such a change?

c) Their test currently uses a 5% level of significance. What are the advantages and disadvantages of changing to an alpha level of 1%?

d) Suppose that, as a day passes, one of the machines on the assembly line produces more and more items that are defective. How will this affect the power of the test?

**23. Equal opportunity?** A company is sued for job discrimination because only 19% of the newly hired candidates were minorities when 27% of all applicants were minorities. Is this strong evidence that the company's hiring practices are discriminatory?

a) Is this a one-tailed or a two-tailed test? Why?
b) In this context, what would a Type I error be?
c) In this context, what would a Type II error be?
d) In this context, describe what is meant by the power of the test.
e) If the hypothesis is tested at the 5% level of significance instead of 1%, how will this affect the power of the test?
f) The lawsuit is based on the hiring of 37 employees. Is the power of the test higher than, lower than, or the same as it would be if it were based on 87 hires?

**24. Stop signs.** Highway safety engineers test new road signs, hoping that increased reflectivity will make them more visible to drivers. Volunteers drive through a test course with several of the new- and old-style signs and rate which kind shows up the best.
a) Is this a one-tailed or a two-tailed test? Why?
b) In this context, what would a Type I error be?
c) In this context, what would a Type II error be?
d) In this context, describe what is meant by the power of the test.
e) If the hypothesis is tested at the 1% level of significance instead of 5%, how will this affect the power of the test?
f) The engineers hoped to base their decision on the reactions of 50 drivers, but time and budget constraints may force them to cut back to 20. How would this affect the power of the test? Explain.

**25. Dropouts.** A Statistics professor has observed that for several years about 13% of the students who initially enroll in his Introductory Statistics course withdraw before the end of the semester. A salesman suggests that he try a statistics software package that gets students more involved with computers, predicting that it will cut the dropout rate. The software is expensive, and the salesman offers to let the professor use it for a semester to see if the dropout rate goes down significantly. The professor will have to pay for the software only if he chooses to continue using it.
a) Is this a one-tailed or two-tailed test? Explain.
b) Write the null and alternative hypotheses.
c) In this context, explain what would happen if the professor makes a Type I error.
d) In this context, explain what would happen if the professor makes a Type II error.
e) What is meant by the power of this test?

**26. Ads.** A company is willing to renew its advertising contract with a local radio station only if the station can prove that more than 20% of the residents of the city have heard the ad and recognize the company's product. The radio station conducts a random phone survey of 400 people.
a) What are the hypotheses?
b) The station plans to conduct this test using a 10% level of significance, but the company wants the significance level lowered to 5%. Why?
c) What is meant by the power of this test?
d) For which level of significance will the power of this test be higher? Why?
e) They finally agree to use $\alpha = 0.05$, but the company proposes that the station call 600 people instead of the 400 initially proposed. Will that make the risk of Type II error higher or lower? Explain.

**27. Dropouts, part II.** Initially, 203 students signed up for the Stats course in Exercise 25. They used the software suggested by the salesman, and only 11 dropped out of the course.
a) Should the professor spend the money for this software? Support your recommendation with an appropriate test.
b) Explain carefully what your P-value means in this context.

**28. Testing the ads.** The company in Exercise 26 contacts 600 people selected at random, and only 133 remember the ad.
a) Should the company renew the contract? Support your recommendation with an appropriate test.
b) Explain carefully what your P-value means in this context.

**29. Two coins.** In a drawer are two coins. They look the same, but one coin produces heads 90% of the time when spun while the other one produces heads only 30% of the time. You select one of the coins. You are allowed to spin it *once* and then must decide whether the coin is the 90%- or the 30%-head coin. Your null hypothesis is that your coin produces 90% heads.
a) What is the alternative hypothesis?
b) Given that the outcome of your spin is tails, what would you decide? What if it were heads?
c) How large is $\alpha$ in this case?
d) How large is the power of this test? (*Hint:* How many possibilities are in the alternative hypothesis?)
e) How could you lower the probability of a Type I error and increase the power of the test at the same time?

**30. Faulty or not?** You are in charge of shipping computers to customers. You learn that a faulty disk drive was put into some of the machines. There's a simple test you can perform, but it's not perfect. All but 4% of the time, a good disk drive passes the test, but unfortunately, 35% of the bad disk drives pass the test, too. You have to decide on the basis of one test whether the disk drive is good or bad. Make this a hypothesis test.
a) What are the null and alternative hypotheses?
b) Given that a computer fails the test, what would you decide? What if it passes the test?
c) How large is $\alpha$ for this test?
d) What is the power of this test? (*Hint:* How many possibilities are in the alternative hypothesis?)

**31. Hoops.** A basketball player with a poor foul-shot record practices intensively during the off-season. He tells the coach that he has raised his proficiency from 60% to 80%. Dubious, the coach asks him to take 10 shots, and is surprised when the player hits 9 out of 10. Did the player prove that he has improved?
a) Suppose the player really is no better than before—still a 60% shooter. What's the probability he can hit at least 9 of 10 shots anyway? (*Hint:* Use a Binomial model.)
b) If that is what happened, now the coach thinks the player has improved when he has not. Which type of error is that?
c) If the player really can hit 80% now, and it takes at least 9 out of 10 successful shots to convince the coach, what's the power of the test?

d) List two ways the coach and player could increase the power to detect any improvement.

**32. Pottery.** An artist experimenting with clay to create pottery with a special texture has been experiencing difficulty with these special pieces. About 40% break in the kiln during firing. Hoping to solve this problem, she buys some more expensive clay from another supplier. She plans to make and fire 10 pieces and will decide to use the new clay if at most one of them breaks.
   a) Suppose the new, expensive clay really is no better than her usual clay. What's the probability that this test convinces her to use it anyway? (*Hint:* Use a Binomial model.)
   b) If she decides to switch to the new clay and it is no better, what kind of error did she commit?
   c) If the new clay really can reduce breakage to only 20%, what's the probability that her test will not detect the improvement?
   d) How can she improve the power of her test? Offer at least two suggestions.

**33. Survey.** A company has surveyed a stratified sample of its employees to find out how many might take advantage of a program to help people stop smoking. You may assume that the sampling strategy was properly random and that the data-gathering methodology avoided biases. The table below shows the results. For which of the groups could we use our methods of inference to determine a 95% confidence interval for the proportion of employees who would participate in the stop-smoking program?

| Group | Number of Employees | Number Surveyed | Percent to Participate |
|---|---|---|---|
| Laborers | 6235 | 300 | 9% |
| Clerical | 1520 | 200 | 7% |
| Management | 342 | 25 | 8% |

**34. Fire safety.** A city law requires all buildings to have a fire safety inspection at least once every three years. Concerned that some of these inspections are not being done, the mayor orders a survey to see what fraction of the city's buildings may be out of compliance. Results for the sample appear in the table below. For which of the building classifications could you use our methods of inference to create 95% confidence intervals for the proportion of buildings lacking the required inspection?

| Class | Number of Buildings | Number Surveyed | Percent Not Inspected |
|---|---|---|---|
| Single-family home | 7742 | 200 | 7% |
| Apartment building | 205 | 20 | 10% |
| Commercial | 407 | 70 | 16% |

**35. Little League.** In a 1999–2000 longitudinal study of youth baseball, researchers found that 26% of 298 young pitchers complained of elbow pain after pitching.
   a) Create a 90% confidence interval for the percentage of young players who may develop elbow pain after pitching.
   b) A coach claims that only about 1 player in 5 is at risk of arm injury from pitching. Is this claim consistent with your confidence interval?

**36. Global warming.** A survey by the Pew Research Center for the People & the Press, conducted January 10–15, 2007 among 1708 Americans, found 55% saying that global warming is a problem that requires immediate government action. Pew reports that this is a decline from the previously established level of 61% holding this opinion. Pew reports a margin of error of ±3% for this result. Does the Pew result provide strong evidence that the percentage has decreased? Use the confidence interval to test an appropriate hypothesis, and state your conclusion.

### JUST CHECKING
*Answers*

1. With a *z*-score of 0.62, you can't reject the null hypothesis. The experiment shows no evidence that the wheel is not fair.

2. At $\alpha = 0.05$, you can't reject the null hypothesis because 0.30 is contained in the 90% confidence interval—it's plausible that sending the DVDs is no more effective than just sending letters.

3. The confidence interval is from 29% to 45%. The DVD strategy is more expensive and may not be worth it. We can't distinguish the success rate from 30% given the results of this experiment, but 45% would represent a large improvement. The bank should consider another trial, increasing their sample size to get a narrower confidence interval.

4. A Type I error would mean deciding that the DVD success rate is higher than 30% when it really isn't. They would adopt a more expensive method for collecting payments that's no better than the less expensive strategy.

5. A Type II error would mean deciding that there's not enough evidence to say that the DVD strategy works when in fact it does. The bank would fail to discover an effective method for increasing their revenue from delinquent accounts.

6. 60%; the larger the effect size, the greater the power. It's easier to detect an improvement to a 60% success rate than to a 32% rate.

# Comparing Two Proportions

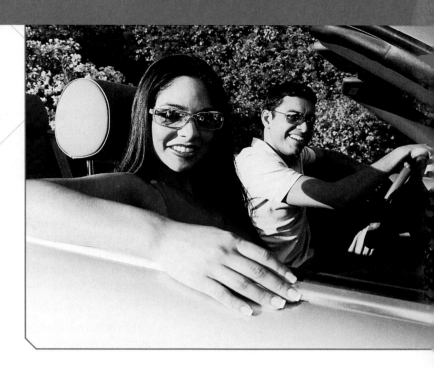

## Where are we going?

Is the proportion of men who like our new Web page the same as the proportion of women who like it? Do people really feel better about the economy this month compared to last month, or was that increase just sampling variation? In practice, it's much more common to compare two proportions than to test whether one is equal to a given number. That's how we'll see whether two groups are different or whether there's been a change over time. Comparing two proportions is very much like testing one. The standard error is different, but the concepts are really the same.

| | |
|---|---|
| **WHO** | 6971 male drivers |
| **WHAT** | Seat-belt use |
| **WHY** | Highway safety |
| **WHEN** | 2007 |
| **WHERE** | Massachussetts |

D o men take more risks than women? Psychologists have documented that, in many situations, men choose riskier behavior than women do. But what is the effect of having a woman by their side? A recent seat-belt observation study in Massachusetts[1] found that, not surprisingly, male drivers wear seat belts less often than women do. The study also noted that men's belt-wearing jumped more than 16 percentage points when they had a female passenger. Seat-belt use was recorded at 161 locations in Massachusetts, using random-sampling methods developed by the National Highway Traffic Safety Administration (NHTSA). Female drivers wore belts more than 70% of the time, regardless of the sex of their passengers. Of 4208 male drivers with female passengers, 2777 (66.0%) were belted. But among 2763 male drivers with male passengers only, 1363 (49.3%) wore seat belts. This was only a random sample, but it suggests there may be a shift in men's risk-taking behavior when women are present. What would we estimate the true size of that gap to be?

Comparisons between two percentages are much more common than questions about isolated percentages. And they are more interesting. We often want to know how two groups differ, whether a treatment is better than a placebo control, or whether this year's results are better than last year's.

---

[1] Massachusetts Traffic Safety Research Program [June 2007].

## Another Ruler

We know the difference between the proportions of men wearing seat belts seen in the *sample*. It's 16.7%. But what's the *true* difference for all men? We know that our estimate probably isn't exactly right. To say more, we need a new ruler—the standard deviation of the sampling distribution model for the difference in the proportions. Now we have two proportions, and each will vary from sample to sample. We are interested in the difference between them. So what is the correct standard deviation?

The answer is simple, but not obvious. (You may have seen it in Chapter 16.) It makes sense that the difference between two random quantities should vary more than either one of them. After all, there are two varying quantities. But it isn't obvious how much more variation to expect. It turns out that we add their *variances* (not the standard deviations) and take a square root to get back to natural units:

*The variance of the sum or difference of two independent random variables is the sum of their variances.*

This is such an important (and powerful) idea in Statistics that it's worth pausing a moment to review the reasoning. Here's some intuition about why variation increases even when we subtract two random quantities.

Grab a full box of cereal. The box claims to contain 16 ounces of cereal. We know that's not exact: There's some small variation from box to box. Now pour a bowl of cereal. Of course, your 2-ounce serving will not be exactly 2 ounces. There'll be some variation there, too. How much cereal would you guess was left in the box? Do you think your guess will be as close as your guess for the full box? *After* you pour your bowl, the amount of cereal in the box is still a random quantity (with a smaller mean than before), but it is even *more variable* because of the additional variation in the amount you poured.

According to our rule, the variance of the amount of cereal left in the box would now be the *sum* of the two *variances.*

We want a standard deviation, not a variance, but that's just a square root away. We can write symbolically what we've just said:

$$Var(X - Y) = Var(X) + Var(Y), \text{so}$$

$$SD(X - Y) = \sqrt{SD^2(X) + SD^2(Y)} = \sqrt{Var(X) + Var(Y)}.$$

That formula may look sort of familiar. Think of a right triangle. Remember the Pythagorean Theorem?[2] It says that the length of the longest side of a right triangle is the square root of the sum of the squares of the other two sides. Standard deviations add in exactly the same way. (You can think of this as the Pythagorean Theorem of Statistics.)

Be careful, though—this simple formula applies only when $X$ and $Y$ are independent. Just as the Pythagorean Theorem works only for right triangles, our formula works only for independent random variables. Always check for independence before using it.

For independent random variables, **variances add.**

**A S** **Activity: Compare Two Proportions.** Does a preschool program help disadvantaged children later in life?

SD(Y)

SD(X)

$\sqrt{SD^2(X) + SD^2(Y)}$

---

[2] If you don't remember the formula, don't rely on the Scarecrow's version from *The Wizard of Oz*. He may have a brain, and have been awarded his Th.D. (Doctor of Thinkology), but he gets the formula wrong.

# The Standard Deviation of the Difference Between Two Proportions

> Combining independent random quantities always *increases* the overall variation, so even for *differences* of independent random variables, **variances add.**

Fortunately, proportions observed in independent random samples *are* independent, so we can put the two proportions in for $X$ and $Y$ and add their variances. We just need to use careful notation to keep things straight.

When we have two samples, each can have a different size and proportion value, so we keep them straight with subscripts. Often we choose subscripts that remind us of the groups. For our example, we might use "$_M$" and "$_F$", but generically we'll just use "$_1$" and "$_2$". We will represent the two sample proportions as $\hat{p}_1$ and $\hat{p}_2$, and the two sample sizes as $n_1$ and $n_2$.

The standard deviations of the sample proportions are $SD(\hat{p}_1) = \sqrt{\dfrac{p_1 q_1}{n_1}}$ and $SD(\hat{p}_2) = \sqrt{\dfrac{p_2 q_2}{n_2}}$, so the variance of the difference in the proportions is

$$Var(\hat{p}_1 - \hat{p}_2) = \left(\sqrt{\frac{p_1 q_1}{n_1}}\right)^2 + \left(\sqrt{\frac{p_2 q_2}{n_2}}\right)^2 = \frac{p_1 q_1}{n_1} + \frac{p_2 q_2}{n_2}.$$

The standard deviation is the square root of that variance:

$$SD(\hat{p}_1 - \hat{p}_2) = \sqrt{\frac{p_1 q_1}{n_1} + \frac{p_2 q_2}{n_2}}.$$

We usually don't know the true values of $p_1$ and $p_2$. When we have the sample proportions in hand from the data, we use them to estimate the variances. So the standard error is

$$SE(\hat{p}_1 - \hat{p}_2) = \sqrt{\frac{\hat{p}_1 \hat{q}_1}{n_1} + \frac{\hat{p}_2 \hat{q}_2}{n_2}}.$$

---

### FOR EXAMPLE | Finding the standard error of a difference in proportions

A recent survey of 886 randomly selected teenagers (aged 12–17) found that more than half of them had online profiles.[3] Some researchers and privacy advocates are concerned about the possible access to personal information about teens in public places on the Internet. There appear to be differences between boys and girls in their online behavior. Among teens aged 15–17, 57% of the 248 boys had posted profiles, compared to 70% of the 256 girls. Let's start the process of estimating how large the true gender gap might be.

**Question:** What's the standard error of the difference in sample proportions?

Because the boys and girls were selected at random, it's reasonable to assume their behaviors are independent, so it's okay to use the Pythagorean Theorem of Statistics:

$$SE(\hat{p}_{boys}) = \sqrt{\frac{0.57 \times 0.43}{248}} = 0.0314$$

$$SE(\hat{p}_{girls}) = \sqrt{\frac{0.70 \times 0.30}{256}} = 0.0286$$

$$SE(\hat{p}_{girls} - \hat{p}_{boys}) = \sqrt{0.0314^2 + 0.0286^2} = 0.0425$$

---

[3] Princeton Survey Research Associates International for the Pew Internet & American Life Project.

# Assumptions and Conditions

Before we look at our example, we need to check assumptions and conditions.

## INDEPENDENCE ASSUMPTIONS

**Independence Assumption:** Within each group, the data should be based on results for independent individuals. We can't check that for certain, but we *can* check the following:

**Randomization Condition:** The data in each group should be drawn independently and at random from a homogeneous population or generated by a randomized comparative experiment.

**The 10% Condition:** If the data are sampled without replacement, the sample should not exceed 10% of the population.

Because we are comparing two groups in this way, we need an additional Independence Assumption. In fact, this is the most important of these assumptions. If it is violated, these methods just won't work.

**Independent Groups Assumption:** The two groups we're comparing must also be independent *of each other*. Usually, the independence of the groups from each other is evident from the way the data were collected.

Why is the Independent Groups Assumption so important? If we compare husbands with their wives, or a group of subjects before and after some treatment, we can't just add the variances. Subjects' performance before a treatment might very well be related to their performance after the treatment. So the proportions are not independent and the Pythagorean-style variance formula does not hold. We'll see a way to compare a common kind of nonindependent samples in a later chapter.

## SAMPLE SIZE CONDITION

*Each* of the groups must be big enough. As with individual proportions, we need larger groups to estimate proportions that are near 0% or 100%. We usually check the Success/Failure Condition for each group.

**Success/Failure Condition:** Both groups are big enough that at least 10 successes and at least 10 failures have been observed in each.

---

**FOR EXAMPLE** Checking assumptions and conditions

**Recap:** Among randomly sampled teens aged 15–17, 57% of the 248 boys had posted online profiles, compared to 70% of the 256 girls.

**Question:** Can we use these results to make inferences about all 15–17-year-olds?

✔ **Randomization Condition:** The sample of boys and the sample of girls were both chosen randomly.

✔ **10% Condition:** 248 boys and 256 girls are each less than 10% of all teenage boys and girls.

✔ **Independent Groups Assumption:** Because the samples were selected at random, it's reasonable to believe the boys' online behaviors are independent of the girls' online behaviors.

✔ **Success/Failure Condition:** Among the boys, 248(0.57) = 141 had online profiles and the other 248(0.43) = 107 did not. For the girls, 256(0.70) = 179 successes and 256(0.30) = 77 failures. All counts are at least 10.

Because all the assumptions and conditions are satisfied, it's okay to proceed with inference.

(Note that when we find the *observed* counts of successes and failures, we round off to whole numbers. We're using the reported percentages to recover the actual counts.)

## The Sampling Distribution

We're almost there. We just need one more fact about proportions. We know already that for large enough samples, each of our proportions has an approximately Normal sampling distribution. The same is true of their difference.

**Why Normal?**

In Chapter 16 we learned that sums and differences of independent Normal random variables also follow a Normal model. That's the reason we use a Normal model for the difference of two independent proportions.

> **THE SAMPLING DISTRIBUTION MODEL FOR A DIFFERENCE BETWEEN TWO INDEPENDENT PROPORTIONS**
>
> Provided that the sampled values are independent, the samples are independent, and the sample sizes are large enough, the sampling distribution of $\hat{p}_1 - \hat{p}_2$ is modeled by a Normal model with mean $\mu = p_1 - p_2$ and standard deviation
>
> $$SD(\hat{p}_1 - \hat{p}_2) = \sqrt{\frac{p_1 q_1}{n_1} + \frac{p_2 q_2}{n_2}}.$$

The sampling distribution model and the standard deviation give us all we need to find a margin of error for the difference in proportions—or at least they would if we knew the true proportions, $p_1$ and $p_2$. However, we don't know the true values, so we'll work with the observed proportions, $\hat{p}_1$ and $\hat{p}_2$, and use $SE(\hat{p}_1 - \hat{p}_2)$ to estimate the standard deviation. The rest is just like a one-proportion z-interval.

> **A TWO-PROPORTION z-INTERVAL**
>
> When the conditions are met, we are ready to find the confidence interval for the difference of two proportions, $p_1 - p_2$. The confidence interval is
>
> $$(\hat{p}_1 - \hat{p}_2) \pm z^* \times SE(\hat{p}_1 - \hat{p}_2)$$
>
> where we find the standard error of the difference,
>
> $$SE(\hat{p}_1 - \hat{p}_2) = \sqrt{\frac{\hat{p}_1 \hat{q}_1}{n_1} + \frac{\hat{p}_2 \hat{q}_2}{n_2}},$$
>
> from the observed proportions.
>
> The critical value $z^*$ depends on the particular confidence level, $C$, that we specify.

**FOR EXAMPLE**    Finding a two-proportion z-interval

**Recap:** Among randomly sampled teens aged 15–17, 57% of the 248 boys had posted online profiles, compared to 70% of the 256 girls. We calculated the standard error for the difference in sample proportions to be $SE(\hat{p}_{girls} - \hat{p}_{boys}) = 0.0425$ and found that the assumptions and conditions required for inference checked out okay.

*(continued)*

For Example (*continued*)

**Question:** What does a confidence interval say about the difference in online behavior?

A 95% confidence interval for $p_{girls} - p_{boys}$ is

$$(\hat{p}_{girls} - \hat{p}_{boys}) \pm z^*SE(\hat{p}_{girls} - \hat{p}_{boys})$$
$$(0.70 - 0.57) \pm 1.96(0.0425)$$
$$0.13 \pm 0.083$$
$$(4.7\%, 21.3\%)$$

We can be 95% confident that, among teens aged 15–17, the proportion of girls who post online profiles is between 4.7 and 21.3 percentage points higher than the proportion of boys who do. It seems clear that teen girls are more likely to post profiles than are boys the same age.

---

## STEP-BY-STEP EXAMPLE    A Two-Proportion *z*-Interval

Now we are ready to be more precise about the passenger-based gap in male drivers' seat-belt use. We'll estimate the difference with a confidence interval using a method called the **two-proportion z-interval** and follow the four confidence interval steps.

**Question:** How much difference is there in the proportion of male drivers who wear seat belts when sitting next to a male passenger and the proportion who wear seat belts when sitting next to a female passenger?

**Plan** State what you want to know. Discuss the variables and the W's.

Identify the parameter you wish to estimate. (It usually doesn't matter in which direction we subtract, so, for convenience, we usually choose the direction with a positive difference.)

Choose and state a confidence level.

**Model** Think about the assumptions and check the conditions.

I want to know the true difference in the population proportion, $p_M$, of male drivers who wear seat belts when sitting next to a man and $p_F$, the proportion who wear seat belts when sitting next to a woman. The data are from a random sample of drivers in Massachusetts in 2007, observed according to procedures developed by the NHTSA. The parameter of interest is the difference $p_F - p_M$.

I will find a 95% confidence interval for this parameter.

✔ **Independence Assumption:** Driver behavior was independent from car to car.
✔ **Randomization Condition:** The NHTSA methods are more complex than a SRS, but they result in a suitable random sample.
✔ **10% Condition:** The samples include far fewer than 10% of all male drivers accompanied by male or by female passengers.
✔ **Independent Groups Assumption:** There's no reason to believe that drivers with male passengers and those with female passengers are not independent.

| | |
|---|---|
| The Success/Failure Condition must hold for each group. | ✔ **Success Failure Condition:** Among male drivers with female passengers, 2777 wore seat belts and 1431 did not; of those driving with male passengers, 1363 wore seat belts and 1400 did not. Each group contained far more than 10 successes and 10 failures. |
| State the sampling distribution model for the statistic.<br><br>Choose your method. | Under these conditions, the sampling distribution of the difference between the sample proportions is approximately Normal, so I'll find a **two-proportion z-interval.** |

**Mechanics** Construct the confidence interval.

I know

$$n_F = 4208, n_M = 2763.$$

The observed sample proportions are

$$\hat{p}_F = \frac{2777}{4208} = 0.660, \hat{p}_M = \frac{1363}{2763} = 0.493$$

As often happens, the key step in finding the confidence interval is estimating the standard deviation of the sampling distribution model of the statistic. Here the statistic is the difference in the proportions of men who wear seat belts when they have a female passenger and the proportion who do so with a male passenger. Substitute the data values into the formula.

I'll estimate the SD of the difference with

$$SE(\hat{p}_F - \hat{p}_M) = \sqrt{\frac{\hat{p}_F \hat{q}_F}{n_F} + \frac{\hat{p}_M \hat{q}_M}{n_M}}$$

$$= \sqrt{\frac{(0.660)(0.340)}{4208} + \frac{(0.493)(0.507)}{2763}}$$

$$= 0.012$$

The sampling distribution is Normal, so the critical value for a 95% confidence interval, $z^*$, is 1.96. The margin of error is the critical value times the SE.

$$ME = z^* \times SE(\hat{p}_F - \hat{p}_M)$$
$$= 1.96(0.012) = 0.024$$

The confidence interval is the statistic ± ME.

The observed difference in proportions is $\hat{p}_F - \hat{p}_M = 0.660 - 0.493 = 0.167$, so the 95% confidence interval is

$$0.167 \pm 0.024$$

or 14.3% to 19.1%

**Conclusion** Interpret your confidence interval in the proper context. (Remember: We're 95% confident that our interval captured the true difference.)

I am 95% confident that the proportion of male drivers who wear seat belts when driving next to a female passenger is between 14.3 and 19.1 percentage points higher than the proportion who wear seat belts when driving next to a male passenger.

This is an interesting result—but be careful not to try to say too much! In Massachusetts, overall seat-belt use is lower than the national average, so we can't be certain that these results generalize to other states. And these were two different groups of men, so we can't say that, individually, men are more likely to buckle up when they have a woman passenger. You can probably think of several alternative explanations; we'll suggest just a couple. Perhaps age is a lurking variable: Maybe older men are more likely to wear seat belts and also more likely to be driving with their wives. Or maybe men who don't wear seat belts have trouble attracting women!

---

## JUST CHECKING

A public broadcasting station plans to launch a special appeal for additional contributions from current members. Unsure of the most effective way to contact people, they run an experiment. They randomly select two groups of current members. They send the same request for donations to everyone, but it goes to one group by e-mail and to the other group by regular mail. The station was successful in getting contributions from 26% of the members they e-mailed but only from 15% of those who received the request by regular mail. A 90% confidence interval estimated the difference in donation rates to be 11% ± 7%.

**1.** Interpret the confidence interval in this context.

**2.** Based on this confidence interval, what conclusion would we reach if we tested the hypothesis that there's no difference in the response rates to the two methods of fund raising? Explain.

---

# Will I Snore When I'm 64?

| | |
|---|---|
| **WHO** | Randomly selected U.S. adults over age 18 |
| **WHAT** | Proportion who snore, categorized by age (less than 30, 30 or older) |
| **WHEN** | 2001 |
| **WHERE** | United States |
| **WHY** | To study sleep behaviors of U.S. adults |

The National Sleep Foundation asked a random sample of 1010 U.S. adults questions about their sleep habits. The sample was selected in the fall of 2001 from random telephone numbers, stratified by region and sex, guaranteeing that an equal number of men and women were interviewed (2002 Sleep in America Poll, National Sleep Foundation, Washington, DC).

One of the questions asked about snoring. Of the 995 respondents, 37% of adults reported that they snored at least a few nights a week during the past year. Would you expect that percentage to be the same for all age groups? Split into two age categories, 26% of the 184 people under 30 snored, compared with 39% of the 811 in the older group. Is this difference of 13% real, or due only to natural fluctuations in the sample we've chosen?

The question calls for a hypothesis test. Now the parameter of interest is the true *difference* between the (reported) snoring rates of the two age groups.

What's the appropriate null hypothesis? That's easy here. We hypothesize that there is no difference in the proportions. This is such a natural null hypothesis that we rarely consider any other. But instead of writing $H_0: p_1 = p_2$, we usually express it in a slightly different way. To make it relate directly to the *difference*, we hypothesize that the difference in proportions is zero:

$$H_0: p_1 - p_2 = 0.$$

# Everyone into the Pool

Our hypothesis is about a new parameter: the *difference* in proportions. We'll need a standard error for that. Wait—don't we know that already? Yes and no. We know that the standard error of the difference in proportions is

$$SE(\hat{p}_1 - \hat{p}_2) = \sqrt{\frac{\hat{p}_1\hat{q}_1}{n_1} + \frac{\hat{p}_2\hat{q}_2}{n_2}},$$

and we could just plug in the numbers, but we can do even better. The secret is that proportions and their standard deviations are linked. There are two proportions in the standard error formula—but look at the null hypothesis. It says that these proportions are equal. To do a hypothesis test, we *assume* that the null hypothesis is true. So there should be just a single value of $\hat{p}$ in the SE formula (and, of course, $\hat{q}$ is just $1 - \hat{p}$).

How would we do this for the snoring example? If the null hypothesis is true, then, among all adults, the two groups have the same proportion. Overall, we saw $48 + 318 = 366$ snorers out of a total of $184 + 811 = 995$ adults who responded to this question. The overall proportion of snorers was $366/995 = 0.3678$.

Combining the counts like this to get an overall proportion is called **pooling**. Whenever we have data from different sources or different groups but we believe that they really came from the same underlying population, we pool them to get better estimates.

When we have counts for each group, we can find the pooled proportion as

$$\hat{p}_{\text{pooled}} = \frac{Success_1 + Success_2}{n_1 + n_2},$$

where $Success_1$ is the number of successes in group 1 and $Success_2$ is the number of successes in group 2. That's the overall proportion of success.

When we have only proportions and not the counts, as in the snoring example, we have to reconstruct the number of successes by multiplying the sample sizes by the proportions:

$$Success_1 = n_1\hat{p}_1 \text{ and } Success_2 = n_2\hat{p}_2.$$

If these calculations don't come out to whole numbers, round them first. There must have been a whole number of successes, after all. (This is the *only* time you should round values in the middle of a calculation.)

We then put this pooled value into the formula, substituting it for *both* sample proportions in the standard error formula:

$$SE_{\text{pooled}}(\hat{p}_1 - \hat{p}_2) = \sqrt{\frac{\hat{p}_{\text{pooled}}\hat{q}_{\text{pooled}}}{n_1} + \frac{\hat{p}_{\text{pooled}}\hat{q}_{\text{pooled}}}{n_2}}$$

$$= \sqrt{\frac{0.3678 \times (1 - 0.3678)}{184} + \frac{0.3678 \times (1 - 0.3678)}{811}}.$$

This comes out to 0.039.

> When finding the number of successes, round the values to integers. For example, the 48 snorers among the 184 under-30 respondents are actually 26.1% of 184. We round back to the nearest whole number to find the count that could have yielded the rounded percent we were given.

# Improving the Success/Failure Condition

The vaccine Gardasil® was introduced to prevent the strains of human papillomavirus (HPV) that are responsible for almost all cases of cervical cancer. In randomized placebo-controlled clinical trials,[4] only 1 case of HPV was diagnosed

---

[4] *Quadrivalent Human Papillomavirus Vaccine: Recommendations of the Advisory Committee on Immunization Practices (ACIP)*, National Center for HIV/AIDS, Viral Hepatitis, STD and TB Prevention [May 2007].

among 7897 women who received the vaccine, compared with 91 cases diagnosed among 7899 who received a placebo. The one observed HPV case ("success") doesn't meet the at-least-10-successes criterion. Surely, though, we should not refuse to test the effectiveness of the vaccine just because it failed so rarely; that would be absurd.

For that reason, in a two-proportion z-test, the proper Success/Failure test uses the *expected* frequencies, which we can find from the pooled proportion. In this case,

$$\hat{p}_{\text{pooled}} = \frac{91 + 1}{7899 + 7897} = 0.0058$$

$$n_1 \hat{p}_{\text{pooled}} = 7899(0.0058) = 46$$

$$n_2 \hat{p}_{\text{pooled}} = 7897(0.0058) = 46,$$

so we can proceed with the hypothesis test.

Often it is easier just to check the observed numbers of successes and failures. If they are both greater than 10, you don't need to look further. But keep in mind that the correct test uses the expected frequencies rather than the observed ones.

## Compared to What?

Naturally, we'll reject our null hypothesis if we see a large enough difference in the two proportions. How can we decide whether the difference we see, $\hat{p}_1 - \hat{p}_2$, is large? The answer is the same as always: We just compare it to its standard deviation.

Unlike previous hypothesis-testing situations, the null hypothesis doesn't provide a standard deviation, so we'll use a standard error (here, pooled). Since the sampling distribution is Normal, we can divide the observed difference by its standard error to get a z-score. The z-score will tell us how many standard errors the observed difference is away from 0. We can then use the 68–95–99.7 Rule to decide whether this is large, or some technology to get an exact P-value. The result is a **two-proportion z-test.**

> **A S** *Activity:* **Test for a Difference Between Two Proportions.** Is premium-brand chicken less likely to be contaminated than store-brand chicken?

---

**TWO-PROPORTION z-TEST**

The conditions for the two-proportion z-test are the same as for the two-proportion z-interval. We are testing the hypothesis

$$H_0: p_1 - p_2 = 0.$$

Because we hypothesize that the proportions are equal, we pool the groups to find

$$\hat{p}_{\text{pooled}} = \frac{Success_1 + Success_2}{n_1 + n_2}$$

and use that pooled value to estimate the standard error:

$$SE_{\text{pooled}}(\hat{p}_1 - \hat{p}_2) = \sqrt{\frac{\hat{p}_{\text{pooled}}\,\hat{q}_{\text{pooled}}}{n_1} + \frac{\hat{p}_{\text{pooled}}\,\hat{q}_{\text{pooled}}}{n_2}}.$$

Now we find the test statistic,

$$z = \frac{(\hat{p}_1 - \hat{p}_2) - 0}{SE_{\text{pooled}}(\hat{p}_1 - \hat{p}_2)}.$$

When the conditions are met and the null hypothesis is true, this statistic follows the standard Normal model, so we can use that model to obtain a P-value.

---

**STEP-BY-STEP EXAMPLE** | **A Two-Proportion *z*-Test**

**Question: Are the snoring rates of the two age groups really different?**

---

**Plan** State what you want to know. Discuss the variables and the W's.

I want to know whether snoring rates differ for those under and over 30 years old. The data are from a random sample of 1010 U.S. adults surveyed in the 2002 Sleep in America Poll. Of these, 995 responded to the question about snoring, indicating whether or not they had snored at least a few nights a week in the past year.

**Hypotheses** The study simply broke down the responses by age, so there is no sense that either alternative was preferred. A two-sided alternative hypothesis is appropriate.

$H_0$: There is no difference in snoring rates in the two age groups:

$$p_{old} - p_{young} = 0.$$

$H_A$: The rates are different: $p_{old} - p_{young} \neq 0.$

**Model** Think about the assumptions and check the conditions.

✓ **Independence Assumption:** The National Sleep Foundation selected respondents at random, so they should be independent.

✓ **Randomization Condition:** The respondents were randomly selected by telephone number and stratified by sex and region.

✓ **10% Condition:** The number of adults surveyed in each age group is certainly far less than 10% of that population.

✓ **Independent Groups Assumption:** The two groups are independent of each other because the sample was selected at random.

✓ **Success/Failure Condition:** In the younger age group, 48 snored and 136 didn't. In the older group, 318 snored and 493 didn't. The observed numbers of both successes and failures are much more than 10 for both groups.[5]

State the null model.

Choose your method.

Because the conditions are satisfied, I'll use a Normal model and perform a **two-proportion *z*-test.**

---

[5] This is one of those situations in which the traditional term "success" seems a bit weird. A success here could be that a person snores. "Success" and "failure" are arbitrary labels left over from studies of gambling games.

**SHOW**

### Mechanics

$n_{young} = 184$, $y_{young} = 48$, $\hat{p}_{young} = 0.261$

$n_{old} = 811$, $y_{old} = 318$, $\hat{p}_{old} = 0.392$

The hypothesis is that the proportions are equal, so pool the sample data.

$$\hat{p}_{pooled} = \frac{y_{old} + y_{young}}{n_{old} + n_{young}} = \frac{318 + 48}{811 + 184} = 0.3678$$

Use the pooled SE to estimate $SD(p_{old} - p_{young})$.

$SE_{pooled}(\hat{p}_{old} - \hat{p}_{young})$

$$= \sqrt{\frac{\hat{p}_{pooled}\,\hat{q}_{pooled}}{n_{old}} + \frac{\hat{p}_{pooled}\,\hat{q}_{pooled}}{n_{young}}}$$

$$= \sqrt{\frac{(0.3678)(0.6322)}{811} + \frac{(0.3678)(0.6322)}{184}}$$

$$\approx 0.039375$$

The observed difference in sample proportions is
$\hat{p}_{old} - \hat{p}_{young} = 0.392 - 0.261 = 0.131$

Make a picture. Sketch a Normal model centered at the hypothesized difference of 0. Shade the region to the right of the observed difference, and because this is a two-tailed test, also shade the corresponding region in the other tail.

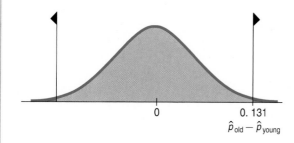

Find the z-score for the observed difference in proportions, 0.131.

Find the P-value using Table Z or technology. Because this is a two-tailed test, we must *double* the probability we find in the upper tail.

$$z = \frac{(\hat{p}_{old} - \hat{p}_{young}) - 0}{SE_{pooled}(\hat{p}_{old} - \hat{p}_{young})} = \frac{0.131 - 0}{0.039375} = 3.33$$

$$P = 2P(z \geq 3.33) = 0.0008$$

 **TELL**

### Conclusion

Link the P-value to your decision about the null hypothesis, and state your conclusion in context.

The P-value of 0.0008 says that if there really were no difference in (reported) snoring rates between the two age groups, then the difference observed in this study would happen only 8 times in 10,000. This is so small that I reject the null hypothesis of no difference and conclude that there is a difference in the rate of snoring between older adults and younger adults. It appears that older adults are more likely to snore.

# JUST CHECKING

**3.** A June 2004 public opinion poll asked 1000 randomly selected adults whether the United States should decrease the amount of immigration allowed; 49% of those responding said "yes." In June of 1995, a random sample of 1000 had found that 65% of adults thought immigration should be curtailed. To see if that percentage has decreased, why can't we just use a one-proportion $z$-test of $H_0$: $p = 0.65$ and see what the P-value of $\hat{p} = 0.49$ is?

**4.** For opinion polls like this, which has more variability, the percentage of respondents answering "yes" in either year or the difference in the percentages between the two years?

---

## FOR EXAMPLE     Another 2-proportion z-test

**Recap:** One concern of the study on teens' online profiles was safety and privacy. In the random sample, girls were less likely than boys to say that they are easy to find online from their profiles. Only 19% (62 girls) of 325 teen girls with profiles say that they are easy to find, while 28% (75 boys) of the 268 boys with profiles say the same.

**Question:** Are these results evidence of a real difference between boys and girls? Perform a two-proportion $z$-test and discuss what you find.

$$H_O: p_{boys} - p_{girls} = 0$$
$$H_A: p_{boys} - p_{girls} \neq 0$$

✔ **Randomization Condition:** The sample of boys and the sample of girls were both chosen randomly.

✔ **10% Condition:** 268 boys and 325 girls are each less than 10% of all teenage boys and girls with online profiles.

✔ **Independent Groups Assumption:** Because the samples were selected at random, it's reasonable to believe the boys' perceptions are independent of the girls'.

✔ **Success/Failure Condition:** Among the girls, there were 62 "successes" and 263 failures, and among boys, 75 successes and 193 failures. These counts are at least 10 for each group.

Because all the assumptions and conditions are satisfied, it's okay to do a **two-proportion z-test**:

$$\hat{p}_{pooled} = \frac{75 + 62}{268 + 325} = 0.231$$

$$SE_{pooled}(\hat{p}_{boys} - \hat{p}_{girls}) = \sqrt{\frac{0.231 \times 0.769}{268} + \frac{0.231 \times 0.769}{325}} = 0.0348$$

$$z = \frac{(0.28 - 0.19) - 0}{0.0348} = 2.59$$

$$P(z > 2.59) = 0.0048$$

This is a two-tailed test, so the P-value = 2(0.0048) = 0.0096. Because this P-value is very small, I reject the null hypothesis. This study provides strong evidence that there really is a difference in the proportions of teen girls and boys who say they are easy to find online.

## WHAT CAN GO WRONG?

▶ **Don't use two-sample proportion methods when the samples aren't independent.** These methods give wrong answers when this assumption of independence is violated. Good random sampling is usually the best insurance of independent groups. Make sure there is no relationship between the two groups. For example, you can't compare the proportion of respondents who own SUVs with the proportion of those same respondents who think the tax on gas should be eliminated. The responses are not independent because you've asked many of the same people. To use these methods to estimate or test the difference, you'd need to survey two different groups of people.

Alternatively, if you have a random sample, you can split your respondents according to their answers to one question and treat the two resulting groups as independent samples. So, you could test whether the proportion of SUV owners who favored eliminating the gas tax was the same as the corresponding proportion among non–SUV owners.

▶ **Don't apply inference methods where there was no randomization.** If the data do not come from representative random samples or from a properly randomized experiment, then the inference about the differences in proportions will be wrong.

▶ **Don't interpret a significant difference in proportions causally.** It turns out that people with higher incomes are more likely to snore. Does that mean money affects sleep patterns? Probably not. We have seen that older people are more likely to snore, and they are also likely to earn more. In a prospective or retrospective study, there is always the danger that other lurking variables not accounted for are the real reason for an observed difference. Be careful not to jump to conclusions about causality.

# CONNECTIONS

In Chapter 3 we looked at contingency tables for two categorical variables. Differences in proportions are just $2 \times 2$ contingency tables. You'll often see data presented in this way. For example, the snoring data could be shown as

|  | 18–29 | 30 and over | Total |
|---|---|---|---|
| **Snore** | 48 | 318 | 366 |
| **Don't snore** | 136 | 493 | 629 |
| Total | 184 | 811 | 995 |

We tested whether the column percentages of snorers were the same for the two age groups.

This chapter gives the first examples we've seen of inference methods for a parameter other than a simple proportion. Although we have a different standard error, the step-by-step procedures are almost identical. In particular, once again we divide the statistic (the difference in proportions) by its standard error and get a z-score. You should feel right at home.

# WHAT HAVE WE LEARNED?

In the last few chapters we began our exploration of statistical inference; we learned how to create confidence intervals and test hypotheses about a proportion. Now we've looked at inference for the difference in two proportions. In doing so, perhaps the most important thing we've learned is that the concepts and interpretations are essentially the same—only the mechanics have changed slightly.

We've learned that hypothesis tests and confidence intervals for the difference in two proportions are based on Normal models. Both require us to find the standard error of the difference in two proportions. We do that by adding the variances of the two sample proportions, assuming our two groups are independent. When we test a hypothesis that the two proportions are equal, we pool the sample data; for confidence intervals, we don't pool.

## Terms

**Variances of independent random variables add**

558. The variance of a sum or difference of independent random variables is the sum of the variances of those variables.

**Sampling distribution of the difference between two proportions**

559, 561. The sampling distribution of $\hat{p}_1 - \hat{p}_2$ is, under appropriate assumptions, modeled by a Normal model with mean $\mu = p_1 - p_2$ and standard deviation $SD(\hat{p}_1 - \hat{p}_2) = \sqrt{\dfrac{p_1 q_1}{n_1} + \dfrac{p_2 q_2}{n_2}}$

**Two-proportion z-interval**

561. A two-proportion z-interval gives a confidence interval for the true difference in proportions, $p_1 - p_2$, in two independent groups.

The confidence interval is $(\hat{p}_1 - \hat{p}_2) \pm z^* \times SE(\hat{p}_1 - \hat{p}_2)$, where $z^*$ is a critical value from the standard Normal model corresponding to the specified confidence level.

**Pooling**

565. When we have data from different sources that we believe are homogeneous, we can get a better estimate of the common proportion and its standard deviation. We can combine, or pool, the data into a single group for the purpose of estimating the common proportion. The resulting pooled standard error is based on more data and is thus more reliable (if the null hypothesis is true and the groups are truly homogeneous).

**Two-proportion z-test**

566. Test the null hypothesis $H_0: p_1 - p_2 = 0$ by referring the statistic

$$z = \frac{\hat{p}_1 - \hat{p}_2}{SE_{\text{pooled}}(\hat{p}_1 - \hat{p}_2)}$$

to a standard Normal model.

## Skills

▸ Be able to state the null and alternative hypotheses for testing the difference between two population proportions.

▸ Know how to examine your data for violations of conditions that would make inference about the difference between two population proportions unwise or invalid.

▸ Understand that the formula for the standard error of the difference between two independent sample proportions is based on the principle that when finding the sum or difference of two independent random variables, their variances add.

▸ Know how to find a confidence interval for the difference between two proportions.

▸ Be able to perform a significance test of the natural null hypothesis that two population proportions are equal.

▸ Know how to write a sentence describing what is said about the difference between two population proportions by a confidence interval.

▸ Know how to write a sentence interpreting the results of a significance test of the null hypothesis that two population proportions are equal.

▸ Be able to interpret the meaning of a P-value in nontechnical language, making clear that the probability claim is made about computed values and not about the population parameter of interest.

▸ Know that we do not "accept" a null hypothesis if we fail to reject it.

# ON THE COMPUTER

## Inferences for the Difference Between Two Proportions

It is so common to test against the null hypothesis of no difference between the two true proportions that most statistics programs simply assume this null hypothesis. And most will automatically use the pooled standard deviation. If you wish to test a different null (say, that the true difference is 0.3), you may have to search for a way to do it.

Many statistics packages don't offer special commands for inference for differences between proportions. As with inference for single proportions, most statistics programs want the "success" and "failure" status for each case. Usually these are given as 1 or 0, but they might be category names like "yes" and "no." Often we just know the proportions of successes, $\hat{p}_1$ and $\hat{p}_2$, and the counts, $n_1$ and $n_2$. Computer packages don't usually deal with summary data like these easily. Calculators typically do a better job.

In some programs, you can reconstruct the original values. But even when you have (or can reconstruct) the raw data values, often you won't get *exactly* the same test statistic from a computer package as you would find working by hand. The reason is that when the packages treat the proportion as a mean, they make some approximations. The result is very close, but not exactly the same.

### DATA DESK

Data Desk does not offer built-in methods for inference with proportions. Use **Replicate Y by X** to construct data corresponding to given proportions and totals.

COMMENTS

For summarized data, open a Scratchpad to compute the standard deviations and margin of error by typing the calculation.

### EXCEL

Inference methods for proportions are not part of the standard Excel tool set.

COMMENTS

For summarized data, type the calculation into any cell and evaluate it.

### JMP

For a **categorical** variable that holds category labels, the **Distribution** platform includes tests and intervals of proportions.

For summarized data, put the category names in one variable and the frequencies in an adjacent variable. Designate the frequency column to have the **role** of **frequency.** Then use the **Distribution** platform.

COMMENTS

JMP uses slightly different methods for proportion inferences than those discussed in this text. Your answers are likely to be slightly different.

## MINITAB

To find a hypothesis test for a proportion, Choose **Basic Statistics** from the **Stat** menu.
Choose **2Proportions . . .** from the Basic Statistics submenu. If the data are organized as category names in one column and case IDs in another, assign the variables from the variable list box to the **Samples in one column** box. If the data are organized as two separate columns of responses, click on **Samples in different columns:** and assign the variables from the variable list box. If you have summarized data, click the **Summarized Data** button and fill in the number of trials and the number of successes for each group.
Click the **Options** button and specify the remaining details. Remember to click the **Use pooled estimate of _p_ for test** box when testing the null hypothesis of no difference between proportions. Click the **OK** button.

### COMMENTS

When working from a variable that names categories, MINITAB treats the last category as the "success" category. You can specify how the categories should be ordered.

## SPSS

SPSS does not find hypothesis tests for proportions.

## TI-83/84 PLUS

To calculate a confidence interval for the difference between two population proportions,
▶ Select **B:2-PropZInt** from the **STAT TESTS** menu.
▶ Enter the observed counts and the sample sizes for both samples.
▶ Specify a confidence level.
▶ Calculate the interval.
To do the mechanics of a hypothesis test for equality of population proportions,
▶ Select **6:2-PropZTest** from the **STAT TESTS** menu.
▶ Enter the observed counts and sample sizes.
▶ Indicate what kind of test you want: one-tail upper tail, lower tail, or two-tail.
▶ Calculate the result.

### COMMENTS

*Beware:* When you enter the value of _x_, you need the *count,* not the percentage. The count must be a whole number.

## TI-89

To calculate a confidence interval for the difference between two population proportions,
▶ Select **6:2-PropZInt** from the **STAT Ints** menu.
▶ Enter the observed counts and the sample sizes for both samples.
▶ Specify a confidence level.
▶ Calculate the interval.
To do the mechanics of a hypothesis test for equality of population proportions,
▶ Select **6:2-PropZTest** from the **STAT Tests** menu.
▶ Enter the observed counts and sample sizes.
▶ Indicate what kind of test you want: one-tail upper tail, lower tail, or two-tail.
▶ Specify whether results should simply be calculated or displayed with the area corresponding to the P-value of the test shaded.

### COMMENTS

*Beware:* When you enter the value of _x_, you need the *count,* not the percentage. The count must be a whole number. If the number of successes is given as a percent, you must first multiply _np_ and round the result to obtain _x_.

**1. Online social networking.** The Parents & Teens 2006 Survey of 935 12- to 17-year-olds found that, among teens aged 15–17, girls were significantly more likely to have used social networking sites and online profiles. 70% of the girls surveyed had used an online social network, compared to 54% of the boys. What does it mean to say that the difference in proportions is "significant"?

**2. Science news.** In 2007 a Pew survey asked 1447 Internet users about their sources of news and information about science. Among those who had broadband access at home, 34% said they would turn to the Internet for most of their science news. The report on this survey claims that this is not significantly different from the percentage (33%) who said they ordinarily get their science news from television. What does it mean to say that the difference is not significant?

**3. Revealing information.** 886 randomly sampled teens were asked which of several personal items of information they thought it okay to share with someone they had just met. 44% said it was okay to share their e-mail addresses, but only 29% said they would give out their cell phone numbers. A researcher claims that a two-proportion z-test could tell whether there was a real difference among all teens. Explain why that test would not be appropriate for these data.

**4. Regulating access.** When a random sample of 935 parents were asked about rules in their homes, 77% said they had rules about the kinds of TV shows their children could watch. Among the 790 of those parents whose teenage children had Internet access, 85% had rules about the kinds of Internet sites their teens could visit. That looks like a difference, but can we tell? Explain why a two-sample z-test would not be appropriate here.

**5. Gender gap.** A presidential candidate fears he has a problem with women voters. His campaign staff plans to run a poll to assess the situation. They'll randomly sample 300 men and 300 women, asking if they have a favorable impression of the candidate. Obviously, the staff can't know this, but suppose the candidate has a positive image with 59% of males but with only 53% of females.
a) What kind of sampling design is his staff planning to use?
b) What difference would you expect the poll to show?
c) Of course, sampling error means the poll won't reflect the difference perfectly. What's the standard deviation for the difference in the proportions?
d) Sketch a sampling model for the size difference in proportions of men and women with favorable impressions of this candidate that might appear in a poll like this.
e) Could the campaign be misled by the poll, concluding that there really is no gender gap? Explain.

**6. Buy it again?** A consumer magazine plans to poll car owners to see if they are happy enough with their vehicles that they would purchase the same model again.

They'll randomly select 450 owners of American-made cars and 450 owners of Japanese models. Obviously, the actual opinions of the entire population couldn't be known, but suppose 76% of owners of American cars and 78% of owners of Japanese cars would purchase another.
a) What kind of sampling design is the magazine planning to use?
b) What difference would you expect their poll to show?
c) Of course, sampling error means the poll won't reflect the difference perfectly. What's the standard deviation for the difference in the proportions?
d) Sketch a sampling model for the difference in proportions that might appear in a poll like this.
e) Could the magazine be misled by the poll, concluding that owners of American cars are much happier with their vehicles than owners of Japanese cars? Explain.

**7. Arthritis.** The Centers for Disease Control and Prevention reported a survey of randomly selected Americans age 65 and older, which found that 411 of 1012 men and 535 of 1062 women suffered from some form of arthritis.
a) Are the assumptions and conditions necessary for inference satisfied? Explain.
b) Create a 95% confidence interval for the difference in the proportions of senior men and women who have this disease.
c) Interpret your interval in this context.
d) Does this confidence interval suggest that arthritis is more likely to afflict women than men? Explain.

**8. Graduation.** In October 2000 the U.S. Department of Commerce reported the results of a large-scale survey on high school graduation. Researchers contacted more than 25,000 Americans aged 24 years to see if they had finished high school; 84.9% of the 12,460 males and 88.1% of the 12,678 females indicated that they had high school diplomas.
a) Are the assumptions and conditions necessary for inference satisfied? Explain.
b) Create a 95% confidence interval for the difference in graduation rates between males and females.
c) Interpret your confidence interval.
d) Does this provide strong evidence that girls are more likely than boys to complete high school? Explain.

**9. Pets.** Researchers at the National Cancer Institute released the results of a study that investigated the effect of weed-killing herbicides on house pets. They examined 827 dogs from homes where an herbicide was used on a regular basis, diagnosing malignant lymphoma in 473 of them. Of the 130 dogs from homes where no herbicides were used, only 19 were found to have lymphoma.
a) What's the standard error of the difference in the two proportions?
b) Construct a 95% confidence interval for this difference.
c) State an appropriate conclusion.

10. **Carpal tunnel.** The painful wrist condition called carpal tunnel syndrome can be treated with surgery or less invasive wrist splints. In September 2002, *Time* magazine reported on a study of 176 patients. Among the half that had surgery, 80% showed improvement after three months, but only 48% of those who used the wrist splints improved.
    a) What's the standard error of the difference in the two proportions?
    b) Construct a 95% confidence interval for this difference.
    c) State an appropriate conclusion.

11. **Prostate cancer.** There has been debate among doctors over whether surgery can prolong life among men suffering from prostate cancer, a type of cancer that typically develops and spreads very slowly. In the summer of 2003, *The New England Journal of Medicine* published results of some Scandinavian research. Men diagnosed with prostate cancer were randomly assigned to either undergo surgery or not. Among the 347 men who had surgery, 16 eventually died of prostate cancer, compared with 31 of the 348 men who did not have surgery.
    a) Was this an experiment or an observational study? Explain.
    b) Create a 95% confidence interval for the difference in rates of death for the two groups of men.
    c) Based on your confidence interval, is there evidence that surgery may be effective in preventing death from prostate cancer? Explain.

12. **Race and smoking 2005.** In 2005 the New Jersey Adult Tobacco Survey found that 22.5% of 464 blacks surveyed said that they smoked cigarettes while 18.3% of 2449 white respondents reported smoking.
    a) Create a 90% confidence interval for the difference in the percentage of smokers between black and white adults in New Jersey.
    b) Does this survey indicate a race-based difference in smoking among American adults? Explain, using your confidence interval to test an appropriate hypothesis.
    c) What alpha level did your test use?

13. **Politics.** A poll checking on the level of public support for proposed antiterrorist legislation reported that 68% of the respondents were in favor. The pollsters reported a sampling error of ±3%. When the responses were broken down by party affiliation, support was 2% higher among Republican respondents than Democrats. The pollsters said the margin of error for this difference was ±4%.
    a) Why is the margin of error larger for the difference in support between the parties than for the overall level of support?
    b) Based on these results, can we conclude that support is significantly higher among Republicans? Explain.

14. **War.** In September 2002, a Gallup Poll found major differences of opinion based on political affiliation over whether Congress should give President Bush authority to take military action in Iraq. Overall, about 50% of the 1010 respondents were in favor, with a margin of error of ±3%. Opinion differed greatly among Republicans, Democrats, and Independents. (See the bar graph in the next column.)

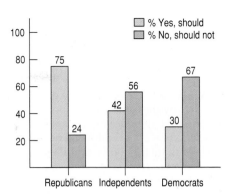

    a) How large did this poll estimate the difference in support between Republicans and Democrats to be?
    b) Was the margin of error for that difference equal to, greater than, or less than 3%? Explain.

15. **Ear infections.** A new vaccine was recently tested to see if it could prevent the painful and recurrent ear infections that many infants suffer from. *The Lancet*, a medical journal, reported a study in which babies about a year old were randomly divided into two groups. One group received vaccinations; the other did not. During the following year, only 333 of 2455 vaccinated children had ear infections, compared to 499 of 2452 unvaccinated children in the control group.
    a) Are the conditions for inference satisfied?
    b) Find a 95% confidence interval for the difference in rates of ear infection.
    c) Use your confidence interval to explain whether you think the vaccine is effective.

16. **Anorexia.** The *Journal of the American Medical Association* reported on an experiment intended to see if the drug Prozac® could be used as a treatment for the eating disorder anorexia nervosa. The subjects, women being treated for anorexia, were randomly divided into two groups. Of the 49 who received Prozac, 35 were deemed healthy a year later, compared to 32 of the 44 who got the placebo.
    a) Are the conditions for inference satisfied?
    b) Find a 95% confidence interval for the difference in outcomes.
    c) Use your confidence interval to explain whether you think Prozac is effective.

17. **Another ear infection.** In Exercise 15 you used a confidence interval to examine the effectiveness of a vaccine against ear infections in babies. Suppose that instead you had conducted a hypothesis test. (Answer these questions *without* actually doing the test.)
    a) What hypotheses would you test?
    b) State a conclusion based on your confidence interval.
    c) If that conclusion is wrong, which type of error did you make?
    d) What would be the consequences of such an error?

18. **Anorexia again.** In Exercise 16 you used a confidence interval to examine the effectiveness of Prozac in treating anorexia nervosa. Suppose that instead you had conducted a hypothesis test. (Answer these questions *without* actually doing the test.)

a) What hypotheses would you test?

b) State a conclusion based on your confidence interval.

c) If that conclusion is wrong, which type of error did you make?

d) What would be the consequences of such an error?

**19. Teen smoking, part I.** A Vermont study published in December 2001 by the American Academy of Pediatrics examined parental influence on teenagers' decisions to smoke. A group of students who had never smoked were questioned about their parents' attitudes toward smoking. These students were questioned again two years later to see if they had started smoking. The researchers found that, among the 284 students who indicated that their parents disapproved of kids smoking, 54 had become established smokers. Among the 41 students who initially said their parents were lenient about smoking, 11 became smokers. Do these data provide strong evidence that parental attitude influences teenagers' decisions about smoking?

a) What kind of design did the researchers use?

b) Write appropriate hypotheses.

c) Are the assumptions and conditions necessary for inference satisfied?

d) Test the hypothesis and state your conclusion.

e) Explain in this context what your P-value means.

f) If that conclusion is actually wrong, which type of error did you commit?

**20. Depression.** A study published in the *Archives of General Psychiatry* in March 2001 examined the impact of depression on a patient's ability to survive cardiac disease. Researchers identified 450 people with cardiac disease, evaluated them for depression, and followed the group for 4 years. Of the 361 patients with no depression, 67 died. Of the 89 patients with minor or major depression, 26 died. Among people who suffer from cardiac disease, are depressed patients more likely to die than non-depressed ones?

a) What kind of design was used to collect these data?

b) Write appropriate hypotheses.

c) Are the assumptions and conditions necessary for inference satisfied?

d) Test the hypothesis and state your conclusion.

e) Explain in this context what your P-value means.

f) If your conclusion is actually incorrect, which type of error did you commit?

**21. Teen smoking, part II.** Consider again the Vermont study discussed in Exercise 19.

a) Create a 95% confidence interval for the difference in the proportion of children who may smoke and have approving parents and those who may smoke and have disapproving parents.

b) Interpret your interval in this context.

c) Carefully explain what "95% confidence" means.

**22. Depression revisited.** Consider again the study of the association between depression and cardiac disease survivability in Exercise 20.

a) Create a 95% confidence interval for the difference in survival rates.

b) Interpret your interval in this context.

c) Carefully explain what "95% confidence" means.

**23. Pregnancy.** In 1998, a San Diego reproductive clinic reported 42 live births to 157 women under the age of 38, but only 7 live births for 89 clients aged 38 and older. Is this strong evidence of a difference in the effectiveness of the clinic's methods for older women?

a) Test an appropriate hypothesis and state your conclusion.

b) If you concluded there was a difference, estimate that difference with a confidence interval and interpret your interval in context.

**24. Birthweight.** In 2003 the *Journal of the American Medical Association* reported a study examining the possible impact of air pollution caused by the 9/11 attack on New York's World Trade Center on the weight of babies. Researchers found that 8% of 182 babies born to mothers who were exposed to heavy doses of soot and ash on September 11 were classified as having low birth weight. Only 4% of 2300 babies born in another New York City hospital whose mothers had not been near the site of the disaster were similarly classified. Does this indicate a possibility that air pollution might be linked to a significantly higher proportion of low-weight babies?

a) Test an appropriate hypothesis and state your conclusion.

b) If you concluded there is a difference, estimate that difference with a confidence interval and interpret that interval in context.

**25. Politics and sex.** One month before the election, a poll of 630 randomly selected voters showed 54% planning to vote for a certain candidate. A week later it became known that he had had an extramarital affair, and a new poll showed only 51% of 1010 voters supporting him. Do these results indicate a decrease in voter support for his candidacy?

a) Test an appropriate hypothesis and state your conclusion.

b) If you concluded there was a difference, estimate that difference with a confidence interval and interpret your interval in context.

**26. Retirement.** The Employee Benefit Research Institute reports that 27% of males anticipate having enough money to live comfortably in retirement, but only 18% of females express that confidence. If these results were based on samples of 200 people of each sex, would you consider this strong evidence that men and women have different outlooks?

a) Test an appropriate hypothesis and state your conclusion.

b) If you concluded there was a difference, estimate that difference with a confidence interval and interpret your interval in context.

**27. Twins.** In 2001, one county reported that, among 3132 white women who had babies, 94 were multiple births. There were also 20 multiple births to 606 black women. Does this indicate any racial difference in the likelihood of multiple births?

a) Test an appropriate hypothesis and state your conclusion.

b) If your conclusion is incorrect, which type of error did you commit?

**28. Shopping.** A survey of 430 randomly chosen adults found that 21% of the 222 men and 18% of the 208 women had purchased books online.

a) Is there evidence that men are more likely than women to make online purchases of books? Test an appropriate hypothesis and state your conclusion in context.

b) If your conclusion in fact proves to be wrong, did you make a Type I or Type II error?

**29. Mammograms.** It's widely believed that regular mammogram screening may detect breast cancer early, resulting in fewer deaths from that disease. One study that investigated this issue over a period of 18 years was published during the 1970s. Among 30,565 women who had never had mammograms, 196 died of breast cancer, while only 153 of 30,131 who had undergone screening died of breast cancer.

a) Do these results suggest that mammograms may be an effective screening tool to reduce breast cancer deaths?

b) If your conclusion is incorrect, what type of error have you committed?

**30. Mammograms redux.** In 2001, the conclusion of the study outlined in Exercise 29 was questioned. A new 9-year study was conducted in Sweden, comparing 21,088 women who had mammograms with 21,195 who did not. Of the women who underwent screening, 63 died of breast cancer, compared to 66 deaths among the control group. (*The New York Times*, Dec 9, 2001)

a) Do these results support the effectiveness of regular mammograms in preventing deaths from breast cancer?

b) If your conclusion is incorrect, what kind of error have you committed?

**31. Pain.** Researchers comparing the effectiveness of two pain medications randomly selected a group of patients who had been complaining of a certain kind of joint pain. They randomly divided these people into two groups, then administered the pain killers. Of the 112 people in the group who received medication A, 84 said this pain reliever was effective. Of the 108 people in the other group, 66 reported that pain reliever B was effective.

a) Write a 95% confidence interval for the percent of people who may get relief from this kind of joint pain by using medication A. Interpret your interval.

b) Write a 95% confidence interval for the percent of people who may get relief by using medication B. Interpret your interval.

c) Do the intervals for A and B overlap? What do you think this means about the comparative effectiveness of these medications?

d) Find a 95% confidence interval for the difference in the proportions of people who may find these medications effective. Interpret your interval.

e) Does this interval contain zero? What does that mean?

f) Why do the results in parts c and e seem contradictory? If we want to compare the effectiveness of these two pain relievers, which is the correct approach? Why?

**32. Gender gap.** Candidates for political office realize that different levels of support among men and women may be a crucial factor in determining the outcome of an election.

One candidate finds that 52% of 473 men polled say they will vote for him, but only 45% of the 522 women in the poll express support.

a) Write a 95% confidence interval for the percent of male voters who may vote for this candidate. Interpret your interval.

b) Write a 95% confidence interval for the percent of female voters who may vote for him. Interpret your interval.

c) Do the intervals for males and females overlap? What do you think this means about the gender gap?

d) Find a 95% confidence interval for the difference in the proportions of males and females who will vote for this candidate. Interpret your interval.

e) Does this interval contain zero? What does that mean?

f) Why do the results in parts c and e seem contradictory? If we want to see if there is a gender gap among voters with respect to this candidate, which is the correct approach? Why?

**33. Convention bounce.** Political pundits talk about the "bounce" that a presidential candidate gets after his party's convention. In the last forty years, it has averaged about 6 percentage points. Just before the 2004 Democratic convention, Rasmussen Reports polled 1500 likely voters at random and found that 47% favored John Kerry. Just afterward they took another random sample of 1500 likely voters and found that 49% favored Kerry. That's a two percentage point increase, but the pollsters claimed that there was no bounce. Explain.

**34. Stay-at-home dads.** In August 2004, a *Time* magazine article about a survey of men's attitudes reported that 11 of 161 black respondents and 20 of 358 Latino respondents responded "Yes" to the question "Are you a stay-at-home dad?" How big is the difference in proportions in the two populations?

a) Construct and interpret an appropriate confidence interval.

b) Overall, the survey contacted 1302 men and claims a margin of error of $\pm 2.9\%$. Why is the margin of error different for your confidence interval?

**35. Sensitive men.** In August 2004, *Time* magazine, reporting on a survey of men's attitudes, noted that "Young men are more comfortable than older men talking about their problems." The survey reported that 80 of 129 surveyed 18- to 24-year-old men and 98 of 184 25- to 34-year-old men said they were comfortable. What do you think? Is *Time's* interpretation justified by these numbers?

**36. Carbs.** In July of 2004, the Gallup Poll asked 1005 U.S. adults if they actively try to avoid carbohydrates in their diet. That number increased to 27% from 20% in a similar 2002 poll. Is this a statistically significant increase? Explain.

**37. Intentional walk.** During the 2004 baseball season, San Francisco Giants' slugger Barry Bonds was such a dangerous hitter that many teams simply chose to walk him rather than throw him a pitch he could hit. Just before a series of games in New York, an analyst advised the Mets that they should pitch to Bonds. As evidence, he reported that thus far in the season the Giants had scored in 37 of 79 innings when Bonds was walked intentionally, but in only 107 of 298 innings when the opponents did not walk him. Does this provide evidence that teams should not intentionally walk Barry Bonds?

38. **Retention rates.** In 2004 the testing company ACT, Inc., reported on the percentage of first-year students at 4-year colleges who return for a second year. Their sample of 1139 students in private colleges showed a 74.9% retention rate, while the rate was 71.9% for the sample of 505 students at public colleges. Does this provide evidence that there's a difference in retention rates of first-year students at public and private colleges?

39. **Online activity checks.** Are more parents checking up on their teen's online activities? A Pew survey in 2004 found that 33% of 868 randomly sampled teens said that their parents checked to see what Web sites they visited. In 2006 the same question posed to 811 teens found 41% reporting such checks. Do these results provide evidence that more parents are checking?

40. **Computer gaming.** Who plays online or electronic games? A survey in 2006 found that 69% of 223 boys aged 12–14 said they "played computer or console games like Xbox or PlayStation . . . or games online." Of 248 boys aged 15–17, only 62% played these games. Is this evidence of a real age-based difference?

41. **Food preference.** GfK Roper Consulting gathers information on consumer preferences around the world to help companies monitor attitudes about health, food, and healthcare products. They asked people in many different cultures how they felt about the following statement:

    *I have a strong preference for regional or traditional products and dishes from where I come from.*

    In a random sample of 800 respondents, 417 of 646 people who live in urban environments agreed (either completely or somewhat) with that statement, compared to 78 out of 154 people who live in rural areas.

    Based on this sample, is there evidence that the percentage of people agreeing with the statement about regional preferences differs between all urban and rural dwellers?

42. **Fast food.** The global survey we learned about in Exercise 41 also asked respondents how they felt about the statement "I try to avoid eating fast foods." The random sample of 800 included 411 people 35 years old or younger, and of those, 197 agreed (completely or somewhat) with the statement. Of the 389 people over 35 years old, 246 people agreed with the statement. Is there evidence that the percentage of people avoiding fast food is different in the two age groups?

**JUST CHECKING**
**Answers**

1. We're 90% confident that if members are contacted by e-mail, the donation rate will be between 4 and 18 percentage points higher than if they received regular mail.

2. Since a difference of 0 is not in the confidence interval, we'd reject the null hypothesis. There is evidence that more members will donate if contacted by e-mail.

3. The proportion from the sample in 1995 has variability, too. If we do a one-proportion z-test, we won't take that variability into account and our P-value will be incorrect.

4. The difference in the proportions between the two years has more variability than either individual proportion. The variance of the difference is the sum of the two variances.

7

**PART**

**V**

# REVIEW OF PART V

## From the Data at Hand to the World at Large

### Quick Review

What do samples really tell us about the populations from which they are drawn? Are the results of an experiment meaningful, or are they just sampling error? Statistical inference based on our understanding of sampling models can help answer these questions. Here's a brief summary of the key concepts and skills:

- Sampling models describe the variability of sample statistics using a remarkable result called the Central Limit Theorem.
  - When the number of trials is sufficiently large, proportions found in different samples vary according to an approximately Normal model.
  - When samples are sufficiently large, the means of different samples vary, with an approximately Normal model.
  - The variability of sample statistics decreases as sample size increases.
  - Statistical inference procedures are based on the Central Limit Theorem.
  - No inference procedure is valid unless the underlying assumptions are true. Always check the conditions before proceeding.
- A confidence interval uses a sample statistic (such as a proportion) to estimate a range of plausible values for the parameter of a population model.
  - All confidence intervals involve an estimate of the parameter, a margin of error, and a level of confidence.
  - For confidence intervals based on a given sample, the greater the margin of error, the higher the confidence.
  - At a given level of confidence, the larger the sample, the smaller the margin of error.

- A hypothesis test proposes a model for the population, then examines the observed statistics to see if that model is plausible.
  - A null hypothesis suggests a parameter value for the population model. Usually, we assume there is nothing interesting, unusual, or different about the sample results.
  - The alternative hypothesis states what we will believe if the sample results turn out to be inconsistent with our null model.
  - We compare the difference between the statistic and the hypothesized value with the standard deviation of the statistic. It's the sampling distribution of this ratio that gives us a P-value.
  - The P-value of the test is the probability that the null model could produce results at least as extreme as those observed in the sample or the experiment just as a result of sampling error.
  - A low P-value indicates evidence against the null model. If it is sufficiently low, we reject the null model.
  - A high P-value indicates that the sample results are not inconsistent with the null model, so we cannot reject it. However, this does not prove the null model is true.
  - Sometimes we will mistakenly reject the null hypothesis even though it's actually true—that's called a Type I error. If we fail to reject a false null hypothesis, we commit a Type II error.
  - The power of a test measures its ability to detect a false null hypothesis.
  - You can lower the risk of a Type I error by requiring a higher standard of proof (lower P-value) before rejecting the null hypothesis. But this will raise the risk of a Type II error and decrease the power of the test.
  - The only way to increase the power of a test while decreasing the chance of committing either error is to design a study based on a larger sample.

And now for some opportunities to review these concepts and skills . . .

# REVIEW EXERCISES

**1. Herbal cancer.**   A report in the *New England Journal of Medicine* (June 6, 2000) notes growing evidence that the herb *Aristolochia fangchi* can cause urinary tract cancer in those who take it. Suppose you are asked to design an experiment to study this claim. Imagine that you have data on urinary tract cancers in subjects who have used this herb and similar subjects who have not used it and that you can measure incidences of cancer and precancerous lesions in these subjects. State the null and alternative hypotheses you would use in your study.

**2. Colorblind.**   Medical literature says that about 8% of males are colorblind. A university's introductory psychology course is taught in a large lecture hall. Among the students, there are 325 males. Each semester when the professor discusses visual perception, he shows the class a test for colorblindness. The percentage of males who are colorblind varies from semester to semester.
a) Is the sampling distribution model for the sample proportion likely to be Normal? Explain.
b) What are the mean and standard deviation of this sampling distribution model?
c) Sketch the sampling model, using the 68–95–99.7 Rule.
d) Write a few sentences explaining what the model says about this professor's class.

**3. Birth days.**   During a 2-month period in 2002, 72 babies were born at the Tompkins Community Hospital in upstate New York. The table shows how many babies were born on each day of the week.
a) If births are uniformly distributed across all days of the week, how many would you expect on each day?
b) Only 7 births occurred on a Monday. Does this indicate that women might be less likely to give birth on a Monday? Explain.
c) Are the 17 births on Tuesdays unusually high? Explain.
d) Can you think of any reasons why births may not occur completely at random?

| Day | Births |
|------|--------|
| Mon. | 7 |
| Tues. | 17 |
| Wed. | 8 |
| Thurs. | 12 |
| Fri. | 9 |
| Sat. | 10 |
| Sun. | 9 |

**4. Polling 2004.**   In the 2004 U.S. presidential election, the official results showed that George W. Bush received 50.7% of the vote and John Kerry received 48.3%. Ralph Nader, running as a third-party candidate, picked up only 0.4%. After the election, there was much discussion about exit polls, which had initially indicated a different result. Suppose you had taken a random sample of 1000 voters in an exit poll and asked them for whom they had voted.
a) Would you always get 507 votes for Bush and 483 for Kerry?
b) In 95% of such polls, your sample proportion of voters for Bush should be between what two values?
c) In 95% of such polls, your sample proportion of voters for Nader should be between what two numbers?

d) Would you expect the sample proportion of Nader votes to vary more, less, or about the same as the sample proportion of Bush votes? Why?

**5. Leaky gas tanks.**   Nationwide, it is estimated that 40% of service stations have gas tanks that leak to some extent. A new program in California is designed to lessen the prevalence of these leaks. We want to assess the effectiveness of the program by seeing if the percentage of service stations whose tanks leak has decreased. To do this, we randomly sample 27 service stations in California and determine whether there is any evidence of leakage. In our sample, only 7 of the stations exhibit any leakage. Is there evidence that the new program is effective?
a) What are the null and alternative hypotheses?
b) Check the assumptions necessary for inference.
c) Test the null hypothesis.
d) What do you conclude (in plain English)?
e) If the program actually works, have you made an error? What kind?
f) What two things could you do to decrease the probability of making this kind of error?
g) What are the advantages and disadvantages of taking those two courses of action?

**6. Surgery and germs.**   Joseph Lister (for whom Listerine is named!) was a British physician who was interested in the role of bacteria in human infections. He suspected that germs were involved in transmitting infection, so he tried using carbolic acid as an operating room disinfectant. In 75 amputations, he used carbolic acid 40 times. Of the 40 amputations using carbolic acid, 34 of the patients lived. Of the 35 amputations without carbolic acid, 19 patients lived. The question of interest is whether carbolic acid is effective in increasing the chances of surviving an amputation.
a) What kind of a study is this?
b) What do you conclude? Support your conclusion by testing an appropriate hypothesis.
c) What reservations do you have about the design of the study?

**7. Scrabble.**   Using a computer to play many simulated games of Scrabble, researcher Charles Robinove found that the letter "A" occurred in 54% of the hands. This study had a margin of error of ±10%. (*Chance*, 15, no. 1 [2002])
a) Explain what the margin of error means in this context.
b) Why might the margin of error be so large?
c) Probability theory predicts that the letter "A" should appear in 63% of the hands. Does this make you concerned that the simulation might be faulty? Explain.

**8. Dice.**   When one die is rolled, the number of spots showing has a mean of 3.5 and a standard deviation of 1.7. Suppose you roll 10 dice. What's the approximate probability that your total is between 30 and 40 (that is, the average for the 10 dice is between 3 and 4)? Specify the model you use and the assumptions and conditions that justify your approach.

**9. News sources.**   In May of 2000, the Pew Research Foundation sampled 1593 respondents and asked how they obtain news. In Pew's report, 33% of respondents say that they now obtain news from the Internet at least once a week.
a) Pew reports a margin of error of ±3% for this result. Explain what the margin of error means.
b) Pew also asked about investment information, and 21% of respondents reported that the Internet is their main source of this information. When limited to the 780 respondents who identified themselves as investors, the percent who rely on the Internet rose to 28%. How would you expect the margin of error for this statistic to change in comparison with the margin of error for the percentage of all respondents?
c) When restricted to the 239 active traders in the sample, Pew reports that 45% rely on the Internet for investment information. Find a confidence interval for this statistic.
d) How does the margin of error for your confidence interval compare with the values in parts a and b? Explain why.

**10. Death penalty 2006.**   In May of 2006, the Gallup Organization asked a random sample of 537 American adults this question:

*If you could choose between the following two approaches, which do you think is the better penalty for murder, the death penalty or life imprisonment, with absolutely no possibility of parole?*

Of those polled, 47% chose the death penalty, the lowest percentage in the 21 years that Gallup has asked this question.
a) Create a 95% confidence interval for the percentage of all American adults who favor the death penalty.
b) Based on your confidence interval, is it clear that the death penalty no longer has majority support? Explain.
c) If pollsters wanted to follow up on this poll with another survey that could determine the level of support for the death penalty to within 2% with 98% confidence, how many people should they poll?

**11. Bimodal.**   We are sampling randomly from a distribution known to be bimodal.
a) As our sample size increases, what's the expected shape of the sample's distribution?
b) What's the expected value of our sample's mean? Does the size of the sample matter?
c) How is the variability of this sample's mean related to the standard deviation of the population? Does the size of the sample matter?
d) How is the shape of the sampling distribution model affected by the sample size?

**12. Vitamin D.**   In July 2002 the *American Journal of Clinical Nutrition* reported that 42% of 1546 African-American women studied had vitamin D deficiency. The data came from a national nutrition study conducted by the Centers for Disease Control and Prevention in Atlanta.
a) Do these data meet the assumptions necessary for inference? What would you like to know that you don't?
b) Create a 95% confidence interval.
c) Interpret the interval in this context.
d) Explain in this context what "95% confidence" means.

**13. Archery.**   A champion archer can generally hit the bull's-eye 80% of the time. Suppose she shoots 200 arrows during competition. Let $\hat{p}$ represent the percentage of bull's-eyes she gets (the sample proportion).
a) What are the mean and standard deviation of the sampling distribution model for $\hat{p}$?
b) Is a Normal model appropriate here? Explain.
c) Sketch the sampling model, using the 68–95–99.7 Rule.
d) What's the probability that she gets at least 85% bull's-eyes?

**14. Free throws 2007.**   During the 2006–2007 NBA season, Kyle Korver led the league by making 191 of 209 free throws, for a success rate of 91.39%. But Matt Carroll was close behind, with 188 of 208 (90.39%).
a) Find a 95% confidence interval for the difference in their free throw percentages.
b) Based on your confidence interval, is it certain that Korver is better than Carroll at making free throws?

**15. Twins.**   There is some indication in medical literature that doctors may have become more aggressive in inducing labor or doing preterm cesarean sections when a woman is carrying twins. Records at a large hospital show that, of the 43 sets of twins born in 1990, 20 were delivered before the 37th week of pregnancy. In 2000, 26 of 48 sets of twins were born preterm. Does this indicate an increase in the incidence of early births of twins? Test an appropriate hypothesis and state your conclusion.

**16. Eclampsia.**   It's estimated that 50,000 pregnant women worldwide die each year of eclampsia, a condition involving elevated blood pressure and seizures. A research team from 175 hospitals in 33 countries investigated the effectiveness of magnesium sulfate in preventing the occurrence of eclampsia in at-risk patients. Results are summarized below. (*Lancet*, June 1, 2002)

| | | Total Subjects | Reported side effects | Developed eclampsia | Deaths |
|---|---|---|---|---|---|
| Treatment | Magnesium sulfide | 4999 | 1201 | 40 | 11 |
| | Placebo | 4993 | 228 | 96 | 20 |

a) Write a 95% confidence interval for the increase in the proportion of women who may develop side effects from this treatment. Interpret your interval.
b) Is there evidence that the treatment may be effective in preventing the development of eclampsia? Test an appropriate hypothesis and state your conclusion.

**17. Eclampsia.**   Refer again to the research summarized in Exercise 16. Is there any evidence that when eclampsia does occur, the magnesium sulfide treatment may help prevent the woman's death?
a) Write an appropriate hypothesis.
b) Check the assumptions and conditions.
c) Find the P-value of the test.
d) What do you conclude about the magnesium sulfide treatment?
e) If your conclusion is wrong, which type of error have you made?

f) Name two things you could do to increase the power of this test.

g) What are the advantages and disadvantages of those two options?

**18. Eggs.** The ISA Babcock Company supplies poultry farmers with hens, advertising that a mature B300 Layer produces eggs with a mean weight of 60.7 grams. Suppose that egg weights follow a Normal model with standard deviation 3.1 grams.

a) What fraction of the eggs produced by these hens weigh more than 62 grams?

b) What's the probability that a dozen randomly selected eggs average more than 62 grams?

c) Using the 68–95–99.7 Rule, sketch a model of the total weights of a dozen eggs.

**19. Polling disclaimer.** A newspaper article that reported the results of an election poll included the following explanation:

*The Associated Press poll on the 2000 presidential campaign is based on telephone interviews with 798 randomly selected registered voters from all states except Alaska and Hawaii. The interviews were conducted June 21–25 by ICR of Media, Pa.*

*The results were weighted to represent the population by demographic factors such as age, sex, region, and education.*

*No more than 1 time in 20 should chance variations in the sample cause the results to vary by more than 4 percentage points from the answers that would be obtained if all Americans were polled.*

*The margin of sampling error is larger for responses of subgroups, such as income categories or those in political parties. There are other sources of potential error in polls, including the wording and order of questions.*

a) Did they describe the 5 W's well?

b) What kind of sampling design could take into account the several demographic factors listed?

c) What was the margin of error of this poll?

d) What was the confidence level?

e) Why is the margin of error larger for subgroups?

f) Which kinds of potential bias did they caution readers about?

**20. Enough eggs?** One of the important issues for poultry farmers is the production rate—the percentage of days on which a given hen actually lays an egg. Ideally, that would be 100% (an egg every day), but realistically, hens tend to lay eggs on about 3 of every 4 days. ISA Babcock wants to advertise the production rate for the B300 Layer (see Exercise 18) as a 95% confidence interval with a margin of error of ±2%. How many hens must they collect data on?

**21. Teen deaths.** Traffic accidents are the leading cause of death among people aged 15 to 20. In May 2002, the National Highway Traffic Safety Administration reported that even though only 6.8% of licensed drivers are between 15 and 20 years old, they were involved in 14.3% of all fatal crashes. Insurance companies have long known

that teenage boys were high risks, but what about teenage girls? One insurance company found that the driver was a teenage girl in 44 of the 388 fatal accidents they investigated. Is this strong evidence that the accident rate is lower for girls than for teens in general?

a) Test an appropriate hypothesis and state your conclusion.

b) Explain what your P-value means in this context.

**22. Perfect pitch.** A recent study of perfect pitch tested 2700 students in American music conservatories. It found that 7% of non-Asian and 32% of Asian students have perfect pitch. A test of the difference in proportions resulted in a P-value of $< 0.0001$.

a) What are the researchers' null and alternative hypotheses?

b) State your conclusion.

c) Explain in this context what the P-value means.

d) The researchers claimed that the data prove that genetic differences between the two populations cause a difference in the frequency of occurrence of perfect pitch. Do you agree? Why or why not?

**23. Largemouth bass.** Organizers of a fishing tournament believe that the lake holds a sizable population of largemouth bass. They assume that the weights of these fish have a model that is skewed to the right with a mean of 3.5 pounds and a standard deviation of 2.2 pounds.

a) Explain why a skewed model makes sense here.

b) Explain why you cannot determine the probability that a largemouth bass randomly selected ("caught") from the lake weighs over 3 pounds.

c) Each fisherman in the contest catches 5 fish each day. Can you determine the probability that someone's catch averages over 3 pounds? Explain.

d) The 12 fishermen competing each caught the limit of 5 fish. What's the probability that the total catch of 60 fish averaged more than 3 pounds?

**24. Cheating.** A Rutgers University study released in 2002 found that many high school students cheat on tests. The researchers surveyed a random sample of 4500 high school students nationwide; 74% of them said they had cheated at least once.

a) Create a 90% confidence interval for the level of cheating among high school students. Don't forget to check the appropriate conditions.

b) Interpret your interval.

c) Explain what "90% confidence" means.

d) Would a 95% confidence interval be wider or narrower? Explain without actually calculating the interval.

**25. Language.** Neurological research has shown that in about 80% of people language abilities reside in the brain's left side. Another 10% display right-brain language centers, and the remaining 10% have two-sided language control. (The latter two groups are mainly left-handers.) (*Science News,* 161, no. 24 [2002])

a) We select 60 people at random. Is it reasonable to use a Normal model to describe the possible distribution of the proportion of the group that has left-brain language control? Explain.

b) What's the probability that our group has at least 75% left-brainers?

c) If the group had consisted of 100 people, would that probability be higher, lower, or about the same? Explain why, without actually calculating the probability.

d. How large a group would almost certainly guarantee at least 75% left-brainers? Explain.

**26. Cigarettes 2006.** In 1999 the Centers for Disease Control and Prevention estimated that about 34.8% of high school students smoked cigarettes. They established a national health goal of reducing that figure to 16% by the year 2010. To that end, they hoped to achieve a reduction to 20% by 2006. In 2006 they released a research study in which 23% of a random sample of 1815 high school students said they were current smokers. Is this evidence that progress toward the goal is off track?

a) Write appropriate hypotheses.

b) Verify that the appropriate assumptions are satisfied.

c) Find the P-value of this test.

d) Explain what the P-value means in this context.

e) State an appropriate conclusion.

f) Of course, your conclusion may be incorrect. If so, which kind of error did you commit?

**27. Crohn's disease.** In 2002 the medical journal *The Lancet* reported that 335 of 573 patients suffering from Crohn's disease responded positively to injections of the arthritis-fighting drug infliximab.

a) Create a 95% confidence interval for the effectiveness of this drug.

b) Interpret your interval in context.

c) Explain carefully what "95% confidence" means in this context.

**28. Teen smoking 2006.** The Centers for Disease Control and Prevention say that about 23% of teenagers smoke tobacco (down from a high of 38% in 1997). A college has 522 students in its freshman class. Is it likely that more than 30% of them are smokers? Explain.

**29. Alcohol abuse.** Growing concern about binge drinking among college students has prompted one large state university to conduct a survey to assess the size of the problem on its campus. The university plans to randomly select students and ask how many have been drunk during the past week. If the school hopes to estimate the true proportion among all its students with 90% confidence and a margin of error of $\pm 4\%$, how many students must be surveyed?

**30. Errors.** An auto parts company advertises that its special oil additive will make the engine "run smoother, cleaner, longer, with fewer repairs." An independent laboratory decides to test part of this claim. It arranges to use a taxicab company's fleet of cars. The cars are randomly divided into two groups. The company's mechanics will use the additive in one group of cars but not in the other. At the end of a year the laboratory will compare the percentage of cars in each group that required engine repairs.

a) What kind of a study is this?

b) Will they do a one-tailed or a two-tailed test?

c) Explain in this context what a Type I error would be.

d) Explain in this context what a Type II error would be.

e) Which type of error would the additive manufacturer consider more serious?

f) If the cabs with the additive do indeed run significantly better, can the company conclude it is an effect of the additive? Can they generalize this result and recommend the additive for all cars? Explain.

**31. Preemies.** Among 242 Cleveland-area children born prematurely at low birth weights between 1977 and 1979, only 74% graduated from high school. Among a comparison group of 233 children of normal birth weight, 83% were high school graduates. ("Outcomes in Young Adulthood for Very-Low-Birth-Weight Infants," *New England Journal of Medicine*, 346, no. 3 [2002])

a) Create a 95% confidence interval for the difference in graduation rates between children of normal and children of very low birth weights. Be sure to check the appropriate assumptions and conditions.

b) Does this provide evidence that premature birth may be a risk factor for not finishing high school? Use your confidence interval to test an appropriate hypothesis.

c) Suppose your conclusion is incorrect. Which type of error did you make?

**32. Safety.** Observers in Texas watched children at play in eight communities. Of the 814 children seen biking, roller skating, or skateboarding, only 14% wore a helmet.

a) Create and interpret a 95% confidence interval.

b) What concerns do you have about this study that might make your confidence interval unreliable?

c) Suppose we want to do this study again, picking various communities and locations at random, and hope to end up with a 98% confidence interval having a margin of error of $\pm 4\%$. How many children must we observe?

**33. Fried PCs.** A computer company recently experienced a disastrous fire that ruined some of its inventory. Unfortunately, during the panic of the fire, some of the damaged computers were sent to another warehouse, where they were mixed with undamaged computers. The engineer responsible for quality control would like to check out each computer in order to decide whether it's undamaged or damaged. Each computer undergoes a series of 100 tests. The number of tests it fails will be used to make the decision. If it fails more than a certain number, it will be classified as damaged and then scrapped. From past history, the distribution of the number of tests failed is known for both undamaged and damaged computers. The probabilities associated with each outcome are listed in the table below:

| Number of tests failed | 0 | 1 | 2 | 3 | 4 | 5 | >5 |
|---|---|---|---|---|---|---|---|
| Undamaged (%) | 80 | 13 | 2 | 4 | 1 | 0 | 0 |
| Damaged (%) | 0 | 10 | 70 | 5 | 4 | 1 | 10 |

The table indicates, for example, that 80% of the undamaged computers have no failures, while 70% of the damaged computers have 2 failures.

a) To the engineers, this is a hypothesis-testing situation. State the null and alternative hypotheses.

b) Someone suggests classifying a computer as damaged if it fails any of the tests. Discuss the advantages and disadvantages of this test plan.

c) What number of tests would a computer have to fail in order to be classified as damaged if the engineers want to have the probability of a Type I error equal to 5%?

d) What's the power of the test plan in part c?

e) A colleague points out that by increasing $\alpha$ just 2%, the power can be increased substantially. Explain.

**34. Power.** We are replicating an experiment. How will each of the following changes affect the power of our test? Indicate whether it will increase, decrease, or remain the same, assuming that all other aspects of the situation remain unchanged.

a) We increase the number of subjects from 40 to 100.

b) We require a higher standard of proof, changing from $\alpha = 0.05$ to $\alpha = 0.01$.

**35. Approval 2007.** Of all the post–World War II presidents, Richard Nixon had the highest *disapproval* rating near the end of his presidency. His disapproval rating peaked at 66% in July 1974, just before he resigned. In May 2007, George W. Bush's disapproval rating was 63%, according to a Gallup poll of 1000 voters. Pundits started discussing whether his rating was still discernibly better than Nixon's. What do you think?

**36. Grade inflation.** In 1996, 20% of the students at a major university had an overall grade point average of 3.5 or higher (on a scale of 4.0). In 2000, a random sample of 1100 student records found that 25% had a GPA of 3.5 or higher. Is this evidence of grade inflation?

**37. Name recognition.** An advertising agency won't sign an athlete to do product endorsements unless it is sure the person is known to more than 25% of its target audience. The agency always conducts a poll of 500 people to investigate the athlete's name recognition before offering a contract. Then it tests $H_0: p = 0.25$ against $H_A: p > 0.25$ at a 5% level of significance.

a) Why does the company use upper tail tests in this situation?

b) Explain what Type I and Type II errors would represent in this context, and describe the risk that each error poses to the company.

c) The company is thinking of changing its test to use a 10% level of significance. How would this change the company's exposure to each type of risk?

**38. Name recognition, part II.** The advertising company described in Exercise 37 is thinking about signing a WNBA star to an endorsement deal. In its poll, 27% of the respondents could identify her.

a) Fans who never took Statistics can't understand why the company did not offer this WNBA player an endorsement contract even though the 27% recognition rate in the poll is above the 25% threshold. Explain it to them.

b) Suppose that further polling reveals that this WNBA star really is known to about 30% of the target audience. Did the company initially commit a Type I or Type II error in not signing her?

c) Would the power of the company's test have been higher or lower if the player were more famous? Explain.

**39. NIMBY.** In March 2007, the Gallup Poll split a sample of 1003 randomly selected U.S. adults into two groups at random. Half ($n = 502$) of the respondents were asked,

*"Overall, do you strongly favor, somewhat favor, somewhat oppose, or strongly oppose the use of nuclear energy as one of the ways to provide electricity for the U.S.?"*

They found that 53% were either "somewhat" or "strongly" in favor. The other half ($n = 501$) were asked,

*"Overall, would you strongly favor, somewhat favor, somewhat oppose, or strongly oppose the construction of a nuclear energy plant in your area as one of the ways to provide electricity for the U.S.?"*

Only 40% were somewhat or strongly in favor. This difference is an example of the *NIMBY* (Not In My Back-Yard) phenomenon and is a serious concern to policy makers and planners. How large is the difference between the proportion of American adults who think nuclear energy is a good idea and the proportion who would be willing to have a nuclear plant in their area? Construct and interpret an appropriate confidence interval.

**40. Dropouts.** One study comparing various treatments for the eating disorder anorexia nervosa initially enlisted 198 subjects, but found overall that 105 failed to complete their assigned treatment programs. Construct and interpret an appropriate confidence interval. Discuss any reservations you have about this inference.

PART

# VI

# Learning About the World

## Instructor's Guide

# Inferences About Means

## What's It About?

Chapter 23 examines confidence intervals and hypothesis tests for a population mean. We introduce the $t$-models to deal with the extra variation caused by not knowing the population's standard deviation, and examine the assumptions and conditions necessary for inference. We use this new application of the concepts of inference to re-examine the correct interpretation of a confidence interval, the relationship between confidence intervals and hypothesis tests, and the difference between statistical significance and importance. We show how to determine the sample size necessary for a study about means, and how to interpret output from software packages. An optional section presents and illustrates the sign test—a simple distribution-free method.

## Comments

We almost never do inference pretending to know the population standard deviation. We have emphasized throughout this course that Statistics is about the real world, and we won't change that now. In the real world no one ever knows the population standard deviation. (Well, almost never. There are cases when experience suggests that the standard deviation is known—the hospital example in the book is a case in point. In that rare case, we can use the $z$ instead). Gosset discovered the $t$-distributions to resolve this dilemma. What worked for Gosset works for us, too.

And we never mention the outdated pretechnology approach of using a Normal model for "large samples." You might think there was a compelling mathematical justification for switching over to $z$ when the sample size exceeds 30, but there wasn't. Typesetters, not mathematicians, are the source of that rule of thumb. About 30 lines of a $t$-table fit conveniently on a page. After that, the old advice was, turn to the $z$-table because it's pretty close. In the age of graphing calculators and statistics software, there's no reason to shy away from $t$ for any number of degrees of freedom, so we can do better than

approximate it with $z$. We can do inference for means the right way, using $t$. Always.

The bottom line is that nothing in this chapter is really new. We still create and interpret confidence intervals the same old way. We still use the same reasoning and four-step procedure for testing a hypothesis. The only new issue is the need to scrap the trusty Normal model in favor of a $t$-model, an adjustment students will readily make.

This is true even of the optional section on the sign test. That just looks back to inference for proportions, so once again, nothing is new. Students gain insight by seeing alternative methods for addressing essentially the same questions.

## Looking Ahead

In the next two chapters we expand our abilities to do inference for means when there are two groups. Chapter 24 explains the proper procedures if the two groups are independent, and Chapter 25 looks at inference for paired differences if the groups are matched. Both chapters continue to rely on $t$-models. Student's $t$ returns again in Chapter 27 where we discuss inference for regression.

## Class Do's

Start right in with an example involving data—like the coffee machine example that follows. Students will be able to set up the outline of the hypothesis test. After all, these tests are all the same.

▸ **Hypotheses.** This time they're about $\mu$. (Never $\bar{y}$, of course. We *know* $\bar{y}$; that value comes to us from the sample. It's the mean of the population we wonder about.)

▸ **Model.** Some of the conditions are obvious. We need a simple random sample of less than 10% of the population (and we won't worry as much about the 10% Condition for quantitative data). We'll add another condition after some more discussion.

▶ *Mechanics.* It seems pretty straightforward at first. Find $\bar{y}$, then try to find $z$. Trouble. The Central Limit Theorem tells us the sampling model for $\bar{y}$ has a standard deviation of $\sigma$ divided by the square root of the sample size. Strike One: we don't know $\sigma$. Students suggest using $s$, the sample's standard deviation, as an estimate. Great idea. This shows they have caught on to the kind of statistical thinking we want them to develop in this course. But there's a problem. Unlike proportions, where the null hypothesis specifies $p$, and that in turn tells us the SD, here there is *no link* to the SD. The hypothesized population mean tells us nothing about the population's standard deviation. And the sample standard deviation, $s$, varies from sample to sample. This introduces variation in the denominator, something that wasn't there before. How can we deal with this extra uncertainty? Some students may suggest cutting ourselves a little more slack to make up for the increased variability, and that's exactly what a $t$-model does.

Spend some time briefly describing $t$ (suggestions follow). Note that the mathematics underlying the use of $t$ requires the assumption that the sample comes from a population that is Normal. Strike Two: we don't know the population's center (our hypothesis is about that), we don't know its spread (that's why we need $t$), and we don't (indeed can't) know its shape, either. All we can do is take a look at the distribution of the data in the sample to see if it's plausible that these data were chosen at random from a Normal population. We hope to see a roughly mound-shaped, symmetric distribution without skewness or outliers. That's the Nearly Normal Condition, telling us it's OK to use a one-sample $t$-test for means.

With the conditions now complete, get right on with the hypothesis test. Calculate $t$, draw the curve (indicating the degrees of freedom), shade the region representing the P-value, and find P (using technology or a $t$ table for critical values).

▶ *Conclusion.* It's the same old story: linkage, decision, and conclusion in context. Be sure the conclusion talks about the *mean* of the *population*.

It's a great idea to follow the hypothesis test with a confidence interval, looking up the critical value in the table. Spend some time with the interpretation. There are all kinds of new ways to be wrong about what the interval means! Most common are that some students will think that 95% of the population or 95% of all sample means must lie in the interval. Help students understand the correct interpretation. The investigative task on means (in the *PTBRG*) will help.

Since the $t$-models are new, it helps to discuss their relationship to the Normal model. Common sense says that the increased uncertainty caused by using $s$ to estimate $\sigma$ makes this model more spread out, and that this uncertainty (and therefore the spread) must be greater for small samples. These ideas tell us that there are different $t$-models for different $n$'s, pointing to the new issue of degrees of freedom. Greater spread tells us that confidence intervals must be wider, so critical values of $t$ must be larger than the corresponding critical value of $z$. A quick glance down one of the columns of the table will show that, and also show that $t$-models look increasingly Normal as $n$ increases.

The Nearly Normal Condition is intentionally vague. First, be sure students understand that the issue is not whether the sample is Normal. Samples aren't; they can't be. We must have a sample drawn from a population that's Normal, but we can never be sure about the population. The $t$-test is fairly robust. What we really need is that the distribution is roughly symmetric—i.e., nearly Normal. We're particularly concerned about outliers and skewness. However, the usefulness of a $t$-model also depends on the sample size. As the sample size increases, the Normality of the population becomes less critical. (We say that the $t$-models with larger degrees of freedom are increasingly *robust* with respect to the assumption of Normality.) For $n$'s near 20, some skewness is okay. For $n$'s near 30, we can use $t$ unless the sample is strongly skewed or there are far outliers. For larger samples, we often don't even look at the histogram, justifying use of a $t$-model simply by saying the sample is large.

Talk about what to do with outliers. We recommend performing the analysis twice. The concern, of course, is that the outlier will distort the results. If the conclusions don't change (if, for example, we reject a hypothesis when we include the outlier in the data, and also reject it after we remove the outlier), then it's clear that the decision is not based on the impact of the outlier. Generally, outliers inflate the standard error more than they move the sample mean, so they make confidence intervals wider and P-values larger.

We resort to $z$ only when we do a sample size calculation, because not knowing $n$ leaves us unable to pick a critical value for $t$. This calculation will always underestimate the sample size we should use. If it calls for a very large sample, that's fine. But if it points to a small sample, then we need to use that first estimate for $n$ to determine a critical $t$ and rerun the calculation.

## The Importance of What You Don't Say

*Suppose we know $\sigma$, the standard deviation of the population.* We almost never will.

*For large samples, use $z$ instead of $t$.* For inference about means, use $t$. Always. (Almost.)

We find it confusing to write $\sigma_{\bar{y}} = \sigma/\sqrt{n}$. Instead use $SD(\bar{y})$. Of course it's the same thing, but students seem to get confused with $\sigma$'s all over the place. And the difference between $SD(\bar{y})$ and $SE(\bar{y})$ reminds them of the difference in terminology and meaning.

## Class Examples

1. A coffee machine dispenses coffee into paper cups. You're supposed to get 10 ounces of coffee, but the amount varies slightly from cup to cup. Here are the amounts measured in a random sample of 20 cups. Is there evidence that the machine is shortchanging customers?

| | | | |
|---|---|---|---|
| 9.9 | 9.7 | 10.0 | 10.1 |
| 9.9 | 9.6 | 9.8 | 9.8 |
| 10.0 | 9.5 | 9.7 | 10.1 |
| 9.9 | 9.6 | 10.2 | 9.8 |
| 10.0 | 9.9 | 9.5 | 9.9 |

*Hypotheses:* $H_0: \mu = 10.0$ $\qquad H_A: \mu < 10.0$

**Plan:** Random sample; 20 < 10% of all cups (no reason to doubt independence). The histogram of sample data below looks roughly unimodal and symmetric, so it's reasonable to believe that the amount of coffee in all possible cups could be described by a Normal model. Okay to do a *t*-test for the mean.

9.845          10.0

**Mechanics:** $n = 20$   $df = 19$   $\bar{y} = 9.845$   $s = 0.199$

$$t = \frac{9.845 - 10}{0.199/\sqrt{20}} = -3.49$$

P-value = $P(t_{19} < -3.49) = 0.0012$

**Conclusion:** Such a small P-value makes it unlikely that the low sample mean resulted from sampling error, so we reject the null hypothesis. There is strong evidence that the mean amount of coffee dispensed by this machine is less than the stated 10 fluid ounces.

**Confidence interval:** The conditions have been met, so we can create a one-sample *t*-interval. (Note that all confidence intervals look alike: estimate ± margin of error.)

$$\bar{y} \pm t^*_{19} \times SE(\bar{y}) = 9.845 \pm 2.093 \frac{0.199}{\sqrt{20}} = (9.75, 9.94)$$

We are 95% confident that the machine dispenses an average of between 9.75 and 9.94 fluid ounces of coffee per cup.

2. A company has set a goal of developing a battery that lasts 5 hours (300 minutes) in continuous use. In a first test of 12 of these batteries measured the following lifespans (in minutes): 321, 295, 332, 351, 281, 336, 311, 253, 270, 326, 311, and 288.

- Is there evidence that the company has met its goal?
- Find a 90% confidence interval for the mean lifespan of this type of battery.
- If we wish to conduct another trial, how many batteries must we test to be 95% sure of estimating the mean lifespan to within 15 minutes? To within 5 minutes?

3. After you finish this chapter, have students complete the Investigative Task (in the *PTBRG*). Each student will have created a confidence interval based on a different sample. Tell them what the true mean for the population was. Ask them how many caught it in their intervals. Then ask who missed it. There will probably be a few whose intervals do not contain the true mean—yet they did nothing wrong. This teachable moment really helps students understand what "90% confidence" means, and why we are so picky about those pesky interpretations.

## RESOURCES

### ActivStats

▸ Chapter 23. The interactive tool in *ActivStats* that shows confidence intervals and P-values dynamically is valuable in cementing student understanding. One activity in this chapter differentiates the effects of smaller sample size on degrees of freedom from the effects of sample size on the standard error (in which we divide by the sample size). The change in standard error has a far greater impact than the spreading of the *t*-distribution due to smaller degrees of freedom.

### Web Links

▸ You'll find several good data sets at the DASL Web site. http://lib.stat.cmu.edu/DASL

### Printed Test Bank and Resource Guide

The *Printed Test Bank and Resource Guide* has an Investigative Task that is the first of two. Here, students draw their own samples and construct confidence intervals. In Chapter 25, they'll return to their data for a second Investigative Task. And, of course, there are three chapter quizzes.

**Instructor's Guide**

**CHAPTER**

**24**

# Comparing Means

## What's It About?

We extend inference for means to comparing the means of two groups. We look at both confidence intervals and hypothesis tests. We emphasize that these methods are appropriate only when the groups are independent. This allows us to determine the standard error for the sampling distribution by adding variances (again). We advise students against pooling for inference about means of independent groups.

## Comments

The development in this chapter parallels our look at inference for two proportions. Students are now familiar with one-sample *t*-tests and confidence intervals, and can adapt those procedures to investigate the difference in two means. They see that once again the key is in adding the variances, and that makes it necessary that the two groups be independent.

In our look at proportions, we introduced the idea of pooling the samples to provide our best estimate of the population standard deviation. It may at first seem logical to follow that route again here. However, the key difference is that the population proportion determines the population standard deviation. A hypothesis that two populations have equal proportions implies that they also have equal variances. That package deal does not exist here. The null hypothesis of equal means implies nothing about the standard deviations.

## Looking Ahead

Chapters 24 and 25 both look at inference about means when there are two sets of data. Both use *t*-models. There the similarity ends. In Chapter 24 our two groups will be independent. Under that condition variances add. In Chapter 25 our two groups are paired, hence not independent. That means we're unable to add variances, so we cannot use the methods we see in this chapter. It is critical that students start thinking about the independence issue now, because that is the vital determining factor in the decision they'll soon face—whether to use two-sample or paired-*t* methods. The decision is forced by the design of the study, and therefore not a "choice" a student can make.

## Class Do's

Present the class with a two-group example to consider, and expect them to be able to do the inference.

*Hypotheses.*   Students should be able to write the hypotheses correctly. Be sure the notation is clear and correct, using parameters with well-defined or mnemonic subscripts.

*Model.*   Students can also write the assumptions and conditions, needing only to apply those for the one-sample *t* methods to both groups. Note that this means checking *both* groups for signs of Normality, so they need to do *two* histograms. Students may or may not foresee the need to add the assumption that the groups are independent, but you can return to that when the issue arises.

*Mechanics.*   As always, write the sample statistics using proper notation. Sketch the curve, centered on the hypothesized difference (usually 0), mark the observed difference, and shade the proper tails. Then there are two problems to face: degrees of freedom and standard deviation. We'll let technology tell us the degrees of freedom. (Show them the formula—they'll be happy for technology!) And once again the secret for finding the standard error of the difference in sample means is in adding the variances. That requires believing that the groups are independent. There's no condition to check for that; we just need to think carefully about how the data were collected. This

is a key point—in the next chapter we'll encounter situations where the groups are not independent and we'll need a different technique.

*Conclusion.*   By now, a familiar story: linkage, decision, and conclusion in context. Be sure that the conclusion clearly talks about *means* of the *populations*.

*Confidence Interval.*   As we often do, follow the hypothesis test with a confidence interval to see just how big the difference in means might be.

Emphasize that we need to believe that Normal models are appropriate for both populations. We test the plausibility of that assumption by looking at the distributions of both groups. We can look at histograms, dotplots, stem-and-leaf displays, or boxplots. We're more worried about outliers and skewness when the groups are small; if the samples are large enough, we can simply rely on the robustness of the *t*-procedures and go ahead with inference.

Some students will want to use two separate confidence intervals to see if there is a significant difference in the means. They will argue that if the two intervals overlap, then the means may be the same, but if the intervals do not overlap, the means are probably different. This analysis is not precise enough. We should instead look for a significant difference using a single confidence interval for the difference in means. If 0 is in the interval, the means may be the same; if not, then we can conclude they are probably different. This approach correctly adds variances. Since confidence intervals have margins of error based on standard deviations, to look for an overlap in two separate intervals is to incorrectly add the standard deviations. (It's a Pythagorean issue: $3 + 4 = 7$, but $\sqrt{3^2 + 4^2} = 5$.) When there are two groups, we must use two-sample methods.

Tukey's Quick Test (optional) is fun in this context because it is so different. Showing (or having students read about) an alternative method can help keep them from thinking that there is One True Method.

## The Importance of What You Don't Say

▸ *Suppose we know the standard deviations of the populations.*   We almost never will.

▸ *If both groups are large, use z instead of t.*   For inference about means, use *t*. Always.

▸ *Pooled t-test.*   Don't suggest that students pool to achieve an estimate for a common population variance. It's rare that such an assumption is warranted, there's no good way to test it, and little is gained (perhaps a few degrees of freedom, but with additional risk.) It's never wrong not to pool.

▸ *df = smaller n − 1.*   Discourage students from using the "smaller sample size − 1" guideline for degrees of freedom. It's overly cautious, and can make a sizeable difference in the results. With technology available there's no reason to shortchange ourselves.

## Class Examples

1. Resting pulse rates for a random sample of 26 smokers had a mean of 80 beats per minute (bpm) and a standard deviation of 5 bpm. Among 32 randomly chosen nonsmokers, the mean and standard deviation were 74 and

6 bpm. Both sets of data were roughly symmetric and had no outliers. Is there evidence of a difference in mean pulse rate between smokers and nonsmokers? How big?

**Hypotheses:** $H_0: \mu_S - \mu_{NS} = 0$   $H_A: \mu_S - \mu_{NS} \neq 0$

**Model:** We have independent random samples, each less than 10% of the population, and are told that the data appear to be approximately Normal. OK to proceed with a two-sample $t$-test.

**Mechanics:** $n_S = 26$   $\bar{y}_S = 80$   $s_S = 5$
$\qquad\qquad\quad n_{NS} = 32$   $\bar{y}_{NS} = 74$   $s_{NS} = 6$

$$t = \frac{(80 - 74) - 0}{\sqrt{\dfrac{5^2}{26} + \dfrac{6^2}{32}}} = 4.15$$

$$P \approx 0.0001 \quad df \approx 56$$

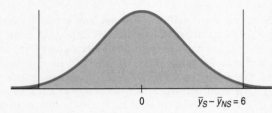

$$0 \qquad \bar{y}_S - \bar{y}_{NS} = 6$$

**Conclusion:** Because the P-value is so small, the observed difference is unlikely to be just sampling error. We reject the null hypothesis. We have strong evidence of a difference in mean pulse rates for smokers and nonsmokers.

**Follow-up:** We can be 95% confident that the average pulse rate for smokers is between 3.1 and 8.9 beats per minute higher than for nonsmokers.

2. Here is the saturated fat content (in grams) for pizzas sold by two national chains. Be sure that in checking the conditions, students plot both sets of data.

| Brand D | 17 | 12 | 10 | 8 | 8 | 10 | 10 | 5 | 16 | 16 |
|---------|----|----|----|---|----|----|----|----|----|----|
|         | 8  | 12 | 15 | 7 | 11 | 11 | 13 | 13 | 11 | 12 |
| Brand PJ | 6 | 7 | 11 | 9 | 4 | 4 | 7 | 9 | | |
|          | 11 | 3 | 4 | 5 | 8 | 5 | 5 | | | |

3. Exercises 13 and 14 address the important issue of using one confidence interval for the difference in means (correct) rather than seeing if separate confidence intervals for the two means overlap (incorrect). Here are some easy (made-up) statistics you can use to demonstrate the point.

They deal with a hypothetical experiment to see if there is any difference in the amount of weight gained by two groups of pigs fed different diets. Based on these data, we estimate (with 95% confidence) that Diet A would produce a mean weight gain between 53.99 and 56.01 pounds, and Diet B between 51.65 and 54.35 pounds. These two intervals overlap, making it appear that the two diets might each produce the same mean weight gain (maybe 54.2 pounds, for example). This analysis is incorrect. It rests on the fact that the 2-pound difference is smaller than the sum of the two separate margins of error. Each of those margins of error is based on the standard error of the individual means, here $3/\sqrt{36} = 0.5$ and $4/\sqrt{36} = 0.67$. We must instead sum the *variances* to examine the difference between the two means: $\sqrt{\left(\dfrac{3}{\sqrt{36}}\right)^2 + \left(\dfrac{4}{\sqrt{36}}\right)^2} = 0.83$, less than $0.5 + 0.67$. The 95% confidence interval for the difference in mean weight gains is 0.34 to 3.66 pounds. It does not look likely that the two diets produce the same results, because 0 is not in the confidence interval. (Note also that the correct method uses 65 degrees of freedom rather than only 35.)

| | | Feed | |
|---|---|---|---|
| | | Diet A | Diet B |
| **Number of pigs** | | 36 | 36 |
| **Mean weight gain** | | 55 lb | 53 lb |
| **Standard deviation** | | 3 lb | 4 lb |

## RESOURCES

### ActivStats

▸ Chapter 24: Comparing Two Means discusses the question of whether a restricted-calorie diet can prolong life. This topic keeps popping up in the news.

### Web Links

▸ The Fast Food Nutrition Fact Explorer offers a lot of data for comparing groups. (www.fatcalories.com)

### *Printed Test Bank and Resource Guide*

The *Printed Test Bank and Resource Guide* has three chapter quizzes.

# Paired Samples and Blocks

## What's It About?

Chapter 25 examines data collected from subjects that have been paired. We want to test whether the means of two groups are equal, but we can't use the independent two-sample $t$-test. We discuss the assumptions and conditions, and present examples of paired-$t$ procedures for both hypothesis tests and confidence intervals. Many exercises require students to distinguish between groups of data that are matched and those that are independent.

## Comments

The procedures we use for inference in this chapter are not new. Paired-$t$ procedures are mechanically identical to the one-sample $t$ procedures we first saw in Chapter 23. We simply apply those methods to the differences observed between the two measurements for each pair.

The problem students face is less in learning *how* to perform this kind of inference than in deciding *when* these procedures are necessary. We hope that our decision to write a separate chapter helps send the message that we face two different situations, both involving two sets of data. In Chapter 24 the data came from two different and independent groups. Now the data are two different measurements for the same group or two groups in which individuals were paired. To use the procedures from Chapter 24, the groups must be independent. Paired measurements are clearly not independent, so the two-sample procedures are not viable. The decision about what procedure to use must be based on the way the data were collected, requiring students to (you guessed it) *Think* before they *Show* and *Tell*.

And the "when" problem is, of course, much larger than that. Chapters 19 through 25 show students many different methods for inference about means and proportions. Even students who are very adept at performing each of the individual procedures may find it quite difficult to decide which one is appropriate when they encounter a question outside the tell-tale chapter. We offer suggestions here for helping them learn to make those important decisions. We summarize the methods and assumptions and conditions in the Part VI Quick Review, and offer comprehensive Review Exercises.

## Looking Ahead

We'll encounter the importance of considering the design under which the data were collected again in Chapter 26, where students must decide whether to use a $\chi^2$ test for goodness of fit, for homogeneity, or for independence.

The versatility of Gosset's $t$ in serving as a useful model for a wide variety sampling distributions is highlighted again in Chapter 27, where we discuss inference for regression.

## Class Do's

When you first present students with data in matched pairs, expect them to raise the red flag when they get to the assumption of independence. It should be clear that paired data are not independent, and that the methods of Chapter 24 are therefore not useful. Specifically, the lack of independence prevents us from adding variances to determine the standard error of the difference in means. Those formulas cannot be used here; we need something new. Ask students what they should look at instead. They are likely to suggest examining the actual difference in measurements for each individual—exactly what we want.

As always, notation is critical. Proper notation enhances both understanding and communication. Here we are examining differences, $d$, not the actual measurements themselves. Our statistic is the mean of those differences, $\bar{d}$, not the difference in means, $\bar{y}_1 - \bar{y}_2$, even though they have the same value. Similarly, our parameter of interest is the mean of those differences, $\mu_d$, not the difference of the means, $\mu_1 - \mu_2$.

But it's not just the notation and the formulas that must be different. Each stage of our procedure reflects the fact that we are looking at paired differences rather than independent measurements.

*Hypothesis.* The null hypothesis is about the mean of the *differences*, $\mu_d$.

*Model.* We note that the data are paired, and check a histogram of the differences for plausible Normality—one histogram, not two as in the last chapter.

*Mechanics.* Our method looks like the one-sample $t$ approach, but our statistic is, $\bar{d}$ and degrees of freedom are simply $n - 1$, the number of *pairs* $- 1$.

*Conclusion.* We talk about what these data reveal about the mean difference. Our statements say things like "There is strong evidence that the training results in an increased test score on average."

*Confidence Interval.* Again, our interpretation is about mean difference, as in "We are 95% confident that training increases an individual's test score by an average of between 8 and 11.5 points."

When pairing is a form of blocking in a designed experiment, there is rarely any question about it. But observational data may be matched for a variety of reasons, making the pairing less clear. We can't assume that samples of 50 men and 50 women are paired just because there are 50 of each. But we might learn subsequently that these are really 50 married couples and conclude that they should be paired. This potential ambiguity emphasizes the need to determine the details of the study design first and determine whether the data are paired at the *Think* step, before performing any analysis.

After students have learned how to do inference for means, it's important to help them decide when. At this point in the course, they can find confidence intervals and do hypothesis tests for situations involving one proportion, two proportions, one mean, two independent means, or matched pairs. They may (we hope) be very good at each individual procedure. That's only part of the problem, however. Students also need to be able to read about the situation and the questions to be investigated, and then to decide which type of inference is called for. Some find this extremely difficult. Try to help them gain this key ability in several ways.

▸ A large set of inference questions that includes all the various types makes for a good in-class group discussion. It may be more important to have students decide what the proper procedure would be for each rather than spend time having them fully complete each analysis.

▸ In the Part VI Review, there's a one-page summary of the procedures and the assumptions and conditions. Not only will that help students check to see if it's appropriate to forge ahead with their chosen inference procedure, it also helps them see what the key issues are. Are we looking at proportions or means? For one group or two? If two, are they independent or matched?

▸ The Part VI Review Exercises aren't just about means. They offer a cumulative review of all inference so far. There are problems dealing with both means and proportions, mixed together in random order. Since these exercises are not clearly attached to a particular chapter, students have to *Think* carefully about what to do. They need plenty of practice with this.

## The Importance of What You Don't Say

***Don't say "choose" two-sample or paired t.*** There is no choice. We are compelled to use the method that is appropriate based on our knowledge of how the data were collected. There is an appropriate method and an inappropriate method, not an option.

***Don't say we "lose" degrees of freedom when we use matched pairs.*** No, we don't; they were never there. True, there are more degrees of freedom when we have two independent samples, but if the data are matched, those degrees of freedom don't exist. Nothing was lost. And we now have the greater control of variability afforded by matched and blocked designs. Usually that makes for a more powerful analysis, even though there are fewer degrees of freedom.

## Class Examples

1. As we have in the last several chapters, we offer an example that allows you to start with a hypothesis test, then immediately find a confidence interval as further analysis. If you elect not to try to do both in one day, this chapter leads with the hypothesis test.

One indicator of physical fitness is resting pulse rate. Ten men volunteered to test an exercise device advertised on television by using it three times a week for 20 minutes. Their resting pulse rates (beats per minute) were measured before the test began, and then again after six weeks. Results are shown in the table. Is there evidence that this kind of exercise can reduce resting pulse rates? How much?

| Subject | Pulse Rates (beats/min) | |
| --- | --- | --- |
| | **Before** | **After** |
| Allen | 73 | 73 |
| Brandon | 83 | 79 |
| Carlos | 85 | 81 |
| David | 87 | 86 |
| Edwin | 91 | 87 |
| Franco | 99 | 91 |
| Graeme | 87 | 84 |
| Hans | 85 | 83 |
| Ivan | 83 | 84 |
| Jorge | 79 | 76 |

Your students should see that the methods they know aren't viable here. The *before* and *after* measurements are *not* independent. Someone will likely suggest looking at the change. Seeing that they should apply our one-sample *t*-procedure to the paired differences should allow the class to lead you through the solution.

***Hypotheses:*** $H_0: \mu_d = 0$    $H_A: \mu_d < 0$ (because we're interested in a *decrease*)

***Model:*** Although the results are independent from one subject to the next, the measurements are paired by subject. A histogram of the paired differences is approximately unimodal and symmetric. Okay to do a matched pairs *t*-test.

***Mechanics:*** $n = 10$, $df = 9$, $\bar{d} = -2.8$, $s_d = 2.53$

$$t = \frac{(-2.8) - 0}{2.53/\sqrt{10}} = -3.5$$

P-value = $P(t_9^* < -3.5) = 0.0034$

***Conclusion:*** With a P-value this low, we reject the null hypothesis. There is strong evidence that this form of exercise can reduce resting pulse rates.

***Confidence Interval:*** The interval looks just like those we saw in Chapter 23; only the notation changes to represent the differences. We choose 95% as our confidence level.

$$\bar{d} \pm t_9^* \times SE(\bar{d}) = -2.8 \pm 2.262 \frac{2.53}{\sqrt{10}} = (-4.61, -0.99)$$

We are 95% confident that six weeks of this exercise program can produce a mean decrease in resting pulse rate of between 1 and 4.6 beats per minute.

2. Discussions of assigned homework problems should provide ample additional examples of matched pairs analysis. When you assign exercises from Chapters 24 and 25, think about mixing in both paired and independent sample problems so students learn to make the distinction.

3. You'll need to review all the inference procedures if you use the test in the Instructor's Resources. The test is comprehensive—it includes questions about both means and proportions. Students need practice deciding what kind of inference is called for in a wide variety of exercises. They must be able to tell whether they are investigating proportions or means, and whether they have one group, two independent groups, or two groups that are paired in some way. This is not easy. It may help to assign practice questions of all types, randomly ordered. (We offer a sample set in the *PTBRG*.) Students will also find the Part VI Review helpful. Along with the usual Quick Review, we include a Quick Guide to Inference and a summary of the Assumptions and Conditions covering all of the different procedures so far. The Review Exercises are comprehensive, covering all the different kinds of inference, with questions in random order. Be sure to have students spend time there. Even students who are adept at using each individual procedure can find it difficult to choose among them. While you'll probably want to assign a few exercises to be worked out in full, it's also very productive to just ask students to read exercises and classify them with respect to the type of inference called for.

## RESOURCES

### *ActivStats*

▸ Chapter 25—"Paired Comparisons."

### *Printed Test Bank and Resource Guide*

The *Printed Test Bank and Resource Guide* provides two chapter quizzes. Then there's an Investigative Task that continues the task from Chapter 23. Students draw their own samples of data and perform two hypothesis tests, one based on independent samples and the other on matched pairs. There's also a group project that covers all of the types of inference covered so far. Finally, this being the end of Part VI, there are 3 Part Tests on inference topics from Chapters 18–25.

# Inferences About Means

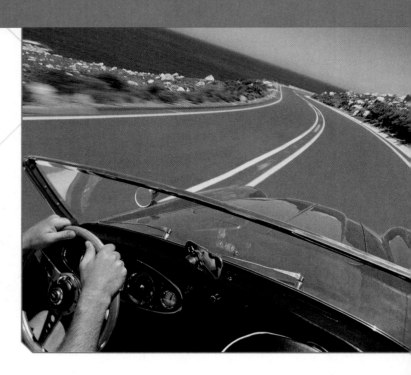

## Where are we going?

We've learned how to generalize from the data at hand to the world at large for proportions. But not all data are as simple as Yes or No. In this chapter we'll learn how to make confidence intervals and test hypotheses for the mean of a quantitative variable.

| | |
|---|---|
| **WHO** | Vehicles on Triphammer Road |
| **WHAT** | Speed |
| **UNITS** | Miles per hour |
| **WHEN** | April 11, 2000, 1 p.m. |
| **WHERE** | A small town in the northeastern United States |
| **WHY** | Concern over impact on residential neighborhood |

Motor vehicle crashes are the leading cause of death for people between 4 and 33 years old. In the year 2006, motor vehicle accidents claimed the lives of 43,300 people in the United States. This means that, on average, motor vehicle crashes resulted in 117 deaths each day, or 1 death every 12 minutes. Speeding is a contributing factor in 31% of all fatal accidents, according to the National Highway Traffic Safety Administration.

Triphammer Road is a busy street that passes through a residential neighborhood. Residents there are concerned that vehicles traveling on Triphammer often exceed the posted speed limit of 30 miles per hour. The local police sometimes place a radar speed detector by the side of the road; as a vehicle approaches, this detector displays the vehicle's speed to its driver.

The local residents are not convinced that such a passive method is helping the problem. They wish to persuade the village to add extra police patrols to encourage drivers to observe the speed limit. To help their case, a resident stood where he could see the detector and recorded the speed of vehicles passing it during a 15-minute period one day. When clusters of vehicles went by, he noted only the speed of the front vehicle. The data and the histogram appear in Figure 23.1.

We're interested both in estimating the true mean speed and in testing whether it exceeds the posted speed limit. Although the sample of vehicles is a convenience sample, not a truly random sample, there's no compelling reason to

**FIGURE 23.1**

*The speeds of cars on Triphammer Road seem to be unimodal and symmetric, at least at this scale.*

| Speed | | |
|---|---|---|
| 29 | 29 | 24 |
| 34 | 34 | 34 |
| 34 | 32 | 36 |
| 28 | 31 | 31 |
| 30 | 27 | 34 |
| 29 | 37 | 36 |
| 38 | 29 | 21 |
| 31 | 26 | |

believe that vehicles at one time of day are driving faster or slower than vehicles at another time of day,[1] so we can take the sample to be representative.

These data differ from data on proportions in one important way. Proportions are usually reported as summaries. After all, individual responses are just "success" and "failure" or "1" and "0." Quantitative data, though, usually report a value for each individual. When you have a value for each individual, you should remember the three rules of data analysis and plot the data, as we have done here.

We have quantitative data, so we summarize with means and standard deviations. Because we want to make inferences, we'll think about sampling distributions, too, and we already know most of the facts we need.

## Getting Started

You've learned how to create confidence intervals and test hypotheses about proportions. We always center confidence intervals at our best guess of the unknown parameter. Then we add and subtract a margin of error. For proportions, that means $\hat{p} \pm ME$.

We found the margin of error as the product of the standard error, $SE(\hat{p})$, and a critical value, $z^*$, from the Normal table. So we had $\hat{p} \pm z^*SE(\hat{p})$.

We knew we could use $z$ because the Central Limit Theorem told us (back in Chapter 18) that the sampling distribution model for proportions is Normal.

Now we want to do exactly the same thing for means, and fortunately, the Central Limit Theorem (still in Chapter 18) told us that the same Normal model works as the sampling distribution for means.

---

**THE CENTRAL LIMIT THEOREM**

When a random sample is drawn from any population with mean $\mu$ and standard deviation $\sigma$, its sample mean, $\bar{y}$, has a sampling distribution with the same *mean $\mu$* but whose *standard deviation is* $\frac{\sigma}{\sqrt{n}}$ (and we write $\sigma(\bar{y}) = SD(\bar{y}) = \frac{\sigma}{\sqrt{n}}$).

No matter what population the random sample comes from, the *shape* of the sampling distribution is approximately Normal as long as the sample size is large enough. The larger the sample used, the more closely the Normal approximates the sampling distribution for the mean.

---

[1] Except, perhaps, at rush hour. But at that time, traffic is slowed. Our concern is with ordinary traffic during the day.

---

**FOR EXAMPLE** | Using the CLT (as if we knew $\sigma$)

---

Based on weighing thousands of animals, the American Angus Association reports that mature Angus cows have a mean weight of 1309 pounds with a standard deviation of 157 pounds. This result was based on a very large sample of animals from many herds over a period of 15 years, so let's assume that these summaries are the population parameters and that the distribution of the weights was unimodal and reasonably symmetric.

**Question:** What does the CLT predict about the mean weight seen in random samples of 100 mature Angus cows?

It's given that weights of all mature Angus cows have $\mu = 1309$ and $\sigma = 157$ pounds. Because $n = 100$ animals is a fairly large sample, I can apply the Central Limit Theorem. I expect the resulting sample means $\bar{y}$ will average 1309 pounds and have a standard deviation of $SD(\bar{y}) = \dfrac{\sigma}{\sqrt{n}} = \dfrac{157}{\sqrt{100}} = 15.7$ pounds.

The CLT also says that the distribution of sample means follows a Normal model, so the 68–95–99.7 Rule applies. I'd expect that

▸ in 68% of random samples of 100 mature Angus cows, the mean weight will be between $1309 - 15.7 = 1293.3$ and $1309 + 15.7 = 1324.7$ pounds;

▸ in 95% of such samples, $1277.6 \leq \bar{y} \leq 1340.4$ pounds;

▸ in 99.7% of such samples, $1261.9 \leq \bar{y} \leq 1356.1$ pounds.

---

The CLT says that all we need to model the sampling distribution of $\bar{y}$ is a random sample of quantitative data.

And the true population standard deviation, $\sigma$.

Uh oh. That could be a problem. How are we supposed to know $\sigma$? With proportions, we had a link between the proportion value and the standard deviation of the sample proportion: $SD(\hat{p}) = \sqrt{\dfrac{pq}{n}}$. And there was an obvious way to estimate the standard deviation from the data: $SE(\hat{p}) = \sqrt{\dfrac{\hat{p}\hat{q}}{n}}$. But for means, $SD(\bar{y}) = \dfrac{\sigma}{\sqrt{n}}$, so knowing $\bar{y}$ doesn't tell us anything about $SD(\bar{y})$. We know $n$, the sample size, but the population standard deviation, $\sigma$, could be *anything*. So what should we do? We do what any sensible person would do: We estimate the population parameter $\sigma$ with $s$, the sample standard deviation based on the data. The resulting standard error is $SE(\bar{y}) = \dfrac{s}{\sqrt{n}}$.

> Because we estimate the standard deviation of the sampling distribution model from the data, it's a *standard error*. So we use the $SE(\bar{y})$ notation. Remember, though, that it's just the estimated standard deviation of the sampling distribution model for means.

A century ago, people used this standard error with the Normal model, assuming it would work. And for large sample sizes it *did* work pretty well. But they began to notice problems with smaller samples. The sample standard deviation, $s$, like any other statistic, varies from sample to sample. And this extra variation in the standard error was messing up the P-values and margins of error.

> **A S** *Activity:* **Estimating the Standard Error.** What's the average age at which people have heart attacks? A confidence interval gives a good answer, but we must estimate the standard error from the data to construct the interval.

William S. Gosset is the man who first investigated this fact. He realized that not only do we need to allow for the extra variation with larger margins of error and P-values, but we even need a new sampling distribution model. In fact, we need a whole *family* of models, depending on the sample size, $n$. These models are unimodal, symmetric, bell-shaped models, but the smaller our sample, the more we must stretch out the tails. Gosset's work transformed Statistics, but most people who use his work don't even know his name.

## Gosset's *t*

*To find the sampling distribution of*
$$\frac{\bar{y}}{s/\sqrt{n}},$$ *Gosset simulated it by hand. He drew paper slips of small samples from a hat hundreds of times and computed the means and standard deviations with a mechanically cranked calculator. Today you could repeat in seconds on a computer the experiment that took him over a year. Gosset's work was so meticulous that not only did he get the shape of the new histogram approximately right, but he even figured out the exact formula for it from his sample. The formula was not confirmed mathematically until years later by Sir R. A. Fisher.*

Gosset had a job that made him the envy of many. He was the quality control engineer for the Guinness Brewery in Dublin, Ireland. His job was to make sure that the stout (a thick, dark beer) leaving the brewery was of high enough quality to meet the demands of the brewery's many discerning customers. It's easy to imagine why a large sample with many observations might be undesirable when testing stout, not to mention dangerous to one's health. So Gosset often used small samples of 3 or 4. But he noticed that with samples of this size, his tests for quality weren't quite right. He knew this because when the batches that he rejected were sent back to the laboratory for more extensive testing, too often they turned out to be OK.

Gosset checked the stout's quality by performing hypothesis tests. He knew that the test would make some Type I errors and reject about 5% of the *good* batches of stout. However, the lab told him that he was in fact rejecting about 15% of the good batches. Gosset knew something was wrong, and it bugged him.

Gosset took time off to study the problem (and earn a graduate degree in the emerging field of Statistics). He figured out that when he used the estimated standard error, $\frac{s}{\sqrt{n}}$, the shape of the sampling model changed. He even figured out what the new model should be and called it a *t*-distribution.

The Guinness Company didn't give Gosset a lot of support for his work. In fact, it had a policy against publishing results. Gosset had to convince the company that he was not publishing an industrial secret, and (as part of getting permission to publish) he had to use a pseudonym. The pseudonym he chose was "Student," and ever since, the model he found has been known as **Student's *t*.**

Gosset's model is always bell-shaped, but the details change with different sample sizes. So the Student's *t*-models form a whole *family* of related distributions that depend on a parameter known as **degrees of freedom.** We often denote degrees of freedom as *df*, and the model as $t_{df}$, with the degrees of freedom as a subscript.

## A Confidence Interval for Means

To make confidence intervals or test hypotheses for means, we need to use Gosset's model. Which one? Well, for means, it turns out the right value for degrees of freedom is $df = n - 1$.

**A PRACTICAL SAMPLING DISTRIBUTION MODEL FOR MEANS**
When certain assumptions and conditions[2] are met, the standardized sample mean,

$$t = \frac{\bar{y} - \mu}{SE(\bar{y})},$$

follows a Student's *t*-model with $n - 1$ degrees of freedom. We estimate the standard error with

$$SE(\bar{y}) = \frac{s}{\sqrt{n}}.$$

---

[2] You can probably guess what they are. We'll see them in the next section.

When Gosset corrected the model for the extra uncertainty, the margin of error got bigger, as you might have guessed. When you use Gosset's model instead of the Normal model, your confidence intervals will be just a bit wider and your P-values just a bit larger. That's the correction you need. By using the *t*-model, you've compensated for the extra variability in precisely the right way.

---

**ONE-SAMPLE *t*-INTERVAL FOR THE MEAN**

When the assumptions and conditions[3] are met, we are ready to find the confidence interval for the population mean, $\mu$. The confidence interval is

$$\bar{y} \pm t^*_{n-1} \times SE(\bar{y}),$$

where the standard error of the mean, $SE(\bar{y}) = \dfrac{s}{\sqrt{n}}$.

The critical value $t^*_{n-1}$ depends on the particular confidence level, $C$, that you specify and on the number of degrees of freedom, $n - 1$, which we get from the sample size.

---

**FOR EXAMPLE**     A one-sample *t*-interval for the mean

In 2004, a team of researchers published a study of contaminants in farmed salmon.[4] Fish from many sources were analyzed for 14 organic contaminants. The study expressed concerns about the level of contaminants found. One of those was the insecticide mirex, which has been shown to be carcinogenic and is suspected to be toxic to the liver, kidneys, and endocrine system. One farm in particular produced salmon with very high levels of mirex. After those outliers are removed, summaries for the mirex concentrations (in parts per million) in the rest of the farmed salmon are:

$$n = 150 \qquad \bar{y} = 0.0913 \text{ ppm} \qquad s = 0.0495 \text{ ppm}.$$

**Question:** What does a 95% confidence interval say about mirex?

$$df = 150 - 1 = 149$$

$$SE(\bar{y}) = \frac{s}{\sqrt{n}} = \frac{0.0495}{\sqrt{150}} = 0.0040$$

$$t^*_{149} \approx 1.977 \text{ (from table T, using 140 df)}$$

$$(\text{actually, } t^*_{149} \approx 1.976 \text{ from technology})$$

So the confidence interval for $\mu$ is

$$\bar{y} \pm t^*_{149} \times SE(\bar{y})$$

$$0.0913 \pm 1.977(0.0040)$$

$$0.0913 \pm 0.0079$$

$$(0.0834, 0.0992)$$

I'm 95% confident that the mean level of mirex concentration in farm-raised salmon is between 0.0834 and 0.0992 parts per million.

---

[3] Yes, the same ones, and they're still coming in the next section.
[4] Ronald A. Hites, Jeffery A. Foran, David O. Carpenter, M. Coreen Hamilton, Barbara A. Knuth, and Steven J. Schwager, "Global Assessment of Organic Contaminants in Farmed Salmon," *Science* 9 January 2004: Vol. 303., no. 5655, pp. 226–229.

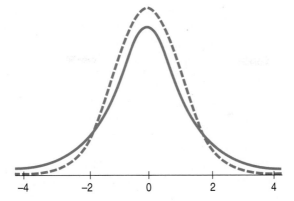

**FIGURE 23.2**

*The t-model (solid curve) on 2 degrees of freedom has fatter tails than the Normal model (dashed curve). So the 68–95–99.7 Rule doesn't work for t-models with only a few degrees of freedom.*

---

**z or t?**

If you know $\sigma$, use z. (That's rare!) Whenever you use s to estimate $\sigma$, use t.

---

Student's *t*-models are unimodal, symmetric, and bell-shaped, just like the Normal. But *t*-models with only a few degrees of freedom have much fatter tails than the Normal. (That's what makes the margin of error bigger.) As the degrees of freedom increase, the *t*-models look more and more like the Normal. In fact, the *t*-model with infinite degrees of freedom is exactly Normal.[5] This is great news if you happen to have an infinite number of data values. Unfortunately, that's not practical. Fortunately, above a few hundred degrees of freedom it's very hard to tell the difference. Of course, in the rare situation that we *know* $\sigma$, it would be foolish not to use that information, and if we don't have to estimate it, we can use the Normal model.

> **When $\sigma$ is known** Administrators of a hospital were concerned about the prenatal care given to mothers in their part of the city. To study this, they examined the gestation times of babies born there. They drew a sample of 25 babies born in their hospital in the previous 6 months. Human gestation times for healthy pregnancies are thought to be well-modeled by a Normal with a mean of 280 days and a standard deviation of 14 days. The hospital administrators wanted to test the mean gestation time of their sample of babies against the known standard. For this test, they should use the established value for the standard deviation, 14 days, rather than estimating the standard deviation from their sample. Because they use the model parameter value for $\sigma$, they should base their test on the Normal model rather than Student's *t*.

# Assumptions and Conditions

Gosset found the *t*-model by simulation. Years later, when Sir Ronald A. Fisher[6] showed mathematically that Gosset was right, he needed to make some assumptions to make it work. These are the assumptions we need to use the Student's *t*-models.

### INDEPENDENCE ASSUMPTION

**Independence Assumption:** The data values should be independent. There's really no way to check independence of the data by looking at the sample, but we should think about whether the assumption is reasonable.

---

[5] Formally, in the limit as *n* goes to infinity.
[6] We met Fisher back in Chapter 21. You can see his picture on page 538.

**Randomization Condition:** The data arise from a random sample or suitably randomized experiment. Randomly sampled data—and especially data from a Simple Random Sample—are ideal.

When a sample is drawn without replacement, technically we ought to confirm that we haven't sampled a large fraction of the population, which would threaten the independence of our selections. We check the

**10% Condition:** The sample is no more than 10% of the population.

> ### We Don't *Want* to Stop
>
> We check conditions hoping that we can make a meaningful analysis of our data. The conditions serve as *disqualifiers*—we keep going unless there's a serious problem. If we find minor issues, we note them and express caution about our results. If the sample is not an SRS, but we believe it's representative of some populations, we limit our conclusions accordingly. If there are outliers, rather than stop, we perform the analysis both with and without them. If the sample looks bimodal, we try to analyze subgroups separately. Only when there's major trouble—like a strongly skewed small sample or an obviously nonrepresentative sample—are we unable to proceed at all.

In practice, though, we often don't mention the 10% Condition for means. Why not? When we made inferences about proportions, this condition was crucial because we usually had large samples. But for means our samples are generally smaller, so the independence problem arises only if we're sampling from a small population (and then there's a correction formula we could use—but let's not get into that here). And sometimes we're dealing with a randomized experiment; then there's no sampling at all.

## NORMAL POPULATION ASSUMPTION

Student's *t*-models won't work for data that are badly skewed. How skewed is too skewed? Well, formally, we assume that the data are from a population that follows a Normal model. Practically speaking, there's no way to be certain this is true.

And it's almost certainly *not* true. Models are idealized; real data are, well, real. The good news, however, is that even for small samples, it's sufficient to check the . . .

**Nearly Normal Condition:** The data come from a distribution that is unimodal and symmetric.

Check this condition by making a histogram or Normal probability plot. The importance of Normality for Student's *t* depends on the sample size. Just our luck: It matters most when it's hardest to check.[7]

For very small samples (*n* < 15 or so), the data should follow a Normal model pretty closely. Of course, with so little data, it's rather hard to tell. But if you do find outliers or strong skewness, don't use these methods.

For moderate sample sizes (*n* between 15 and 40 or so), the *t* methods will work well as long as the data are unimodal and reasonably symmetric. Make a histogram.

When the sample size is larger than 40 or 50, the *t* methods are safe to use unless the data are extremely skewed. Be sure to make a histogram. If you find outliers in the data, it's always a good idea to perform the analysis twice, once with and once without the outliers, even for large samples. They may well hold additional information about the data that deserves special attention. If you find multiple modes, you may well have different groups that should be analyzed and understood separately.

**FOR EXAMPLE**     Checking assumptions and conditions for Student's *t*

**Recap:** Researchers purchased whole farmed salmon from 51 farms in eight regions in six countries. The histogram shows the concentrations of the insecticide mirex in 150 farmed salmon.

**Question:** Are the assumptions and conditions for inference satisfied?

*(continued)*

---

[7] There are formal tests of Normality, but they don't really help. When we have a small sample—just when we really care about checking Normality—these tests have very little power. So it doesn't make much sense to use them in deciding whether to perform a *t*-test. We don't recommend that you use them.

For Example (*continued*)

✔ **Independence Assumption:** The fish were raised in many different places, and samples were purchased independently from several sources.

✔ **Randomization Condition:** The fish were selected randomly from those available for sale.

✔ **10% Conditions:** There's lots of fish in the sea (and at the fish farms); 150 is certainly far fewer than 10% of the population.

✔ **Nearly Normal Condition:** The histogram of the data is unimodal. Although it may be somewhat skewed to the right, this is not a concern with a sample size of 150.

It's okay to use these data for inference about farm-raised salmon.

---

# JUST CHECKING

Every 10 years, the United States takes a census. The census tries to count every resident. There are two forms, known as the "short form," answered by most people, and the "long form," slogged through by about one in six or seven households chosen at random. According to the Census Bureau (www.census.gov), ". . . each estimate based on the long form responses has an associated confidence interval."

**1.** Why does the Census Bureau need a confidence interval for long-form information, but not for the questions that appear on both the long and short forms?

**2.** Why must the Census Bureau base these confidence intervals on *t*-models?

The Census Bureau goes on to say, "These confidence intervals are wider . . . for geographic areas with smaller populations and for characteristics that occur less frequently in the area being examined (such as the proportion of people in poverty in a middle-income neighborhood)."

**3.** Why is this so? For example, why should a confidence interval for the mean amount families spend monthly on housing be wider for a sparsely populated area of farms in the Midwest than for a densely populated area of an urban center? How does the formula show this will happen?

To deal with this problem, the Census Bureau reports long-form data only for ". . . geographic areas from which about two hundred or more long forms were completed—which are large enough to produce good quality estimates. If smaller weighting areas had been used, the confidence intervals around the estimates would have been significantly wider, rendering many estimates less useful . . ."

**4.** Suppose the Census Bureau decided to report on areas from which only 50 long forms were completed. What effect would that have on a 95% confidence interval for, say, the mean cost of housing? Specifically, which values used in the formula for the margin of error would change? Which would change a lot and which would change only slightly?

**5.** Approximately how much wider would that confidence interval based on 50 forms be than the one based on 200 forms?

---

**A S** *Activity:* **Intuition for *t*-based Intervals.** A narrated review of Student's *t*.

---

**STEP-BY-STEP EXAMPLE** | **A One-Sample *t*-Interval for the Mean**

Let's build a 90% confidence interval for the mean speed of all vehicles traveling on Triphammer Road. The interval that we'll make is called the **one-sample *t*-interval**.

**Question: What can we say about the mean speed of all cars on Triphammer Road?**

---

 **THINK**

**Plan** State what we want to know. Identify the parameter of interest.

Identify the variables and review the W's.

Make a picture. Check the distribution shape and look for skewness, multiple modes, and outliers.

**REALITY CHECK** The histogram centers around 30 mph, and the data lie between 20 and 40 mph. We'd expect a confidence interval to place the population mean within a few mph of 30.

**Model** Think about the assumptions and check the conditions.

Note that with this small sample we probably didn't need to check the 10% Condition.

On the other hand, doing so gives us a chance to think about what the population is.

State the sampling distribution model for the statistic.

Choose your method.

---

I want to find a 90% confidence interval for the mean speed, $\mu$, of vehicles driving on Triphammer Road. I have data on the speeds of 23 cars there, sampled on April 11, 2000.

Here's a histogram of the 23 observed speeds.

✔ **Independence Assumption:** This is a convenience sample, but care was taken to select cars that were not driving near each other, so their speeds are plausibly independent.

✔ **Randomization Condition:** Not really met. This is a convenience sample, but I have reason to believe that it is representative.

✔ **10% Condition:** The cars I observed were fewer than 10% of all cars that travel Triphammer Road.

✔ **Nearly Normal Condition:** The histogram of the speeds is unimodal and symmetric.

The conditions are satisfied, so I will use a Student's *t*-model with

$$(n - 1) = 22 \text{ degrees of freedom}$$

and find a **one-sample *t*-interval for the mean.**

---

 **SHOW**

**Mechanics** Construct the confidence interval.

Be sure to include the units along with the statistics.

---

Calculating from the data (see p. 587):

$$n = 23 \text{ cars}$$
$$\bar{y} = 31.0 \text{ mph}$$
$$s = 4.25 \text{ mph.}$$

The critical value we need to make a 90% interval comes from a Student's t table, a computer program, or a calculator. We have $23 - 1 = 22$ degrees of freedom. The selected confidence level says that we want 90% of the probability to be caught in the middle, so we exclude 5% in *each* tail, for a total of 10%. The degrees of freedom and 5% tail probability are all we need to know to find the critical value.

**REALITY CHECK** ▶ The result looks plausible and in line with what we thought.

The standard error of $\bar{y}$ is

$$SE(\bar{y}) = \frac{s}{\sqrt{n}} = \frac{4.25}{\sqrt{23}} = 0.886 \text{ mph.}$$

The 90% critical value is $t^*_{22} = 1.717$, so the margin of error is

$$ME = t^*_{22} \times SE(\bar{y})$$
$$= 1.717(0.886)$$
$$= 1.521 \text{ mph.}$$

The 90% confidence interval for the mean speed is $31.0 \pm 1.5$ mph.

---

**TELL**

**Conclusion** Interpret the confidence interval in the proper context.

When we construct confidence intervals in this way, we expect 90% of them to cover the true mean and 10% to miss the true value. That's what "90% confident" means.

I am 90% confident that the interval from 29.5 mph to 32.5 mph contains the true mean speed of all vehicles on Triphammer Road.

Caveat: This was not a random sample of vehicles. It was a convenience sample taken at one time on one day. And the participants were not blinded. Drivers could see the police device, and some may have slowed down. I'm reluctant to extend this inference to other situations.

---

*Using Table T to look up the critical value t\* for a 90% confidence level with 22 degrees of freedom.*

| | 0.25 | 0.2 | 0.15 | 0.1 | 0.05 | 0.025 | 0.02 |
|---|---|---|---|---|---|---|---|
| 19 | .6876 | .8610 | 1.066 | 1.328 | 1.729 | 2.093 | 2.205 |
| 20 | .6870 | .8600 | 1.064 | 1.325 | 1.725 | 2.086 | 2.197 |
| 21 | .6864 | .8591 | 1.063 | 1.323 | 1.721 | 2.080 | 2.189 |
| 22 | .6858 | .8583 | 1.061 | 1.321 | 1.717 | 2.074 | 2.183 |
| 23 | .6853 | .8575 | 1.060 | 1.319 | 1.714 | 2.069 | 2.177 |
| 24 | .6848 | .8569 | 1.059 | 1.318 | 1.711 | 2.064 | 2.172 |
| 25 | .6844 | .8562 | 1.058 | 1.316 | 1.708 | 2.060 | 2.167 |
| 26 | .6840 | .8557 | 1.058 | 1.315 | 1.706 | 2.056 | 2.162 |
| 27 | .6837 | .8551 | 1.057 | 1.314 | 1.703 | 2.052 | 2.158 |
| C | | | | 80% | 90% | 95% | |

**A S** *Activity:* **The Real Effect of Small Sample Size.** We know that smaller sample sizes lead to wider confidence intervals, but is that just because they have fewer degrees of freedom?

Here's the part of the Student's t table that gives the critical value we needed. (See Table T in the back of the book.) To find a critical value, locate the row of the table corresponding to the degrees of freedom and the column corresponding to the probability you want. Our 90% confidence interval leaves 5% of the values on either side, so look for 0.05 at the top of the column or 90% at the bottom. The value in the table at that intersection is the critical value we need: 1.717.

Of course, you can also create the confidence interval with computer software or a calculator.

## More Cautions About Interpreting Confidence Intervals

<table>
<tr><td>

**So What *Should* We Say?**
Since 90% of random samples yield an interval that captures the true mean, we *should* say, "I am 90% confident that the interval from 29.5 to 32.5 mph contains the mean speed of all the vehicles on Triphammer Road." It's also okay to say something less formal: "I am 90% confident that the average speed of all vehicles on Triphammer Road is between 29.5 and 32.5 mph." Remember: *Our uncertainty is about the interval, not the true mean.* The interval varies randomly. The true mean speed is neither variable nor random—just unknown.

</td><td>

Confidence intervals for means offer new tempting wrong interpretations. Here are some things you *shouldn't* say:

▶ *Don't say,* "*90% of all the vehicles* on Triphammer Road drive at a speed between 29.5 and 32.5 mph." The confidence interval is about the *mean* speed, not about the speeds of *individual* vehicles.

▶ *Don't say,* "We are 90% confident that *a randomly selected vehicle* will have a speed between 29.5 and 32.5 mph." This false interpretation is also about individual vehicles rather than about the *mean* of the speeds. We are 90% confident that the *mean* speed of all vehicles on Triphammer Road is between 29.5 and 32.5 mph.

▶ *Don't say,* "The mean speed of the vehicles is 31.0 mph 90% *of the time.*" That's about means, but still wrong. It implies that the true mean varies, when in fact it is the confidence interval that would have been different had we gotten a different sample.

▶ Finally, *don't say,* "90% of all *samples* will have mean speeds between 29.5 and 32.5 mph." That statement suggests that *this* interval somehow sets a standard for every other interval. In fact, this interval is no more (or less) likely to be correct than any other. You could say that 90% of all possible samples will produce intervals that actually do contain the true mean speed. (The problem is that, because we'll never know where the true mean speed really is, we can't know if our sample was one of those 90%.)

▶ *Do say,* "90% of intervals found in this way cover the true value." Or make it more personal and say, "I am 90% confident that the true mean speed is between 29.5 and 32.5 mph."

</td></tr>
</table>

## Make a Picture, Make a Picture, Make a Picture

**FIGURE 23.3**

*A Normal probability plot of speeds looks reasonably straight.*

The only reasonable way to check the Nearly Normal Condition is with graphs of the data. Make a histogram of the data and verify that its distribution is unimodal and symmetric and that it has no outliers. You may also want to make a Normal probability plot to see that it's reasonably straight. You'll be able to spot deviations from the Normal model more easily with a Normal probability plot, but it's easier to understand the particular nature of the deviations from a histogram.

If you have a computer or graphing calculator doing the work, there's no excuse not to look at *both* displays as part of checking the Nearly Normal Condition.

# A Test for the Mean

The residents along Triphammer Road have a more specific concern. It appears that the mean speed along the road is higher than it ought to be. To get the police to patrol more frequently, though, they'll need to show that the true mean speed is *in fact greater* than the 30 mph speed limit. This calls for a hypothesis test called the **one-sample $t$-test for the mean.**

You already know enough to construct this test. The test statistic looks just like the others we've seen. It compares the difference between the observed statistic and a hypothesized value to the standard error of the observed statistic. We already know that, for means, the appropriate probability model to use for P-values is Student's $t$ with $n - 1$ degrees of freedom.

We're ready to go:

---

**A S**    *Activity: A t-Test for Wind Speed.* Watch the video in the preceding activity, and then use the interactive tool to test whether, there's enough wind for electricity generation at a site under investigation.

---

### ONE-SAMPLE $t$-TEST FOR THE MEAN

The assumptions and conditions for the one-sample $t$-test for the mean are the same as for the one-sample $t$-interval. We test the hypothesis $H_0: \mu = \mu_0$ using the statistic

$$t_{n-1} = \frac{\bar{y} - \mu_0}{SE(\bar{y})}.$$

The standard error of $\bar{y}$ is $SE(\bar{y}) = \dfrac{s}{\sqrt{n}}.$

When the conditions are met and the null hypothesis is true, this statistic follows a Student's $t$-model with $n - 1$ degrees of freedom. We use that model to obtain a P-value.

---

### FOR EXAMPLE    A one-sample $t$-test for the mean

**Recap:** Researchers tested 150 farm-raised salmon for organic contaminants. They found the mean concentration of the carcinogenic insecticide mirex to be 0.0913 parts per million, with standard deviation 0.0495 ppm. As a safety recommendation to recreational fishers, the Environmental Protection Agency's (EPA) recommended "screening value" for mirex is 0.08 ppm.

**Question:** Are farmed salmon contaminated beyond the level permitted by the EPA? (We've already checked the conditions; see p. 592–3.)

$$H_0: \mu = 0.08$$
$$H_A: \mu > 0.08$$

These data satisfy the conditions for inference; I'll do a one-sample $t$-test for the mean:

$$n = 150, \; df = 149$$
$$\bar{y} = 0.0913, \; s = 0.0495$$
$$SE(\bar{y}) = \frac{0.0495}{\sqrt{150}} = 0.0040$$
$$t_{149} = \frac{0.0913 - 0.08}{0.0040} = 2.825$$

*(continued)*

For Example (*continued*)

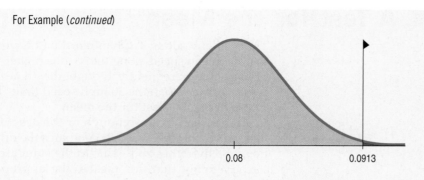

$$P(t_{149} > 2.825) = 0.0027 \text{ (from technology)}.$$

With a P-value that low, I reject the null hypothesis and conclude that, in farm-raised salmon, the mirex contamination level does exceed the EPA screening value.

---

**STEP-BY-STEP EXAMPLE**    A One-Sample *t*-Test for the Mean

Let's apply the one-sample *t*-test to the Triphammer Road car speeds. The speed limit is 30 mph, so we'll use that as the null hypothesis value.

**Question: Does the mean speed of all cars exceed the posted speed limit?**

 **THINK**

**Plan** State what we want to know. Make clear what the population and parameter are.

Identify the variables and review the W's.

**Hypotheses** The null hypothesis is that the true mean speed is equal to the limit. Because we're interested in whether the vehicles are speeding, the alternative is one-sided.

Make a picture. Check the distribution for skewness, multiple modes, and outliers.

**REALITY CHECK** The histogram of the observed speeds is clustered around 30, so we'd be surprised to find that the mean was much higher than that. (The fact that 30 is within the confidence interval that we've just found confirms this suspicion.)

**Model** Think about the assumptions and check the conditions.

(We won't worry about the 10% Condition—it's a small sample.)

I want to know whether the mean speed of vehicles on Triphammer Road exceeds the posted speed limit of 30 mph. I have a sample of 23 car speeds on April 11, 2000.

$$H_0: \text{Mean speed, } \mu = 30 \text{ mph}$$
$$H_A: \text{Mean speed, } \mu > 30 \text{ mph}$$

✓ **Independence Assumption:** These cars are a convenience sample, but they were selected so no two cars were driving near each other, so I am justified in believing that their speeds are independent.

✔ **Randomization Condition:** Although I have a convenience sample, I have reason to believe that it is a representative sample.

✔ **Nearly Normal Condition:** The histogram of the speeds is unimodal and reasonably symmetric.

State the sampling distribution model. (Be sure to include the degrees of freedom.)

Choose your method.

The conditions are satisfied, so I'll use a Student's t-model with $(n - 1) = 22$ degrees of freedom to do a **one-sample t-test for the mean.**

**Mechanics** Be sure to include the units when you write down what you know from the data.

We use the null model to find the P-value. Make a picture of the *t*-model centered at $\mu = 30$. Since this is an upper-tail test, shade the region to the right of the observed mean speed.

The *t*-statistic calculation is just a standardized value, like *z*. We subtract the hypothesized mean and divide by the standard error.

The P-value is the probability of observing a sample mean as large as 31.0 (or larger) *if* the true mean were 30.0, as the null hypothesis states. We can find this P-value from a table, calculator, or computer program.

**REALITY CHECK** We're not surprised that the difference isn't statistically significant.

From the data,

$$n = 23 \text{ cars}$$
$$\bar{y} = 31.0 \text{ mph}$$
$$s = 4.25 \text{ mph}$$

$$SE(\bar{y}) = \frac{s}{\sqrt{n}} = \frac{4.25}{\sqrt{23}} = 0.886 \text{ mph.}$$

$$t = \frac{\bar{y} - \mu_0}{SE(\bar{y})} = \frac{31.0 - 30.0}{0.886} = 1.13$$

(The observed mean is 1.13 standard errors above the hypothesized value.)

$$P\text{-value} = P(t_{22} > 1.13) = 0.136$$

**Conclusion** Link the P-value to your decision about $H_0$, and state your conclusion in context.

Unfortunately for the residents, there is no course of action associated with failing to reject this particular null hypothesis.

The P-value of 0.136 says that if the true mean speed of vehicles on Triphammer Road were 30 mph, samples of 23 vehicles can be expected to have an observed mean of at least 31.0 mph 13.6% of the time. That P-value is not small enough for me to reject the hypothesis that the true mean is 30 mph at any reasonable alpha level. I conclude that there is not enough evidence to say the average speed is too high.

# Finding *t*-Values by Hand

*Part of Table T*

As degrees of freedom increase, the shape of
Student's *t*-models changes more gradually.
Table T at the back of the book includes degrees of
freedom between 100 and 1000 selected so that you
can pin down the P-value for just about any df. If
your df's aren't listed, take the cautious approach
by using the next lower value, or use technology.

The Student's *t*-model is different for each value of degrees of freedom. Usually
we find critical values and margins of error for Student's *t*-based intervals with
technology. Calculators or statistics programs can give critical values for a
*t*-model for any number of degrees of freedom and for any confidence level you
please.

But you can also use tables such as Table T at the back of this book. The tables
run down the page for as many degrees of freedom as can fit. For *enough* degrees
of freedom, the *t*-model gets closer and closer to the Normal, so the tables give a
final row with the critical values from the Normal model and label it "∞ df."

These tables are only a portion of the full tables, such as the one we used for
the Normal model. We could have printed a table like table Z for every df, but
that's a lot of pages and not likely to be a best seller. One way to shorten the book
is to limit ourselves to only a few values. Although it might be nice to be able to
get a critical value for a 93.4% confidence interval with 179 df, in practice we usually limit ourselves to 90%, 95%, 99%, and 99.9% and selected degrees of freedom.
So, Table T fits on a single page with columns for selected confidence levels and
rows for selected df's.[8]

For confidence intervals, the values in the table are usually
enough to cover most cases of interest. If you can't find a row
for the df you need, just use the next smaller df in the table.

For hypothesis tests, the computed *t*-statistic can take on
any value, so the value you get is not likely to be one found in
the table. The best we can do is to trap a calculated *t*-value between two columns. Just look across the row with the appropriate degrees of freedom to find where the *t*-statistic falls. The
P-value will be between the two values at the heads of the
columns.[9] Report that the P-value falls between these two values. Usually that's good enough.

---

**FOR EXAMPLE**   Finding P-values from Table T

**Recap:** We've computed a one-sample *t*-test for the mean mirex contamination in farmed salmon, finding
$t = 2.825$ with 149 df. In the earlier example we found the P-value with technology.

**Question:** How can we estimate the P-value for this upper-tail test using Table T?

I seek $P(t_{149} > 2.825)$. Table T has neither a row for 149 df nor an entry that is exactly 2.825. Here's the part of Table T where I'll need to work; roughly the right degrees of freedom and *t*-values:

| Two-tail probability | | 0.20 | 0.10 | 0.05 | 0.02 | 0.01 |
| **One-tail probability** | | 0.10 | 0.05 | 0.025 | 0.01 | 0.005 |
|---|---|---|---|---|---|---|
| Values of $t_\alpha$ | df | | | | | |
| | 140 | 1.288 | 1.656 | 1.977 | 2.353 | 2.611 |
| | 180 | 1.286 | 1.653 | 1.973 | 2.347 | 2.603 |

*(continued)*

---

[8] You can also find tables and interactive tools on the Internet.
[9] Don't be confused that the *t*-values in the table *increase* from left to right while the
P-values labeling the columns *decrease* from left to right. Think about it, and you'll see that
it makes sense.

For Example (*continued*)

*Since 149 df doesn't appear in the table, I'll be conservative and use the next lower df value that does appear. In this table, that's 140 df. Looking across the row for 140 df, I see that the largest t-value in the table is 2.611. According to the column heading, a t-value this large or larger will occur with probability 0.005. My t-value of 2.825 is larger than this, so I know that the probability of a t-value that large must be even smaller. I can report P < 0.005.*

## Significance and Importance

Recall that "statistically significant" does not mean "actually important" or "meaningful," even though it sort of sounds that way. In this example, it does seem that speeds may be a bit above 30 miles per hour. If so, it's possible that a larger sample would show statistical significance.

But would that be the right decision? The difference between 31 miles per hour and 30 miles per hour doesn't seem meaningful, and rejecting the null hypothesis wouldn't change that. Even with a statistically significant result, it would be hard to convince the police that vehicles on Triphammer Road were driving at dangerously fast speeds. It would probably also be difficult to persuade the town that spending more money to lower the average speed on Triphammer Road would be a good use of the town's resources. Looking at the confidence interval, we can say with 90% confidence, that the mean speed is somewhere between 29.5 and 32.5 mph. Even in the worst case, if the mean speed is 32.5 mph, would this be a bad enough situation to convince the town to spend more money? Probably not. It's always a good idea when we test a hypothesis to also check the confidence interval and think about the likely values for the mean.

### JUST CHECKING

In discussing estimates based on the long-form samples, the Census Bureau notes, "The disadvantage . . . is that . . . estimates of characteristics that are also reported on the short form will not match the [long-form estimates]."

The short-form estimates are values from a complete census, so they are the "true" values—something we don't usually have when we do inference.

6. Suppose we use long-form data to make 95% confidence intervals for the mean age of residents for each of 100 of the Census-defined areas. How many of these 100 intervals should we expect will fail to include the true mean age (as determined from the complete short-form Census data)?

7. Based only on the long-form sample, we might test the null hypothesis about the mean household income in a region. Would the power of the test increase or decrease if we used an area with more long forms?

## Intervals and Tests

The 90% confidence interval for the mean speed was 31.0 mph ± 1.5, or (29.5 mph, 32.5 mph). If someone hypothesized that the mean speed was really 30 mph, how would you feel about it? How about 35 mph?

Because the confidence interval included the speed limit of 30 mph, it certainly looked like 30 mph might be a plausible value for the true mean speed of the vehicles on Triphammer Road. In fact, 30 mph gave a P-value of 0.136—too large to reject the null hypothesis. We should have seen this coming. The hypothesized mean of 30 mph lies *within the confidence interval*. It's one of the reasonable values for the mean.

Confidence intervals and significance tests are built from the same calculations. In fact, they are really complementary ways of looking at the same question. Here's the connection: The confidence interval contains all the null hypothesis values we can't reject with these data.

More precisely, a level C confidence interval contains *all* of the plausible null hypothesis values that would *not* be rejected by a two-sided hypothesis test at alpha level $1 - C$. So a 95% confidence interval matches a $1 - 0.95 = 0.05$ level test for these data.

Confidence intervals are naturally two-sided, so they match exactly with two-sided hypothesis tests. When, as in our example, the hypothesis is one-sided, the corresponding alpha level is $(1 - C)/2$.

> **Fail to reject** Our 90% confidence interval was 29.5 to 32.5 mph. If any of these values had been the null hypothesis for the mean, then the corresponding hypothesis test at $\alpha = 0.05$ (because $\dfrac{1 - 0.90}{2} = 0.05$) would not have been able to reject the null. That is, the corresponding one-sided P-value for our observed mean of 31 mph would be greater than 0.05. So, we would not reject any hypothesized value between 29.5 and 32.5 mph.

# Sample Size

How large a sample do we need? The simple answer is "more." But more data cost money, effort, and time, so how much is enough? Suppose your computer just took an hour to download a movie you wanted to watch. You're not happy. You hear about a program that claims to download movies in under a half-hour. You're interested enough to spend $29.95 for it, but only if it really delivers. So you get the free evaluation copy and test it by downloading that movie 10 different times. Of course, the mean download time is not exactly 30 minutes as claimed. Observations vary. If the margin of error were 8 minutes, though, you'd probably be able to decide whether the software is worth the money. Doubling the sample size would require another 5 hours of testing and would reduce your margin of error to a bit under 6 minutes. You'll need to decide whether that's worth the effort.

As we make plans to collect data, we should have some idea of how small a margin of error we need to be able to draw a conclusion or detect a difference we want to see. If the size of the effect we're studying is large, then we may be able to tolerate a larger *ME*. If we need great precision, however, we'll want a smaller *ME*, and, of course, that means a larger sample size.

Armed with the *ME* and confidence level, we can find the sample size we'll need. Almost.

We know that for a mean, $ME = t^*_{n-1} \times SE(\bar{y})$ and that $SE(\bar{y}) = \dfrac{s}{\sqrt{n}}$, so we can determine the sample size by solving this equation for $n$:

$$ME = t^*_{n-1}\frac{s}{\sqrt{n}}.$$

The good news is that we have an equation; the bad news is that we won't know most of the values we need to solve it. When we thought about sample

**SAMPLE SIZE CALCULATIONS BY HAND**

Let's give the sample size formula a spin. Suppose we want an *ME* of 8 minutes, and we think the standard deviation of download times is about 10 minutes. Using a 95% confidence interval and $z^* = 1.96$, we solve

$$8 = 1.96 \frac{10}{\sqrt{n}}$$

$$\sqrt{n} = \frac{1.96 \times 10}{8} = 2.45$$

$$n = (2.45)^2 = 6.0025$$

That's a small sample size, so we use $(6 - 1) = 5$ degrees of freedom[10] to substitute an appropriate $t^*$ value. At 95%, $t^*_5 = 2.571$. Now solve the equation one more time:

$$8 = 2.571 \frac{10}{\sqrt{n}}$$

$$\sqrt{n} = \frac{2.571 \times 10}{8} \approx 3.214$$

$$n = (3.214)^2 \approx 10.33$$

To make sure the *ME* is no larger than you want, you should always round *up*, which gives $n = 11$ runs. So, to get an *ME* of 8 minutes, we should find the downloading times for $n = 11$ movies.

size for proportions back in Chapter 19, we ran into a similar problem. There we had to guess a working value for *p* to compute a sample size. Here, we need to know *s*. We don't know *s* until we get some data, but we want to calculate the sample size *before* collecting the data. We might be able to make a good guess, and that is often good enough for this purpose. If we have no idea what the standard deviation might be, or if the sample size really matters (for example, because each additional individual is very expensive to sample or experiment on), it might be a good idea to run a small *pilot study* to get some feeling for the standard deviation.

That's not all. Without knowing *n*, we don't know the degrees of freedom and we can't find the critical value, $t^*_{n-1}$. One common approach is to use the corresponding $z^*$ value from the Normal model. If you've chosen a 95% confidence level, then just use 2, following the 68–95–99.7 Rule. If your estimated sample size is, say, 60 or more, it's probably okay—$z^*$ was a good guess. If it's smaller than that, you may want to add a step, using $z^*$ at first, finding *n*, and then replacing $z^*$ with the corresponding $t^*_{n-1}$ and calculating the sample size once more.

Sample size calculations are *never* exact. The margin of error you find *after* collecting the data won't match exactly the one you used to find *n*. The sample size formula depends on quantities that you won't have until you collect the data, but using it is an important first step. Before you collect data, it's always a good idea to know whether the sample size is large enough to give you a good chance of being able to tell you what you want to know.

# Degrees of Freedom

Some calculators offer an alternative button for standard deviation that divides by *n* instead of *n* – 1. Why don't you stick a wad of gum over the "*n*" button so you won't be tempted to use it? Use *n* – 1.

The number of degrees of freedom, $(n - 1)$, might have reminded you of the value we divide by to find the standard deviation of the data (since, in fact, it's the same number). When we introduced that formula, we promised to say a bit more about why we divide by $n - 1$ rather than by *n*. The reason is closely tied to the reasoning behind the *t*-distribution.

If only we knew the true population mean, $\mu$, we would find the sample standard deviation as

$$s = \sqrt{\frac{\sum (y - \mu)^2}{n}} \qquad \text{(Equation 23.1)[11]}$$

We use $\bar{y}$ instead of $\mu$, though, and that causes a problem. For any sample, the data values will generally be closer to their own sample mean than to the true population mean, $\mu$. Why is that? Imagine that we take a random sample of

---

[10] Ordinarily we'd round the sample size *up*. But at this stage of the calculation, rounding *down* is the safer choice. Can you see why?

[11] Statistics textbooks usually have equation numbers so they can talk about equations by name. We haven't needed equation numbers yet, but we admit it's useful here, so this is our first.

10 high-school seniors. The mean SAT verbal score is 500 in the United States. But the sample mean, $\bar{y}$, for *these* 10 seniors won't be exactly 500. Are the 10 seniors' scores closer to 500 or $\bar{y}$? They'll always be closer to their own average $\bar{y}$. If we used $\sum (y - \bar{y})^2$ instead of $\sum (y - \mu)^2$ in Equation 23.1 to calculate $s$, our standard deviation estimate would be too small. How can we fix it? The amazing mathematical fact is that we can compensate for the smaller sum exactly by dividing by $n - 1$ instead of by $n$. So that's all the $n - 1$ is doing in the denominator of $s$. And we call $n - 1$ the degrees of freedom.

# WHAT CAN GO WRONG?

The most fundamental issue you face is knowing when to use Student's $t$ methods.

▶ **Don't confuse proportions and means.** When you treat your data as categorical, counting successes and summarizing with a sample proportion, make inferences using the Normal model methods you learned about in Chapters 19 through 22. When you treat your data as quantitative, summarizing with a sample mean, make your inferences using Student's $t$ methods.

Student's $t$ methods work only when the Normality Assumption is true. Naturally, many of the ways things can go wrong turn out to be different ways that the Normality Assumption can fail. It's always a good idea to look for the most common kinds of failure. It turns out that you can even fix some of them.

▶ **Beware of multimodality.** The Nearly Normal Condition clearly fails if a histogram of the data has two or more modes. When you see this, look for the possibility that your data come from two groups. If so, your best bet is to try to separate the data into different groups. (Use the variables to help distinguish the modes, if possible. For example, if the modes seem to be composed mostly of men in one and women in the other, split the data according to sex.) Then you could analyze each group separately.

▶ **Beware of skewed data.** Make a Normal probability plot and a histogram of the data. If the data are very skewed, you might try re-expressing the variable. Re-expressing may yield a distribution that is unimodal and symmetric, more appropriate for Student's $t$ inference methods for means. Re-expression cannot help if the sample distribution is not unimodal. Some people may object to re-expressing the data, but unless your sample is very large, you just can't use the methods of this chapter on skewed data.

▶ **Set outliers aside.** Student's $t$ methods are built on the mean and standard deviation, so we should beware of outliers when using them. When you make a histogram to check the Nearly Normal Condition, be sure to check for outliers as well. If you find some, consider doing the analysis twice, both with the outliers excluded and with them included in the data, to get a sense of how much they affect the results.

The suggestion that you can perform an analysis with outliers removed may be controversial in some disciplines. Setting aside outliers is seen by some as "cheating." But an analysis of data with outliers left in place is *always* wrong. The outliers violate the Nearly Normal Condition and also the implicit assumption of a homogeneous population, so they invalidate inference procedures. An analysis of the non-outlying points, along with a separate discussion of the outliers, is often much more informative and can reveal important aspects of the data.

How can you tell whether there are outliers in your data? The "outlier nomination rule" of boxplots can offer some guidance, but it's just a rule of thumb and not an absolute definition. The best practical definition is that a value is an outlier if removing it substantially changes your conclusions about the data. You won't want a single value

As tempting as it is to get rid of annoying values, you can't just throw away outliers and not discuss them. It isn't appropriate to lop off the highest or lowest values just to improve your results.

to determine your understanding of the world unless you are very, very sure that it is absolutely correct. Of course, when the outliers affect your conclusion, this can lead to the uncomfortable state of not really knowing what to conclude. Such situations call for you to use your knowledge of the real world and your understanding of the data you are working with.[12]

Of course, Normality issues aren't the only risks you face when doing inferences about means. Remember to *Think* about the usual suspects.

▶ **Watch out for bias.** Measurements of all kinds can be biased. If your observations differ from the true mean in a systematic way, your confidence interval may not capture the true mean. And there is no sample size that will save you. A bathroom scale that's 5 pounds off will be 5 pounds off even if you weigh yourself 100 times and take the average. We've seen several sources of bias in surveys, and measurements can be biased, too. Be sure to think about possible sources of bias in your measurements.

▶ **Make sure cases are independent.** Student's *t* methods also require the sampled values to be mutually independent. We check for random sampling and the 10% Condition. You should also think hard about whether there are likely violations of independence in the data collection method. If there are, be very cautious about using these methods.

▶ **Make sure that data are from an appropriately randomized sample.** Ideally, all data that we analyze are drawn from a simple random sample or generated by a randomized experiment. When they're not, be careful about making inferences from them. You may still compute a confidence interval correctly, or get the mechanics of the P-value right, but this might not save you from making a serious mistake in inference.

▶ **Interpret your confidence interval correctly.** Many statements that sound tempting are, in fact, misinterpretations of a confidence interval for a mean. You might want to have another look at some of the common mistakes, explained on page 596. Keep in mind that a confidence interval is about the mean of the population, not about the means of samples, individuals in samples, or individuals in the population. ⊘

# CONNECTIONS

The steps for finding a confidence interval or hypothesis test for means are just like the corresponding steps for proportions. Even the form of the calculations is similar. As the *z*-statistic did for proportions, the *t*-statistic tells us how many standard errors our sample mean is from the hypothesized mean. For means, though, we have to estimate the standard error separately. This added uncertainty changes the model for the sampling distribution from *z* to *t*.

As with all of our inference methods, the randomization applied in drawing a random sample or in randomizing a comparative experiment is what generates the sampling distribution. Randomization is what makes inference in this way possible at all.

The new concept of degrees of freedom connects back to the denominator of the sample standard deviation calculation, as shown earlier.

There's just no escaping histograms and Normal probability plots. The Nearly Normal Condition required to use Student's *t* can be checked best by making appropriate displays of the data. Back when we first used histograms, we looked at their shape and, in particular, checked whether they were unimodal and symmetric, and whether they showed any outliers. Those are just the features we check for here. The Normal probability plot zeros in on the Normal model a little more precisely.

---

[12] An important reason for you to know Statistics rather than let someone else analyze your data.

# WHAT HAVE WE LEARNED?

We first learned to create confidence intervals and test hypotheses about proportions. Now we've turned our attention to means, and learned that statistical inference for means relies on the same concepts; only the mechanics and our model have changed.

▶ We've learned that what we can say about a population mean is inferred from data, using the mean of a representative random sample.

▶ We've learned to describe the sampling distribution of sample means using a new model we select from the Student's $t$ family based on our degrees of freedom.

▶ We've learned that our ruler for measuring the variability in sample means is the standard error $SE(\bar{y}) = \dfrac{s}{\sqrt{n}}$.

▶ We've learned to find the margin of error for a confidence interval using that ruler and critical values based on a Student's $t$-model.

▶ And we've also learned to use that ruler to test hypotheses about the population mean.

Above all, we've learned that the reasoning of inference, the need to verify that the appropriate assumptions are met, and the proper interpretation of confidence intervals and P-values all remain the same regardless of whether we are investigating means or proportions.

## Terms

**Student's $t$**
**Degrees of freedom (df)**

589. A family of distributions indexed by its degrees of freedom. The $t$-models are unimodal symmetric, and bell shaped, but generally have fatter tails and a narrower center than the Normal model. As the degrees of freedom increase, $t$-distributions approach the Normal.

**One-sample $t$-interval for the mean**

590. A one-sample $t$-interval for the population mean is

$$\bar{y} \pm t^*_{n-1} \times SE(\bar{y}), \text{ where } SE(\bar{y}) = \frac{s}{\sqrt{n}}.$$

The critical value $t^*_{n-1}$ depends on the particular confidence level, $C$, that you specify and on the number of degrees of freedom, $n - 1$.

**One-sample $t$-test for the mean**

597. The one-sample $t$-test for the mean tests the hypothesis $H_0: \mu = \mu_0$ using the statistic

$$t_{n-1} = \frac{\bar{y} - \mu_0}{SE(\bar{y})}.$$

The standard error of $\bar{y}$ is

$$SE(\bar{y}) = \frac{s}{\sqrt{n}}.$$

## Skills

▶ Know the assumptions required for $t$-tests and $t$-based confidence intervals.

▶ Know how to examine your data for violations of conditions that would make inference about the population mean unwise or invalid.

▶ Understand that a confidence interval and a hypothesis test are essentially equivalent. You can do a two-tailed hypothesis test at level of significance $\alpha$ with a $1 - \alpha$ confidence interval, or a one-tailed test with a $1 - 2\alpha$ confidence interval.

▶ Be able to compute and interpret a $t$-test for the population mean using a statistics package or working from summary statistics for a sample.

▶ Be able to compute and interpret a $t$-based confidence interval for the population mean using a statistics package or working from summary statistics for a sample.

▶ Be able to explain the meaning of a confidence interval for a population mean. Make clear that the randomness associated with the confidence level is a statement about the interval bounds and not about the population parameter value.

▸ Understand that a 95% confidence interval does not trap 95% of the sample values.

▸ Be able to interpret the result of a test of a hypothesis about a population mean.

▸ Know that we do not "accept" a null hypothesis if we cannot reject it. We say that we fail to reject it.

▸ Understand that the P-value of a test does not give the probability that the null hypothesis is correct.

# ON THE COMPUTER

## Inference for Means

Statistics packages offer convenient ways to make histograms of the data. Even better for assessing near-Normality is a Normal probability plot. When you work on a computer, there is simply no excuse for skipping the step of plotting the data to check that it is nearly Normal. *Beware:* Statistics packages don't agree on whether to place the Normal scores on the x-axis (as we have done) or the y-axis. Read the axis labels.

Any standard statistics package can compute a hypothesis test. Here's what the package output might look like in general (although no package we know gives the results in exactly this form):[13]

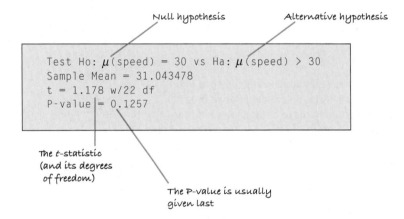

**A S** *Activity:* **Student's *t* in Practice.** We almost always use technology to do inference with Student's *t*. Here's a chance to do that as you investigate several questions.

The package computes the sample mean and sample standard deviation of the variable and finds the P-value from the *t*-distribution based on the appropriate number of degrees of freedom. All modern statistics packages report P-values. The package may also provide additional information such as the sample mean, sample standard deviation, *t*-statistic value, and degrees of freedom. These are useful for interpreting the resulting P-value and telling the difference between a meaningful result and one that is merely statistically significant. Statistics packages that report the estimated standard deviation of the sampling distribution usually label it "standard error" or "SE."

Inference results are also sometimes reported in a table. You may have to read carefully to find the values you need. Often, test results and the corresponding confidence interval bounds are given together. And often you must read carefully to find the alternative hypotheses. Here's an example of that kind of output:

---

[13] Many statistics packages keep as many as 16 digits for all intermediate calculations. If we had kept as many, our results in the Step-By-Step section would have been closer to these.

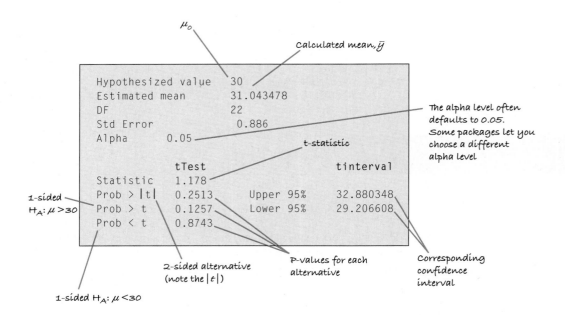

The commands to do inference for means on common statistics programs and calculators are not always obvious. (By contrast, the resulting output is usually clearly labeled and easy to read.) The guides for each program can help you start navigating.

## DATA DESK

Select variables.
From the **Calc** menu, choose **Estimate** for confidence intervals or **Test** for hypothesis tests. Select the interval or test from the drop-down menu and make other choices in the dialog.

## EXCEL

Specify formulas. Find $t*$ with the TINV(alpha, df) function.

### COMMENTS

Not really automatic. There's no easy way to find P-values in Excel.

## JMP

From the **Analyze** menu, select **Distribution.** For a confidence interval, scroll down to the "Moments" section to find the interval limits. For a hypothesis test, click the red triangle next to the variable's name and choose **Test Mean** from the menu. Then fill in the resulting dialog.

### COMMENTS

"Moment" is a fancy statistical term for means, standard deviations, and other related statistics.

## MINITAB

From the **Stat** menu, choose the **Basic Statistics** submenu. From that menu, choose **1-sample t. . . .** Then fill in the dialog.

### COMMENTS

The dialog offers a clear choice between confidence interval and test.

## SPSS

From the **Analyze** menu, choose the **Compare Means** submenu. From that, choose the **One-Sample t-test** command.

### COMMENTS

The commands suggest neither a single mean nor an interval. But the results provide both a test and an interval.

## TI-83/84 PLUS

Finding a confidence interval:
In the **STAT TESTS** menu, choose **8:TInterval.** You may specify that you are using data stored in a list, or you may enter the mean, standard deviation, and sample size. You must also specify the desired level of confidence.

Testing a hypothesis:
In the **STAT TESTS** menu, choose **2:T-Test.** You may specify that you are using data stored in a list, or you may enter the mean, standard deviation, and size of your sample. You must also specify the hypothesized model mean and whether the test is to be two-tail, lower-tail, or upper-tail.

## TI-89

Finding a confidence interval:
In the **STAT Ints** menu, choose **2:TInterval.** Specify whether you are using data stored in a list or whether you will enter the mean, standard deviation, and sample size. You must also specify the desired level of confidence.

Testing a hypothesis:
In the **STAT Tests** menu, choose **2:T-Test.** You must specify whether you are using data stored in a list or whether you will enter the mean, standard deviation, and size of your sample. You must also specify the hypothesized model mean and whether the test is to be two-tail, lower-tail, or upper-tail. Select whether the test is to be simply computed or whether to display the distribution curve and highlight the area corresponding to the P-value of the test.

# EXERCISES

**1. $t$-models, part I.** Using the $t$ tables, software, or a calculator, estimate
   a) the critical value of $t$ for a 90% confidence interval with df = 17.
   b) the critical value of $t$ for a 98% confidence interval with df = 88.
   c) the P-value for $t \geq 2.09$ with 4 degrees of freedom.
   d) the P-value for $|t| > 1.78$ with 22 degrees of freedom.

**2. $t$-models, part II.** Using the $t$ tables, software, or a calculator, estimate
   a) the critical value of $t$ for a 95% confidence interval with df = 7.
   b) the critical value of $t$ for a 99% confidence interval with df = 102.
   c) the P-value for $t \leq 2.19$ with 41 degrees of freedom.
   d) the P-value for $|t| > 2.33$ with 12 degrees of freedom.

**3. $t$-models, part III.** Describe how the shape, center, and spread of $t$-models change as the number of degrees of freedom increases.

**4. $t$-models, part IV (last one!).** Describe how the critical value of $t$ for a 95% confidence interval changes as the number of degrees of freedom increases.

**5. Cattle.** Livestock are given a special feed supplement to see if it will promote weight gain. Researchers report that the 77 cows studied gained an average of 56 pounds, and that a 95% confidence interval for the mean weight gain this supplement produces has a margin of error of ±11 pounds. Some students wrote the following conclusions.

Did anyone interpret the interval correctly? Explain any misinterpretations.
   a) 95% of the cows studied gained between 45 and 67 pounds.
   b) We're 95% sure that a cow fed this supplement will gain between 45 and 67 pounds.
   c) We're 95% sure that the average weight gain among the cows in this study was between 45 and 67 pounds.
   d) The average weight gain of cows fed this supplement will be between 45 and 67 pounds 95% of the time.
   e) If this supplement is tested on another sample of cows, there is a 95% chance that their average weight gain will be between 45 and 67 pounds.

**6. Teachers.** Software analysis of the salaries of a random sample of 288 Nevada teachers produced the confidence interval shown below. Which conclusion is correct? What's wrong with the others?

t-Interval for $\mu$: with 90.00% Confidence, $38944 < \mu(\text{TchPay}) < 42893$

   a) If we took many random samples of Nevada teachers, about 9 out of 10 of them would produce this confidence interval.
   b) If we took many random samples of Nevada teachers, about 9 out of 10 of them would produce a confidence interval that contained the mean salary of all Nevada teachers.
   c) About 9 out of 10 Nevada teachers earn between $38,944 and $42,893.

d) About 9 out of 10 of the teachers surveyed earn between $38,944 and $42,893.

e) We are 90% confident that the average teacher salary in the United States is between $38,944 and $42,893.

**7. Meal plan.** After surveying students at Dartmouth College, a campus organization calculated that a 95% confidence interval for the mean cost of food for one term (of three in the Dartmouth trimester calendar) is ($1102, $1290). Now the organization is trying to write its report and is considering the following interpretations. Comment on each.

a) 95% of all students pay between $1102 and $1290 for food.

b) 95% of the sampled students paid between $1102 and $1290.

c) We're 95% sure that students in this sample averaged between $1102 and $1290 for food.

d) 95% of all samples of students will have average food costs between $1102 and $1290.

e) We're 95% sure that the average amount all students pay is between $1102 and $1290.

**8. Rain.** Based on meteorological data for the past century, a local TV weather forecaster estimates that the region's average winter snowfall is 23", with a margin of error of ±2 inches. Assuming he used a 95% confidence interval, how should viewers interpret this news? Comment on each of these statements:

a) During 95 of the last 100 winters, the region got between 21" and 25" of snow.

b) There's a 95% chance the region will get between 21" and 25" of snow this winter.

c) There will be between 21" and 25" of snow on the ground for 95% of the winter days.

d) Residents can be 95% sure that the area's average snowfall is between 21" and 25".

e) Residents can be 95% confident that the average snowfall during the last century was between 21" and 25" per winter.

**Ⓣ 9. Pulse rates.** A medical researcher measured the pulse rates (beats per minute) of a sample of randomly selected adults and found the following Student's $t$-based confidence interval:

With 95.00% Confidence,
$70.887604 < \mu(\text{Pulse}) < 74.497011$

a) Explain carefully what the software output means.
b) What's the margin of error for this interval?
c) If the researcher had calculated a 99% confidence interval, would the margin of error be larger or smaller? Explain.

**10. Crawling.** Data collected by child development scientists produced this confidence interval for the average age (in weeks) at which babies begin to crawl:

t-Interval for $\mu$
(95.00% Confidence): $\quad 29.202 < \mu(\text{age}) < 31.844$

a) Explain carefully what the software output means.
b) What is the margin of error for this interval?

c) If the researcher had calculated a 90% confidence interval, would the margin of error be larger or smaller? Explain.

**11. CEO compensation.** A sample of 20 CEOs from the Forbes 500 shows total annual compensations ranging from a minimum of $0.1 to $62.24 million. The average for these 20 CEOs is $7.946 million. The histogram and boxplot are as follows:

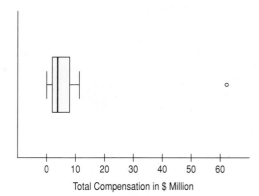

Based on these data, a computer program found that a 95% confidence interval for the mean annual compensation of all Forbes 500 CEOs is (1.69, 14.20) $ million. Why should you be hesitant to trust this confidence interval?

**12. Credit card charges.** A credit card company takes a random sample of 100 cardholders to see how much they charged on their card last month. A histogram and boxplot are as follows:

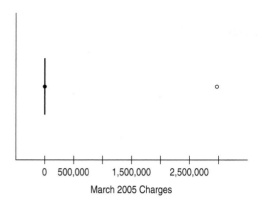

March 2005 Charges

A computer program found that the resulting 95% confidence interval for the mean amount spent in March 2005 is (−$28366.84, $90691.49). Explain why the analysts didn't find the confidence interval useful, and explain what went wrong.

**T  13. Normal temperature.**   The researcher described in Exercise 9 also measured the body temperatures of that randomly selected group of adults. The data he collected are summarized below. We wish to estimate the average (or "normal") temperature among the adult population.

| Summary | Temperature |
|---|---|
| **Count** | 52 |
| **Mean** | 98.285 |
| **Median** | 98.200 |
| **MidRange** | 98.600 |
| **StdDev** | 0.6824 |
| **Range** | 2.800 |
| **IntQRange** | 1.050 |

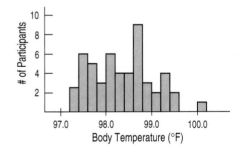

a) Are the necessary conditions for a *t*-interval satisfied? Explain.
b) Find a 98% confidence interval for mean body temperature.
c) Explain the meaning of that interval.
d) Explain what "98% confidence" means in this context.
e) 98.6°F is commonly assumed to be "normal." Do these data suggest otherwise? Explain.

**14. Parking.**   Hoping to lure more shoppers downtown, a city builds a new public parking garage in the central business district. The city plans to pay for the structure

through parking fees. During a two-month period (44 weekdays), daily fees collected averaged $126, with a standard deviation of $15.
a) What assumptions must you make in order to use these statistics for inference?
b) Write a 90% confidence interval for the mean daily income this parking garage will generate.
c) Explain in context what this confidence interval means.
d) Explain what "90% confidence" means in this context.
e) The consultant who advised the city on this project predicted that parking revenues would average $130 per day. Based on your confidence interval, do you think the consultant was correct? Why?

**T  15. Normal temperatures, part II.**   Consider again the statistics about human body temperature in Exercise 13.
a) Would a 90% confidence interval be wider or narrower than the 98% confidence interval you calculated before? Explain. (You should not need to compute the new interval.)
b) What are the advantages and disadvantages of the 98% confidence interval?
c) If we conduct further research, this time using a sample of 500 adults, how would you expect the 98% confidence interval to change? Explain.
d) How large a sample would you need to estimate the mean body temperature to within 0.1 degrees with 98% confidence?

**16. Parking II.**   Suppose that, for budget planning purposes, the city in Exercise 14 needs a better estimate of the mean daily income from parking fees.
a) Someone suggests that the city use its data to create a 95% confidence interval instead of the 90% interval first created. How would this interval be better for the city? (You need not actually create the new interval.)
b) How would the 95% interval be worse for the planners?
c) How could they achieve an interval estimate that would better serve their planning needs?
d) How many days' worth of data must they collect to have 95% confidence of estimating the true mean to within $3?

**17. Hot dogs.**   A nutrition laboratory tests 40 "reduced sodium" hot dogs, finding that the mean sodium content is 310 mg, with a standard deviation of 36 mg.
a) Find a 95% confidence interval for the mean sodium content of this brand of hot dog.
b) What assumptions have you made in this inference? Are the appropriate conditions satisfied?
c) Explain clearly what your interval means.

**18. Speed of light.**   In 1882 Michelson measured the speed of light (usually denoted $c$ as in Einstein's famous equation $E = mc^2$). His values are in km/sec and have 299,000 subtracted from them. He reported the results of 23 trials with a mean of 756.22 and a standard deviation of 107.12.
a) Find a 95% confidence interval for the true speed of light from these statistics.
b) State in words what this interval means. Keep in mind that the speed of light is a physical constant that, as

far as we know, has a value that is true throughout the universe.

c) What assumptions must you make in order to use your method?

**19. Second dog.** The nutrition lab in Exercise 17 tests the hot dogs again, this time using a sample of 60 "reduced sodium" frankfurters. The new sample produces a mean of 318 mg of sodium, and the standard deviation is 32 mg.

a) Should this larger sample of hot dogs produce a more accurate estimate of the mean sodium content? Explain.

b) What is the standard error of the mean sodium content?

c) Find and interpret a 95% confidence interval.

d) Food labeling regulations require that any food identified as "reduced sodium" must have at least 30% less sodium than its regular counterpart. If regular franks average 465 mg of sodium, should this brand be labeled "reduced"? Explain, using your confidence interval.

**20. Better light.** After his first attempt to determine the speed of light (described in Exercise 18), Michelson conducted an "improved" experiment. In 1897 he reported results of 100 trials with a mean of 852.4 and a standard deviation of 79.0.

a) What is the standard error of the mean for these data?

b) Without computing it, how would you expect a 95% confidence interval for the second experiment to differ from the confidence interval for the first? Note at least three specific reasons why they might differ, and indicate the ways in which these differences would change the interval.

c) According to Stigler (who reports these values), the true speed of light is 299,710.5 km/sec, corresponding to a value of 710.5 for Michelson's 1897 measurements. What does this indicate about Michelson's two experiments? Explain, using your confidence interval.

**21. Departures.** What are the chances your flight will leave on time? The U.S. Bureau of Transportation Statistics of the Department of Transportation publishes information about airline performance. Here are a histogram and summary statistics for the percentage of flights departing on time each month from 1995 thru 2006.

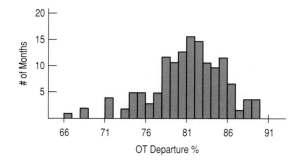

| $n$ | 144 |
|---|---|
| $\bar{y}$ | 81.1838 |
| $s$ | 4.47094 |

There is no evidence of a trend over time. (The correlation of On Time Departure% with time is $r = -0.016$.)

a) Check the assumptions and conditions for inference.

b) Find a 90% confidence interval for the true percentage of flights that depart on time.

c) Interpret this interval for a traveler planning to fly.

**22. Late arrivals.** Will your flight get you to your destination on time? The U.S. Bureau of Transportation Statistics reported the percentage of flights that were late each month from 1995 through 2006. Here's a histogram, along with some summary statistics:

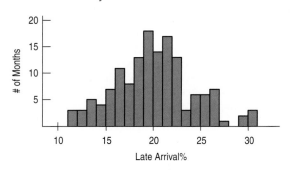

| $n$ | 144 |
|---|---|
| $\bar{y}$ | 20.0757 |
| $s$ | 4.08837 |

We can consider these data to be a representative sample of all months. There is no evidence of a time trend ($r = -0.07$).

a) Check the assumptions and conditions for inference about the mean.

b) Find a 99% confidence interval for the true percentage of flights that arrive late.

c) Interpret this interval for a traveler planning to fly.

**23. For Example, 2nd look.** This chapter's For Examples looked at mirex contamination in farmed salmon. We first found a 95% confidence interval for the mean concentration to be 0.0834 to 0.0992 parts per million. Later we rejected the null hypothesis that the mean did not exceed the EPA's recommended safe level of 0.08 ppm based on a P-value of 0.0027. Explain how these two results are consistent. Your explanation should discuss the confidence level, the P-value, and the decision.

**24. Step-By-Step, 2nd look.** This chapter's Step-By-Steps looked at the speeds of cars traveling on Triphammer Road in Ithaca, New York. We first found a 90% confidence interval for the mean speed to be 31.0 ± 1.5 miles per hour. Later, based on a P-value of 0.136, we failed to reject the null hypothesis that the mean was no higher than the posted 30 mph speed limit. Explain how these two results are consistent. Your explanation should discuss the confidence level, the P-value, and the decision.

**25. Pizza.** A researcher tests whether the mean cholesterol level among those who eat frozen pizza exceeds the value considered to indicate a health risk. She gets a P-value of 0.07. Explain in this context what the "7%" represents.

**26. Golf balls.** The United States Golf Association (USGA) sets performance standards for golf balls. For example, the initial velocity of the ball may not exceed 250 feet per second when measured by an apparatus approved by the USGA. Suppose a manufacturer introduces a new kind of ball and provides a sample for testing. Based on the mean speed in the test, the USGA comes up with a P-value of 0.34. Explain in this context what the "34%" represents.

**27. TV safety.** The manufacturer of a metal stand for home TV sets must be sure that its product will not fail under the weight of the TV. Since some larger sets weigh nearly 300 pounds, the company's safety inspectors have set a standard of ensuring that the stands can support an average of over 500 pounds. Their inspectors regularly subject a random sample of the stands to increasing weight until they fail. They test the hypothesis $H_0: \mu = 500$ against $H_A: \mu > 500$, using the level of significance $\alpha = 0.01$. If the sample of stands fail to pass this safety test, the inspectors will not certify the product for sale to the general public.
a) Is this an upper-tail or lower-tail test? In the context of the problem, why do you think this is important?
b) Explain what will happen if the inspectors commit a Type I error.
c) Explain what will happen if the inspectors commit a Type II error.

**28. Catheters.** During an angiogram, heart problems can be examined via a small tube (a catheter) threaded into the heart from a vein in the patient's leg. It's important that the company that manufactures the catheter maintain a diameter of 2.00 mm. (The standard deviation is quite small.) Each day, quality control personnel make several measurements to test $H_0: \mu = 2.00$ against $H_A: \mu \neq 2.00$ at a significance level of $\alpha = 0.05$. If they discover a problem, they will stop the manufacturing process until it is corrected.
a) Is this a one-sided or two-sided test? In the context of the problem, why do you think this is important?
b) Explain in this context what happens if the quality control people commit a Type I error.
c) Explain in this context what happens if the quality control people commit a Type II error.

**29. TV safety revisited.** The manufacturer of the metal TV stands in Exercise 27 is thinking of revising its safety test.
a) If the company's lawyers are worried about being sued for selling an unsafe product, should they increase or decrease the value of $\alpha$? Explain.
b) In this context, what is meant by the power of the test?
c) If the company wants to increase the power of the test, what options does it have? Explain the advantages and disadvantages of each option.

**30. Catheters again.** The catheter company in Exercise 28 is reviewing its testing procedure.
a) Suppose the significance level is changed to $\alpha = 0.01$. Will the probability of a Type II error increase, decrease, or remain the same?
b) What is meant by the power of the test the company conducts?
c) Suppose the manufacturing process is slipping out of proper adjustment. As the actual mean diameter of the catheters produced gets farther and farther above the desired 2.00 mm, will the power of the quality control test increase, decrease, or remain the same?
d) What could they do to improve the power of the test?

**31. Marriage.** In 1960, census results indicated that the age at which American men first married had a mean of 23.3 years. It is widely suspected that young people today are waiting longer to get married. We want to find out if the mean age of first marriage has increased during the past 40 years.
a) Write appropriate hypotheses.
b) We plan to test our hypothesis by selecting a random sample of 40 men who married for the first time last year. Do you think the necessary assumptions for inference are satisfied? Explain.
c) Describe the approximate sampling distribution model for the mean age in such samples.
d) The men in our sample married at an average age of 24.2 years, with a standard deviation of 5.3 years. What's the P-value for this result?
e) Explain (in context) what this P-value means.
f) What's your conclusion?

**32. Fuel economy.** A company with a large fleet of cars hopes to keep gasoline costs down and sets a goal of attaining a fleet average of at least 26 miles per gallon. To see if the goal is being met, they check the gasoline usage for 50 company trips chosen at random, finding a mean of 25.02 mpg and a standard deviation of 4.83 mpg. Is this strong evidence that they have failed to attain their fuel economy goal?
a) Write appropriate hypotheses.
b) Are the necessary assumptions to make inferences satisfied?
c) Describe the sampling distribution model of mean fuel economy for samples like this.
d) Find the P-value.
e) Explain what the P-value means in this context.
f) State an appropriate conclusion.

**T 33. Ruffles.** Students investigating the packaging of potato chips purchased 6 bags of Lay's Ruffles marked with a net weight of 28.3 grams. They carefully weighed the contents of each bag, recording the following weights (in grams): 29.3, 28.2, 29.1, 28.7, 28.9, 28.5.
a) Do these data satisfy the assumptions for inference? Explain.
b) Find the mean and standard deviation of the observed weights.
c) Create a 95% confidence interval for the mean weight of such bags of chips.
d) Explain in context what your interval means.
e) Comment on the company's stated net weight of 28.3 grams.

**T 34. Doritos.** Some students checked 6 bags of Doritos marked with a net weight of 28.3 grams. They carefully weighed the contents of each bag, recording the following weights (in grams): 29.2, 28.5, 28.7, 28.9, 29.1, 29.5.
a) Do these data satisfy the assumptions for inference? Explain.
b) Find the mean and standard deviation of the observed weights.
c) Create a 95% confidence interval for the mean weight of such bags of chips.

d) Explain in context what your interval means.
e) Comment on the company's stated net weight of 28.3 grams.

**35. Popcorn.** Yvon Hopps ran an experiment to test optimum power and time settings for microwave popcorn. His goal was to find a combination of power and time that would deliver high-quality popcorn with only 10% of the kernels left unpopped, on average. After experimenting with several bags, he determined that power 9 at 4 minutes was the best combination.
a) He concluded that this popping method achieved the 10% goal. If it really does not work that well, what kind of error did Hopps make?
b) To be sure that the method was successful, he popped 8 more bags of popcorn (selected at random) at this setting. All were of high quality, with the following percentages of uncooked popcorn: 7, 13.2, 10, 6, 7.8, 2.8, 2.2, 5.2. Does this provide evidence that he met his goal of an average of no more than 10% uncooked kernels? Explain.

**36. Ski wax.** Bjork Larsen was trying to decide whether to use a new racing wax for cross-country skis. He decided that the wax would be worth the price if he could average less than 55 seconds on a course he knew well, so he planned to test the wax by racing on the course 8 times.
a) Suppose that he eventually decides not to buy the wax, but it really would lower his average time to below 55 seconds. What kind of error would he have made?
b) His 8 race times were 56.3, 65.9, 50.5, 52.4, 46.5, 57.8, 52.2, and 43.2 seconds. Should he buy the wax? Explain.

**37. Cars.** One of the important factors in auto safety is the weight of the vehicle. Insurance companies are interested in knowing the average weight of cars currently licensed in the United States; they believe it is 3000 pounds. To see if that estimate is correct, they checked a random sample of 91 cars. For that group, the mean weight was 2919 pounds, with a standard deviation of 531.5 pounds. Is this strong evidence that the mean weight of all cars is not 3000 pounds?

**38. Portable phones.** A manufacturer claims that a new design for a portable phone has increased the range to 150 feet, allowing many customers to use the phone throughout their homes and yards. An independent testing laboratory found that a random sample of 44 of these phones worked over an average distance of 142 feet, with a standard deviation of 12 feet. Is there evidence that the manufacturer's claim is false?

**39. Chips Ahoy.** In 1998, as an advertising campaign, the Nabisco Company announced a "1000 Chips Challenge," claiming that every 18-ounce bag of their Chips Ahoy cookies contained at least 1000 chocolate chips. Dedicated Statistics students at the Air Force Academy (no kidding) purchased some randomly selected bags of cookies, and counted the chocolate chips. Some of their data are given below. (*Chance,* 12, no. 1[1999])

1219 1214 1087 1200 1419 1121 1325 1345
1244 1258 1356 1132 1191 1270 1295 1135

a) Check the assumptions and conditions for inference. Comment on any concerns you have.
b) Create a 95% confidence interval for the average number of chips in bags of Chips Ahoy cookies.
c) What does this evidence say about Nabisco's claim? Use your confidence interval to test an appropriate hypothesis and state your conclusion.

**40. Yogurt.** *Consumer Reports* tested 14 brands of vanilla yogurt and found the following numbers of calories per serving:

| 160 | 200 | 220 | 230 | 120 | 180 | 140 |
|-----|-----|-----|-----|-----|-----|-----|
| 130 | 170 | 190 | 80 | 120 | 100 | 170 |

a) Check the assumptions and conditions for inference.
b) Create a 95% confidence interval for the average calorie content of vanilla yogurt.
c) A diet guide claims that you will get 120 calories from a serving of vanilla yogurt. What does this evidence indicate? Use your confidence interval to test an appropriate hypothesis and state your conclusion.

**41. Maze.** Psychology experiments sometimes involve testing the ability of rats to navigate mazes. The mazes are classified according to difficulty, as measured by the mean length of time it takes rats to find the food at the end. One researcher needs a maze that will take rats an average of about one minute to solve. He tests one maze on several rats, collecting the data shown.
a) Plot the data. Do you think the conditions for inference are satisfied? Explain.
b) Test the hypothesis that the mean completion time for this maze is 60 seconds. What is your conclusion?
c) Eliminate the outlier, and test the hypothesis again. What is your conclusion?
d) Do you think this maze meets the "one-minute average" requirement? Explain.

| Time (sec) | |
|------|------|
| 38.4 | 57.6 |
| 46.2 | 55.5 |
| 62.5 | 49.5 |
| 38.0 | 40.9 |
| 62.8 | 44.3 |
| 33.9 | 93.8 |
| 50.4 | 47.9 |
| 35.0 | 69.2 |
| 52.8 | 46.2 |
| 60.1 | 56.3 |
| 55.1 | |

**42. Braking.** A tire manufacturer is considering a newly designed tread pattern for its all-weather tires. Tests have indicated that these tires will provide better gas mileage and longer tread life. The last remaining test is for braking effectiveness. The company hopes the tire will allow a car traveling at 60 mph to come to a complete stop within an average of 125 feet after the brakes are applied. They will adopt the new tread pattern unless there is strong evidence that the tires do not meet this objective. The distances (in feet) for 10 stops on a test track were 129, 128, 130, 132, 135, 123, 102, 125, 128, and 130. Should the company adopt the new tread pattern? Test an appropriate hypothesis and state your conclusion. Explain how you dealt with the outlier and why you made the recommendation you did.

**43. Driving distance.** How far do professional golfers drive a ball? (For non-golfers, the drive is the shot hit from a tee at the start of a hole and is typically the longest shot.) A histogram of the average driving distances of the

202 leading professional golfers in 2006 is shown here, along with summary statistics.

| Count | 202 |
|-------|-----|
| **Mean** | 288.6 yd |
| **StdDev** | 9.31 yd |

a) Find a 95% confidence interval for the mean drive distance.
b) Interpreting this interval raises some problems. Discuss.
c) The data are the mean driving distance for each golfer. Is that a concern in interpreting the interval? (*Hint:* Review the What Can Go Wrong warnings of Chapter 9. Chapter 9?! Yes, Chapter 9.)

**T** 44. **Wind power.** Should you generate electricity with your own personal wind turbine? That depends on whether you have enough wind on your site. To produce enough energy, your site should have an annual average wind speed of at least 8 miles per hour, according to the Wind Energy Association. One candidate site was monitored for a year, with wind speeds recorded every 6 hours. A total of 1114 readings of wind speed averaged 8.019 mph with a standard deviation of 3.813 mph. You've been asked to make a statistical report to help the landowner decide whether to place a wind turbine at this site.

a) Discuss the assumptions and conditions for using Student's *t* inference methods with these data. Here are some plots that may help you decide whether the methods can be used:

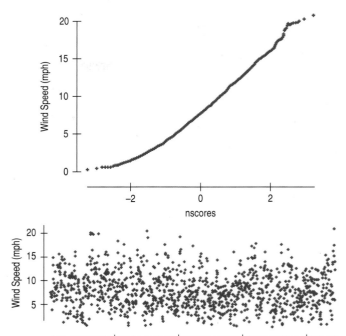

b) What would you tell the landowner about whether this site is suitable for a small wind turbine? Explain.

**JUST CHECKING**
**Answers**

1. Questions on the short form are answered by everyone in the population. This is a census, so means or proportions *are* the true population values. The long forms are given just to a sample of the population. When we estimate parameters from a sample, we use a confidence interval to take sample-to-sample variability into account.

2. They don't know the population standard deviation, so they must use the sample SD as an estimate. The additional uncertainty is taken into account by *t*-models.

3. The margin of error for a confidence interval for a mean depends, in part, on the standard error,
$$SE(\bar{y}) = \frac{s}{\sqrt{n}}.$$
Since *n* is in the denominator, smaller sample sizes lead to larger SEs and correspondingly wider intervals. Long forms returned by one in every six or seven households in a less populous area will be a smaller sample.

4. The critical values for *t* with fewer degrees of freedom would be slightly larger. The $\sqrt{n}$ part of the standard error changes a lot, making the SE much larger. Both would increase the margin of error.

5. The smaller sample is one fourth as large, so the confidence interval would be roughly twice as wide.

6. We expect 95% of such intervals to cover the true value, so 5 of the 100 intervals might be expected to miss.

7. The power would increase if we have a larger sample size.

# Comparing Means

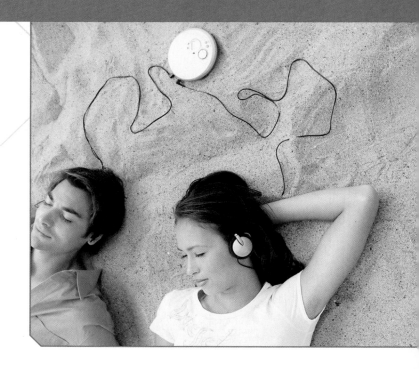

## Where are we going?

Does taking echinacea help you get over a cold faster? Does playing Mozart to babies in the womb make them smarter? Which last longer, generic or brand-name batteries? Many of the decisions made in business, medicine, and science compare the mean of two groups. In this chapter, we'll learn how.

| WHO | AA alkaline batteries |
|---|---|
| WHAT | Length of battery life while playing a CD continuously |
| UNITS | Minutes |
| WHY | Class project |
| WHEN | 1998 |

Should you buy generic rather than brand-name batteries? A Statistics student designed a study to test battery life. He wanted to know whether there was any real difference between brand-name batteries and a generic brand. To estimate the difference in mean lifetimes, he kept a battery-powered CD player continuously playing the same CD, with the volume control fixed at 5, and measured the time until no more music was heard through the headphones. (He ran an initial trial to find out approximately how long that would take, so that he didn't have to spend the first 3 hours of each run listening to the same CD.) For his trials he used six sets of AA alkaline batteries from two major battery manufacturers: a well-known brand name and a generic brand. He measured the time in minutes until the sound stopped. To account for changes in the CD player's performance over time, he randomized the run order by choosing sets of batteries at random.

Here are his data (times in minutes):

| Brand Name | Generic |
|---|---|
| 194.0 | 190.7 |
| 205.5 | 203.5 |
| 199.2 | 203.5 |
| 172.4 | 206.5 |
| 184.0 | 222.5 |
| 169.5 | 209.4 |

**A S** *Video:* **Can Diet Prolong Life?** Watch a video that tells the story of an experiment. We'll analyze the data later in this chapter.

Studies that compare two groups are common throughout both science and industry. We might want to compare the effects of a new drug with the traditional therapy, the fuel efficiency of two car engine designs, or the sales of new products in two different test cities. In fact, battery manufacturers do research like this on their products and competitors' products themselves.

## Plot the Data

**FIGURE 24.1**

*Boxplots comparing the brand-name and generic batteries suggest a difference in duration.*

The natural display for comparing two groups is boxplots of the data for the two groups, placed side by side. Although we can't make a confidence interval or test a hypothesis from the boxplots themselves, you should always start with boxplots when comparing groups. Let's look at the boxplots of the battery test data.

It sure looks like the generic batteries lasted longer. And we can see that they were also more consistent. But is the difference large enough to change our battery-buying behavior? Can we be confident that the difference is more than just random fluctuation? That's why we need statistical inference.

The boxplot for the generic data identifies two possible outliers. That's interesting, but with only six measurements in each group, the outlier nomination rule is not very reliable. Both of the extreme values are plausible results, and the range of the generic values is smaller than the range of the brand-name values, even with the outliers. So we're probably better off just leaving these values in the data.

## Comparing Two Means

Comparing two means is not very different from comparing two proportions. In fact, it's not different in concept from any of the methods we've seen. Now, the population model parameter of interest is the difference between the *mean* battery lifetimes of the two brands, $\mu_1 - \mu_2$.

The rest is the same as before. The statistic of interest is the difference in the two observed means, $\bar{y}_1 - \bar{y}_2$. We'll start with this statistic to build our confidence interval, but we'll need to know its standard deviation and its sampling model. Then we can build confidence intervals and find P-values for hypothesis tests.

We know that, for independent random quantities, the variance of their *difference* is the *sum* of their variances, $Var(Y - X) = Var(Y) + Var(X)$. To find the standard deviation of the difference between the two independent sample means, we add their variances and then take a square root:

$$SD(\bar{y}_1 - \bar{y}_2) = \sqrt{Var(\bar{y}_1) + Var(\bar{y}_2)}$$

$$= \sqrt{\left(\frac{\sigma_1}{\sqrt{n_1}}\right)^2 + \left(\frac{\sigma_2}{\sqrt{n_2}}\right)^2}$$

$$= \sqrt{\frac{\sigma_1^2}{n_1} + \frac{\sigma_2^2}{n_2}}.$$

Of course, we still don't know the true standard deviations of the two groups, $\sigma_1$ and $\sigma_2$, so as usual, we'll use the estimates, $s_1$ and $s_2$. Using the estimates gives us the *standard error*:

$$SE(\bar{y}_1 - \bar{y}_2) = \sqrt{\frac{s_1^2}{n_1} + \frac{s_2^2}{n_2}}.$$

We'll use the standard error to see how big the difference really is. Because we are working with means and estimating the standard error of their difference using the data, we shouldn't be surprised that the sampling model is a Student's $t$.

---

**FOR EXAMPLE**    Finding the standard error of the difference in sample means

Can you tell how much you are eating from how full you are? Or do you need visual cues? Researchers[1] constructed a table with two ordinary 18 oz soup bowls and two identical-looking bowls that had been modified to slowly, imperceptibly, refill as they were emptied. They assigned experiment participants to the bowls randomly and served them tomato soup. Those eating from the ordinary bowls had their bowls refilled by ladle whenever they were one-quarter full. If people judge their portions by internal cues, they should eat about the same amount. How big a difference was there in the amount of soup consumed? The table summarizes their results.

|  | Ordinary bowl | Refilling bowl |
|---|---|---|
| $n$ | 27 | 27 |
| $\bar{y}$ | 8.5 oz | 14.7 oz |
| $s$ | 6.1 oz | 8.4 oz |

**Question:** How much variability do we expect in the difference between the two means? Find the standard error.

$$SE(\bar{y}_{refill} - \bar{y}_{ordinary}) = \sqrt{\frac{s_r^2}{n_r} + \frac{s_o^2}{n_o}} = \sqrt{\frac{8.4^2}{27} + \frac{6.1^2}{27}} = 2.0 \text{ oz.}$$

---

The confidence interval we build is called a **two-sample $t$-interval** (for the difference in means). The corresponding hypothesis test is called a **two-sample $t$-test.** The interval looks just like all the others we've seen—the statistic plus or minus an estimated margin of error:

$$(\bar{y}_1 - \bar{y}_2) \pm ME$$
$$\text{where } ME = t^* \times SE(\bar{y}_1 - \bar{y}_2).$$

Compare this formula with the one for the confidence interval for the difference of two proportions we saw in Chapter 22 (p. 561). The formulas are almost the same. It's just that here we use a Student's $t$-model instead of a Normal model to find the appropriate critical $t^*$-value corresponding to our chosen confidence level.

What are we missing? Only the degrees of freedom for the Student's $t$-model. Unfortunately, *that* formula is strange.

The deep, dark secret is that the sampling model isn't *really* Student's $t$, but only something close. The trick is that by using a special, adjusted degrees-of-freedom value, we can make it so close to a Student's $t$-model that nobody can tell the difference. The adjustment formula is straightforward but doesn't help our

---

[1] Brian Wansink, James E. Painter, and Jill North, "Bottomless Bowls: Why Visual Cues of Portion Size May Influence Intake," *Obesity Research*, Vol. 13, No. 1, January 2005.

understanding much, so we leave it to the computer or calculator. (If you are curious and really want to see the formula, look in the footnote.[2])

---

**A SAMPLING DISTRIBUTION FOR THE DIFFERENCE BETWEEN TWO MEANS**

When the conditions are met, the sampling distribution of the standardized sample difference between the means of two independent groups,

$$t = \frac{(\bar{y}_1 - \bar{y}_2) - (\mu_1 - \mu_2)}{SE(\bar{y}_1 - \bar{y}_2)},$$

can be modeled by a Student's $t$-model with a number of degrees of freedom found with a special formula. We estimate the standard error with

$$SE(\bar{y}_1 - \bar{y}_2) = \sqrt{\frac{s_1^2}{n_1} + \frac{s_2^2}{n_2}}.$$

---

# Assumptions and Conditions

Now we've got everything we need. Before we can make a two-sample $t$-interval or perform a two-sample $t$-test, though, we have to check the assumptions and conditions.

## INDEPENDENCE ASSUMPTION

**Independence Assumption:** The data in each group must be drawn independently and at random from a homogeneous population, or generated by a randomized comparative experiment. We can't expect that the data, taken as one big group, come from a homogeneous population, because that's what we're trying to test. But without randomization of some sort, there are no sampling distribution models and no inference. We can check two conditions:

**Randomization Condition:** Were the data collected with suitable randomization? For surveys, are they a representative random sample? For experiments, was the experiment randomized?

**10% Condition:** We usually don't check this condition for differences of means. We'll check it only if we have a very small population or an extremely large sample. We needn't worry about it at all for randomized experiments.

## NORMAL POPULATION ASSUMPTION

As we did before with Student's $t$-models, we should check the assumption that the underlying populations are *each* Normally distributed. We check the . . .

**Nearly Normal Condition:** We must check this for *both* groups; a violation by either one violates the condition. As we saw for single sample means, the

---

[2]

$$df = \frac{\left(\frac{s_1^2}{n_1} + \frac{s_2^2}{n_2}\right)^2}{\frac{1}{n_1 - 1}\left(\frac{s_1^2}{n_1}\right)^2 + \frac{1}{n_2 - 1}\left(\frac{s_2^2}{n_2}\right)^2}$$

Are you sorry you looked? This formula usually doesn't even give a whole number. If you are using a table, you'll need a whole number, so round down to be safe. If you are using technology, it's even easier. The approximation formulas that computers and calculators use for the Student's $t$-distribution can deal with fractional degrees of freedom, so it's OK to pass the fractional degrees of freedom from this formula through to those formulas.

Normality Assumption matters most when sample sizes are small. For samples of $n < 15$ in either group, you should not use these methods if the histogram or Normal probability plot shows severe skewness. For $n$'s closer to 40, a mildly skewed histogram is OK, but you should remark on any outliers you find and not work with severely skewed data. When both groups are bigger than 40, the Central Limit Theorem starts to kick in no matter how the data are distributed, so the Nearly Normal Condition for the data matters less. Even in large samples, however, you should still be on the lookout for outliers, extreme skewness, and multiple modes.

## INDEPENDENT GROUPS ASSUMPTION

**Independent Groups Assumption:** To use the two-sample $t$ methods, the two groups we are comparing must be independent of each other. In fact, this test is sometimes called the two *independent samples t*-test. No statistical test can verify this assumption. You have to think about how the data were collected. The assumption would be violated, for example, if one group consisted of husbands and the other group, their wives. Whatever we measure on couples might naturally be related. Similarly, if we compared subjects' performances before some treatment with their performances afterward, we'd expect a relationship of each "before" measurement with its corresponding "after" measurement. In cases such as these, where the observational units in the two groups are related or matched, *the two-sample methods of this chapter can't be applied.* When this happens, we need a different procedure that we'll see in the next chapter.

> **A S** *Activity:* **Does Restricting Diet Prolong Life?** This activity lets you construct a confidence interval to compare life spans of rats fed two different diets.

---

**FOR EXAMPLE**     Checking assumptions and conditions

**Recap:** Researchers randomly assigned people to eat soup from one of two bowls: 27 got ordinary bowls that were refilled by ladle, and 27 others bowls that secretly refilled slowly as the people ate.

**Question:** Can the researchers use their data to make inferences about the role of visual cues in determining how much people eat?

✔ **Independence Assumption:** The amount consumed by one person should be independent of the amount consumed by others.

✔ **Randomization Condition:** Subjects were randomly assigned to the treatments.

✔ **Nearly Normal Condition:** The histograms for both groups look unimodal but somewhat skewed to the right. I believe both groups are large enough (27) to allow use of $t$-methods.

✔ **Independent Groups Assumption:** Randomization to treatment groups guarantees this.

It's okay to construct a two-sample $t$-interval for the difference in means.

**An Easier Rule?**
The formula for the degrees of freedom of the sampling distribution of the difference between two means is long, but the number of degrees of freedom is always at *least* the smaller of the two $n$'s, minus 1. So wouldn't it be easier to just use that value? You could do that, but you'd have to be conservative and use the lower value. And *that* approximation can be a poor choice because it can give fewer than *half* the degrees of freedom you're entitled to from the correct formula.

> ## TWO-SAMPLE $t$-INTERVAL FOR THE DIFFERENCE BETWEEN MEANS
>
> When the conditions are met, we are ready to find the confidence interval for the difference between means of two independent groups, $\mu_1 - \mu_2$. The confidence interval is
>
> $$(\bar{y}_1 - \bar{y}_2) \pm t^*_{df} \times SE(\bar{y}_1 - \bar{y}_2),$$
>
> where the standard error of the difference of the means
>
> $$SE(\bar{y}_1 - \bar{y}_2) = \sqrt{\frac{s_1^2}{n_1} + \frac{s_2^2}{n_2}}.$$
>
> The critical value $t^*_{df}$ depends on the particular confidence level, $C$, that you specify and on the number of degrees of freedom, which we get from the sample sizes and a special formula.

### FOR EXAMPLE

Finding a confidence interval for the difference in sample means

**Recap:** Researchers studying the role of internal and visual cues in determining how much people eat conducted an experiment in which some people ate soup from bowls that secretly refilled. The results are summarized in the table.

|  | Ordinary bowl | Refilling bowl |
|---|---|---|
| $n$ | 27 | 27 |
| $\bar{y}$ | 8.5 oz | 14.7 oz |
| $s$ | 6.1 oz | 8.4 oz |

We've already checked the assumptions and conditions, and have found the standard error for the difference in means to be $SE(\bar{y}_{refill} - \bar{y}_{ordinary}) = 2.0$ oz.

**Question:** What does a 95% confidence interval say about the difference in mean amounts eaten?

The observed difference in means is

$$\bar{y}_{refill} - \bar{y}_{ordinary} = (14.7 - 8.5) = 6.2 \ oz$$
$$df = 47.46 \quad t^*_{47.46} = 2.011 \ (Table \ gives \ t^*_{45} = 2.014.)$$
$$ME = t^* \times SE(\bar{y}_{refill} - \bar{y}_{ordinary}) = 2.011(2.0) = 4.02 \ oz$$

The 95% confidence interval for $\mu_{refill} - \mu_{ordinary}$ is

$$6.2 \pm 4.02, \ or \ (2.18, 10.22) \ oz.$$

I am 95% confident that people eating from a subtly refilling bowl will eat an average of between 2.18 and 10.22 more ounces of soup than those eating from an ordinary bowl.

### STEP-BY-STEP EXAMPLE

A Two-Sample $t$-Interval

Judging from the boxplot, the generic batteries seem to have lasted about 20 minutes longer than the brand-name batteries. Before we change our buying habits, what should we expect to happen with the next batteries we buy?

**Question:** How much longer might the generic batteries last?

**Plan** State what we want to know.

Identify the *parameter* you wish to estimate. Here our parameter is the difference in the means, not the individual group means.

Identify the *population(s)* about which you wish to make statements. We hope to make decisions about purchasing batteries, so we're interested in all the AA batteries of these two brands.

Identify the variables and review the W's.

Make a picture. Boxplots are the display of choice for comparing groups. We'll also want to check the distribution of each group. Histograms or Normal probability plots do a better job there.

**REALITY CHECK** From the boxplots, it appears our confidence interval should be centered near a difference of 20 minutes. We don't have a lot of intuition about how far the interval should extend on either side of 20.

**Model** Think about the appropriate assumptions and check the conditions to be sure that a Student's *t*-model for the sampling distribution is appropriate.

For very small samples like these, we often don't worry about the 10% Condition.

I have measurements of the lifetimes (in minutes) of 6 sets of generic and 6 sets of brand-name AA batteries from a randomized experiment. I want to find an interval that is likely, with 95% confidence, to contain the true difference $\mu_G - \mu_B$ between the mean lifetime of the generic AA batteries and the mean lifetime of the brand-name batteries.

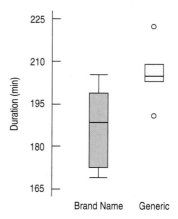

✔ **Randomization Condition:** The batteries were selected at random from those available for sale. Not exactly an SRS, but a reasonably representative random sample.

✔ **Independence Assumption:** The batteries were packaged together, so they may not be independent. For example, a storage problem might affect all the batteries in the same pack. Repeating the study for several different packs of batteries would make the conclusions stronger.

✔ **Independent Groups Assumption:** Batteries manufactured by two different companies and purchased in separate packages should be independent.

✔ **Nearly Normal Condition:** The samples are small, but the histograms look unimodal and symmetric:

State the sampling distribution model for the statistic. Here the degrees of freedom will come from that messy approximation formula.

Under these conditions, it's okay to use a Student's t-model.

Specify your method.

I'll use a **two-sample t-interval.**

**Mechanics** Construct the confidence interval.

Be sure to include the units along with the statistics. Use meaningful subscripts to identify the groups.

I know $n_G = 6$ $n_B = 6$

$\bar{y}_G = 206.0$ min $\bar{y}_B = 187.4$ min

$s_G = 10.3$ min $s_B = 14.6$ min

Use the sample standard deviations to find the standard error of the sampling distribution.

The groups are independent, so

$$SE(\bar{y}_G - \bar{y}_B) = \sqrt{SE^2(\bar{y}_G) + SE^2(\bar{y}_B)}$$

$$= \sqrt{\frac{s_G^2}{n_G} + \frac{s_B^2}{n_B}}$$

$$= \sqrt{\frac{10.3^2}{6} + \frac{14.6^2}{6}}$$

$$= \sqrt{\frac{106.09}{6} + \frac{213.16}{6}}$$

$$= \sqrt{53.208}$$

$$= 7.29 \text{ min.}$$

We have three choices for degrees of freedom. The best alternative is to let the computer or calculator use the approximation formula for df. This gives a fractional degree of freedom (here df = 8.98), and technology can find a corresponding critical value. In this case, it is $t^* = 2.263$.

The approximation formula calls for 8.98 degrees of freedom.[3]

The corresponding critical value for a 95% confidence level from a Student's t-model with 8.98 df is $t^* = 2.263$.

Or we could round the approximation formula's df value down to an integer so we can use a t table. That gives 8 df and a critical value $t^* = 2.306$.

So the margin of error is

$$ME = t^* \times SE(\bar{y}_G - \bar{y}_B)$$

$$= 2.263(7.29)$$

$$= 16.50 \text{ min.}$$

The 95% confidence interval is

The easy rule says to use only $6 - 1 = 5$ df. That gives a critical value $t^* = 2.571$. The corresponding confidence interval is about 14% wider—a high price to pay for a small savings in effort.

$$(206.0 - 187.4) \pm 16.5 \text{ min.}$$

$$\text{or } 18.6 \pm 16.5 \text{ min.}$$

$$= (2.1, 35.1) \text{ min.}$$

---

[3] If you try to find the degrees of freedom with that messy approximation formula (We dare you! It's in the footnote on page 619) using the values above, you'll get 8.99. The minor discrepancy is because we rounded the standard deviations to make the exposition clearer.

**Conclusion** Interpret the confidence interval in the proper context.

Less formally, you could say, "I'm 95% confident that generic batteries last an average of 2.1 to 35.1 minutes longer than brand-name batteries."

*I am 95% confident that the interval from 2.1 minutes to 35.1 minutes captures the mean amount of time by which generic batteries outlast brand-name batteries for this task. If generic batteries are cheaper, there seems little reason not to use them. If it is more trouble or costs more to buy them, then I'd consider whether the additional performance is worth it.*

# Another One Just Like the Other Ones?

**A S** *Activity:* **Find Two-Sample** *t*-**Intervals.** Who wants to deal with that ugly df formula? We usually find these intervals with a statistics package. Learn how here.

Yes. That's been our point all along. Once again we see a statistic plus or minus the margin of error. And the ME is just a critical value times the standard error. Just look out for that crazy degrees of freedom formula.

## JUST CHECKING

Carpal tunnel syndrome (CTS) causes pain and tingling in the hand. It can be bad enough to keep sufferers awake at night and restrict their daily activities. Researchers studied the effectiveness of two alternative surgical treatments for CTS (Mackenzie, Hainer, and Wheatley, *Annals of Plastic Surgery*, 2000). Patients were randomly assigned to have endoscopic or open-incision surgery. Four weeks later the endoscopic surgery patients demonstrated a mean pinch strength of 9.1 kg compared to 7.6 kg for the open-incision patients.

**1.** Why is the randomization of the patients into the two treatments important?

**2.** A 95% confidence interval for the difference in mean strength is about (0.04 kg, 2.96 kg). Explain what this interval means.

**3.** Why might we want to examine such a confidence interval in deciding between these two surgical procedures?

**4.** Why might you want to see the data before trusting the confidence interval?

# Testing the Difference Between Two Means

If you bought a used camera in good condition from a friend, would you pay the same as you would if you bought the same item from a stranger? A researcher at Cornell University (J. J. Halpern, "The Transaction Index: A Method for Standardizing Comparisons of Transaction Characteristics Across Different Contexts," *Group Decision and Negotiation*, 6: 557–572) wanted to know how friendship might affect simple sales such as this. She randomly divided subjects into two groups and gave each group descriptions of items they might want to buy. One group was told to imagine buying from a friend whom they expected to see again. The other group was told to imagine buying from a stranger.

Here are the prices they offered for a used camera in good condition:

| WHO | University students |
|---|---|
| WHAT | Prices offered for a used camera |
| UNITS | $ |
| WHY | Study of the effects of friendship on transactions |
| WHEN | 1990s |
| WHERE | U.C. Berkeley |

| PRICE OFFERED FOR A USED CAMERA ($) | |
|---|---|
| Buying from a Friend | Buying from a Stranger |
| 275 | 260 |
| 300 | 250 |
| 260 | 175 |
| 300 | 130 |
| 255 | 200 |
| 275 | 225 |
| 290 | 240 |
| 300 | |

The researcher who designed this study had a specific concern. Previous theories had doubted that friendship had a measurable effect on pricing. She hoped to find an effect on friendship. This calls for a hypothesis test—in this case a **two-sample t-test for the difference between means.**[4]

# A Test for the Difference Between Two Means

You already know enough to construct this test. The test statistic looks just like the others we've seen. It finds the difference between the observed group means and compares this with a hypothesized value for that difference. We'll call that hypothesized difference $\Delta_0$ ("delta naught"). It's so common for that hypothesized difference to be zero that we often just assume $\Delta_0 = 0$. We then compare the difference in the means with the standard error of that difference. We already know that, for a difference between independent means, we can find P-values from a Student's t-model on that same special number of degrees of freedom.

**A S**  *Activity: The Two-Sample t-Test.* How different are beef hot dogs and chicken dogs? Test whether measured differences are statistically significant.

**NOTATION ALERT:**

$\Delta_0$—delta naught—isn't so standard that you can assume everyone will understand it. We use it because it's the Greek letter (good for a parameter) "D" for "difference." You should say "delta naught" rather than "delta zero"—that's standard for parameters associated with null hypotheses.

> **TWO-SAMPLE t-TEST FOR THE DIFFERENCE BETWEEN MEANS**
>
> The conditions for the two-sample t-test for the difference between the means of two independent groups are the same as for the two-sample t-interval. We test the hypothesis
>
> $$H_0: \mu_1 - \mu_2 = \Delta_0$$
>
> where the hypothesized difference is almost always 0, using the statistic
>
> $$t = \frac{(\bar{y}_1 - \bar{y}_2) - \Delta_0}{SE(\bar{y}_1 - \bar{y}_2)}.$$
>
> The standard error of $\bar{y}_1 - \bar{y}_2$ is
>
> $$SE(\bar{y}_1 - \bar{y}_2) = \sqrt{\frac{s_1^2}{n_1} + \frac{s_2^2}{n_2}}.$$
>
> When the conditions are met and the null hypothesis is true, this statistic can be closely modeled by a Student's t-model with a number of degrees of freedom given by a special formula. We use that model to obtain a P-value.

---

[4] Because it is performed so often, this test is usually just called a "two-sample t-test."

---

**STEP-BY-STEP EXAMPLE**     A Two-Sample *t*-Test for the Difference Between Two Means

The usual null hypothesis is that there's no difference in means. That's just the right null hypothesis for the camera purchase prices.

**Question:** Is there a difference in the price people would offer a friend rather than a stranger?

| | |
|---|---|
| **Plan** State what we want to know. | I want to know whether people are likely to offer a different amount for a used camera when buying from a friend than when buying from a stranger. I wonder whether the difference between mean amounts is zero. I have bid prices from 8 subjects buying from a friend and 7 buying from a stranger, found in a randomized experiment. |

Identify the *parameter* you wish to estimate. Here our parameter is the difference in the means, not the individual group means.

Identify the variables and check the W's.

**Hypotheses** State the null and alternative hypotheses.

The research claim is that friendship changes what people are willing to pay.[5] The natural null hypothesis is that friendship makes no difference.

We didn't start with any knowledge of whether friendship might increase or decrease the price, so we choose a two-sided alternative.

$H_O$: The difference in mean price offered to friends and the mean price offered to strangers is zero:

$$\mu_F - \mu_S = 0.$$

$H_A$: The difference in mean prices is not zero:

$$\mu_F - \mu_S \neq 0.$$

Make a picture. Boxplots are the display of choice for comparing groups. We'll also want to check the distribution of each group. Histograms or Normal probability plots do a better job there.

**REALITY CHECK** Looks like the prices are higher if you buy from a friend, but we can't be sure. You can't tell from looking at the boxplots whether the difference is statistically significant—the plot shows spreads on the same scale as the data, and we know those don't add. You'll need to add the *variances* to get a suitable ruler for comparing the difference.

---

[5] This claim is a good example of what is called a "research hypothesis" in many social sciences. The only way to check it is to deny that it's true and see where the resulting null hypothesis leads us.

**Model** Think about the assumptions and check the conditions. (Note that, because this is a randomized experiment, we haven't sampled at all, so the 10% Condition does not apply.)

✔ **Randomization Condition:** The experiment was randomized. Subjects were assigned to treatment groups at random.

✔ **Independence Assumption:** This is an experiment, so there is no need for the subjects to be randomly selected from any particular population. All we need to check is whether they were assigned randomly to treatment groups.

✔ **Independent Groups Assumption:** Randomizing the experiment gives independent groups.

✔ **Nearly Normal Condition:** Histograms of the two sets of prices are unimodal and symmetric:

State the sampling distribution model.

Specify your method.

The assumptions are reasonable and the conditions are okay, so I'll use a Student's t-model to perform a **two-sample t-test.**

 **Mechanics** List the summary statistics. Be sure to use proper notation.

From the data:

$$n_F = 8 \qquad n_S = 7$$
$$\bar{y}_F = \$281.88 \qquad \bar{y}_S = \$211.43$$
$$s_F = \$18.31 \qquad s_S = \$46.43$$

Use the null model to find the P-value. First determine the standard error of the difference between sample means.

For independent groups,

$$SE(\bar{y}_F - \bar{y}_S) = \sqrt{SE^2(\bar{y}_F) + SE^2(\bar{y}_S)}$$
$$= \sqrt{\frac{s_F^2}{n_F} + \frac{s_S^2}{n_S}}$$
$$= \sqrt{\frac{18.31^2}{8} + \frac{46.43^2}{7}}$$
$$= 18.70$$

The observed difference is

$$(\bar{y}_F - \bar{y}_S) = 281.88 - 211.43 = \$70.45$$

Make a picture. Sketch the *t*-model centered at the hypothesized difference of zero. Because this is a two-tailed test, shade the region to the right of the observed difference and the corresponding region in the other tail.

Find the *t*-value.

A statistics program or graphing calculator can find the P-value using the fractional degrees of freedom from the approximation formula. If you are doing a test like this without technology, you could use the smaller sample size to determine degrees of freedom. In this case, $n_2 - 1 = 6$.

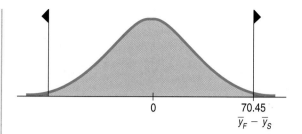

$$t = \frac{(\bar{y}_F - \bar{y}_S) - (0)}{SE(\bar{y}_F - \bar{y}_S)} = \frac{70.45}{18.70} = 3.77$$

The approximation formula gives 7.62 degrees of freedom.[6]

$$\text{P-value} = 2P(t_{7.62} > 3.77) = 0.006$$

**Conclusion** Link the P-value to your decision about the null hypothesis, and state the conclusion in context.

Be cautious about generalizing to items whose prices are outside the range of those in this study.

If there were no difference in the mean prices, a difference this large would occur only 6 times in 1000. That's too rare to believe, so I reject the null hypothesis and conclude that people are likely to offer a friend more than they'd offer a stranger for a used camera (and possibly for other, similar items).

## JUST CHECKING

Recall the experiment comparing patients 4 weeks after surgery for carpal tunnel syndrome. The patients who had endoscopic surgery demonstrated a mean pinch strength of 9.1 kg compared to 7.6 kg for the open-incision patients.

**5.** What hypotheses would you test?

**6.** The P-value of the test was less than 0.05. State a brief conclusion.

**7.** The study reports work on 36 "hands," but there were only 26 patients. In fact, 7 of the endoscopic surgery patients had both hands operated on, as did 3 of the open-incision group. Does this alter your thinking about any of the assumptions? Explain.

---

[6] If you were daring enough to calculate that messy degrees of freedom formula by hand with the values given here, you'd get about 7.74. Computers work with more precision for the standard deviations than we gave in our example. Many computer programs will round the final result down to 7 degrees of freedom. All give about the same result for the P-value, so it doesn't really matter—the conclusion would be the same.

## FOR EXAMPLE

**A two-sample $t$-test**

Many office "coffee stations" collect voluntary payments for the food consumed. Researchers at the University of Newcastle upon Tyne performed an experiment to see whether the image of eyes watching would change employee behavior.[7] They alternated pictures (seen here) of eyes looking at the viewer with pictures of flowers each week on the cupboard behind the "honesty box." They measured the consumption of milk to approximate the amount of food consumed and recorded the contributions (in £) each week per liter of milk. The table summarizes their results.

|  | Eyes | Flowers |
|---|---|---|
| $n$ (# weeks) | 5 | 5 |
| $\bar{y}$ | 0.417 £/l | 0.151 £/l |
| $s$ | 0.1811 £/l | 0.067 £/l |

**Question:** Do these results provide evidence that there really is a difference in honesty even when it's only photographs of eyes that are "watching"?

$$H_O: \mu_{eyes} - \mu_{flowers} = 0$$
$$H_A: \mu_{eyes} - \mu_{flowers} \neq 0$$

✓ **Independence Assumption:** The amount paid by one person should be independent of the amount paid by others.

✓ **Randomization Condition:** This study was observational. Treatments alternated a week at a time and were applied to the same group of office workers.

✓ **Nearly Normal Condition:** I don't have the data to check, but it seems unlikely there would be outliers in either group. I could be more certain if I could see histograms for both groups.

✓ **Independent Groups Assumption:** The same workers were recorded each week, but week-to-week independence is plausible.

It's okay to do a two-sample $t$-test for the difference in means:

$$SE(\bar{y}_{eyes} - \bar{y}_{flowers}) = \sqrt{\frac{s^2_{eyes}}{n_{eyes}} + \frac{s^2_{flowers}}{n_{flowers}}} = \sqrt{\frac{0.1811^2}{5} + \frac{0.067^2}{5}} = 0.0864$$

$$df = 5.07$$

$$t_5 = \frac{(\bar{y}_{eyes} - \bar{y}_{flowers}) - 0}{SE(\bar{y}_{eyes} - \bar{y}_{flowers})} = \frac{0.417 - 0.151}{0.0864} = 3.08$$

$$P(|t_5| > 3.08) = 0.027$$

Assuming the data were free of outliers, the very low P-value leads me to reject the null hypothesis. This study provides evidence that people will leave higher average voluntary payments for food if pictures of eyes are "watching."

(Note: In Table T we can see that at 5 df, $t = 3.08$ lies between the critical values for $P = 0.02$ and $P = 0.05$, so we could report $P < 0.05$.)

---

[7] Melissa Bateson, Daniel Nettle, and Gilbert Roberts, "Cues of Being Watched Enhance Cooperation in a Real-World Setting," *Biol. Lett. doi*:10.1098/rsbl.2006.0509.

# Back into the Pool

Remember that when we know a proportion, we know its standard deviation. When we tested the null hypothesis that two proportions were equal, that link meant we could assume their variances were equal as well. This led us to pool our data to estimate a standard error for the hypothesis test.

For means, there is also a pooled *t*-test. Like the two-proportions *z*-test, this test assumes that the variances in the two groups are equal. But be careful: Knowing the mean of some data doesn't tell you anything about their variance. And knowing that two means are equal doesn't say anything about whether their variances are equal. If we were willing to *assume* that their variances are equal, we could pool the data from two groups to estimate the common variance. We'd estimate this pooled variance from the data, so we'd still use a Student's *t*-model. This test is called a **pooled *t*-test (for the difference between means).**

Pooled *t*-tests have a couple of advantages. They often have a few more degrees of freedom than the corresponding two-sample test and a much simpler degrees of freedom formula. But these advantages come at a price: You have to pool the variances and think about another assumption. The assumption of equal variances is a strong one, is often not true, and is difficult to check. For these reasons, we recommend that you use a two-sample *t*-test instead.

The pooled *t*-test is the theoretically correct method only when we have a good reason to believe that the variances are equal. And (as we will see shortly) there are times when this makes sense. Keep in mind, however, that it's never wrong *not* to pool.

# *The Pooled *t*-Test

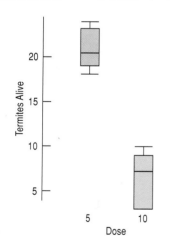

Termites cause billions of dollars of damage each year, to homes and other buildings, but some tropical trees seem to be able to resist termite attack. A researcher extracted a compound from the sap of one such tree and tested it by feeding it at two different concentrations to randomly assigned groups of 25 termites.[8] After 5 days, 8 groups fed the lower dose had an average of 20.875 termites alive, with a standard deviation of 2.23. But 6 groups fed the higher dose had an average of only 6.667 termites alive, with a standard deviation of 3.14. Is this a large enough difference to declare the sap compound effective in killing termites? In order to use the pooled *t*-test, we must make the **Equal Variance Assumption** that the variances of the two populations from which the samples have been drawn are equal. That is, $\sigma_1^2 = \sigma_2^2$. (Of course, we could think about the standard deviations being equal instead.) The corresponding **Similar Spreads Condition** really just consists of looking at the boxplots to check that the spreads are not wildly different. We were going to make boxplots anyway, so there's really nothing new here.

Once we decide to pool, we estimate the common variance by combining numbers we already have:

$$s_{\text{pooled}}^2 = \frac{(n_1 - 1)s_1^2 + (n_2 - 1)s_2^2}{(n_1 - 1) + (n_2 - 1)}.$$

$$s_{\text{pooled}}^2 = \frac{(8 - 1)2.23^2 + (6 - 1)3.14^2}{(8 - 1) + (6 - 1)} = 7.01$$

(If the two sample sizes are equal, this is just the average of the two variances.)

Now we just substitute this pooled variance in place of each of the variances in the standard error formula. Remember, the standard error formula for the difference of two independent means is

$$SE(\bar{y}_1 - \bar{y}_2) = \sqrt{\frac{s_1^2}{n_1} + \frac{s_2^2}{n_2}}.$$

---

[8] Adam Messer, Kevin McCormick, Sunjaya, H. H. Hagedorm, Ferny Tumbel and J. Meinwald, "Defensive role of tropical tree resins: antitermitic sesquiterpenes from Southeast Asian Dipterocarpaceae," *J Chem Ecology*, 16:122, pp. 3333–3352.

$$SE_{\text{pooled}}(\bar{y}_1 - \bar{y}_2) = \sqrt{\frac{7.01}{8} + \frac{7.01}{6}} = 1.43$$

$$t = \frac{20.875 - 6.667}{1.43} = 9.935$$

**A S** *Activity:* **The Pooled *t*-Test.** It's those hot dogs again. The same interactive tool can handle a pooled *t*-test, too. Take it for a spin here.

We just substitute the common pooled variance for each of the two variances in this formula and simplify. That makes the pooled standard error formula much simpler:

$$SE_{\text{pooled}}(\bar{y}_1 - \bar{y}_2) = \sqrt{\frac{s^2_{\text{pooled}}}{n_1} + \frac{s^2_{\text{pooled}}}{n_2}} = s_{\text{pooled}}\sqrt{\frac{1}{n_1} + \frac{1}{n_2}}.$$

The formula for degrees of freedom for the Student's *t*-model is simpler, too. It was so complicated for the two-sample *t* that we stuck it in a footnote.[9] Now it's just df $= n_1 + n_2 - 2$.

Substitute the pooled-*t* estimate of the standard error and its degrees of freedom into the steps of the confidence interval or hypothesis test, and you'll be using the pooled-*t* method. For the termites, $\bar{y}_1 - \bar{y}_2 = 14.208$, giving a *t*-value $= 9.935$ with 12 df and a P-value $\leq 0.0001$. Of course, if you decide to use a pooled-*t* method, you must defend your assumption that the variances of the two groups are equal.

How can we defend an assumption like that? We're testing whether the means are equal, so we admit that we don't *know* whether they are equal. Doesn't it seem a bit much to just *assume* that the variances are equal? Well, yes—but there are some special cases to consider.

---

**POOLED *t*-TEST AND CONFIDENCE INTERVAL FOR MEANS**

The conditions for the pooled *t*-test for the difference between the means of two independent groups (commonly called a "pooled *t*-test") are the same as for the two-sample *t*-test with the additional assumption that the variances of the two groups are the same. We test the hypothesis

$$H_0: \mu_1 - \mu_2 = \Delta_0,$$

where the hypothesized difference, $\Delta_0$, is almost always 0, using the statistic

$$t = \frac{(\bar{y}_1 - \bar{y}_2) - \Delta_0}{SE_{\text{pooled}}(\bar{y}_1 - \bar{y}_2)}.$$

The standard error of $\bar{y}_1 - \bar{y}_2$ is

$$SE_{\text{pooled}}(\bar{y}_1 - \bar{y}_2) = \sqrt{\frac{s^2_{\text{pooled}}}{n_1} + \frac{s^2_{\text{pooled}}}{n_2}} = s_{\text{pooled}}\sqrt{\frac{1}{n_1} + \frac{1}{n_2}},$$

where the pooled variance is

$$s^2_{\text{pooled}} = \frac{(n_1 - 1)s^2_1 + (n_2 - 1)s^2_2}{(n_1 - 1) + (n_2 - 1)}.$$

When the conditions are met and the null hypothesis is true, we can model this statistic's sampling distribution with a Student's *t*-model with $(n_1 - 1) + (n_2 - 1)$ degrees of freedom. We use that model to obtain a P-value for a test or a margin of error for a confidence interval.

The corresponding confidence interval is

$$(\bar{y}_1 - \bar{y}_2) \pm t^*_{\text{df}} \times SE_{\text{pooled}}(\bar{y}_1 - \bar{y}_2),$$

where the critical value $t^*$ depends on the confidence level and is found with $(n_1 - 1) + (n_2 - 1)$ degrees of freedom.

---

[9] But not this one. See page 619.

## Is the Pool All Wet?

So when *should* you use pooled-*t* methods rather than two-sample *t* methods?

Never.

What, never?

Well, hardly ever.

You see, when the variances of the two groups are in fact equal, the two methods give pretty much the same result. (For the termites, the two-sample *t* statistic is barely different—9.436 with 8 df—and the P-value is still < 0.001.) Pooled methods have a small advantage (slightly narrower confidence intervals, slightly more powerful tests) mostly because they usually have a few more degrees of freedom, but the advantage is slight.

When the variances are *not* equal, the pooled methods are just not valid and can give poor results. You have to use the two-sample methods instead.

As the sample sizes get bigger, the advantages that come from a few more degrees of freedom make less and less difference. So the advantage (such as it is) of the pooled method is greatest when the samples are small—just when it's hardest to check the conditions. And the difference in the degrees of freedom is greatest when the variances are not equal—just when you can't use the pooled method anyway. Our advice is to use the two-sample *t* methods to compare means.

Why did we devote a whole section to a method that we don't recommend using? Good question. The answer is that pooled methods are actually very important in Statistics. It's just that the simplest of the pooled methods—those for comparing two means—have good alternatives in the two-sample methods that don't require the extra assumption. Lacking the burden of the Equal Variances Assumption, the two-sample methods apply to more situations and are safer to use.

> Because the advantages of pooling are small, and you are allowed to pool only rarely (when the Equal Variances Assumption is met), *don't*.
>
> It's never wrong *not* to pool.

## Why Not Test the Assumption that the Variances Are Equal?

There is a hypothesis test that would do this. However, it is very sensitive to failures of the assumptions and works poorly for small sample sizes—just the situation in which we might care about a difference in the methods. When the choice between two-sample *t* and pooled-*t* methods makes a difference (that is, when the sample sizes are small), the test for whether the variances are equal hardly works at all.

## Is There Ever a Time When Assuming Equal Variances Makes Sense?

Yes. In a randomized comparative experiment, we start by assigning our experimental units to treatments at random, as the experimenter did with the termites. We know that at the start of the experiment each treatment group is a random sample from the same population,[10] so each treatment group begins with the same population variance. In this case, assuming that the variances are equal after we apply the treatment is the same as assuming that the treatment doesn't change the variance. When we test whether the true means are equal, we may be

---

[10] That is, the population of experimental subjects. Remember that to be valid, experiments do not need a representative sample drawn from a population because we are not trying to estimate a population model parameter.

willing to go a bit farther and say that the treatments made no difference *at all.* For example, we might suspect that the treatment is no different from the placebo offered as a control. Then it's not much of a stretch to assume that the variances have remained equal. It's still an assumption, and there are conditions that need to be checked (make the boxplots, make the boxplots, make the boxplots), but at least it's a plausible assumption.

This line of reasoning is important. The methods used to analyze comparative experiments *do* pool variances in exactly this way and defend the pooling with a version of this argument. The chapter on Analysis of Variance on the DVD introduces these methods.

---

## FOR EXAMPLE    A pooled *t*-test

**Recap:** Remember the experiment showing that people would consume more soup if their bowls were secretly being refilled as they ate? Could it be that those subjects with the refilling bowl just enjoyed eating soup more? The experimenters asked the participants to estimate how many ounces of soup they had eaten. Their responses are summarized in the table.

|       | Ordinary bowl | Refilling bowl |
|-------|:-------------:|:--------------:|
| $n$   | 27            | 27             |
| $\bar{y}$ | 8.2       | 9.8            |
| $s$   | 6.9           | 9.2            |

**Question:** Is there evidence that those who ate more knew what they had done?

$$H_O: \mu_{refill} - \mu_{ordinary} = 0$$
$$H_A: \mu_{refill} - \mu_{ordinary} \neq 0$$

The independence assumptions and randomization condition checked out earlier. Also,

**?  Nearly Normal Condition:** The histograms for both groups look unimodal and skewed to the right. The presence of skewness and outliers in groups this size (27) suggests that using *t*-methods may be risky.

✓ **Equal Variances Assumption:** Subjects were assigned randomly to the two treatments, so I can assume that before they ate any soup, both groups' volume-estimating abilities had equal variances.

✓ **Similar Spreads Condition:** The boxplots show comparable spreads for the two groups.

*(continued)*

For Example (*continued*)

I'll perform a pooled *t*-test, with caution.

$$s^2_{pooled} = \frac{(n_r - 1)s^2_r + (n_o - 1)s^2_o}{(n_r - 1) + (n_o - 1)} = \frac{26 \times 9.2^2 + 26 \times 6.9^2}{(26) + (26)} = 8.13$$

$$SE_{pooled}(\bar{y}_o - \bar{y}_r) = \sqrt{\frac{s^2_{pooled}}{n_p} + \frac{s^2_{pooled}}{n_o}} = s_{pooled}\sqrt{\frac{1}{n_p} + \frac{1}{n_o}} = 5.09\sqrt{\frac{1}{27} + \frac{1}{27}} = 2.213$$

$$df = (27 - 1) + (27 - 1) = 52$$

$$t_{52} = \frac{(9.8 - 8.2) - 0}{2.213} = 0.723$$

$$P\text{-value} = P(|t_{52}| > 0.723) = 0.473$$

An event that happens nearly half of the time by chance isn't very extraordinary, so I would not reject the null hypothesis. There's no evidence that the subjects who ate more soup from the refilling bowl could tell that they did so.

## WHAT CAN GO WRONG?

▶ **Watch out for paired data.** The Independent Groups Assumption deserves special attention. If the samples are not independent, you can't use these two-sample methods. This is probably the main thing that can go wrong when using these two-sample methods. The methods of this chapter can be used *only* if the observations in the two groups are *independent*. Matched-pairs designs in which the observations are deliberately related arise often and are important. The next chapter deals with them.

▶ **Look at the plots.** The usual (by now) cautions about checking for outliers and non-Normal distributions apply, of course. The simple defense is to make and examine boxplots. You may be surprised how often this simple step saves you from the wrong or even absurd conclusions that can be generated by a single undetected outlier. You don't want to conclude that two methods have very different means just because one observation is atypical.

> **Do what we say, not what we do...** Precision machines used in industry often have a bewildering number of parameters that have to be set, so experiments are performed in an attempt to try to find the best settings. Such was the case for a hole-punching machine used by a well-known computer manufacturer to make printed circuit boards. The data were analyzed by one of the authors, but because he was in a hurry, he didn't look at the boxplots first and just performed *t*-tests on the experimental factors. When he found extremely small P-values even for factors that made no sense, he plotted the data. Sure enough, there was one observation 1,000,000 times bigger than the others. It turns out that it had been recorded in microns (millionths of an inch), while all the rest were in inches.

# CONNECTIONS

The structure and reasoning of inference methods for comparing two means are very similar to what we used for comparing two proportions. Here we must estimate the standard errors independent of the means, so we use Student's *t*-models rather than the Normal.

We first learned about side-by-side boxplots in Chapter 5. There we made general statements about the shape, center, and spread of each group. When we compared groups, we asked whether their centers looked different compared to how spread out the distributions were. Here we've made that kind of thinking precise, with confidence intervals for the difference and tests of whether the means are the same.

We use Student's *t* as we did for single sample means, and for the same reasons: We are using standard errors from the data to estimate the standard deviation of the sample statistic. As before, to work with Student's *t*-models, we need to check the Nearly Normal Condition. Histograms and Normal probability plots are the best methods for such checks.

As always, we've decided whether a statistic is large by comparing it with its standard error. In this case, our statistic is the difference in means.

We pooled data to find a standard deviation when we tested the hypothesis of equal proportions. For that test, the assumption of equal variances was a consequence of the null hypothesis that the proportions were equal, so it didn't require an extra assumption. When two proportions are equal, so are their variances. But means don't have a linkage with their corresponding variances; so to use pooled-*t* methods, we must make the additional assumption of equal variances. When we can make this assumption, the pooled variance calculations are very similar to those for proportions, combining the squared deviations of each group from its own mean to find a common variance.

# WHAT HAVE WE LEARNED?

Are the means of two groups the same? If not, how different are they? We've learned to use statistical inference to compare the means of two independent groups.

▶ We've seen that confidence intervals and hypothesis tests about the difference between two means, like those for an individual mean, use *t*-models.

▶ Once again we've seen the importance of checking assumptions that tell us whether our method will work.

▶ We've seen that, as when comparing proportions, finding the standard error for the difference in sample means depends on believing that our data come from independent groups. Unlike proportions, however, pooling is usually not the best choice here.

▶ And we've seen once again that we can add variances of independent random variables to find the standard deviation of the difference in two independent means.

▶ Finally, we've learned that the reasoning of statistical inference remains the same; only the mechanics change.

## Terms

**Two-sample *t* methods**

618. Two-sample *t* methods allow us to draw conclusions about the difference between the means of two independent groups. The two-sample methods make relatively few assumptions about the underlying populations, so they are usually the method of choice for comparing two sample means. However, the Student's *t*-models are only approximations for their true sampling distribution. To make that approximation work well, the two-sample *t* methods have a special rule for estimating degrees of freedom.

**Two-sample *t*-interval for the difference between means**

621. A confidence interval for the difference between the means of two independent groups found as

$$(\bar{y}_1 - \bar{y}_2) \pm t^*_{df} \times SE(\bar{y}_1 - \bar{y}_2)$$

where

$$SE(\bar{y}_1 - \bar{y}_2) = \sqrt{\frac{s_1^2}{n_1} + \frac{s_2^2}{n_2}}$$

and the number of degrees of freedom is given by a special formula (see footnote 2 on page 619).

**Two-sample *t*-test for the difference between means**

625. A hypothesis test for the difference between the means of two independent groups. It tests the null hypothesis

$$H_0: \mu_1 - \mu_2 = \Delta_0,$$

where the hypothesized difference, $\Delta_0$, is almost always 0, using the statistic

$$t_{df} = \frac{(\bar{y}_1 - \bar{y}_2) - \Delta_0}{SE(\bar{y}_1 - \bar{y}_2)},$$

with the number of degrees of freedom given by the special formula.

**Pooling**

630. Data from two or more populations may sometimes be combined, or *pooled*, to estimate a statistic (typically a pooled variance) when we are willing to assume that the estimated value is the same in both populations. The resulting larger sample size may lead to an estimate with lower sample variance. However, pooled estimates are appropriate only when the required assumptions are true.

**Pooled-*t* methods**

630. Pooled-*t* methods provide inferences about the difference between the means of two independent populations under the assumption that both populations have the same standard deviation. When the assumption is justified, pooled-*t* methods generally produce slightly narrower confidence intervals and more powerful significance tests than two-sample *t* methods. When the assumption is not justified, they generally produce worse results—sometimes substantially worse.

We recommend that you use two-sample *t* methods instead.

**\*Pooled *t*-intervals**

631. A confidence interval for the difference between the means of two independent groups used when we are willing and able to make the additional assumption that the variances of the groups are equal. It is found as

$$(\bar{y}_1 - \bar{y}_2) \pm t^*_{df} \times SE_{pooled}(\bar{y}_1 - \bar{y}_2),$$

where

$$SE_{pooled}(\bar{y}_1 - \bar{y}_2) = \sqrt{\frac{s^2_{pooled}}{n_1} + \frac{s^2_{pooled}}{n_2}} = s_{pooled}\sqrt{\frac{1}{n_1} + \frac{1}{n_2}},$$

the pooled variance is

$$s^2_{pooled} = \frac{(n_1 - 1)s^2_1 + (n_2 - 1)s^2_2}{(n_1 - 1) + (n_2 - 1)},$$

and the number of degrees of freedom is $(n_1 - 1) + (n_2 - 1)$.

**\*Pooled *t*-test**

631. A hypothesis test for the difference in the means of two independent groups when we are willing and able to assume that the variances of the groups are equal. It tests the null hypothesis

$$H_0: \mu_1 - \mu_2 = \Delta_0,$$

where the hypothesized difference, $\Delta_0$, is almost always 0, using the statistic

$$t_{df} = \frac{(\bar{y}_1 - \bar{y}_2) - \Delta_0}{SE_{pooled}(\bar{y}_1 - \bar{y}_2)},$$

where the pooled standard error is defined as for the pooled interval and the degrees of freedom is $(n_1 - 1) + (n_2 - 1)$.

## Skills

**THINK**

▸ Be able to recognize situations in which we want to do inference on the difference between the means of two independent groups.

▸ Know how to examine your data for violations of conditions that would make inference about the difference between two population means unwise or invalid.

▸ Be able to recognize when a pooled-*t* procedure might be appropriate and be able to explain why you decided to use a two-sample method anyway.

**SHOW**

▸ Be able to perform a two-sample *t*-test using a statistics package or calculator (at least for finding the degrees of freedom).

**TELL**

▸ Be able to interpret a test of the null hypothesis that the means of two independent groups are equal. (If the test is a pooled *t*-test, your interpretation should include a defense of your assumption of equal variances.)

# ON THE COMPUTER

## Two-Sample Methods

Here's some typical computer package output with comments:

*May just say "difference of means"*

*Test Statistic*

```
2-Sample t-Test of μ1-μ2 = 0 vs ≠ 0

Difference Between Means = 0.99145299 t-Statistic = 1.540
w/196 df
Fail to reject Ho at Alpha = 0.05
P = 0.1251
```

*Some programs will draw a conclusion about the test. Others just give the P-value and let you decide for yourself.*

*df found from approximation formula and rounded down. The unrounded value may be given, or may be used to find the P-value.*

*Many programs give far too many digits. Ignore the excess digits.*

Most statistics packages compute the test statistic for you and report a P-value corresponding to that statistic. And, of course, statistics packages make it easy to examine the boxplots of the two groups, so you have no excuse for skipping this important check.

Some statistics software automatically tries to test whether the variances of the two groups are equal. Some automatically offer both the two-sample-*t* and pooled-*t* results. Ignore the test for the variances; it has little power in any situation in which its results could matter. If the pooled and two-sample methods differ in any important way, you should stick with the two-sample method. Most likely, the Equal Variance Assumption needed for the pooled method has failed.

The degrees of freedom approximation usually gives a fractional value. Most packages seem to round the approximate value down to the next smallest integer (although they may actually compute the P-value with the fractional value, gaining a tiny amount of power).

There are two ways to organize data when we want to compare two independent groups. The data can be in two lists, as in the table at the start of this chapter. Each list can be thought of as a variable. In this method, the variables in the batteries example would be *Brand Name* and *Generic*. Graphing calculators usually prefer this form, and some computer programs can use it as well.

There's another way to think about the data. What is the response variable for the battery life experiment? It's the *Time* until the music stopped. But the values of this variable are in both columns, and actually there's an experiment factor here, too—namely, the *Brand* of the battery. So, we could put the data into two different columns, one with the *Times* in it and one with the *Brand*. Then the data would look like this:

| Time | Brand |
|------|-------|
| 194.0 | Brand name |
| 205.5 | Brand name |
| 199.2 | Brand name |
| 172.4 | Brand name |
| 184.0 | Brand name |
| 169.5 | Brand name |
| 190.7 | Generic |
| 203.5 | Generic |
| 203.5 | Generic |
| 206.5 | Generic |
| 222.5 | Generic |
| 209.4 | Generic |

This way of organizing the data makes sense as well. Now the factor and the response variables are clearly visible. You'll have to see which method your program requires. Some packages even allow you to structure the data either way.

The commands to do inference for two independent groups on common statistics technology are not always found in obvious places. Here are some starting guidelines.

## DATA DESK

Select variables.
From the **Calc** menu, choose **Estimate** for confidence intervals or **Test** for hypothesis tests. Select the interval or test from the drop-down menu and make other choices in the dialog.

COMMENTS

Data Desk expects the two groups to be in separate variables.

## EXCEL

From the Data Tab, Analysis Group, choose **Data Analysis.**
Alternatively (if the Data Analysis Tool Pack is not installed), in the Formulas Tab, choose More functions > Statistical > TTEST, and specify Type=3 in the resulting dialog.
Fill in the cell ranges for the two groups, the hypothesized difference, and the alpha level.

COMMENTS

Excel expects the two groups to be in separate cell ranges. Notice that, contrary to Excel's wording, we do not need to assume that the variances are *not* equal; we simply choose not to assume that they *are* equal.

## JMP

From the **Analyze** menu, select **Fit y by x.** Select variables: a **Y, Response** variable that holds the data and an **X, Factor** variable that holds the group names. JMP will make a dotplot. Click the **red triangle** in the dotplot title, and choose **Unequal variances.** The *t*-test is at the bottom of the resulting table. Find the P-value from the Prob>F section of the table (they are the same).

COMMENTS

JMP expects data in one variable and category names in the other. Don't be misled: There is no need for the variances to be unequal to use two-sample *t* methods.

## MINITAB

From the **Stat** menu, choose the **Basic Statistics** submenu. From that menu, choose **2-sample t....** Then fill in the dialog.

COMMENTS

The dialog offers a choice of data in two variables, or data in one variable and category names in the other.

## SPSS

From the **Analyze** menu, choose the **Compare Means** submenu. From that, choose the **Independent-Samples t-test** command. Specify the data variable and "group variable." Then type in the labels used in the group variable. SPSS offers both the two-sample and pooled-*t* results in the same table.

COMMENTS

SPSS expects the data in one variable and group names in the other. If there are more than two group names in the group variable, only the two that are named in the dialog box will be compared.

## TI-83/84 PLUS

For a confidence interval:
In the **STAT TESTS** menu, choose **0:2-SampTInt.** You may specify that you are using data stored in two lists, or you may enter the means, standard deviations, and sizes of both samples. You must also indicate whether to pool the variances (when in doubt, say no) and specify the desired level of confidence.

To test a hypothesis,
In the **STAT TESTS** menu, choose
**4:2-SampTTest.** You may specify if you are using data stored in two lists, or you may enter the means, standard deviations, and sizes of both samples. You must also indicate whether to pool the variances (when in doubt, say no) and specify whether the test is to be two-tail, lower-tail, or upper-tail.

---

**TI-89**

For a confidence interval:
In the **STAT Ints** menu, choose **4:2-SampTInt.** You must specify if you are using data stored in two lists or if you will enter the means, standard deviations, and sizes of both samples. You must also indicate whether to pool the variances (when in doubt, say no) and specify the desired level of confidence.

To test a hypothesis:
In the **STAT TESTS** menu, choose **4:2-SampTTest.** You must specify if you are using data stored in two lists or if you will enter the means, standard deviations, and sizes of both samples. You must also indicate whether to pool the variances (when in doubt, say no) and specify whether the test is to be two-tail, lower-tail, or upper-tail.

---

# EXERCISES

1. **Dogs and calories.** In the July 2007 issue, *Consumer Reports* examined the calorie content of two kinds of hot dogs: meat (usually a mixture of pork, turkey, and chicken) and all beef. The researchers purchased samples of several different brands. The meat hot dogs averaged 111.7 calories, compared to 135.4 for the beef hot dogs. A test of the null hypothesis that there's no difference in mean calorie content yields a P-value of 0.124. Would a 95% confidence interval for $\mu_{Meat} - \mu_{Beef}$ include 0? Explain.

2. **Dogs and sodium.** The *Consumer Reports* article described in Exercise 1 also listed the sodium content (in mg) for the various hot dogs tested. A test of the null hypothesis that beef hot dogs and meat hot dogs don't differ in the mean amounts of sodium yields a P-value of 0.11. Would a 95% confidence interval for $\mu_{Meat} - \mu_{Beef}$ include 0? Explain.

3. **Dogs and fat.** The *Consumer Reports* article described in Exercise 1 also listed the fat content (in grams) for samples of beef and meat hot dogs. The resulting 90% confidence interval for $\mu_{Meat} - \mu_{Beef}$ is $(-6.5, -1.4)$.
   a) The endpoints of this confidence interval are negative numbers. What does that indicate?
   b) What does the fact that the confidence interval does not contain 0 indicate?
   c) If we use this confidence interval to test the hypothesis that $\mu_{Meat} - \mu_{Beef} = 0$, what's the corresponding alpha level?

4. **Washers.** In the June 2007 issue, *Consumer Reports* examined the relative merits of top-loading and front-loading washing machines, testing samples of several different brands of each type. One of the variables the article reported was "cycle time", the number of minutes it took each machine to wash a load of clothes. Among the machines rated good to excellent, the 98% confidence interval for the difference in mean cycle time ($\mu_{Top} - \mu_{Front}$) is $(-40, -22)$.
   a) The endpoints of this confidence interval are negative numbers. What does that indicate?
   b) What does the fact that the confidence interval does not contain 0 indicate?

   c) If we use this confidence interval to test the hypothesis that $\mu_{Top} - \mu_{Front} = 0$, what's the corresponding alpha level?

5. **Dogs and fat, second helping.** In Exercise 3, we saw a 90% confidence interval of $(-6.5, -1.4)$ grams for $\mu_{Meat} - \mu_{Beef}$, the difference in mean fat content for meat vs. all-beef hot dogs. Explain why you think each of the following statements is true or false:
   a) If I eat a meat hot dog instead of a beef dog, there's a 90% chance I'll consume less fat.
   b) 90% of meat hot dogs have between 1.4 and 6.5 grams less fat than a beef hot dog.
   c) I'm 90% confident that meat hot dogs average 1.4–6.5 grams less fat than the beef hot dogs.
   d) If I were to get more samples of both kinds of hot dogs, 90% of the time the meat hot dogs would average 1.4–6.5 grams less fat than the beef hot dogs.
   e) If I tested more samples, I'd expect about 90% of the resulting confidence intervals to include the true difference in mean fat content between the two kinds of hot dogs.

6. **Second load of wash.** In Exercise 4, we saw a 98% confidence interval of $(-40, -22)$ minutes for $\mu_{Top} - \mu_{Front}$, the difference in time it takes top-loading and front-loading washers to do a load of clothes. Explain why you think each of the following statements is true or false:
   a) 98% of top loaders are 22 to 40 minutes faster than front loaders.
   b) If I choose the laundromat's top loader, there's a 98% chance that my clothes will be done faster than if I had chosen the front loader.
   c) If I tried more samples of both kinds of washing machines, in about 98% of these samples I'd expect the top loaders to be an average of 22 to 40 minutes faster.
   d) If I tried more samples, I'd expect about 98% of the resulting confidence intervals to include the true difference in mean cycle time for the two types of washing machines.
   e) I'm 98% confident that top loaders wash clothes an average of 22 to 40 minutes faster than front-loading machines.

**7. Learning math.** The Core Plus Mathematics Project (CPMP) is an innovative approach to teaching Mathematics that engages students in group investigations and mathematical modeling. After field tests in 36 high schools over a three-year period, researchers compared the performances of CPMP students with those taught using a traditional curriculum. In one test, students had to solve applied Algebra problems using calculators. Scores for 320 CPMP students were compared to those of a control group of 273 students in a traditional Math program. Computer software was used to create a confidence interval for the difference in mean scores. (*Journal for Research in Mathematics Education,* 31, no. 3[2000])

Conf level: 95%   Variable: Mu(CPMP) − Mu(Ctrl)
Interval: (5.573, 11.427)

a) What's the margin of error for this confidence interval?
b) If we had created a 98% CI, would the margin of error be larger or smaller?
c) Explain what the calculated interval means in this context.
d) Does this result suggest that students who learn Mathematics with CPMP will have significantly higher mean scores in Algebra than those in traditional programs? Explain.

**8. Stereograms.** Stereograms appear to be composed entirely of random dots. However, they contain separate images that a viewer can "fuse" into a three-dimensional (3D) image by staring at the dots while defocusing the eyes. An experiment was performed to determine whether knowledge of the form of the embedded image affected the time required for subjects to fuse the images. One group of subjects (group NV) received no information or just verbal information about the shape of the embedded object. A second group (group VV) received both verbal information and visual information (specifically, a drawing of the object). The experimenters measured how many seconds it took for the subject to report that he or she saw the 3D image.

2-Sample t-Interval for $\mu 1 - \mu 2$
Conf level = 90%   df = 70
$\mu$(NV) − $\mu$(VV) interval: (0.55, 5.47)

a) Interpret your interval in context.
b) Does it appear that viewing a picture of the image helps people "see" the 3D image in a stereogram?
c) What's the margin of error for this interval?
d) Explain carefully what the 90% confidence level means.
e) Would you expect a 99% confidence level to be wider or narrower? Explain.
f) Might that change your conclusion in part b? Explain.

**9. CPMP, again.** During the study described in Exercise 7, students in both CPMP and traditional classes took another Algebra test that did not allow them to use calculators. The table below shows the results. Are the mean scores of the two groups significantly different?

| Math Program | n | Mean | SD |
|---|---|---|---|
| **CPMP** | 312 | 29.0 | 18.8 |
| **Traditional** | 265 | 38.4 | 16.2 |

*Performance on Algebraic Symbolic Manipulation Without Use of Calculators*

a) Write an appropriate hypothesis.
b) Do you think the assumptions for inference are satisfied? Explain.
c) Here is computer output for this hypothesis test. Explain what the P-value means in this context.

2-Sample t-Test of $\mu 1 - \mu 2 \neq 0$
t-Statistic = −6.451 w/574.8761 df
P < 0.0001

d) State a conclusion about the CPMP program.

**10. CPMP and word problems.** The study of the new CPMP Mathematics methodology described in Exercise 7 also tested students' abilities to solve word problems. This table shows how the CPMP and traditional groups performed. What do you conclude?

| Math Program | n | Mean | SD |
|---|---|---|---|
| **CPMP** | 320 | 57.4 | 32.1 |
| **Traditional** | 273 | 53.9 | 28.5 |

**11. Commuting.** A man who moves to a new city sees that there are two routes he could take to work. A neighbor who has lived there a long time tells him Route A will average 5 minutes faster than Route B. The man decides to experiment. Each day he flips a coin to determine which way to go, driving each route 20 days. He finds that Route A takes an average of 40 minutes, with standard deviation 3 minutes, and Route B takes an average of 43 minutes, with standard deviation 2 minutes. Histograms of travel times for the routes are roughly symmetric and show no outliers.

a) Find a 95% confidence interval for the difference in average commuting time for the two routes.
b) Should the man believe the old-timer's claim that he can save an average of 5 minutes a day by always driving Route A? Explain.

**12. Pulse rates.** A researcher wanted to see whether there is a significant difference in resting pulse rates for men and women. The data she collected are displayed in the boxplots on the next page and summarized below.

| | Sex | |
|---|---|---|
| | **Male** | **Female** |
| **Count** | 28 | 24 |
| **Mean** | 72.75 | 72.625 |
| **Median** | 73 | 73 |
| **StdDev** | 5.37225 | 7.69987 |
| **Range** | 20 | 29 |
| **IQR** | 9 | 12.5 |

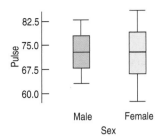

a) What do the boxplots suggest about differences between male and female pulse rates?
b) Is it appropriate to analyze these data using the methods of inference discussed in this chapter? Explain.
c) Create a 90% confidence interval for the difference in mean pulse rates.
d) Does the confidence interval confirm your answer to part a? Explain.

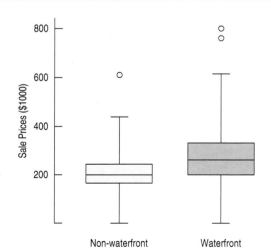

**13. View of the water.** How much extra is having a waterfront property worth? A student took a random sample of 170 recently sold properties in Upstate New York to examine the question. Here are her summaries and boxplots of the two groups of prices:

| Non-Waterfront Properties | | Waterfront Properties | |
|---|---|---|---|
| $n$ | 100 | $n$ | 70 |
| $\bar{y}$ | $219,896.60 | $\bar{y}$ | $319,906.40 |
| $s$ | $94,627.15 | $s$ | $153,303.80 |

Construct and interpret a 95% confidence interval for the mean additional amount that waterfront property is worth.

**14. New construction.** The sample of 100 house sales we looked at in Exercise 13 also listed whether the home was new construction or not. Find and interpret a 95% confidence interval for how much more an agent can expect to sell a new home for. Here are the summaries and boxplots of the *Sale Prices*:

| Old Construction | | New Construction | |
|---|---|---|---|
| $n$ | 100 | $n$ | 100 |
| $\bar{y}$ | $201,707.50 | $\bar{y}$ | $267,878.10 |
| $s$ | $96,116.88 | $s$ | $93,302.18 |

**15. Cereal.** The data below show the sugar content (as a percentage of weight) of several national brands of children's and adults' cereals. Create and interpret a 95% confidence interval for the difference in mean sugar content. Be sure to check the necessary assumptions and conditions.

**Children's cereals:** 40.3, 55, 45.7, 43.3, 50.3, 45.9, 53.5, 43, 44.2, 44, 47.4, 44, 33.6, 55.1, 48.8, 50.4, 37.8, 60.3, 46.6

**Adults' cereals:** 20, 30.2, 2.2, 7.5, 4.4, 22.2, 16.6, 14.5, 21.4, 3.3, 6.6, 7.8, 10.6, 16.2, 14.5, 4.1, 15.8, 4.1, 2.4, 3.5, 8.5, 10, 1, 4.4, 1.3, 8.1, 4.7, 18.4

**16. Egyptians.** Some archaeologists theorize that ancient Egyptians interbred with several different immigrant populations over thousands of years. To see if there is any indication of changes in body structure that might have resulted, they measured 30 skulls of male Egyptians dated from 4000 B.C.E and 30 others dated from 200 B.C.E. (A. Thomson and R. Randall-Maciver, *Ancient Races of the Thebaid*, Oxford: Oxford University Press, 1905)
a) Are these data appropriate for inference? Explain.
b) Create a 95% confidence interval for the difference in mean skull breadth between these two eras.
c) Do these data provide evidence that the mean breadth of males' skulls changed over this period? Explain.

| Maximum Skull Breadth (mm) | | | |
|---|---|---|---|
| 4000 B.C.E. | 4000 B.C.E. | 200 B.C.E. | 200 B.C.E. |
| 131 | 131 | 141 | 131 |
| 125 | 135 | 141 | 129 |
| 131 | 132 | 135 | 136 |
| 119 | 139 | 133 | 131 |
| 136 | 132 | 131 | 139 |
| 138 | 126 | 140 | 144 |
| 139 | 135 | 139 | 141 |
| 125 | 134 | 140 | 130 |
| 131 | 128 | 138 | 133 |
| 134 | 130 | 132 | 138 |
| 129 | 138 | 134 | 131 |
| 134 | 128 | 135 | 136 |
| 126 | 127 | 133 | 132 |
| 132 | 131 | 136 | 135 |
| 141 | 124 | 134 | 141 |

**T** **17. Reading.** An educator believes that new reading activities for elementary school children will improve reading comprehension scores. She randomly assigns third graders to an eight-week program in which some will use these activities and others will experience traditional teaching methods. At the end of the experiment, both groups take a reading comprehension exam. Their scores are shown in the back-to-back stem-and-leaf display. Do these results suggest that the new activities are better? Test an appropriate hypothesis and state your conclusion.

| New Activities | | Control |
|---|---|---|
| | 1 | 07 |
| 4 | 2 | 068 |
| 3 | 3 | 377 |
| 96333 | 4 | 12222238 |
| 9876432 | 5 | 355 |
| 721 | 6 | 02 |
| 1 | 7 | |
| | 8 | 5 |

**T** **18. Streams.** Researchers collected samples of water from streams in the Adirondack Mountains to investigate the effects of acid rain. They measured the pH (acidity) of the water and classified the streams with respect to the kind of substrate (type of rock over which they flow). A lower pH means the water is more acidic. Here is a plot of the pH of the streams by substrate (limestone, mixed, or shale):

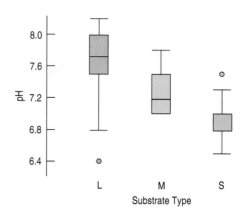

Here are selected parts of a software analysis comparing the pH of streams with limestone and shale substrates:

2-Sample t-Test of $\mu_1 - \mu_2$
Difference Between Means = 0.735
t-Statistic = 16.30 w/133 df
$p \leq 0.0001$

a) State the null and alternative hypotheses for this test.
b) From the information you have, do the assumptions and conditions appear to be met?
c) What conclusion would you draw?

**T** **19. Hurricanes 2006.** The data below show the number of hurricanes recorded annually before and after 1970. Create an appropriate visual display, and determine whether these data are appropriate for testing whether there has been a change in the frequency of hurricanes.

| **1944–1969** | **1970–2006** |
|---|---|
| 3, 2, 1, 2, 4, 3, 7, 2, 3, 3, 2, 5, 2, 2, 4, 2, 2, 6, 0, 2, 5, 1, 3, 1, 0, 3 | 2, 1, 0, 1, 2, 3, 2, 1, 2, 2, 2, 3, 1, 1, 1, 3, 0, 1, 3, 2, 1, 2, 1, 1, 0, 5, 6, 1, 3, 5, 3, 3, 2, 3, 6, 7, 2 |

**T** **20. Memory.** Does ginkgo biloba enhance memory? In an experiment to find out, subjects were assigned randomly to take ginkgo biloba supplements or a placebo. Their memory was tested to see whether it improved. Here are boxplots comparing the two groups and on the next page some computer output from a two-sample t-test computed for the data.

2-Sample t-Test of $\mu_G - \mu_P > 0$
Difference Between Means $= -0.9914$
t-Statistic $= -1.540$ w/196 df
P $= 0.9374$

a) Explain in this context what the P-value means.
b) State your conclusion about the effectiveness of ginkgo biloba.
c) Proponents of ginkgo biloba continue to insist that it works. What type of error do they claim your conclusion makes? Explain.

**T  21. Baseball 2006.**   American League baseball teams play their games with the designated hitter rule, meaning that pitchers do not bat. The league believes that replacing the pitcher, traditionally a weak hitter, with another player in the batting order produces more runs and generates more interest among fans. Below are the average numbers of runs scored in American League and National League stadiums for the 2006 season.

| American | National |
|----------|----------|
| 11.4 | 10.5 |
| 10.5 | 10.3 |
| 10.4 | 10.0 |
| 10.3 | 10.0 |
| 10.2 | 9.7 |
| 10.0 | 9.7 |
| 9.9 | 9.6 |
| 9.9 | 9.5 |
| 9.7 | 9.5 |
| 9.1 | 9.4 |
| 9.0 | 9.1 |
| 9.0 | 9.0 |
| 8.9 | 9.0 |
| 8.8 | 8.9 |
|  | 8.9 |
|  | 7.9 |

a) Create an appropriate display of these data. What do you see?
b) With a 95% confidence interval, estimate the mean number of runs scored in American League games.
c) Coors Field, in Denver, stands a mile above sea level, an altitude far greater than that of any other major league ball park. Some believe that the thinner air makes it harder for pitchers to throw curve balls and easier for batters to hit the ball a long way. Do you think the 10.5 runs scored per game at Coors is unusual? Explain.
d) Explain why you should not use two separate confidence intervals to decide whether the two leagues differ in average number of runs scored.

**22. Handy.**   A factory hiring people to work on an assembly line gives job applicants a test of manual agility. This test counts how many strangely shaped pegs the applicant can fit into matching holes in a one-minute period. The table below summarizes the data by sex of the job applicant. Assume that all conditions necessary for inference are met.

|  | Male | Female |
|---|------|--------|
| Number of subjects | 50 | 50 |
| Pegs placed: |  |  |
| Mean | 19.39 | 17.91 |
| SD | 2.52 | 3.39 |

a) Find 95% confidence intervals for the average number of pegs that males and females can each place.
b) Those intervals overlap. What does this suggest about any sex-based difference in manual agility?
c) Find a 95% confidence interval for the difference in the mean number of pegs that could be placed by men and women.
d) What does this interval suggest about any difference in manual agility between men and women?
e) The two results seem contradictory. Which method is correct: doing two-sample inference or doing one-sample inference twice?
f) Why don't the results agree?

**T  23. Double header 2006.**   Do the data in Exercise 21 suggest that the American League's designated hitter rule may lead to more runs?
a) Using a 95% confidence interval, estimate the difference between the mean number of runs scored in American and National League games.
b) Interpret your interval.
c) Does that interval suggest that the two leagues may differ in average number of runs scored per game?

**T  24. Hard water.**   In an investigation of environmental causes of disease, data were collected on the annual mortality rate (deaths per 100,000) for males in 61 large towns in England and Wales. In addition, the water hardness was recorded as the calcium concentration (parts per million, ppm) in the drinking water. The data set also notes, for each town, whether it was south or north of Derby. Is there a significant difference in mortality rates in the two regions? Here are the summary statistics.

Summary of:   mortality
For categories in:   Derby

| Group | Count | Mean | Median | StdDev |
|-------|-------|---------|--------|---------|
| North | 34 | 1631.59 | 1631 | 138.470 |
| South | 27 | 1388.85 | 1369 | 151.114 |

a) Test appropriate hypotheses and state your conclusion.
b) The boxplots of the two distributions show an outlier among the data north of Derby. What effect might that have had on your test?

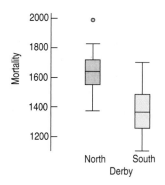

**25. Job satisfaction.** A company institutes an exercise break for its workers to see if this will improve job satisfaction, as measured by a questionnaire that assesses workers' satisfaction. Scores for 10 randomly selected workers before and after implementation of the exercise program are shown. The company wants to assess the effectiveness of the exercise program. Explain why you can't use the methods discussed in this chapter to do that. (Don't worry, we'll give you another chance to do this the right way.)

| Worker Number | Job Satisfaction Index | |
|---|---|---|
| | **Before** | **After** |
| 1 | 34 | 33 |
| 2 | 28 | 36 |
| 3 | 29 | 50 |
| 4 | 45 | 41 |
| 5 | 26 | 37 |
| 6 | 27 | 41 |
| 7 | 24 | 39 |
| 8 | 15 | 21 |
| 9 | 15 | 20 |
| 10 | 27 | 37 |

**26. Summer school.** Having done poorly on their math final exams in June, six students repeat the course in summer school, then take another exam in August. If we consider these students representative of all students who might attend this summer school in other years, do these results provide evidence that the program is worthwhile?

| June | 54 | 49 | 68 | 66 | 62 | 62 |
|---|---|---|---|---|---|---|
| Aug. | 50 | 65 | 74 | 64 | 68 | 72 |

**27. Sex and violence.** In June 2002, the *Journal of Applied Psychology* reported on a study that examined whether the content of TV shows influenced the ability of viewers to recall brand names of items featured in the commercials. The researchers randomly assigned volunteers to watch one of three programs, each containing the same nine commercials. One of the programs had violent content, another sexual content, and the third neutral content. After the shows ended, the subjects were asked to recall the brands of products that were advertised. Results are summarized in the next column.

| | Program Type | | |
|---|---|---|---|
| | **Violent** | **Sexual** | **Neutral** |
| **No. of subjects** | 108 | 108 | 108 |
| **Brands recalled** | | | |
| **Mean** | 2.08 | 1.71 | 3.17 |
| **SD** | 1.87 | 1.76 | 1.77 |

a) Do these results indicate that viewer memory for ads may differ depending on program content? A test of the hypothesis that there is no difference in ad memory between programs with sexual content and those with violent content has a P-value of 0.136. State your conclusion.
b) Is there evidence that viewer memory for ads may differ between programs with sexual content and those with neutral content? Test an appropriate hypothesis and state your conclusion.

**28. Ad campaign.** You are a consultant to the marketing department of a business preparing to launch an ad campaign for a new product. The company can afford to run ads during one TV show, and has decided not to sponsor a show with sexual content. You read the study described in Exercise 19, then use a computer to create a confidence interval for the difference in mean number of brand names remembered between the groups watching violent shows and those watching neutral shows.

TWO-SAMPLE T
95% CI FOR MUviol – MUneut: (−1.578, −0.602)

a) At the meeting of the marketing staff, you have to explain what this output means. What will you say?
b) What advice would you give the company about the upcoming ad campaign?

**29. Sex and violence II.** In the study described in Exercise 27, the researchers also contacted the subjects again, 24 hours later, and asked them to recall the brands advertised. Results are summarized below.

| | Program Type | | |
|---|---|---|---|
| | **Violent** | **Sexual** | **Neutral** |
| **No. of subjects** | 101 | 106 | 103 |
| **Brands recalled** | | | |
| **Mean** | 3.02 | 2.72 | 4.65 |
| **SD** | 1.61 | 1.85 | 1.62 |

a) Is there a significant difference in viewers' abilities to remember brands advertised in shows with violent vs. neutral content?
b) Find a 95% confidence interval for the difference in mean number of brand names remembered between the groups watching shows with sexual content and those watching neutral shows. Interpret your interval in this context.

**30. Ad recall.** In Exercises 27 and 29, we see the number of advertised brand names people recalled immediately after watching TV shows and 24 hours later. Strangely enough, it appears that they remembered more about the ads the next day. Should we conclude this is true in general about people's memory of TV ads?
   a) Suppose one analyst conducts a two-sample hypothesis test to see if memory of brands advertised during violent TV shows is higher 24 hours later. The P-value of his test is 0.00013. What might he conclude?
   b) Explain why his procedure was inappropriate. Which of the assumptions for inference was violated?
   c) How might the design of this experiment have tainted the results?
   d) Suggest a design that could compare immediate brand-name recall with recall one day later.

**31. Hungry?** Researchers investigated how the size of a bowl affects how much ice cream people tend to scoop when serving themselves.[10] At an "ice cream social," people were randomly given either a 17 oz or a 34 oz bowl (both large enough that they would not be filled to capacity). They were then invited to scoop as much ice cream as they liked. Did the bowl size change the selected portion size? Here are the summaries:

| Small Bowl | | Large Bowl | |
|---|---|---|---|
| $n$ | 26 | $n$ | 22 |
| $\bar{y}$ | 5.07 oz | $\bar{y}$ | 6.58 oz |
| $s$ | 1.84 oz | $s$ | 2.91 oz |

Test an appropriate hypothesis and state your conclusions. For assumptions and conditions that you cannot test, you may assume that they are sufficiently satisfied to proceed.

**32. Thirsty?** Researchers randomly assigned participants either a tall, thin "highball" glass or a short, wide "tumbler," each of which held 355 ml. Participants were asked to pour a shot (1.5 oz = 44.3 ml) into their glass. Did the shape glass make a difference in how much liquid they poured?[11] Here are the summaries:

| highball | | tumbler | |
|---|---|---|---|
| $n$ | 99 | $n$ | 99 |
| $\bar{y}$ | 42.2 ml | $\bar{y}$ | 60.9 ml |
| $s$ | 16.2 ml | $s$ | 17.9 ml |

Test an appropriate hypothesis and state your conclusions. For assumptions and conditions that you cannot test, you may assume that they are sufficiently satisfied to proceed.

---

[10] Brian Wansink, Koert van Ittersum, and James E. Painter, "Ice Cream Illusions: Bowls, Spoons, and Self-Served Portion Sizes," *Am J Prev Med* 2006.
[11] Brian Wansink and Koert van Ittersum, "Shape of Glass and Amount of Alcohol Poured: Comparative Study of Effect of Practice and Concentration," *BMJ* 2005;331;1512–1514.

**33. Lower scores?** Newspaper headlines recently announced a decline in science scores among high school seniors. In 2000, a total of 15,109 seniors tested by The National Assessment in Education Program (NAEP) scored a mean of 147 points. Four years earlier, 7537 seniors had averaged 150 points. The standard error of the difference in the mean scores for the two groups was 1.22.
   a) Have the science scores declined significantly? Cite appropriate statistical evidence to support your conclusion.
   b) The sample size in 2000 was almost double that in 1996. Does this make the results more convincing or less? Explain.

**34. The Internet.** The NAEP report described in Exercise 33 compared science scores for students who had home Internet access to the scores of those who did not, as shown in the graph. They report that the differences are statistically significant.
   a) Explain what "statistically significant" means in this context.
   b) If their conclusion is incorrect, which type of error did the researchers commit?
   c) Does this prove that using the Internet at home can improve a student's performance in science?

**35. Crossing Ontario.** Between 1954 and 2003, swimmers have crossed Lake Ontario 43 times. Both women and men have made the crossing. Here are some plots (we've omitted a crossing by Vikki Keith, who swam a round trip—North to South to North—in 3390 minutes):

Summary statistics are as follows:

| | Summary of Time (min) | | |
|---|---|---|---|
| Group | Count | Mean | StdDev |
| F | 22 | 1271.59 | 261.111 |
| M | 20 | 1196.75 | 304.369 |

How much difference is there between the mean amount of time (in minutes) it would take female and male swimmers to swim the lake?

a) Construct and interpret a 95% confidence interval for the difference between female and male crossing times.

b) Comment on the assumptions and conditions.

36. **Still swimming.**   Here's some additional information about the Ontario crossing times presented in Exercise 35. It is generally thought to be harder to swim across the lake from north to south. Indeed, this has been done only 5 times. Every one of those crossings was by a woman. If we omit those 5 crossings, the boxplots look like this:

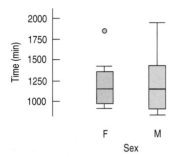

The female outlier is Vikki Keith, who crossed the lake swimming only butterfly stroke. Omitting that extraordinary swim gives the following summary statistics:

| Summary of Time (min) | | | |
|---|---|---|---|
| Group | **Count** | **Mean** | **StdDev** |
| **F** | 16 | 1175.25 | 177.794 |
| **M** | 20 | 1196.75 | 304.369 |

a) Do women or men appear to be faster at swimming across the lake? Support your answer by interpreting a confidence interval.

b) Vikki Keith was responsible for two of the more remarkable crossings, but she also swam Lake Ontario two other times. In fact, of the 36 crossings in this analysis, 7 were repeat crossings by a swimmer who'd crossed the lake before. How does this fact affect your thoughts about the confidence interval?

Ⓣ 37. **Running heats.**   In Olympic running events, preliminary heats are determined by random draw, so we should expect that the abilities of runners in the various heats to be about the same, on average. Here are the times (in seconds) for the 400–m women's run in the 2004 Olympics in Athens for preliminary heats 2 and 5. Is there any evidence that the mean time to finish is different for randomized heats? Explain. Be sure to include a discussion of assumptions and conditions for your analysis.

| Country | Name | Heat | Time |
|---|---|---|---|
| USA | HENNAGAN Monique | 2 | 51.02 |
| BUL | DIMITROVA Mariyana | 2 | 51.29 |
| CHA | NADJINA Kaltouma | 2 | 51.50 |

*(continued)*

| | | | |
|---|---|---|---|
| JAM | DAVY Nadia | 2 | 52.04 |
| BRA | ALMIRAO Maria Laura | 2 | 52.10 |
| FIN | MYKKANEN Kirsi | 2 | 52.53 |
| CHN | BO Fanfang | 2 | 56.01 |
| BAH | WILLIAMS-DARLING Tonique | 5 | 51.20 |
| BLR | USOVICH Svetlana | 5 | 51.37 |
| UKR | YEFREMOVA Antonina | 5 | 51.53 |
| CMR | NGUIMGO Mireille | 5 | 51.90 |
| JAM | BECKFORD Allison | 5 | 52.85 |
| TOG | THIEBAUD-KANGNI Sandrine | 5 | 52.87 |
| SRI | DHARSHA K V Damayanthi | 5 | 54.58 |

Ⓣ 38. **Swimming heats.**   In Exercise 37 we looked at the times in two different heats for the 400-m women's run from the 2004 Olympics. Unlike track events, swimming heats are *not* determined at random. Instead, swimmers are seeded so that better swimmers are placed in later heats. Here are the times (in seconds) for the women's 400-m freestyle from heats 2 and 5. Do these results suggest that the mean times of seeded heats are not equal? Explain. Include a discussion of assumptions and conditions for your analysis.

| Country | Name | Heat | Time |
|---|---|---|---|
| ARG | BIAGIOLI Cecilia Elizabeth | 2 | 256.42 |
| SLO | CARMAN Anja | 2 | 257.79 |
| CHI | KOBRICH Kristel | 2 | 258.68 |
| MKD | STOJANOVSKA Vesna | 2 | 259.39 |
| JAM | ATKINSON Janelle | 2 | 260.00 |
| NZL | LINTON Rebecca | 2 | 261.58 |
| KOR | HA Eun-Ju | 2 | 261.65 |
| UKR | BERESNYEVA Olga | 2 | 266.30 |
| FRA | MANAUDOU Laure | 5 | 246.76 |
| JPN | YAMADA Sachiko | 5 | 249.10 |
| ROM | PADURARU Simona | 5 | 250.39 |
| GER | STOCKBAUER Hannah | 5 | 250.46 |
| AUS | GRAHAM Elka | 5 | 251.67 |
| CHN | PANG Jiaying | 5 | 251.81 |
| CAN | REIMER Brittany | 5 | 252.33 |
| BRA | FERREIRA Monique | 5 | 253.75 |

39. **Tees.**   Does it matter what kind of tee a golfer places the ball on? The company that manufactures "Stinger" tees claims that the thinner shaft and smaller head will lessen resistance and drag, reducing spin and allowing the ball to travel farther. In August 2003, Golf Laboratories, Inc., compared the distance traveled by golf balls hit off regular wooden tees to those hit off Stinger tees. All the balls were struck by the same golf club using a robotic device set to swing the club head at approximately 95 miles per hour. Summary statistics from the test are shown in the table on the next page. Assume that 6 balls were hit off each tee and that the data were suitable for inference.

| | | Total Distance (yards) | Ball Velocity (mph) | Club Velocity (mph) |
|---|---|---|---|---|
| **Regular tee** | Avg. | 227.17 | 127.00 | 96.17 |
| | SD | 2.14 | 0.89 | 0.41 |
| **Stinger tee** | Avg. | 241.00 | 128.83 | 96.17 |
| | SD | 2.76 | 0.41 | 0.52 |

Is there evidence that balls hit off the Stinger tees would have a higher initial velocity?

**40. Golf again.** Given the test results on golf tees described in Exercise 39, is there evidence that balls hit off Stinger tees would travel farther? Again, assume that 6 balls were hit off each tee and that the data were suitable for inference.

**41. Statistics journals.** When a professional statistician has information to share with colleagues, he or she will submit an article to one of several Statistics journals for publication. This can be a lengthy process; typically, the article must be circulated for "peer review" and perhaps edited before being accepted for publication. Then the article must wait in line with other articles before actually appearing in print. In the Winter 1998 issue of *Chance* magazine, Eric Bradlow and Howard Wainer reported on this delay for several journals between 1990 and 1994. For 288 articles published in *The American Statistician*, the mean length of time between initial submission and publication was 21 months, with a standard deviation of 8 months. For 209 *Applied Statistics* articles, the mean time to publication was 31 months, with a standard deviation of 12 months. Create and interpret a 90% confidence interval for the difference in mean delay, and comment on the assumptions that underlie your analysis.

**42. Music and memory.** Is it a good idea to listen to music when studying for a big test? In a study conducted by some Statistics students, 62 people were randomly assigned to listen to rap music, music by Mozart, or no music while attempting to memorize objects pictured on a page. They were then asked to list all the objects they could remember. Here are summary statistics for each group:

| | Rap | Mozart | No Music |
|---|---|---|---|
| **Count** | 29 | 20 | 13 |
| **Mean** | 10.72 | 10.00 | 12.77 |
| **SD** | 3.99 | 3.19 | 4.73 |

a) Does it appear that it is better to study while listening to Mozart than to rap music? Test an appropriate hypothesis and state your conclusion.

b) Create a 90% confidence interval for the mean difference in memory score between students who study to Mozart and those who listen to no music at all. Interpret your interval.

**43. Rap.** Using the results of the experiment described in Exercise 42, does it matter whether one listens to rap music while studying, or is it better to study without music at all?
a) Test an appropriate hypothesis and state your conclusion.
b) If you concluded there is a difference, estimate the size of that difference with a confidence interval and explain what your interval means.

**44. Cuckoos.** Cuckoos lay their eggs in the nests of other (host) birds. The eggs are then adopted and hatched by the host birds. But the potential host birds lay eggs of different sizes. Does the cuckoo change the size of her eggs for different foster species? The numbers in the table are lengths (in mm) of cuckoo eggs found in nests of three different species of other birds. The data are drawn from the work of O.M. Latter in 1902 and were used in a fundamental textbook on statistical quality control by L.H.C. Tippett (1902–1985), one of the pioneers in that field.

| CUCKOO EGG LENGTH (MM) | | |
|---|---|---|
| Foster Parent Species | | |
| **Sparrow** | **Robin** | **Wagtail** |
| 20.85 | 21.05 | 21.05 |
| 21.65 | 21.85 | 21.85 |
| 22.05 | 22.05 | 21.85 |
| 22.85 | 22.05 | 21.85 |
| 23.05 | 22.05 | 22.05 |
| 23.05 | 22.25 | 22.45 |
| 23.05 | 22.45 | 22.65 |
| 23.05 | 22.45 | 23.05 |
| 23.45 | 22.65 | 23.05 |
| 23.85 | 23.05 | 23.25 |
| 23.85 | 23.05 | 23.45 |
| 23.85 | 23.05 | 24.05 |
| 24.05 | 23.05 | 24.05 |
| 25.05 | 23.05 | 24.05 |
| | 23.25 | 24.85 |
| | 23.85 | |

Investigate the question of whether the mean length of cuckoo eggs is the same for different species, and state your conclusion.

## JUST CHECKING
### Answers

1. Randomization should balance unknown sources of variability in the two groups of patients and helps us believe the two groups are independent.

2. We can be 95% confident that after 4 weeks endoscopic surgery patients will have a mean pinch strength between 0.04 kg and 2.96 kg higher than open-incision patients.

3. The lower bound of this interval is close to 0, so the difference may not be great enough that patients could actually notice the difference. We may want to consider other issues such as cost or risk in making a recommendation about the two surgical procedures.

4. Without data, we can't check the Nearly Normal Condition.

5. $H_0$: Mean pinch strength is the same after both surgeries.

   $H_A$: Mean pinch strength is different after the two surgeries.

6. With a P-value this low, we reject the null hypothesis. We can conclude that mean pinch strength differs after 4 weeks in patients who undergo endoscopic surgery vs. patients who have open-incision surgery. Results suggest that the endoscopic surgery patients may be stronger, on average.

7. If some patients contributed two hands to the study, then the groups may not be internally independent. It is reasonable to assume that two hands from the same patient might respond in similar ways to similar treatments.

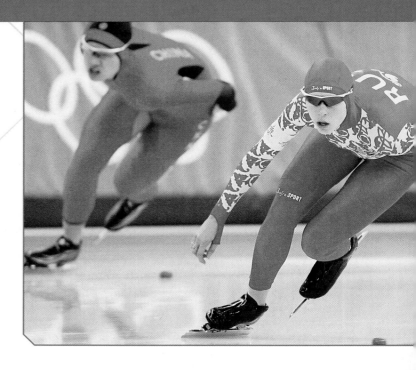

# CHAPTER 25

# Paired Samples and Blocks

## Where are we going?

How much will an LSAT prep course raise scores? Are boys better at computer games than their sisters? Questions like this look at paired variables. When pairs of observations go together naturally, they can't be independent, so the methods we used in the last chapter won't work. In this chapter you'll see what to do with paired data.

| | |
|---|---|
| **WHO** | Olympic speed-skaters |
| **WHAT** | Time for women's 1500 m |
| **UNITS** | Seconds |
| **WHEN** | 2006 |
| **WHERE** | Torino, Italy |
| **WHY** | To see whether one lane is faster than the other |

Speed-skating races are run in pairs. Two skaters start at the same time, one on the inner lane and one on the outer lane. Halfway through the race, they cross over, switching lanes so that each will skate the same distance in each lane. Even though this seems fair, at the 2006 Olympics some fans thought there might have been an advantage to starting on the outside. After all, the winner, Cindy Klassen, started on the outside and skated a remarkable 1.47 seconds faster than the Silver medalist.

Here are the data for the women's 1500-m race:

| Inner lane | | Outer lane | |
|---|---|---|---|
| **Name** | **Time** | **Name** | **Time** |
| OLTEAN Daniela | 129.24 | NEMOTO Nami | 122.34 |
| ZHANG Xiaolei | 125.75 | LAMB Maria | 122.12 |
| ABRAMOVA Yekaterina | 121.63 | NOH Seon Yeong | 123.35 |
| REMPEL Shannon | 122.24 | TIMMER Marianne | 120.45 |
| LEE Ju-Youn | 120.85 | MARRA Adelia | 123.07 |
| ROKITA Anna Natalia | 122.19 | OPITZ Lucille | 122.75 |
| YAKSHINA Valentina | 122.15 | HAUGLI Maren | 121.22 |
| BJELKEVIK Hedvig | 122.16 | WOJCICKA Katarzyna | 119.96 |
| ISHINO Eriko | 121.85 | BJELKEVIK Annette | 121.03 |
| RANEY Catherine | 121.17 | LOBYSHEVA Yekaterina | 118.87 |

*(continued)*

**FIGURE 25.1**

*Using boxplots to compare times in the inner and outer lanes shows little because it ignores the fact that the skaters raced in pairs.*

| | | | | |
|---|---|---|---|---|
| OTSU Hiromi | 124.77 | JI Jia | 121.85 |
| SIMIONATO Chiara | 118.76 | WANG Fei | 120.13 |
| ANSCHUETZ THOMS Daniela | 119.74 | van DEUTEKOM Paulien | 120.15 |
| BARYSHEVA Varvara | 121.60 | GROVES Kristina | 116.74 |
| GROENEWOLD Renate | 119.33 | NESBITT Christine | 119.15 |
| RODRIGUEZ Jennifer | 119.30 | KLASSEN Cindy | 115.27 |
| FRIESINGER Anni | 117.31 | TABATA Maki | 120.77 |
| WUST Ireen | 116.90 | | |

We can view this skating event as an experiment testing whether the lanes were equally fast. Skaters were assigned to lanes randomly. The boxplots of times recorded in the inner and outer lanes don't show much difference. But that's not the right way to compare these times. Conditions can change during the day. The data are recorded for races run two at a time, so the two groups are not independent.

## Paired Data

Data such as these are called **paired.** We have the times for skaters in each lane for each race. The races are run in pairs, so they can't be independent. And since they're not independent, we can't use the two-sample *t* methods. Instead, we can focus on the *differences* in times for each racing pair.

Paired data arise in a number of ways. Perhaps the most common way is to compare subjects with themselves before and after a treatment. When pairs arise from an experiment, the pairing is a type of *blocking*. When they arise from an observational study, it is a form of *matching*.

---

**FOR EXAMPLE**    Identifying paired data

Do flexible schedules reduce the demand for resources? The Lake County, Illinois, Health Department experimented with a flexible four-day work week. For a year, the department recorded the mileage driven by 11 field workers on an ordinary five-day work week. Then it changed to a flexible four-day work week and recorded mileage for another year.[1] Here are the data:

| Name | 5-Day mileage | 4-Day mileage |
|---|---|---|
| Jeff | 2798 | 2914 |
| Betty | 7724 | 6112 |
| Roger | 7505 | 6177 |
| Tom | 838 | 1102 |
| Aimee | 4592 | 3281 |
| Greg | 8107 | 4997 |
| Larry G. | 1228 | 1695 |
| Tad | 8718 | 6606 |
| Larry M. | 1097 | 1063 |
| Leslie | 8089 | 6392 |
| Lee | 3807 | 3362 |

*(continued)*

---

[1] Charles S. Catlin, "Four-day Work Week Improves Environment," *Journal of Environmental Health*, Denver, 59:7.

For Example (*continued*)

Question: Why are these data paired?

*The mileage data are paired because each driver's mileage is measured before and after the change in schedule. I'd expect drivers who drove more than others before the schedule change to continue to drive more afterwards, so the two sets of mileages can't be considered independent.*

Pairing isn't a problem; it's an opportunity. If you know the data are paired, you can take advantage of that fact—in fact, you *must* take advantage of it. You *may not* use the two-sample and pooled methods of the previous chapter when the data are paired. You must decide whether the data are paired from understanding how they were collected and what they mean (check the W's). There is no test to determine whether the data are paired.

Once we recognize that the speed-skating data are matched pairs, it makes sense to consider the difference in times for each two-skater race. So we look at the *pairwise* differences:

> *A S* **Activity: Differences in Means of Paired Groups.** Are married couples typically the same age, or do wives tend to be younger than their husbands, on average?

| Skating Pair | Inner Time | Outer Time | Inner − Outer |
|:---:|:---:|:---:|:---:|
| 1 | 129.24 | | . |
| 2 | 125.75 | 122.34 | 3.41 |
| 3 | 121.63 | 122.12 | −0.49 |
| 4 | 122.24 | 123.35 | −1.11 |
| 5 | 120.85 | 120.45 | 0.40 |
| 6 | 122.19 | 123.07 | −0.88 |
| 7 | 122.15 | 122.75 | −0.60 |
| 8 | 122.16 | 121.22 | 0.94 |
| 9 | 121.85 | 119.96 | 1.89 |
| 10 | 121.17 | 121.03 | 0.14 |
| 11 | 124.77 | 118.87 | 5.90 |
| 12 | 118.76 | 121.85 | −3.09 |
| 13 | 119.74 | 120.13 | −0.39 |
| 14 | 121.60 | 120.15 | 1.45 |
| 15 | 119.33 | 116.74 | 2.59 |
| 16 | 119.30 | 119.15 | 0.15 |
| 17 | 117.31 | 115.27 | 2.04 |
| 18 | 116.90 | 120.77 | −3.87 |

One skater raced alone, so we'll omit that race. Because it is the *differences* we care about, we'll treat them as if *they* were the data, ignoring the original two columns. Now that we have only one column of values to consider, we can use a simple one-sample *t*-test. Mechanically, a **paired *t*-test** is just a one-sample *t*-test for the means of these pairwise differences. The sample size is the number of pairs.

So you've already seen the *Show*.

# Assumptions and Conditions

## PAIRED DATA ASSUMPTION

**Paired Data Assumption:** The data must be paired. You can't just decide to pair data when in fact the samples are independent. When you have two groups with the same number of observations, it may be tempting to match them up.

Don't, unless you are prepared to justify your claim that the data are paired.

On the other hand, be sure to recognize paired data when you have them. Remember, two-sample *t* methods aren't valid without independent groups, and paired groups aren't independent. Although this is a strictly required assumption, it is one that can be easy to check if you understand how the data were collected.

## INDEPENDENCE ASSUMPTION

**Independence Assumption:** If the data are paired, the *groups* are not independent. For these methods, it's the *differences* that must be independent of each other. There's no reason to believe that the difference in speeds of one pair of races could affect the difference in speeds for another pair.

**Randomization Condition:** Randomness can arise in many ways. The pairs may be a random sample. In an experiment, the order of the two treatments may be randomly assigned, or the treatments may be randomly assigned to one member of each pair. In a before-and-after study, we may believe that the observed differences are a representative sample from a population of interest. If we have any doubts, we'll need to include a control group to be able to draw conclusions. What we want to know usually focuses our attention on where the randomness should be.

In our example, skaters were assigned to the lanes at random.

**10% Condition:** We're thinking of the speed-skating data as an experiment testing the difference between lanes. The 10% Condition doesn't apply to randomized experiments, where no sampling takes place.

## NORMAL POPULATION ASSUMPTION

We need to assume that the population of *differences* follows a Normal model. We don't need to check the individual groups.

**Nearly Normal Condition:** This condition can be checked with a histogram or Normal probability plot of the *differences*—but not of the individual groups. As with the one-sample *t*-methods, this assumption matters less the more pairs we have to consider. You may be pleasantly surprised when you check this condition. Even if your original measurements are skewed or bimodal, the *differences* may be nearly Normal. After all, the individual who was way out in the tail on an initial measurement is likely to still be out there on the second one, giving a perfectly ordinary difference.

> **10% of what?**
> A fringe benefit of checking the 10% Condition is that it forces us to think about what population we're hoping to make inferences about.

---

**FOR EXAMPLE**    Checking assumptions and conditions

**Recap:** Field workers for a health department compared driving mileage on a five-day work schedule with mileage on a new four-day schedule. To see if the new schedule changed the amount of driving they did, we'll look at paired differences in mileages before and after.

*(continued)*

For Example (*continued*)

| Name | 5-Day mileage | 4-Day mileage | Difference |
|------|---------------|---------------|------------|
| Jeff | 2798 | 2914 | −116 |
| Betty | 7724 | 6112 | 1612 |
| Roger | 7505 | 6177 | 1328 |
| Tom | 838 | 1102 | −264 |
| Aimee | 4592 | 3281 | 1311 |
| Greg | 8107 | 4997 | 3110 |
| Larry G. | 1228 | 1695 | −467 |
| Tad | 8718 | 6606 | 2112 |
| Larry M. | 1097 | 1063 | 34 |
| Leslie | 8089 | 6392 | 1697 |
| Lee | 3807 | 3362 | 445 |

**Question:**  Is it okay to use these data to test whether the new schedule changed the amount of driving?

✓ **Paired Data Assumption:** The data are paired because each value is the mileage driven by the same person before and after a change in work schedule.

✓ **Independence Assumption:** The driving behavior of any individual worker is independent of the others, so the differences are mutually independent.

✓ **Randomization Condition:** The mileages are the sums of many individual trips, each of which experienced random events that arose while driving. Repeating the experiment in two new years would give randomly different values.

✓ **Nearly Normal Condition:** The histogram of the mileage differences is unimodal and symmetric:

Since the assumptions and conditions are satisfied, it's okay to use paired-t methods for these data.

---

The steps of testing a hypothesis for paired differences are very much like the steps for a one-sample *t*-test for a mean.

---

**THE PAIRED *t*-TEST**

When the conditions are met, we are ready to test whether the mean of paired differences is significantly different from zero. We test the hypothesis

$$H_0: \mu_d = \Delta_0,$$

where the *d*'s are the pairwise differences and $\Delta_0$ is almost always 0.

We use the statistic

$$t_{n-1} = \frac{\bar{d} - \Delta_0}{SE(\bar{d})},$$

where $\bar{d}$ is the mean of the pairwise differences, $n$ is the number of *pairs*, and

$$SE(\bar{d}) = \frac{s_d}{\sqrt{n}}.$$

$SE(\bar{d})$ is the ordinary standard error for the mean, applied to the differences.

When the conditions are met and the null hypothesis is true, we can model the sampling distribution of this statistic with a Student's *t*-model with $n-1$ degrees of freedom, and use that model to obtain a P-value.

---

## STEP-BY-STEP EXAMPLE  A Paired *t*-Test

**Question: Was there a difference in speeds between the inner and outer speed-skating lanes at the 2006 Winter Olympics?**

| | |
|---|---|
| **THINK** **Plan** State what we want to know. | I want to know whether there really was a difference in the speeds of the two lanes for speed skating at the 2006 Olympics. I have data for the women's 1500-m race. |
| Identify the *parameter* we wish to estimate. Here our parameter is the mean difference in race times. | |
| Identify the variables and check the W's. | |
| **Hypotheses** State the null and alternative hypotheses. | $H_O$: Neither lane offered an advantage: |
| Although fans suspected one lane was faster, we can't use the data we have to specify the direction of a test. We (and Olympic officials) would be interested in a difference in either direction, so we'd better test a two-sided alternative. | $\mu_d = 0.$ <br> $H_A$: The mean difference is different from zero: <br> $\mu_d \neq 0.$ |
| **REALITY CHECK** The individual differences are all in seconds. We should expect the mean difference to be comparable in magnitude. | ✔ **Paired Data Assumption:** The data are paired because racers compete in pairs. |
| **Model** Think about the assumptions and check the conditions. | ✔ **Independence Assumption:** Each race is independent of the others, so the differences are mutually independent. |
| State why you think the data are paired. Simply having the same number of individuals in each group, displaying them in side-by-side columns, doesn't make them paired. | ✔ **Randomization Condition:** Skaters are assigned to lanes at random. Repeating the experiment with different pairings and lane assignments would give randomly different values. |
| Think about what we hope to learn and where the randomization comes from. Here, the randomization comes from the racer pairings and lane assignments. | ✔ **Nearly Normal Condition:** The histogram of the differences is unimodal and symmetric: |

Make a picture—just one. Don't plot separate distributions of the two groups—that entirely misses the pairing. For paired data, it's the Normality of the *differences* that we care about. Treat those paired differences as you would a single variable, and check the Nearly Normal Condition with a histogram or a Normal probability plot.

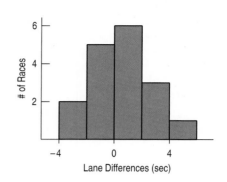

Specify the sampling distribution model.

Choose the method.

The conditions are met, so I'll use a Student's t-model with $(n - 1) = 16$ degrees of freedom, and perform a **paired t-test.**

---

**SHOW**

### Mechanics

$n$ is the number of *pairs*—in this case, the number of races.

$\bar{d}$ is the mean difference.

$s_d$ is the standard deviation of the differences.

Find the standard error and the *t*-score of the observed mean difference. There is nothing new in the mechanics of the paired-*t* methods. These are the mechanics of the *t*-test for a mean applied to the differences.

Make a picture. Sketch a *t*-model centered at the hypothesized mean of 0. Because this is a two-tail test, shade both the region to the right of the observed mean difference of 0.499 seconds and the corresponding region in the lower tail.

Find the P-value, using technology.

**REALITY CHECK** The mean difference is 0.499 seconds. That may not seem like much, but a smaller difference determined the Silver and Bronze medals. The standard error is about this big, so a *t*-value less than 1.0 isn't surprising. Nor is a large P-value.

The data give

$$n = 17 \text{ pairs}$$
$$\bar{d} = 0.499 \text{ seconds}$$
$$s_d = 2.333 \text{ seconds.}$$

I estimate the standard deviation of $\bar{d}$ using

$$SE(\bar{d}) = \frac{s_d}{\sqrt{n}} = \frac{2.333}{\sqrt{17}} = 0.5658$$

So $t_{16} = \dfrac{\bar{d} - 0}{SE(\bar{d})} = \dfrac{0.499}{0.5658} = 0.882$

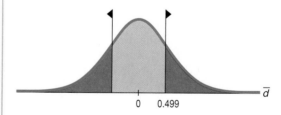

P-value $= 2P(t_{16} > 0.882) = 0.39$

**Conclusion** Link the P-value to your decision about $H_0$, and state your conclusion in context.

The P-value is large. Events that happen more than a third of the time are not remarkable. So, even though there is an observed difference between the lanes, I can't conclude that it isn't due simply to random chance. It appears the fans may have interpreted a random fluctuation in the data as favoring one lane. There's insufficient evidence to declare any lack of fairness.

---

### FOR EXAMPLE    Doing a paired *t*-test

**Recap:** We want to test whether a change from a five-day work week to a four-day work week could change the amount driven by field workers of a health department. We've already confirmed that the assumptions and conditions for a paired *t*-test are met.

**Question:** Is there evidence that a four-day work week would change how many miles workers drive?

$H_0$: The change in the health department workers' schedules didn't change the mean mileage driven; the mean difference is zero:

$$\mu_d = 0.$$

$H_A$: The mean difference is different from zero:

$$\mu_d \neq 0.$$

The conditions are met, so I'll use a Student's *t*-model with $(n - 1) = 10$ degrees of freedom and perform a **paired *t*-test.**

The data give

$$n = 11 \text{ pairs}$$

$$\bar{d} = 982 \text{ miles}$$

$$s_d = 1139.6 \text{ miles.}$$

$$SE(\bar{d}) = \frac{s_d}{\sqrt{n}} = \frac{1139.6}{\sqrt{11}} = 343.6$$

$$\text{So } t_{10} = \frac{\bar{d} - 0}{SE(\bar{d})} = \frac{982.0}{343.6} = 2.86$$

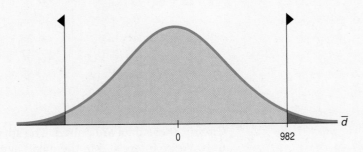

$$\text{P-value} = 2P(t_{10} > 2.86) = 0.017$$

*(continued)*

For Example (*continued*)

The P-value is small, so I reject the null hypothesis and conclude that the change in work week did lead to a change in average driving mileage.

It appears that changing the work schedule may reduce the mileage driven by workers. We should propose a course of action, but it's hard to tell from the hypothesis test whether the reduction matters. Is the difference in mileage important in the sense of reducing air pollution or costs, or is it merely statistically significant? To help make that decision, we should look at a confidence interval. If the difference in mileage proves to be large in a practical sense, then we might recommend a change in schedule for the rest of the department.

# Confidence Intervals for Matched Pairs

In developed countries, the average age of women is generally higher than that of men. After all, women tend to live longer. But if we look at *married couples,* husbands tend to be slightly older than wives. How much older, on average, are husbands? We have data from a random sample of 200 British couples, the first 16 of which are shown below. Only 170 couples provided ages for both husband and wife, so we can work only with that many pairs. Let's form a confidence interval for the mean difference of husband's and wife's age for these 170 couples. Here are the first 16 pairs:

| | |
|---|---|
| **WHO** | 170 Randomly sampled couples |
| **WHAT** | Ages |
| **UNITS** | Years |
| **WHEN** | Recently |
| **WHERE** | Britain |

| Wife's Age | Husband's Age | Difference (husband − wife) |
|:---:|:---:|:---:|
| 43 | 49 | 6 |
| 28 | 25 | −3 |
| 30 | 40 | 10 |
| 57 | 52 | −5 |
| 52 | 58 | 6 |
| 27 | 32 | 5 |
| 52 | 43 | −9 |
| 43 | 47 | 4 |
| 23 | 31 | 8 |
| 25 | 26 | 1 |
| 39 | 40 | 1 |
| 32 | 35 | 3 |
| 35 | 35 | 0 |
| 33 | 35 | 2 |
| 43 | 47 | 4 |
| 35 | 38 | 3 |
| ⋮ | ⋮ | ⋮ |

Clearly, these data are paired. The survey selected *couples* at random, not individuals. We're interested in the mean age difference within couples. How would we construct a confidence interval for the true mean difference in ages?

**PAIRED *t*-INTERVAL**

When the conditions are met, we are ready to find the confidence interval for the mean of the paired differences. The confidence interval is

$$\bar{d} \pm t^*_{n-1} \times SE(\bar{d}),$$

where the standard error of the mean difference is $SE(\bar{d}) = \dfrac{s_d}{\sqrt{n}}$.

The critical value $t^*$ from the Student's $t$-model depends on the particular confidence level, $C$, that you specify and on the degrees of freedom, $n - 1$, which is based on the number of pairs, $n$.

Making confidence intervals for matched pairs follows exactly the steps for a one-sample $t$-interval.

---

**STEP-BY-STEP EXAMPLE**    **A Paired $t$-Interval**

**Question: How big a difference is there, on average, between the ages of husbands and wives?**

---

 **THINK**

**Plan** State what we want to know.

Identify the variables and check the W's.

Identify the parameter you wish to estimate. For a paired analysis, the parameter of interest is the mean of the differences. The population of interest is the population of differences.

**Model** Think about the assumptions and check the conditions.

I want to estimate the mean difference in age between husbands and wives. I have a random sample of 200 British couples, 170 of whom provided both ages.

✔ **Paired Data Assumption:** The data are paired because they are on members of married couples.

✔ **Independence Assumption:** The data are from a randomized survey, so couples should be independent of each other.

✔ **Randomization Condition:** These couples were randomly sampled.

✔ **10% Condition:** The sample is less than 10% of the population of married couples in Britain.

✔ **Nearly Normal Condition:** The histogram of the husband–wife differences is unimodal and symmetric:

**REALITY CHECK** Make a picture. We focus on the differences, so a histogram or Normal probability plot is best here.

The histogram shows husbands are often older than wives (because most of the differences are greater than 0). The mean difference seen here of about 2 years is reasonable.

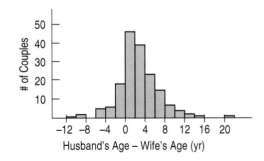

State the sampling distribution model.

Choose your method.

The conditions are met, so I can use a Student's $t$-model with $(n - 1) = 169$ degrees of freedom and find a **paired $t$-interval.**

**Mechanics**

$n$ is the number of *pairs*, here, the number of couples.

$\bar{d}$ is the mean difference.

$s_d$ is the standard deviation of the differences.

Be sure to include the units along with the statistics.

The critical value we need to make a 95% interval comes from a Student's $t$ table, a computer program, or a calculator.

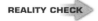 This result makes sense. Our everyday experience confirms that an average age difference of about 2 years is reasonable.

$n = 170$ couples
$\bar{d} = 2.2$ years
$s_d = 4.1$ years

I estimate the standard error of $\bar{d}$ as

$$SE(\bar{d}) = \frac{s_d}{\sqrt{n}} = \frac{4.1}{\sqrt{170}} = 0.31 \text{ years.}$$

The df for the $t$-model is $n - 1 = 169$.

The 95% critical value for $t_{169}$ (from the table) is 1.97.

The margin of error is

$$ME = t^*_{169} \times SE(\bar{d}) = 1.97(0.31) = 0.61$$

So the 95% confidence interval is

$$2.2 \pm 0.6 \text{ years,}$$

or an interval of (1.6, 2.8) years.

**Conclusion** Interpret the confidence interval in context.

I am 95% confident that British husbands are, on average, 1.6 to 2.8 years older than their wives.

## Effect Size

When we examined the speed-skating times, we failed to reject the null hypothesis, so we couldn't be certain whether there really was a difference between the lanes. Maybe there wasn't any difference, or maybe whatever difference there might have been was just too small to matter at all. Were the fans right to be concerned?

We can't tell from the hypothesis test, but using the same summary statistics, we can find that the corresponding 95% confidence interval for the mean difference is $(-0.70 < \mu_d < 1.70)$ seconds.

A confidence interval is a good way to get a sense for the size of the effect we're trying to understand. That gives us a plausible range of values for the true mean difference in lane times. If differences of 1.7 seconds were too small to matter in 1500-m Olympic speed skating, we'd be pretty sure there was no need for concern.

But in fact, except for the Gold–Silver gap, the successive gaps between each skater and the next–faster one were *all* less than the high end of this interval, and most were right around the middle of the interval:

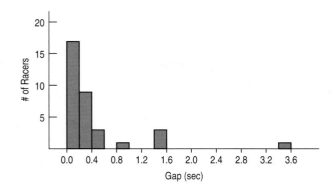

So even though we were unable to discern a real difference, the confidence interval shows that the effects we're considering may be big enough to be important. We may want to continue this investigation by checking out other races on this ice and being alert for possible differences at other venues.

---

**FOR EXAMPLE**      Looking at effect size with a paired-*t* confidence interval

**Recap:** We know that, on average, the switch from a five-day work week to a four-day work week reduced the amount driven by field workers in that Illinois health department. However, finding that there is a significant difference doesn't necessarily mean that difference is meaningful or worthwhile. To assess the size of the effect, we need a confidence interval. We already know the assumptions and conditions are met.

**Question:** By how much, on average, might a change in work week schedule reduce the amount driven by workers?

$$\bar{d} = 982 \; mi \qquad SE(\bar{d}) = 343.6 \qquad t_{10}^{*} = 2.228 \,(for \; 95\%)$$
$$ME = t_{10}^{*} \times SE(\bar{d}) = 2.228(343.6) = 765.54$$

So the 95 % confidence interval for $\mu_d$ is

$$982 \pm 765.54 \; or \; (216.46, 1747.54) \; fewer \; miles.$$

With 95% confidence, I estimate that by switching to a four-day work week employees would drive an average of between 216 and 1748 fewer miles per year. With high gas prices, this could save a lot of money.

---

# Blocking

**FIGURE 25.2**

*This display is worthless. It does no good to compare all the wives as a group with all the husbands. We care about the paired differences.*

Because the sample of British husbands and wives includes both older and younger couples, there's a lot of variation in the ages of the men and in the ages of the women. In fact, that variation is so great that a boxplot of the two groups would show little difference. But that would be the wrong plot. It's the *difference* we care about. Pairing isolates the extra variation and allows us to focus on the individual differences. In Chapter 13 we saw how we could design an experiment with blocking to isolate the variability between identifiable groups of subjects, allowing us to better see variability among treatment groups due to their response to the treatment. A paired design is an example of blocking.

When we pair, we have roughly half the degrees of freedom of a two-sample test. You may see discussions that suggest that in "choosing" a paired analysis we "give up" these degrees of freedom. This isn't really true, though. If the data are paired, then there never were additional degrees of freedom, and we have no "choice." The fact of the pairing determines how many degrees of freedom are available.

Matching pairs generally removes so much extra variation that it more than compensates for having only half the degrees of freedom. Of course, inappropriate matching when the groups are in fact independent (say, by matching on the first letter of the last name of subjects) would cost degrees of freedom without the benefit of reducing the variance. When you design a study or experiment, you should consider using a paired design if possible.

## JUST CHECKING

Think about each of the situations described below.

▸ Would you use a two-sample *t* or paired-*t* method (or neither)? Why?

▸ Would you perform a hypothesis test or find a confidence interval?

1. Random samples of 50 men and 50 women are asked to imagine buying a birthday present for their best friend. We want to estimate the difference in how much they are willing to spend.

2. Mothers of twins were surveyed and asked how often in the past month strangers had asked whether the twins were identical.

3. Are parents equally strict with boys and girls? In a random sample of families, researchers asked a brother and sister from each family to rate how strict their parents were.

4. Forty-eight overweight subjects are randomly assigned to either aerobic or stretching exercise programs. They are weighed at the beginning and at the end of the experiment to see how much weight they lost.
   **a)** We want to estimate the mean amount of weight lost by those doing aerobic exercise.
   **b)** We want to know which program is more effective at reducing weight.

5. Couples at a dance club were separated and each person was asked to rate the band. Do men or women like this band more?

## WHAT CAN GO WRONG?

▸ **Don't use a two-sample *t*-test when you have paired data.** See the What Can Go Wrong? discussion in Chapter 24.

▸ **Don't use a paired-*t* method when the samples aren't paired.** When two groups don't have the same number of values, it's pretty easy to see that they can't be paired. But just because two groups have the same number of observations doesn't mean they can be paired, even if they are shown side-by-side in a table. We might have 25 men and 25 women in our study, but they might be completely independent of one another. If they were siblings or spouses, we might consider them paired. Remember that you cannot *choose* which method to use based on your preferences. If the data are from two independent samples, use two-sample *t* methods. If the data are from an experiment in which observations were paired, you must use a paired method. If the data are from an observational study, you must be able to defend your decision to use matched pairs or independent groups.

▸ **Don't forget outliers.** The outliers we care about now are in the differences. A subject who is extraordinary both before and after a treatment may still have a perfectly typical difference. But one outlying difference can completely distort your conclusions. Be sure to plot the differences (even if you also plot the data).

▶ **Don't look for the difference between the means of paired groups with side-by-side boxplots.** The point of the paired analysis is to remove extra variation. The boxplots of each group still contain that variation. Comparing them is likely to be misleading.

# CONNECTIONS

The most important connection is to the concept of blocking that we first discussed when we considered designed experiments in Chapter 13. Pairing is a basic and very effective form of blocking.

Of course, the details of the mechanics for paired $t$-tests and intervals are identical to those for the one-sample $t$-methods. Everything we know about those methods applies here.

The connection to the two-sample and pooled methods of the previous chapter is that when the data are naturally paired, those methods are not appropriate because paired data fail the required condition of independence.

## WHAT HAVE WE LEARNED?

When we looked at various ways to design experiments, back in Chapter 13, we saw that pairing can be a very effective strategy. Because pairing can help control variability between individual subjects, paired methods are usually more powerful than methods that compare independent groups. Now we've learned that analyzing data from matched pairs requires different inference procedures.

▶ We've learned that paired $t$-methods look at pairwise differences. Based on these differences, we test hypotheses and generate confidence intervals. These procedures are mechanically identical to the one-sample $t$-methods we saw in Chapter 23.

▶ We've also learned to *Think* about the design of the study that collected the data before we proceed with inference. We must be careful to recognize pairing when it is present but not assume it when it is not. Making the correct decision about whether to use independent $t$-procedures or paired $t$-methods is the first critical step in analyzing the data.

## Terms

**Paired data**  651. Data are paired when the observations are collected in pairs or the observations in one group are naturally related to observations in the other. The simplest form of pairing is to measure each subject twice—often before and after a treatment is applied. More sophisticated forms of pairing in experiments are a form of blocking and arise in other contexts. Pairing in observational and survey data is a form of matching.

**Paired $t$-test**  654. A hypothesis test for the mean of the pairwise differences of two groups. It tests the null hypothesis

$$H_0: \mu_d = \Delta_0,$$

where the hypothesized difference is almost always 0, using the statistic

$$t = \frac{\bar{d} - \Delta_0}{SE(\bar{d})}$$

with $n - 1$ degrees of freedom, where $SE(\bar{d}) = \frac{s_d}{\sqrt{n}}$, and $n$ is the number of pairs.

Paired-*t* confidence interval

658. A confidence interval for the mean of the pairwise differences between independent groups found as

$$\bar{d} \pm t_{n-1}^* \times SE(\bar{d}), \text{ where } SE(\bar{d}) = \frac{s_d}{\sqrt{n}} \text{ and } n \text{ is the number of pairs.}$$

# Skills

▸ Be able to recognize whether a design that compares two groups is paired.

▸ Be able to find a paired confidence interval, recognizing that it is mechanically equivalent to doing a one-sample *t*-interval applied to the differences.

▸ Be able to perform a paired *t*-test, recognizing that it is mechanically equivalent to a one-sample *t*-test applied to the differences.

▸ Be able to interpret a paired *t*-test, recognizing that the hypothesis tested is about the mean of the differences between paired values rather than about the differences between the means of two independent groups.

▸ Be able to interpret a paired *t*-interval, recognizing that it gives an interval for the mean difference in the pairs.

# ON THE COMPUTER

# Paired *t*

Most statistics programs can compute paired-*t* analyses. Some may want you to find the differences yourself and use the one-sample *t* methods. Those that perform the entire procedure will need to know the two variables to compare. The computer, of course, cannot verify that the variables are naturally paired. Most programs will check whether the two variables have the same number of observations, but some stop there, and that can cause trouble. Most programs will automatically omit any pair that is missing a value for either variable (as we did with the British couples). You must look carefully to see whether that has happened.

As we've seen with other inference results, some packages pack a lot of information into a simple table, but you must locate what you want for yourself. Here's a generic example with comments:

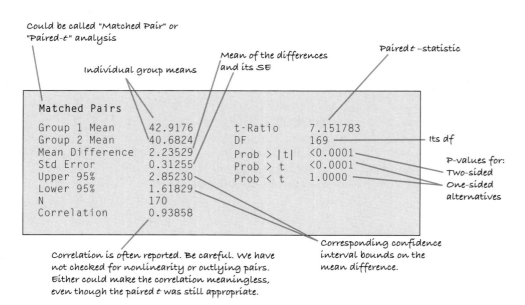

Other packages try to be more descriptive. It may be easier to find the results, but you may get less information from the output table.

Groups may have missing values. Only cases with both values present are used in a paired-*t* analysis. You may not learn that from some packages.

Even simple tables can have superfluous numbers such as these.

SD (differences)

SE($\bar{d}$)

CI corresponds to specified α.

$\bar{d}$

Some packages let you specify the alternative and report only results for that alternative.

*t*-statistic and its P-value (You may need to calculate $n_d - 1$ for yourself to get the df.)

Computers make it easy to examine the boxplots of the two groups and the histogram of the differences—both important steps. Some programs offer a scatterplot of the two variables. That can be helpful. In terms of the scatterplot, a paired *t*-test is about whether the points tend to be above or below the 45° line $y = x$. (Note, though, that pairing says nothing about whether the scatterplot should be straight. That doesn't matter for our *t*-methods.)

## DATA DESK

Select variables.
From the **Calc** menu, choose **Estimate** for confidence intervals or **Test** for hypothesis tests. Select the interval or test from the drop-down menu, and make other choices in the dialog.

### COMMENTS

Data Desk expects the two groups to be in separate variables and in the same "Relation"—that is, about the same cases.

## EXCEL

In Excel 2003 and earlier, select **Data Analysis** from the **Tools** menu.
In Excel 2007, select **Data Analysis** from the **Analysis** Group on the **Data** Tab.
From the **Data Analysis** menu, choose **t-test: paired two-sample for Means.** Fill in the cell ranges for the two groups, the hypothesized difference, and the alpha level.

### COMMENTS

Excel expects the two groups to be in separate cell ranges.
**Warning:** Do not compute this test in Excel without checking for missing values. If there are any missing values (empty cells), Excel will usually give a wrong answer. Excel compacts each list, pushing values up to cover the missing cells, and then checks only that it has the same number of values in each list. The result is mismatched pairs and an entirely wrong analysis.

## JMP

From the **Analyze** menu, select **Matched Pairs.** Specify the columns holding the two groups in the **Y Paired Response** Dialog. Click **OK.**

## MINITAB

From the **Stat** menu, choose the **Basic Statistics** submenu. From that menu, choose **Paired t...** Then fill in the dialog.

### COMMENTS

Minitab takes "First sample" minus "Second sample."

# EXERCISES

1. **More eggs?**   Can a food additive increase egg production? Agricultural researchers want to design an experiment to find out. They have 100 hens available. They have two kinds of feed: the regular feed and the new feed with the additive. They plan to run their experiment for a month, recording the number of eggs each hen produces.
   a) Design an experiment that will require a two-sample *t* procedure to analyze the results.
   b) Design an experiment that will require a matched-pairs *t* procedure to analyze the results.
   c) Which experiment would you consider the stronger design? Why?

2. **MTV.**   Some students do homework with the TV on. (Anyone come to mind?) Some researchers want to see if people can work as effectively with as without distraction. The researchers will time some volunteers to see how long it takes them to complete some relatively easy crossword puzzles. During some of the trials, the room will be quiet; during other trials in the same room, a TV will be on, tuned to MTV.
   a) Design an experiment that will require a two-sample *t* procedure to analyze the results.
   b) Design an experiment that will require a matched-pairs *t* procedure to analyze the results.
   c) Which experiment would you consider the stronger design? Why?

3. **Sex sells?**   Ads for many products use sexual images to try to attract attention to the product. But do these ads bring people's attention to the item that was being advertised? We want to design an experiment to see if the presence of sexual images in an advertisement affects people's ability to remember the product.
   a) Describe an experimental design that would require a matched-pairs *t* procedure to analyze the results.
   b) Describe an experimental design that would require an independent sample procedure to analyze the results.

4. **Freshman 15?**   Many people believe that students gain weight as freshmen. Suppose we plan to conduct a study to see if this is true.
   a) Describe a study design that would require a matched-pairs *t* procedure to analyze the results.
   b) Describe a study design that would require a two-sample *t* procedure to analyze the results.

5. **Women.**   Values for the labor force participation rate of women (LFPR) are published by the U.S. Bureau of Labor Statistics. We are interested in whether there was a difference between female participation in 1968 and 1972, a time of rapid change for women. We check LFPR values for 19 randomly selected cities for 1968 and 1972. Shown on the next page is software output for two possible tests:

Paired t-Test of $\mu(1 - 2)$
Test Ho: $\mu(1972\text{-}1968) = 0$ vs Ha: $\mu(1972\text{-}1968) \neq 0$
Mean of Paired Differences = 0.0337
t-Statistic = 2.458 w/18 df
p = 0.0244

2-Sample t-Test of $\mu 1 - \mu 2$
Ho: $\mu 1 - \mu 2 = 0$ Ha: $\mu 1 - \mu 2 \neq 0$
Test Ho: $\mu(1972) - \mu(1968) = 0$ vs
Ha: $\mu(1972) - \mu(1968) \neq 0$
Difference Between Means = 0.0337
t-Statistic = 1.496 w/35 df
p = 0.1434

a) Which of these tests is appropriate for these data? Explain.
b) Using the test you selected, state your conclusion.

**T** **6. Rain.** Simpson, Alsen, and Eden (*Technometrics* 1975) report the results of trials in which clouds were seeded and the amount of rainfall recorded. The authors report on 26 seeded and 26 unseeded clouds in order of the amount of rainfall, largest amount first. Here are two possible tests to study the question of whether cloud seeding works. Which test is appropriate for these data? Explain your choice. Using the test you select, state your conclusion.

Paired t-Test of $\mu(1 - 2)$
Mean of Paired Differences = –277.39615
t-Statistic = –3.641 w/25 df
p = 0.0012

2-Sample t-Test of $\mu 1 - \mu 2$
Difference Between Means = –277.4
t-Statistic = –1.998 w/33 df
p = 0.0538

a) Which of these tests is appropriate for these data? Explain.
b) Using the test you selected, state your conclusion.

**T** **7. Friday the 13th, I.** In 1993 the *British Medical Journal* published an article titled, "Is Friday the 13th Bad for Your Health?" Researchers in Britain examined how Friday the 13th affects human behavior. One question was whether people tend to stay at home more on Friday the 13th. The data below are the number of cars passing Junctions 9 and 10 on the M25 motorway for consecutive Fridays (the 6th and 13th) for five different periods.

| Year | Month | 6th | 13th |
|------|-------|-----|------|
| 1990 | July | 134,012 | 132,908 |
| 1991 | September | 133,732 | 131,843 |
| 1991 | December | 121,139 | 118,723 |
| 1992 | March | 124,631 | 120,249 |
| 1992 | November | 117,584 | 117,263 |

Here are summaries of two possible analyses:

Paired t-Test of mu(1 – 2) = 0 vs. mu(1 – 2) > 0
Mean of Paired Differences: 2022.4
t-Statistic = 2.9377 w/4 df
P = 0.0212

2-Sample t-Test of mu1 = mu2 vs. mu1 > mu2
Difference Between Means: 2022.4
t-Statistic = 0.4273 w/7.998 df
P = 0.3402

a) Which of the tests is appropriate for these data? Explain.
b) Using the test you selected, state your conclusion.
c) Are the assumptions and conditions for inference met?

**T** **8. Friday the 13th, II:** The researchers in Exercise 7 also examined the number of people admitted to emergency rooms for vehicular accidents on 12 Friday evenings (6 each on the 6th and 13th).

| Year | Month | 6th | 13th |
|------|-------|-----|------|
| 1989 | October | 9 | 13 |
| 1990 | July | 6 | 12 |
| 1991 | September | 11 | 14 |
| 1991 | December | 11 | 10 |
| 1992 | March | 3 | 4 |
| 1992 | November | 5 | 12 |

Based on these data, is there evidence that more people are admitted, on average, on Friday the 13th? Here are two possible analyses of the data:

Paired t-Test of mu(1 – 2) = 0 vs. mu(1 – 2) < 0
Mean of Paired Differences = 3.333
t-Statistic = 2.7116 w/5 df
P = 0.0211

2-Sample t-Test of mu1 = mu2 vs. mu1 < mu2
Difference Between Means = 3.333
t-Statistic = 1.6644 w/9.940 df
P = 0.0636

a) Which of these tests is appropriate for these data? Explain.
b) Using the test you selected, state your conclusion.
c) Are the assumptions and conditions for inference met?

**9. Online insurance I.** After seeing countless commercials claiming one can get cheaper car insurance from an online company, a local insurance agent was concerned that he might lose some customers. To investigate, he randomly selected profiles (type of car, coverage, driving record, etc.) for 10 of his clients and checked online price quotes for their policies. The comparisons are shown in the table on the next page. His statistical software produced the following summaries (where *PriceDiff = Local – Online*):

| Variable | Count | Mean | StdDev |
|----------|-------|------|--------|
| Local | 10 | 799.200 | 229.281 |
| Online | 10 | 753.300 | 256.267 |
| PriceDiff | 10 | 45.9000 | 175.663 |

| Local | Online | PriceDiff |
|-------|--------|-----------|
| 568 | 391 | 177 |
| 872 | 602 | 270 |
| 451 | 488 | −37 |
| 1229 | 903 | 326 |
| 605 | 677 | −72 |
| 1021 | 1270 | −249 |
| 783 | 703 | 80 |
| 844 | 789 | 55 |
| 907 | 1008 | −101 |
| 712 | 702 | 10 |

At first, the insurance agent wondered whether there was some kind of mistake in this output. He thought the Pythagorean Theorem of Statistics should work for finding the standard deviation of the price differences—in other words, that $SD(Local − Online) = \sqrt{SD^2(Local) + SD^2(Online)}$. But when he checked, he found that $\sqrt{(229.281)^2 + (256.267)^2} = 343.864$, not 175.663 as given by the software. Tell him where his mistake is.

**T 10. Windy, part I.** To select the site for an electricity-generating wind turbine, wind speeds were recorded at several potential sites every 6 hours for a year. Two sites not far from each other looked good. Each had a mean wind speed high enough to qualify, but we should choose the site with a higher average daily wind speed. Because the sites are near each other and the wind speeds were recorded at the same times, we should view the speeds as paired. Here are the summaries of the speeds (in miles per hour):

| Variable | Count | Mean | StdDev |
|----------|-------|------|--------|
| site2 | 1114 | 7.452 | 3.586 |
| site4 | 1114 | 7.248 | 3.421 |
| site2 − site4 | 1114 | 0.204 | 2.551 |

Is there a mistake in this output? Why doesn't the Pythagorean Theorem of Statistics work here? In other words, shouldn't

$$SD(site2 − site4) = \sqrt{SD^2(site2) + SD^2(site4)}?$$

But $\sqrt{(3.586)^2 + (3.421)^2} = 4.956$, not 2.551 as given by the software. Explain why this happened.

**11. Online insurance II.** In Exercise 9, we saw summary statistics for 10 drivers' car insurance premiums quoted by a local agent and an online company. Here are displays for each company's quotes and for the difference (*Local − Online*):

a) Which of the summaries would help you decide whether the online company offers cheaper insurance? Why?

b) The standard deviation of *PriceDiff* is quite a bit smaller than the standard deviation of prices quoted by either the local or online companies. Discuss why.

c) Using the information you have, discuss the assumptions and conditions for inference with these data.

**T 12. Windy, part II.** In Exercise 10, we saw summary statistics for wind speeds at two sites near each other, both being considered as locations for an electricity-generating wind turbine. The data, recorded every 6 hours for a year, showed each of the sites had a mean wind speed high enough to qualify, but how can we tell which site is best? Here are some displays:

a) The boxplots show outliers for each site, yet the histogram shows none. Discuss why.
b) Which of the summaries would you use to select between these sites? Why?
c) Using the information you have, discuss the assumptions and conditions for paired $t$ inference for these data. (*Hint:* Think hard about the independence assumption in particular.)

**13. Online insurance 3.** Exercises 9 and 11 give summaries and displays for car insurance premiums quoted by a local agent and an online company. Test an appropriate hypothesis to see if there is evidence that drivers might save money by switching to the online company.

**14. Windy, part III.** Exercises 10 and 12 give summaries and displays for two potential sites for a wind turbine. Test an appropriate hypothesis to see if there is evidence that either of these sites has a higher average wind speed.

**15. Wheelchair marathon 2007.** The Boston Marathon has had a wheelchair division since 1977. Who do you think is typically faster, the men's marathon winner on foot or the women's wheelchair marathon winner? Because the conditions differ from year to year, and speeds have improved over the years, it seems best to treat these as paired measurements. Here are summary statistics for the pairwise differences in finishing time (in minutes): (www.boston.com/sports/marathon)

Summary of wheelchrF – runM
N = 31
Mean = –2.12097
SD = 36.4434

a) Comment on the assumptions and conditions.
b) Assuming that these times are representative of such races and the differences appeared acceptable for

inference, construct and interpret a 95% confidence interval for the mean difference in finishing times.
c) Would a hypothesis test at $\alpha = 0.05$ reject the null hypothesis of no difference? What conclusion would you draw?

**16. Boston startup years 2007.** When we considered the Boston Marathon in Exercise 15, we were unable to check the Nearly Normal Condition. Here's a histogram of the differences:

Those three large differences are the first three years of wheelchair competition: 1977, 1978, and 1979. Often the start-up years of new events are different; later on, more athletes train and compete. If we omit those three years, the summary statistics change as follows:

Summary of wheelchrF – runM
N = 28
Mean = –12.1780
SD = 19.5116

a) Comment on the assumptions and conditions.
b) Assuming that these times are representative of such races, construct and interpret a 95% confidence interval for the mean difference in finishing time.
c) Would a hypothesis test at $\alpha = 0.05$ reject the null hypothesis of no difference? What conclusion would you draw?

**17. BST.** Many dairy cows now receive injections of BST, a hormone intended to spur greater milk production. After the first injection, a test herd of 60 Ayrshire cows increased their mean daily production from 47 pounds to 61 pounds of milk. The standard deviation of the increases was 5.2 pounds. We want to estimate the mean increase a farmer could expect in his own cows.
a) Check the assumptions and conditions for inference.
b) Write a 95% confidence interval.
c) Explain what your interval means in this context.
d) Given the cost of BST, a farmer believes he cannot afford to use it unless he is sure of attaining at least a 25% increase in milk production. Based on your confidence interval, what advice would you give him?

**18. BST II.** In the experiment about hormone injections in cows described in Exercise 17, a group of 52 Jersey cows increased average milk production from 43 pounds to 52 pounds per day, with a standard deviation of 4.8 pounds. Is this evidence that the hormone may be more effective in one breed than the other? Test an appropriate hypothesis and state your conclusion. Be sure to discuss any assumptions you make.

**19. Temperatures.**   The table below gives the average high temperatures in January and July for several European cities. Write a 90% confidence interval for the mean temperature difference between summer and winter in Europe. Be sure to check conditions for inference, and clearly explain what your interval means.

| City | Mean High Temperatures (°F) | |
|------|------|------|
| | **Jan.** | **July** |
| Vienna | 34 | 75 |
| Copenhagen | 36 | 72 |
| Paris | 42 | 76 |
| Berlin | 35 | 74 |
| Athens | 54 | 90 |
| Rome | 54 | 88 |
| Amsterdam | 40 | 69 |
| Madrid | 47 | 87 |
| London | 44 | 73 |
| Edinburgh | 43 | 65 |
| Moscow | 21 | 76 |
| Belgrade | 37 | 84 |

**20. Marathons 2006.**   Shown are the winning times (in minutes) for men and women in the New York City Marathon between 1978 and 2006. Assuming that performances in the Big Apple resemble performances elsewhere, we can think of these data as a sample of performance in marathon competitions. Create a 90% confidence interval for the mean difference in winning times for male and female marathon competitors. (www.nycmarathon.org)

| Year | Men | Women | Year | Men | Women |
|------|------|------|------|------|------|
| 1978 | 132.2 | 152.5 | 1993 | 130.1 | 146.4 |
| 1979 | 131.7 | 147.6 | 1994 | 131.4 | 147.6 |
| 1980 | 129.7 | 145.7 | 1995 | 131.0 | 148.1 |
| 1981 | 128.2 | 145.5 | 1996 | 129.9 | 148.3 |
| 1982 | 129.5 | 147.2 | 1997 | 128.2 | 148.7 |
| 1983 | 129.0 | 147.0 | 1998 | 128.8 | 145.3 |
| 1984 | 134.9 | 149.5 | 1999 | 129.2 | 145.1 |
| 1985 | 131.6 | 148.6 | 2000 | 130.2 | 145.8 |
| 1986 | 131.1 | 148.1 | 2001 | 127.7 | 144.4 |
| 1987 | 131.0 | 150.3 | 2002 | 128.1 | 145.9 |
| 1988 | 128.3 | 148.1 | 2003 | 130.5 | 142.5 |
| 1989 | 128.0 | 145.5 | 2004 | 129.5 | 143.2 |
| 1990 | 132.7 | 150.8 | 2005 | 129.5 | 144.7 |
| 1991 | 129.5 | 147.5 | 2006 | 130.0 | 145.1 |
| 1992 | 129.5 | 144.7 | | | |

**21. Push-ups.**   Every year the students at Gossett High School take a physical fitness test during their gym classes. One component of the test asks them to do as many push-ups as they can. Results for one class are shown below, separately for boys and girls. Assuming that students at Gossett are assigned to gym classes at random, create a 90% confidence interval for how many more push-ups boys can do than girls, on average, at that high school.

| Boys | 17 | 27 | 31 | 17 | 25 | 32 | 28 | 23 | 25 | 16 | 11 | 34 |
|------|----|----|----|----|----|----|----|----|----|----|----|----|
| Girls | 24 | 7 | 14 | 16 | 2 | 15 | 19 | 25 | 10 | 27 | 31 | 8 |

**22. Exercise.**   An August 2001 article in the journal *Medicine and Science in Sports and Exercise* compared how long it would take men and women to burn 200 calories during light or heavy workouts on various kinds of exercise equipment. The results summarized in the table are the average times for a group of physically active young men and women whose performances were measured on each type of equipment.
a) On average, how many minutes longer than a man must a woman exercise at a light exertion rate in order to burn 200 calories? Give a 95% confidence interval.
b) Estimate the average number of minutes longer a woman must work out at light exertion than at heavy exertion to get the same benefit. Give a 95% confidence interval.
c) These data are actually averages rather than individual times. How might this affect the margins of error in these confidence intervals?

| | Average Minutes to Burn 200 Calories | | | |
|------|------|------|------|------|
| | Hard Exertion | | Light Exertion | |
| Machine Type | **Men** | **Women** | **Men** | **Women** |
| Treadmill | 12 | 17 | 14 | 22 |
| X-C skier | 12 | 16 | 16 | 23 |
| Stair climber | 13 | 18 | 20 | 37 |
| Rowing machine | 14 | 16 | 21 | 25 |
| Exercise rider | 22 | 24 | 27 | 36 |
| Exercise bike | 16 | 20 | 29 | 44 |

**23. Job satisfaction.**   (When you first read about this exercise break plan in Chapter 24, you did not have an inference method that would work. Try again now.) A company institutes an exercise break for its workers to see if it will improve job satisfaction, as measured by a questionnaire that assesses workers' satisfaction. Scores for 10 randomly selected workers before and after the implementation of the exercise program are shown in the table on the next page.
a) Identify the procedure you would use to assess the effectiveness of the exercise program, and check to see if the conditions allow the use of that procedure.
b) Test an appropriate hypothesis and state your conclusion.

| Worker | Job Satisfaction Index | |
|---|---|---|
| Number | Before | After |
| 1 | 34 | 33 |
| 2 | 28 | 36 |
| 3 | 29 | 50 |
| 4 | 45 | 41 |
| 5 | 26 | 37 |
| 6 | 27 | 41 |
| 7 | 24 | 39 |
| 8 | 15 | 21 |
| 9 | 15 | 20 |
| 10 | 27 | 37 |

**24. Summer school.** (When you first read about the summer school issue in Chapter 24 you did not have an inference method that would work. Try again now.) Having done poorly on their Math final exams in June, six students repeat the course in summer school and take another exam in August. If we consider these students to be representative of all students who might attend this summer school in other years, do these results provide evidence that the program is worthwhile?

| June | 54 | 49 | 68 | 66 | 62 | 62 |
|---|---|---|---|---|---|---|
| Aug. | 50 | 65 | 74 | 64 | 68 | 72 |

**25. Sleep.** W.S. Gosset (Student) refers to data recording the number of hours of additional sleep gained by 10 patients from the use of *laevohyoscyamine hydrobromide*. We want to see if there is strong evidence that the herb can help people get more sleep.
a) State the null and alternative hypotheses clearly.
b) A *t*-test of the null hypothesis of no gain has a *t*-statistic of 3.680 with 9 degrees of freedom. Find the P-value.
c) Interpret this result by explaining the meaning of the P-value.
d) State your conclusion regarding the hypotheses.
e) This conclusion, of course, may be incorrect. If so, which type of error was made?

**26. Gasoline.** Many drivers of cars that can run on regular gas actually buy premium in the belief that they will get better gas mileage. To test that belief, we use 10 cars from a company fleet in which all the cars run on regular gas. Each car is filled first with either regular or premium gasoline, decided by a coin toss, and the mileage for that tankful is recorded. Then the mileage is recorded again for the same cars for a tankful of the other kind of gasoline. We don't let the drivers know about this experiment.
Here are the results (miles per gallon):

| Car # | 1 | 2 | 3 | 4 | 5 | 6 | 7 | 8 | 9 | 10 |
|---|---|---|---|---|---|---|---|---|---|---|
| Regular | 16 | 20 | 21 | 22 | 23 | 22 | 27 | 25 | 27 | 28 |
| Premium | 19 | 22 | 24 | 24 | 25 | 25 | 26 | 26 | 28 | 32 |

a) Is there evidence that cars get significantly better fuel economy with premium gasoline?
b) How big might that difference be? Check a 90% confidence interval.
c) Even if the difference is significant, why might the company choose to stick with regular gasoline?
d) Suppose you had done a "bad thing." (We're sure you didn't.) Suppose you had mistakenly treated these data as two independent samples instead of matched pairs. What would the significance test have found? Carefully explain why the results are so different.

**27. Yogurt.** Do these data suggest that there is a significant difference in calories between servings of strawberry and vanilla yogurt? Test an appropriate hypothesis and state your conclusion. Don't forget to check assumptions and conditions!

| | | Calories per Serving | |
|---|---|---|---|
| | | Strawberry | Vanilla |
| **Brand** | America's Choice | 210 | 200 |
| | Breyer's Lowfat | 220 | 220 |
| | Columbo | 220 | 180 |
| | Dannon Light 'n Fit | 120 | 120 |
| | Dannon Lowfat | 210 | 230 |
| | Dannon la Crème | 140 | 140 |
| | Great Value | 180 | 80 |
| | La Yogurt | 170 | 160 |
| | Mountain High | 200 | 170 |
| | Stonyfield Farm | 100 | 120 |
| | Yoplait Custard | 190 | 190 |
| | Yoplait Light | 100 | 100 |

**28. Caffeine.** A student experiment investigating the potential impact of caffeine on studying for a test involved 30 subjects randomly divided into two groups. Each group took a memory test. The subjects then each drank two cups of regular (caffeinated) cola or caffeine-free cola. Thirty minutes later they each took another version of the memory test, and the changes in their scores were noted. Among the 15 subjects who drank caffeine, scores fell an average of −0.933 points, with a standard deviation of 2.988 points. Among the no-caffeine group, scores went up an average of 1.429 points, with a standard deviation of 2.441 points. Assumptions of Normality were deemed reasonable based on histograms of differences in scores.
a) Did scores change significantly for the group that drank caffeine? Test an appropriate hypothesis and state your conclusion.
b) Did scores change significantly for the no-caffeine group? Test an appropriate hypothesis and state your conclusion.
c) Does this indicate that some mystery substance in noncaffeinated soda may aid memory? What other explanation is plausible?

**29. Braking.** In a test of braking performance, a tire manufacturer measured the stopping distance for one of its tire models. On a test track, a car made repeated stops from 60 miles per hour. The test was run on both dry and wet pavement, with results as shown in the table. (Note that actual *braking distance,* which takes into account the driver's reaction time, is much longer, typically nearly 300 feet at 60 mph!)

a) Write a 95% confidence interval for the mean dry pavement stopping distance. Be sure to check the appropriate assumptions and conditions, and explain what your interval means.

b) Write a 95% confidence interval for the mean increase in stopping distance on wet pavement. Be sure to check the appropriate assumptions and conditions, and explain what your interval means.

| Stopping Distance (ft) | |
|---|---|
| **Dry Pavement** | **Wet Pavement** |
| 145 | 211 |
| 152 | 191 |
| 141 | 220 |
| 143 | 207 |
| 131 | 198 |
| 148 | 208 |
| 126 | 206 |
| 140 | 177 |
| 135 | 183 |
| 133 | 223 |

**30. Brain waves.** An experiment was performed to see whether sensory deprivation over an extended period of time has any effect on the alpha-wave patterns produced by the brain. To determine this, 20 subjects, inmates in a Canadian prison, were randomly split into two groups. Members of one group were placed in solitary confinement. Those in the other group were allowed to remain in their own cells. Seven days later, alpha-wave frequencies were measured for all subjects, as shown in the following table. (P. Gendreau et al., "Changes in EEG Alpha Frequency and Evoked Response Latency During Solitary Confinement," *Journal of Abnormal Psychology* 79 [1972]: 54–59)

| Nonconfined | Confined |
|---|---|
| 10.7 | 9.6 |
| 10.7 | 10.4 |
| 10.4 | 9.7 |
| 10.9 | 10.3 |
| 10.5 | 9.2 |
| 10.3 | 9.3 |
| 9.6 | 9.9 |
| 11.1 | 9.5 |
| 11.2 | 9.0 |
| 10.4 | 10.9 |

a) What are the null and alternative hypotheses? Be sure to define all the terms and symbols you use.

b) Are the assumptions necessary for inference met?

c) Perform the appropriate test, indicating the formula you used, the calculated value of the test statistic, and the P-value.

d) State your conclusion.

**31. Braking, test 2.** For another test of the tires in Exercise 29, the company tried them on 10 different cars, recording the stopping distance for each car on both wet and dry pavement. Results are shown in the table.

| | Stopping Distance (ft) | |
|---|---|---|
| Car # | **Dry Pavement** | **Wet Pavement** |
| 1 | 150 | 201 |
| 2 | 147 | 220 |
| 3 | 136 | 192 |
| 4 | 134 | 146 |
| 5 | 130 | 182 |
| 6 | 134 | 173 |
| 7 | 134 | 202 |
| 8 | 128 | 180 |
| 9 | 136 | 192 |
| 10 | 158 | 206 |

a) Write a 95% confidence interval for the mean dry pavement stopping distance. Be sure to check the appropriate assumptions and conditions, and explain what your interval means.

b) Write a 95% confidence interval for the mean increase in stopping distance on wet pavement. Be sure to check the appropriate assumptions and conditions, and explain what your interval means.

**32. Tuition 2006.** How much more do public colleges and universities charge out-of-state students for tuition per semester? A random sample of 19 public colleges and universities listed at www.collegeboard.com yielded the following data. Tuition figures per semester are rounded to the nearest hundred dollars.

| Institution | Resident | Nonresident |
|---|---|---|
| Univ of Akron (OH) | 4200 | 8800 |
| Athens State (AL) | 1900 | 3600 |
| Ball State (IN) | 3400 | 8600 |
| Bloomsburg U (PA) | 3200 | 7000 |
| UC Irvine (CA) | 3400 | 12700 |
| Central State (OH) | 2600 | 5700 |
| Clarion U (PA) | 3300 | 5900 |
| Dakota State | 2900 | 3400 |
| Fairmont State (WV) | 2200 | 4600 |
| Johnson State (VT) | 3400 | 7300 |
| Lock Haven U (PA) | 3200 | 6000 |
| New College of Florida | 1600 | 8300 |
| Oakland U (MI) | 3300 | 7700 |
| U Pittsburgh | 6100 | 10700 |
| Savannah State (GA) | 1600 | 5400 |
| SE Louisiana | 1700 | 4400 |
| W Liberty State (WV) | 2000 | 4800 |
| W Texas College | 800 | 1000 |
| Worcester State (MA) | 2800 | 5800 |

a) Create a 90% confidence interval for the mean difference in cost. Be sure to justify the procedure you use.

b) Interpret your interval in context.

c) A national magazine claims that public institutions charge state residents an average of $3500 less for tuition each semester. What does your confidence interval indicate about the validity of this assertion?

**T** **33. Sex sells, part II.** In Exercise 3 you considered the question of whether sexual images in ads affected people's abilities to remember the item being advertised. To investigate, a group of Statistics students cut ads out of magazines. They were careful to find two ads for each of 10 similar items, one with a sexual image and one without. They arranged the ads in random order and had 39 subjects look at them for one minute. Then they asked the subjects to list as many of the products as they could remember. Their data are shown in the table. Is there evidence that the sexual images mattered?

| Subject Number | Ads Remembered Sexual Image | No Sex | Subject Number | Ads Remembered Sexual Image | No Sex |
|---|---|---|---|---|---|
| 1 | 2 | 2 | 21 | 2 | 3 |
| 2 | 6 | 7 | 22 | 4 | 2 |
| 3 | 3 | 1 | 23 | 3 | 3 |
| 4 | 6 | 5 | 24 | 5 | 3 |
| 5 | 1 | 0 | 25 | 4 | 5 |
| 6 | 3 | 3 | 26 | 2 | 4 |
| 7 | 3 | 5 | 27 | 2 | 2 |
| 8 | 7 | 4 | 28 | 2 | 4 |
| 9 | 3 | 7 | 29 | 7 | 6 |
| 10 | 5 | 4 | 30 | 6 | 7 |
| 11 | 1 | 3 | 31 | 4 | 3 |
| 12 | 3 | 2 | 32 | 4 | 5 |
| 13 | 6 | 3 | 33 | 3 | 0 |
| 14 | 7 | 4 | 34 | 4 | 3 |
| 15 | 3 | 2 | 35 | 2 | 3 |
| 16 | 7 | 4 | 36 | 3 | 3 |
| 17 | 4 | 4 | 37 | 5 | 5 |
| 18 | 1 | 3 | 38 | 3 | 4 |
| 19 | 5 | 5 | 39 | 4 | 3 |
| 20 | 2 | 2 | | | |

**T** **34. Freshman 15, revisited.** In Exercise 4 you thought about how to design a study to see if it's true that students tend to gain weight during their first year in college. Well, Cornell Professor of Nutrition David Levitsky did just that. He recruited students from two large sections of an introductory health course. Although they were volunteers, they appeared to match the rest of the freshman class in terms of demographic variables such as sex and ethnicity. The students were weighed during the first week of the semester, then again 12 weeks later. Based on Professor Levitsky's data, estimate the mean weight gain in first-semester freshmen and comment on the "freshman 15." (Weights are in pounds.)

| Subject Number | Initial Weight | Terminal Weight | Subject Number | Initial Weight | Terminal Weight |
|---|---|---|---|---|---|
| 1 | 171 | 168 | 35 | 148 | 150 |
| 2 | 110 | 111 | 36 | 164 | 165 |
| 3 | 134 | 136 | 37 | 137 | 138 |
| 4 | 115 | 119 | 38 | 198 | 201 |
| 5 | 150 | 155 | 39 | 122 | 124 |
| 6 | 104 | 106 | 40 | 146 | 146 |
| 7 | 142 | 148 | 41 | 150 | 151 |
| 8 | 120 | 124 | 42 | 187 | 192 |
| 9 | 144 | 148 | 43 | 94 | 96 |
| 10 | 156 | 154 | 44 | 105 | 105 |
| 11 | 114 | 114 | 45 | 127 | 130 |
| 12 | 121 | 123 | 46 | 142 | 144 |
| 13 | 122 | 126 | 47 | 140 | 143 |
| 14 | 120 | 115 | 48 | 107 | 107 |
| 15 | 115 | 118 | 49 | 104 | 105 |
| 16 | 110 | 113 | 50 | 111 | 112 |
| 17 | 142 | 146 | 51 | 160 | 162 |
| 18 | 127 | 127 | 52 | 134 | 134 |
| 19 | 102 | 105 | 53 | 151 | 151 |
| 20 | 125 | 125 | 54 | 127 | 130 |
| 21 | 157 | 158 | 55 | 106 | 108 |
| 22 | 119 | 126 | 56 | 185 | 188 |
| 23 | 113 | 114 | 57 | 125 | 128 |
| 24 | 120 | 128 | 58 | 125 | 126 |
| 25 | 135 | 139 | 59 | 155 | 158 |
| 26 | 148 | 150 | 60 | 118 | 120 |
| 27 | 110 | 112 | 61 | 149 | 150 |
| 28 | 160 | 163 | 62 | 149 | 149 |
| 29 | 220 | 224 | 63 | 122 | 121 |
| 30 | 132 | 133 | 64 | 155 | 158 |
| 31 | 145 | 147 | 65 | 160 | 161 |
| 32 | 141 | 141 | 66 | 115 | 119 |
| 33 | 158 | 160 | 67 | 167 | 170 |
| 34 | 135 | 134 | 68 | 131 | 131 |

**T** **35. Strikes.** Advertisements for an instructional video claim that the techniques will improve the ability of Little League pitchers to throw strikes and that, after undergoing the training, players will be able to throw strikes on at least 60% of their pitches. To test this claim, we have 20 Little Leaguers throw 50 pitches each, and we record the number of strikes. After the players participate in the training program, we repeat the test. The table on the next page shows the number of strikes each player threw before and after the training.

a) Is there evidence that after training players can throw strikes more than 60% of the time?

b) Is there evidence that the training is effective in improving a player's ability to throw strikes?

| Number of Strikes (out of 50) | | Number of Strikes (out of 50) | |
|---|---|---|---|
| **Before** | **After** | **Before** | **After** |
| 28 | 35 | 33 | 33 |
| 29 | 36 | 33 | 35 |
| 30 | 32 | 34 | 32 |
| 32 | 28 | 34 | 30 |
| 32 | 30 | 34 | 33 |
| 32 | 31 | 35 | 34 |
| 32 | 32 | 36 | 37 |
| 32 | 34 | 36 | 33 |
| 32 | 35 | 37 | 35 |
| 33 | 36 | 37 | 32 |

**36. Uninsured.** During the economic recession of 2000–2001, unemployment increased and job benefits were scaled back. The table shows the percentage of people in each state who lacked health insurance during the '99–'00 and '00–'01 fiscal years, as reported by the U.S. Census Bureau. Is there any evidence that more people were without health insurance during the recession?

| State | '99–'00 | '00–'01 | State | '99–'00 | '00–'01 |
|---|---|---|---|---|---|
| AL | 13.3 | 13.2 | MT | 17.3 | 15.2 |
| AK | 18.6 | 17.3 | NE | 17.7 | 16.5 |
| AZ | 18.6 | 17.3 | NV | 17.7 | 16.5 |
| AR | 14.4 | 15.2 | NH | 8.7 | 8.9 |
| CA | 19.0 | 19.0 | NJ | 12.1 | 12.6 |
| CO | 14.9 | 14.9 | NM | 24.4 | 22.4 |
| CT | 9.4 | 10.0 | NY | 15.9 | 15.9 |
| DE | 9.6 | 9.2 | NC | 14.0 | 14.0 |
| DC | 14.1 | 13.4 | ND | 11.5 | 10.5 |
| FL | 17.6 | 17.9 | OH | 10.7 | 11.2 |
| GA | 14.7 | 15.5 | OK | 17.7 | 18.6 |
| HI | 9.8 | 9.5 | OR | 13.3 | 12.7 |
| ID | 16.8 | 15.7 | PA | 8.5 | 9.0 |
| IL | 13.6 | 13.7 | RI | 6.9 | 7.6 |
| IN | 10.3 | 11.5 | SC | 13.8 | 12.2 |
| IA | 8.2 | 8.2 | SD | 10.9 | 10.2 |
| KS | 11.4 | 11.1 | TN | 10.6 | 11.1 |
| KY | 13.4 | 13.0 | TX | 22.7 | 23.2 |
| LA | 19.9 | 18.7 | UT | 13.0 | 13.7 |
| ME | 10.8 | 10.6 | VT | 9.8 | 9.1 |
| MD | 10.8 | 11.3 | VA | 12.4 | 11.3 |
| MA | 9.0 | 8.5 | WA | 13.7 | 13.3 |
| MI | 9.7 | 9.8 | WV | 14.7 | 13.6 |
| MN | 7.8 | 8.1 | WI | 8.9 | 7.6 |
| MS | 14.6 | 15.0 | WY | 15.4 | 15.8 |
| MO | 8.1 | 9.9 | | | |

**37. Seasonal spending.** The success of the Christmas spending season (in the United States, roughly from Thanksgiving to Christmas) drives much of retail sales for the year. Financial analysts for credit card companies know that January credit card charges will generally be much lower than the month before and so must plan for the decrease in revenue. A simple random sample of 99 cardholders' spending for each month from December 2004 to February 2005 can be found in the data set **Ch25_Seasonal_Spending.** Construct a 95% confidence interval for the mean change in charges between December and January.

**38. Seasonal spending II.** As we saw in Exercise 37, financial analysts know that January credit card charges will generally be much lower than the month before. What about the difference between January and February? Does the trend continue into the next month? A simple random sample of 99 cardholders' spending for each month from December 2004 to February 2005 can be found in the data set **Ch25_Seasonal_Spending.**
a) Test the hypothesis of no change in the mean charges of cardholders between January and February.
b) Construct a 95% confidence interval for the mean change in charges between January and February.

**JUST CHECKING**
**Answers**

1. These are independent groups sampled at random, so use a two-sample *t* confidence interval to estimate the size of the difference.

2. There is only one sample. Use a one-sample *t*-interval.

3. A brother and sister from the same family represent a matched pair. The question calls for a paired *t*-test.

4. a) A before-and-after study calls for paired *t*-methods. To estimate the loss, find a confidence interval for the before–after differences.

   b) The two treatment groups were assigned randomly, so they are independent. Use a two-sample *t*-test to assess whether the mean weight losses differ.

5. Sometimes it just isn't clear. Most likely, couples would discuss the band or even decide to go to the club because they both like a particular band. If we think that's likely, then these data are paired. But maybe not. If we asked them their opinions of, say, the decor or furnishings at the club, the fact that they were couples might not affect the independence of their answers.

# REVIEW OF PART VI

## Learning About the World

### Quick Review

We continue to explore how to answer questions about the statistics we get from samples and experiments. In this part, those questions have been about means—means of one sample, two independent samples, or matched pairs. Here's a brief summary of the key concepts and skills:

▶ A confidence interval uses a sample statistic to estimate a range of possible values for a parameter of interest.

▶ A hypothesis test proposes a model, then examines the plausibility of that model by seeing how surprising our observed data would be if the model were true.

▶ Statistical inference procedures for proportions are based on the Central Limit Theorem. We can make inferences about a single proportion or the difference of two proportions using Normal models.

▶ Statistical inference procedures for means are also based on the Central Limit Theorem, but we don't usually know the population standard deviation. Student's $t$-models take into account the additional uncertainty of independently estimating the standard deviation.

  • We can make inferences about one mean, the difference of two independent means, or the mean of paired differences using $t$-models.

  • No inference procedure is valid unless the underlying assumptions are true. Always check the conditions before proceeding.

• Because $t$-models assume that samples are drawn from Normal populations, data in the sample should appear to be nearly Normal. Skewness and outliers are particularly problematic, especially for small samples.

• When there are two variables, you must think carefully about how the data were collected. You may use two-sample $t$ procedures only if the groups are independent.

• Unless there is some obvious reason to suspect that two independent populations have the same standard deviation, you should not pool the variances. It is never wrong to use unpooled $t$ procedures.

• If the two groups are somehow paired, the data are *not* from independent groups. You must use matched-pairs $t$ procedures.

Now for some opportunities to review these concepts. Be careful. You have a lot of thinking to do. These review exercises mix questions about proportions and means. You have to determine which of our inference procedures is appropriate in each situation. Then you have to check the proper assumptions and conditions. Keeping track of those can be difficult, so first we summarize the many procedures with their corresponding assumptions and conditions on the next page. Look them over carefully . . . then, on to the Exercises!

## Quick Guide to Inference

| Think | | | | | | | Show | Tell? |
|---|---|---|---|---|---|---|---|---|
| Inference about? | One group or two? | Procedure | Model | Parameter | Estimate | | SE | Chapter |
| Proportions | One sample | 1-Proportion z-Interval | $z$ | $p$ | $\hat{p}$ | | $\sqrt{\dfrac{\hat{p}\hat{q}}{n}}$ | 19 |
| | | 1-Proportion z-Test | | | | | $\sqrt{\dfrac{p_0 q_0}{n}}$ | 20, 21 |
| | Two independent groups | 2-Proportion z-Interval | $z$ | $p_1 - p_2$ | $\hat{p}_1 - \hat{p}_2$ | | $\sqrt{\dfrac{\hat{p}_1\hat{q}_1}{n_1} + \dfrac{\hat{p}_2\hat{q}_2}{n_2}}$ | 22 |
| | | 2-Proportion z-Test | | | | | $\sqrt{\dfrac{\hat{p}\hat{q}}{n_1} + \dfrac{\hat{p}\hat{q}}{n_2}}, \ \hat{p} = \dfrac{y_1 + y_2}{n_1 + n_2}$ | 22 |
| Means | One sample | t-Interval  t-Test | $t$  df $= n - 1$ | $\mu$ | $\bar{y}$ | | $\dfrac{s}{\sqrt{n}}$ | 23 |
| | Two independent groups | 2-Sample t-Test  2-Sample t-Interval | $t$  df from technology | $\mu_1 - \mu_2$ | $\bar{y}_1 - \bar{y}_2$ | | $\sqrt{\dfrac{s_1^2}{n_1} + \dfrac{s_2^2}{n_2}}$ | 24 |
| | Matched pairs | Paired t-Test  Paired t-Interval | $t$  df $= n - 1$ | $\mu_d$ | $\bar{d}$ | | $\dfrac{s_d}{\sqrt{n}}$ | 25 |

## Assumptions for Inference     And the Conditions That Support or Override Them

**Proportions ($z$)**

- **One sample**
  1. Individuals are independent.
  2. Sample is sufficiently large.

  1. SRS and $n < 10\%$ of the population.
  2. Successes and failures each $\geq 10$.

- **Two groups**
  1. Groups are independent.
  2. Data in each group are independent.

  3. Both groups are sufficiently large.

  1. (Think about how the data were collected.)
  2. Both are SRSs and $n < 10\%$ of populations OR random allocation.
  3. Successes and failures each $\geq 10$ for both groups.

**Means ($t$)**

- **One sample** (df $= n - 1$)
  1. Individuals are independent.
  2. Population has a Normal model.

  1. SRS and $n < 10\%$ of the population.
  2. Histogram is unimodal and symmetric.*

- **Matched pairs** (df $= n - 1$)
  1. Data are matched.
  2. Individuals are independent.
  3. Population of differences is Normal.

  1. (Think about the design.)
  2. SRS and $n < 10\%$ OR random allocation.
  3. Histogram of differences is unimodal and symmetric.*

- **Two independent groups** (df from technology)
  1. Groups are independent.
  2. Data in each group are independent.
  3. Both populations are Normal.

  1. (Think about the design.)
  2. SRSs and $n < 10\%$ OR random allocation.
  3. Both histograms are unimodal and symmetric.*

(*less critical as $n$ increases)

## REVIEW EXERCISES

1. **Crawling.**   A study published in 1993 found that babies born at different times of the year may develop the ability to crawl at different ages! The author of the study suggested that these differences may be related to the temperature at the time the infant is 6 months old. (Benson and Janette, *Infant Behavior and Development* [1993])
   a) The study found that 32 babies born in January crawled at an average age of 29.84 weeks, with a standard deviation of 7.08 weeks. Among 21 July babies, crawling ages averaged 33.64 weeks, with a standard deviation of 6.91 weeks. Is this difference significant?
   b) For 26 babies born in April the mean and standard deviation were 31.84 and 6.21 weeks, while for 44 October babies the mean and standard deviation of crawling ages were 33.35 and 7.29 weeks. Is this difference significant?
   c) Are these results consistent with the researcher's claim? (We'll examine these data in more detail in a later chapter.)

2. **Mazes and smells.**   Can pleasant smells improve learning? Researchers timed 21 subjects as they tried to complete paper-and-pencil mazes. Each subject attempted a maze both with and without the presence of a floral aroma. Subjects were randomized with respect to whether they did the scented trial first or second. Some of the data collected are shown in the table. Is there any evidence that the floral scent improved the subjects' ability to complete the mazes? (A. R. Hirsch and L. H. Johnston, "Odors and Learning." Chicago: Smell and Taste Treatment and Research Foundation)

| Time to Complete the Maze (sec) | |
|---|---|
| Unscented | Scented |
| 25.7 | 30.2 |
| 41.9 | 56.7 |
| 51.9 | 42.4 |
| 32.2 | 34.4 |
| 64.7 | 44.8 |
| 31.4 | 42.9 |
| 40.1 | 42.7 |
| 43.2 | 24.8 |
| 33.9 | 25.1 |
| 40.4 | 59.2 |
| 58.0 | 42.2 |
| 61.5 | 48.4 |
| 44.6 | 32.0 |
| 35.3 | 48.1 |
| 37.2 | 33.7 |
| 39.4 | 42.6 |
| 77.4 | 54.9 |
| 52.8 | 64.5 |
| 63.6 | 43.1 |
| 56.6 | 52.8 |
| 58.9 | 44.3 |

3. **Women.**   The U.S. Census Bureau reports that 26% of all U.S. businesses are owned by women. A Colorado consulting firm surveys a random sample of 410 businesses in the Denver area and finds that 115 of them have women owners. Should the firm conclude that its area is unusual? Test an appropriate hypothesis and state your conclusion.

4. **Drugs.**   In a full-page ad that ran in many U.S. newspapers in August 2002, a Canadian discount pharmacy listed costs of drugs that could be ordered from a Web site in Canada. The table compares prices (in US$) for commonly prescribed drugs.

| | Cost per 100 Pills | | |
|---|---|---|---|
| Drug Name | United States | Canada | Percent savings |
| Cardizem | 131 | 83 | 37 |
| Celebrex | 136 | 72 | 47 |
| Cipro | 374 | 219 | 41 |
| Pravachol | 370 | 166 | 55 |
| Premarin | 61 | 17 | 72 |
| Prevacid | 252 | 214 | 15 |
| Prozac | 263 | 112 | 57 |
| Tamoxifen | 349 | 50 | 86 |
| Vioxx | 243 | 134 | 45 |
| Zantac | 166 | 42 | 75 |
| Zocor | 365 | 200 | 45 |
| Zoloft | 216 | 105 | 51 |

   a) Give a 95% confidence interval for the average savings in dollars.
   b) Give a 95% confidence interval for the average savings in percent.
   c) Which analysis do you think is more appropriate? Why?
   d) In small print the newspaper ad says, "Complete list of all 1500 drugs available on request." How does this comment affect your conclusions above?

5. **Pottery.**   Archaeologists can use the chemical composition of clay found in pottery artifacts to determine whether different sites were populated by the same ancient people. They collected five samples of Romano–British pottery from each of two sites in Great Britain—the Ashley Rails site and the New Forest site—and measured the percentage of aluminum oxide in each. Based on these data, do you think the same people used these two kiln sites? Base your conclusion on a 95% confidence interval for the difference in aluminum oxide content of pottery made at the sites. (A. Tubb, A. J. Parker, and G. Nickless, "The Analysis of Romano–British Pottery by Atomic Absorption Spectrophotometry." *Archaeometry*, 22[1980]:153–171)

| Ashley Rails | 19.1 | 14.8 | 16.7 | 18.3 | 17.7 |
|---|---|---|---|---|---|
| New Forest | 20.8 | 18.0 | 18.0 | 15.8 | 18.3 |

6. **Streams.**   Researchers in the Adirondack Mountains collect data on a random sample of streams each year. One of the variables recorded is the substrate of the streams—the type of soil and rock over which they flow.

The researchers found that 69 of the 172 sampled streams had a substrate of shale. Construct a 95% confidence interval for the proportion of Adirondack streams with a shale substrate. Clearly interpret your interval in this context.

7. **Gehrig.** Ever since Lou Gehrig developed amyotrophic lateral sclerosis (ALS), this deadly condition has been commonly known as Lou Gehrig's disease. Some believe that ALS is more likely to strike athletes or the very fit. Columbia University neurologist Lewis P. Rowland recorded personal histories of 431 patients he examined between 1992 and 2002. He diagnosed 280 as having ALS; 38% of them had been varsity athletes. The other 151 had other neurological disorders, and only 26% of them had been varsity athletes. (*Science News*, Sept. 28 [2002])
   a) Is there evidence that ALS is more common among athletes?
   b) What kind of study is this? How does that affect the inference you made in part a?

8. **Teen drinking.** A study of the health behavior of school-aged children asked a sample of 15-year-olds in several different countries if they had been drunk at least twice.

| | Percent of 15-Year-Olds Drunk at Least Twice | |
| Country | Female | Male |
| --- | --- | --- |
| Denmark | 63 | 71 |
| Wales | 63 | 72 |
| Greenland | 59 | 58 |
| England | 62 | 51 |
| Finland | 58 | 52 |
| Scotland | 56 | 53 |
| No. Ireland | 44 | 53 |
| Slovakia | 31 | 49 |
| Austria | 36 | 49 |
| Canada | 42 | 42 |
| Sweden | 40 | 40 |
| Norway | 41 | 37 |
| Ireland | 29 | 42 |
| Germany | 31 | 36 |
| Latvia | 23 | 47 |
| Estonia | 23 | 44 |
| Hungary | 22 | 43 |
| Poland | 21 | 39 |
| USA | 29 | 34 |
| Czech Rep. | 22 | 36 |
| Belgium | 22 | 36 |
| Russia | 25 | 32 |
| Lithuania | 20 | 32 |
| France | 20 | 29 |
| Greece | 21 | 24 |
| Switzerland | 16 | 25 |
| Israel | 10 | 18 |

The results are shown in the table, by gender. Give a 95% confidence interval for the difference in the rates for males and females. Be sure to check the assumptions that support your chosen procedure, and explain what your interval means. (*Health and Health Behavior Among Young People.* Copenhagen: World Health Organization, 2000)

9. **Babies.** The National Perinatal Statistics Unit of the Sydney Children's Hospital reports that the mean birth weight of all babies born in Australia in 1999 was 3360 grams—about 7.41 pounds. A Missouri hospital reports that the average weight of 112 babies born there last year was 7.68 pounds, with a standard deviation of 1.31 pounds. If we believe the Missouri babies fairly represent American newborns, is there any evidence that U.S. babies and Australian babies do not weigh the same amount at birth?

10. **Petitions.** To get a voter initiative on a state ballot, petitions that contain at least 250,000 valid voter signatures must be filed with the Elections Commission. The board then has 60 days to certify the petitions. A group wanting to create a statewide system of universal health insurance has just filed petitions with a total of 304,266 signatures. As a first step in the process, the Board selects an SRS of 2000 signatures and checks them against local voter lists. Only 1772 of them turn out to be valid.
   a) What percent of the sample signatures were valid?
   b) What percent of the petition signatures submitted must be valid in order to have the initiative certified by the Elections Commission?
   c) What will happen if the Elections Commission commits a Type I error?
   d) What will happen if the Elections Commission commits a Type II error?
   e) Does the sample provide evidence in support of certification? Explain.
   f) What could the Elections Commission do to increase the power of the test?

11. **Feeding fish.** In the midwestern United States, a large aquaculture industry raises largemouth bass. Researchers wanted to know whether the fish would grow better if fed a natural diet of fathead minnows or an artificial diet of food pellets. They stocked six ponds with bass fingerlings weighing about 8 grams. For one year, the fish in three of the ponds were fed minnows, and the others were fed the commercially prepared pellets. The fish were then harvested, weighed, and measured. The bass fed a natural food source had a higher average length (19.6 cm) and weight (95.9 g) than those fed the commercial fish food (17.3 cm and 72.0 g, respectively). The researchers reported P-values for both measurements to be less than 0.001.
   a) Explain to someone who has not studied Statistics what the P-values mean here.
   b) What advice should the researchers give the people who raise largemouth bass?
   c) If that advice turns out to be incorrect, what type of error occurred?

**12. Risk.** A study of auto safety determined the number of driver deaths per million vehicle sales for the model years 1995–1999, classified by type of vehicle. The data below are for 6 midsize models and 6 SUVs. Wondering if there is evidence that drivers of SUVs are safer, we hope to create a 95% confidence interval for the difference in driver death rates for the two types of vehicles. Are these data appropriate for this inference? Explain. (Ross and Wenzel, *An Analysis of Traffic Deaths by Vehicle Type and Model*, March 2002)

| Midsize | 47 | 54 | 64 | 76 | 88 | 97 |
|---------|----|----|----|----|----|----|
| SUV | 55 | 60 | 62 | 76 | 91 | 109 |

**13. Age.** In a study of how depression may affect one's ability to survive a heart attack, the researchers reported the ages of the two groups they examined. The mean age of 2397 patients without cardiac disease was 69.8 years (SD = 8.7 years), while for the 450 patients with cardiac disease, the mean and standard deviation of the ages were 74.0 and 7.9, respectively.
a) Create a 95% confidence interval for the difference in mean ages of the two groups.
b) How might an age difference confound these research findings about the relationship between depression and ability to survive a heart attack?

**14. Smoking.** In the depression and heart attack research described in Exercise 13, 32% of the diseased group were smokers, compared with only 23.7% of those free of heart disease.
a) Create a 95% confidence interval for the difference in the proportions of smokers in the two groups.
b) Is this evidence that the two groups in the study were different? Explain.
c) Could this be a problem in analyzing the results of the study? Explain.

**15. Computer use.** A Gallup telephone poll of 1240 teens conducted in 2001 found that boys were more likely than girls to play computer games, by a margin of 77% to 65%. Equal numbers of boys and girls were surveyed.
a) What kind of sampling design was used?
b) Give a 95% confidence interval for the difference in game playing by gender.
c) Does your confidence interval suggest that among all teens a higher percentage of boys than girls play computer games?

**16. Recruiting.** In September 2002, CNN reported on a method of grad student recruiting by the Haas School of Business at U.C.-Berkeley. The school notifies applicants by formal letter that they have been admitted, and also e-mails the accepted students a link to a Web site that greets them with personalized balloons, cheering, and applause. The director of admissions says this extra effort at recruiting has really worked well. The school accepts 500 applicants each year, and the percentage that actually choose to enroll at Berkeley increased from 52% the year before the Web greeting to 54% this year.
a) Create a 95% confidence interval for the change in enrollment rates.
b) Based on your confidence interval, are you convinced that this new form of recruiting has been effective? Explain.

**17. Hearing.** Fitting someone for a hearing aid requires assessing the patient's hearing ability. In one method of assessment, the patient listens to a tape of 50 English words. The tape is played at low volume, and the patient is asked to repeat the words. The patient's hearing ability score is the number of words perceived correctly. Four tapes of equivalent difficulty are available so that each ear can be tested with more than one hearing aid. These lists were created to be equally difficult to perceive in silence, but hearing aids must work in the presence of background noise. Researchers had 24 subjects with normal hearing compare two of the tapes when a background noise was present, with the order of the tapes randomized. Is it reasonable to assume that the two lists are still equivalent for purposes of the hearing test when there is background noise? Base your decision on a confidence interval for the mean difference in the number of words people might misunderstand. (Faith Loven, *A Study of the Interlist Equivalency of the CID W-22 Word List Presented in Quiet and in Noise.* University of Iowa [1981])

| Subject | List A | List B |
|---------|--------|--------|
| 1 | 24 | 26 |
| 2 | 32 | 24 |
| 3 | 20 | 22 |
| 4 | 14 | 18 |
| 5 | 32 | 24 |
| 6 | 22 | 30 |
| 7 | 20 | 22 |
| 8 | 26 | 28 |
| 9 | 26 | 30 |
| 10 | 38 | 16 |
| 11 | 30 | 18 |
| 12 | 16 | 34 |
| 13 | 36 | 32 |
| 14 | 32 | 34 |
| 15 | 38 | 32 |
| 16 | 14 | 18 |
| 17 | 26 | 20 |
| 18 | 14 | 20 |
| 19 | 38 | 40 |
| 20 | 20 | 26 |
| 21 | 14 | 14 |
| 22 | 18 | 14 |
| 23 | 22 | 30 |
| 24 | 34 | 42 |

**18. Cesareans.** Some people fear that differences in insurance coverage can affect healthcare decisions. A survey of several randomly selected hospitals found that 16.6% of 223 recent births in Vermont involved cesarean deliveries, compared to 18.8% of 186 births in New Hampshire. Is this evidence that the rate of cesarean births in the two states is different?

**19. Newspapers.** Who reads the newspaper more, men or women? Eurostat, an agency of the European Union (EU), conducts surveys on several aspects of daily life in EU countries. Recently, the agency asked samples of 1000 respondents in each of 14 European countries whether they read the newspaper on a daily basis. Below are the data by country and gender.

| Country | % Reading a Newspaper Daily | |
|---|---|---|
| | **Men** | **Women** |
| Belgium | 56.3 | 45.5 |
| Denmark | 76.8 | 70.3 |
| Germany | 79.9 | 76.8 |
| Greece | 22.5 | 17.2 |
| Spain | 46.2 | 24.8 |
| Ireland | 58.0 | 54.0 |
| Italy | 50.2 | 29.8 |
| Luxembourg | 71.0 | 67.0 |
| Netherlands | 71.3 | 63.0 |
| Austria | 78.2 | 74.1 |
| Portugal | 58.3 | 24.1 |
| Finland | 93.0 | 90.0 |
| Sweden | 89.0 | 88.0 |
| UK | 32.6 | 30.4 |

a) Examine the differences in the percentages for each country. Which of these countries seem to be outliers? What do they have in common?
b) After eliminating the outliers, is there evidence that in Europe men are more likely than women to read the newspaper?

**T  20. Meals.** A college student is on a "meal program." His budget allows him to spend an average of $10 per day for the semester. He keeps track of his daily food expenses for 2 weeks; the data are given in the table. Is there strong evidence that he will overspend his food allowance? Explain.

| Date | Cost ($) |
|---|---|
| 7/29 | 15.20 |
| 7/30 | 23.20 |
| 7/31 | 3.20 |
| 8/1 | 9.80 |
| 8/2 | 19.53 |
| 8/3 | 6.25 |
| 8/4 | 0 |
| 8/5 | 8.55 |
| 8/6 | 20.05 |
| 8/7 | 14.95 |
| 8/8 | 23.45 |
| 8/9 | 6.75 |
| 8/10 | 0 |
| 8/11 | 9.01 |

**21. Wall Street.** In September of 2000, the Harris Poll organization asked 1002 randomly sampled American adults whether they agreed or disagreed with the following statement:

Most people on Wall Street would be willing to break the law if they believed they could make a lot of money and get away with it.

Of those asked, 60% said they agreed with this statement. We know that if we could ask the entire population of American adults, we would not find that exactly 60% think that Wall Street workers would be willing to break the law to make money. Construct a 95% confidence interval for the true percentage of American adults who agree with the statement.

**22. Teach for America.** Several programs attempt to address the shortage of qualified teachers by placing uncertified instructors in schools with acute needs—often in inner cities. A 1999–2000 study compared students taught by certified teachers to others taught by uncertified teachers in the same schools. Reading scores of the students of certified teachers averaged 35.62 points with standard deviation 9.31. The scores of students instructed by uncertified teachers had mean 32.48 points with standard deviation 9.43 points on the same test. There were 44 students in each group. The appropriate $t$ procedure has 86 degrees of freedom. Is there evidence of lower scores with uncertified teachers? Discuss. (*The Effectiveness of "Teach for America" and Other Under-certified Teachers on Student Academic Achievement: A Case of Harmful Public Policy.* Education Policy Analysis Archives [2002])

**T  23. Legionnaires' disease.** In 1974, the Bellevue-Stratford Hotel in Philadelphia was the scene of an outbreak of what later became known as legionnaires' disease. The cause of the disease was finally discovered to be bacteria that thrived in the air-conditioning units of the hotel. Owners of the Rip Van Winkle Motel, hearing about the Bellevue-Stratford, replace their air-conditioning system. The following data are the bacteria counts in the air of eight rooms, before and after a new air-conditioning system was installed (measured in colonies per cubic foot of air). The objective is to find out whether the new system has succeeded in lowering the bacterial count. You are the statistician assigned to report to the hotel whether the strategy has worked. Base your analysis on a confidence interval. Be sure to list all your assumptions, methods, and conclusions.

| Room Number | Before | After |
|---|---|---|
| 121 | 11.8 | 10.1 |
| 163 | 8.2 | 7.2 |
| 125 | 7.1 | 3.8 |
| 264 | 14 | 12 |
| 233 | 10.8 | 8.3 |
| 218 | 10.1 | 10.5 |
| 324 | 14.6 | 12.1 |
| 325 | 14 | 13.7 |

**24. Teach for America, Part II.** The study described in Exercise 22 also looked at scores in mathematics and language. Here are software outputs for the appropriate tests. Explain what they show.

**Mathematics**

T-TEST OF Mu(1) − Mu(2) = O
Mu(Cert) − Mu(NoCert) = 4.53   t (86) = 2.95   p = 0.002

**Language**

T-TEST OF Mu(1) − Mu(2) = O
Mu(Cert) − Mu(NoCert) = 2.13   t (84) = 1.71   p = 0.045

**25. Bipolar kids.** The June 2002 *American Journal of Psychiatry* reported that researchers used medication and psychotherapy to treat children aged 7 to 16 who exhibit bipolar symptoms. After 2 years, symptoms had cleared up in only 26 of the 89 children involved in the study.
   a) Write a 95% confidence interval, and interpret it in this context.
   b) If researchers subsequently hope to produce an estimate of treatment effectiveness for bipolar disorder that has a margin of error of only 6%, how many patients should they study?

**26. Online testing.** The Educational Testing Service is now administering several of its standardized tests online—the CLEP and GMAT exams, for example. Since taking a test on a computer is different from taking a test with pencil and paper, one wonders if the scores will be the same. To investigate this question, researchers created two versions of an SAT-type test and got 20 volunteers to participate in an experiment. Each volunteer took both versions of the test, one with pencil and paper and the other online. Subjects were randomized with respect to the order in which they sat for the tests (online/paper) and which form they took (Test A, Test B) in which environment. The scores (out of a possible 20) are summarized in the table.

| Subject | Paper | Online |
|---|---|---|
|  | Test A | Test B |
| 1 | 14 | 13 |
| 2 | 10 | 13 |
| 3 | 16 | 8 |
| 4 | 15 | 14 |
| 5 | 17 | 16 |
| 6 | 14 | 11 |
| 7 | 9 | 12 |
| 8 | 12 | 12 |
| 9 | 16 | 16 |
| 10 | 7 | 14 |
|  | Test B | Test A |
| 11 | 8 | 13 |
| 12 | 11 | 13 |
| 13 | 15 | 17 |
| 14 | 11 | 13 |
| 15 | 13 | 14 |
| 16 | 9 | 9 |
| 17 | 15 | 9 |
| 18 | 14 | 15 |
| 19 | 16 | 12 |
| 20 | 8 | 10 |

   a) Were the two forms (A/B) of the test equivalent in terms of difficulty? Test an appropriate hypothesis and state your conclusion.
   b) Is there evidence that the testing environment (paper/online) matters? Test an appropriate hypothesis and state your conclusion.

**27. Bread.** Clarksburg Bakery is trying to predict how many loaves of bread to bake. In the last 100 days, the bakery has sold between 95 and 140 loaves per day. Here are a histogram and the summary statistics for the number of loaves sold for the last 100 days.

**Summary of Sales**

| | |
|---|---|
| Mean | 103 |
| Median | 100 |
| SD | 9.000 |
| Min | 95 |
| Max | 140 |
| Lower 25th %tile | 97 |
| Upper 25th %tile | 105.5 |

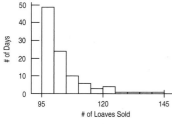

   a) Can you use these data to estimate the number of loaves sold on the busiest 10% of all days? Explain.
   b) Explain why you can use these data to construct a 95% confidence interval for the mean number of loaves sold per day.
   c) Calculate a 95% confidence interval and carefully interpret what that confidence interval means.
   d) If the bakery would have been satisfied with a confidence interval whose margin of error was twice as wide, how many days' data could they have used?
   e) When the bakery opened, the owners estimated that they would sell an average of 100 loaves per day. Does your confidence interval provide strong evidence that this estimate was incorrect? Explain.

**28. Irises.** Can measurements of the petal length of flowers be of value when you need to determine the species of a certain flower? Here are the summary statistics from measurements of the petals of two species of irises. (R. A. Fisher, "The Use of Multiple Measurements in Axonomic Problems." *Annals of Eugenics 7* [1936]:179–188)

| | Species | |
|---|---|---|
| | Versicolor | Virginica |
| **Count** | 50 | 50 |
| **Mean** | 55.52 | 43.22 |
| **Median** | 55.50 | 44.00 |
| **SD** | 5.519 | 5.362 |
| **Min** | 45 | 30 |
| **Max** | 69 | 56 |
| **Lower Quartile** | 51 | 40 |
| **Upper Quartile** | 59 | 47 |

   a) Make parallel boxplots of petal lengths for the two species.
   b) Describe the differences seen in the boxplots.
   c) Write a 95% confidence interval for this difference.

d) Explain what your interval means.

e) Based on your confidence interval, is there evidence of a difference in petal length? Explain.

**29. Insulin and diet.** A study published in the *Journal of the American Medical Association* examined people to see if they showed any signs of IRS (insulin resistance syndrome) involving major risk factors for Type 2 diabetes and heart disease. Among 102 subjects who consumed dairy products more than 35 times per week, 24 were identified with IRS. In comparison, IRS was identified in 85 of 190 individuals with the lowest dairy consumption, fewer than 10 times per week.

a) Is this strong evidence that IRS risk is different in people who frequently consume dairy products than in those who do not?

b) Does this prove that diary consumption influences the development of IRS? Explain.

**30. Speeding.** A newspaper report in August 2002 raised the issue of racial bias in the issuance of speeding tickets. The following facts were noted:

- 16% of drivers registered in New Jersey are black.
- Of the 324 speeding tickets issued in one month on a 65-mph section of the New Jersey Turnpike, 25% went to black drivers.

a) Is the percentage of speeding tickets issued to blacks unusually high compared to the state's registration information?

b) Does this prove that racial profiling may be present?

c) What other statistics would you like to know about this situation?

**T 31. Rainmakers?** In an experiment to determine whether seeding clouds with silver iodide increases rainfall, 52 clouds were randomly assigned to be seeded or not. The amount of rain they generated was then measured (in acre-feet). Create a 95% confidence interval for the average amount of additional rain created by seeding clouds. Explain what your interval means.

|  | Unseeded Clouds | Seeded Clouds |
|---|---|---|
| **Count** | 26 | 26 |
| **Mean** | 164.588 | 441.985 |
| **Median** | 44.200 | 221.600 |
| **SD** | 278.426 | 650.787 |
| **IntQRange** | 138.600 | 337.600 |
| **25 %ile** | 24.400 | 92.400 |
| **75 %ile** | 163 | 430 |

**32. Fritos.** As a project for an introductory Statistics course, students checked 6 bags of Fritos marked with a net weight of 35.4 grams. They carefully weighed the contents of each bag, recording the following weights (in grams): 35.5, 35.3, 35.1, 36.4, 35.4, 35.5. Is there evidence that the mean weight of bags of Fritos is less than advertised?

a) Write appropriate hypotheses.

b) Do these data satisfy the assumptions for inference? Explain.

c) Test your hypothesis using all 6 weights.

d) Retest your hypothesis with the one unusually high weight removed.

e) What would you conclude about the stated net weight?

**T 33. Color or text?** In an experiment, 32 volunteer subjects are briefly shown seven cards, each displaying the name of a color printed in a different color (example: red, blue, and so on). The subject is asked to perform one of two tasks: memorize the order of the words or memorize the order of the colors. Researchers record the number of cards remembered correctly. Then the cards are shuffled and the subject is asked to perform the other task. The table displays the results for each subject. Is there any evidence that either the color or the written word dominates perception?

a) What role does randomization play in this experiment?

b) State appropriate hypotheses.

c) Are the assumptions necessary for inference reasonable here?

d) Perform the test.

e) State your conclusion.

| Subject | Color | Word | Subject | Color | Word |
|---|---|---|---|---|---|
| 1 | 4 | 7 | 17 | 4 | 3 |
| 2 | 1 | 4 | 18 | 7 | 4 |
| 3 | 5 | 6 | 19 | 4 | 3 |
| 4 | 1 | 6 | 20 | 0 | 6 |
| 5 | 6 | 4 | 21 | 3 | 3 |
| 6 | 4 | 5 | 22 | 3 | 5 |
| 7 | 7 | 3 | 23 | 7 | 3 |
| 8 | 2 | 5 | 24 | 3 | 7 |
| 9 | 7 | 5 | 25 | 5 | 6 |
| 10 | 4 | 3 | 26 | 3 | 4 |
| 11 | 2 | 0 | 27 | 3 | 5 |
| 12 | 5 | 4 | 28 | 1 | 4 |
| 13 | 6 | 7 | 29 | 2 | 3 |
| 14 | 3 | 6 | 30 | 5 | 3 |
| 15 | 4 | 6 | 31 | 3 | 4 |
| 16 | 4 | 7 | 32 | 6 | 7 |

**34. And it means?** Every statement about a confidence interval contains two parts: the level of confidence and the interval. Suppose that an insurance agent estimating the mean loss claimed by clients after home burglaries created the 95% confidence interval ($1644, $2391).

a) What's the margin of error for this estimate?

b) Carefully explain what the interval means.

c) Carefully explain what the 95% confidence level means.

**35. Batteries.** We work for the "Watchdog for the Consumer" consumer advocacy group. We've been asked to look at a battery company that claims its batteries last an average of 100 hours under normal use. There have been several complaints that the batteries don't last that long, so we decide to test them. To do this, we select 16 batteries and run them until they die. They lasted a mean of 97 hours, with a standard deviation of 12 hours.

a) One of the editors of our newsletter (who does not know statistics) says that 97 hours is a lot less than the advertised 100 hours, so we should reject the company's claim. Explain to him the problem with doing that.

b) What are the null and alternative hypotheses?

c) What assumptions must we make in order to proceed with inference?

d) At a 5% level of significance, what do you conclude?

e) Suppose that, in fact, the average life of the company's batteries is only 98 hours. Has an error been made in part d? If so, what kind?

**36. Hamsters.** How large are hamster litters? Among 47 golden hamster litters recorded, there were an average of 7.72 baby hamsters, with a standard deviation of 2.5 hamsters per litter.

a) Create and interpret a 90% confidence interval.

b) Would a 98% confidence interval have a larger or smaller margin of error? Explain.

c) How many litters must be used to estimate the average litter size to within 1 baby hamster with 95% confidence?

# PART VII

# Inference When Variables Are Related

The final part of the text looks forward as well as backward. We apply just about everything we've learned. But we also look beyond this course to possible future studies.

The theme of this Part is understanding and modeling relationships between variables. In Chapter 26, we look at categorical data with $\chi^2$ models. In Chapter 27, the subject is inference for regression models.

The next steps are the two chapters found on the DVD: Chapter 28 on ANOVA and Chapter 29 on Multiple Regression. These can be considered chapters in this Part. Each lays the foundation for studies that can fill an entire course.

## Instructor's Guide

**CHAPTER 26**

# Comparing Counts

## What's It About?

Chapter 26 introduces $\chi^2$ models. We see how to use the $\chi^2$ statistic to test goodness of fit and homogeneity for distributions of categorical variables, as well as independence of categorical variables. We discuss the assumptions and conditions, present step-by-step examples, and look at how to use residuals to better interpret the results of our tests.

## Comments

Having spent all of Part VI on inference for means, we now return to questions we first raised in Chapter 3 about categorical variables. In Chapter 20 we looked at how to test hypotheses about a single proportion. In Chapter 22 the issue was the difference between two proportions. Now we consider entire distributions. Is an observed distribution consistent with what we expected? Are observed differences among several distributions large enough to be significant?

To answer such questions, we need a new family of models: $\chi^2$. Students first learned to work with Normal models and then made the transition to $t$-models. While the $t$-models looked familiarly "normal," the $\chi^2$ models are different. It's important to consider the family in general so that students develop a "feel" for what their calculations and results mean. Fortunately, we always calculate the test statistic in essentially the same way, squaring the differences between what we observed and what our hypothesis says we should have expected. We always perform a test, rather than estimating with an interval. And the test always asks only whether the computed statistic is sufficiently large. So, mechanically, this is a pretty easy chapter. But we do need to *Think*.

While the first two $\chi^2$ procedures look at distributions, the same kind of calculation can allow us to decide whether we think two categorical variables are independent. That question has been hanging over our heads since Chapter 3 and the *Titanic*. In a way, we're completing a voyage begun there.

## Looking Ahead

The $\chi^2$ test of independence tests the significance of associations between categorical variables. Inference about associations between quantitative variables requires a linear regression $t$-procedure, coming next in Chapter 27.

## Class Do's

Help students understand the family of $\chi^2$ models. Unlike the now familiar Normal and $t$-models, these models do not measure distances in standard deviation (or standard error) units, cannot take on negative values, and are skewed to the right. It's harder to develop a feel for what the calculated result means. With $z$ or $t$, a calculated result of 5 is pretty clearly significant; we can tell even without knowing the P-value, as it's rare for anything to be five standard deviations from what was anticipated. With the $\chi^2$ statistic, the picture is murkier. Values that are highly significant when there are few degrees of freedom fade into nonsignificance as the curve shifts to the right for greater degrees of freedom. You can help your students understand this in three ways:

▶ The more degrees of freedom, the more terms in the summation. We'd naturally expect the sum to be bigger when there are 10 cells in the table than when there are only 4. It takes a much larger value to surprise us when there are more degrees of freedom.

▶ It's helpful to look at the $\chi^2$ table. Pick a column, say $\alpha = 0.05$. Look down the column to see how the critical value increases with higher degrees of freedom. Note that it can take a pretty large number to attain statistical significance when there are many degrees of freedom. You can watch this effect with the interactive $\chi^2$ table in the Appendix of *ActivStats* on the DVD. Drag down the table into higher degrees of freedom and watch the illustrative density at the top of the table as it shifts to the right and its shape gradually becomes more like a Normal.

▸ A fit that's almost perfect would be somewhat unusual, so we don't really expect to calculate a $\chi^2$ value near 0. In fact, the expected value for a $\chi^2$ model is equal to the number of degrees of freedom. We should be a little surprised by a calculated value of $\chi^2 = 9$ when there are 3 degrees of freedom, but not at all surprised if there are 12 degrees of freedom. Having that initial feel for whether or not the calculated value is unusually large helps make the P-value we'll find next a little less mysterious.

How much of the calculations must students be able to do? Well, they should *be able* to do it all—but most of the time they'll use a calculator or software. Be sure students can:

▸ determine the number of degrees of freedom for any table;

▸ determine the expected value for any cell;

▸ calculate the component of $\chi^2$ for any cell;

▸ write out an expression showing how the complete calculation would be done.

Be sure students can distinguish among the three situations, and choose the correct type of test.

▸ A goodness-of-fit test compares the distribution of observed outcomes for a single categorical variable to the expected outcomes predicted by a probability model to see if the model is viable. We start with one variable, one sample.

▸ A test of homogeneity compares observed distributions for several groups to each other to see if there are differences among the respective populations. There are several samples but still only one variable.

▸ A test of independence cross-categorizes one group on two variables to see if there is an association between them. Now there's just one sample, but two variables.

The homogeneity/independence decision can be a difficult one. The data, usually summarized in a two-way table, look the same. We find ourselves in a position similar to that we faced in making the two-samples/matched-pairs decision when doing inference about means. Now, as then, it is the design of the study that matters. How were the data collected? Suppose we wonder what voters consider to be the biggest problem the country currently faces. Did we purposefully select a sample of Republicans, a sample of Democrats, and a sample of other voters to query? If so, that's a question of homogeneity. We'll examine whether the distribution of answers is the same for each of the three groups. Or did we select one large sample of voters, asking them to name the problem and tell us their political party, too. If so, we've categorized each voter with respect to two variables and will examine whether the two variables are independent.

Another way to make the distinction is to think about the inference we'd like to make. In a clinical trial, we might give patients three treatments: a placebo, an herbal remedy, and a pharmaceutical, and then measure the responses (say in three different categories—"much better," "about the same," "much worse"). Compare that to an observational study relating baldness in men to heart disease. We might have three categories of baldness (none/little, some, much) and three categories of heart disease (severe, little, none). The two situations look the same, but the inference is quite different. The first concerns

three *specific* treatments: placebo, herbal remedy, and drug. We don't generalize from there. We're interested in whether the proportions are the same across those three (and only those three) groups. On the other hand, with baldness, we are interested in whether baldness (as a variable) and heart disease are related. The specific levels of baldness are measured—they're not specific categories—and represent the entire range of baldness. This is the essential difference. Homogeneity is about specific groups. Independence is about two variables.

Although the degrees of freedom are determined differently, the distinctions among the three types of tests have no impact on the actual calculation of $\chi^2$. This makes the mechanics fairly straightforward, and students readily learn to find the P-value of the test. Writing the hypotheses and interpreting the results, however, require clear understanding of the differences among the tests.

▸ The null hypothesis for a goodness-of-fit test is that the probability model is correct. (All faces of the die are equally likely to occur.) Our test assesses whether the observed results are consistent with that model. (Do the actual results from tossing the die vary so much from a perfect 1:1:1:1:1:1 ratio as to cast doubt on the die's fairness?) The conclusion either rejects the model (the die is unfair) or fails to reject it (a fair die might behave like this one did).

▸ The null hypothesis for a test of homogeneity is that the two groups are drawn from populations in which the variable has the same model. (The distribution of eye color among boys is the same as it is among girls.) The test assesses whether the differences we found in the two sample distributions are consistent with that belief. (Are the percentages of the various eye colors in the sample of boys so different from those in the sample of girls that we can no longer believe the distribution of eye color is the same for all boys as it is for all girls?) Our conclusion either decides it's unlikely that the populations follow the same model (frequencies of various eye colors differ by gender) or finds the observed discrepancy isn't great enough to make us think so (if boys' and girls' eye colors don't really differ, results like ours could be reasonably expected to turn up in samples like these).

▸ The null hypothesis for a test of independence is that there is no association between the two variables. (Smoking is independent of level of education.) The test assesses whether the observed differences in conditional distributions are greater than sampling variability reasonably allows. (Is the percentage of smokers among the well-educated subjects so much lower than the percentage among those who had only been to high school that the difference can't be attributed to sampling error?) Our conclusion claims either that there is an association (well-educated people are less likely to smoke cigarettes) or that we don't have convincing proof of that (there's no evidence of an association between smoking and education level).

As usual, pay attention to the assumptions and conditions. Be sure students recognize that $\chi^2$ tests are appropriate only for categorical data. Beware of this when you search for other examples to use for discussion in class. There are textbooks out there (written by nonstatisticians) that incorrectly apply these procedures to variables like weight. We include some examples in the exercises to help students see what can go wrong.

We check to see that our sample is large enough by looking at the expected counts in each cell.

▸ All expected cell frequencies must be at least 5.

▸ That's *expected* counts, not observed counts.

▸ Note that while observed counts must be integers, expected counts usually are not.

▸ Students must demonstrate that they checked this condition by actually showing all the expected frequencies. They can either find them themselves or copy them off a calculator- or computer-generated table, but it is not sufficient to just claim that it's true without showing the evidence.

▸ If a *small* number of cells have expected counts slightly below 5, it's okay to proceed with caution. However, if you end up rejecting the null hypothesis, check the $\chi^2$ components to be sure that it was not the offending cells that triggered the rejection.

▸ When it makes sense to do so, it's better to combine cells to achieve expected counts that are sufficiently large.

When you reject the $\chi^2$ null hypothesis, the initial conclusion you reach is rarely satisfying. We've decided the die is not fair. That just makes us want to know what's wrong with it. We can identify which cells contributed most to the high value of $\chi^2$ by examining the components of the calculation. A good rule of thumb is to think of each component as the square of a z-score. Cells with components below 3 or 4 (z within ±2) usually don't arouse our suspicion. Cells with larger components do. Often, when the calculated value of $\chi^2$ is large, there are one or two cells with glaringly large components that dominate the sum. So after our initial conclusion that a very low P-value causes us to reject the null hypothesis and conclude that there is evidence that the die is not fair, we get to add that there's an indication that 3's are unusually likely to appear (or that boys are more likely to have brown eyes, or that the high-school dropouts are over-represented among smokers).

Are $\chi^2$ tests one-tailed or two? The test itself is almost always one sided. We reject the null only if we calculate an unusually large test statistic, so the rejection region is in the upper tail of the curve we draw. But whether a cell shows results higher or lower than expected, we square the deviation, always making it positive. We are essentially checking discrepancies in both directions at once.

You can ask the students what it would mean if the $\chi^2$ statistic (say for a goodness of fit) is too low? They might say that the data fit the model too well—and that's right. There is some question, for example, as to whether the data in Mendel's original experiments on pea breeding were *too* good. The $\chi^2$ statistic for the genetic model proportions is extremely low. Perhaps some of his helpers were overzealous, knowing what Brother Mendel was expecting to see in his peas.

## The Importance of What You Don't Say

*It's usually best not to express these hypotheses symbolically.* The mathematical notation required to express these hypotheses is complicated and not very meaningful to most students. Just say it in words.

*Don't suggest that it doesn't matter whether it's homogeneity or independence.* It does matter. The hypotheses and the

conclusions must be stated differently. Only the mechanics are the same. Don't let students forget to *Think* and *Tell* properly just because the *Show* steps are the same.

## Class Examples

1. Buy enough small packages of M&M's to have one per pair of students—and treat yourself to one, too. Everyone should count the number of candies of each color in his or her package. Tell them the proportions claimed by the candy company: 13% brown, 14% yellow, 13% red, 24% blue, 20% orange, and 16% green at this writing—but check at the M&M's Web site (www.mms.com) for any changes. (Note that other kinds of M&M's have different color distributions.) Calculate how many of each color you should have found in your bag (based on your total number of candies), and have each group do the same for theirs. Lead them through the goodness-of-fit test.

   *Hypotheses:* $H_0$: The distribution of candy colors is as the manufacturer claims.
   $H_A$: The distribution is not what the manufacturer claims it to be.

   *Model:* We have categorical data (counts), a random sample of M&M's (we think), fewer than 10% of all the candies in the world (unfortunately), and we expected at least five of each color to show up in each group's total (if we arrange for enough candies in each group).

   *Mechanics:* Demonstrate your calculation of $\chi^2$, and let the students do their own as they follow along. Explain $\chi^2$ models, and find your P-value, having them each find theirs.

   *Conclusion:* Many will fail to reject the null hypothesis, concluding that the content of their bags does not cast doubt on the claimed color distribution. Others will have P-values that are small enough to reject the null hypothesis. Use one of those to show everyone how to examine the components in order to be able to say more about how the distribution seems to be wrong.

2. Medical researchers enlisted 90 subjects for an experiment comparing treatments for depression. The subjects were randomly divided into three groups and given pills to take for a period of three months. Unknown to them, one group received a placebo, the second group the "natural" remedy St. John's wort, and the third group the prescription drug Posrex. After six months, psychologists and physicians (who did not know which treatment each person had received) evaluated the subjects to see if their depression had returned.

|  | | Treatment | |
|---|---|---|---|
| | Placebo | StJ | Posrex |
| **Depression returned** | 24 | 22 | 14 |
| **No sign of depression** | 6 | 8 | 16 |

(Diagnosis, at left, spans both data rows.)

   *Hypotheses:* $H_0$: The rate of recurrence is the same for all three treatments.
   $H_A$: The rate of recurrence differs for some treatments.

*Model:* These are counts of categorical data. Subjects were randomly assigned to treatments. But now we run into an issue we need to resolve: expected counts.

- Add row and column totals to the table, and challenge students to tell how many subjects they'd expect to have returned to depression for each treatment (if the treatments are equally effective). They should see that those 60 subjects would be expected to divide 20–20–20 under the null hypothesis. We can look at this three ways. Since $30/90 = 1/3$ of all subjects got the placebo, $1/3$ of the 60 with recurrent depression should have been in the placebo group. Or, since $60/90 = 2/3$ of the subjects suffered returning depression, we'd expect that to be true of $2/3$ of the 30 who got the placebo. Or, there's always the mindless explanation: row total $\times$ column total/grand total $= (60 \times 30)/90 = 20$.

| | | Treatment | | | |
|---|---|---|---|---|---|
| | | Placebo | St J | Posrex | Total |
| Diagnosis | Depression returned | 24 (20) | 22 (20) | 14 (20) | 60 |
| | No sign of depression | 6 (10) | 8 (10) | 16 (10) | 30 |
| | Total | 30 | 30 | 30 | 90 |

- Display all the expected counts in the table (or make a separate table) to confirm that none is less than 5. It's okay to proceed with a $\chi^2$ test of homogeneity.

*Mechanics:* We now face another issue: degrees of freedom.

- Note that if you start with these row and column totals, you could freely assign a count to only two cells in any row. The remaining cell count in that row is now fixed (to make the row total come out right), as are the cell counts in the next row (to make all the column totals work). Draw a $3 \times 5$ grid on the board and make up some row and column totals. Then ask students how many degrees of freedom there are. They should see that you can freely play with all but one row and all but one column. That's $(3 - 1)(5 - 1) = 8$ df.

Here we have $(2 - 1)(3 - 1) = 2$ degrees of freedom. Write out the calculation of $\chi^2$:

$$\chi^2 = \frac{(24 - 20)^2}{20} + \frac{(22 - 20)^2}{20} + \frac{(14 - 20)^2}{20} + \frac{(6 - 10)^2}{10}$$

$$+ \frac{(8 - 10)^2}{10} + \frac{(16 - 10)^2}{10}$$

$$\chi^2 = 0.8 + 0.2 + 1.8 + 1.6 + 0.4 + 3.6**$$

$$= 8.4$$

$$\text{P-value} = P(\chi^2_2 > 8.4) = 0.015$$

*Conclusion:* We'll state a general conclusion and then note that one cell** contributed greatly to the high $\chi^2$ value. Looking back at that cell in the table reveals more individuals there than we expected. Here goes: Because $P < 0.05$, we reject the null hypothesis. There is strong evidence that the tested treatments are not all equally effective in preventing the recurrence of depression. It appears that people who take the prescription drug Posrex are more likely

to remain free of the disease than those who took a placebo or the natural remedy St. John's wort.

3. You can collect data about eye color and handedness from your classes. Here are some sample data. Note that expected cell counts for lefties with green eyes and "other" are too small (3.83 and 2.67) to allow use of a $\chi^2$ procedure. We surmount this obstacle by combining "green" and "other," as seen in the second table. We have one group of respondents who answered questions about two categorical variables, so this will be a test of independence.

| | | Handedness | |
|---|---|---|---|
| | | Left | Right |
| Eye Color | Brown | 6 | 36 |
| | Blue | 7 | 26 |
| | Green | 2 | 21 |
| | Other | 4 | 12 |

*Hypotheses:* $H_0$: Handedness and eye color are independent.

$H_A$: There is an association between handedness and eye color.

*Model:* We have counts of categorical variables. Our sample, though not random, may be representative of all students. After combining cells for students with green and other color eyes, all expected counts are greater than 5.

*Mechanics:* $df = 2$, $\chi^2 = 0.71$, P − value $= 0.70$

*Conclusion:* With such a high P-value, we do not reject the null hypothesis. There is no evidence of any association between handedness and eye color in high-school students.

| | | Handedness | |
|---|---|---|---|
| | | Left | Right |
| Eye Color | Brown | 6 (7) | 36 (35) |
| | Blue | 7 (5.5) | 26 (27.5) |
| | Other | 6 (6.5) | 33 (32.5) |

## RESOURCES

### ActivStats

▸ Chapter 26—"Chi-Square." These activities include both a simulation illustrating independence and a return to the *Titanic* story.

### Web Links

▸ If you use the M&M Classroom activity, you can check the M&M color distribution at http://us.mms.com/us/about/products/

### Printed Test Bank and Resource Guide

The *Printed Test Bank and Resource Guide* offers an Investigative Task and three chapter quizzes.

## What's It About?

In Chapter 27 we return to the question of associations between quantitative variables, examining the regression model, with its underlying assumptions and conditions. We see that that $t$-models describe the sampling distribution of slopes of regression lines. We present step-by-step examples of hypothesis tests and confidence intervals for slope. Here we emphasize computer output, because that is the way that most people calculate and encounter regression.

## Comments

The last chapter closed with the chi-square test for independence, allowing us to check for evidence of an association between categorical variables. Our tour of introductory statistics is not complete until we can make inferences about associations between quantitative variables as well.

We last looked at linear regression back in Part II, many weeks ago. It's a very important topic, involving a number of key concepts and skills. Students need to remember how to create and describe a scatterplot and how to find and interpret the correlation. They need to understand the concept of residuals and be able to use a residuals plot to confirm the appropriateness of a linear model. They need to be able to find the equation of the regression line and interpret its slope and $y$-intercept.

## Looking Ahead

The ideas presented here form the basis for understanding multiple regression, an optional topic on the DVD that accompanies this text.

## Class Do's

Start with a review of the key regression concepts from Chapters 7, 8, and 9. A set of data and a list of questions should do it. If possible, have students work in groups, helping each other to remember the concepts, the mechanics, and the interpretations.

▶ How do we make a scatterplot?

▶ What do we look for in a scatterplot?

▶ How do we find the correlation?

▶ What does the correlation mean?

▶ What does $R^2$ mean?

▶ How do we create a linear model?

▶ How do we know if the linear model is appropriate?

▶ How do we create a residuals plot?

▶ What do we look for in the residuals plot?

▶ What does the slope mean?

▶ What does the $y$-intercept mean?

We also get to review the idea of a sampling distribution. Remind students about the two sampling distribution models from Chapter 18. We know that sample proportions vary from sample to sample, and their distribution has a Normal model. That knowledge allows us to do inference for proportions. We know that sample means vary from sample to sample, also following a Normal model. Not knowing the population's standard deviation, though, forces us to use the almost-Normal $t$-models when we do inference. Now we are interested in examining how slopes of regression lines vary from sample to sample. Recall our earlier heights and weights example. Have students imagine the scatterplot for the entire population, a dense cloud of points. We must believe that for this population there is an ideal line that captures the association between height and weight. Our sample produces a line that approximates the true line. Other samples would also produce such approximating lines, each with a slightly different slope. Slopes, then, vary from sample to sample. Each slope, $b_1$, is an estimate of the true slope, $\beta_1$. The distribution of all such slopes has a $t$-model, with $n - 2$ degrees of freedom. Knowing the model enables us to do inference about slope. Almost.

The $t$-model we want to use is appropriate only if the population behaves according to certain assumptions. When students understand the assumptions that create the perfect model of linear association (illustrated in Figure 27.7 on page 724), they're better able to remember the conditions they need to check.

▶ We believe that there is an underlying linear relationship between $x$ and $y$ that we can model with the least squares line. We check the Straight Enough Condition with a scatterplot. If the relationship is straight enough, we can find the least squares line.

▶ We believe that the errors—the (signed) distances of points from the ideal line, akin to residuals in the sample—are independent, that one person's heavier-than-expected weight does not tell whether another person might be heavier or lighter than their height might predict. (Check the residuals plot for random scatter.)

▶ We believe that at each value of $x$ the $y$'s follow a Normal model. For example, a Normal model describes the weights of all the people who are, say, 60 inches tall—or any other height. (Moreover, we believe that the means of all those Normal models lie on the line relating $y$ and $x$, so this can be seen as a statement about the distribution of the errors around the ideal line.)

▶ We believe that all those Normal models have the same standard deviation. In other words, we believe the variability of weights is the same at each height. This assumption is called "homoskedasticity," a term students don't need to know—but they love the word! We can examine the residuals plot for uniform spread—checking whether the Plot Thickens. If the spread seems constant, then we can pool the residuals together and look at a histogram or Normal probability plot to check whether their distribution really does seem nearly Normal.

But what are we doing inference *about*? Help students see that even if there is no association present in the population, a sample might draw points that appear to show an association. The question we ask is whether the association we see in our sample is so strong that it could not just have popped up by chance during the sampling process. We want to know if the apparent association in our sample provides evidence that there must be an association in the population. Our null hypothesis, then, is that in the population there is no association—in other words, that the ideal line is really horizontal: $\beta_1 = 0$.

When a hypothesis test indicates that an association exists, have students create a confidence interval for the slope of the true line. Earlier in the course they learned to interpret slope and to interpret confidence intervals. That does not mean they'll easily get the phrasing right when dealing with both.

▶ *Slope:* The model suggests that weights of teenage boys increase about 4.2 pounds for every additional inch of height.

▶ *Confidence interval:* We are 95% confident that the interval from 5'8" to 5'10" contains the mean height of teenage boys.

▶ *Confidence interval for slope:* We are 95% confident that the interval from 3.8 to 4.6 pounds per inch contains the average weight difference associated with differences in height among teenage boys.

Invest time in looking at regression output. Most regression analyses are produced by statistics software packages. Be sure students can find, use, and properly interpret the key results. The annotated output on page 743 should be a big help.

Students will also find the Part VII Review helpful. Along with the usual Quick Review, we include the rest of our Quick Guide to Inference and summary of assumptions and conditions covering all of the different procedures we've seen. These are designed to help students organize their understanding of the last three units, and to become adept at deciding which of the many inference procedures to apply in a given situation. The Review Exercises are comprehensive, covering all the different kinds of inference with questions in random order. Be sure to have students spend time there. Even students who are adept at using each individual procedure can find it difficult to choose among them. While you'll probably want to assign a few exercises to be worked out in full, it's also very productive to just ask students to read exercises and classify them with respect to the type of inference called for.

## The Importance of What You Don't Say

*Dependent Variable/Independent Variable.* We warned about this back in Chapter 8, but it is still true. We have by now made so much of checking for independence that to introduce the term in an entirely different context and meaning can only be harmful. Speak of response variables and predictors (or, if you get to ANOVA, possibly factors.)

*Coefficient of Determination.* "R-squared" is what the statistics packages call it and what we've been calling it. This is another term the students don't need to know at this point.

*Don't spend time on the formulas for calculating s, SE(b₁), and so on.* Students need to understand the concepts and be able to interpret regression output from software packages. Don't distract them from these central issues with scary formulas. If they can conduct a hypothesis test and create a confidence interval using software or calculator to do the mechanics, that will be fine.

## Class Examples

1. Review the concepts of regression by examining the association between anxiety level and math test scores. You can give students the data in the table on the next page and let students work on it in groups. By putting their heads together they should collectively remember enough to do everything, and the discussion will help everyone get back up to speed on these concepts and skills.

2. Students need to understand that a low correlation may be evidence of a weak association between two variables. But it may also simply arise from sampling error even when there is no association at all between the two variables. To demonstrate, have each student create two sets of 20 random numbers. Look at the scatterplot and find the correlation. Clearly, there should be no association between random numbers, yet some will see patterns and many will have correlations of 0.20 or more. We need a way to see if the correlation is high enough to be meaningful—a hypothesis test, in other words. It turns out that we test correlations by looking at the slope of the regression line. After all, a true correlation of 0 would make the slope of the ideal line also 0. We suspect that the slopes of the lines we fit to our random scatterplots, though not exactly 0, aren't statistically significant.

3. Run through the key steps of a hypothesis test and confidence interval (including careful attention to the assumptions and conditions) for the anxiety and math test data, or use the average temperature vs. electrical usage worksheet in the Instructor's Resources.

4. Once students understand the linear regression *t*-test, have them check the significance of the associations that appeared between their two lists of random numbers. Almost all will turn out to be too weak to reject the null hypothesis. And when the occasional significant correlation does appear, you can remind them of the risk of Type I error that's always present—we're willing to take a 5% risk of rejecting a true null.

5. Return to the Instructor's Guide Chapter 8 example involving the price of plane tickets for flights originating in Atlanta, and have students create a confidence interval for the cost per mile.

| Student Number | Anxiety Level | Math Test |
|:---:|:---:|:---:|
| 1 | 10 | 35 |
| 2 | 8 | 61 |
| 3 | 7 | 68 |
| 4 | 7 | 39 |
| 5 | 6 | 79 |
| 6 | 2 | 94 |
| 7 | 3 | 87 |
| 8 | 5 | 81 |
| 9 | 6 | 80 |
| 10 | 8 | 57 |
| 11 | 8 | 45 |
| 12 | 10 | 44 |
| 13 | 10 | 27 |
| 14 | 9 | 47 |
| 15 | 7 | 60 |
| 16 | 6 | 85 |
| 17 | 4 | 29 |
| 18 | 6 | 100 |
| 19 | 6 | 41 |
| 20 | 10 | 37 |
| 21 | 3 | 66 |
| 22 | 9 | 72 |
| 23 | 2 | 68 |
| 24 | 8 | 80 |

6. The large selection of homework exercises will provide you with plenty of additional examples for discussion. Start mixing in the Part VII Review Exercises, too. Those exercises include, in random order, all the different types of inference. By now we expect students to be able to decide what inference procedure is called for in any situation.

## RESOURCES

### ActivStats

▶ Chapter 27—"Inference for Regression." Simulations in this chapter can help students understand what our inference for slope is about. Another activity helps them explore the regression output for the selected statistics package.

### Printed Test Bank and Resource Guide

The *Printed Test Bank and Resource Guide* has two chapter quizzes. And, since this is the end of Part VII, there are also 3 Part Tests covering inference topics (Chapters 18–27).

**Instructor's Guide**

**CHAPTER 28**

# Analysis of Variance

## What's It About?

We looked at equality of means for two groups in Chapter 24. Here, in Chapter 28, we extend our concern to more than two groups. Another way of looking at this question is to think of it as the association between a quantitative and a categorical variable. In Chapter 24, we saw that the ratio of the difference of two means to its standard error was the natural statistic to use to test the null hypothesis and that the $t$-model gave us its sampling distribution. Now we have the generalization of that ratio: the ratio of two mean squares, modeled by the $F$-distribution. We present step-by-step examples of hypothesis tests. In the case that the null hypothesis is rejected, we may want to go further and examine confidence intervals for pairwise differences. We do this using the Bonferroni adjustment.

## Comments

Chapter 26 introduced the chi-square test for homogeneity, testing whether proportions are the same across different groups. It can be useful to point out that the ANOVA test generalizes the $t$-test for means in much the same way that the chi-square test generalizes the $z$-test for proportions. The chi-square statistic rejects the null hypothesis of equal proportions when the sum of squared differences between expected and observed becomes too large. Similarly, the $F$ statistic rejects the null when the variance of the group means is too large. The connection is that the numerator of that variance is the squared differences of the group means from the grand average.

ANOVA becomes difficult to learn when too much time is spent on the formulas themselves. Rarely will students need to calculate these quantities by hand. More important is to emphasize that the F-statistic measures the ratio of the variation among the group means to the (average) variation within each group. Students intuitively know that large differences lead to rejecting the null hypothesis, and that differences are easier to discern when the variation is smaller. Students need to understand that the variation within the groups is based on an average of *all* the groups and so, that variation needs to be similar for the average to make sense. The assumption of equal variances is easily checked by the equal variance condition. They've used residual plots to check conditions for regression, so this check is natural.

## Looking Ahead

In Chapter 29, we'll look at models where the predictor variables can be either all quantitative (multiple regression) or a mix of quantitative and categorical variables (multiple regression with indicator variables, or analysis of covariance, depending on your point of view).

## Class Do's

Start with a review of the *t*-test and when it rejects the null hypothesis of equal means. Use boxplots of various situations to ask students what their intuition says about equality of means with more than two groups. (Watch out for extremely large or small group sample sizes where the intuition may not match well.)

Start right in with data. Show the boxplots and ask students whether they think there is evidence of differences in group means. Ask whether the assumptions and conditions of ANOVA are satisfied:

▸ We believe that all the groups have the same standard deviation. This is the same "homoskedasticity" as regression. This is pretty easy to believe for randomized experiments because when we randomly assign subjects to treatments, the resulting treatments groups start out with the same underlying standard deviation. So we only need to assume that (under the null hypothesis of no difference in treatment effect), treatments that didn't change the means also didn't change the standard deviations. The assumption's crucial here because the $MS_E$ needs to make sense. It is dangerous to average essentially different quantities (we learned that in the Simpson's paradox examples of Chapter 3). To check a corresponding condition, we can look at group boxplots and/or check the scatterplot of residuals vs. predicted for uniform spread.

▸ We believe that the errors—the differences of the observations from the group means—are independent. (We need to think about how the data were collected. If an experiment, were the treatments appropriately randomized? If an observational study, were the respondents chosen at random?)

▸ We also believe that the errors are normally distributed. (Check a normal probability plot of the residuals.)

Examine the ANOVA table. Without getting too caught up in the sums of squares and degrees of freedom, look at the two mean squares. The error mean square estimates the (average) error variance across the groups. So, its square root ($s_p$) should give a reasonable estimate of the spread of the boxplots. Does

it? Now, if the group means *are* equal, the treatment mean square should be about the same size as the error mean square. Is it? If it's a lot larger, the F-test will reject the null hypothesis, and the larger the ratio, the more evidence there is against the null hypothesis. That's the F-test in a nutshell.

Be careful to say what rejecting the null hypothesis doesn't say. We don't know *which* means are different. For that we need to do multiple comparisons.

## The Importance of What You Don't Say

*Don't dwell on the sums of squares formulas for getting to the mean squares.* Students need to understand the concepts and be able to interpret ANOVA output from software packages or a calculator. Don't distract them from these central issues with scary formulas. If they can conduct a hypothesis test using software or a calculator to do the mechanics, they will be fine.

## Class Examples

1. Resting pulse rates for a random sample of 26 heavy smokers had a mean of 80 beats per minute (bpm) and a standard deviation of 5 bpm. Among 32 randomly chosen light smokers the mean and standard deviation were 77 and 6 bpm. Among 30 non-smokers the mean was 74 bpm with a standard deviation of 5 bpm. All three sets of data were roughly symmetric and had no outliers. The ANOVA table shows:

### Analysis of Variance Table

| Source | Sum of Squares | df | Mean Square | F-ratio | P-value |
|---|---|---|---|---|---|
| Smoking | 502.364 | 2 | 251.1818 | 7.639 | < 0.001 |
| Error | 2466.000 | 85 | 32.88 | | |
| Total | 2968.364 | 31 | | | |

Is there evidence of a difference in mean pulse rate between these groups?

**Hypotheses.**  $H_0$: $\mu_{HS} = \mu_{LS} = \mu_{NS}$ *vs.* $H_A$: not all the means are equal.

**Model.**  We have independent random samples, the spreads of the three groups appear to be about the same, and we are told that the data appear to be approximately Normal. OK to proceed with an ANOVA.

**Mechanics.**  The F-test shows that there is strong evidence of a difference. The observed differences are unlikely to be due to sampling error. We reject the null hypothesis, concluding we have strong evidence of a difference in mean pulse rates across the three groups. In other words, we reject the hypothesis that the mean plus is the same for all three groups.

To get a 95% confidence interval for the difference between two groups, say light smokers and non-smokers, we would start by creating a confidence interval for the difference as in Chapter 24, replacing the two sided $t^*$ critical value at $\alpha = 0.05$ with a $t^{**}$ value at $\alpha = 0.05/3 = 0.01667$. For 85 degrees of freedom, $t^{**} = 2.442$ (Be careful, we have to split $\alpha = 0.01667$ into two because it's a confidence interval). So the Bonferroni confidence interval for the difference is:

$$77 - 74 \pm t^{**} \times s_p \sqrt{\frac{1}{n_{LS}} + \frac{1}{n_{NS}}}$$

$$= 3 \pm 2.163 \times 5.73 \sqrt{\frac{1}{32} + \frac{1}{30}} = (-0.150, 6.150)\,bpm$$

With a margin of error that large, we can not conclude that there is a significant difference in the mean pulse rates between light smokers and non-smokers.

2. Here is the saturated fat content (in grams) for pizzas sold by ten national chains:

| Pizza | Number | Mean | SD |
|-------|--------|-------|------|
| A | 8 | 12.13 | 2.53 |
| B | 8 | 11.75 | 1.58 |
| C | 8 | 10.13 | 3.64 |
| D | 8 | 11.25 | 2.49 |
| E | 8 | 13.75 | 3.20 |
| F | 8 | 11.25 | 1.16 |
| G | 8 | 12.50 | 2.88 |
| H | 8 | 13.25 | 3.20 |
| I | 8 | 13.00 | 3.93 |
| J | 8 | 13.50 | 3.66 |

**Analysis of Variance Table**

| Source | Sum of Squares | df | Mean Square | F-ratio | P-value |
|--------|---------------|-----|-------------|---------|---------|
| Pizza | 97.75 | 9 | 10.861 | 1.2438 | 0.2833 |
| Error | 611.25 | 70 | 8.732 | | |
| Total | 709.00 | 79 | | | |

Do you find any systematic differences in the fat content from one brand to another? What concerns do you have about the design of the study?

## RESOURCES

### ActivStats

▸ Lesson 28—ANOVA

### Web Links

▸ The Fast Food Nutrition Fact Explorer: http://www.fatcalories.com/index.cfm

### *Printed Test Bank and Resource Guide*

The *Printed Test Bank* offers a chapter quiz. Students will need access to technology to compute the ANOVA required.

## Instructor's Guide

**CHAPTER 29**

# Multiple Regression

## What's It About?

We first looked at simple regression in Chapters 8 and 9. There we learned about interpreting regression coefficients and $R^2$. Then we discussed inference for regression in Chapter 27 and explained most of the other numbers in the computer regression table. But the simple linear model isn't rich enough to deal with the complexities of the real world. Linear models (almost) never account for all of the variation in the data (as the $R^2$ shows us). Adding more predictors to the model can help account for more of the behavior of the response variable. And the linear model accommodates more predictors naturally.

With a statistics program it's easy and natural to add more predictors to a regression. Fortunately, most of what we learned in Chapter 27 still holds. The $R^2$ still gives the fraction of variability accounted for by the regression. The coefficients table gives standard errors, $t$-statistics, and corresponding $P$-values for each coefficient.

But the regression coefficients have a subtly different interpretation that needs to be understood. The chapter provides a careful discussion of what multiple regression coefficients mean, and a visualization of those ideas in Figure 29.2.

The assumptions and conditions also receive renewed attention. The linearity assumption is now an assumption about the multiple regression model, and is harder to check with corresponding conditions. And it matters what order we do things in. Students should look at the ordered list of what to compute and what to check.

## Comments

The theme of this chapter is that multiple regression is pretty much just like what we've been doing with inference and what we've already seen for simple regression inference. Students who have used a statistics package for simple regression should be able to figure out on their own how to throw in a few more predictors. All students, having seen package output for simple regression, should be able to read most of the regression table for a multiple regression.

The most important new concepts here relate to interpreting multiple regression coefficients. A multiple regression coefficient measures the linear association between its predictor and the response variable *after allowing for the linear effects of the other predictors.*

Don't let your students interpret coefficients either as causally predicting what will happen if a variable is changed or as the relationship "when other variables are held constant". Both interpretations are common; neither is really correct.

We now begin to see more of the challenges of multivariate data. Now we have a collection of predictors that may—and probably do—have correlations with each other. That adds new depth and complexity.

## Looking Ahead

At this point, "ahead" really means beyond this course. Analysis of Variance and multiple regression are the foundations of the most widely used statistics methods. Together they are aspects of a Statistics model known as the General Linear Model. Students who take more advanced statistics courses are bound to encounter General Linear Model applications and generalizations. The better their understanding of ANOVA and multiple regression at this point in their study of Statistics, the sounder will be their understanding of the more advanced methods.

## Class Do's

Do encourage students to interpret multiple regression models, but insist that they do so carefully and correctly. Do insist that they plot residuals and check conditions. And be sure that they understand that it is a good idea to maintain alternative regression models for the same data while trying to understand how best to model the data.

It is a good idea to work through one of the step-by-step examples. None of it is really new, but once put together into a full multiple regression analysis, there's quite a bit here.

Start with a review of the key regression concepts from Chapters 7, 8, 9, and 27. A set of data and a list of questions should do it. If possible, have students work in groups helping each other to remember the concepts, the mechanics, and the interpretations.

▶ What does $R^2$ mean?

▶ How do we find a linear model?

▶ How do we know whether the linear model is appropriate?

▶ How do we plot residuals? (Remind them about plotting residuals against the predicted values rather than against $x$; that's what we'll need to do for the multiple regression.)

▶ What do we look for in the residuals plot?

▶ What does the slope of a simple regression mean?

▶ What does the $y$-intercept mean?

▶ What does it mean for the coefficients to have standard errors?

▶ How do we interpret the $t$-tests that come with each coefficient in a simple regression?

▶ What additional conditions did we need to check for those $t$-tests to be appropriate? How do we check them?

All of these concepts continue into the multiple regression framework. The mechanics are increasingly turned over to the computer. The interpretations are the place where we need to think a bit more carefully.

Now we must believe that for this population there is an ideal regression model that captures the association between shoe size and height and weight. Our sample produces a model that approximates the true model. Other samples would also produce such approximating models, each with slightly different coefficients. Coefficients, then, vary from sample to sample. Each coefficient, $b_j$, is an estimate of a population model coefficient, $\beta_j$. The sampling distribution of each of these coefficients has a $t$-model, with $n - k - 1$ degrees of freedom. Knowing the model enables us to do inference about the coefficients. Almost.

The $t$-model we want to use is appropriate only if the population behaves according to certain assumptions. When students understand the assumptions we needed for simple regression inference in Chapter 27, they're better able to remember the conditions they need to check for multiple regression.

▶ We believe that at every possible combination of values of the $x$ variables, the $y$'s follow a Normal model. In other words, a Normal model describes the shoe sizes of all the people who are, say, 60 inches tall and weigh 150 pounds. Or any other height and weight. (Checking a histogram of the residuals for approximate normality addresses this question, provided the linear model itself is appropriate and the variation around the model is the same everywhere.)

▶ We believe that the means of all those Normal models can be modeled with a linear model, and that the ideal model they determine is approximated by the regression model we fit to our sample. (Check the scatterplot of residuals against the predicted value for structure that suggests we don't have the right model.)

▶ We believe that all those Normal models have the same standard deviation. In other words, we believe the variability of shoe sizes is the same at each height and weight combination. This assumption is called "homoskedasticity," a term students don't need to know, but usually enjoy knowing. (Check the residuals plot for uniform spread.)

▶ We believe that the errors—the distances of points from the ideal model, akin to residuals in the sample—are independent, that one person's bigger than expected feet do not tell whether another person might have bigger or smaller feet than their height and weight might predict. (Check the residuals plot for random scatter.)

But what are we doing inference *about*? Help students see that even if there is no association present in the population, a sample might draw points that appear to show an association. The question we ask is whether the association we see in our sample is so strong that it could not just have popped up by chance during the sampling process. We want to know if the apparent association in our sample provides evidence that there must be an association in the population.

Now, however, life is more interesting than it was back in Chapter 27 when we had only one predictor. Now we have a null hypothesis associated with each predictor. We hypothesize that each $\beta_j = 0$ in the model. Be sure that students understand that this is not the same as the simple hypothesis that there is no linear association between $y$ and that predictor. These null hypotheses talk about the relationship between $y$ and the predictor *after allowing for the linear effects of the other predictors*. The null hypothesis can be viewed as saying that *after* doing the best we can with the other predictors, there's nothing more that this one brings to the model.

When a hypothesis test rejects the null hypothesis, have students interpret the coefficient carefully. The coefficient talks about the slope of the linear relationship between the $y$ variable and that predictor after allowing for the linear effects of the other predictors.

Invest time in looking at regression output. Students are most likely to be given a multiple regression analysis produced by a software package. Be sure they can find, use, and properly interpret the key results. The annotated output on page 743 should be a big help.

## The Importance of What You Don't Say

*Don't imply that changing x will cause a change in y corresponding to the regression coefficient.* Regression does not establish a causal relationship, it only models a linear association. For example (as discussed below), although weight is a good predictor of shoe size in a multiple regression, nobody goes on a diet to get dainty feet. And while taller people generally have bigger feet, it makes little sense to talk about the consequences of making an adult shorter.

*Don't be lured into prediction—especially into the future.* It is tempting to interpret regression models that have time as a predictor as if they provided a computerized crystal ball. We warned against this back in Chapter 9. But it is so tempting to do that it is worth repeating the warning here. Regression models do not have "inertia". Just because they are headed in a particular direction when we lose sight of them off the edge of our plots, we can't assume that they'll continue indefinitely on the same path—indeed, a little thought usually shows that they couldn't possibly do that.

*Don't even think about the formulas for calculating SE(b).* Students need to understand the concepts and be able to interpret regression output from software packages. In Chapter 27 we advised against considering these formulas. Now we'll just point out that for multiple regression, they are just not worth considering at all. It is technically possible to write expressions for the standard errors in a regression with two predictors, but it doesn't generalize. The general formula needs matrix algebra; you don't want to go there.

*Don't say "holding the other predictors constant . . ."* Yes, mathematically, it is technically true that if all the other $x$'s are held constant, then a coefficient tells how our prediction for $y$ changes were the corresponding $x$ to change. But in the real world it is often meaningless to hold things constant. Children can't grow taller without also getting older (and probably heavier). Workers gain experience, get raises, and also get older. Unless you are discussing a situation in which the predictors are under control and can be held constant while one other predictor is varied (e.g., an industrial quality experiment in which the speed of the conveyor belt, the oven temperature, and the amounts of various chemicals in the mix) it probably isn't possible to hold predictors constant while another changes. If you lose weight (while holding your height constant) you still won't fit into smaller shoes. That's just not what the regression says.

## Class Examples

Students in a large statistics class were surveyed. Here is a regression predicting shoe size from height (inches), and weight (lbs):

Dependent variable is: shoe size
R squared = 71.2% R squared (adjusted) = 71.0%
s = 1.033 with 216 – 3 = 213 degrees of freedom

| Source | Sum of Squares | df | Mean Square | F-ratio |
|---|---|---|---|---|
| Regression | 562.446 | 2 | 281.223 | 264 |
| Residual | 227.247 | 213 | 1.06689 | |

| Variable | Coefficient | SE(Coeff) | t-ratio | P-value |
|---|---|---|---|---|
| Intercept | –13.2086 | 1.245 | –10.6 | ≤ 0.0001 |
| height | 0.290390 | 0.0220 | 13.2 | ≤ 0.0001 |
| weight | 0.020321 | 0.0030 | 6.75 | ≤ 0.0001 |

Students should be able to find the coefficients in a typical regression table and write the regression model. They should be able to interpret $R^2$ as the fraction of variability in shoe size accounted for by the regression model.

Multiple regressions are always found using a computer. Students should have some experience with finding multiple regressions using a statistics package, or at least reading package output such as the previous table.

1. Students need to understand that a high $R^2$ may be evidence of a good regression model, but it may also simply arise from sampling error even when there is no association at all between the two variables. To demonstrate, have each student create 11 sets of 50 random numbers. Clearly there should be no association among random numbers, yet a regression of one of these "variables" on the 9 others will have a reasonably high $R^2$, possibly around 20%. Is the $R^2$ high enough to be meaningful? We can address this question with hypothesis tests on the coefficients. After all, a true correlation of 0 would make the coefficients of the ideal regression model also 0. We suspect that the coefficients of the model we fit to our random data, though not exactly 0, aren't statistically significant.

2. Run through the key steps of a hypothesis test and confidence interval (including careful attention to the assumptions and conditions) using the shoe size vs height and weight example.

3. Once students understand the linear regression *t*-test, have them check the hypotheses associated with the coefficients of the regression on their random numbers. Almost all will turn out to be too weak to reject the null hypothesis. And when the occasional significant correlation *does* appear you can remind them of the risk of Type I Error that's always present—we're willing to take a 5% risk of rejecting a true null.

4. The large selection of homework exercises will provide you with plenty of additional examples for discussion.

## RESOURCES

### ActivStats

▸ Lesson 29: Multiple Regression, pages 1–3. *ActivStats* offers a number of visualizations that can be useful for individual student use or as classroom demonstrations.

### Statistics software

▸ The user manual of whatever statistics software your students are using will discuss the statistics and graphics associated with multiple regression that the package makes available. Most also provide examples. Some offer additional wisdom.

### Printed Test Bank and Resource Guide

The *Printed Test Bank* has a chapter quiz. The quiz provides the data so students can take it using a statistics package. But it also provides generic package output for students to interpret, so they can take the quiz without access to technology.

# CHAPTER 26

# Comparing Counts

## Where are we going?

Is your favorite color related to how much education you've had? A survey found a higher percentage of those naming blue, and a lower percentage saying red, among adults with only a high school education compared to adults with more education. Could this be just random fluctuation, or is the distribution of color preference different for different education levels? We saw tables of counts and percentages in Chapter 3. In this chapter we'll see how to test the strength of the patterns we saw in those tables.

D oes your zodiac sign predict how successful you will be later in life? *Fortune* magazine collected the zodiac signs of 256 heads of the largest 400 companies. Here are the number of births for each sign:

| WHO | Executives of Fortune 400 companies |
|-----|-------------------------------------|
| WHAT | Zodiac birth sign |
| WHY | Maybe the researcher was a Gemini and naturally curious? |

| Births | Sign |
|--------|------|
| 23 | Aries |
| 20 | Taurus |
| 18 | Gemini |
| 23 | Cancer |
| 20 | Leo |
| 19 | Virgo |
| 18 | Libra |
| 21 | Scorpio |
| 19 | Sagittarius |
| 22 | Capricorn |
| 24 | Aquarius |
| 29 | Pisces |

Birth totals by sign for 256 Fortune 400 executives.

**A S**   *Activity:* **Children at Risk.**
See how a contingency table helps
us understand the different risks to
which an incident exposed children.

We can see some variation in the number of births per sign, and there *are* more Pisces, but is that enough to claim that successful people are more likely to be born under some signs than others?

# Goodness-of-Fit

*"All creatures have their determined time for giving birth and carrying fetus, only a man is born all year long, not in determined time, one in the seventh month, the other in the eighth, and so on till the beginning of the eleventh month."*

—Aristotle

If births were distributed uniformly across the year, we would expect about 1/12 of them to occur under each sign of the zodiac. That suggests 256/12, or about 21.3 births per sign. How closely do the observed numbers of births per sign fit this simple "null" model?

A hypothesis test to address this question is called a test of **"goodness-of-fit."** The name suggests a certain badness-of-grammar, but it is quite standard. After all, we are asking whether the model that births are uniformly distributed over the signs fits the data good, . . . er, well. Goodness-of-fit involves testing a hypothesis. We have specified a model for the distribution and want to know whether it fits. There is no single parameter to estimate, so a confidence interval wouldn't make much sense.

If the question were about only one astrological sign (for example, "Are executives more likely to be Pisces?"[1]), we could use a one-proportion $z$-test and ask if the true proportion of executives with that sign is equal to 1/12. However, here we have 12 hypothesized proportions, one for each sign. We need a test that considers all of them together and gives an overall idea of whether the observed distribution differs from the hypothesized one.

---

**FOR EXAMPLE**   Finding expected counts

Birth month may not be related to success as a CEO, but what about on the ball field? It has been proposed by some researchers that children who are the older ones in their class at school naturally perform better in sports and that these children then get more coaching and encouragement. Could that make a difference in who makes it to the professional level in sports?

Baseball is a remarkable sport, in part because so much data are available. We have the birth dates of every one of the 16,804 players who ever played in a major league game. Since the effect we're suspecting may be due to relatively recent policies (and to keep the sample size moderate), we'll consider the birth months of the 1478 major league players born since 1975 and who have played through 2006. We can also look up the national demographic statistics to find what percentage of people were born in each month. Let's test whether the observed distribution of ballplayers' birth months shows just random fluctuations or whether it represents a real deviation from the national pattern.

| Month | Ballplayer count | National birth % | Month | Ballplayer count | National birth % |
|---|---|---|---|---|---|
| 1 | 137 | 8% | 7 | 102 | 9% |
| 2 | 121 | 7% | 8 | 165 | 9% |
| 3 | 116 | 8% | 9 | 134 | 9% |
| 4 | 121 | 8% | 10 | 115 | 9% |
| 5 | 126 | 8% | 11 | 105 | 8% |
| 6 | 114 | 8% | 12 | 122 | 9% |
| | | | **Total** | 1478 | 100% |

*(continued)*

---

[1] A question actually asked us by someone who was undoubtedly a Pisces.

For Example (*continued*)

Question: We need expected counts. How can we find those?

There are 1478 players in this set of data. I'd expect 8% of them to have been born in January, and 1478(0.08) = 118.24. I won't round off, because expected "counts" needn't be integers. Multiplying 1478 by each of the birth percentages gives the expected counts shown in the table.

| Month | Expected |
|-------|----------|
| 1 | 118.24 |
| 2 | 103.46 |
| 3 | 118.24 |
| 4 | 118.24 |
| 5 | 118.24 |
| 6 | 118.24 |
| 7 | 133.02 |
| 8 | 133.02 |
| 9 | 133.02 |
| 10 | 133.02 |
| 11 | 118.24 |
| 12 | 133.02 |

# Assumptions and Conditions

These data are organized in tables as we saw in Chapter 3, and the assumptions and conditions reflect that. Rather than having an observation for each individual, we typically work with summary counts in categories. In our example, we don't know the birth signs of each of the 256 executives, only the totals for each sign.

**Counted Data Condition:** The data must be *counts* for the categories of a categorical variable. This might seem a simplistic, even silly condition. But many kinds of values can be assigned to categories, and it is unfortunately common to find the methods of this chapter applied incorrectly to proportions or amounts just because they happen to be organized in a two-way table. So check to be sure you really have counts.

### INDEPENDENCE ASSUMPTION

**Independence Assumption:** The counts in the cells should be independent of each other. The easiest case is when the individuals who are counted in the cells are sampled independently from some population. That's what we'd like to have if we want to draw conclusions about that population. Randomness can arise in other ways, though. For example, these Fortune 400 executives are not a random sample, but we might still think that their birth dates are randomly distributed throughout the year. If we want to generalize to a large population, we should check the Randomization Condition.

**Randomization Condition:** The individuals who have been counted and whose counts are available for analysis should be a random sample from some population.

### SAMPLE SIZE ASSUMPTION

We must have enough data for the methods to work. We usually check the following:

**Expected Cell Frequency Condition:** We should expect to see at least 5 individuals in each cell.

The Expected Cell Frequency Condition sounds like—and is, in fact, quite similar to—the condition that $np$ and $nq$ be at least 10 when we tested proportions. In our astrology example, assuming equal births in each month leads us to expect 21.3 births per month, so the condition is easily met here.

---

### FOR EXAMPLE — Checking assumptions and conditions

**Recap:** Are professional baseball players more likely to be born in some months than in others? We have observed and expected counts for the 1478 players born since 1975.

**Question:** Are the assumptions and conditions met for performing a goodness-of-fit test?

✔ **Counted Data Condition:** I have month-by-month counts of ballplayer births.

✔ **Independence Assumption:** These births were independent.

✔ **Randomization Condition:** Although they are not a random sample, we can take these players to be representative of players past and future.

✔ **Expected Cell Frequency Condition:** The expected counts range from 103.46 to 133.02, all much greater than 5.

✔ **10% Condition:** These 1478 players are less than 10% of the population of 16,804 players who have ever played (or will play) major league baseball.

It's okay to use these data for a goodness-of-fit test.

---

## Calculations

**NOTATION ALERT:**

We compare the counts *observed* in each cell with the counts we *expect* to find. The usual notation uses $O$'s and $E$'s or abbreviations such as those we've used here. The method for finding the expected counts depends on the model.

We have observed a count in each category from the data, and have an expected count for each category from the hypothesized proportions. Are the differences just natural sampling variability, or are they so large that they indicate something important? It's natural to look at the *differences* between these observed and expected counts, denoted $(Obs - Exp)$. We'd like to think about the total of the differences, but just adding them won't work because some differences are positive, others negative. We've been in this predicament before—once when we looked at deviations from the mean and again when we dealt with residuals. In fact, these *are* residuals. They're just the differences between the observed data and the counts given by the (null) model. We handle these residuals in essentially the same way we did in regression: We square them. That gives us positive values and focuses attention on any cells with large differences from what we expected. Because the differences between observed and expected counts generally get larger the more data we have, we also need to get an idea of the *relative* sizes of the differences. To do that, we divide each squared difference by the expected count for that cell.

The test statistic, called the **chi-square** (or chi-squared) **statistic,** is found by adding up the sum of the squares of the deviations between the observed and expected counts divided by the expected counts:

$$\chi^2 = \sum_{all\ cells} \frac{(Obs - Exp)^2}{Exp}.$$

The chi-square statistic is denoted $\chi^2$, where $\chi$ is the Greek letter chi (pronounced "ky" as in "sky"). It refers to a family of sampling distribution models we have not seen before called (remarkably enough) the **chi-square models.**

This family of models, like the Student's *t*-models, differ only in the number of degrees of freedom. The number of degrees of freedom for a goodness-of-fit test is $n - 1$. Here, however, $n$ is *not* the sample size, but instead is the number of categories. For the zodiac example, we have 12 signs, so our $\chi^2$ statistic has 11 degrees of freedom.

## Chi-Square P-Values

The chi-square statistic is used only for testing hypotheses, not for constructing confidence intervals. If the observed counts don't match the expected, the statistic will be large. It can't be "too small." That would just mean that our model *really* fit the data well. So the chi-square test is always one-sided. If the calculated statistic value is large enough, we'll reject the null hypothesis. What could be simpler?

If you don't have technology handy, it's easy to read the $\chi^2$ table (Table X in Appendix D).

A portion of Table X.

| Right-Tail Probability | 0.10 | 0.05 | 0.025 | 0.01 | 0.005 |
|---|---|---|---|---|---|
| df | | | | | |
| 1 | 2.706 | 3.841 | 5.024 | 6.635 | 7.879 |
| 2 | 4.605 | 5.991 | 7.378 | 9.210 | 10.597 |
| 3 | 6.251 | 7.815 | 9.348 | 11.345 | 12.838 |
| 4 | 7.779 | 9.488 | 11.143 | 13.277 | 14.860 |
| 5 | 9.236 | 11.070 | 12.833 | 15.086 | 16.750 |
| 6 | 10.645 | 12.592 | 14.449 | 16.812 | 18.548 |
| 7 | 12.017 | 14.067 | 16.013 | 18.475 | 20.278 |
| 8 | 13.362 | 15.507 | 17.535 | 20.090 | 21.955 |
| 9 | 14.684 | 16.919 | 19.023 | 21.666 | 23.589 |
| 10 | 15.987 | 18.307 | 20.483 | 23.209 | 25.188 |
| 11 | 17.275 | 19.675 | 21.920 | 24.725 | 26.757 |
| 12 | 18.549 | 21.026 | 23.337 | 26.217 | 28.300 |
| 13 | 19.812 | 22.362 | 24.736 | 27.688 | 29.819 |
| 14 | 21.064 | 23.685 | 26.119 | 29.141 | 31.319 |

Values of $\chi_{\alpha}^2$

The usual selected probability values are at the top of the columns. As with the *t*-tables, we have only selected probabilities, so the best we can do is to trap a P-value between two of the values in the table. Just find the row for the correct number of degrees of freedom and read across to find where your calculated $\chi^2$ value falls. Of course, technology can find an exact P-value, and that's usually what we'll see.

Even though its mechanics work like a one-sided test, the interpretation of a chi-square test is in some sense *many*-sided. With more than two proportions, there are many ways the null hypothesis can be wrong. By squaring the differences, we made all the deviations positive, whether our observed counts were higher or lower than expected. There's no direction to the rejection of the null model. All we know is that it doesn't fit.

---

## FOR EXAMPLE Doing a goodness-of-fit test

**Recap:** We're looking at data on the birth months of major league baseball players. We've checked the assumptions and conditions for performing a $\chi^2$ test.

**Questions:** What are the hypotheses, and what does the test show?

$H_0$: The distribution of birth months for major league ballplayers is the same as that for the general population.

$H_A$: The distribution of birth months for major league ballplayers differs from that of the rest of the population.

Using technology, $\chi^2 = \sum \dfrac{(Obs - Exp)^2}{Exp} = 26.48$ with df = $12 - 1 = 11$

$P(\chi^2_{11} \geq 26.48) = 0.0055.$ (The row for 11 df in table X shows that the P-value is less than 0.01 and just slightly greater than 0.005.)

Because of the small P-value, I reject $H_0$; there's evidence that birth months of major league ballplayers have a different distribution from the rest of us.

---

## STEP-BY-STEP EXAMPLE A Chi-Square Test for Goodness-of-Fit

We have counts of 256 executives in 12 zodiac sign categories. The natural null hypothesis is that birth dates of executives are divided equally among all the zodiac signs. The test statistic looks at how closely the observed data match this idealized situation.

**Question:** Are zodiac signs of CEOs distributed uniformly?

**Plan** State what you want to know.

Identify the variables and check the W's.

**Hypotheses** State the null and alternative hypotheses. For $\chi^2$ tests, it's usually easier to do that in words than in symbols.

**Model** Make a picture. The null hypothesis is that the frequencies are equal, so a bar chart (with a line at the hypothesized "equal" value) is a good display.

I want to know whether births of successful people are uniformly distributed across the signs of the zodiac. I have counts of 256 Fortune 400 executives, categorized by their birth sign.

$H_0$: Births are uniformly distributed over zodiac signs.[2]

$H_A$: Births are not uniformly distributed over zodiac signs.

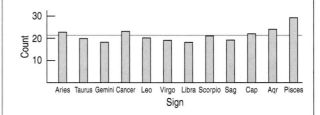

---

[2] It may seem that we have broken our rule of thumb that null hypotheses should specify parameter values. If you want to get formal about it, the null hypothesis is that

$$p_{Aries} = p_{Taurus} = \cdots = p_{Pisces}.$$

That is, we hypothesize that the true proportions of births of CEOs under each sign are equal. The role of the null hypothesis is to specify the model so that we can compute the test statistic. That's what this one does.

The bar chart shows some variation from sign to sign, and Pisces is the most frequent. But it is hard to tell whether the variation is more than I'd expect from random variation.

Think about the assumptions and check the conditions.

✔ **Counted Data Condition:** I have counts of the number of executives in 12 categories.

✔ **Independence Assumption:** The birth dates of executives should be independent of each other.

✔ **Randomization Condition:** This is a convenience sample of executives, but there's no reason to suspect bias.

✔ **Expected Cell Frequency Condition:** The null hypothesis expects that 1/12 of the 256 births, or 21.333, should occur in each sign. These expected values are all at least 5, so the condition is satisfied.

Specify the sampling distribution model.

Name the test you will use.

The conditions are satisfied, so I'll use a $\chi^2$ model with $12 - 1 = 11$ degrees of freedom and do a **chi-square goodness-of-fit test.**

---

 **Mechanics** Each cell contributes an $\dfrac{(Obs - Exp)^2}{Exp}$ value to the chi-square sum. We add up these components for each zodiac sign. If you do it by hand, it can be helpful to arrange the calculation in a table. We show that after this Step-By-Step.

The P-value is the area in the upper tail of the $\chi^2$ model above the computed $\chi^2$ value.

The $\chi^2$ models are skewed to the high end, and change shape depending on the degrees of freedom. The P-value considers only the right tail. Large $\chi^2$ statistic values correspond to small P-values, which lead us to reject the null hypothesis.

The expected value for each zodiac sign is 21.333.

$$\chi^2 = \sum \frac{(Obs - Exp)^2}{Exp} = \frac{(23 - 21.333)^2}{21.333}$$
$$+ \frac{(20 - 21.333)^2}{21.333} + \cdots$$
$$= 5.094 \text{ for all 12 signs.}$$

P-value $= P(\chi^2 > 5.094) = 0.926$

---

**Conclusion** Link the P-value to your decision. Remember to state your conclusion in terms of what the data mean, rather than just making a statement about the distribution of counts.

The P-value of 0.926 says that if the zodiac signs of executives were in fact distributed uniformly, an observed chi-square value of 5.09 or higher would occur about 93% of the time. This certainly isn't unusual, so I fail to reject the null hypothesis, and conclude that these data show virtually no evidence of nonuniform distribution of zodiac signs among executives.

# The Chi-Square Calculation

Let's make the chi-square procedure very clear. Here are the steps:

1. **Find the expected values.** These come from the null hypothesis model. Every model gives a hypothesized proportion for each cell. The expected value is the product of the total number of observations times this proportion.

   For our example, the null model hypothesizes *equal* proportions. With 12 signs, 1/12 of the 256 executives should be in each category. The expected number for each sign is 21.333.

2. **Compute the residuals.** Once you have expected values for each cell, find the residuals, *Observed − Expected*.

3. **Square the residuals.**

4. **Compute the components.** Now find the component, $\frac{(Observed - Expected)^2}{Expected}$, for each cell.

5. **Find the sum of the components.** That's the chi-square statistic.

6. **Find the degrees of freedom.** It's equal to the number of cells minus one. For the zodiac signs, that's $12 - 1 = 11$ degrees of freedom.

7. **Test the hypothesis.** Large chi-square values mean lots of deviation from the hypothesized model, so they give small P-values. Look up the critical value from a table of chi-square values, or use technology to find the P-value directly.

The steps of the chi-square calculations are often laid out in tables. Use one row for each category, and columns for observed counts, expected counts, residuals, squared residuals, and the contributions to the chi-square total like this:

| Sign | Observed | Expected | Residual = $(Obs - Exp)$ | $(Obs - Exp)^2$ | Component = $\frac{(Obs - Exp)^2}{Exp}$ |
|------|----------|----------|--------------------------|------------------|------------------------------------------|
| Aries | 23 | 21.333 | 1.667 | 2.778889 | 0.130262 |
| Taurus | 20 | 21.333 | −1.333 | 1.776889 | 0.083293 |
| Gemini | 18 | 21.333 | −3.333 | 11.108889 | 0.520737 |
| Cancer | 23 | 21.333 | 1.667 | 2.778889 | 0.130262 |
| Leo | 20 | 21.333 | −1.333 | 1.776889 | 0.083293 |
| Virgo | 19 | 21.333 | −2.333 | 5.442889 | 0.255139 |
| Libra | 18 | 21.333 | −3.333 | 11.108889 | 0.520737 |
| Scorpio | 21 | 21.333 | −0.333 | 0.110889 | 0.005198 |
| Sagittarius | 19 | 21.333 | −2.333 | 5.442889 | 0.255139 |
| Capricorn | 22 | 21.333 | 0.667 | 0.444889 | 0.020854 |
| Aquarius | 24 | 21.333 | 2.667 | 7.112889 | 0.333422 |
| Pisces | 29 | 21.333 | 7.667 | 58.782889 | 2.755491 |
| | | | | | $\Sigma = 5.094$ |

**How big is big?**  When we calculated $\chi^2$ for the zodiac sign example, we got 5.094. That value would have been big for $z$ or $t$, leading us to reject the null hypothesis. Not here. Were you surprised that $\chi^2 = 5.094$ had a huge P-value of 0.926? What *is* big for a $\chi^2$ statistic, anyway?

   Think about how $\chi^2$ is calculated. In every cell, any deviation from the expected count contributes to the sum. Large deviations generally contribute more, but if there are a lot of cells, even small deviations can add up, making the $\chi^2$ value larger.

So the more cells there are, the higher the value of $\chi^2$ has to get before it becomes noteworthy. For $\chi^2$, then, the decision about how big is big depends on the number of degrees of freedom.

Unlike the Normal and $t$ families, $\chi^2$ models are skewed. Curves in the $\chi^2$ family change both shape and center as the number of degrees of freedom grows. Here, for example, are the $\chi^2$ curves for 5 and 9 degrees of freedom.

Notice that the value $\chi^2 = 10$ might seem somewhat extreme when there are 5 degrees of freedom, but appears to be rather ordinary for 9 degrees of freedom. Here are two simple facts to help you think about $\chi^2$ models:

▶ The mode is at $\chi^2 = df - 2$. (Look at the curves; their peaks are at 3 and 7, see?)

▶ The expected value (mean) of a $\chi^2$ model is its number of degrees of freedom. That's a bit to the right of the mode—as we would expect for a skewed distribution.

Our test for zodiac birthdays had 11 df, so the relevant $\chi^2$ curve peaks at 9 and has a mean of 11. Knowing that, we might have easily guessed that the calculated $\chi^2$ value of 5.094 wasn't going to be significant.

**A S** *Lesson:* **The Chi-Square Family of Curves.** (Not an activity like the others, but there's no better way to see how $\chi^2$ changes with more df.) Click on the Lesson Book's Resources tab and open the chi-square table. Watch the curve at the top as you click on a row and scroll down the degrees-of freedom column.

# But I Believe the Model . . .

Goodness-of-fit tests are likely to be performed by people who have a theory of what the proportions *should* be in each category and who believe their theory to be true. Unfortunately, the only *null* hypothesis available for a goodness-of-fit test is that the theory is true. And as we know, the hypothesis-testing procedure allows us only to *reject* the null or *fail to reject* it. We can never confirm that a theory is in fact true, which is often what people want to do.

Unfortunately, they're stuck. At best, we can point out that the data are consistent with the proposed theory. But this doesn't *prove* the theory. The data *could* be consistent with the model even if the theory were wrong. In that case, we fail to reject the null hypothesis but can't conclude anything for sure about whether the theory is true.

And we can't fix the problem by turning things around. Suppose we try to make our favored hypothesis the alternative. Then it is impossible to pick a single null. For example, suppose, as a doubter of astrology, you want to prove that the distribution of executive births is uniform. If you choose uniform as the null hypothesis, you can only *fail* to reject it. So you'd like uniformity to be your alternative hypothesis. Which particular violation of equally distributed births would you choose as your null? The problem is that the model can be wrong in many, many ways. There's no way to frame a null hypothesis the other way around. There's just no way to prove that a favored model is true.

**Why can't we prove the null?** A biologist wanted to show that her inheritance theory about fruit flies is valid. It says that 10% of the flies should be type 1, 70% type 2, and 20% type 3. After her students collected data on 100 flies, she did a goodness-of-fit test and found a P-value of 0.07. She started celebrating, since her null hypothesis wasn't rejected—that is, until her students collected data on 100 more flies. With 200 flies, the P-value dropped to 0.02. Although she knew the answer was probably no, she asked the statistician somewhat hopefully if she could just ignore half the data and stick with the original 100. By this reasoning we could always "prove the null" just by not collecting much data. With only a little data, the chances are good that they'll be consistent with almost anything. But they also have little chance of disproving anything either. In this case, the test has no power. Don't let yourself be lured into this scientist's reasoning. With data, more is always better. But you can't ever prove that your null hypothesis is true.

# Comparing Observed Distributions

Many colleges survey graduating classes to determine the plans of the graduates. We might wonder whether the plans of students are the same at different colleges. Here's a summary table for Class of 2006 graduates from several colleges at one university. Each **cell** of the table shows how many students from a particular college made a certain choice.

<table>
<tr><td></td><td>Agriculture</td><td>Arts & Sciences</td><td>Engineering</td><td>Social Science</td><td>Total</td></tr>
<tr><td>**Employed**</td><td>379</td><td>305</td><td>243</td><td>125</td><td>**1052**</td></tr>
<tr><td>**Grad School**</td><td>186</td><td>238</td><td>202</td><td>96</td><td>**722**</td></tr>
<tr><td>**Other**</td><td>104</td><td>123</td><td>37</td><td>58</td><td>**322**</td></tr>
<tr><td>Total</td><td>**669**</td><td>**666**</td><td>**482**</td><td>**279**</td><td>**2096**</td></tr>
</table>

**Table 26.1**

Post-graduation activities of the class of 2006 for several colleges of a large university.

Because class sizes are so different, we see differences better by examining the proportions for each class rather than the counts:

<table>
<tr><td></td><td>Agriculture</td><td>Arts & Sciences</td><td>Engineering</td><td>Social Science</td><td>Total</td></tr>
<tr><td>**Employed**</td><td>56.7%</td><td>45.8</td><td>50.4</td><td>44.8</td><td>**50.2**</td></tr>
<tr><td>**Grad School**</td><td>27.8</td><td>35.7</td><td>41.9</td><td>34.4</td><td>**34.4**</td></tr>
<tr><td>**Other**</td><td>15.5</td><td>18.5</td><td>7.7</td><td>20.8</td><td>**15.4**</td></tr>
<tr><td>Total</td><td>**100**</td><td>**100**</td><td>**100**</td><td>**100**</td><td>**100**</td></tr>
</table>

**Table 26.2**

Activities of graduates as a percentage of respondents from each college.

We already know how to test whether *two* proportions are the same. For example, we could use a two-proportion $z$-test to see whether the proportion of students choosing graduate school is the same for Agriculture students as for Engineering students. But now we have more than two groups. We want to test whether the students' choices are the same across all four colleges. The $z$-test for two proportions generalizes to a **chi-square test of homogeneity.**

Chi-square again? It turns out that the mechanics of this test are *identical* to the chi-square test for goodness-of-fit that we just saw. (How similar can you get?) Why a different name, then? The goodness-of-fit test compared counts with a theoretical model. But here we're asking whether choices are the same among different groups, so we find the expected counts for each category directly from the data. As a result, we count the degrees of freedom slightly differently as well.

The term "homogeneity" means that things are the same. Here, we ask whether the post-graduation choices made by students are the *same* for these four colleges. The homogeneity test comes with a built-in null hypothesis: We hypothesize that the distribution does not change from group to group. The test looks for

---

**WHO** Graduates from 4 colleges at an upstate New York university

**WHAT** Post-graduation activities

**WHEN** 2006

**WHY** Survey for general information

---

**A S** *Video:* **The Incident.** You may have guessed which famous incident put women and children at risk. Here you can view the story complete with rare film footage.

differences large enough to step beyond what we might expect from random sample-to-sample variation. It can reveal a large deviation in a single category or small, but persistent, differences over all the categories—or anything in between.

## Assumptions and Conditions

The assumptions and conditions are the same as for the chi-square test for goodness-of-fit. The **Counted Data Condition** says that these data must be counts. You can't do a test of homogeneity on proportions, so we have to work with the counts of graduates given in the first table. Also, you can't do a chi-square test on measurements. For example, if we had recorded GPAs for these same groups, we wouldn't be able to determine whether the mean GPAs were different using this test.[3]

Often when we test for homogeneity, we aren't interested in some larger population, so we don't really need a random sample. (We would need one if we wanted to draw a more general conclusion—say, about the choices made by all members of the Class of '06.) Don't we need *some* randomness, though? Fortunately, the null hypothesis can be thought of as a model in which the counts in the table are distributed as if each student chose a plan randomly according to the overall proportions of the choices, regardless of the student's class. As long as we don't want to generalize, we don't have to check the **Randomization Condition** or the **10% Condition.**

We still must be sure we have enough data for this method to work. The **Expected Cell Frequency Condition** says that the expected count in each cell must be at least 5. We'll confirm that as we do the calculations.

## Calculations

The null hypothesis says that the proportions of graduates choosing each alternative should be the same for all four colleges. So for each choice, the expected proportion is just the overall proportion of students making that choice. The expected counts are those proportions applied to the number of students in each graduating class.

For example, overall, 1052, or about 50.2%, of the 2096 students who responded to the survey were employed. If the distributions are homogeneous (as the null hypothesis asserts), then 50.2% of the 669 Agriculture school graduates (or about 335.8 students) should be employed. Similarly, 50.2% of the 482 Engineering grads (or about 241.96) should be employed.

Working in this way, we (or, more likely, the computer) can fill in expected values for each cell. Because these are theoretical values, they don't have to be integers. The expected values look like this:

|  | Agriculture | Arts & Sciences | Engineering | Social Science | Total |
|---|---|---|---|---|---|
| **Employed** | **335.777** | 334.271 | 241.290 | 140.032 | **1052** |
| **Grad School** | 230.448 | 229.414 | 166.032 | 96.106 | **722** |
| **Other** | 102.776 | 102.315 | 74.048 | 42.862 | **322** |
| Total | **669** | **666** | **482** | **279** | **2096** |

**Table 26.3** Expected values for the '06 graduates.

---

[3] To do that, you'd use a method called Analysis of Variance, discussed in a supplementary chapter on the DVD and in ActivStats.

Now check the **Expected Cell Frequency Condition.** Indeed, there are at least 5 individuals expected in each cell.

Following the pattern of the goodness-of-fit test, we compute the component for each cell of the table. For the highlighted cell, employed students graduating from the Ag school, that's

$$\frac{(Obs - Exp)^2}{Exp} = \frac{(379 - 335.777)^2}{335.777} = 5.564$$

Summing these components across all cells gives

$$\chi^2 = \sum_{all\ cells} \frac{(Obs - Exp)^2}{Exp} = 54.51$$

How about the degrees of freedom? We don't really need to calculate all the expected values in the table. We know there is a total of 1052 employed students, so once we find the expected values for three of the colleges, we can determine the expected number for the fourth by just subtracting. Similarly, we know how many students graduated from each college, so after filling in three rows, we can find the expected values for the remaining row by subtracting. To fill out the table, we need to know the counts in only $R - 1$ rows and $C - 1$ columns. So the table has $(R - 1)(C - 1)$ degrees of freedom.

In our example, we need to calculate only 2 choices in each column and counts for 3 of the 4 colleges, for a total of $2 \times 3 = 6$ degrees of freedom. We'll need the degrees of freedom to find a P-value for the chi-square statistic.

**NOTATION ALERT:**

For a contingency table, $R$ represents the number of rows and $C$ the number of columns.

---

| **STEP-BY-STEP EXAMPLE** | **A Chi-Square Test for Homogeneity** |

We have reports from four colleges on the post-graduation activities of their 2006 graduating classes.

**Question: Are students' choices of post-graduation activities the same across all the colleges?**

**Plan** State what you want to know.

Identify the variables and check the W's.

I want to know whether post-graduation choices are the same for students from each of four colleges. I have a table of counts classifying each college's Class of 2006 respondents according to their activities.

**Hypotheses** State the null and alternative hypotheses.

$H_0$: Students' post-graduation activities are distributed in the same way for all four colleges.

$H_A$: Students' plans do not have the same distribution.

**Model** Make a picture: A side-by-side bar chart shows the four distributions of post-graduation activities. Plot column percents to remove the effect of class size differences. A split bar chart would also be an appropriate choice.

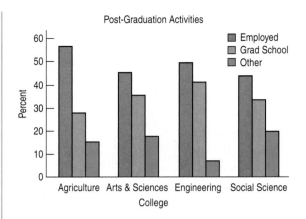

A side-by-side bar chart shows how the distributions of choices differ across the four colleges.

Think about the assumptions and check the conditions.

✔ **Counted Data Condition:** I have counts of the number of students in categories.

✔ **Independence Assumption:** Student plans should be largely independent of each other. The occasional friends who decide to join Teach for America together or couples who make grad school decisions together are too rare to affect this analysis.

✔ **Randomization Condition:** I don't want to draw inferences to other colleges or other classes, so there is no need to check for a random sample.

✔ **Expected Cell Frequency Condition:** The expected values (shown below) are all at least 5.

State the sampling distribution model.

Name the test you will use.

The conditions seem to be met, so I can use a $\chi^2$ model with $(3 - 1) \times (4 - 1) = 6$ degrees of freedom and do a **chi-square test of homogeneity.**

**Mechanics** Show the expected counts for each cell of the data table. You could make separate tables for the observed and expected counts, or put both counts in each cell as shown here. While observed counts must be whole numbers, expected counts rarely are—don't be tempted to round those off.

|  | Ag | A&S | Eng | Soc Sci |
|---|---|---|---|---|
| **Empl.** | 379 / 335.777 | 305 / 334.271 | 243 / 241.290 | 125 / 140.032 |
| **Grad sch.** | 186 / 230.448 | 238 / 229.414 | 202 / 166.032 | 96 / 96.106 |
| **Other** | 104 / 102.776 | 123 / 102.315 | 37 / 74.048 | 58 / 42.862 |

Calculate $\chi^2$.

The shape of a $\chi^2$ model depends on the degrees of freedom. A $\chi^2$ model with 6 df is skewed to the high end.

The P-value considers only the right tail. Here, the calculated value of the $\chi^2$ statistic is off the scale, so the P-value is quite small.

$$\chi^2 = \sum_{all \ cells} \frac{(Obs - Exp)^2}{Exp} = 54.52$$

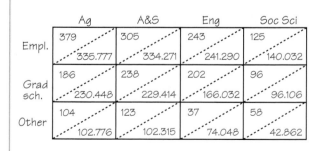

$$P\text{-value} = P(\chi^2 > 54.52) < 0.0001$$

| | Conclusion State your conclusion in the context of the data. You should specifically talk about whether the distributions for the groups appear to be different. | The P-value is very small, so I reject the null hypothesis and conclude that there's evidence that the post-graduation activities of students from these four colleges don't have the same distribution. |
|---|---|---|

If you find that simply rejecting the hypothesis of homogeneity is a bit unsatisfying, you're in good company. Ok, so the post-graduation plans are different. What we'd really like to know is what the differences are, where they're the greatest, and where they're smallest. The test for homogeneity doesn't answer these interesting questions, but it does provide some evidence that can help us.

## Examining the Residuals

Whenever we reject the null hypothesis, it's a good idea to examine residuals. (We don't need to do that when we fail to reject because when the $\chi^2$ value is small, all of its components must have been small.) For chi-square tests, we want to compare residuals for cells that may have very different counts. So we're better off standardizing the residuals. We know the mean residual is zero,[4] but we need to know each residual's standard deviation. When we tested proportions, we saw a link between the expected proportion and its standard deviation. For counts, there's a similar link. To standardize a cell's residual, we just divide by the square root of its expected value:

$$c = \frac{(Obs - Exp)}{\sqrt{Exp}}.$$

Notice that these **standardized residuals** are just the square roots of the **components** we calculated for each cell, and their sign indicates whether we observed more cases than we expected, or fewer.

The standardized residuals give us a chance to think about the underlying patterns and to consider the ways in which the distribution of post-graduation plans may differ from college to college. Now that we've subtracted the mean (zero) and divided by their standard deviations, these are z-scores. If the null hypothesis were true, we could even appeal to the Central Limit Theorem, think of the Normal model, and use the 68–95–99.7 Rule to judge how extraordinary the large ones are.

Here are the standardized residuals for the Class of '06 data:

| | Ag | A&S | Eng | Soc Sci |
|---|---|---|---|---|
| **Employed** | 2.359 | −1.601 | 0.069 | −1.270 |
| **Grad School** | −2.928 | 0.567 | 2.791 | −0.011 |
| **Other** | 0.121 | 2.045 | −4.305 | 2.312 |

**Table 26.4**

Standardized residuals can help show how the table differs from the null hypothesis pattern.

---

[4] Residual = observed − expected. Because the total of the expected values is set to be the same as the observed total, the residuals must sum to zero.

The column for Engineering students immediately attracts our attention. It holds both the largest positive and the largest negative standardized residuals. It looks like Engineering college graduates are more likely to go on to graduate work and very unlikely to take time off for "volunteering and travel, among other activities" (as the "Other" category is explained). By contrast, Ag school graduates seem to be readily employed and less likely to pursue graduate work immediately after college.

---

**FOR EXAMPLE** | Looking at $\chi^2$ residuals

**Recap:** Some people suggest that school children who are the older ones in their class naturally perform better in sports and therefore get more coaching and encouragement. To see if there's any evidence for this, we looked at major league baseball players born since 1975. A goodness-of-fit test found their birth months to have a distribution that's significantly different from the rest of us. The table shows the standardized residuals.

**Question:** What's different about the distribution of birth months among major league ballplayers?

It appears that, compared to the general population, fewer ballplayers than expected were born in July and more than expected in August. Either month would make them the younger kids in their grades in school, so these data don't offer support for the conjecture that being older is an advantage in terms of a career as a pro athlete.

| Month | Residual |
|-------|----------|
| 1 | 1.73 |
| 2 | 1.72 |
| 3 | −0.21 |
| 4 | 0.25 |
| 5 | 0.71 |
| 6 | −0.39 |
| 7 | −2.69 |
| 8 | 2.77 |
| 9 | 0.08 |
| 10 | −1.56 |
| 11 | −1.22 |
| 12 | −0.96 |

---

## JUST CHECKING

Tiny black potato flea beetles can damage potato plants in a vegetable garden. These pests chew holes in the leaves, causing the plants to wither or die. They can be killed with an insecticide, but a canola oil spray has been suggested as a non-chemical "natural" method of controlling the beetles. To conduct an experiment to test the effectiveness of the natural spray, we gather 500 beetles and place them in three Plexiglas® containers. Two hundred beetles go in the first container, where we spray them with the canola oil mixture. Another 200 beetles go in the second container; we spray them with the insecticide. The remaining 100 beetles in the last container serve as a control group; we simply spray them with water. Then we wait 6 hours and count the number of surviving beetles in each container.

**1.** Why do we need the control group?

**2.** What would our null hypothesis be?

**3.** After the experiment is over, we could summarize the results in a table like this. How many degrees of freedom does our $\chi^2$ test have?

|          | Natural spray | Insecticide | Water | Total |
|----------|---------------|-------------|-------|-------|
| Survived |               |             |       |       |
| Died     |               |             |       |       |
| Total    | 200           | 200         | 100   | 500   |

> **4.** Suppose that, all together, 125 beetles survived. (That's the first-row total.) What's the expected count in the first cell—survivors among those sprayed with the natural spray?
>
> **5.** If it turns out that only 40 of the beetles in the first container survived, what's the calculated component of $\chi^2$ for that cell?
>
> **6.** If the total calculated value of $\chi^2$ for this table turns out to be around 10, would you expect the P-value of our test to be large or small? Explain.

## Independence

A study from the University of Texas Southwestern Medical Center examined whether the risk of hepatitis C was related to whether people had tattoos and to where they got their tattoos. Hepatitis C causes about 10,000 deaths each year in the United States, but often lies undetected for years after infection.

The data from this study can be summarized in a two-way table, as follows:

| | Hepatitis C | No Hepatitis C | Total |
|---|---|---|---|
| **Tattoo, parlor** | 17 | 35 | 52 |
| **Tattoo, elsewhere** | 8 | 53 | 61 |
| **None** | 22 | 491 | 513 |
| Total | 47 | 579 | 626 |

**Table 26.5**

Counts of patients classified by their hepatitis C test status according to whether they had a tattoo from a tattoo parlor or from another source, or had no tattoo.

| | |
|---|---|
| **WHO** | Patients being treated for non–blood-related disorders |
| **WHAT** | Tattoo status and hepatitis C status |
| **WHEN** | 1991, 1992 |
| **WHERE** | Texas |

**A S** *Activity:* **Independence and Chi-Square.** This unusual simulation shows how independence arises (and fails) in contingency tables.

> The only difference between the test for homogeneity and the test for independence is in what you . . .

These data differ from the kinds of data we've considered before in this chapter because they categorize subjects from a single group on two categorical variables rather than on only one. The categorical variables here are *Hepatitis C Status* ("Hepatitis C" or "No Hepatitis C") and *Tattoo Status* ("Parlor," "Elsewhere," "None"). We've seen counts classified by two categorical variables displayed like this in Chapter 3, so we know such tables are called contingency tables. **Contingency tables** categorize counts on two (or more) variables so that we can see whether the distribution of counts on one variable is contingent on the other.

The natural question to ask of these data is whether the chance of having hepatitis C is *independent* of tattoo status. Recall that for events **A** and **B** to be independent $P(\mathbf{A})$ must equal $P(\mathbf{A} \mid \mathbf{B})$. Here, this means the probability that a randomly selected patient has hepatitis C should not change when we learn the patient's tattoo status. We examined the question of independence in just this way back in Chapter 15, but we lacked a way to test it. The rules for independent events are much too precise and absolute to work well with real data. A **chi-square test for independence** is the test called for here.

If *Hepatitis Status* is independent of tattoos, we'd expect the proportion of people testing positive for hepatitis to be the same for the three levels of *Tattoo Status*. This sounds a lot like the test of homogeneity. In fact, the mechanics of the calculation are identical.

The difference is that now we have two categorical variables measured on a single population. For the homogeneity test, we had a single categorical variable measured independently on two or more populations. But now we ask a different question: "Are the variables independent?" rather than "Are the groups homogeneous?" These are subtle differences, but they are important when we draw conclusions.

Which $\chi^2$ test?

Many states and localities now collect data on traffic stops regarding the race of the driver. The initial concern was that Black drivers were being stopped more often (the "crime" ironically called "Driving While Black"). With more data in hand, attention has turned to other issues. For example, data from 2533 traffic stops in Cincinnati[5] report the race of the driver (Black, White, or Other) and whether the traffic stop resulted in a search of the vehicle.

|  |  | Race | | | |
|---|---|---|---|---|---|
|  |  | **Black** | **White** | **Other** | **Total** |
| **Search** | **No** | 787 | 594 | 27 | **1408** |
|  | **Yes** | 813 | 293 | 19 | **1125** |
|  | Total | **1600** | **887** | **46** | **2533** |

**Questions:**  Which test would be appropriate to examine whether race is a factor in vehicle searches? What are the hypotheses?

*These data represent one group of traffic stops in Cincinnati, categorized on two variables, Race and Search. I'll do a chi-square test of independence.*

$H_O$: *Whether or not police search a vehicle is independent of the race of the driver.*

$H_A$: *Decisions to search vehicles are not independent of the driver's race.*

## Assumptions and Conditions

**Activity: Chi-Square Tables.** Work with *ActivStats'* interactive chi-square table to perform a hypothesis test.

Of course, we still need counts and enough data so that the expected values are at least 5 in each cell.

If we're interested in the independence of variables, we usually want to generalize from the data to some population. In that case, we'll need to check that the data are a representative random sample from, and fewer than 10% of, that population.

**STEP-BY-STEP EXAMPLE**   A Chi-Square Test for Independence

We have counts of 626 individuals categorized according to their "tattoo status" and their "hepatitis status."

**Question: Are tattoo status and hepatitis status independent?**

| | |
|---|---|
| **THINK** **Plan** State what you want to know. <br><br> Identify the variables and check the W's. <br><br> **Hypotheses** State the null and alternative hypotheses. | *I want to know whether the categorical variables Tattoo Status and Hepatitis Status are statistically independent. I have a contingency table of 626 Texas patients with an unrelated disease.* |

---

[5] John E. Eck, Lin Liu, and Lisa Growette Bostaph, Police Vehicle Stops in Cincinnati, Oct. 1, 2003, available at http://www.cincinnati-oh.gov. Data for other localities can be found by searching from http://www.racialprofilinganalysis.neu.edu.

We perform a test of independence when we suspect the variables may not be independent. We are on the familiar ground of making a claim (in this case, that knowing *Tattoo Status* will change probabilities for *Hepatitis C Status*) and testing the null hypothesis that it is *not* true.

**Model**  Make a picture. Because these are only two categories—Hepatitis C and No Hepatitis C—a simple bar chart of the distribution of tattoo sources for Hep C patients shows all the information.

$H_O$: *Tattoo Status* and *Hepatitis Status* are independent.[6]

$H_A$: *Tattoo Status* and *Hepatitis Status* are not independent.

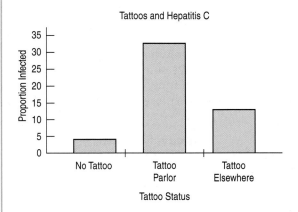

The bar chart suggests strong differences in the relative frequency of tattoo sources among Hepatitis C patients.

Think about the assumptions and check the conditions.

✔ **Counted Data Condition:** I have counts of individuals categorized on two categorical variables.

✔ **Independence Assumption:** The people in this study are likely to be independent of each other.

✔ **Randomization Condition:** These data are from a retrospective study of patients being treated for something unrelated to hepatitis. Although they are not an SRS, they were selected to avoid biases.

✔ **10% Condition:** These 626 patients are far fewer than 10% of all those with tattoos or hepatitis.

✘ **Expected Cell Frequency Condition:** The expected values do not meet the condition that all are at least 5.

---

[6] Once again, parameters are hard to express. The hypothesis of independence itself tells us how to find expected values for each cell of the contingency table. That's all we need.

This table shows both the observed and expected counts for each cell. The expected counts are calculated exactly as they were for a test of homogeneity; in the first cell, for example, we expect $\frac{52}{626}$ (that's 8.3%) of 47.

|  | Hepatitis C | No Hepatitis C | Total |
|---|---|---|---|
| Tattoo, parlor | 17     3.904 | 35     48.096 | 52 |
| Tattoo, elsewhere | 8     4.580 | 53     56.420 | 61 |
| None | 22     38.516 | 491     474.484 | 513 |
| Total | 47 | 579 | 626 |

*Warning:* Be wary of proceeding when there are small expected counts, If we see expected counts that fall far short of 5, or if many cells violate the condition, we should not use $\chi^2$. (We will soon discuss ways you can fix the problem.) If you do continue, always check the residuals to be sure those cells did not have a major influence on your result.

Specify the model.

Name the test you will use.

Although the Expected Cell Frequency Condition is not satisfied, the values are close to 5. I'll go ahead, but I'll check the residuals carefully. I'll use a $\chi^2$ model with $(3 - 1) \times (2 - 1) = 2$ df and do a **chi-square test of independence.**

**Mechanics**  Calculate $\chi^2$.

The shape of a chi-square model depends on its degrees of freedom. With 2 df, the model looks quite different, as you can see here. We still care only about the right tail.

$$\chi^2 = \sum_{all\ cells} \frac{(Obs - Exp)^2}{Exp} = 57.91$$

P-Value = $P(\chi^2 > 57.91) < 0.0001$

**Conclusion**  Link the P-value to your decision. State your conclusion about the independence of the two variables.

(We should be wary of this conclusion because of the small expected counts. A complete solution must include the additional analysis, recalculation, and final conclusion discussed in the following section.)

The P-value is very small, so I reject the null hypothesis and conclude that *Hepatitis Status* is not independent of *Tattoo Status*. Because the Expected Cell Frequency Condition was violated, I need to check that the two cells with small expected counts did not influence this result too greatly.

**FOR EXAMPLE**    *Chi-square mechanics*

**Recap:** We have data that allow us to investigate whether police searches of vehicles they stop are independent of the driver's race.

| | | Black | White | Other | Total |
|---|---|---|---|---|---|
| | | | Race | | |
| Search | No | 787 | 594 | 27 | 1408 |
| | Yes | 813 | 293 | 19 | 1125 |
| | Total | 1600 | 887 | 46 | 2533 |

**Questions:** What are the degrees of freedom for this test? What is the expected frequency of searches for the Black drivers who were stopped? What's that cell's component in the $\chi^2$ computation? And how is the standardized residual for that cell computed?

This is a 2 × 3 contingency table, so $df = (2 - 1)(3 - 1) = 2$. Overall, 1125 of 2533 vehicles were searched. If searches are conducted independent of race, then I'd expect $\frac{1125}{2533}$ of the 1600 Black drivers to have been searched: $\frac{1125}{2533} \times 1600 \approx 710.62$. That cell's term in the $\chi^2$ calculation is

$$\frac{(Obs - Exp)^2}{Exp} = \frac{(813 - 710.62)^2}{710.62} = 14.75$$

The standardized residual for that cell is

$$\frac{Obs - Exp}{\sqrt{Exp}} = \frac{813 - 710.62}{\sqrt{710.62}} = 3.84$$

# Examine the Residuals

Each cell of the contingency table contributes a term to the chi-square sum. As we did earlier, we should examine the residuals because we have rejected the null hypothesis. In this instance, we have an additional concern that the cells with small expected frequencies not be the ones that make the chi-square statistic large.

Our interest in the data arises from the potential for improving public health. If patients with tattoos are more likely to test positive for hepatitis C, perhaps physicians should be advised to suggest blood tests for such patients.

The standardized residuals look like this:

| | Hepatitis C | No Hepatitis C |
|---|---|---|
| **Tattoo, parlor** | 6.628 | −1.888 |
| **Tattoo, elsewhere** | 1.598 | −0.455 |
| **None** | −2.661 | 0.758 |

**Table 26.6**

Standardized residuals for the hepatitis and tattoos data. Are any of them particularly large in magnitude?

The chi-square value of 57.91 is the sum of the squares of these six values. The cell for people with tattoos obtained in a tattoo parlor who have hepatitis C is large and positive, indicating there are more people in that cell than the null hypothesis of independence would predict. Maybe tattoo parlors are a source of infection or maybe those who go to tattoo parlors also engage in risky behavior.

The second-largest component is a negative value for those with no tattoos who test positive for hepatitis C. A negative value says that there are fewer people in this cell than independence would expect. That is, those who have no tattoos are less likely to be infected with hepatitis C than we might expect if the two variables were independent.

What about the cells with small expected counts? The formula for the chi-square standardized residuals divides each residual by the square root of the expected frequency. Too small an expected frequency can arbitrarily inflate the residual and lead to an inflated chi-square statistic. Any expected count close to the arbitrary minimum of 5 calls for checking that cell's standardized residual to be sure it is not particularly large. In this case, the standardized residual for the "Hepatitis C and Tattoo, elsewhere" cell is not particularly large, but the standardized residual for the "Hepatitis C and Tattoo, parlor" cell is large.

**MORE**

We might choose not to report the results because of concern with the small expected frequency. Alternatively, we could include a warning along with our report of the results. Yet another approach is to combine categories to get a larger sample size and correspondingly larger expected frequencies, if there are some categories that can be appropriately combined. Here, we might naturally combine the two rows for tattoos, obtaining a 2 × 2 table:

|  | Hepatitis C | No Hepatitis C | Total |
|---|---|---|---|
| **Tattoo** | 25 | 88 | **113** |
| **None** | 22 | 491 | **513** |
| Total | **47** | **579** | **626** |

**Table 26.7**
Combining the two tattoo categories gives a table with all expected counts greater than 5.

This table has expected values of at least 5 in every cell, and a chi-square value of 42.42 on 1 degree of freedom. The corresponding P-value is <0.0001.

We conclude that *Tattoo Status* and *Hepatitis C Status* are not independent. The data *suggest* that tattoo parlors may be a particular problem, but we haven't enough data to draw that conclusion.

**TELL**

**ALL**

---

**FOR EXAMPLE**          Writing conclusions for $\chi^2$ tests

**Recap:** We're looking at Cincinnati traffic stop data to see if police decisions about searching cars show evidence of racial bias. With 3 df, technology calculates $\chi^2 = 73.25$, a P-value less than 0.0001, and these standardized residuals:

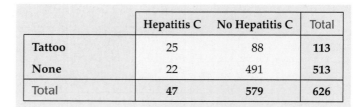

|  |  | Black | White | Other |
|---|---|---|---|---|
| Search | No | −3.43 | 4.55 | 0.28 |
|  | Yes | 3.84 | −5.09 | −0.31 |

**Question:** What's your conclusion?

The very low P-value leads me to reject the null hypothesis. There's strong evidence that police decisions to search cars at traffic stops are associated with the driver's race.

    The largest residuals are for White drivers, who are searched less often than independence would predict. It appears that Black drivers' cars are searched more often.

---

## JUST CHECKING

    Which of the three chi-square tests—goodness-of-fit, homogeneity, or independence—would you use in each of the following situations?

**7.** A restaurant manager wonders whether customers who dine on Friday nights have the same preferences among the four "chef's special" entrées as those who dine on Saturday nights. One weekend he has the wait staff record which entrées were ordered each night. Assuming these customers to be typical of all weekend diners, he'll compare the distributions of meals chosen Friday and Saturday.

**8.** Company policy calls for parking spaces to be assigned to everyone at random, but you suspect that may not be so. There are three lots of equal size: lot A, next to the building; lot B, a bit farther away; and lot C, on the other side of the highway. You gather data about employees at middle management level and above to see how many were assigned parking in each lot.

**9.** Is a student's social life affected by where the student lives? A campus survey asked a random sample of students whether they lived in a dormitory, in off-campus housing, or at home, and whether they had been out on a date 0, 1–2, 3–4, or 5 or more times in the past two weeks.

---

# Chi-Square and Causation

Chi-square tests are common. Tests for independence are especially widespread. Unfortunately, many people interpret a small P-value as proof of causation. We know better. Just as correlation between quantitative variables does not demonstrate causation, a failure of independence between two categorical variables does not show a cause-and-effect relationship between them, nor should we say that one variable *depends* on the other.

    The chi-square test for independence treats the two variables symmetrically. There is no way to differentiate the direction of any possible causation from one variable to the other. In our example, it is unlikely that having hepatitis causes one to crave a tattoo, but other examples are not so clear.

    In this case it's easy to imagine that lurking variables are responsible for the observed lack of independence. Perhaps the lifestyles of some people include both tattoos and behaviors that put them at increased risk of hepatitis C, such as body piercings or even drug use. Even a small subpopulation of people with such a lifestyle among those with tattoos might be enough to create the observed result. After all, we observed only 25 patients with both tattoos and hepatitis.

    In some sense, a failure of independence between two categorical variables is less impressive than a strong, consistent, linear association between quantitative variables. Two categorical variables can fail the test of independence in many ways, including ways that show no consistent pattern of failure. Examination of the chi-square standardized residuals can help you think about the underlying patterns.

# WHAT CAN GO WRONG?

▶ **Don't use chi-square methods unless you have counts.** All three of the chi-square tests apply only to counts. Other kinds of data can be arrayed in two-way tables. Just because numbers are in a two-way table doesn't make them suitable for chi-square analysis. Data reported as proportions or percentages can be suitable for chi-square procedures, *but only after they are converted to counts.* If you try to do the calculations without first finding the counts, your results will be wrong.

▶ **Beware large samples.** Beware *large* samples?! That's not the advice you're used to hearing. The chi-square tests, however, are unusual. You should be wary of chi-square tests performed on very large samples. No hypothesized distribution fits perfectly, no two groups are exactly homogeneous, and two variables are rarely perfectly independent. The degrees of freedom for chi-square tests don't grow with the sample size. With a sufficiently large sample size, a chi-square test can always reject the null hypothesis. But we have no measure of how far the data are from the null model. There are no confidence intervals to help us judge the effect size.

▶ **Don't say that one variable "depends" on the other just because they're not independent.** Dependence suggests a model or a pattern, but variables can fail to be independent in many different ways. When variables fail the test for independence, you might just say they are "associated."

 **A S**   *Simulation:* **Sample Size and Chi-Square.** Chi-square statistics have a peculiar problem. They don't respond to increasing the sample size in quite the same way you might expect.

# CONNECTIONS

Chi-square methods relate naturally to inference methods for proportions. We can think of a test of homogeneity as stepping from a comparison of two proportions to a question of whether three or more proportions are equal. The standard deviations of the residuals in each cell are linked to the expected counts much like the standard deviations we found for proportions.

Independence is, of course, a fundamental concept in Statistics. But chi-square tests do not offer a general way to check on independence for all those times when we have had to assume it.

Stacked bar charts or side-by-side pie charts can help us think about patterns in two-way tables. A histogram or boxplot of the standardized residuals can help locate extraordinary values.

# WHAT HAVE WE LEARNED?

We've learned how to test hypotheses about categorical variables. We use one of three related methods. All look at counts of data in categories, and all rely on chi-square models, a new family indexed by degrees of freedom.

▶ Goodness-of-fit tests compare the observed distribution of a single categorical variable to an expected distribution based on a theory or model.

▶ Tests of homogeneity compare the distribution of several groups for the same categorical variable.

▶ Tests of independence examine counts from a single group for evidence of an association between two categorical variables.

We've seen that, mechanically, these tests are almost identical. Although the tests appear to be one-sided, we've learned that conceptually they are many-sided, because there are many ways that a table of counts can deviate significantly from what we hypothesized. When that happens and we reject the null hypothesis, we've learned to examine standardized residuals in order to better understand patterns as in the table.

# Terms

| | |
|---|---|
| Chi-square model | 690. Chi-square models are skewed to the right. They are parameterized by their degrees of freedom and become less skewed with increasing degrees of freedom. |
| Cell | 688. A cell of a two-way table is one element of the table corresponding to a specific row and a specific column. Table cells can hold counts, percentages, or measurements on other variables. Or they can hold several values. |
| Chi-square statistic | 689, 693. The chi-square statistic can be used to test whether the observed counts in a frequency distribution or contingency table match the counts we would expect according to some model. It is calculated as |

$$\chi^2 = \sum_{all\ cells} \frac{(Obs - Exp)^2}{Exp}.$$

Chi-square statistics differ in how expected counts are found, depending on the question asked.

| | |
|---|---|
| Chi-square test of goodness-of-fit | 687, 691. A test of whether the distribution of counts in one categorical variable matches the distribution predicted by a model is called a test of goodness-of-fit. In a chi-square goodness-of-fit test, the expected counts come from the predicting model. The test finds a P-value from a chi-square model with $n - 1$ degrees of freedom, where $n$ is the number of categories in the categorical variable. |
| Chi-square test of homogeneity | 695. A test comparing the distribution of counts for two or more groups on the same categorical variable is called a test of *homogeneity*. A chi-square test of homogeneity finds expected counts based on the overall frequencies, adjusted for the totals in each group under the (null hypothesis) assumption that the distributions are the same for each group. We find a P-value from a chi-square distribution with $(\#Rows - 1) \times (\#Cols - 1)$ degrees of freedom, where $\#Rows$ gives the number of categories and $\#Cols$ gives the number of independent groups. |
| Chi-square test of independence | 701. A test of whether two categorical variables are independent examines the distribution of counts for one group of individuals classified according to both variables. A chi-square test of *independence* finds expected counts by assuming that knowing the marginal totals tells us the cell frequencies, assuming that there is no association between the variables. This turns out to be the same calculation as a test of homogeneity. We find a P-value from a chi-square distribution with $(\#Rows - 1) \times (\#Cols - 1)$ degrees of freedom, where $\#Rows$ gives the number of categories in one variable and $\#Cols$ gives the number of categories in the other. |
| Chi-square component | 693, 699. The components of a chi-square calculation are |

$$\frac{(Observed - Expected)^2}{Expected},$$

found for each cell of the table.

| | |
|---|---|
| Standardized residual | 699, 705. In each cell of a two-way table, a standardized residual is the square root of the chi-square component for that cell with the sign of the *Observed - Expected* difference: |

$$\frac{(Obs - Exp)}{\sqrt{Exp}}.$$

When we reject a chi-square test, an examination of the standardized residuals can sometimes reveal more about how the data deviate from the null model.

| | |
|---|---|
| Two-way table | 695, 701. Each *cell* of a two-way table shows counts of individuals. One way classifies a sample according to a categorical variable. The other way can classify different groups of individuals according to the same variable or classify the same individuals according to a different categorical variable. |
| Contingency table | 701. A two-way table that classifies individuals according to two categorical variables is called a *contingency table*. |

# Skills

▶ Be able to recognize when a test of goodness-of-fit, a test of homogeneity, or a test of independence would be appropriate for a table of counts.

▶ Understand that the degrees of freedom for a chi-square test depend on the dimensions of the table and not on the sample size. Understand that this means that increasing the sample size increases the ability of chi-square procedures to reject the null hypothesis.

▶ Be able to display and interpret counts in a two-way table.

▶ Know how to use the chi-square tables to perform chi-square tests.

▶ Know how to compute a chi-square test using your statistics software or calculator.

▶ Be able to examine the standardized residuals to explain the nature of the deviations from the null hypothesis.

▶ Know how to interpret chi-square as a test of goodness-of-fit in a few sentences.

▶ Know how to interpret chi-square as a test of homogeneity in a few sentences.

▶ Know how to interpret chi-square as a test of independence in a few sentences.

# ON THE COMPUTER

## Chi-Square

Most statistics packages associate chi-square tests with contingency tables. Often chi-square is available as an option only when you make a contingency table. This organization can make it hard to locate the chi-square test and may confuse the three different roles that the chi-square test can take. In particular, chi-square tests for goodness-of-fit may be hard to find or missing entirely. Chi-square tests for homogeneity are computationally the same as chi-square tests for independence, so you may have to perform the mechanics as if they were tests of independence and interpret them afterwards as tests of homogeneity.

Most statistics packages work with data on individuals rather than with the summary counts. If the only information you have is the table of counts, you may find it more difficult to get a statistics package to compute chi-square. Some packages offer a way to reconstruct the data from the summary counts so that they can then be passed back through the chi-square calculation, finding the cell counts again. Many packages offer chi-square standardized residuals (although they may be called something else).

### DATA DESK

Select variables.
From the **Calc** menu, choose **Contingency Table.** From the table's HyperView menu, choose **Table Options.** (Or Choose **Calc > Calculation Options >Table Options.**) In the dialog, check the boxes for **Chi Square** and for **Standardized Residuals.** Data Desk will display the chi-square and its P-value below the table, and the standardized residuals within the table.

#### COMMENTS

Data Desk automatically treats variables selected for this command as categorical variables even if their elements are numerals.
The **Compute Counts** command in the table's HyperView menu will make variables that hold the table contents (as selected in the Table Options dialog), including the standardized residuals.

### EXCEL

Excel offers the function
**CHITEST(actual_range, expected_range),** which computes a chi-square value for homogeneity. Both ranges are of the form UpperleftCell:LowerRightCell, specifying two rectangular tables that must hold counts (although Excel will not check for integer values). The two tables must be of the same size and shape.

#### COMMENTS

Excel's documentation claims this is a test for independence and labels the input ranges accordingly, but Excel offers no way to find expected counts, so the function is not particularly useful for testing independence. You can use this function only if you already know both tables of counts or are willing to program additional calculations.

### JMP

From the **Analyze** menu, select **Fit Y by X**. Select variables: a Y, Response variable that holds responses for one variable, and an X, Factor variable that holds responses for the other. Both selected variables must be Nominal or Ordinal. JMP will make a plot and a contingency table. Below the contingency table, **JMP** offers a **Tests** panel. In that panel, the Chi Square for independence is called a **Pearson ChiSquare**. The table also offers the P-value.

Click on the Contingency Table title bar to drop down a menu that offers to include a **Deviation** and **Cell Chi square** in each cell of the table.

#### COMMENTS

JMP will choose a chi-square analysis for a **Fit Y by X** if both variables are nominal or ordinal (marked with an N or O), but not otherwise. Be sure the variables have the right type. Deviations are the observed − expected differences in counts. Cell chi-squares are the squares of the standardized residuals. Refer to the deviations for the sign of the difference.

Look under **Distributions** in the **Analyze** menu to find a chi-square test for goodness-of-fit.

### MINITAB

From the **Stat** menu, choose the **Tables** submenu. From that menu, choose **Chi Square Test . . . .** In the dialog, identify the columns that make up the table. Minitab will display the table and print the chi-square value and its P-value.

#### COMMENTS

Alternatively, select the **Cross Tabulation . . .** command to see more options for the table, including expected counts and standardized residuals.

### SPSS

From the **Analyze** menu, choose the **Descriptive Statistics** submenu. From that submenu, choose **Crosstabs . . . .** In the Crosstabs dialog, assign the row and column variables from the variable list. Both variables must be categorical. Click the **Cells** button to specify that standardized residuals should be displayed. Click the **Statistics** button to specify a chi-square test.

#### COMMENTS

SPSS offers only variables that it knows to be categorical in the variable list for the Crosstabs dialog. If the variables you want are missing, check that they have the right type.

### TI-83/84 PLUS

The TI-83 does not have a routine for the chi-square goodness-of-fit test.

To test a hyphothesis of homogeneity or independence, you need to enter the data as a matrix. Push the **MATRIX** button, and choose to **EDIT** matrix. Specify the dimensions of the table, rows × columns, then enter the appropriate counts. To do the test, choose **C: $\chi^2$-Test** from the **STAT TESTS** menu. Note that the calculator automatically stores the expected counts in a matrix you specify.

### TI-89

To test goodness-of-fit, enter the observed counts in a list and the expected counts in another list. Expected counts can be entered as n*p, and the calculator will compute them for you.

From the **STAT Tests** menu, select **7:Chi2 GOF.** Enter the list names using VAR-LINK and the degrees of freedom, k − 1, where k is the number of categories. Select whether to simply calculate or display the result with the area corresponding to the P-value highlighted.

To test a hypothesis of homogeneity or independence, you need to enter the data as a matrix. From the home screen, press APPS and select **6:Data/Matrix Editor,** then select **3:New.** Specify type as Matrix and name the matrix in the **Variable** box. Specify the number of rows and columns. Type the entries, pressing ENTER after each. Press 2nd ESC to leave the editor.

To do the test, choose **8:Chi2 2-way** from the **STAT Tests** menu.

# EXERCISES

1. **Which test?** For each of the following situations, state whether you'd use a chi-square goodness-of-fit test, a chi-square test of homogeneity, a chi-square test of independence, or some other statistical test:
   a) A brokerage firm wants to see whether the type of account a customer has (Silver, Gold, or Platinum) affects the type of trades that customer makes (in person, by phone, or on the Internet). It collects a random sample of trades made for its customers over the past year and performs a test.
   b) That brokerage firm also wants to know if the type of account affects the size of the account (in dollars). It performs a test to see if the mean size of the account is the same for the three account types.
   c) The academic research office at a large community college wants to see whether the distribution of courses chosen (Humanities, Social Science, or Science) is different for its residential and nonresidential students. It assembles last semester's data and performs a test.

2. **Which test again?** For each of the following situations, state whether you'd use a chi-square goodness-of-fit test, a chi-square test of homogeneity, a chi-square test of independence, or some other statistical test:
   a) Is the quality of a car affected by what day it was built? A car manufacturer examines a random sample of the warranty claims filed over the past two years to test whether defects are randomly distributed across days of the work week.
   b) A medical researcher wants to know if blood cholesterol level is related to heart disease. She examines a database of 10,000 patients, testing whether the cholesterol level (in milligrams) is related to whether or not a person has heart disease.
   c) A student wants to find out whether political leaning (liberal, moderate, or conservative) is related to choice of major. He surveys 500 randomly chosen students and performs a test.

3. **Dice.** After getting trounced by your little brother in a children's game, you suspect the die he gave you to roll may be unfair. To check, you roll it 60 times, recording the number of times each face appears. Do these results cast doubt on the die's fairness?
   a) If the die is fair, how many times would you expect each face to show?
   b) To see if these results are unusual, will you test goodness-of-fit, homogeneity, or independence?
   c) State your hypotheses.
   d) Check the conditions.
   e) How many degrees of freedom are there?
   f) Find $\chi^2$ and the P-value.
   g) State your conclusion.

| Face | Count |
|------|-------|
| 1 | 11 |
| 2 | 7 |
| 3 | 9 |
| 4 | 15 |
| 5 | 12 |
| 6 | 6 |

4. **M&M's.** As noted in an earlier chapter, the Masterfoods Company says that until very recently yellow candies made up 20% of its milk chocolate M&M's, red another 20%, and orange, blue, and green 10% each. The rest are brown. On his way home from work the day he was writing these exercises, one of the authors bought a bag of plain M&M's. He got 29 yellow ones, 23 red, 12 orange, 14 blue, 8 green, and 20 brown. Is this sample consistent with the company's stated proportions? Test an appropriate hypothesis and state your conclusion.
   a) If the M&M's are packaged in the stated proportions, how many of each color should the author have expected to get in his bag?
   b) To see if his bag was unusual, should he test goodness-of-fit, homogeneity, or independence?
   c) State the hypotheses.
   d) Check the conditions.
   e) How many degrees of freedom are there?
   f) Find $\chi^2$ and the P-value.
   g) State a conclusion.

5. **Nuts.** A company says its premium mixture of nuts contains 10% Brazil nuts, 20% cashews, 20% almonds, and 10% hazelnuts, and the rest are peanuts. You buy a large can and separate the various kinds of nuts. Upon weighing them, you find there are 112 grams of Brazil nuts, 183 grams of cashews, 207 grams of almonds, 71 grams of hazelnuts, and 446 grams of peanuts. You wonder whether your mix is significantly different from what the company advertises.
   a) Explain why the chi-square goodness-of-fit test is not an appropriate way to find out.
   b) What might you do instead of weighing the nuts in order to use a $\chi^2$ test?

6. **Mileage.** A salesman who is on the road visiting clients thinks that, on average, he drives the same distance each day of the week. He keeps track of his mileage for several weeks and discovers that he averages 122 miles on Mondays, 203 miles on Tuesdays, 176 miles on Wednesdays, 181 miles on Thursdays, and 108 miles on Fridays. He wonders if this evidence contradicts his belief in a uniform distribution of miles across the days of the week. Explain why it is not appropriate to test his hypothesis using the chi-square goodness-of-fit test.

7. **NYPD and race.** Census data for New York City indicate that 29.2% of the under-18 population is white, 28.2% black, 31.5% Latino, 9.1% Asian, and 2% other ethnicities. The New York Civil Liberties Union points out that, of 26,181 police officers, 64.8% are white, 14.5% black, 19.1% Hispanic, and 1.4% Asian. Do the police officers reflect the ethnic composition of the city's youth? Test an appropriate hypothesis and state your conclusion.

8. **Violence against women 2005.** In its study *When Men Murder Women*, the Violence Policy Center (www.vpc.org) reported that 1857 women were murdered by men in

2005. Of these victims, a weapon could be identified for 1752 of them. Of those for whom a weapon could be identified, 966 were killed by guns, 390 by knives or other cutting instruments, 136 by other weapons, and 260 by personal attack (battery, strangulation, etc.). The FBI's Uniform Crime Report says that, among all murders nationwide, the weapon use rates were as follows: guns 63.4%, knives 13.1%, other weapons 16.8%, personal attack 6.7%. Is there evidence that violence against women involves different weapons than other violent attacks in the United States?

**9. Fruit flies.** Offspring of certain fruit flies may have yellow or ebony bodies and normal wings or short wings. Genetic theory predicts that these traits will appear in the ratio 9:3:3:1 (9 yellow, normal: 3 yellow, short: 3 ebony, normal: 1 ebony, short). A researcher checks 100 such flies and finds the distribution of the traits to be 59, 20, 11, and 10, respectively.
a) Are the results this researcher observed consistent with the theoretical distribution predicted by the genetic model?
b) If the researcher had examined 200 flies and counted exactly twice as many in each category—118, 40, 22, 20—what conclusion would he have reached?
c) Why is there a discrepancy between the two conclusions?

**10. Pi.** Many people know the mathematical constant $\pi$ is approximately 3.14. But that's not exact. To be more precise, here are 20 decimal places: 3.14159265358979323846. Still not exact, though. In fact, the actual value is irrational, a decimal that goes on forever without any repeating pattern. But notice that there are no 0's and only one 7 in the 20 decimal places above. Does that pattern persist, or do all the digits show up with equal frequency? The table shows the number of times each digit appears in the first million digits. Test the hypothesis that the digits 0 through 9 are uniformly distributed in the decimal representation of $\pi$.

| The first million digits of $\pi$ | |
|---|---|
| **Digit** | **Count** |
| 0 | 99,959 |
| 1 | 99,758 |
| 2 | 100,026 |
| 3 | 100,229 |
| 4 | 100,230 |
| 5 | 100,359 |
| 6 | 99,548 |
| 7 | 99,800 |
| 8 | 99,985 |
| 9 | 100,106 |

**11. Hurricane frequencies.** The National Hurricane Center provides data that list the numbers of large (category 3, 4, or 5) hurricanes that have struck the United States, by decade since 1851 (http://www.nhc.noaa.gov/Deadliest_Costliest.shtml). Here are the data:

| Decade | Count | Decade | Count |
|---|---|---|---|
| 1851–1860 | 6 | 1931–1940 | 8 |
| 1861–1870 | 1 | 1941–1950 | 10 |
| 1871–1880 | 7 | 1951–1960 | 9 |
| 1881–1890 | 5 | 1961–1970 | 6 |
| 1891–1900 | 8 | 1971–1980 | 4 |
| 1901–1910 | 4 | 1981–1990 | 4 |
| 1911–1920 | 7 | 1991–2000 | 5 |
| 1921–1930 | 5 | 2001–2006 | 7 |

Recently, there's been some concern that perhaps the number of large hurricanes has been increasing. The natural null hypothesis would be that the frequency of such hurricanes has remained constant.
a) With 96 large hurricanes observed over the 16 periods, what are the expected value(s) for each cell?
b) What kind of chi-square test would be appropriate?
c) State the null and alternative hypotheses.
d) How many degrees of freedom are there?
e) The value of $\chi^2$ is 12.67. What's the P-value of the test?
f) State your conclusion.
g) Look again at the definition of the last "decade". Does that alter your conclusion at all?

**12. Lottery numbers.** The fairness of the South African lottery was recently challenged by one of the country's political parties. The lottery publishes historical statistics at its Website (http://www.nationallottery.co.za/lotto/statistics.aspx). Here is a table of the number of times each of the 49 numbers has been drawn in the main lottery and as the "bonus ball" number as of June 2007:

| Number | Count | Bonus | Number | Count | Bonus |
|---|---|---|---|---|---|
| 1 | 81 | 14 | 26 | 78 | 12 |
| 2 | 91 | 16 | 27 | 83 | 16 |
| 3 | 78 | 14 | 28 | 76 | 7 |
| 4 | 77 | 12 | 29 | 76 | 12 |
| 5 | 67 | 16 | 30 | 99 | 16 |
| 6 | 87 | 12 | 31 | 78 | 10 |
| 7 | 88 | 15 | 32 | 73 | 15 |
| 8 | 90 | 16 | 33 | 81 | 14 |
| 9 | 80 | 9 | 34 | 81 | 13 |
| 10 | 77 | 19 | 35 | 77 | 15 |
| 11 | 84 | 12 | 36 | 73 | 8 |
| 12 | 68 | 14 | 37 | 64 | 17 |
| 13 | 79 | 9 | 38 | 70 | 11 |
| 14 | 90 | 12 | 39 | 67 | 14 |
| 15 | 82 | 9 | 40 | 75 | 13 |
| 16 | 103 | 15 | 41 | 84 | 11 |
| 17 | 78 | 14 | 42 | 79 | 8 |
| 18 | 85 | 14 | 43 | 74 | 14 |
| 19 | 67 | 18 | 44 | 87 | 14 |
| 20 | 90 | 13 | 45 | 82 | 19 |
| 21 | 77 | 13 | 46 | 91 | 10 |
| 22 | 78 | 17 | 47 | 86 | 16 |
| 23 | 90 | 14 | 48 | 88 | 21 |
| 24 | 80 | 8 | 49 | 76 | 13 |
| 25 | 65 | 11 | | | |

a) What kind of test should we perform?
b) There are 655 bonus ball observations. What are the appropriate expected value(s) for the test?
c) State the null and alternative hypotheses.
d) How many degrees of freedom are there?
e) The value of $\chi^2$ is 34.5. What's the P-value of the test?
f) State your conclusion.

**13. Childbirth, part 1.** There is some concern that if a woman has an epidural to reduce pain during childbirth, the drug can get into the baby's bloodstream, making the baby sleepier and less willing to breastfeed. In December 2006, the *International Breastfeeding Journal* published results of a study conducted at Sydney University. Researchers followed up on 1178 births, noting whether the mother had an epidural and whether the baby was still nursing after 6 months. Results are summarized in the table.

|  |  | Epidural? | | |
|---|---|---|---|---|
|  |  | **Yes** | **No** | **Total** |
| Breastfeeding | **Yes** | 206 | 498 | **704** |
| @ 6 months? | **No** | 190 | 284 | **474** |
|  | Total | **396** | **782** | **1178** |

a) What kind of test would be appropriate?
b) State the null and alternative hypotheses.

**14. Does your doctor know?** A survey[7] of articles from the *New England Journal of Medicine* (*NEJM*) classified them according to the principal statistics methods used. The articles recorded were all non-editorial articles appearing during the indicated years. Let's just look at whether these articles used statistics at all.

|  | Publication Year | | | |
|---|---|---|---|---|
|  | **1978–79** | **1989** | **2004–05** | Total |
| **No stats** | 90 | 14 | 40 | **144** |
| **Stats** | 242 | 101 | 271 | **614** |
| Total | **332** | **115** | **311** | **758** |

Has there been a change in the use of Statistics over the decades?
a) What kind of test would be appropriate?
b) State the null and alternative hypotheses.

**15. Childbirth, part 2.** In Exercise 13, the table shows results of a study investigating whether aftereffects of epidurals administered during childbirth might interfere with successful breastfeeding. We're planning to do a chi-square test.
a) How many degrees of freedom are there?
b) The smallest expected count will be in the epidural/no breastfeeding cell. What is it?
c) Check the assumptions and conditions for inference.

**16. Does your doctor know? (part 2).** The table in Exercise 14 shows whether *NEJM* medical articles during various time periods included statistics or not. We're planning to do a chi-square test.
a) How many degrees of freedom are there?
b) The smallest expected count will be in the 1989/No cell. What is it?
c) Check the assumptions and conditions for inference.

**17. Childbirth, part 3.** In Exercises 13 and 15, we've begun to examine the possible impact of epidurals on successful breastfeeding.
a) Calculate the component of chi-square for the epidural/no breastfeeding cell.
b) For this test, $\chi^2 = 14.87$. What's the P-value?
c) State your conclusion.

**18. Does your doctor know? (part 3).** In Exercises 14 and 16, we've begun to examine whether the use of statistics in *NEJM* medical articles has changed over time.
a) Calculate the component of chi-square for the 1989/No cell.
b) For this test, $\chi^2 = 59.08$. What's the P-value?
c) State your conclusion.

**19. Childbirth, part 4.** In Exercises 13, 15, and 17, we've tested a hypothesis about the impact of epidurals on successful breastfeeding. The table shows the test's residuals.

|  |  | Epidural? | |
|---|---|---|---|
|  |  | **Yes** | **No** |
| Breastfeeding | **Yes** | $-1.99$ | 1.42 |
| at 6 months? | **No** | 2.43 | $-1.73$ |

a) Show how the residual for the epidural/no breastfeeding cell was calculated.
b) What can you conclude from the standardized residuals?

**20. Does your doctor know? (part 4).** In Exercises 14, 16, and 18, we've tested a hypothesis about whether the use of statistics in *NEJM* medical articles has changed over time. The table shows the test's residuals.

|  | **1978–79** | **1989** | **2004–05** |
|---|---|---|---|
| **No stats** | 3.39 | $-1.68$ | $-2.48$ |
| **Stats** | $-1.64$ | 0.81 | 1.20 |

a) Show how the residual for the 1989/No cell was calculated.
b) What can you conclude from the patterns in the standardized residuals?

**21. Childbirth, part 5.** In Exercises 13, 15, 17, and 19, we've looked at a study examining epidurals as one factor that might inhibit successful breastfeeding of newborn babies. Suppose a broader study included several additional issues, including whether the mother drank alcohol, whether this was a first child, and whether the parents occasionally supplemented breastfeeding with bottled formula. Why would it not be appropriate to use chi-square methods on the 2 × 8 table with yes/no columns for each potential factor?

**22. Does your doctor know? (part 5).** In Exercises 14, 16, 18, and 20, we considered data on articles in the *NEJM*. The original study listed 23 different Statistics methods. (The list read: *t*-tests, contingency tables, linear regression, . . . .) Why would it not be appropriate to use chi-square methods on the 23 × 3 table with a row for each method?

---

[7]Suzanne S. Switzer and Nicholas J. Horton, "What Your Doctor Should Know about Statistics (but Perhaps Doesn't)" *Chance*, 20:1, 2007.

**23. Titanic.** Here is a table we first saw in Chapter 3 showing who survived the sinking of the *Titanic* based on whether they were crew members, or passengers booked in first-, second-, or third-class staterooms:

|       | Crew | First | Second | Third | Total |
|-------|------|-------|--------|-------|-------|
| Alive | 212  | 202   | 118    | 178   | 710   |
| Dead  | 673  | 123   | 167    | 528   | 1491  |
| Total | 885  | 325   | 285    | 706   | 2201  |

a) If we draw an individual at random from this table, what's the probability that we will draw a member of the crew?
b) What's the probability of randomly selecting a third-class passenger who survived?
c) What's the probability of a randomly selected passenger surviving, given that the passenger was a first-class passenger?
d) If someone's chances of surviving were the same regardless of their status on the ship, how many members of the crew would you expect to have lived?
e) State the null and alternative hypotheses we would test here.
f) Give the degrees of freedom for the test.
g) The chi-square value for the table is 187.8, and the corresponding P-value is barely greater than 0. State your conclusions about the hypotheses.

**24. NYPD and sex discrimination.** The table below shows the rank attained by male and female officers in the New York City Police Department (NYPD). Do these data indicate that men and women are equitably represented at all levels of the department?

|      |              | Male   | Female |
|------|--------------|--------|--------|
| Rank | Officer      | 21,900 | 4,281  |
|      | Detective    | 4,058  | 806    |
|      | Sergeant     | 3,898  | 415    |
|      | Lieutenant   | 1,333  | 89     |
|      | Captain      | 359    | 12     |
|      | Higher ranks | 218    | 10     |

a) What's the probability that a person selected at random from the NYPD is a female?
b) What's the probability that a person selected at random from the NYPD is a detective?
c) Assuming no bias in promotions, how many female detectives would you expect the NYPD to have?
d) To see if there is evidence of differences in ranks attained by males and females, will you test goodness-of-fit, homogeneity, or independence?
e) State the hypotheses.
f) Test the conditions.
g) How many degrees of freedom are there?
h) Find $\chi^2$ and the P-value.
i) State your conclusion.
j) If you concluded that the distributions are not the same, analyze the differences using the standardized residuals of your calculations.

**25. Birth order and college choice.** Students in an Introductory Statistics class at a large university were classified by birth order and by the college they attend.

|         |                    | Birth Order (1 = oldest or only child) | | | | |
|---------|--------------------|-----|-----|-----|-----------|-------|
|         |                    | 1   | 2   | 3   | 4 or more | Total |
| College | Arts and Sciences  | 34  | 14  | 6   | 3         | 57    |
|         | Agriculture        | 52  | 27  | 5   | 9         | 93    |
|         | Social Science     | 15  | 17  | 8   | 3         | 43    |
|         | Professional       | 13  | 11  | 1   | 6         | 31    |
|         | Total              | 114 | 69  | 20  | 21        | 224   |

|         |                    | Expected Values Birth Order (1 = oldest or only child) | | | |
|---------|--------------------|---------|---------|--------|---------------|
|         |                    | 1       | 2       | 3      | 4 or more     |
| College | Arts and Sciences  | 29.0089 | 17.5580 | 5.0893 | 5.3438        |
|         | Agriculture        | 47.3304 | 28.6473 | 8.3036 | 8.7188        |
|         | Social Science     | 21.8839 | 13.2455 | 3.8393 | 4.0313        |
|         | Professional       | 15.7768 | 9.5491  | 2.7679 | 2.9063        |

a) What kind of chi-square test is appropriate—goodness-of-fit, homogeneity, or independence?
b) State your hypotheses.
c) State and check the conditions.
d) How many degrees of freedom are there?
e) The calculation yields $\chi^2 = 17.78$, with P = 0.0378. State your conclusion.
f) Examine and comment on the standardized residuals. Do they challenge your conclusion? Explain.

|         |                    | Standardized Residuals Birth Order (1 = oldest or only child) | | | |
|---------|--------------------|----------|----------|----------|---------------|
|         |                    | 1        | 2        | 3        | 4 or more     |
| College | Arts and Sciences  | 0.92667  | −0.84913 | 0.40370  | −1.01388      |
|         | Agriculture        | 0.67876  | −0.30778 | −1.14640 | 0.09525       |
|         | Social Science     | −1.47155 | 1.03160  | 2.12350  | −0.51362      |
|         | Professional       | −0.69909 | 0.46952  | −1.06261 | 1.81476       |

**26. Bingeing and politics.** Students in a large Statistics class at a university in the Northeast were asked to describe their political position and whether they had engaged in binge drinking (5 drinks at a sitting for a man; 4 for a woman).

|               |                   | Political Position | | | |
|---------------|-------------------|--------------|----------|---------|-------|
|               |                   | Conservative | Moderate | Liberal | Total |
| Binge Drinking| In the past 3 days| 7            | 19       | 14      | 40    |
|               | In the past week  | 9            | 19       | 28      | 56    |
|               | In the past month | 3            | 8        | 23      | 34    |
|               | Some other time   | 8            | 15       | 22      | 45    |
|               | Never             | 9            | 22       | 20      | 51    |
|               | Total             | 36           | 83       | 107     | 226   |

| Expected Values | | | |
|---|---|---|---|
| | **Conservative** | **Moderate** | **Liberal** |
| **In the past 3 days** | 6.37168 | 14.6903 | 18.9381 |
| **In the past week** | 8.92035 | 20.5664 | 26.5133 |
| **In the past month** | 5.41593 | 12.4867 | 16.0973 |
| **Some other time** | 7.16814 | 16.5265 | 21.3053 |
| **Never** | 8.12389 | 18.7301 | 24.1460 |

a) What kind of chi-square test is appropriate—goodness-of-fit, homogeneity, or independence?
b) State your hypotheses.
c) State and check the conditions.
d) How many degrees of freedom are there?
e) The calculation yields $\chi^2 = 10.10$, with $P = 0.2578$. State your conclusion.
f) Would you expect that a larger sample might find statistical significance? Explain.

**T 27. Cranberry juice.** It's common folk wisdom that drinking cranberry juice can help prevent urinary tract infections in women. In 2001 the *British Medical Journal* reported the results of a Finnish study in which three groups of 50 women were monitored for these infections over 6 months. One group drank cranberry juice daily, another group drank a lactobacillus drink, and the third drank neither of those beverages, serving as a control group. In the control group, 18 women developed at least one infection, compared to 20 of those who consumed the lactobacillus drink and only 8 of those who drank cranberry juice. Does this study provide supporting evidence for the value of cranberry juice in warding off urinary tract infections?
a) Is this a survey, a retrospective study, a prospective study, or an experiment? Explain.
b) Will you test goodness-of-fit, homogeneity, or independence?
c) State the hypotheses.
d) Test the conditions.
e) How many degrees of freedom are there?
f) Find $\chi^2$ and the P-value.
g) State your conclusion.
h) If you concluded that the groups are not the same, analyze the differences using the standardized residuals of your calculations.

**T 28. Cars.** A random survey of autos parked in the student lot and the staff lot at a large university classified the brands by country of origin, as seen in the table. Are there differences in the national origins of cars driven by students and staff?

| | | Driver | |
|---|---|---|---|
| | | **Student** | **Staff** |
| **Origin** | **American** | 107 | 105 |
| | **European** | 33 | 12 |
| | **Asian** | 55 | 47 |

a) Is this a test of independence or homogeneity?
b) Write appropriate hypotheses.

c) Check the necessary assumptions and conditions.
d) Find the P-value of your test.
e) State your conclusion and analysis.

**T 29. Montana.** A poll conducted by the University of Montana classified respondents by whether they were male or female and political party, as shown in the table. We wonder if there is evidence of an association between being male or female and party affiliation.

| | **Democrat** | **Republican** | **Independent** |
|---|---|---|---|
| **Male** | 36 | 45 | 24 |
| **Female** | 48 | 33 | 16 |

a) Is this a test of homogeneity or independence?
b) Write an appropriate hypothesis.
c) Are the conditions for inference satisfied?
d) Find the P-value for your test.
e) State a complete conclusion.

**T 30. Fish diet.** Medical researchers followed 6272 Swedish men for 30 years to see if there was any association between the amount of fish in their diet and prostate cancer. ("Fatty Fish Consumption and Risk of Prostate Cancer," *Lancet*, June 2001)

| Fish Consumption | Total Subjects | Prostate Cancers |
|---|---|---|
| **Never/seldom** | 124 | 14 |
| **Small part of diet** | 2621 | 201 |
| **Moderate part** | 2978 | 209 |
| **Large part** | 549 | 42 |

a) Is this a survey, a retrospective study, a prospective study, or an experiment? Explain.
b) Is this a test of homogeneity or independence?
c) Do you see evidence of an association between the amount of fish in a man's diet and his risk of developing prostate cancer?
d) Does this study prove that eating fish does not prevent prostate cancer? Explain.

**T 31. Montana revisited.** The poll described in Exercise 29 also investigated the respondents' party affiliations based on what area of the state they lived in. Test an appropriate hypothesis about this table and state your conclusions.

| | **Democrat** | **Republican** | **Independent** |
|---|---|---|---|
| **West** | 39 | 17 | 12 |
| **Northeast** | 15 | 30 | 12 |
| **Southeast** | 30 | 31 | 16 |

**T 32. Working parents.** In July 1991 and again in April 2001, the Gallup Poll asked random samples of 1015 adults about their opinions on working parents. The table on the next page summarizes responses to the question "Considering the needs of both parents and children, which of the following do you see as the ideal family in today's society?"

|  | 1991 | 2001 |
|---|---|---|
| **Both work full time** | 142 | 131 |
| **One works full time, other part time** | 274 | 244 |
| **One works, other works at home** | 152 | 173 |
| **One works, other stays home for kids** | 396 | 416 |
| **No opinion** | 51 | 51 |

a) Is this a survey, a retrospective study, a prospective study, or an experiment? Explain.
b) Will you test goodness-of-fit, homogeneity, or independence?
c) Based on these results, do you think there was a change in people's attitudes during the 10 years between these polls?

**33. Grades.** Two different professors teach an introductory Statistics course. The table shows the distribution of final grades they reported. We wonder whether one of these professors is an "easier" grader.

|  | Prof. Alpha | Prof. Beta |
|---|---|---|
| **A** | 3 | 9 |
| **B** | 11 | 12 |
| **C** | 14 | 8 |
| **D** | 9 | 2 |
| **F** | 3 | 1 |

a) Will you test goodness-of-fit, homogeneity, or independence?
b) Write appropriate null hypotheses.
c) Find the expected counts for each cell, and explain why the chi-square procedures are not appropriate for this table.

**34. Full moon.** Some people believe that a full moon elicits unusual behavior in people. The table shows the number of arrests made in a small town during weeks of six full moons and six other randomly selected weeks in the same year. We wonder if there is evidence of a difference in the types of illegal activity that take place.

|  | Full Moon | Not Full |
|---|---|---|
| **Violent (murder, assault, rape, etc.)** | 2 | 3 |
| **Property (burglary, vandalism, etc.)** | 17 | 21 |
| **Drugs/Alcohol** | 27 | 19 |
| **Domestic abuse** | 11 | 14 |
| **Other offenses** | 9 | 6 |

a) Will you test goodness-of-fit, homogeneity, or independence?
b) Write appropriate null hypotheses.
c) Find the expected counts for each cell, and explain why the chi-square procedures are not appropriate for this table.

**35. Grades again.** In some situations where the expected cell counts are too small, as in the case of the grades given

by Professors Alpha and Beta in Exercise 33, we can complete an analysis anyway. We can often proceed after combining cells in some way that makes sense and also produces a table in which the conditions are satisfied. Here we create a new table displaying the same data, but calling D's and F's "Below C":

|  | Prof. Alpha | Prof. Beta |
|---|---|---|
| **A** | 3 | 9 |
| **B** | 11 | 12 |
| **C** | 14 | 8 |
| **Below C** | 12 | 3 |

a) Find the expected counts for each cell in this new table, and explain why a chi-square procedure is now appropriate.
b) With this change in the table, what has happened to the number of degrees of freedom?
c) Test your hypothesis about the two professors, and state an appropriate conclusion.

**36. Full moon, next phase.** In Exercise 34 you found that the expected cell counts failed to satisfy the conditions for inference.
a) Find a sensible way to combine some cells that will make the expected counts acceptable.
b) Test a hypothesis about the full moon and state your conclusion.

**37. Eating in front of the TV.** Roper Reports asked a random sample of people in 30 countries whether they agreed with the statement "I like to nibble while reading or watching TV." Allowable responses were "Agree completely", "Agree somewhat", "Neither disagree nor agree", "Disagree somewhat", "Disagree completely", and "I Don't Know/No Response". Does a person's age influence their response? Here are data from 3792 respondents in the 2006 sample of five countries (China, India, France, United Kingdom, and United States) for three age groups (Teens, 30's (30–39) and Over 60):

|  | Agree Completely | Agree Somewhat | Neither Disagree Nor Agree | Disagree Somewhat | Disagree Completely |
|---|---|---|---|---|---|
| **Teen** | 369 | 540 | 299 | 175 | 106 |
| **30's** | 272 | 522 | 325 | 229 | 170 |
| **60 +** | 93 | 207 | 153 | 154 | 178 |

a) Make an appropriate display of these data.
b) Does a person's age seem to affect their response to the question about nibbling?

**38. Eating in front of the TV, II.** In Exercise 37 we saw a survey of people who were asked if they agreed with the statement "I like to nibble while reading or watching TV." Does a person's culture tend to influence the response? On the next page we have random samples from each of the five countries that responded:

|  | **Agree Completely** | **Agree Somewhat** | **Neither Disagree Nor Agree** | **Disagree Somewhat** | **Disagree Completely** |
|---|---|---|---|---|---|
| **China** | 253 | 479 | 382 | 244 | 139 |
| **France** | 188 | 407 | 328 | 296 | 308 |
| **India** | 315 | 395 | 246 | 227 | 332 |
| **U.K.** | 307 | 578 | 330 | 218 | 114 |
| **USA** | 308 | 632 | 331 | 201 | 73 |

a) Make an appropriate display of the data.
b) Does what country a person lives in seem to affect their response to the question about nibbling? Explain.

**39. Racial steering.** A subtle form of racial discrimination in housing is "racial steering." Racial steering occurs when real estate agents show prospective buyers only homes in neighborhoods already dominated by that family's race. This violates the Fair Housing Act of 1968. According to an article in *Chance* magazine (Vol. 14, no. 2 [2001]), tenants at a large apartment complex recently filed a lawsuit alleging racial steering. The complex is divided into two parts: Section A and Section B. The plaintiffs claimed that white potential renters were steered to Section A, while African-Americans were steered to Section B. The table displays the data that were presented in court to show the locations of recently rented apartments. Do you think there is evidence of racial steering?

|  | **New Renters** | | |
|---|---|---|---|
|  | **White** | **Black** | **Total** |
| **Section A** | 87 | 8 | 95 |
| **Section B** | 83 | 34 | 117 |
| **Total** | 170 | 42 | 212 |

**40. *Titanic*, redux.** Newspaper headlines at the time, and traditional wisdom in the succeeding decades, have held that women and children escaped the *Titanic* in greater proportions than men. Here's a table with the relevant data. Do you think that survival was independent of whether the person was male or female? Defend your conclusion.

|  | **Female** | **Male** | **Total** |
|---|---|---|---|
| **Alive** | 343 | 367 | 710 |
| **Dead** | 127 | 1364 | 1491 |
| **Total** | 470 | 1731 | 2201 |

**41. Steering revisited.** You could have checked the data in Exercise 39 for evidence of racial steering using two-proportion $z$ procedures.
a) Find the $z$–value for this approach, and show that when you square your $z$-value, you get the value of $\chi^2$ you calculated in Exercise 39.
b) Show that the resulting P-values are the same.

**42. Survival on the *Titanic*, one more time.** In Exercise 40 you could have checked for a difference in the chances of survival for men and women using two-proportion $z$ procedures.
a) Find the $z$–value for this approach.
b) Show that the square of your calculated value of $z$ is the value of $\chi^2$ you calculated in Exercise 40.
c) Show that the resulting P-values are the same.

**43. Race and education.** Data from the U.S. Census Bureau show levels of education attained by age 30 for a sample of U.S. residents.

|  | **Not HS Grad** | **HS Diploma** | **College Grad** | **Adv. Degree** |
|---|---|---|---|---|
| **White** | 810 | 6429 | 4725 | 1127 |
| **Black** | 263 | 1598 | 549 | 117 |
| **Hispanic** | 1031 | 1269 | 412 | 99 |
| **Other** | 66 | 341 | 305 | 197 |

Do these data highlight significant differences in education levels attained by these groups?

**44. Pregnancies.** Most pregnancies result in live births, but some end in miscarriages or stillbirths. A June 2001 National Vital Statistics Report examined those outcomes in the United States during 1997, broken down by the age of the mother. The table shows counts consistent with that report. Is there evidence that the distribution of outcomes is not the same for these age groups?

|  |  | **Live Births** | **Fetal Losses** |
|---|---|---|---|
| **Age of Mother** | **Under 20** | 49 | 13 |
|  | **20–29** | 201 | 41 |
|  | **30–34** | 88 | 21 |
|  | **35 or over** | 49 | 21 |

**45. Race and education, part 2.** Consider only the people who have graduated from high school from Exercise 43. Do these data suggest there are significant differences in opportunities for black and Hispanic Americans who have completed high school to pursue college or advanced degrees?

|  | **HS Diploma** | **College Grad** | **Adv. Degree** |
|---|---|---|---|
| **Black** | 1598 | 549 | 117 |
| **Hispanic** | 1269 | 412 | 99 |

**46. Education by age.** Use the survey results in the table to investigate differences in education level attained among different age groups in the United States.

|  |  | **Age Group** | | | | |
|---|---|---|---|---|---|---|
|  |  | **25–34** | **35–44** | **45–54** | **55–64** | **≥ 65** |
| **Education Level** | **Not HS grad** | 27 | 50 | 52 | 71 | 101 |
|  | **HS** | 82 | 19 | 88 | 83 | 59 |
|  | **1–3 years college** | 43 | 56 | 26 | 20 | 20 |
|  | **≥ 4 years college** | 48 | 75 | 34 | 26 | 20 |

**47. Ranking universities.** In 2004 the Institute of Higher Education at Shanghai's Jiao Tong University evaluated the world's universities. Among their criteria were the size of the institution, the number of Nobel Prizes and Fields Medals won by faculty and alumni, and the faculty's research output. This ranking of the top 502 universities included 200 in North or Latin America, 209 in Europe, and 93 in the rest of the world (Asia/Pacific/Africa). A closer examination of the top 100 showed 55 in the Americas, 37 in Europe, and 8 elsewhere. Is there anything unusual about the geographical distribution of the world's top 100 universities?

**48. Ranking universities, redux.** In Exercise 47 you read about the world's top universities, as ranked by the Institute of Higher Education. The table shows the geographical distribution of these universities by groups of 100. (Not all groups have exactly 100 because of ties in the rankings.) Do these institutions appear to be randomly distributed around the world, or does there appear to be an association between ranking and location?

| Location | Ranking | | | | |
|---|---|---|---|---|---|
| | 1–100 | 101–200 | 201–300 | 301–400 | 401–500 |
| North/Latin America | 55 | 46 | 37 | 26 | 36 |
| Europe | 37 | 42 | 46 | 46 | 38 |
| Asia/Africa/Pacific | 8 | 13 | 17 | 30 | 25 |

## JUST CHECKING
### Answers

1. We need to know how well beetles can survive 6 hours in a Plexiglas® box so that we have a baseline to compare the treatments.

2. There's no difference in survival rate in the three groups.

3. $(2 - 1)(3 - 1) = 2\ df$

4. 50

5. 2

6. The mean value for a $\chi^2$ with 2 df is 2, so 10 seems pretty large. The P-value is probably small.

7. This is a test of homogeneity. The clue is that the question asks whether the distributions are alike.

8. This is a test of goodness-of-fit. We want to test the model of equal assignment to all lots against what actually happened.

9. This is a test of independence. We have responses on two variables for the same individuals.

# CHAPTER 27

# Inferences for Regression

## Where are we going?

A scatterplot of IQ vs brain size shows a mildly positive association. Could this just be due to chance? A hypothesis test is clearly what we need. We can estimate the slope, but how reliable is our estimate? In this chapter we'll step from what we know about tests and confidence intervals for means to regression.

| WHO | 250 Male subjects |
|---|---|
| WHAT | Body fat and waist size |
| UNITS | % Body fat and inches |
| WHEN | 1990s |
| WHERE | United States |
| WHY | Scientific research |

Three percent of a man's body is essential fat. (For a woman, the percentage is closer to 12.5%.) As the name implies, essential fat is necessary for a normal, healthy body. Fat is stored in small amounts throughout your body. Too much body fat, however, can be dangerous to your health. For men between 18 and 39 years old, a healthy percent body fat ranges from 8% to 19%. (For women of the same age, it's 21% to 32%.)

Measuring body fat can be tedious and expensive. The "standard reference" measurement is by dual-energy X-ray absorptiometry (DEXA), which involves two low-dose X-ray generators and takes from 10 to 20 minutes.

How close can we get to a useable prediction of body fat from easily measurable variables such as *Height, Weight,* or *Waist* size? Figure 27.1 shows a scatterplot of *%Body Fat* plotted against *Waist* size for a sample of 250 males of various ages.

Back in Chapter 8 we modeled relationships like this by fitting a least squares line. The plot is clearly straight, so we can find that line. The equation of the least squares line for these data is

$$\widehat{\%Body\ Fat} = -42.7 + 1.7\ Waist.$$

The slope says that, on average, *%Body Fat* is greater by 1.7 percent for each additional inch around the waist.

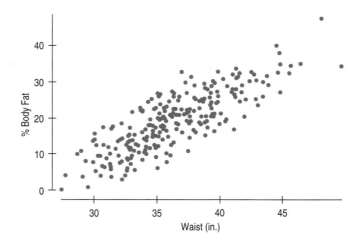

**FIGURE 27.1**

*Percent Body Fat vs. Waist size for 250 men of various ages. The scatterplot shows a strong, positive, linear relationship.*

How useful is this model? When we fit linear models before, we used them to describe the relationship between the variables and we interpreted the slope and intercept as descriptions of the data. Now we'd like to know what the regression model can tell us beyond the 250 men in this study. To do that, we'll want to make confidence intervals and test hypotheses about the slope and intercept of the regression line.

## The Population and the Sample

When we found a confidence interval for a mean, we could imagine a single, true underlying value for the mean. When we tested whether two means or two proportions were equal, we imagined a true underlying difference. But what does it mean to do inference for regression? We know better than to think that even if we knew every population value, the data would line up perfectly on a straight line. After all, even in our sample, not all men who have 38-inch waists have the same *%Body Fat*. In fact, there's a whole distribution of *%Body Fat* for these men:

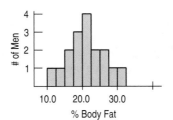

**FIGURE 27.2**

*The distribution of %Body Fat for men with a Waist size of 38 inches is unimodal and symmetric.*

This is true at each *Waist* size. In fact, we could depict the distribution of *%Body Fat* at different *Waist* sizes like this:

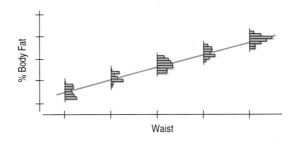

**FIGURE 27.3**

*There's a distribution of %Body Fat for each value of Waist size. We'd like the means of these distributions to line up.*

But we want to *model* the relationship between *%Body Fat* and *Waist* size for all men. To do that, we imagine an idealized regression line. The model assumes that the *means* of the distributions of *%Body Fat* for each *Waist* size fall along the line, even though the individuals are scattered around it. We know that this model is not a perfect description of how the variables are associated, but it may be useful for predicting *%Body Fat* and for understanding how it's related to *Waist* size.

If only we had all the values in the population, we could find the slope and intercept of this *idealized regression line* explicitly by using least squares. Following our usual conventions, we write the idealized line with Greek letters and consider the coefficients (the slope and intercept) to be *parameters:* $\beta_0$ is the intercept and $\beta_1$ is the slope. Corresponding to our fitted line of $\hat{y} = b_0 + b_1 x$, we write

$$\mu_y = \beta_0 + \beta_1 x.$$

Why $\mu_y$ instead of $\hat{y}$? Because this is a model. There is a distribution of *%Body Fat* for each *Waist* size. The model places the *means* of the distributions of *%Body Fat* for each *Waist* size on the same straight line.

Of course, not all the individual $y$'s are at these means. (In fact, the line will miss most—and quite possibly all—of the plotted points.) Some individuals lie above and some below the line, so, like all models, this one makes **errors.** Lots of them. In fact, one at each point. These errors are random and, of course, can be positive or negative. They are model errors, so we use a Greek letter and denote them by $\varepsilon$.

When we put the errors into the equation, we can account for each individual $y$:

$$y = \beta_0 + \beta_1 x + \varepsilon.$$

This equation is now true for each data point (since there is an $\varepsilon$ to soak up the deviation), so the model gives a value of $y$ for any value of $x$.

For the body fat data, an idealized model such as this provides a summary of the relationship between *%Body Fat* and *Waist* size. Like all models, it simplifies the real situation. We know there is more to predicting body fat than waist size alone. But the advantage of a model is that the simplification might help us to think about the situation and assess how well *%Body Fat* can be predicted from simpler measurements.

We estimate the $\beta$'s by finding a regression line, $\hat{y} = b_0 + b_1 x$, as we did in Chapter 8. The residuals, $e = y - \hat{y}$, are the sample-based versions of the errors, $\varepsilon$. We'll use them to help us assess the regression model.

We know that least squares regression will give reasonable estimates of the parameters of this model from a random sample of data. Our challenge is to account for our uncertainty in how well they do. For that, we need to make some assumptions about the model and the errors.

## Assumptions and Conditions

**A S**   *Activity:* **Conditions for Regression Inference.** View an illustrated discussion of the conditions for regression inference.

Back in Chapter 8 when we fit lines to data, we needed to check only the Straight Enough Condition. Now, when we want to make inferences about the coefficients of the line, we'll have to make more assumptions. Fortunately, we can check conditions to help us judge whether these assumptions are reasonable for our data. And as we've done before, we'll make some checks *after* we find the regression equation.

Also, we need to be careful about the order in which we check conditions. If our initial assumptions are not true, it makes no sense to check the later ones. So now we number the assumptions to keep them in order.

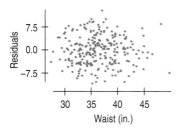

**FIGURE 27.4**

*The residuals show only random scatter when plotted against Waist size.*

**FIGURE 27.5**

*A scatterplot of residuals against predicted values can help check for plot thickening. Note that this plot looks identical to the plot of residuals against Waist size. For a regression of one response variable on one predictor, these plots differ only in the labels on the x-axis.*

## 1. LINEARITY ASSUMPTION

If the true relationship is far from linear and we use a straight line to fit the data, our entire analysis will be useless, so we always check this first.

The **Straight Enough Condition** is satisfied if a scatterplot looks straight. It's generally not a good idea to draw a line through the scatterplot when checking. That can fool your eye into seeing the plot as more straight. Sometimes it's easier to see violations of the Straight Enough Condition by looking at a scatterplot of the residuals against $x$ or against the predicted values, $\hat{y}$. That plot will have a horizontal direction and should have no pattern if the condition is satisfied.

If the scatterplot is straight enough, we can go on to some assumptions about the errors. If not, stop here, or consider re-expressing the data (see Chapter 10) to make the scatterplot more nearly linear. For the *%Body Fat* data, the scatterplot is beautifully linear. Of course, the data must be quantitative for this to make sense. Check the **Quantitative Data Condition.**

## 2. INDEPENDENCE ASSUMPTION

**Independence Assumption:** The errors in the true underlying regression model (the $\varepsilon$'s) must be mutually independent. As usual, there's no way to be sure that the Independence Assumption is true.

Usually when we care about inference for the regression parameters, it's because we think our regression model might apply to a larger population. In such cases, we can check a **Randomization Condition** that the individuals are a representative sample from that population.

We can also check displays of the regression residuals for evidence of patterns, trends, or clumping, any of which would suggest a failure of independence. In the special case when the $x$-variable is related to time, a common violation of the Independence Assumption is for the errors to be correlated. (The error our model makes today may be similar to the one it made for yesterday.) This violation can be checked by plotting the residuals against the $x$-variable and looking for patterns.

The *%Body Fat* data were collected on a sample of men taken to be representative. The subjects were not related in any way, so we can be pretty sure that their measurements are independent. The residuals plot shows no pattern.

## 3. EQUAL VARIANCE ASSUMPTION

The variability of $y$ should be about the same for all values of $x$. In Chapter 8 we looked at the standard deviation of the residuals ($s_e$) to measure the size of the scatter. Now we'll need this standard deviation to build confidence intervals and test hypotheses. The standard deviation of the residuals is the building block for the standard errors of all the regression parameters. But it makes sense only if the scatter of the residuals is the same everywhere. In effect, the standard deviation of the residuals "pools" information across all of the individual distributions at each $x$-value, and pooled estimates are appropriate only when they combine information for groups with the same variance.

Practically, what we can check is the **Does the Plot Thicken? Condition.** A scatterplot of $y$ against $x$ offers a visual check. Fortunately, we've already made one. Make sure the spread around the line is nearly constant. Be alert for a "fan" shape or other tendency for the variation to grow or shrink in one part of the scatterplot. Often it is better to look at the residuals plotted against the predicted values, $\hat{y}$. With the slope of the line removed, it's easier to see patterns left behind. For the body fat data, the spread of *%Body Fat* around the line is remarkably constant across *Waist* sizes from 30 inches to about 45 inches.

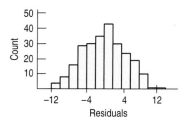

**Check a histogram of the residuals.**
The distribution of the residuals should be unimodal and symmetric.

**FIGURE 27.6**
*A histogram of the residuals is one way to check whether they are nearly Normal. Alternatively, we can look at a Normal probability plot.*

If the plot is straight enough, the data are independent, and the plot doesn't thicken, you can now move on to the final assumption.

## 4. NORMAL POPULATION ASSUMPTION

We assume the errors around the idealized regression line at each value of $x$ follow a Normal model. We need this assumption so that we can use a Student's $t$-model for inference.

As we have at other times when we've used Student's $t$, we'll settle for the residuals satisfying the **Nearly Normal Condition** and the **Outlier Condition.** Look at a histogram or Normal probability plot of the residuals.[1]

The histogram of residuals in the *%Body Fat* regression certainly looks nearly Normal. As we have noted before, the Normality Assumption becomes less important as the sample size grows, because the model is about means and the Central Limit Theorem takes over.

If all four assumptions were true, the idealized regression model would look like this:

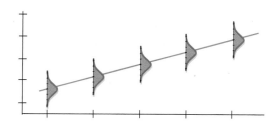

**FIGURE 27.7**
*The regression model has a distribution of y-values for each x-value. These distributions follow a Normal model with means lined up along the line and with the same standard deviations.*

At each value of $x$ there is a distribution of $y$-values that follows a Normal model, and each of these Normal models is centered on the line and has the same standard deviation. Of course, we don't expect the assumptions to be exactly true, and we know that all models are wrong, but the linear model is often close enough to be very useful.

| FOR EXAMPLE | Checking assumptions and conditions |

Look at the moon with binoculars or a telescope, and you'll see craters formed by thousands of impacts. The earth, being larger, has been hit even more often. Meteor Crater in Arizona was the first recognized impact crater and was identified as such only in the 1920s. With the help of satellite images, more and more craters have been identified; now more than 180 are known. These, of course, are only a small sample of all the impacts the earth has experienced: Only 29% of earth's surface is land, and many craters have been covered or eroded away. Astronomers have recognized a roughly 35 million-year cycle in the frequency of cratering, although the cause of this cycle is not fully understood. On the next page is a scatterplot of the known impact craters from the most recent 35 million years.[2] We've taken logs of both age (in millions of years ago) and diameter (km) to make the relationship simpler. (See Chapter 10.)

---

[1] *This* is why we have to check the conditions in order. We have to check that the residuals are independent and that the variation is the same for all $x$'s, so that we can lump all the residuals together for a single check of the Nearly Normal Condition.

[2] Data, pictures, and much more information at the Earth Impact Database found at http://www.unb.ca.

**Question:** Are the assumptions and conditions satisfied for fitting a linear regression model to these data?

✓ **Linearity Assumption:** The scatterplot satisfies the Straight Enough Condition.

✓ **Independence Assumption:** Impacts are likely to be generally independent.

✓ **Randomization Condition:** These are the only known craters, and may differ from others that have disappeared and not yet been found. I'll need to be careful not to generalize my conclusions too broadly.

✓ **Does the Plot Thicken? Condition:** After fitting a linear model, I find these residuals:

Two points seem to give the impression that the residuals may be more variable for higher predicted values than for lower ones, but this doesn't seem to be a serious violation of the Equal Variance Assumption.

✓ **Nearly Normal Condition:** A Normal probability plot suggests a bit of skewness in the distribution of residuals, and the histogram confirms that.

There are no violations severe enough to stop my regression analysis, but I'll be cautious about my conclusions.

# Which Come First: the Conditions or the Residuals?

In regression, there's a little catch. The best way to check many of the conditions is with the residuals, but we get the residuals only *after* we compute the regression. Before we compute the regression, however, we should check at least one of the conditions.

So we work in this order:

1. Make a scatterplot of the data to check the Straight Enough Condition. (If the relationship is curved, try re-expressing the data. Or stop.)
2. If the data are straight enough, fit a regression and find the residuals, *e*, and predicted values, $\hat{y}$.
3. Make a scatterplot of the residuals against *x* or the predicted values. This plot should have no pattern. Check in particular for any bend (which would suggest that the data weren't all that straight after all), for any thickening (or thinning), and, of course, for any outliers. (If there are outliers, and you can correct them or justify removing them, do so and go back to step 1, or consider performing two regressions—one with and one without the outliers.)
4. If the data are measured over time, plot the residuals against time to check for evidence of patterns that might suggest they are not independent.
5. If the scatterplots look OK, then make a histogram and Normal probability plot of the residuals to check the Nearly Normal Condition.
6. If all the conditions seem to be reasonably satisfied, go ahead with inference.

---

**STEP-BY-STEP EXAMPLE** | **Regression Inference**

If our data can jump through all these hoops, we're ready to do regression inference. Let's see how much more we can learn about body fat and waist size from a regression model.

**Questions:** What is the relationship between *%Body Fat* and *Waist* size in men?
What model best predicts body fat from waist size, and how well does it do the job?

| | |
|---|---|
|  **Plan** Specify the question of interest.<br><br>Name the variables and report the W's.<br><br>Identify the parameters you want to estimate.<br><br>**Model** Think about the assumptions and check the conditions.<br><br>Make pictures. For regression inference, you'll need a scatterplot, a residuals plot, and either a histogram or a Normal probability plot of the residuals. | I have quantitative body measurements on 250 adult males from the BYU Human Performance Research Center. I want to understand the relationship between *%Body Fat* and *Waist* size.<br><br>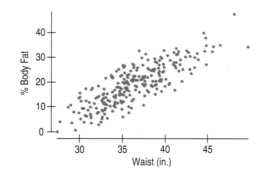 |

(We've seen plots of the residuals already. See Figures 27.5 and 27.6.)

✔ **Straight Enough Condition:** There's no obvious bend in the original scatterplot of the data or in the plot of residuals against predicted values.

✔ **Independence Assumption:** These data are not collected over time, and there's no reason to think that the %Body Fat of one man influences the %Body Fat of another.

✔ **Does the Plot Thicken? Condition:** Neither the original scatterplot nor the residual scatterplot shows any changes in the spread about the line.

✔ **Nearly Normal Condition, Outlier Condition:** A histogram of the residuals is unimodal and symmetric. The Normal probability plot of the residuals is quite straight, indicating that the Normal model is reasonable for the errors.

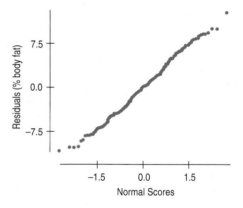

Choose your method.

Under these conditions a **regression model** is appropriate.

---

**Mechanics**  Let's just "push the button" and see what the regression looks like.

The formula for the regression equation can be found in Chapter 8, and the standard error formulas will be shown a bit later, but regressions are almost always computed with a computer program or calculator.

Write the regression equation.

Here's the computer output for this regression:

Dependent variable is: %BF
R-squared = 67.8%
s = 4.713 with 250 − 2 = 248 degrees of freedom

| Variable | Coeff | SE(Coeff) | t-ratio | P-value |
|----------|-------|-----------|---------|---------|
| Intercept | −42.734 | 2.717 | −15.7 | <0.0001 |
| Waist | 1.70 | 0.0743 | 22.9 | <0.0001 |

The estimated regression equation is

$$\widehat{\%Body\ Fat} = -42.73 + 1.70\ Waist.$$

| **Conclusion** Interpret your results in context. | *The $R^2$ for the regression is 67.8%. Waist size seems to account for about 2/3 of the %Body Fat variation in men. The slope of the regression says that %Body Fat increases by about 1.7 percentage points per inch of Waist size, on average.* |
|---|---|
| **More Interpretation** We haven't worked it out in detail yet, but the output gives us numbers labeled as *t*-statistics and corresponding P-values, and we have a general idea of what those mean. (Now it's time to learn more about regression inference, so we can figure out what the rest of the output means.) | *The standard error of 0.07 for the slope is much smaller than the slope itself, so it looks like the estimate is reasonably precise. And there are a couple of t-ratios and P-values given. Because the P-values are small, it appears that some null hypotheses can be rejected.* |

# Intuition About Regression Inference

> **A S** *Simulation:* **Simulate the Sampling Distribution of a Regression Slope.** Draw samples repeatedly to see for yourself how slope can vary from sample to sample. This simulation experiment lets you build up a histogram to see the sampling distribution.

Wait a minute! We've just pulled a fast one. We've pushed the "regression button" on our computer or calculator but haven't discussed where the standard errors for the slope or intercept come from. We know that if we had collected similar data on a different random sample of men, the slope and intercept would be different. Each sample would have produced its own regression line, with slightly different $b_0$'s and $b_1$'s . This sample-to-sample variation is what generates the sampling distributions for the coefficients.

There's only one regression model; each sample regression is trying to estimate the same parameters, $\beta_0$ and $\beta_1$. We expect any sample to produce a $b_1$ whose expected value is the true slope, $\beta_1$. What about its standard deviation? What aspects of the data affect how much the slope (and intercept) vary from sample to sample?

> **Spread around the line.** Here are two situations in which we might do regression. Which situation would yield the more consistent slope? That is, if we were to sample over and over from the two underlying populations that these samples come from and compute all the slopes, which group of slopes would vary less?

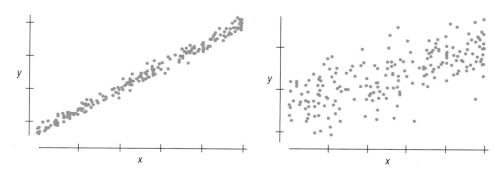

**FIGURE 27.8**

*Which of these scatterplots shows a situation that would give the more consistent regression slope estimate if we were to sample repeatedly from its underlying population?*

Clearly, data like those in the left plot give more consistent slopes.

Less scatter around the line means the slope will be more consistent from sample to sample. The spread around the line is measured with the **residual standard deviation,** $s_e$. You can always find $s_e$ in the regression output, often just labeled $s$. You're probably not going to calculate the residual standard deviation by hand. As we noted when we first saw this formula in Chapter 8, it looks a lot like the standard deviation of $y$, only now subtracting the predicted values rather than the mean and dividing by $n - 2$ instead of $n - 1$:

$$s_e = \sqrt{\frac{\sum (y - \hat{y})^2}{n - 2}}.$$

The less scatter around the line, the smaller the residual standard deviation and the stronger the relationship between $x$ and $y$.

Some people prefer to assess the strength of a regression by looking at $s_e$ rather than $R^2$. After all, $s_e$ has the same units as $y$, and because it's the standard deviation of the errors around the line, it tells you how close the data are to our model. By contrast, $R^2$ is the proportion of the variation of $y$ accounted for by $x$. We say, why not look at both?

▶ **Spread of the $x$'s:** Here are two more situations. Which of these would yield more consistent slopes?

**FIGURE 27.9**

*Which of these scatterplots shows a situation that would give the more consistent regression slope estimate if we were to sample repeatedly from the underlying population?*

A plot like the one on the right has a broader range of $x$-values, so it gives a more stable base for the slope. We'd expect the slopes of samples from situations like that to vary less from sample to sample. A large standard deviation of $x$, $s_x$, provides a more stable regression.

▶ **Sample size.** Here we go again. What about these two?

 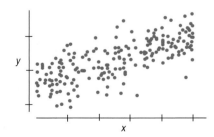

**FIGURE 27.10**

*Which of these scatterplots shows a situation that would give the more consistent regression slope estimate if we were to sample repeatedly from the underlying population?*

It shouldn't be a surprise that having a larger sample size, $n$, gives more consistent estimates from sample to sample.

**n − 2?**

For standard deviation (in Chapter 4), we divided by $n - 1$ because we didn't know the true mean and had to estimate it. Now it's later in the course and there's even more we don't know. Here we don't know *two* things: the slope and the intercept. If we knew them both, we'd divide by $n$ and have $n$ degrees of freedom. When we estimate both, however, we adjust by subtracting 2, so we divide by $n - 2$ and (as we will see soon) have 2 fewer degrees of freedom.

# Standard Error for the Slope

Three aspects of the scatterplot, then, affect the standard error of the regression slope:

- Spread around the line: $s_e$
- Spread of $x$ values: $s_x$
- Sample size: $n$

These are in fact the *only* things that affect the standard error of the slope. Although you'll probably never have to calculate it by hand, the formula for the standard error is

$$SE(b_1) = \frac{s_e}{\sqrt{n-1}\, s_x}.$$

The error standard deviation, $s_e$, is in the *numerator*, since spread around the line *increases* the slope's standard error. The denominator has both a sample size term $\sqrt{n-1}$ and $s_x$, because increasing either of these *decreases* the slope's standard error.

We know the $b_1$'s vary from sample to sample. As you'd expect, their sampling distribution model is centered at $\beta_1$, the slope of the idealized regression line. Now we can estimate its standard deviation with $SE(b_1)$. What about its shape? Here the Central Limit Theorem and "Wild Bill" Gosset come to the rescue again. When we standardize the slopes by subtracting the model mean and dividing by their standard error, we get a Student's $t$-model, this time with $n-2$ degrees of freedom:

$$\frac{b_1 - \beta_1}{SE(b_1)} \sim t_{n-2}.$$

**A S** **Activity: Regression Slope Standard Error.** See how $SE(b_1)$ is constructed and where the values used in the formula are found in the regression output table.

**A S** **Simulation: x-Variance and Slope Variance.** You don't have to just imagine how the variability of the slope depends on the spread of the $x$'s.

**NOTATION ALERT:**

Don't confuse the standard deviation of the residuals, $s_e$, with the standard error of the slope, $SE(b_1)$. The first measures the scatter around the line, and the second tells us how reliably we can estimate the slope.

---

**A SAMPLING DISTRIBUTION FOR REGRESSION SLOPES**

When the conditions are met, the standardized estimated regression slope,

$$t = \frac{b_1 - \beta_1}{SE(b_1)},$$

follows a Student's $t$-model with $n-2$ degrees of freedom. We estimate the standard error with

$$SE(b_1) = \frac{s_e}{\sqrt{n-1}\, s_x}, \text{ where } s_e = \sqrt{\frac{\sum (y - \hat{y})^2}{n-2}},$$

$n$ is the number of data values, and $s_x$ is the ordinary standard deviation of the $x$-values.

---

**FOR EXAMPLE**  Finding standard errors

**Recap:** Recent terrestrial impact craters seem to show a relationship between age and size that is linear when re-expressed using logarithms (see Chapter 10).

Here are summary statistics and regression output from a statistics package:

| Variable | Count | Mean | StdDev |
|----------|-------|------|--------|
| LogAge | 39 | −0.656310 | 1.57682 |
| LogDiam | 39 | 0.012600 | 1.04104 |

Dependent variable is: LogDiam
R squared = 63.6%
s = 0.6362 with 39 − 2 = 37 degrees of freedom

| Variable | Coefficient | Se(coeff) | t-ratio | P-value |
|----------|-------------|-----------|---------|---------|
| Intercept | 0.358262 | 0.1106 | 3.24 | 0.0025 |
| LogAge | 0.526674 | 0.0655 | 8.05 | ≤ 0.0001 |

**Questions:** How are the standard error of the slope and the *t*-ratio for the slope calculated? (And aren't you glad the software does this for you?)

$$SE(b_1) = \frac{s_e}{\sqrt{n-1} \times s_x} = \frac{0.6362}{\sqrt{39-1} \times 1.57682} = 0.0655$$

$$\text{Assuming no association } (\beta_1 = 0), \quad t_{37} = \frac{b_1 - \beta_1}{SE(b_1)} = \frac{0.526674 - 0}{0.0655} = 8.05$$

# What About the Intercept?

The same reasoning applies for the intercept. We could write

$$\frac{b_0 - \beta_0}{SE(b_0)} \sim t_{n-2}$$

and use it to construct confidence intervals and test hypotheses, but often the value of the intercept isn't something we care about. The intercept usually isn't interesting. Most hypothesis tests and confidence intervals for regression are about the slope. But in case you really want to see the formula for the standard error of the intercept, we've parked it in a footnote.[3]

# Regression Inference

Now that we have the standard error of the slope and its sampling distribution, we can test a hypothesis about it and make confidence intervals. The usual null hypothesis about the slope is that it's equal to 0. Why? Well, a slope of zero would say that $y$ doesn't tend to change linearly when $x$ changes—in other words, that there is no linear association between the two variables. If the slope were zero, there wouldn't be much left of our regression equation.

So a null hypothesis of a zero slope questions the entire claim of a linear relationship between the two variables—and often that's just what we want to know. In fact, every software package or calculator that does regression simply assumes that you want to test the null hypothesis that the slope is really zero.

To test $H_0: \beta_1 = 0$, we find

$$t_{n-2} = \frac{b_1 - 0}{SE(b_1)}.$$

This is just like every *t*-test we've seen: a difference between the statistic and its hypothesized value, divided by its standard error.

For our body fat data, the computer found the slope (1.7), its standard error (0.0743), and the ratio of the two: $\frac{1.7 - 0}{0.0743} = 22.9$ (see p. 727). Nearly 23 standard errors from the hypothesized value certainly seems big. The P-value ($<0.0001$) confirms that a *t*-ratio this large would be very unlikely to occur if the true slope were zero.

> **What if the Slope Were 0?**
>
> If $b_1 = 0$, our prediction is $\hat{y} = b_0 + 0x$. The equation collapses to just $\hat{y} = b_0$. Now $x$ is nowhere in sight, so $y$ doesn't depend on $x$ at all.
>
> And $b_0$ would turn out to be $\bar{y}$. Why? We know that $b_0 = \bar{y} - b_1\bar{x}$, but when $b_1 = 0$, that becomes simply $b_0 = \bar{y}$. It turns out, then, that when the slope is 0, the equation is just $\hat{y} = \bar{y}$; at every value of $x$, we always predict the mean value for $y$.

---

[3] $SE(b_0) = s_e \sqrt{\dfrac{1}{n} + \dfrac{\bar{x}^2}{\sum (x - \bar{x})^2}}$

Maybe the standard null hypothesis isn't all that interesting here. Did you have any doubts that *%Body Fat* is related to *Waist* size? A more sensible use of these same values might be to make a confidence interval for the slope instead.

We can build a confidence interval in the usual way, as an estimate plus or minus a margin of error. As always, the margin of error is just the product of the standard error and a critical value. Here the critical value comes from the *t*-distribution with $n - 2$ degrees of freedom, so a 95% **confidence interval for $\beta$** is

$$b_1 \pm t^*_{n-2} \times SE(b_1).$$

For the body fat data, $t^*_{248} = 1.970$, so that comes to $1.7 \pm 1.97 \times 0.074$, or an interval from 1.55 to 1.85 *%Body Fat* per inch of *Waist* size.

---

**FOR EXAMPLE** | Interpreting a regression model

**Recap:** On a log scale, there seems to be a linear relationship between the diameter and the age of recent terrestrial impact craters. We have regression output from statistics software:

Dependent variable is: LogDiam
R squared = 63.6%
s = 0.6362 with 39 − 2 = 37 degrees of freedom

| Variable | Coefficient | Se(coeff) | t-ratio | P-value |
|----------|-------------|-----------|---------|---------|
| Intercept | 0.358262 | 0.1106 | 3.24 | 0.0025 |
| LogAge | 0.526674 | 0.0655 | 8.05 | ≤0.0001 |

**Questions:** What's the regression model, and what can it tell us?

For terrestrial impact craters younger than 35 million years, the logarithm of *Diameter* grows linearly with the logarithm of *Age*: $\widehat{\log Diam} = 0.358 + 0.527 \log Age$. The P-value for each coefficient's *t*-statistic is very small, so I'm quite confident that neither is zero. Based on my model, I conclude that, on average, the older a crater is, the larger it tends to be. This model accounts for 63.6% of the variation in *logDiam*.

Although it is possible that impacts (and their craters) are getting smaller, it is more likely that I'm seeing the effects of age on craters. Small craters are probably more likely to erode or become buried, or otherwise be difficult to find as they age. Larger craters may survive the huge expanses of geologic time more successfully.

---

## ✓ JUST CHECKING

Researchers in Food Science studied how big people's mouths tend to be. They measured mouth volume by pouring water into the mouths of subjects who lay on their backs. Unless this is your idea of a good time, it would be helpful to have a model to estimate mouth volume more simply. Fortunately, mouth volume is related to height. (Mouth volume is measured in cubic centimeters and height in meters.)

The data were checked and deemed suitable for regression. Here is some computer output:

| Summary of | Mouth Volume |
|------------|--------------|
| Mean | 60.2704 |
| StdDev | 16.8777 |

Dependent variable is: Mouth Volume

R squared = 15.3%
s = 15.66 with 61 − 2 = 59 degrees of freedom

| Variable | Coefficient | SE(coeff) | t-ratio | P-value |
|----------|-------------|-----------|---------|---------|
| Intercept | −44.7113 | 32.16 | −1.39 | 0.1697 |
| Height | 61.3787 | 18.77 | 3.27 | 0.0018 |

**1.** What does the $t$-ratio of 3.27 tell us about this relationship? How does the P-value help our understanding?

**2.** Would you say that measuring a person's height could reliably be used as a substitute for the wetter method of determining how big a person's mouth is? What numbers in the output helped you reach that conclusion?

**3.** What does the value of $s_e$ add to this discussion?

# Another Example

Every spring, Nenana, Alaska, hosts a contest in which participants try to guess the exact minute that a wooden tripod placed on the frozen Tanana River will fall through the breaking ice. The contest started in 1917 as a diversion for railroad engineers, with a jackpot of $800 for the closest guess. It has grown into an event in which hundreds of thousands of entrants enter their guesses on the Internet[4] and vie for as much as $300,000.

Because so much money and interest depends on the time of breakup, it has been recorded to the nearest minute with great accuracy ever since 1917. And because a standard measure of breakup has been used throughout this time, the data are consistent. An article in *Science*[5] used the data to investigate global warming—whether greenhouse gasses and other human actions have been making the planet warmer. Others might just want to make a good prediction of next year's breakup time.

Of course, we can't use regression to tell the *causes* of any change. But we can estimate the *rate* of change (if any) and use it to make better predictions.

Here are some of the data:

| | |
|---|---|
| **WHO** | Years |
| **WHAT** | Year, day, and hour of ice breakup |
| **UNITS** | $x$ is in years since 1900. |
| | $y$ is in days after midnight Dec. 31. |
| **WHEN** | 1917–present |
| **WHERE** | Nenana, Alaska |
| **WHY** | Wagering, but proposed to look at global warming |

| Year (since 1900) | Breakup Date (days after Jan. 1) | Year (since 1900) | Breakup Date (days after Jan. 1) |
|-------------------|-------------------------------|-------------------|-------------------------------|
| 17 | 119.4792 | 30 | 127.7938 |
| 18 | 130.3979 | 31 | 129.3910 |
| 19 | 122.6063 | 32 | 121.4271 |
| 20 | 131.4479 | 33 | 127.8125 |
| 21 | 130.2792 | 34 | 119.5882 |
| 22 | 131.5556 | 35 | 134.5639 |
| 23 | 128.0833 | 36 | 120.5403 |
| 24 | 131.6319 | 37 | 131.8361 |
| 25 | 126.7722 | 38 | 125.8431 |
| 26 | 115.6688 | 39 | 118.5597 |
| 27 | 131.2375 | 40 | 110.6437 |
| 28 | 126.6840 | 41 | 122.0764 |
| 29 | 124.6535 | ⋮ | ⋮ |

---

[4] http://www.nenanaakiceclassic.com
[5] "Climate Change in Nontraditional Data Sets." *Science* 294 [26 October 2001]: 811.

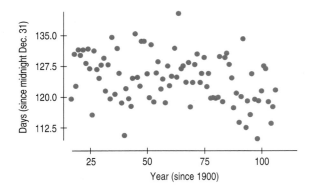

**FIGURE 27.11**

*Has the Date of ice breakup on the Tanana River changed since 1917, when record keeping began? Earlier breakup dates might be a sign of global warming.*

*Activity:* **A Hypothesis Test for the Regression Slope.** View an animated discussion of testing the standard null hypothesis for slope.

---

**STEP-BY-STEP EXAMPLE**          **A Regression Slope *t*-Test**

The slope of the regression gives the change in Nenana ice breakup date per year.

**Questions:** Is there sufficient evidence to claim that ice breakup times are changing? If so, how rapid is the change?

---

**THINK**

**Plan** State what you want to know.

Identify the *parameter* you wish to estimate. Here our parameter is the slope.

Identify the variables and review the W's.

**Hypotheses** Write your null and alternative hypotheses.

**Model** Think about the assumptions and check the conditions.

Make pictures. We saw a scatterplot of the data earlier. Because it seems straight enough, we can find and plot the residuals.

Usually, we check for suggestions that the Independence Assumption fails by plotting the residuals against the predicted values. Patterns and clusters in that plot raise our suspicions. But when the data are measured over time, it is always a good idea to plot residuals against time to look for trends and oscillations.

I wonder whether the date of ice breakup in Nenana has changed over time. The slope of that change might indicate climate change. I have the date of ice breakup annually since 1917, recorded as the number of days and fractions of a day until the ice breakup.

$H_0$: There is no change in the date of ice breakup: $\beta_1 = 0$

$H_A$: Yes, there is: $\beta_1 \neq 0$

✓ **Straight Enough Condition:** I have quantitative data with no obvious bend in the scatterplot.

✓ **Independence Assumption:** These data are a time series, which raises my suspicions that they may not be independent. To check, here's a plot of the residuals against time, the x-variable of the regression:

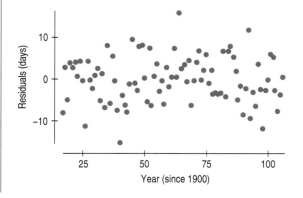

I see a hint that the data oscillate up and down, which suggests some failure of independence, but not so strongly that I can't proceed with the analysis. These data are not a random sample, so I'm reluctant to extend my conclusions beyond this river and these years.

✔ **Does the Plot Thicken? Condition:** The residuals plot shows no obvious trends in the spread.

✔ **Nearly Normal Condition, Outlier Condition:** A histogram of the residuals is unimodal and symmetric.

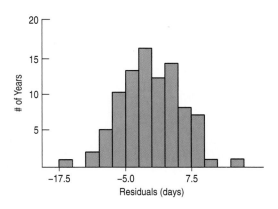

State the sampling distribution model.

Under these conditions, the sampling distribution of the regression slope can be modeled by a Student's t-model with $(n - 2) = 89$ degrees of freedom.

Choose your method.

I'll do a **regression slope t-test.**

**Mechanics** The regression equation can be found from the formulas in Chapter 8, but regressions are almost always found from a computer program or calculator.

The P-values given in the regression output table are from the Student's t-distribution on $(n - 2) = 88$ degrees of freedom. They are appropriate for two-sided alternatives.

Here's the computer output for this regression:

Dependent variable is: Breakup Date

R-squared = 11.3%
s = 5.673 with 91 − 2 = 89 degrees of freedom

| Variable | Coeff | SE(Coeff) | t-ratio | P-value |
|---|---|---|---|---|
| Intercept | 128.950 | 1.525 | 84.6 | <0.0001 |
| Year Since 1900 | −0.07606 | 0.0226 | −3.36 | 0.0012 |

The estimated regression equation is

$$\widehat{\text{Date}} = 128.95 - 0.076 \text{ YearSince1900}.$$

| | | |
|---|---|---|
| **TELL** | **Conclusion** Link the P-value to your decision and state your conclusion in the proper context. | The P-value of 0.0012 means that the association we see in the data is unlikely to have occurred by chance. I reject the null hypothesis, and conclude that there is strong evidence that, on average, the ice breakup is occurring earlier each year. But the oscillation pattern in the residuals raises concerns. |
| **SHOW** **MORE** | **Create a confidence interval for the true slope** | A 95% confidence interval for $\beta_1$ is $$b_1 \pm t^*_{89} \times SE(b_1)$$ $$-0.076 \pm (1.987)(0.0226)$$ $$\text{or } (-0.12, -0.03) \text{ days per year.}$$ |
| **TELL** **MORE** | **Interpret the interval** Simply rejecting the standard null hypothesis doesn't guarantee that the size of the effect is large enough to be important. Whether we want to know the breakup time to the nearest minute or are interested in global warming, a change measured in hours each year is big enough to be interesting. | I am 95% confident that the ice has been breaking up, on average, between 0.03 days (about 40 minutes) and 0.12 days (about 3 hours) earlier each year since 1900. |

**But is it global warming?** So the ice is breaking up earlier. Temperatures are higher. Must be global warming, right?

Maybe.

An article challenging the original analysis of the Nenana data proposed a possible confounding variable. It noted that the city of Fairbanks is upstream from Nenana and suggested that the growth of Fairbanks could have warmed the river. So maybe it's not global warming.

Or maybe global warming is a lurking variable, leading more people to move to a now balmier Fairbanks and also leading to generally earlier ice breakup in Nenana.

Or maybe there's some other variable or combination of variables at work. We can't set up an experiment, so we may never really know.

Only one thing is for sure. When you try to explain an association by claiming cause and effect, you're bound to be on thin ice.[6]

## Standard Errors for Predicted Values

Once we have a useful regression, how can we indulge our natural desire to predict, without being irresponsible? We know how to compute predicted values of $y$ for any value of $x$. We first did that in Chapter 8. This predicted value would be our best estimate, but it's still just an informed guess.

---

[6] How *do* scientists sort out such messy situations? Even though they can't conduct an experiment, they *can* look for replications elsewhere. A number of studies of ice on other bodies of water have also shown earlier ice breakup times in recent years. That suggests they need an explanation that's more comprehensive than just Fairbanks and Nenana.

Now, however, we have standard errors. We can use those to construct a confidence interval for the predictions and to report our uncertainty honestly.

From our model of *%Body Fat* and *Waist* size, we might want to use *Waist* size to get a reasonable estimate of *%Body Fat*. A confidence interval can tell us how precise that prediction will be. The precision depends on the question we ask, however, and there are two questions: Do we want to know the mean *%Body Fat* for *all* men with a *Waist* size of, say, 38 inches? Or do we want to estimate the *%Body Fat* for a particular man with a 38-inch *Waist* without making him climb onto the X-ray table?

What's the difference between the two questions? The predicted *%Body Fat* is the same, but one question leads to an answer much more precise than the other. We can predict the *mean %Body Fat* for *all* men whose *Waist* size is 38 inches with a lot more precision than we can predict the *%Body Fat* of a *particular individual* whose *Waist* size happens to be 38 inches. Both are interesting questions.

We start with the same prediction in both cases. We are predicting the value for a new individual, one that was not part of the original data set. To emphasize this, we'll call his *x*-value "*x* sub new" and write it $x_\nu$.[7] Here, $x_\nu$ is 38 inches. The regression equation predicts *%Body Fat* as $\hat{y}_\nu = b_0 + b_1 x_\nu$.

Now that we have the predicted value, we construct both intervals around this same number. Both intervals take the form

$$\hat{y}_\nu \pm t^*_{n-2} \times SE.$$

Even the $t^*$ value is the same for both. It's the critical value (from Table T or technology) for $n - 2$ degrees of freedom and the specified confidence level. The intervals differ because they have different standard errors. Our choice of ruler depends on which interval we want.

The standard errors for prediction depend on the same kinds of things as the coefficients' standard errors. If there is more spread around the line, we'll be less certain when we try to predict the response. Of course, if we're less certain of the slope, we'll be less certain of our prediction. If we have more data, our estimate will be more precise. And there's one more piece: If we're farther from the center of our data, our prediction will be less precise. This last factor is new, but makes intuitive sense: It's a lot easier to predict a data point near the middle of the data set than to extrapolate far from the center.

Each of these factors contributes uncertainty—that is, variability—to the estimate. Because the factors are independent of each other, we can add their variances to find the total variability. The resulting formula for the standard error of the predicted *mean* value explicitly takes into account each of the factors:

$$SE(\hat{\mu}_\nu) = \sqrt{SE^2(b_1)\cdot(x_\nu - \overline{x})^2 + \frac{s_e^2}{n}}.$$

Individual values vary more than means, so the standard error for a single predicted value has to be larger than the standard error for the mean. In fact, the standard error of a single predicted value has an *extra* source of variability: the variation of individuals around the predicted mean. That appears as the extra variance term, $s_e^2$, at the end under the square root:

$$SE(\hat{y}_\nu) = \sqrt{SE^2(b_1)\cdot(x_\nu - \overline{x})^2 + \frac{s_e^2}{n} + s_e^2}.$$

For the Nenana Ice Classic, someone who planned to place a bet would want to predict this year's breakup time. By contrast, scientists studying global warming are likely to be more interested in the mean breakup time. Unfortunately if you want to gamble, the variability is greater for predicting for a single year.

---

[7] Yes, this is a bilingual pun. The Greek letter $\nu$ is called "nu." Don't blame me; my co-author suggested this.

Remember to keep this distinction between the two kinds of standard errors when looking at computer output. The smaller one is for the predicted *mean* value, and the larger one is for a predicted *individual* value.[8]

# Confidence Intervals for Predicted Values

Now that we have standard errors, we can ask how well our analysis can predict the mean *%Body Fat* for men with 38-inch *Waists*. The regression output table provides most of the numbers we need:

$$s_e = 4.713$$
$$n = 250$$
$$SE(b_1) = 0.074, \text{ and from the data we need to know that}$$
$$\bar{x} = 36.3$$

The regression model gives a predicted value at $x_\nu = 38$ of

$$\hat{y}_\nu = -42.7 + 1.7(38) = 21.9\%.$$

Let's find the 95% confidence interval for the mean *%Body Fat* for all men with 38-inch *Waists*. We find the standard error from the formula:

$$SE(\hat{\mu}_\nu) = \sqrt{0.074^2(38 - 36.3)^2 + \frac{4.713^2}{250}} = 0.32\%.$$

The $t^*$ value that excludes 2.5% in either tail with $250 - 2 = 248$ df is (according to the tables) 1.97.

Putting it all together, we find the margin of error as

$$ME = 1.97(0.32) = 0.63\%.$$

So, we are 95% confident that the mean *%Body Fat* for men with 38-inch *Waists* is

$$21.9\% \pm 0.63\%.$$

Suppose, instead, we want to predict the *%Body Fat* for an individual man with a 38-inch *Waist*. We need the larger standard error:

$$SE(\hat{y}_\nu) = \sqrt{0.074^2(38 - 36.3)^2 + \frac{4.713^2}{250} + 4.713^2} = 4.72\%.$$

The corresponding margin of error is

$$ME = 1.97(4.72) = 9.30\%,$$

so the **prediction interval** is

$$21.9\% \pm 9.30\%.$$

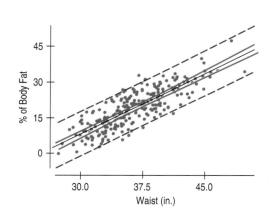

**FIGURE 27.12**

*A scatterplot of %Body Fat vs. Waist size with a least squares regression line. The solid green lines near the regression line show the extent of the 95% confidence intervals for mean %Body Fat at each Waist size. The dashed red lines show the prediction intervals. Most of the points are contained within the prediction intervals, but not within the confidence intervals.*

We can think of this interval as having a 95% chance of capturing the true *%Body Fat* of a randomly selected man whose *Waist* is 38 inches.[9] Notice how much wider this interval is than the previous one. As we've known since Chapter 18, the mean is much less variable than a randomly selected individual value.

---

[8] You may see the standard error expressions written in other, equivalent ways. The most common alternatives are

$$SE(\hat{\mu}_\nu) = s_e\sqrt{\frac{1}{n} + \frac{(x_\nu - \bar{x})^2}{\sum(x - \bar{x})^2}} \quad \text{and} \quad SE(\hat{y}_\nu) = s_e\sqrt{1 + \frac{1}{n} + \frac{(x_\nu - \bar{x})^2}{\sum(x - \bar{x})^2}}.$$

[9] Technically, it's a little more complicated, but it's very close to this.

Keep in mind this distinction between the two kinds of confidence intervals: The narrower interval is a **confidence interval for the predicted mean value** at $x_\nu$, and the wider interval is a **prediction interval for an individual** with that $x$-value.

## FOR EXAMPLE
### Intervals for predictions

**Recap:** We've found a linear model for the relationship between the *logDiam* and *logAge* for terrestrial impact craters: $\widehat{logDiam} = 0.358 + 0.527logAge$.

Let's look at some confidence intervals, keeping in mind that the model is in terms of the logs of these variables, so we must work with logs and then transform back to original units when we are done. (Many of the values substituted into the formulas are from the software outputs shown in the For Examples on pages 730 and 732.)

**Question #1:** If we wish to hunt for new craters that are 5 million years old, what's a 95% confidence interval for the mean size we'd expect them to be?

$$\widehat{logDiam} = 0.358 + 0.527logAge$$
$$= 0.358 + 0.527log(5)$$
$$= 0.726$$

$$SE(\hat{\mu}) = \sqrt{SE^2(b_1)\cdot(x - \bar{x})^2 + \frac{s_e^2}{n}}$$

$$= \sqrt{0.0655^2(log(5) - (-0.65631))^2 + \frac{0.6362^2}{39}}$$

$$= 0.1351$$

From Table T, $t_{37}^* = 2.030$, so a 95% CI is $0.726 \pm 2.030(0.1351)$, or $(0.452, 1.00)$.

Since these represent logs of the diameters, I'll find the original units:

$$10^{0.452} = 2.8 \text{ km and } 10^{1.00} = 10 \text{ km.}$$

I'm 95% confident that terrestrial craters 5 million years old average between 2.8 and 10 kilometers in diameter.

**Question #2:** There's just been a news report announcing the discovery of a new crater that is 10 million years old. How large do you expect it to be? What's a 95% prediction interval for your estimate?

For a crater 10 million years old, $\widehat{logDiam} = 0.358 + 0.527log(10) = 0.885$ and $10^{0.885} = 7.674$. I expect the new crater to be about 7.7 km in diameter.

$$SE(\hat{y}) = \sqrt{SE^2(b_1)\cdot(x - \bar{x})^2 + \frac{s_e^2}{n} + s_e^2}$$

$$= \sqrt{0.0655^2(log(10) - (-0.65631))^2 + \frac{0.6362^2}{39} + 0.6362^2}$$

$$= 0.653$$

A 95% CI is $0.885 \pm 2.030(0.653) = (-0.441, 2.211)$; in original units, that's $(0.36, 162.55)$.

I'm 95% confident that the newly discovered 10 million-year-old crater is between 0.36 and 162.55 kilometers in diameter. (Without a lot of data and a very strong association, prediction intervals often aren't very precise!)

## WHAT CAN GO WRONG?

In this chapter we've added inference to the regression explorations that we did in Chapters 8 and 9. Everything covered in those chapters that could go wrong with regression can still go wrong. It's probably a good time to review Chapter 9. We'll let you do that.

With inference, we've put numbers on our estimates and predictions, but these numbers are only as good as the model. Here are the main things to watch out for:

▶ **Don't fit a linear regression to data that aren't straight.** This is the most fundamental assumption. If the relationship between $x$ and $y$ isn't approximately linear, there's no sense in fitting a straight line to it.

▶ **Watch out for the plot thickening.** The common part of confidence and prediction intervals is the estimate of the error standard deviation, the spread around the line. If it changes with $x$, the estimate won't make sense. Imagine making a prediction interval for these data.

When $x$ is small, we can predict $y$ precisely, but as $x$ gets larger, it's much harder to pin $y$ down. Unfortunately, if the spread changes, the single value of $s_e$ won't pick that up. The prediction interval will use the average spread around the line, with the result that we'll be too pessimistic about our precision for low $x$-values and too optimistic for high $x$-values. A re-expression of $y$ is often a good fix for changing spread.

▶ **Make sure the errors are Normal.** When we make a prediction interval for an individual, the Central Limit Theorem can't come to our rescue. For us to believe the prediction interval, the errors must be from the Normal model. Check the histogram and Normal probability plot of the residuals to see if this assumption looks reasonable.

▶ **Watch out for extrapolation.** It's tempting to think that because we have prediction *intervals*, they'll take care of all of our uncertainty so we don't have to worry about extrapolating. Wrong. The interval is only as good as the model. The uncertainty our intervals predict is correct only if our model is true. There's no way to adjust for wrong models. That's why it's always dangerous to predict for $x$-values that lie far from the center of the data.

▶ **Watch out for high-influence points and outliers.** We always have to be on the lookout for a few points that have undue influence on our estimated model—and regression is certainly no exception.

▶ **Watch out for one-tailed tests.** Because tests of hypotheses about regression coefficients are usually two-tailed, software packages report two-tailed P-values. If you are using software to conduct a one-tailed test about slope, you'll need to divide the reported P-value in half.

# CONNECTIONS

Regression inference is connected to almost everything we've done so far. Scatterplots are essential for checking linearity and whether the plot thickens. Histograms and normal probability plots come into play to check the Nearly Normal condition. And we're still thinking about the same attributes of the data in these plots as we were back in the first part of the book.

Regression inference also is connected to just about every inference method we have seen for measured data. The assumption that the spread of data about the line is constant is essentially the same as the assumption of equal variances required for the pooled-$t$ methods. Our use of all the residuals together to estimate their standard deviation is a form of pooling.

Inference for regression is closely related to inference for means, so your understanding of means transfers directly to your understanding of regression. Here's a table that displays the similarities:

| | Means | Regression Slope |
|---|---|---|
| Parameter | $\mu$ | $\beta_1$ |
| Statistic | $\bar{y}$ | $b_1$ |
| Population spread estimate | $s_y = \sqrt{\dfrac{\Sigma(y - \bar{y})^2}{n - 1}}$ | $s_e = \sqrt{\dfrac{\Sigma(y - \hat{y})^2}{n - 2}}$ |
| Standard error of the statistic | $SE(\bar{y}) = \dfrac{s_y}{\sqrt{n}}$ | $SE(b_1) = \dfrac{s_e}{s_x\sqrt{n - 1}}$ |
| Test statistic | $\dfrac{\bar{y} - \mu_0}{SE(\bar{y})} \sim t_{n - 1}$ | $\dfrac{b_1 - \beta_1}{SE(b_1)} \sim t_{n - 2}$ |
| Margin of error | $ME = t^*_{n - 1} \times SE(\bar{y})$ | $ME = t^*_{n - 2} \times SE(b_1)$ |

# WHAT HAVE WE LEARNED?

In Chapters 7, 8, and 9, we learned to examine the relationship between two quantitative variables in a scatterplot, to summarize its strength with correlation, and to fit linear relationships by least squares regression. And we saw that these methods are particularly powerful and effective for modeling, predicting, and understanding these relationships.

Now we have completed our study of inference methods by applying them to these regression models. We've found that the same methods we used for means—Student's $t$-models—work for regression in much the same way as they did for means. And we've seen that although this makes the mechanics familiar, there are new conditions to check and a need for care in describing the hypotheses we test and the confidence intervals we construct.

▸ We've learned that under certain assumptions, the sampling distribution for the slope of a regression line can be modeled by a Student's $t$-model with $n - 2$ degrees of freedom.

▸ We've learned to check four conditions to verify those assumptions before we proceed with inference. We've learned the importance of checking these conditions in order, and we've seen that most of the checks can be made by graphing the data and the residuals with the methods we learned in Chapters 4, 5, and 8.

▸ We've learned to use the appropriate $t$-model to test a hypothesis about the slope. If the slope of our regression line is significantly different from zero, we have strong evidence that there is an association between the two variables.

▸ We've also learned to create and interpret a confidence interval for the true slope.

▸ And we've been reminded yet again never to mistake the presence of an association for proof of causation.

## Terms

**Conditions for inference in regression (and checks for some of them)**

▸ 723. **Straight Enough Condition** for linearity. (Check that the scatterplot of $y$ against $x$ has linear form and that the scatterplot of residuals against predicted values has no obvious pattern.)

▸ 723. **Independence Assumption.** (Think about the nature of the data. Check a residuals plot.)

▸ 723. **Does the Plot Thicken? Condition** for constant variance. (Check that the scatterplot shows consistent spread across the range of the $x$-variable, and that the residuals plot has constant variance, too. A common problem is increasing spread with increasing predicted values—the *plot thickens!*)

▸ 724. **Nearly Normal Condition** for Normality of the residuals. (Check a histogram of the residuals.)

**Residual standard deviation**

729. The spread of the data around the regression line is measured with the residual standard deviation, $s_e$:

$$s_e = \sqrt{\frac{\sum(y - \hat{y})^2}{n - 2}} = \sqrt{\frac{\sum e^2}{n - 2}}.$$

**t-test for the regression slope**

730. When the assumptions are satisfied, we can perform a test for the slope coefficient. We usually test the null hypothesis that the true value of the slope is zero against the alternative that it is not. A zero slope would indicate a complete absence of linear relationship between $y$ and $x$.

To test $H_0: \beta_1 = 0$, we find

$$t = \frac{b_1 - 0}{SE(b_1)}$$

where

$$SE(b_1) = \frac{s_e}{\sqrt{n - 1}\, s_x}, \quad s_e = \sqrt{\frac{\sum(y - \hat{y})^2}{n - 2}},$$

$n$ is the number of cases, and $s_x$ is the standard deviation of the $x$-values. We find the P-value from the Student's $t$-model with $n - 2$ degrees of freedom.

**Confidence interval for the regression slope**

732. When the assumptions are satisfied, we can find a confidence interval for the slope parameter from $b_1 \pm t_{n-2}^* \times SE(b_1)$. The critical value, $t_{n-2}^*$, depends on the confidence level specified and on Student's $t$-model with $n - 2$ degrees of freedom.

**Confidence interval for a predicted mean value**

738. Different samples will give different estimates of the regression model and, so, different predicted values for the same value of $x$. We find a confidence interval for the mean of these predicted values at a specified $x$-value, $x_\nu$, as $\hat{y}_\nu \pm t_{n-2}^* \times SE(\hat{\mu}_\nu)$, where

$$SE(\hat{\mu}_\nu) = \sqrt{SE^2(b_1) \cdot (x_\nu - \bar{x})^2 + \frac{s_e^2}{n}}.$$

The critical value, $t_{n-2}^*$, depends on the specified confidence level and the Student's $t$-model with $n - 2$ degrees of freedom.

**Prediction interval for an individual**

738. Different samples will give different estimates of the regression model and, so, different predicted values for the same value of $x$. We can make a confidence interval to capture a certain percentage of the entire distribution of predicted values. This makes it much wider than the corresponding confidence interval for the mean. The confidence interval takes the form $\hat{y}_\nu \pm t_{n-2}^* \times SE(\hat{y}_\nu)$, where

$$SE(\hat{y}_\nu) = \sqrt{SE^2(b_1) \cdot (x_\nu - \bar{x})^2 + \frac{s_e^2}{n} + s_e^2}.$$

The critical value, $t_{n-2}^*$, depends on the specified confidence level and the Student's $t$-model with $n - 2$ degrees of freedom.

## Skills

▸ Understand that the "true" regression line does not fit the population data perfectly, but rather is an idealized summary of that data.

▸ Know how to examine your data and a scatterplot of $y$ vs. $x$ for violations of assumptions that would make inference for regression unwise or invalid.

▸ Know how to examine displays of the residuals from a regression to double-check that the conditions required for regression have been met. In particular, know how to judge linearity and constant variance from a scatterplot of residuals against predicted values. Know how to judge Normality from a histogram and Normal probability plot.

▸ Remember to be especially careful to check for failures of the Independence Assumption when working with data recorded over time. To search for patterns, examine scatterplots both of $x$ against time and of the residuals against time.

▸ Know how to test the standard hypothesis that the true regression slope is zero. Be able to state the null and alternative hypotheses. Know where to find the relevant numbers in standard computer regression output.

▸ Be able to find a confidence interval for the slope of a regression based on the values reported in a standard regression output table.

▸ Be able to summarize a regression in words. In particular, be able to state the meaning of the true regression slope, the standard error of the estimated slope, and the standard deviation of the errors.

▸ Be able to interpret the P-value of the *t*-statistic for the slope to test the standard null hypothesis.

▸ Be able to interpret a confidence interval for the slope of a regression.

# ON THE COMPUTER

## Regression Analysis

All statistics packages make a table of results for a regression. These tables differ slightly from one package to another, but all are essentially the same. We've seen two examples of such tables already.

All packages offer analyses of the residuals. With some, you must request plots of the residuals as you request the regression. Others let you find the regression first and then analyze the residuals afterward. Either way, your analysis is not complete if you don't check the residuals with a histogram or Normal probability plot and a scatterplot of the residuals against *x* or the predicted values.

You should, of course, always look at the scatterplot of your two variables before computing a regression.

Regressions are almost always found with a computer or calculator. The calculations are too long to do conveniently by hand for data sets of any reasonable size. No matter how the regression is computed, the results are usually presented in a table that has a standard form. Here's a portion of a typical regression results table, along with annotations showing where the numbers come from:

> **A S** *Activity:* **Regression on the Computer.** How fast is the universe expanding? And how old is it? A prominent astronomer used regression to astound the scientific community. Read the story, analyze the data, and interactively learn about each of the numbers in a typical computer regression output table.

The regression table gives the coefficients (once you find them in the middle of all this other information), so we can see that the regression equation is

$$\widehat{\%BF} = -42.73 + 1.7 \; Waist$$

and that the $R^2$ for the regression is 67.8%. (Is accounting for 68% of the variation in *%Body Fat* good enough to be useful? Is a prediction *ME* of more than 9% good enough? Health professionals might not be satisfied.)

The column of *t*-ratios gives the test statistics for the respective null hypotheses that the true values of the coefficients are zero. The corresponding P-values are also usually reported.

## DATA DESK

- ▸ Select *Y*- and *X*-variables.
- ▸ From the **Calc** menu, choose **Regression.**
- ▸ Data Desk displays the regression table.
- ▸ Select plots of residuals from the Regression table's HyperView menu.

### COMMENTS

You can change the regression by dragging the icon of another variable over either the *Y*- or *X*-variable name in the table and dropping it there. The regression will recompute automatically.

## EXCEL

- ▸ In Excel 2003 and earlier, select Data Analysis from the **Tools** menu. In Excel 2007, select Data Analysis from the **Analysis Group** on the Data Tab.
- ▸ Select Regression from the **Analysis Tools** list.
- ▸ Click the **OK** button.
- ▸ Enter the data range holding the Y-variable in the box labeled "Y-range".
- ▸ Enter the range of cells holding the X-variable in the box labeled "X-range."
- ▸ Select the **New Worksheet Ply** option.
- ▸ Select **Residuals** options. Click the **OK** button.

### COMMENTS

The Y and X ranges do not need to be in the same rows of the spreadsheet, although they must cover the same number of cells. But it is a good idea to arrange your data in parallel columns as in a data table.

Although the dialog offers a Normal probability plot of the residuals, the data analysis add-in does not make a correct probability plot, so don't use this option.

## JMP

- ▸ From the **Analyze** menu, select **Fit Y by X.**
- ▸ Select variables: a Y, Response variable, and an X, Factor variable. Both must be continuous (quantitative).
- ▸ JMP makes a scatterplot.
- ▸ Click on the red triangle beside the heading labeled **Bivariate Fit...** and choose **Fit Line.** JMP draws the least squares regression line on the scatterplot and displays the results of the regression in tables below the plot.
- ▸ The portion of the table labeled "Parameter Estimates" gives the coefficients and their standard errors, *t*-ratios, and P-values.

### COMMENTS

JMP chooses a regression analysis when both variables are "Continuous." If you get a different analysis, check the variable types.

The Parameter table does not include the residual standard deviation $s_e$. You can find that as Root Mean Square Error in the Summary of Fit panel of the output.

## MINITAB

- ▸ Choose **Regression** from the **Stat** menu.
- ▸ Choose **Regression...** from the **Regression** submenu.
- ▸ In the Regression dialog, assign the Y-variable to the Response box and assign the X-variable to the Predictors box.
- ▸ Click the **Graphs** button.
- ▸ In the Regression-Graphs dialog, select **Standardized residuals,** and check **Normal plot of residuals** and **Residuals versus fits.**
- ▸ Click the **OK** button to return to the Regression dialog.
- ▸ Click the **OK** button to compute the regression.

### COMMENTS

You can also start by choosing a Fitted Line plot from the **Regression** submenu to see the scatterplot first—usually good practice.

## SPSS

- ▸ Choose **Regression** from the **Analyze** menu.
- ▸ Choose **Linear** from the **Regression** submenu.
- ▸ In the Linear Regression dialog that appears, select the Y-variable and move it to the dependent target. Then move the X-variable to the independent target.
- ▸ Click the **Plots** button.

- ▸ In the Linear Regression Plots dialog, choose to plot the *SRESIDs against the *ZPRED values.
- ▸ Click the **Continue** button to return to the Linear Regression dialog.
- ▸ Click the **OK** button to compute the regression.

**TI-83/84 PLUS**

Under **STAT TESTS** choose **LinRegTTest**. Specify the two lists where the data are stored and (usually) choose the two-tail option. In addition to reporting the calculated value of $t$ and the P-value, the calculator will tell you the

coefficients of the regression equation ($a$ and $b$), the values of $r^2$ and $r$, and the value of $s$ you need for confidence or prediction intervals.

**TI-89**

Under **STAT Tests** choose **A:LinRegTTest**. Specify the two lists where the data are stored and (usually) choose the two-tail option. Select an equation name to store the resulting line. In addition to reporting the calculated value of $t$ and the P-value, the calculator will tell you the coefficients of the regression equation ($a$ and $b$), the values of $r^2$ and $r$, the value of $s$ used in prediction and confidence intervals, and

the standard error of the slope. For 95% prediction and confidence intervals, choose **7:LinRegTint** from the **STAT Ints** menu. Specify the two lists where the data are stored, and select an equation name to store the resulting line. Select for an interval for the slope or for a response. If for a response, enter the x-value.

# EXERCISES

**1. Hurricane predictions.** In Chapter 7 we looked at data from the National Oceanic and Atmospheric Administration about their success in predicting hurricane tracks. Here is a scatterplot of the error (in nautical miles) for predicting hurricane locations 72 hours in the future vs. the year in which the prediction (and the hurricane) occurred:

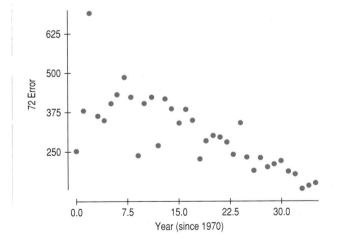

In Chapter 7 we could describe this relationship only in general terms. Now we can learn more. Here is the regression analysis:

Dependent variable is:    72Error
R squared = 58.5%
s = 75.38 with 36 − 2 = 34 degrees of freedom

| Variable | Coefficient | SE(Coeff) | t-ratio | P-value |
|---|---|---|---|---|
| Intercept | 453.223 | 24.61 | 18.4 | ≤0.0001 |
| Year since 1970 | −8.37084 | 1.209 | −6.92 | ≤0.0001 |

a) Explain in words and numbers what the regression says.
b) State the hypothesis about the slope (both numerically and in words) that describes how hurricane prediction quality has changed.
c) Assuming that the assumptions for inference are satisfied, perform the hypothesis test and state your conclusion. Be sure to state it in terms of prediction errors and years.
d) Explain what the R-squared means in terms of this regression.

**2. Drug use.** The *European School Study Project on Alcohol and Other Drugs*, published in 1995, investigated the use of marijuana and other drugs. Data from 11 countries are summarized in the following scatterplot and regression analysis. They show the association between the percentage of a country's ninth graders who report having smoked marijuana and who have used other drugs such as LSD, amphetamines, and cocaine.

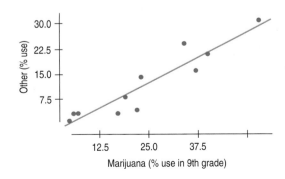

Dependent variable is: Other
R-squared = 87.3%
s = 3.853 with 11 − 2 = 9 degrees of freedom

| Variable | Coefficient | SE(Coeff) | t-ratio | P-value |
|---|---|---|---|---|
| Intercept | −3.06780 | 2.204 | −1.39 | 0.1974 |
| Marijuana | 0.615003 | 0.0784 | 7.85 | <0.0001 |

a) Explain in words and numbers what the regression says.
b) State the hypothesis about the slope (both numerically and in words) that describes how use of marijuana is associated with other drugs.
c) Assuming that the assumptions for inference are satisfied, perform the hypothesis test and state your conclusion in context.
d) Explain what the *R*-squared in this regression means.
e) Do these results indicate that marijuana use leads to the use of harder drugs? Explain.

**T** **3. Movie budgets.** How does the cost of a movie depend on its length? Data on the cost (millions of dollars) and the running time (minutes) for major release films of 2005 are summarized in these plots and computer output:

Dependent variable is: Budget($M)
R squared = 15.4%
s = 32.95 with 120 − 2 = 118 degrees of freedom

| Variable | Coefficient | SE(Coeff) | t-ratio | P-value |
|---|---|---|---|---|
| Intercept | −31.3869 | 17.12 | −1.83 | 0.0693 |
| Run Time | 0.714400 | 0.1541 | 4.64 | ≤0.0001 |

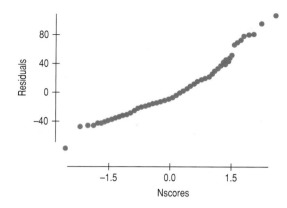

a) Explain in words and numbers what the regression says.
b) The intercept is negative. Discuss its value, taking note of the P-value.
c) The output reports s = 32.95. Explain what that means in this context.
d) What's the value of the standard error of the slope of the regression line?
e) Explain what that means in this context.

**T** **4. House prices.** How does the price of a house depend on its size? Data from Saratoga, New York, on 1064 randomly selected houses that had been sold include data on price ($1000's) and size (1000's ft$^2$), producing the following graphs and computer output:

Dependent variable is: Price
R squared = 59.5%
s = 53.79 with 1064 − 2 = 1062 degrees of freedom

| Variable | Coefficient | SE(Coeff) | t-ratio | P-value |
|---|---|---|---|---|
| Intercept | −3.11686 | 4.688 | −0.665 | 0.5063 |
| Size | 94.4539 | 2.393 | 39.5 | ≤0.0001 |

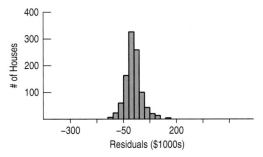

a) Explain in words and numbers what the regression says.
b) The intercept is negative. Discuss its value, taking note of its P-value.
c) The output reports $s = 53.79$. Explain what that means in this context.
d) What's the value of the standard error of the slope of the regression line?
e) Explain what that means in this context.

**5. Movie budgets: the sequel.** Exercise 3 shows computer output examining the association between the length of a movie and its cost.
a) Check the assumptions and conditions for inference.
b) Find a 95% confidence interval for the slope and interpret it.

**6. Second home.** Exercise 4 shows computer output examining the association between the sizes of houses and their sale prices.
a) Check the assumptions and conditions for inference.
b) Find a 95% confidence interval for the slope and interpret it.

**7. Hot dogs.** Healthy eating probably doesn't include hot dogs, but if you are going to have one, you'd probably hope it's low in both calories and sodium. In its July 2007 issue, *Consumer Reports* listed the number of calories and sodium content (in milligrams) for 13 brands of all-beef hot dogs it tested. Examine the association, assuming that the data satisfy the conditions for inference.

Dependent variable is: Sodium
R squared = 60.5%
s = 59.66 with 13 − 2 = 11 degrees of freedom

| Variable | Coefficient | SE(Coeff) | t-ratio | P-value |
|----------|-------------|-----------|---------|---------|
| Constant | 90.9783 | 77.69 | 1.17 | 0.2663 |
| Calories | 2.29959 | 0.5607 | 4.10 | 0.0018 |

a) State the appropriate hypotheses about the slope.
b) Test your hypotheses and state your conclusion in the proper context.

**8. Cholesterol 2007.** Does a person's cholesterol level tend to change with age? Data collected from 1406 adults aged 45 to 62 produced the regression analysis shown. Assuming that the data satisfy the conditions for inference, examine the association between age and cholesterol level.

Dependent variable is: Chol
s = 46.16

| Variable | Coefficient | SE(Coeff) | t-ratio | P-value |
|----------|-------------|-----------|---------|---------|
| Intercept | 194.232 | 13.55 | 14.3 | ≤0.0001 |
| Age | 0.771639 | 0.2574 | 3.00 | 0.0028 |

a) State the appropriate hypothesis for the slope.
b) Test your hypothesis and state your conclusion in the proper context.

**9. Second frank.** Look again at Exercise 7's regression output for the calorie and sodium content of hot dogs.
a) The output reports $s = 59.66$. Explain what that means in this context.
b) What's the value of the standard error of the slope of the regression line?
c) Explain what that means in this context.

**10. More cholesterol.** Look again at Exercise 8's regression output for age and cholesterol level.
a) The output reports $s = 46.16$. Explain what that means in this context.
b) What's the value of the standard error of the slope of the regression line?
c) Explain what that means in this context.

**11. Last dog.** Based on the regression output seen in Exercise 7, create a 95% confidence interval for the slope of the regression line and interpret your interval in the proper context.

**12. Cholesterol, finis.** Based on the regression output seen in Exercise 8, create a 95% confidence interval for the slope of the regression line and interpret your interval in the proper context.

**13. Marriage age 2003.** The scatterplot suggests a decrease in the difference in ages at first marriage for men and women since 1975. We want to examine the regression to see if this decrease is significant.

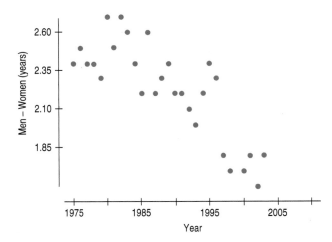

Dependent variable is: Men − Women
R squared = 65.6%
s = 0.1869 with 28 − 2 = 26 degrees of freedom

| Variable | Coefficient | SE(Coeff) | t-ratio | P-value |
|---|---|---|---|---|
| Intercept | 61.8067 | 8.468 | 7.30 | ≤0.0001 |
| Year | −0.02996 | 0.0043 | −7.04 | ≤0.0001 |

a) Write appropriate hypotheses.
b) Here are the residuals plot and a histogram of the residuals. Do you think the conditions for inference are satisfied? Explain.

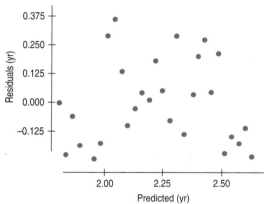

c) Test the hypothesis and state your conclusion about the trend in age at first marriage.

**14. Used cars 2007.** Classified ads in a newspaper offered several used Toyota Corollas for sale. Listed below are the ages of the cars and the advertised prices.

| Age (yr) | Prices Advertised ($) |
|---|---|
| 1 | 13990 |
| 1 | 13495 |
| 3 | 12999 |
| 4 | 9500 |
| 4 | 10495 |
| 5 | 8995 |
| 5 | 9495 |
| 6 | 6999 |
| 7 | 6950 |
| 7 | 7850 |
| 8 | 6999 |
| 8 | 5995 |
| 10 | 4950 |
| 10 | 4495 |
| 13 | 2850 |

a) Make a scatterplot for these data.
b) Do you think a linear model is appropriate? Explain.
c) Find the equation of the regression line.
d) Check the residuals to see if the conditions for inference are met.

**15. Marriage age 2003, again.** Based on the analysis of marriage ages since 1975 given in Exercise 13, give a 95% confidence interval for the rate at which the age gap is closing. Clearly explain what your confidence interval means.

**16. Used cars 2007, again.** Based on the analysis of used car prices you did for Exercise 14, create a 95% confidence interval for the slope of the regression line and explain what your interval means in context.

**17. Fuel economy.** A consumer organization has reported test data for 50 car models. We will examine the association between the weight of the car (in thousands of pounds) and the fuel efficiency (in miles per gallon). Shown are the scatterplot, summary statistics, and regression analysis:

| Variable | Count | Mean | StdDev |
|---|---|---|---|
| MPG | 50 | 25.0200 | 4.83394 |
| wt/1000 | 50 | 2.88780 | 0.511656 |

Dependent variable is: MPG
R-squared = 75.6%
s = 2.413 with 50 − 2 = 48 df

| Variable | Coefficient | SE(Coeff) | t-ratio | P-value |
|---|---|---|---|---|
| Intercept | 48.7393 | 1.976 | 24.7 | ≤0.0001 |
| Weight | −8.21362 | 0.6738 | −12.2 | ≤0.0001 |

a) Is there strong evidence of an association between the weight of a car and its gas mileage? Write an appropriate hypothesis.
b) Are the assumptions for regression satisfied?
c) Test your hypothesis and state your conclusion.

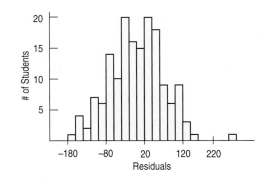

**18. SAT scores.** How strong was the association between student scores on the Math and Verbal sections of the old SAT? Scores on this exam ranged from 200 to 800 and were widely used by college admissions offices. Here are summaries and plots of the scores for a graduating class at Ithaca High School:

| Variable | Count | Mean | Median | StdDev | Range | IntQRange |
|---|---|---|---|---|---|---|
| Verbal | 162 | 596.296 | 610 | 99.5199 | 490 | 140 |
| Math | 162 | 612.099 | 630 | 98.1343 | 440 | 150 |

Dependent variable is: Math
R-squared = 46.9%
s = 71.75 with 162 − 2 = 160 df

| Variable | Coefficient | SE(Coeff) | t-ratio | P-value |
|---|---|---|---|---|
| Intercept | 209.554 | 34.35 | 6.10 | ≤0.0001 |
| Verbal | 0.675075 | 0.0568 | 11.9 | ≤0.0001 |

a) Is there evidence of an association between Math and Verbal scores? Write an appropriate hypothesis.
b) Discuss the assumptions for inference.
c) Test your hypothesis and state an appropriate conclusion.

**19. Fuel economy, part II.** Consider again the data in Exercise 17 about the gas mileage and weights of cars.
a) Create a 95% confidence interval for the slope of the regression line.
b) Explain in this context what your confidence interval means.

**20. SATs, part II.** Consider the high school SAT scores data from Exercise 18.
a) Find a 90% confidence interval for the slope of the true line describing the association between Math and Verbal scores.
b) Explain in this context what your confidence interval means.

**21. Fuel economy, part III.** Consider again the data in Exercise 17 about the gas mileage and weights of cars.
a) Create a 95% confidence interval for the average fuel efficiency among cars weighing 2500 pounds, and explain what your interval means.
b) Create a 95% prediction interval for the gas mileage you might get driving your new 3450-pound SUV, and explain what that interval means.

**22. SATs again.** Consider the high school SAT scores data from Exercise 18 once more.
a) Find a 90% confidence interval for the mean SAT-Math score for all students with an SAT-Verbal score of 500.
b) Find a 90% prediction interval for the Math score of the senior class president if you know she scored 710 on the Verbal section.

**23. Cereal.** A healthy cereal should be low in both calories and sodium. Data for 77 cereals were examined and judged acceptable for inference. The 77 cereals had between 50 and 160 calories per serving and between 0 and 320 mg of sodium per serving. The regression analysis is shown:

Dependent variable is: Sodium
R-squared = 9.0%
s = 80.49 with 77 − 2 = 75 degrees of freedom

| Variable | Coefficient | SE(Coeff) | t-ratio | P-value |
|---|---|---|---|---|
| Intercept | 21.4143 | 51.47 | 0.416 | 0.6786 |
| Calories | 1.29357 | 0.4738 | 2.73 | 0.0079 |

a) Is there an association between the number of calories and the sodium content of cereals? Explain.
b) Do you think this association is strong enough to be useful? Explain.

**24. Brain size.** Does your IQ depend on the size of your brain? A group of female college students took a test that measured their verbal IQs and also underwent an MRI scan to measure the size of their brains (in 1000s of pixels). The scatterplot and regression analysis are shown, and the assumptions for inference were satisfied.

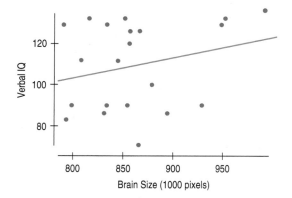

Dependent variable is: IQ_Verbal
R-squared = 6.5%

| Variable | Coefficient | SE(Coeff) |
|---|---|---|
| Intercept | 24.1835 | 76.38 |
| Size | 0.098842 | 0.0884 |

a) Test an appropriate hypothesis about the association between brain size and IQ.
b) State your conclusion about the strength of this association.

**25. Another bowl.** Further analysis of the data for the breakfast cereals in Exercise 23 looked for an association between *Fiber* content and *Calories* by attempting to construct a linear model. Several graphs are shown. Which of the assumptions for inference are violated? Explain.

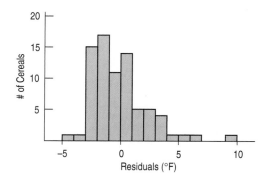

**26. Winter.** The output shows an attempt to model the association between average *January Temperature* (in degrees Fahrenheit) and *Latitude* (in degrees north of the equator) for 59 U.S. cities. Which of the assumptions for inference do you think are violated? Explain.

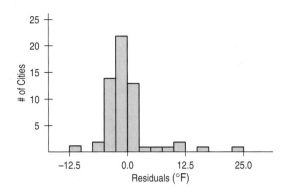

**27. Acid rain.** Biologists studying the effects of acid rain on wildlife collected data from 163 streams in the Adirondack Mountains. They recorded the *pH* (acidity) of the water and the *BCI*, a measure of biological diversity. Following is a scatterplot of *BCI* against *pH*:

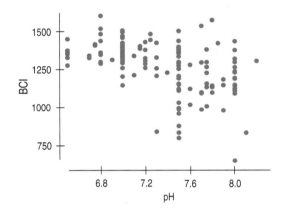

And here is part of the regression analysis:

Dependent variable is: BCI
R-squared = 27.1%
s = 140.4 with 163 − 2 = 161 degrees of freedom

| Variable | Coefficient | SE(Coeff) |
|---|---|---|
| Intercept | 2733.37 | 187.9 |
| pH | −197.694 | 25.57 |

a) State the null and alternative hypotheses under investigation.
b) Assuming that the assumptions for regression inference are reasonable, find the t- and P-values for the test.
c) State your conclusion.

**28. El Niño.** Concern over the weather associated with El Niño has increased interest in the possibility that the climate on earth is getting warmer. The most common theory relates an increase in atmospheric levels of carbon dioxide ($CO_2$), a greenhouse gas, to increases in temperature. Here is part of a regression analysis of the mean annual $CO_2$ concentration in the atmosphere, measured in parts per million (ppm), at the top of Mauna Loa in Hawaii and the mean annual air temperature over both land and sea across the globe, in degrees Celsius. The scatterplots and residuals plots indicated that the data were appropriate for inference.

Dependent variable is: Temp
R-squared = 33.4%
s = 0.0809 with 37 − 2 = 35 degrees of freedom

| Variable | Coefficient | SE(Coeff) |
|---|---|---|
| Intercept | 15.3066 | 0.3139 |
| CO2 | 0.004 | 0.0009 |

a) Write the equation of the regression line.
b) Is there evidence of an association between $CO_2$ level and global temperature?
c) Do you think predictions made by this regression will be very accurate? Explain.

**29. Ozone.** The Environmental Protection Agency is examining the relationship between the ozone level (in parts per million) and the population (in millions) of U.S. cities. Part of the regression analysis is shown.

Dependent variable is: Ozone
R-squared = 84.4%
s = 5.454 with 16 − 2 = 14 df

| Variable | Coefficient | SE(Coeff) |
|---|---|---|
| Intercept | 18.892 | 2.395 |
| Pop | 6.650 | 1.910 |

a) We suspect that the greater the population of a city, the higher its ozone level. Is the relationship significant? Assuming the conditions for inference are satisfied, test an appropriate hypothesis and state your conclusion in context.
b) Do you think that the population of a city is a useful predictor of ozone level? Use the values of both $R^2$ and s in your explanation.

**30. Sales and profits.** A business analyst was interested in the relationship between a company's sales and its profits. She collected data (in millions of dollars) from a random sample of Fortune 500 companies and created the regression analysis and summary statistics shown. The assumptions for regression inference appeared to be satisfied.

| | Profits | Sales |
|---|---|---|
| Count | 79 | 79 |
| Mean | 209.839 | 4178.29 |
| Variance | 635,172 | 49,163,000 |
| Std Dev | 796.977 | 7011.63 |

Dependent variable is: Profits
R-squared = 66.2%    s = 466.2

| Variable | Coefficient | SE(Coeff) |
|---|---|---|
| Intercept | −176.644 | 61.16 |
| Sales | 0.092498 | 0.0075 |

a) Is there a significant association between sales and profits? Test an appropriate hypothesis and state your conclusion in context.
b) Do you think that a company's sales serve as a useful predictor of its profits? Use the values of both $R^2$ and s in your explanation.

**31. Ozone, again.** Consider again the relationship between the population and ozone level of U.S. cities that you analyzed in Exercise 29.
a) Give a 90% confidence interval for the approximate increase in ozone level associated with each additional million city inhabitants.
b) For the cities studied, the mean population was 1.7 million people. The population of Boston is approximately 0.6 million people. Predict the mean ozone level for cities of that size with an interval in which you have 90% confidence.

**32. More sales and profits.** Consider again the relationship between the sales and profits of Fortune 500 companies that you analyzed in Exercise 30.

a) Find a 95% confidence interval for the slope of the regression line. Interpret your interval in context.

b) Last year the drug manufacturer Eli Lilly, Inc., reported gross sales of $9 billion (that's $9,000 million). Create a 95% prediction interval for the company's profits, and interpret your interval in context.

**33. Start the car!** In October 2002, *Consumer Reports* listed the price (in dollars) and power (in cold cranking amps) of auto batteries. We want to know if more expensive batteries are generally better in terms of starting power. Here are several software displays:

Dependent variable is: Power
R-squared = 25.2%
s = 116.0 with 33 − 2 = 31 degrees of freedom

| Variable | Coefficient | SE(Coeff) | t-ratio | P-value |
|----------|-------------|-----------|---------|---------|
| Intercept | 384.594 | 93.55 | 4.11 | 0.0003 |
| Cost | 4.14649 | 1.282 | 3.23 | 0.0029 |

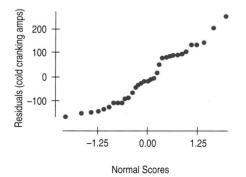

a) How many batteries were tested?

b) Are the conditions for inference satisfied? Explain.

c) Is there evidence of an association between the cost and cranking power of auto batteries? Test an appropriate hypothesis and state your conclusion.

d) Is the association strong? Explain.

e) What is the equation of the regression line?

f) Create a 90% confidence interval for the slope of the true line.

g) Interpret your interval in this context.

**34. Crawling.** Researchers at the University of Denver Infant Study Center wondered whether temperature might influence the age at which babies learn to crawl. Perhaps the extra clothing that babies wear in cold weather would restrict movement and delay the age at which they started crawling. Data were collected on 208 boys and 206 girls. Parents reported the month of the baby's birth and the age (in weeks) at which their child first crawled. The table gives the average *Temperature* (°F) when the babies were 6 months old and average *Crawling Age* (in weeks) for each month of the year. Make the plots and compute the analyses necessary to answer the following questions.

| Birth Month | 6-Month Temperature | Average Crawling Age |
|-------------|---------------------|----------------------|
| Jan. | 66 | 29.84 |
| Feb. | 73 | 30.52 |
| Mar. | 72 | 29.70 |
| April | 63 | 31.84 |
| May | 52 | 28.58 |
| June | 39 | 31.44 |
| July | 33 | 33.64 |
| Aug. | 30 | 32.82 |
| Sept. | 33 | 33.83 |
| Oct. | 37 | 33.35 |
| Nov. | 48 | 33.38 |
| Dec. | 57 | 32.32 |

a) Would this association appear to be weaker, stronger, or the same if data had been plotted for individual babies instead of using monthly averages? Explain.

b) Is there evidence of an association between *Temperature* and *Crawling Age*? Test an appropriate hypothesis and state your conclusion. Don't forget to check the assumptions.

c) Create and interpret a 95% confidence interval for the slope of the true relationship.

**35. Printers.** In March 2002, *Consumer Reports* reviewed several models of inkjet printers. Shown on the next page are the speed of the printer (in pages per minute) and the cost per page printed. Is there evidence of an association between *Speed* and *Cost*? Test an appropriate hypothesis and state your conclusion.

| Speed (ppm) | Cost (cents/page) |
|---|---|
| 4.6 | 12.0 |
| 5.5 | 8.5 |
| 4.5 | 6.2 |
| 3.8 | 3.4 |
| 4.6 | 2.6 |
| 3.7 | 4.0 |
| 4.7 | 5.8 |
| 4.7 | 8.1 |
| 4.0 | 9.4 |
| 3.1 | 14.9 |
| 1.9 | 2.6 |
| 2.2 | 4.3 |
| 1.8 | 4.6 |
| 2.0 | 14.8 |
| 2.0 | 4.4 |

**36. Strike two.** Remember the Little League instructional video discussed in Chapter 25? Ads claimed that the techniques would improve the performances of Little League pitchers. To test this claim, 20 Little Leaguers threw 50 pitches each, and we recorded the number of strikes. After the players participated in the training program, we repeated the test. The table shows the number of strikes each player threw before and after the training. A test of paired differences failed to show that this training was effective in improving a player's ability to throw strikes. Is there any evidence that the effectiveness of the video depends on the player's initial ability to throw strikes? Test an appropriate hypothesis and state your conclusion.

| Number of Strikes (out of 50) | | | |
|---|---|---|---|
| **Before** | **After** | **Before** | **After** |
| 28 | 35 | 33 | 33 |
| 29 | 36 | 33 | 35 |
| 30 | 32 | 34 | 32 |
| 32 | 28 | 34 | 30 |
| 32 | 30 | 34 | 33 |
| 32 | 31 | 35 | 34 |
| 32 | 32 | 36 | 37 |
| 32 | 34 | 36 | 33 |
| 32 | 35 | 37 | 35 |
| 33 | 36 | 37 | 32 |

**37. Body fat.** Do the data shown in the table in the next column indicate an association between *Waist* size and *%Body Fat*?
a) Test an appropriate hypothesis and state your conclusion.
b) Give a 95% confidence interval for the mean *%Body Fat* found in people with 40-inch *Waists*.

| Waist (in.) | Weight (lb) | Body Fat (%) | Waist (in.) | Weight (lb) | Body Fat (%) |
|---|---|---|---|---|---|
| 32 | 175 | 6 | 33 | 188 | 10 |
| 36 | 181 | 21 | 40 | 240 | 20 |
| 38 | 200 | 15 | 36 | 175 | 22 |
| 33 | 159 | 6 | 32 | 168 | 9 |
| 39 | 196 | 22 | 44 | 246 | 38 |
| 40 | 192 | 31 | 33 | 160 | 10 |
| 41 | 205 | 32 | 41 | 215 | 27 |
| 35 | 173 | 21 | 34 | 159 | 12 |
| 38 | 187 | 25 | 34 | 146 | 10 |
| 38 | 188 | 30 | 44 | 219 | 28 |

**38. Body fat, again.** Use the data from Exercise 37 to examine the association between *Weight* and *%Body Fat*.
a) Find a 90% confidence interval for the slope of the regression line of *%Body Fat* on *Weight*.
b) Interpret your interval in context.
c) Give a 95% prediction interval for the *%Body Fat* of an individual who weighs 165 pounds.

**39. Grades.** The data set below shows midterm scores from an Introductory Statistics course.

| First Name | Midterm 1 | Midterm 2 | Homework |
|---|---|---|---|
| Timothy | 82 | 30 | 61 |
| Karen | 96 | 68 | 72 |
| Verena | 57 | 82 | 69 |
| Jonathan | 89 | 92 | 84 |
| Elizabeth | 88 | 86 | 84 |
| Patrick | 93 | 81 | 71 |
| Julia | 90 | 83 | 79 |
| Thomas | 83 | 21 | 51 |
| Marshall | 59 | 62 | 58 |
| Justin | 89 | 57 | 79 |
| Alexandra | 83 | 86 | 78 |
| Christopher | 95 | 75 | 77 |
| Justin | 81 | 66 | 66 |
| Miguel | 86 | 63 | 74 |
| Brian | 81 | 86 | 76 |
| Gregory | 81 | 87 | 75 |
| Kristina | 98 | 96 | 84 |
| Timothy | 50 | 27 | 20 |
| Jason | 91 | 83 | 71 |
| Whitney | 87 | 89 | 85 |
| Alexis | 90 | 91 | 68 |
| Nicholas | 95 | 82 | 68 |
| Amandeep | 91 | 37 | 54 |
| Irena | 93 | 81 | 82 |
| Yvon | 88 | 66 | 82 |
| Sara | 99 | 90 | 77 |
| Annie | 89 | 92 | 68 |
| Benjamin | 87 | 62 | 72 |
| David | 92 | 66 | 78 |

*(Continued)*

| First Name | Midterm 1 | Midterm 2 | Homework |
|---|---|---|---|
| Josef | 62 | 43 | 56 |
| Rebecca | 93 | 87 | 80 |
| Joshua | 95 | 93 | 87 |
| Ian | 93 | 65 | 66 |
| Katharine | 92 | 98 | 77 |
| Emily | 91 | 95 | 83 |
| Brian | 92 | 80 | 82 |
| Shad | 61 | 58 | 65 |
| Michael | 55 | 65 | 51 |
| Israel | 76 | 88 | 67 |
| Iris | 63 | 62 | 67 |
| Mark | 89 | 66 | 72 |
| Peter | 91 | 42 | 66 |
| Catherine | 90 | 85 | 78 |
| Christina | 75 | 62 | 72 |
| Enrique | 75 | 46 | 72 |
| Sarah | 91 | 65 | 77 |
| Thomas | 84 | 70 | 70 |
| Sonya | 94 | 92 | 81 |
| Michael | 93 | 78 | 72 |
| Wesley | 91 | 58 | 66 |
| Mark | 91 | 61 | 79 |
| Adam | 89 | 86 | 62 |
| Jared | 98 | 92 | 83 |
| Michael | 96 | 51 | 83 |
| Kathryn | 95 | 95 | 87 |
| Nicole | 98 | 89 | 77 |
| Wayne | 89 | 79 | 44 |
| Elizabeth | 93 | 89 | 73 |
| John | 74 | 64 | 72 |
| Valentin | 97 | 96 | 80 |
| David | 94 | 90 | 88 |
| Marc | 81 | 89 | 62 |
| Samuel | 94 | 85 | 76 |
| Brooke | 92 | 90 | 86 |

a) Fit a model predicting the second midterm score from the first.
b) Comment on the model you found, including a discussion of the assumptions and conditions for regression. Is the coefficient for the slope statistically significant?
c) A student comments that because the P-value for the slope is very small, Midterm 2 is very well predicted from Midterm 1. So, he reasons, next term the professor can give just one midterm. What do you think?

**T** **40. Grades?** The professor teaching the Introductory Statistics class discussed in Exercise 39 wonders whether performance on homework can accurately predict midterm scores.
a) To investigate it, she fits a regression of the sum of the two midterms scores on homework scores. Fit the regression model.

b) Comment on the model including a discussion of the assumptions and conditions for regression. Is the coefficient for the slope "statistically significant"?
c) Do you think she can accurately judge a student's performance without giving the midterms? Explain.

**T** **41. Swimming Ontario.** Between 1974 and 2003, swimmers have crossed Lake Ontario 37 times. Have swimmers been getting faster or slower, or has there been no change in swimming speed? A regression predicting time for the swim (in minutes) against year of the swim looks like this:

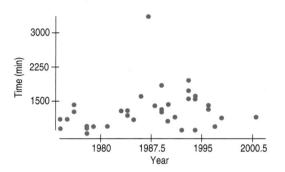

Dependent variable is: Time
R squared = 7.0%
s = 447.3 with 37 − 2 = 35 degrees of freedom

| Variable | Coefficient | SE(Coeff) | t-ratio | P-value |
|---|---|---|---|---|
| Intercept | −29161.9 | 18830 | −1.55 | 0.1305 |
| Year | 15.3323 | 9.479 | 1.62 | 0.1147 |

a) What do you hope to learn from these data? Define the variables, and state the null and alternative hypotheses about the slope.
b) Check assumptions and conditions.
c) If they are satisfied, complete the analysis.
d) The longest time is for a swim in which Vicki Keith swam round-trip, crossing the lake twice. If we remove it from the data, the new analysis is shown. Check the conditions again.

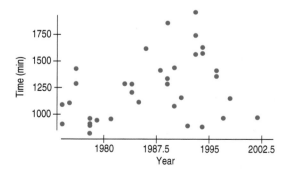

Dependent variable is: Time
R squared = 15.9%
s = 277.2 with 36 − 2 = 34 degrees of freedom

| Variable | Coefficient | SE(Coeff) | t-ratio | P-value |
|---|---|---|---|---|
| Constant | −28399.9 | 11671 | −2.43 | 0.0204 |
| Year | 14.9198 | 5.875 | 2.54 | 0.0158 |

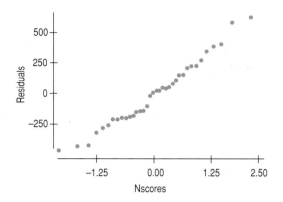

e) If the conditions are satisfied, complete the analysis.

f) The slope itself didn't change very much when we removed the outlier, but the P-value did. Consider the formula for the *t*-ratio and explain what changed.

**T 42. All the efficiency money can buy.** A sample of 84 model-2004 cars from an online information service was examined to see how fuel efficiency (as highway mpg) relates to the cost (Manufacturer's Suggested Retail Price in dollars) of cars. Here are displays and computer output:

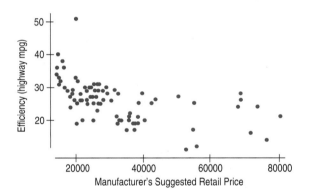

Dependent variable is: Highway MPG
R squared = 30.1%
s = 5.298 with 84 − 2 = 82 degrees of freedom

| Variable | Coefficient | SE(Coeff) | t-ratio | P-value |
|---|---|---|---|---|
| Constant | 33.0581 | 1.299 | 25.5 | ≤ 0.0001 |
| MSRP | −2.16543e-4 | 0.0000 | −5.95 | ≤ 0.0001 |

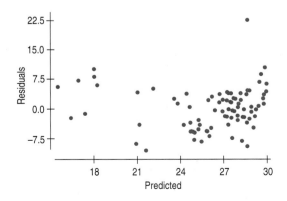

a) State what you want to know, identify the variables, and give the appropriate hypotheses.

b) Check the assumptions and conditions.

c) If the conditions are met, complete the analysis.

**T 43. Education and mortality.** The software output below is based on the mortality rate (deaths per 100,000 people) and the education level (average number of years in school) for 58 U.S. cities.

| Variable | Count | Mean | StdDev |
|---|---|---|---|
| Mortality | 58 | 942.501 | 61.8490 |
| Education | 58 | 11.0328 | 0.793480 |

Dependent variable is: Mortality
R-squared = 41.0%
s = 47.92 with 58 − 2 = 56 degrees of freedom

| Variable | Coefficient | SE(Coeff) |
|---|---|---|
| Intercept | 1493.26 | 88.48 |
| Education | −49.9202 | 8.000 |

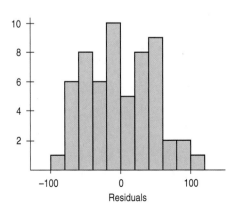

a) Comment on the assumptions for inference.

b) Is there evidence of a strong association between the level of *Education* in a city and the *Mortality* rate? Test an appropriate hypothesis and state your conclusion.

c) Can we conclude that getting more education is likely (on average) to prolong your life? Why or why not?

d) Find a 95% confidence interval for the slope of the true relationship.

e) Explain what your interval means.

f) Find a 95% confidence interval for the average *Mortality* rate in cities where the adult population completed an average of 12 years of school.

**T 44. Property assessments.** The software outputs below provide information about the *Size* (in square feet) of 18 homes in Ithaca, New York, and the city's assessed *Value* of those homes.

| Variable | Count | Mean | StdDev | Range |
|----------|-------|---------|---------|-------|
| Size | 18 | 2003.39 | 264.727 | 890 |
| Value | 18 | 60946.7 | 5527.62 | 19710 |

Dependent variable is: Value
R-squared = 32.5%
s = 4682 with 18 − 2 = 16 degrees of freedom

| Variable | Coefficient | SE(Coeff) |
|-----------|-------------|-----------|
| Intercept | 37108.8 | 8664 |
| Size | 11.8987 | 4.290 |

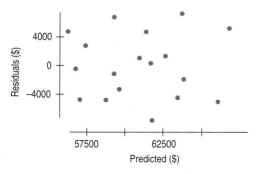

a) Explain why inference for linear regression is appropriate with these data.

b) Is there a significant association between the *Size* of a home and its assessed *Value*? Test an appropriate hypothesis and state your conclusion.

c) What percentage of the variability in assessed *Value* is explained by this regression?

d) Give a 90% confidence interval for the slope of the true regression line, and explain its meaning in the proper context.

e) From this analysis, can we conclude that adding a room to your house will increase its assessed *Value*? Why or why not?

f) The owner of a home measuring 2100 square feet files an appeal, claiming that the $70,200 assessed *Value* is too high. Do you agree? Explain your reasoning.

**T 45. Seasonal spending revisited.** In Exercise 37 of Chapter 25 we saw that spending on credit cards decreased after the Christmas spending season (as measured by amount charged on a credit card in December). The data set on the DVD contains the monthly credit card charges of a random sample of 99 cardholders.

a) Build a regression model to predict January spending from December's spending.

b) How much, on average, will cardholders who charged $2000 in December charge in January?

c) Give a 95% confidence interval for the average January charges of cardholders who charged $2000 in December.

d) From c), give a 95% confidence interval for the average decrease in the charges of cardholders who charged $2000 in December.

e) What reservations, if any, do you have about the confidence intervals you made in c) and d)?

**T 46. Seasonal spending revisited II.** As we saw in Exercise 38 of Chapter 25, financial analysts know that January credit card charges will generally be much lower than those of the month before. What about the difference between January and the next month? Does the trend continue? The data set on the DVD contains the monthly credit card charges of a random sample of 99 cardholders.

a) Build a regression model to predict February charges from January's charges.

b) How much, on average, will cardholders who charged $2000 in January charge in February?

c) Give a 95% confidence interval for the average February charges of cardholders who charged $2000 in January.

d) From c), give a 95% confidence interval for the average decrease in the charges of cardholders who charged $2000 in January.

e) What reservations, if any, do you have about the confidence intervals you made in c) and d)?

## JUST CHECKING
### Answers

1. A high *t*-ratio of 3.27 indicates that the slope is different from zero—that is, that there is a linear relationship between height and mouth size. The small P-value says that a slope this large would be very unlikely to occur by chance if, in fact, there was no linear relationship between the variables.

2. Not really. The $R^2$ for this regression is only 15.3%, so height doesn't account for very much of the variability in mouth size.

3. The value of *s* tells the standard deviation of the residuals. Mouth sizes have a mean of 60.3 cubic centimeters. A standard deviation of 15.7 in the residuals indicates that the errors made by this regression model can be quite large relative to what we are estimating. Errors of 15 to 30 cubic centimeters would be common.

# REVIEW OF PART VII

## Inference When Variables Are Related

### Quick Review

With these last two chapters, you have added important analytical tools to your ways of looking at data. Here's a brief summary of those key concepts and skills, as well as an overview of statistical inference:

▸ Inferences about distributions of counts use chi-square models.

- To see if an observed distribution is consistent with a proposed model, use a goodness-of-fit test.
- To see if two or more observed distributions could have arisen from populations with the same model, use a test of homogeneity.

▸ Inference about association between two variables tests the hypothesis that it is plausible to consider the variables independent.

- If the variables are categorical, display the data in a contingency table and use a chi-square test of independence.
- If the variables are quantitative, display them with a scatterplot. You may use a linear regression t-test if there appears to be a linear association for which the residuals are random, consistent in terms of spread, and approximately Normal.

▸ You can now use statistical inference to answer questions about means, proportions, distributions, and associations.

- No inference procedure is valid unless the underlying assumptions are true. Always check the conditions before proceeding. Many of those checks should be made by examining a graph.
- You can make inferences about a single proportion or the difference of two proportions using Normal models.

- You can make inferences about one mean, the difference of two independent means, or the mean of paired differences using t-models.
- You can make inferences about distributions using chi-square models.
- You can make inferences about associations between categorical variables using chi-square models.
- You can make inferences about linear associations between quantitative variables using t-models.

If you look back at where we've been in this book, you'll see that statistical inference relies on almost everything we've seen. In Chapters 12 and 13 we learned techniques of collecting data using randomization—that's what makes inference possible at all. In Chapters 3, 4, and 7 we learned to plot our data and to look for the patterns and relationships we use to check the conditions that allow inference. In Chapters 3, 5, and 8 we learned about the summary statistics we use to do the mechanics of inference. We use our knowledge of randomness and probability from Chapters 11, 14, and 15 to help us think clearly about uncertainty, and the probability models of Chapters 6, 16, and 17 to measure our uncertainty precisely. Ultimately, the Central Limit Theorem of Chapter 18 makes all of inference possible.

Remember (have we said this often enough yet?): Never use any inference procedure without first checking the assumptions and conditions. On the next page we summarize the new types of inference procedures, the corresponding formulas, and the assumptions and conditions. You'll find complete summaries of all our inference procedures inside the back cover of the book. Have a look. Then you'll be ready for more opportunities to practice using these concepts and skills. . . .

## Quick Guide to Inference

| Think | | | | Show | | | Tell? |
|---|---|---|---|---|---|---|---|
| **Inference about?** | **One group or two?** | **Procedure** | **Model** | **Parameter** | **Estimate** | **SE** | **Chapter** |
| **Distributions** (one categorical variable) | One sample | Goodness-of-Fit | $\chi^2$ <br> df = *cells* − 1 | | | $\displaystyle\sum \frac{(\text{obs} - \text{exp})^2}{\text{exp}}$ | 26 |
| | Many independent groups | Homogeneity $\chi^2$ Test | | | | | |
| **Independence** (two categorical variables) | One sample | Independence $\chi^2$ Test | $\chi^2$ <br> df = $(r-1)(c-1)$ | | | | |
| **Association** (two quantitative variables) | One sample | Linear Regression *t*-Test or Confidence Interval for $\beta$ | $t$ <br> df = $n - 2$ | $\beta_1$ | $b_1$ | $\dfrac{s_e}{s_x\sqrt{n-1}}$ <br> (compute with technology) | 27 |
| | | Confidence Interval for $\mu_\nu$ | | $\mu_\nu$ | $\hat{y}_\nu$ | $\sqrt{SE^2(b_1)\cdot(x_\nu - \bar{x})^2 + \dfrac{s_e^2}{n}}$ | |
| | | Prediction Interval for $y_\nu$ | | $y_\nu$ | $\hat{y}_\nu$ | $\sqrt{SE^2(b_1)\cdot(x_\nu - \bar{x})^2 + \dfrac{s_e^2}{n} + s_e^2}$ | |

---

**Assumptions for Inference**                    **And the Conditions That Support or Override Them**

---

Distributions/Association ($\chi^2$)

- **Goodness-of-fit** (df = # of cells − 1; one variable, one sample compared with population model)
  1. Data are counts.
  2. Data in sample are independent.
  3. Sample is sufficiently large.

  1. (Are they?)
  2. SRS and $n < 10\%$ of the population.
  3. All expected counts $\geq 5$.

- **Homogeneity** [df = $(r-1)(c-1)$; samples from many populations compared on one variable]
  1. Data are counts.
  2. Data in groups are independent.
  3. Groups are sufficiently large.

  1. (Are they?)
  2. SRSs and $n < 10\%$ OR random allocation.
  3. All expected counts $\geq 5$.

- **Independence** [df = $(r-1)(c-1)$; sample from one population classified on two variables]
  1. Data are counts.
  2. Data are independent.
  3. Sample is sufficiently large.

  1. (Are they?)
  2. SRSs and $n < 10\%$ of the population.
  3. All expected counts $\geq 5$.

Regression ($t$, df = $n - 2$)

- **Association** between two quantitative variables ($\beta = 0$?)
  1. Form of relationship is linear.
  2. Errors are independent.
  3. Variability of errors is constant.
  4. Errors have a Normal model.

  1. Scatterplot looks approximately linear.
  2. No apparent pattern in residuals plot.
  3. Residuals plot has consistent spread.
  4. Histogram of residuals is approximately unimodal and symmetric or Normal probability plot reasonably straight.*

---

(*less critical as $n$ increases)

# REVIEW EXERCISES

**1. Genetics.** Two human traits controlled by a single gene are the ability to roll one's tongue and whether one's ear lobes are free or attached to the neck. Genetic theory says that people will have neither, one, or both of these traits in the ratio 1:3:3:9 (1 attached, noncurling; 3 attached, curling; 3 free, noncurling; 9 free, curling). An Introductory Biology class of 122 students collected the data shown. Are they consistent with the genetic theory? Test an appropriate hypothesis and state your conclusion.

| Trait | | | |
|---|---|---|---|
| | Attached, noncurling | Attached, curling | Free, noncurling | Free, curling |
| Count | 10 | 22 | 31 | 59 |

**2. Tableware.** Nambe Mills manufactures plates, bowls, and other tableware made from an alloy of several metals. Each item must go through several steps, including polishing. To better understand the production process and its impact on pricing, the company checked the polishing time (in minutes) and the retail price (in US$) of these items. The regression analysis is shown below. The scatterplot showed a linear pattern, and residuals were deemed suitable for inference.

Dependent variable is: Price
R-squared = 84.5%
s = 20.50 with 59 − 2 = 57 degrees of freedom

| Variable | Coefficient | SE(Coeff) |
|---|---|---|
| Intercept | −2.89054 | 5.730 |
| Time | 2.49244 | 0.1416 |

a) How many different products were included in this analysis?
b) What fraction of the variation in retail price is explained by the polishing time?
c) Create a 95% confidence interval for the slope of this relationship.
d) Interpret your interval in this context.

**3. Hard water.** In an investigation of environmental causes of disease, data were collected on the annual mortality rate (deaths per 100,000) for males in 61 large towns in England and Wales. In addition, the water hardness was recorded as the calcium concentration (parts per million, or ppm) in the drinking water. Here are the scatterplot and regression analysis of the relationship between mortality and calcium concentration.

Dependent variable is: mortality
R-squared = 43%
s = 143.0 with 61 − 2 = 59 degrees of freedom

| Variable | Coefficient | SE(Coeff) |
|---|---|---|
| Intercept | 1676 | 29.30 |
| calcium | −3.23 | 0.48 |

a) Is there an association between the hardness of the water and the mortality rate? Write the appropriate hypothesis.
b) Assuming the assumptions for regression inference are met, what do you conclude?
c) Create a 95% confidence interval for the slope of the true line relating calcium concentration and mortality.
d) Interpret your interval in context.

**4. Mutual funds.** In March 2002, *Consumer Reports* listed the rate of return for several large-cap mutual funds over the previous 3-year and 5-year periods. ("Large cap" refers to companies worth over $10 billion.)
a) Create a 95% confidence interval for the difference in rate of return for the 3- and 5-year periods covered by these data. Clearly explain what your interval means.
b) It's common for advertisements to carry the disclaimer "Past returns may not be indicative of future performance," but do these data indicate that there was an association between 3-year and 5-year rates of return?

| Fund Name | Annualized Returns (%) | |
|---|---|---|
| | 3-year | 5-year |
| Ameristock | 7.9 | 17.1 |
| Clipper | 14.1 | 18.2 |
| Credit Suisse Strategic Value | 5.5 | 11.5 |
| Dodge & Cox Stock | 15.2 | 15.7 |
| Excelsior Value | 13.1 | 16.4 |
| Harbor Large Cap Value | 6.3 | 11.5 |
| ICAP Discretionary Equity | 6.6 | 11.4 |
| ICAP Equity | 7.6 | 12.4 |
| Neuberger Berman Focus | 9.8 | 13.2 |
| PBHG Large Cap Value | 10.7 | 18.1 |
| Pelican | 7.7 | 12.1 |
| Price Equity Income | 6.1 | 10.9 |
| USAA Cornerstone Strategy | 2.5 | 4.9 |
| Vanguard Equity Income | 3.5 | 11.3 |
| Vanguard Windsor | 11.0 | 11.0 |

**5. Resume fraud.** In 2002 the Veritas Software company found out that its chief financial officer did not actually have the MBA he had listed on his resume. They fired him, and the value of the company's stock dropped 19%. Kroll, Inc., a firm that specializes in investigating such matters, said that they believe as many as 25% of background checks might reveal false information. How many such random checks would they have to do to estimate the true percentage of people who misrepresent their backgrounds to within ±5% with 98% confidence?

**6. Paper airplanes.** In preparation for a regional paper airplane competition, a student tried out her latest design. The distances her plane traveled (in feet) in 11 trial flights are given here. (The world record is an astounding 193.01 feet!) The data were 62, 52, 68, 23, 34, 45, 27, 42, 83, 56, and 40 feet. Here are some summaries:

| | |
|---|---|
| Count | 11 |
| Mean | 48.3636 |
| Median | 45 |
| StdDev | 18.0846 |
| StdErr | 5.45273 |
| IntQRange | 25 |
| 25th %tile | 35.5000 |
| 75th %tile | 60.5000 |

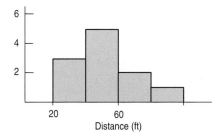

Distance (ft)

a) Construct a 95% confidence interval for the true distance.
b) Based on your confidence interval, is it plausible that the mean distance is 40 ft? Explain.
c) How would a 99% confidence interval for the true distance differ from your answer in part a? Explain briefly, without actually calculating a new interval.
d) How large a sample size would the student need to get a confidence interval half as wide as the one you got in part a, at the same confidence level?

**7. Back to Montana.** The respondents to the Montana poll described in Exercise 29 in Chapter 26 were also classified by income level: low (under $20,000), middle ($20,000–$35,000), or high (over $35,000). Is there any evidence that party enrollment there is associated with income? Test an appropriate hypothesis about this table, and state your conclusions.

| | Democrat | Republican | Independent |
|---|---|---|---|
| **Low** | 30 | 16 | 12 |
| **Middle** | 28 | 24 | 22 |
| **High** | 26 | 38 | 6 |

**8. Wild horses.** Large herds of wild horses can become a problem on some federal lands in the West. Researchers hoping to improve the management of these herds collected data to see if they could predict the number of foals that would be born based on the size of the current herd. Their attempt to model this herd growth is summarized in the output shown.

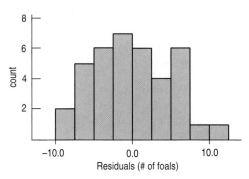

| Variable | Count | Mean | StdDev |
|---|---|---|---|
| Adults | 38 | 110.237 | 71.1809 |
| Foals | 38 | 15.3947 | 11.9945 |

Dependent variable is: Foals
R-squared = 83.5%
s = 4.941 with 38 − 2 = 36 degrees of freedom

| Variable | Coefficient | SE(Coeff) | t-ratio | P-value |
|---|---|---|---|---|
| Intercept | −1.57835 | 1.492 | −1.06 | 0.2970 |
| Adults | 0.153969 | 0.0114 | 13.5 | ≤ 0.0001 |

a) How many herds of wild horses were studied?
b) Are the conditions necessary for inference satisfied? Explain.
c) Create a 95% confidence interval for the slope of this relationship.
d) Explain in this context what that slope means.

e) Suppose that a new herd with 80 adult horses is located. Estimate, with a 90% prediction interval, the number of foals that may be born.

**9. Lefties and music.** In an experiment to see if left- and right-handed people have different abilities in music, subjects heard a tone and were then asked to identify which of several other tones matched the first. Of 76 right-handed subjects, 38 were successful in completing this test, compared with 33 of 53 lefties. Is this strong evidence of a difference in musical abilities based on handedness?

**10. AP Statistics scores.** In 2001, more than 41,000 Statistics students nationwide took the Advanced Placement Examination in Statistics. The national distribution of scores and the results at Ithaca High School are shown in the table.

| | | Ithaca High School | |
|---|---|---|---|
| Score | National Distribution | Number of boys | Number of girls |
| 5 | 11.5% | 13 | 13 |
| 4 | 23.4% | 21 | 15 |
| 3 | 24.9% | 6 | 13 |
| 2 | 19.1% | 7 | 3 |
| 1 | 21.1% | 4 | 2 |

a) Is the distribution of scores at this high school significantly different from the national results?
b) Was there a significant different between the performances of boys and girls at this school?

**11. Polling.** How accurate are pollsters in predicting the outcomes of congressional elections? The table shows the actual number of Democratic party seats in the House of Representatives and the number predicted by the Gallup organization for nonpresidential election years between World War II and 1998.

a) Is there a significant difference between the number of seats predicted for the Democrats and the number they actually held? Test an appropriate hypothesis and state your conclusions.

| Democratic Party Congressmen | | |
|---|---|---|
| Year | Predicted | Actual |
| 1946 | 190 | 188 |
| 1950 | 235 | 234 |
| 1954 | 232 | 232 |
| 1958 | 272 | 283 |
| 1962 | 259 | 258 |
| 1966 | 247 | 248 |
| 1970 | 260 | 255 |
| 1974 | 292 | 291 |
| 1978 | 277 | 277 |
| 1982 | 275 | 269 |
| 1986 | 264 | 258 |
| 1990 | 260 | 267 |
| 1994 | 201 | 204 |
| 1998 | 211 | 211 |

b) Is there a strong association between the pollsters' predictions and the outcomes of the elections? Test an appropriate hypothesis and state your conclusions.

**12. Twins.** In 2000 The *Journal of the American Medical Association* published a study that examined a sample of pregnancies that resulted in the birth of twins. Births were classified as preterm with intervention (induced labor or cesarean), preterm without such procedures, or term or postterm. Researchers also classified the pregnancies by the level of prenatal medical care the mother received (inadequate, adequate, or intensive). The data, from the years 1995–1997, are summarized in the table below. Figures are in thousands of births. (*JAMA* 284 [2000]: 335–341)

| TWIN BIRTHS, 1995–1997 (IN THOUSANDS) | | | | |
|---|---|---|---|---|
| | Preterm (induced or Cesarean) | Preterm (without procedures) | Term or postterm | Total |
| Intensive | 18 | 15 | 28 | **61** |
| Adequate | 46 | 43 | 65 | **154** |
| Inadequate | 12 | 13 | 38 | **63** |
| Total | **76** | **71** | **131** | **278** |

Is there evidence of an association between the duration of the pregnancy and the level of care received by the mother?

**13. Twins, again.** After reading of the *JAMA* study in Exercise 12, a large city hospital examined their records of twin births for several years and found the data summarized in the table below. Is there evidence that the way the hospital deals with pregnancies involving twins may have changed?

| | 1990 | 1995 | 2000 |
|---|---|---|---|
| Preterm (induced or cesarean) | 11 | 13 | 19 |
| Preterm (without procedures) | 13 | 14 | 18 |
| Term or postterm | 27 | 26 | 32 |

**14. Preemies.** Do the effects of being born prematurely linger into adulthood? Researchers examined 242 Cleveland-area children born prematurely between 1977 and 1979, and compared them with 233 children of normal birth weight; 24 of the "preemies" and 12 of the other children were described as being of "subnormal height" as adults. Is this evidence that babies born with a very low birth weight are more likely to be smaller than normal adults? ("Outcomes in Young Adulthood for Very-Low-Birth-Weight Infants," *New England Journal of Medicine*, 346, no. 3 [January 2002])

**T** **15. LA rainfall.** The Los Angeles Almanac Web site reports recent annual rainfall (in inches), as shown in the table.

a) Create a 90% confidence interval for the mean annual rainfall in LA.

b) If you wanted to estimate the mean annual rainfall with a margin of error of only 2 inches, how many years' data would you need?

c) Do these data suggest any change in annual rainfall as time passes? Check for an association between rainfall and year.

| Year | Rain (in.) | Year | Rain (in.) |
|------|------------|------|------------|
| 1980 | 8.96 | 1991 | 21.00 |
| 1981 | 10.71 | 1992 | 27.36 |
| 1982 | 31.28 | 1993 | 8.14 |
| 1983 | 10.43 | 1994 | 24.35 |
| 1984 | 12.82 | 1995 | 12.46 |
| 1985 | 17.86 | 1996 | 12.40 |
| 1986 | 7.66 | 1997 | 31.01 |
| 1987 | 12.48 | 1998 | 9.09 |
| 1988 | 8.08 | 1999 | 11.57 |
| 1989 | 7.35 | 2000 | 17.94 |
| 1990 | 11.99 | 2001 | 4.42 |

**T** **16. Age and party.** The Gallup Poll conducted a representative telephone survey during the first quarter of 1999. Among the reported results was the following table concerning the preferred political party affiliation of respondents and their ages. Is there evidence of age-based differences in party affiliation in the United States?

| | Repub-lican | Demo-cratic | Inde-pendent | Total |
|---|---|---|---|---|
| **18–29** | 241 | 351 | 409 | 1001 |
| **30–49** | 299 | 330 | 370 | 999 |
| **50–64** | 282 | 341 | 375 | 998 |
| **65+** | 279 | 382 | 343 | 1004 |
| **Total** | **1101** | **1404** | **1497** | **4002** |

(Age is the row label on the left side.)

a) Will you conduct a test of homogeneity or independence? Why?

b) Test an appropriate hypothesis.

c) State your conclusion, including an analysis of differences you find (if any).

**T** **17. Eye and hair color.** A survey of 1021 school-age children was conducted by randomly selecting children from several large urban elementary schools. Two of the questions concerned eye and hair color. In the survey, the following codes were used:

| Hair Color | Eye Color |
|------------|-----------|
| 1 = Blond | 1 = Blue |
| 2 = Brown | 2 = Green |
| 3 = Black | 3 = Brown |
| 4 = Red | 4 = Grey |
| 5 = Other | 5 = Other |

The Statistics students analyzing the data were asked to study the relationship between eye and hair color.

a) One group of students produced the output shown below. What kind of analysis is this? What are the null and alternative hypotheses? Is the analysis appropriate? If so, summarize the findings, being sure to include any assumptions you've made and/or limitations to the analysis. If it's not an appropriate analysis, state explicitly why not.

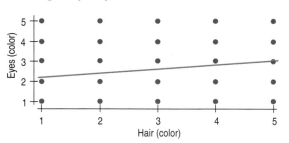

Dependent variable is: Eyes
R-squared = 3.7%
s = 1.112 with 1021 − 2 = 1019 degrees of freedom

| Variable | Coefficient | SE(Coeff) | t-ratio | P-value |
|----------|-------------|-----------|---------|---------|
| Intercept | 1.99541 | 0.08346 | 23.9 | ≤0.0001 |
| Hair | 0.211809 | 0.03372 | 0.28 | ≤0.0001 |

b) A second group of students used the same data to produce the output shown below. The table displays counts and standardized residuals in each cell. What kind of analysis is this? What are the null and alternative hypotheses? Is the analysis appropriate? If so, summarize the findings, being sure to include any assumptions you've made and/or limitations to the analysis. If it's not an appropriate analysis, state explicitly why not.

| Hair Color \ Eye Color | 1 | 2 | 3 | 4 | 5 |
|---|---|---|---|---|---|
| **1** | 143 / 7.67540 | 30 / 0.41799 | 58 / −5.88169 | 15 / −0.63925 | 12 / −0.31451 |
| **2** | 90 / −2.57141 | 45 / 0.29019 | 215 / 1.72235 | 30 / 0.49189 | 20 / −0.08246 |
| **3** | 28 / −5.39425 | 15 / −2.34780 | 190 / 6.28154 | 10 / −1.76376 | 10 / −0.80382 |
| **4** | 30 / 2.06116 | 15 / 2.71589 | 10 / −4.05540 | 10 / 2.37402 | 5 / 0.75993 |
| **5** | 10 / −0.52195 | 5 / 0.33262 | 15 / −0.94192 | 5 / 1.36326 | 5 / 2.07578 |

(Each cell shows the count on the first line and the standardized residual on the second line. "Eye Color" spans columns 1–5; "Hair Color" labels the rows.)

$$\sum \frac{(Observed - Expected)^2}{Expected} = 223.6 \quad \text{P-value} < 0.00001$$

18. **Depression and the Internet.** The September 1998 issue of the *American Psychologist* published an article reporting on an experiment examining "the social and psychological impact of the Internet on 169 people in 73 households during their first 1 to 2 years online." In the experiment, a sample of households was offered free Internet access for one or two years in return for allowing their time and activity online to be tracked. The members of the households who participated in the study were also given a battery of tests at the beginning and again at the end of the study. One of the tests measured the subjects' levels of depression on a 4-point scale, with higher numbers meaning the person was more depressed. Internet usage was measured in average number of hours per week. The regression analysis examines the association between the subjects' depression levels and the amounts of Internet use. The conditions for inference were satisfied.

Dependent variable is: Depression After
R-squared = 4.6%
s = 0.4563 with 162 − 2 = 160 degrees of freedom

| Variable | Coefficient | SE(coeff) | t-ratio | Prob |
|----------|-------------|-----------|---------|------|
| Constant | 0.565485 | 0.0399 | 14.2 | ≤0.0001 |
| Intr_use | 0.019948 | 0.0072 | 2.76 | 0.0064 |

a) Do these data indicate that there is an association between Internet use and depression? Test an appropriate hypothesis and state your conclusion clearly.
b) One conclusion of the study was that those who spent more time online tended to be more depressed at the end of the experiment. News headlines said that too much time on the Internet can lead to depression. Does the study support this conclusion? Explain.
c) As noted, the subjects' depression levels were tested at both the beginning and the end of this study; higher scores indicated the person was more depressed. Results are summarized in the table. Is there evidence that the depression level of the subjects changed during this study?

Depression Level
162 subjects

| Variable | Mean | StdDev |
|----------|------|--------|
| DeprBfore | 0.730370 | 0.487817 |
| DeprAfter | 0.611914 | 0.461932 |
| Difference | −0.118457 | 0.552417 |

19. **Pregnancy.** In 1998 a San Diego reproductive clinic reported 42 live births to 157 women under the age of 38, but only 7 successes for 89 clients aged 38 and older. Is this evidence of a difference in the effectiveness of the clinic's methods for older women?
a) Test the appropriate hypotheses, using the two-proportion z-procedure.
b) Repeat the analysis, using an appropriate chi-square procedure.
c) Explain how the two results are equivalent.

20. **Family planning.** A 1954 study of 1438 pregnant women examined the association between the woman's education level and the occurrence of unplanned pregnancies, producing these data:

| | Education Level | | |
|---|---|---|---|
| | <3 yr HS | 3+ yr HS | Some college |
| **Number of pregnancies** | 591 | 608 | 239 |
| **% unplanned** | 66.2% | 55.4% | 42.7% |

Do these data provide evidence of an association between family planning and education level? (*Fertility Planning and Fertility Rates by Socio-Economic Status*, Social and Psychological Factors Affecting Fertility, 1954)

21. **Old Faithful.** As you saw in an earlier chapter, Old Faithful isn't all that faithful. Eruptions do not occur at uniform intervals and may vary greatly. Can we improve our chances of predicting the time of the next eruption if we know how long the previous eruption lasted?
a) Describe what you see in this scatterplot.

b) Write an appropriate hypothesis.
c) Here are a histogram of the residuals and the residuals plot. Do you think the assumptions for inference are met? Explain.

d) State a conclusion based on this regression analysis:

Dependent variable is: Interval

R-squared = 77.0%

s = 6.159 with 222 − 2 = 220 degrees of freedom

| Variable | Coefficient | SE(Coeff) | t-ratio | P-value |
|---|---|---|---|---|
| Intercept | 33.9668 | 1.428 | 23.8 | ≤0.0001 |
| Duration | 10.3582 | 0.3822 | 27.1 | ≤0.0001 |

| Variable | Mean | StdDev |
|---|---|---|
| Duration | 3.57613 | 1.08395 |
| Interval | 71.0090 | 12.7992 |

e) The second table shows the summary statistics for the two variables. Create a 95% confidence interval for the mean length of time that will elapse following a 2-minute eruption.

f) You arrive at Old Faithful just as an eruption ends. Witnesses say it lasted 4 minutes. Create a 95% prediction interval for the length of time you will wait to see the next eruption.

**22. Togetherness.** Are good grades in high school associated with family togetherness? A simple random sample of 142 high-school students was asked how many meals per week their families ate together. Their responses produced a mean of 3.78 meals per week, with a standard deviation of 2.2. Researchers then matched these responses against the students' grade point averages. The scatterplot appeared to be reasonably linear, so they went ahead with the regression analysis, seen below. No apparent pattern emerged in the residuals plot.

Dependent variable: GPA

R-squared = 11.0%

s = 0.6682 with 142 − 2 = 140 df

| Variable | Coefficient | SE(Coeff) |
|---|---|---|
| Intercept | 2.7288 | 0.1148 |
| Meals/wk | 0.1093 | 0.0263 |

a) Is there evidence of an association? Test an appropriate hypothesis and state your conclusion.

b) Do you think this association would be useful in predicting a student's grade point average? Explain.

c) Are your answers to parts a and b contradictory? Explain.

**23. Learning math.** Developers of a new math curriculum called "Accelerated Math" compared performances of students taught by their system with control groups of students in the same schools who were taught using traditional instructional methods and materials. Statistics about pretest and posttest scores are shown in the table. (J. Ysseldyke and S. Tardrew, *Differentiating Math Instruction*, Renaissance Learning, 2002)

a) Did the groups differ in average math score at the start of this study?

b) Did the group taught using the Accelerated Math program show a significant improvement in test scores?

c) Did the control group show a significant improvement in test scores?

d) Were gains significantly higher for the Accelerated Math group than for the control group?

| | | Instructional Method | |
|---|---|---|---|
| | | **Acc. math** | **Control** |
| Number of students | | 231 | 245 |
| **Pretest** | Mean | 560.01 | 549.65 |
| | St. Dev | 84.29 | 74.68 |
| **Post-test** | Mean | 637.55 | 588.76 |
| | St. Dev | 82.9 | 83.24 |
| **Individual gain** | Mean | 77.53 | 39.11 |
| | St. Dev. | 78.01 | 66.25 |

**24. Pesticides.** A study published in 2002 in the journal *Environmental Health Perspectives* examined the gender ratios of children born to workers exposed to dioxin in Russian pesticide factories. The data covered the years from 1961 to 1988 in the city of Ufa, Bashkortostan, Russia. Of 227 children born to workers exposed to dioxin, only 40% were male. Overall in the city of Ufa, the proportion of males was 51.2%. Is this evidence that human exposure to dioxin may result in the birth of more girls? (An interesting note: It appeared that paternal exposure was most critical; 51% of babies born to mothers exposed to the chemical were boys.)

**25. Dairy sales.** Peninsula Creameries sells both cottage cheese and ice cream. The CEO recently noticed that in months when the company sells more cottage cheese, it seems to sell more ice cream as well. Two of his aides were assigned to test whether this is true or not. The first aide's plot and analysis of sales data for the past 12 months (in millions of pounds for cottage cheese and for ice cream) appear below.

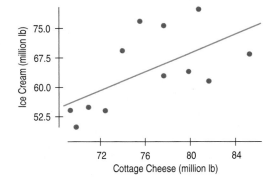

Dependent variable is: Ice cream

R-squared = 36.9%

s = 8.320 with 12 − 2 = 10 degrees of freedom

| Variable | Coefficient | SE(Coeff) | t-ratio | P-value |
|---|---|---|---|---|
| Constant | −26.5306 | 37.68 | −0.704 | 0.4975 |
| Cottage C ... | 1.19334 | 0.4936 | 2.42 | 0.0362 |

The other aide looked at the differences in sales of ice cream and cottage cheese for each month and created the following output:

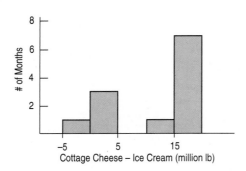

Cottage Cheese – Ice Cream

| | |
|---|---|
| Count | 12 |
| Mean | 11.8000 |
| Median | 15.3500 |
| StdDev | 7.99386 |
| IntQRange | 14.3000 |
| 25th %tile | 3.20000 |
| 75th %tile | 17.5000 |

Test HO: $\mu$(CC – IC) = 0 vs Ha: $\mu$(CC – IC) ≠ 0
Sample Mean = 11.800000 t-Statistic = 5.113 w/11 df
Prob = 0.0003
Lower 95% bound = 6.7209429
Upper 95% bound = 16.879057

a) Which analysis would you use to answer the CEO's question? Why?
b) What would you tell the CEO?
c) Which analysis would you use to test whether the company sells more cottage cheese or ice cream in a typical year? Why?
d) What would you tell the CEO about this other result?
e) What assumptions are you making in the analysis you chose in part a? What assumptions are you making in the analysis in part c?
f) Next month's cottage cheese sales are 82 million pounds. Ice cream sales are not yet available. How much ice cream do you predict Peninsula Creameries will sell?
g) Give a 95% confidence interval for the true slope of the regression equation of ice cream sales by cottage cheese sales.
h) Explain what your interval means.

**26. Infliximab.** In an article appearing in the journal *The Lancet* in 2002, medical researchers reported on the experimental use of the arthritis drug infliximab in treating Crohn's disease. In a trial, 573 patients were given initial 5-mg injections of the drug. Two weeks later, 335 had responded positively. These patients were then randomly assigned to three groups. Group I received continued injections of a placebo, Group II continued with 5 mg of infliximab, and Group III received 10 mg of the drug. After 30 weeks, 23 of 110 Group I patients were in remission, compared with 44 of 113 Group II and 50 of 112 Group III patients. Do these data indicate that continued treatment with infliximab is of value for Crohn's disease patients who exhibit a positive initial response to the drug?

**27. Weight loss.** A weight loss clinic advertises that its program of diet and exercise will allow clients to lose 10 pounds in one month. A local reporter investigating weight reduction gets permission to interview a randomly selected sample of clients who report the given weight losses during their first month in this program. Create a confidence interval to test the clinic's claim that the typical weight loss is 10 pounds.

| Pounds Lost | |
|---|---|
| 9.5 | 9.5 |
| 13 | 9 |
| 9 | 8 |
| 10 | 7.5 |
| 11 | 10 |
| 9 | 7 |
| 5 | 8 |
| 9 | 10.5 |
| 12.5 | 10.5 |
| 6 | 9 |

**28. Education vs. income.** The information below examines the median income and education level (years in school) for several U.S. cities.

| Variable | Count | Mean | StdDev |
|---|---|---|---|
| Education | 57 | 10.9509 | 0.848344 |
| Income | 57 | 32742.6 | 3618.01 |

Dependent variable is: Income
R-squared = 32.9%
s = 2991 with 57 − 2 = 55 degrees of freedom

| Variable | Coefficient | SE(Coeff) | t-ratio | P-value |
|----------|-------------|-----------|---------|---------|
| Intercept | 5970.05 | 5175 | 1.15 | 0.2537 |
| Education | 2444.79 | 471.2 | 5.19 | ≤0.0001 |

a) Do you think the assumptions for inference are met? Explain.
b) Does there appear to be an association between education and income levels in these cities?
c) Would this association appear to be weaker, stronger, or the same if data were plotted for individual people rather than for cities in aggregate? Explain.
d) Create and interpret a 95% confidence interval for the slope of the true line that describes the association between income and education.
e) Predict the median income for cities where residents spent an average of 11 years in school. Describe your estimate with a 90% confidence interval, and interpret that result.

**T 29. Diet.** Thirteen overweight women volunteered for a study to determine whether eating specially prepared crackers before a meal could help them lose weight. The subjects were randomly assigned to eat crackers with different types of fiber (bran fiber, gum fiber, both, and a control cracker). Unfortunately, some of the women developed uncomfortable bloating and upset stomachs. Researchers suspected that some of the crackers might be at fault. The contingency table of "Cracker" versus "Bloat" shows the relationship between the four different types of crackers and the reported bloating. The study was paid for by the manufacturers of the gum fiber. What would you recommend to them about the prospects for marketing their new diet cracker?

|         |         | Bloat | |
|---------|---------|-------------|-----------------|
|         |         | Little/None | Moderate/Severe |
| Cracker | Bran    | 11 | 2 |
|         | Gum     | 4  | 9 |
|         | Combo   | 7  | 6 |
|         | Control | 8  | 4 |

**T 30. Cramming.** Students in two basic Spanish classes were required to learn 50 new vocabulary words. One group of 45 students received the list on Monday and studied the words all week. Statistics summarizing this group's scores on Friday's quiz are given. The other group of 25 students did not get the vocabulary list until Thursday. They also took the quiz on Friday, after "cramming" Thursday night. Then, when they returned to class the following Monday, they were retested—without advance warning. Both sets of test scores for these students are shown.

**Group 1**

Fri.
Number of students = 45
Mean = 43.2 (of 50)
StDev = 3.4
Students passing (score ≥ 40) = 33%

**Group 2**

| Fri. | Mon. | Fri. | Mon. |
|------|------|------|------|
| 42 | 36 | 50 | 47 |
| 44 | 44 | 34 | 34 |
| 45 | 46 | 38 | 31 |
| 48 | 38 | 43 | 40 |
| 44 | 40 | 39 | 41 |
| 43 | 38 | 46 | 32 |
| 41 | 37 | 37 | 36 |
| 35 | 31 | 40 | 31 |
| 43 | 32 | 41 | 32 |
| 48 | 37 | 48 | 39 |
| 43 | 41 | 37 | 31 |
| 45 | 32 | 36 | 41 |
| 47 | 44 |    |    |

a) Did the week-long study group have a mean score significantly higher than that of the overnight crammers?
b) Was there a significant difference in the percentages of students who passed the quiz on Friday?
c) Is there any evidence that when students cram for a test, their "learning" does not last for 3 days?
d) Use a 95% confidence interval to estimate the mean number of words that might be forgotten by crammers.
e) Is there any evidence that how much students forget depends on how much they "learned" to begin with?

# Appendixes

# Answers

Here are the "answers" to the exercises for the chapters and the unit reviews. As we said in Chapter 1, the answers are outlines of the complete solution. Your solution should follow the model of the Step-By-Step examples, where appropriate. You should explain the context, show your reasoning and calculations, and draw conclusions. For some problems, what you decide to include in an argument may differ somewhat from the answers here. But, of course, the numerical part of your answer should match the numbers in the answers shown.

## CHAPTER 2

1. Categorical
2. Categorical
3. Quantitative
4. Quantitative
5. Answers will vary.
6. Answers will vary.
7. *Who*—2500 cars
   *What*—Distance from car to bicycle
   *Population*—All cars passing bicyclists
8. *Who*—30 similar companies
   *What*—401(k) employee participation rates
   *Population*—All similar companies
9. *Who*—Coffee drinkers at a Newcastle University coffee station
   *What*—Amount of money contributed
   *Population*—All people in honor system payment situations
10. *Who*—120 first-run movies in 2005
    *What*—Length of the movie and profit
    *Population*—All first-run movies
11. *Who*—25,892 men aged 30 to 87
    *What*—Fitness level and cause of death
    *Population*—All men
12. *Who*—10 crankshafts at Cleveland Casting
    *What*—The pouring temperature of molten iron
    *Population*—All Cleveland Casting crankshafts
13. *Who*—54 bears
    *Cases*—Each bear is a case.
    *What*—Weight, neck size, length, and sex
    *When*—Not specified
    *Where*—Not specified
    *Why*—To estimate weight from easier-to-measure variables
    *How*—Researchers collected data on 54 bears they were able to catch.
    *Variable*—Weight
       *Type*—Quantitative
       *Units*—Not specified
    *Variable*—Neck size
       *Type*—Quantitative
       *Units*—Not specified
    *Variable*—Length
       *Type*—Quantitative
       *Units*—Not specified
    *Variable*—Sex
       *Type*—Categorical
14. *Who*—Students
    *Cases*—Each student is an individual.

*What*—Age, race or ethnicity, number of absences, grade level, reading score, math score, and disabilities/special needs
*When*—Current
*Where*—Not specified
*Why*—Keeping this information is a state requirement.
*How*—The information is collected and stored as part of school records.
*Variable*—Age
   *Type*—Quantitative
   *Units*—Not specified, probably years (perhaps years, months)
*Variable*—Race or ethnicity
   *Type*—Categorical
*Variable*—Days absent
   *Type*—Quantitative
   *Units*—Number of days
*Variable*—Current grade level
   *Type*—Categorical (could be quantitative for some purposes)
*Variable*—Standardized reading score
   *Type*—Quantitative
   *Units*—Not specified
*Variable*—Standardized math score
   *Type*—Quantitative
   *Units*—Not specified
*Variable*—Disability/special needs
   *Type*—Categorical
15. *Who*—Arby's sandwiches
    *Cases*—Each sandwich is a case.
    *What*—Type of meat, number of calories, and serving size
    *When*—Not specified
    *Where*—Arby's restaurants
    *Why*—To assess nutritional value of sandwiches
    *How*—Report by Arby's restaurants
    *Variable*—Type of meat
       *Type*—Categorical
    *Variable*—Number of calories
       *Type*—Quantitative
       *Units*—Calories
    *Variable*—Serving size
       *Type*—Quantitative
       *Units*—Ounces
16. *Who*—Shipboard firefighters
    *Cases*—Each firefighter is an individual.
    *What*—Pulling force, weight, and gender
    *When*—Reported in 1982
    *Where*—Not specified
    *Why*—The researchers wanted to compare the abilities of men and women.

*How*—Not specified
*Variable*—Pulling force
   *Type*—Quantitative
   *Units*—Newtons
*Variable*—Weight
   *Type*—Quantitative
   *Units*—Not specified, probably pounds
*Variable*—Gender
   *Type*—Categorical

**17.** *Who*—882 births
   *Cases*—Each of the 882 births is a case.
   *What*—Mother's age, length of pregnancy, type of birth, level of
      prenatal care, birth weight of baby, gender of baby, and
      baby's health problems
   *When*—1998–2000
   *Where*—Large city hospital
   *Why*—Researchers were investigating the impact of prenatal care
      on newborn health.
   *How*—Not specified exactly, but probably from hospital records
   *Variable*—Mother's age
      *Type*—Quantitative
      *Units*—Probably years
   *Variable*—Length of pregnancy
      *Type*—Quantitative
      *Units*—Weeks
   *Variable*—Birth weight of baby
      *Type*—Quantitative
      *Units*—Not specified, probably pounds and ounces
   *Variable*—Type of birth
      *Type*—Categorical
   *Variable*—Level of prenatal care
      *Type*—Categorical
   *Variable*—Sex
      *Type*—Categorical
   *Variable*—Baby's health problems
      *Type*—Categorical

**18.** *Who*—385 species of flowers
   *Cases*—Each of the 385 species at each of the 47 years is a case,
      for a total of 18,095 cases.
   *What*—Date of first flowering
   *When*—Not specified
   *Where*—Southern England
   *Why*—The researchers believe that early flowering indicates a
      warming of the overall climate.
   *How*—Not specified
   *Variables*—Date of first flowering
      *Type*—Quantitative
      *Units*—Days

**19.** *Who*—Experiment subjects
   *Cases*—Each subject is an individual.
   *What*—Treatment (herbal cold remedy or sugar solution) and
      cold severity
   *When*—Not specified
   *Where*—Not specified
   *Why*—To test efficacy of herbal remedy on common cold
   *How*—The scientists set up an experiment.
   *Variable*—Treatment
      *Type*—Categorical
   *Variable*—Cold severity rating
      *Type*—Quantitative (perhaps ordinal categorical)
      *Units*—Scale from 0 to 5
   *Concerns*—The severity of a cold seems subjective and difficult to
      quantify. Scientists may feel pressure to report nega-
      tive findings of herbal product.

**20.** *Who*—Customers of a start-up company
   *Cases*—Each customer is an individual.
   *What*—Customer name, ID number, region of the country, date of
      last purchase, amount of purchase, and item purchased

*When*—Now
*Where*—United States
*Why*—The company is building a database of sales information.
*How*—From company database
*Variable*—Customer name
   *Type*—Identifier
*Variable*—Customer ID number
   *Type*—Identifier
*Variable*—Region of country
   *Type*—Categorical
*Variable*—Date of last purchase
   *Type*—Quantitative
   *Units*—Days, years
*Variable*—Amount of purchase
   *Type*—Quantitative
   *Units*—Not specified (dollars?)
*Variable*—Item purchased
   *Type*—Categorical

**21.** *Who*—Automobiles in student and staff lots
   *Cases*—Each car is a case.
   *What*—Make, country of origin, type of vehicle, and age of
      vehicle
   *When*—Not specified
   *Where*—A large university
   *Why*—Not specified
   *How*—A survey was taken in campus parking lots.
   *Variable*—Make
      *Type*—Categorical
   *Variable*—Country of origin
      *Type*—Categorical
   *Variable*—Type of vehicle
      *Type*—Categorical
   *Variable*—Age of vehicle
      *Type*—Quantitative
      *Units*—Years

**22.** *Who*—American vineyards
   *Cases*—Each vineyard is a case.
   *What*—Size of vineyard, number of years in existence, state,
      varieties of grapes grown, average case price, gross sales,
      and percent profit
   *When*—Not specified
   *Where*—United States
   *Why*—To provide information for American grape growers
   *How*—Not specified
   *Variable*—Vineyard size
      *Type*—Quantitative
      *Units*—Acres
   *Variable*—Number of years in existence
      *Type*—Quantitative
      *Units*—Years
   *Variable*—State
      *Type*—Categorical
   *Variable*—Varieties of grapes grown
      *Type*—Categorical
   *Variable*—Average case price
      *Type*—Quantitative
      *Units*—Dollars?
   *Variable*—Gross sales
      *Type*—Quantitative
      *Units*—Dollars?
   *Variables*—Percent profit
      *Type*—Quantitative
      *Units*—Percent

**23.** *Who*—Streams
   *Cases*—Each stream is a case.
   *What*—Name of stream, substrate of the stream, acidity of the
      water, temperature, BCI
   *When*—Not specified

*Where*—Upstate New York
*Why*—To study ecology of streams
*How*—Not specified
*Variable*—Stream name
  *Type*—Identifier
*Variable*—Substrate
  *Type*—Categorical
*Variable*—Acidity of water
  *Type*—Quantitative
  *Units*—pH
*Variable*—Temperature
  *Type*—Quantitative
  *Units*—Degrees Celsius
*Variable*—BCI
  *Type*—Quantitative
  *Units*—Not specified

24. *Who*—1180 Americans
    *Cases*—Each of the 1180 Americans surveyed is an individual in this poll.
    *What*—Region, age, political affiliation, and whether or not the person voted in the 1998 midterm congressional election
    *When*—First quarter of 1999
    *Where*—United States
    *Why*—The information was gathered for presentation in a Gallup public opinion poll.
    *How*—Phone survey
    *Variable*—Region
      *Type*—Categorical
    *Variable*—Age
      *Type*—Quantitative
      *Units*—Not specified (years?)
    *Variable*—Party affiliation
      *Type*—Categorical
    *Variable*—Voted in last election?
      *Type*—Categorical

25. *Who*—All airline flights in the United States
    *Cases*—Each flight is a case.
    *What*—Type of aircraft, number of passengers, whether or not departures and arrivals were on schedule, mechanical problems
    *When*—Current
    *Where*—United States
    *Why*—Required by the Federal Aviation Administration
    *How*—Data are collected from airline flight information.
    *Variable*—Type of aircraft
      *Type*—Categorical
    *Variable*—Number of passengers
      *Type*—Quantitative
      *Units*—Count
    *Variable*—Departed on time?
      *Type*—Categorical
    *Variable*—Arrived on time?
      *Type*—Categorical
    *Variable*—Mechanical problems?
      *Type*—Categorical

26. *Who*—Each model of automobile
    *Cases*—Each vehicle model is a case.
    *What*—Vehicle manufacturer, vehicle type, weight, horsepower, and gas mileage for city and highway driving
    *When*—Current
    *Where*—United States
    *Why*—By the Environmental Protection Agency to track fuel economy of vehicles
    *How*—The data are collected from the manufacturer of each model.
    *Variable*—Manufacturer

      *Type*—Categorical
    *Variable*—Vehicle type
      *Type*—Categorical
    *Variable*—Weight
      *Type*—Quantitative
      *Units*—Not specified (pounds)
    *Variable*—Horsepower
      *Type*—Quantitative
      *Units*—Not specified (horsepower)
    *Variable*—Gas mileage, city
      *Type*—Quantitative
      *Units*—Miles per gallon
    *Variable*—Gas mileage, highway
      *Type*—Quantitative
      *Units*—Miles per gallon
    *Concerns*—Do manufacturers' ratings of their own vehicles' gas mileage reflect customer experience?

27. *Who*—41 refrigerator models
    *Cases*—Each of the 41 refrigerator models is a case.
    *What*—Brand, cost, size, type, estimated annual energy cost, overall rating, and repair history
    *When*—2006
    *Where*—United States
    *Why*—To provide information to the readers of *Consumer Reports*
    *How*—Not specified
    *Variable*—Brand
      *Type*—Categorical
    *Variable*—Cost
      *Type*—Quantitative
      *Units*—Not specified (dollars)
    *Variable*—Size
      *Type*—Quantitative
      *Units*—Cubic feet
    *Variable*—Type
      *Type*—Categorical
    *Variable*—Estimated annual energy cost
      *Type*—Quantitative
      *Units*—Not specified (dollars)
    *Variable*—Overall rating
      *Type*—Categorical (ordinal)
    *Variable*—Percent requiring repair in last 5 years
      *Type*—Quantitative
      *Units*—Percent

28. *Who*—32 volunteers
    *Cases*—Each volunteer is an individual.
    *What*—Sex, height, handedness, distance walked, sideline crossed
    *When*—Not specified
    *Where*—Not specified
    *Why*—To see if people naturally walk in circles
    *How*—Collected during a test on a football field
    *Variable*—Sex
      *Type*—Categorical
    *Variable*—Height
      *Type*—Quantitative
      *Units*—Inches?
    *Variable*—Handedness
      *Type*—Categorical
    *Variable*—Distance
      *Type*—Quantitative
      *Units*—Yards
    *Variable*—Sideline crossed
      *Type*—Categorical

29. *Who*—Kentucky Derby races
    *What*—Date, winner, margin, jockey, net proceed to winner, duration, track condition
    *When*—1875 to 2006
    *Where*—Churchill Downs, Louisville, Kentucky

*Why*—To see trends in horse racing?
*How*—Official statistics collected at race
*Variable*—Year
   *Date*—Quantitative
   *Units*—Day and year
*Variable*—Winner
   *Type*—Identifier
*Variable*—Margin
   *Type*—Quantitative
   *Units*—Horse lengths
*Variable*—Jockey
   *Type*—Categorical
*Variable*—Net proceeds to winner
   *Type*—Quantitative
   *Units*—Dollars
*Variable*—Duration
   *Type*—Quantitative
   *Units*—Minutes and seconds
*Variable*—Track condition
   *Type*—Categorical

**30.** *Who*—Indy 500 races
*What*—Year, winner, pole position, average speed, pole winner, pole speed
*When*—1911 to 2006
*Where*—Indianapolis
*Why*—To see trends in auto racing?
*How*—Official statistics at race
*Variable*—Year
   *Type*—Quantitative
   *Units*—Year
*Variable*—Winner
   *Type*—Categorical
*Variable*—Pole position
   *Type*—Categorical or possibly quantitative
   *Units*—Position number
*Variable*—Average speed
   *Type*—Quantitative
   *Units*—Miles per hour
*Variable*—Pole winner
   *Type*—Categorical
*Variable*—Average pole speed
   *Type*—Quantitative
   *Units*—Miles per hour

# CHAPTER 3

**1.** Answers will vary.
**2.** Answers will vary.
**3.** Answers will vary.
**4.** Answers will vary.
**5.** a) Yes; each is categorized in a single genre.
  b) Thriller/Horror
**6.** a) Yes, each movie falls into only one category.
  b) PG-13
**7.** a) Comedy
  b) It is easier to tell from the bar chart; slices of the pie chart are too close in size.
**8.** a) G
  b) No. These displays show only the distribution of movies in these categories. They do not show any changes over time.
**9.** By far, most eighth-grade smokers preferred Marlboro (53.7%), with Newport and Camel far behind. Although over 20 brands were mentioned, nearly 10% of these smokers indicated that they had no usual brand.
**10.** Only 12% of these students said that they did not participate in sports at all. The largest group (43%) were involved just for fun, 18% were varsity athletes, and the rest participated in other organized sports activities.

**11.** 1755 students applied for admission to the magnet schools program. 53% were accepted, 17% were wait-listed, and the other 30% were turned away.
**12.** Of the 1755 students who applied for admission to the magnet schools program, 29.5% were black or Hispanic, 16.6% were Asian, and 53.9% were white.
**13.** a) Yes. We can add because these categories do not overlap. (Each person is assigned only one cause of death.)
  b) $100 - (27.9 + 22.8 + 6.4 + 5.2 + 4.5) = 33.2\%$
  c) Either a bar chart or pie chart with "other" added would be appropriate. A bar chart is shown.

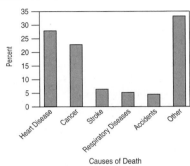

**14.** a) Yes, we can add because each crash was assigned to only one cause category.
  b) $100 - (40 + 5 + 6 + 14 + 6) = 29\%$

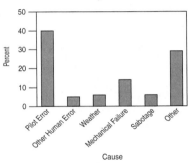

**15.** a) Individuals must have been able to select more than one phenomenon. Because of this, it is not reasonable to add those percents.
  b) No, there may be people who believe in more than one of these or in none. We can't tell from these percentages.
  c) A bar chart displays the percentages well:

**16.** a) *Who*—Illegal gun-trafficking cases
   *What*—Types of violation
   *Where*—United States
   *When*—July 1996 through December 1998
   *Why*—Study by US BATF
   *How*—Survey of 1530 investigations
  b) They total more than 100%. Either a case may be assigned to more than one category, or one or more of these numbers are wrong.

c)

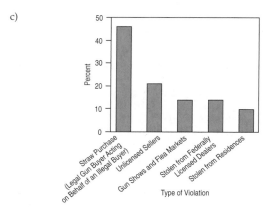

17. The bar chart shows that grounding and collision are the most frequent causes of oil spills. Very few have unknown causes. A pie chart seems appropriate as well.

18. a) There are too many categories to make a meaningful bar chart or pie chart.
    b) One way to reduce the number of categories is to collect many of the countries that didn't win many medals into an "other" category. Here we've put every country with fewer than 6 medals into "Other."

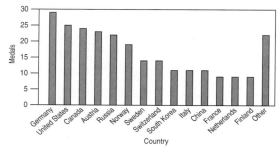

19. There's no title, the percentages total only 92%, and the three-dimensional display distorts the sizes of the regions.

20. a) The bars have false depth, which can be misleading. This is a bar chart, so the bars should have space between them. From a simple design standpoint, running the labels on the bars one way and the vertical axis label the other way is awkward.
    b) The percentages sum to 100%. This is unlikely if the respondents were asked to name three methods each. For example, it would be possible for 80% of respondents to use ice at some time and another 75% to use electric stimulation. This is a case where adding to 100% seems wrong rather than correct.

21. In both the South and West, about 58% of the eighth-grade smokers preferred Marlboro. Newport was the next most popular brand, but was far more popular in the South than in the West, where Camel was cited nearly as often in the two regions. Nearly twice as many smokers in the West as in the South indicated that they had no usual brand (12.9% to 6.7%).

22. Over 76% of guns collected in the buyback program were small-caliber handguns, a type of gun involved in only 20% of the homicides. Most homicides (55%) involved medium-caliber guns, yet these represented fewer than 20% of those collected. While large-caliber and other guns represented only 4% of those collected by the buyback program, such weapons were involved in 25% of the murders.

23. a) The column totals are 100%.
    b) 31.7%
    c) 60%
    d) i. 60%; ii. can't tell; iii. 0%; iv. can't tell

24. a) The row and column margins are not 100%, but the table total is 100%.
    b) PG-13 comedies make up 16.7% of all movies.
    c) 12                    d) 6
    e) Yes. 46.7% + 31.7% = 78.4% of movies are rated PG-13 or R.

25. a) 82.5%       b) 12.9%       c) 11.1%
    d) 13.4%       e) 85.7%

26. a) 59.9%       b) 14.1%       c) 18.3%       d) 10.9%

27. a) 73.9% 4-yr college, 13.4% 2-year college, 1.5% military, 5.2% employment, 6.0% other
    b) 77.2% 4-yr college, 10.5% 2-year college, 1.8% military, 5.3% employment, 5.3% other
    c) Many charts are possible. Here is a side-by-side bar chart.

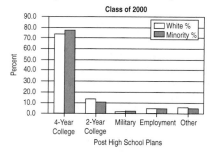

    d) The white and minority students' plans are very similar. The small differences should be interpreted with caution because the total number of minority students is small. There is little evidence of an association between race and plans.

28. a) 45% "Liberal," 47% "Moderate," 8% "Conservative"
    b) 43% "Liberal," 38% "Moderate," 18% "Conservative"
    c)

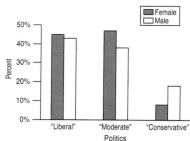

    d) No. Although about the same fraction of males and females classified themselves as politically "Liberal," females were slightly more likely to be "Moderate." A much higher percentage of males (18%) considered themselves to be "Conservative" than did the females (8%).

29. a) 16.6%       b) 11.8%       c) 37.7%       d) 53.0%

30. a)

    b) The overall percentage of females in the class is about 40%, but the percentage of females among "Conservatives" is only about half that.

31. 1755 students applied for admission to the magnet schools program. 53% were accepted, 17% were wait-listed, and the other 30% were turned away. While the overall acceptance rate was

53%, 93.8% of blacks and Hispanics were accepted, compared to only 37.7% of Asians and 35.5% of whites. Overall, 29.5% of applicants were black or Hispanic, but only 6% of those turned away were. Asians accounted for 16.6% of all applicants, but 25.4% of those turned away. Whites were 54% of the applicants and 68.5% of those who were turned away. It appears that the admissions decisions were not independent of the applicant's ethnicity.

**32.** a) Foreign cars are defined as non-American. There are
   $45 + 102 = 147$ non-American cars, or $147/359 = 40.95\%$.
   b) There are 212 American cars, of which 107 or
   $107/212 = 50.47\%$ were owned by students.
   c) There are 195 students, of whom 107 or $107/195 = 54.87\%$
   owned American cars.
   d)

|  | Totals | Percentages |
|---|---|---|
| American | 212 | 59.05% |
| European | 45 | 12.53% |
| Asian | 102 | 28.41% |

(row label: **Origin**)

   e) For students, the origin distribution is

| | Driver | |
|---|---|---|
|  | Student | Percentage |
| American | 107 | 54.87% |
| European | 33 | 16.92% |
| Asian | 55 | 28.21% |
| **Totals** | 195 | 100.00% |

(row label: **Origin**)

   For staff, it is

| | Driver | |
|---|---|---|
|  | Staff | Percentages |
| American | 105 | 64.02% |
| European | 12 | 7.32% |
| Asian | 47 | 28.66% |
| **Totals** | 164 | 100.00% |

(row label: **Origin**)

   f) No, the marginal distributions look slightly different. Bar chars or pie charts could be used to compare.

**33.** a) 9.3%     b) 24.7%     c) 80.8%
   d) No, there appears to be no association between weather and ability to forecast weather. On days it rained, his forecast was correct 79.4% of the time. When there was no rain, his forecast was correct 81.0% of the time.

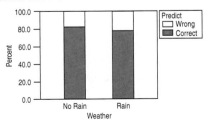

**34.** a) 22.7%     b) 52.9%     c) 39.7%
   d)

   e) It appears that inadequate care leads to more term or post-term births and fewer induced or cesarean births.

**35.** a)

|  | Total | Percent |
|---|---|---|
| Low | 95 | 20.0% |
| Normal | 232 | 48.9% |
| High | 147 | 31.0% |

(row label: **Blood Pressure**)

   b)

|  | Under 30 | Percent |
|---|---|---|
| Low | 27 | 27.6% |
| Normal | 48 | 49.0% |
| High | 23 | 23.5% |

(row label: **Blood Pressure**)

|  | 30–49 | Percent |
|---|---|---|
| Low | 37 | 20.7% |
| Normal | 91 | 50.8% |
| High | 51 | 28.5% |

(row label: **Blood Pressure**)

|  | Over 50 | Percent |
|---|---|---|
| Low | 31 | 15.7% |
| Normal | 93 | 47.2% |
| High | 73 | 37.1% |

(row label: **Blood Pressure**)

   c)

   d) As age increases, the percent of adults with high blood pressure increases. By contrast, the percent of adults with low blood pressure decreases.
   e) No, but it gives an indication that it might. There might be additional reasons that explain the differences in blood pressures.

**36.** a) For each classification of BMI (column), participants' self-reported exercise levels. These are column percentages. The percentages sum to 100% in each column, *not* across each row.

b)

Physical Activity ■ Inactive  ▨ Irregularly active
▨ Regular, not intense  □ Regular, intense

c) No. The graphical displays provide strong evidence that lack of exercise and BMI are not independent. While it may seem logical that lack of exercise causes obesity, the causality could run the other way, or a lurking variable may be the cause of the link between the variables.

**37.** No, there's no evidence that Prozac is effective. The relapse rates were nearly identical: 28.6% among the people treated with Prozac, compared to 27.3% among those who took the placebo.

**38.** Yes, the risk of bone fractures is about twice as high (10%) among the people who were taking SSRIs than among those who were not (5%).

**39.** a) 67.5%   b) 31.0%   c) 94.6%   d) 73.4%

e) No, the percent of Canadian citizens overall speaking French is 31.0%, whereas the percent of citizens of Quebec speaking French is 94.6%. These percentages are very different and should be the same if language knowledge and province of residence were independent.

**40.** a) No. I would suspect horse owners to be more affluent than other pet owners. Horses and their care are much more expensive than the other pets listed and their care.

b) These are column percentages. Each column totals 100%.

c) Yes. Among horse owners, there are relatively fewer households in the lowest income bracket and relatively more households in the highest income bracket. In the middle income ranges, the percentages are about the same for each of the different types of pets.

**41.** The change in attitude in 10 years was fairly small. There was a slight decrease in the response "One works full time, other part time," and there seems to be a similar increase in the response "One works, other works at home."

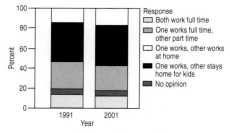

Response
□ Both work full time
▨ One works full time, other part time
□ One works, other works at home
■ One works, other stays home for kids
▨ No opinion

**42.** There seems to be a strong association between having a tattoo and contracting hepatitis C. There appears to be a much greater risk for tattoos done in commercial parlors, less for tattoos done elsewhere, and very little risk for those with no tattoos.

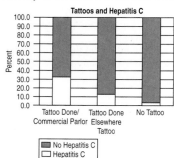

**Tattoos and Hepatitis C**

■ No Hepatitis C
□ Hepatitis C

**43.** a) 4.7%   b) 50.0%.

c) There are about 50% of each sex in each age group, but it ranges from 48.8% female in the youngest group to 54.6% in the oldest. As the age increases, there is a slight increase in the percentage of female drivers.

d) There is a slight association. As the age increases, there is a small increase in the percentage of female drivers.

**44.** a) 34.1%   b) 3.8%

c) In Europe, a greater percentage of toys is sold in toy chains, general merchandise, toy, hobby, and game retailers, as well as department stores. Those distribution channels account for 75% of the sales in Europe. In North America, general merchandise; food, drug, and miscellaneous outlets; and toy chains have the highest percentages, totaling 86% of the toy sales.

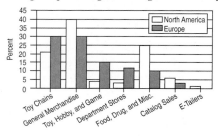

d) The distribution channel varies by region, although general merchandise stores are either the most important or a close second in all regions. Toy chains are especially important in Europe, and toy and hobby shops are significant in Asia. Only in North America are a sizable percentage of toys sold in general food and drug stores. E-tailing of toys was relatively unimportant in the year 1999.

**45.** a) 160 of 1300, or 12.3%

b) Yes. Major surgery: 15.3% vs. minor surgery: 6.7%

c) Large hospital: 13% small hospital: 10%

d) Large hospital: Major 15% vs. minor 5%
Small hospital: Major 20% vs. minor 8%

e) No. Smaller hospitals have a higher rate for both kinds of surgery, even though it's lower "overall."

f) The small hospital has a larger percentage of minor surgeries (83.3%) than the large hospital (20%). Minor surgeries have a lower delay rate, so the small hospital looks better "overall."

**46.** a) Overall, Pack Rats are late 5.6% of the time. Boxes R Us is late 6.0% of the time.

b) Pack Rats have 3% late rate on regular and 16% on overnight. Boxes R Us have 2% late rate on regular and 7% on overnight, so they are better on both.

c) Simpson's paradox

**47.** a) 42.6%

b) A higher percentage of males than females were admitted: Males: 47.2% to females: 30.9%

c) Program 1: Males 61.9%, females 82.4%
Program 2: Males 62.9%, females 68.0%
Program 3: Males 33.7%, females 35.2%
Program 4: Males 5.9%, females 7.0%

d) The comparisons in c) show that males have a *lower* admittance rate in every program, even though the overall rate shows males with a higher rate of admittance. This is an example of Simpson's paradox.

**48.** One possibility

| | Company A | Company B |
|---|---|---|
| **Full-time employees** | 40 local of 100 (40%) | 90 of 200 (45%) |
| **Part-time employees** | 170 of 200 (85%) | 90 of 100 (90%) |
| **Overall** | 210 of 300 (70%) | 180 of 300 (60%) |

# CHAPTER 4

**1.** Answers will vary.   **2.** Answers will vary.
**3.** Answers will vary.   **4.** Answers will vary.
**5.** a) Unimodal (near 0) and skewed. Many seniors will have 0 or 1 speeding tickets. Some may have several, and a few may have more than that.
   b) Probably unimodal and slightly skewed to the right. It is easier to score 15 strokes over the mean than 15 strokes under the mean.
   c) Probably unimodal and symmetric. Weights may be equally likely to be over or under the average.
   d) Probably bimodal. Men's and women's distributions may have different modes. It may also be skewed to the right, since it is possible to have very long hair, but hair length can't be negative.
**6.** a) Bimodal because you have players and parents. It may also be skewed to the right, since parents' ages can be higher than the mean more easily than lower.
   b) Unimodal and skewed to the right. There are probably many students with 0 or 1 sibling and some with 2 or more.
   c) Unimodal and symmetric. It will be unusual to have either very high or low pulse rates.
   d) Uniform. Each face of the die has the same chance of coming up, so the number of times should be about the same for each face.
**7.** a) Bimodal. Looks like two groups. Modes are near 6% and 46%. No real outliers.
   b) Looks like two groups of cereals, a low-sugar and a high-sugar group.
**8.** a) Looks bimodal, one mode near 65 inches, one near 71 inches. Could be two groups that look fairly symmetric within each group.
   b) Probably the mix of men and women in the group.
**9.** a) 78%
   b) Skewed to the right with at least one high outlier. Most of the vineyards are less than 90 acres with a few high ones. The mode is between 0 and 30 acres.
**10.** Skewed to the right, centered at around 30 to 31 minutes, with most observations between 29 to 32 minutes. Skewed to the right because it is easier to run much slower than usual, but hard to run the same amount *faster* than usual.
**11.** a) Because the distribution is skewed to the right, we expect the mean to be larger.
   b) Bimodal and skewed to the right. Center mode near 8 days. Another mode at 1 day (may represent patients who didn't survive). Most of the patients stay between 1 and 15 days. There are some extremely high values above 25 days.
**12.** a) Because the distribution is skewed to the right, we expect the mean to be larger.

b) Skewed to the right. Mode near 1. One outlier very far from rest of data. Spread fairly small. Most of the data less than 5.
**13.** a) 45 points        b) 37 points and 55 (or 55.5) points
**14.** a) 14 points        b) 7 points and 21 (or 21.5) points
**15.** The median and IQR because the distribution is strongly skewed.
**16.** The median and IQR because the distribution is strongly skewed.
**17.** The mean and standard deviation because the distribution is unimodal and symmetric.
**18.** The mean and standard deviation because the distribution is unimodal and symmetric.
**19.** a) The mean is closest to $2.60 because that's the balancing point of the histogram.
   b) The standard deviation is closest to $0.15 since that's a typical distance from the mean. There are no prices as far as $0.50 or $1.00.
**20.** a) The mean is closest to 15 inches because that's the balancing point of the histogram.
   b) The standard deviation is closest to 1 inch because a typical value lies about 1 inch from the mean. There are few points as far as 3 inches from the mean and none as far as 5 inches, so those are too large to be the standard deviation.
**21.** a) About 100 minutes
   b) Yes, only 3 of these movies run that long.
   c) The mean would be higher. The distribution is skewed high.
**22.** a) Unimodal and reasonably symmetric.
   b) About 15%.
   c) $\bar{y} = 288.6$; any estimate between 285 and 290 is a good guess.
   d) The median should be close to the mean because this distribution is symmetric. (In fact, it is 288.35.)
**23.** a) $1001.50      b) 1025, 850, 1200      c) 835, 350
**24.** a) 56.3          b) 40, 36, 68          c) 105, 32
**25.** a) The median will probably be unaffected. The mean will be larger.
   b) The range and standard deviation will increase; the IQR will be unaffected.
**26.** a) The mean will be smaller; the median will not be affected.
   b) The range and standard deviation will be larger; the IQR won't change.
**27.** The publication is using the median; the watchdog group is using the mean, pulled higher by the several very expensive movies in the long right tail.
**28.** The company is using the mean of 7 days, while the union negotiators are using the median of 3 days. There may be high outliers, or a distribution of sick days that is generally skewed to the right.
**29.** a) The standard deviation will be larger for set 2, since the values are more spread out. SD(set 1) = 2.2, SD(set 2) = 3.2.
   b) The standard deviation will be larger for set 2, since 11 and 19 are farther from 15 than are 14 and 16. Other numbers are the same. SD(set 1) = 3.6, SD(set 2) = 4.5.
   c) The standard deviation will be the same for both sets, since the values in the second data set are just the values in the first data set + 80. The spread has not changed. SD(set 1) = 4.2. SD(set 2) = 4.2.
**30.** a) Set 2 will have a larger SD because 6 and 8 in set 2 are farther from 7 than 7 and 7 in set 1. The other numbers are the same. SD(set 1) = 2.1, SD(set 2) = 2.2.
   b) The standard deviation will be the same for both sets, since the values in set 1 are just the values in set 2 + 90. The spread remains the same. SD(set 1) = 36.1, SD(set 2) = 36.1.
   c) Set 2 has a wider range and will have a larger SD. SD(set 1) = 6.0, SD(set 2) = 7.2.
**31.** a) Mean $525, median $450
   b) 2 employees earn more than the mean.
   c) The median because of the outlier.
   d) The IQR will be least sensitive to the outlier of $1200, so it would be the best to report.

**32.** a) Median 66 inches, IQR 5 inches
b) Mean 67.12 inches, SD 3.79 inches
c)

d) The distribution is centered near 67 in., with median 66 in. and mean 67.12 in. The IQR is 15 in., with the middle 50% of heights between 65 and 70 in. The distribution appears to be bimodal, probably due to differences in heights of men and women.

**33.** a)

| Stem | Leaf |
|------|------|
| 25 | |
| 25 | |
| 24 | 5 6 |
| 24 | |
| 23 | 6 8 |
| 23 | 2 3 |
| 22 | 6 7 7 7 8 9 |
| 22 | 1 2 3 4 |

22|1 = $2.21/gallon

b) The distribution of gas prices is unimodal and skewed to the right (upward), centered around $2.27, with most stations charging between $2.26 and $2.33 per gallon. The lowest and highest prices were $2.21 and $2.46.
c) There are two high prices separated from the other gas stations by a gap.

**34.** a)

| Stem | Leaf |
|------|------|
| 8 | 0 0 0 0 0 1 0 2 2 |
| 7 | 9 9 8 8 |
| 7 | 4 3 4 0 |
| 6 | |
| 6 | |
| 5 | 4 |
| 5 | |
| 4 | |
| 4 | 5 8 |

4|5 = 45 games

b) The distribution of games played by Gretzky is skewed to the left.
c) Typically, Gretzky played about 80 games per season. The numbers of games played are tightly clustered in the upper 70s and low 80s.
d) Two seasons are low outliers, when Gretzky played fewer than 50 games. He might have been injured.

**35.** a) The histogram of height is most nearly symmetric and shows no outliers. That makes it the best candidate for summarizing with a mean.
b) The histogram of sip size shows a high outlier. The standard deviation is sensitive to outliers, so we'd prefer to use the IQR for this one.

**36.** The histogram shows some low outliers (or possibly small modes). These are probably poor estimates and will pull the mean down. The median is likely to give a better estimate. Unrealistically small values like 56" were probably meant to be 5'6".

**37.** a) Since these data are strongly skewed to the right, the median and IQR are the best statistics to report.
b) The mean will be larger than the median because the data are skewed to the right.
c) The median is 4 million. The IQR is 4.5 million (Q3 = 6 million, Q1 = 1.5 million).

d) The distribution of populations of the states and Washington, DC, is unimodal and skewed to the right. The median population is 4 million. One state is an outlier, with a population of 34 million.

**38.** a) The distribution is highly skewed to the left.
b) 79 games.
c) The mean should be lower. There are two seasons when Gretzky played an unusually low number of games. Those will pull the mean down.

**39.** Skewed to the right, mode in low 30s. Three low outliers, then a gap from 9 to 22.

**40.** a)

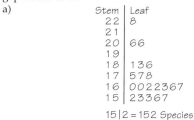

| Stem | Leaf |
|------|------|
| 22 | 8 |
| 21 | |
| 20 | 6 6 |
| 19 | |
| 18 | 1 3 6 |
| 17 | 5 7 8 |
| 16 | 0 0 2 2 3 6 7 |
| 15 | 2 3 3 6 7 |

15|2 = 152 Species

b) Skewed to the right; several high outliers. Center near 163.

**41.** a)

b) Slightly skewed to the right. Unimodal, mode near 2. Possibly a second mode near 5. No outliers.

**42.** This distribution is nearly uniform. Values range from 65 to 155 horsepower. The center is near 105.

| Stem | Leaf |
|------|------|
| 15 | 0 5 |
| 14 | 2 |
| 13 | 0 3 5 8 |
| 12 | 0 5 5 9 |
| 11 | 0 0 5 5 5 |
| 10 | 3 5 9 |
| 9 | 0 0 5 7 7 |
| 8 | 0 0 5 8 |
| 7 | 0 1 1 5 8 |
| 6 | 5 5 8 8 9 |

6|5 = 65 horsepower

**43.** a) This is not a histogram. The horizontal axis should split the number of home runs hit in each year into bins. The vertical axis should show the number of years in each bin.
b)

**44.** a) This is not a histogram. The horizontal axis should split the number of counts from each site into bins. The vertical axis should show the number of sites in each bin.

b)

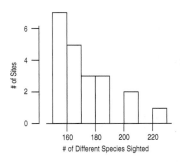

**45.** Skewed to the right, possibly bimodal with one fairly symmetric group near 4.4, another at 5.6. Two outliers in middle seem not to belong to either group.

```
Stem │ Leaf
  57 │ 8
  56 │ 2 7
  55 │ 1
  54 │
  53 │
  52 │ 9
  51 │
  50 │ 8
  49 │
  48 │ 2
  47 │ 3
  46 │ 0 3 4
  45 │ 2 6 7
  44 │ 0 1 5
  43 │ 0 1 9 9
  42 │ 6 6 9
  41 │ 2 2

  41│2 = 4.12 pH
```

**46.** Unimodal with center around 20%, but with a cluster of countries reporting over 35%.

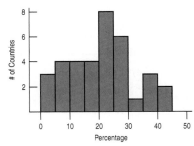

**47.** Histogram bins are too wide to be useful.
**48.** a) Histogram bins are too narrow to be useful.
  b) Skewed to the left, mode near 170, several outliers below 100. Fairly tightly clustered except for outliers.
**49.** Neither appropriate nor useful. Zip codes are categorical data, not quantitative. But they do contain *some* information. The leading digit gives a rough East-to-West placement in the United States. So we see that they have almost no customers in the Northeast, but a bar chart by leading digit would be more appropriate.
**50.** a) The codes are integers, and the width of a bin is less than 1. But the question doesn't make sense, since the codes are categorical, not quantitative.
  b) Question doesn't make sense, since the display is inappropriate.
  c) Display is not appropriate. Data are categorical. He should use a bar chart.
**51.** a) Median 239, IQR 9, Mean 237.6, SD 5.7
  b) Because it's skewed to the left, probably better to report Median and IQR.
  c) Skewed to the left; may be bimodal. The center is around 239. The middle 50% of states scored between 233 and 242.

Alabama, Mississippi, and New Mexico scores were much lower than other states' scores.

**52.** a)

  b) Mean 3.06%, SD 3.32%
  c) The distribution is unimodal and skewed right; South Dakota increased 11.9%. The mean percent increase was 3.06%, with a standard deviation of 3.32%.
**53.** In the year 2004, per capita gasoline use by state in the United States averaged around 500 gallons per person (mean 488.7, median 500.5). States varied in per capita consumption, with a standard deviation of 68.7 gallons. The only outlier is New York. The IQR of 96.9 gallons shows that 50% of the states had per capita consumption of between 447.5 and 544.4 gallons. The data appear to be bimodal, so the median and IQR are better choices of summary statistics.

**54.** a) Here is a histogram of the distribution:

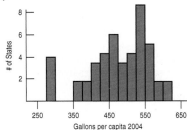

  b) Mean 3.07%, median 2.85%. Mean is higher because of the outlier.
  c) The median, because of the outlier.
  d) IQR 1.1%, SD 1.37%.
  e) The standard deviation is also influenced by the outlier. The better measure of spread is the IQR.
  f) Mean and median would be 1.2% lower. SD and IQR would not change.
  g) Median and IQR won't change very much. The middle value and the two quartiles will shift at most one data value. The mean and SD will decrease.
  h) The distribution of growth rates for the cities is unimodal and symmetric except for the one outlier, Las Vegas, at 7.5%. The median growth rate for these cities is 2.85%. The middle 50% of the cities had growth rates between 2.25% and 3.35%, for an interquartile range of 1.1%. The median and IQR are the best statistics to report when a distribution has outliers, but if the outlier were omitted, the average growth rate would be 2.84%, with a standard deviation of 0.91%.

**55.** a) Although numeric codes have been assigned to the different titles, these data are categorical, not quantitative. The mean of 54.41 is meaningless.
  b) The typical reasons are skewness and/or outliers.
  c) No. Here the numbers are just codes. Most of the people probably had titles of Mr. or Mrs., making the "median" 1, but these summary statistics are meaningless.

**56.** a) Neither. These are not quantitative data.
  b) Neither. These are not quantitative data.
  c) Not very much, since zip codes are categorical. However, there is *some* information in the first digit of zip codes. They indicate a general East (0–1) to West (8–9) direction. So, the distribution shows that a large portion of their sales occurs in the West and another in the 32000 area. But a bar chart of the first digits might be a better display of this.

# CHAPTER 5

**1.** Answers will vary.　　**2.** Answers will vary.
**3.** Answers will vary.　　**4.** Answers will vary.
**5.** a) Prices appear to be both higher on average and more variable in Baltimore than in the other three cities. Prices in Chicago may be slightly higher than in Dallas and Denver, but the difference is very small.
  b) There are outliers on the low end in Baltimore and Chicago and one high outlier in Dallas, but these do not affect the overall conclusions reached in part a).

**6.** a) Coffee, on average is the most expensive.
  b) On average, newspapers are more expensive than public transportation rides, but there are cities in which a ride on public transportation costs more than a newspaper in other cities.
  c) There is one outlying city in each of the three boxplots, but removing this outlier will not affect the conclusions of part a) or b).

**7.** a) 1611 yd
  b) Between 5585.75 yd and 6131 yd
  c) Mean and SD, since this is roughly unimodal and symmetric.
  d) The distribution is fairly symmetric and unimodal. Because of the symmetry, the mean of 5892.91 yd and median of 5928 yd are nearly the same, showing a center near 5900 yd. The standard deviation of the lengths is 386.59 yd. The range is 1611 yd from a minimum 5185 yd to a maximum 6796 yd.

**8.** a) The range is 22.54 seconds.
  b) The central 50% of times are between 192.238 and 200.625 seconds.
  c) We'd prefer the median and IQR.
  d) The distribution of combined times is unimodal and skewed to the right. (Possibly, there's a second mode; that's a matter of opinion.) The median time is 193.27 seconds. The times are not spread out very much; half the times fall between 192.238 and 200.625 seconds, and the winning time, at 189.35 seconds, is less than 3 seconds faster.

**9.** a) Essentially symmetric, very slightly skewed to the right with two high outliers at 36 and 48. Most victims are between the ages of 16 and 24.
  b) The slight increase between ages 22 and 24 is apparent in the histogram but not in the boxplot. It may be a second mode.
  c) The median would be the most appropriate measure of center because of the slight skew and the extreme outliers.
  d) The IQR would be the most appropriate measure of spread because of the slight skew and the extreme outliers.

**10.** a) Both plots show skewness to the high end.
  b) The histogram shows a bimodal distribution and skewness to the high end. Boxplots can't show multiple modes clearly.
  c) We'd prefer the median to the mean because of the skewness and possible outliers.
  d) We'd prefer the IQR to the standard deviation because of the skewness and possible outliers.

**11.** a) About 18%　b) About 59%　　c) Bimodal
  d) Some cereals are very sugary; others are healthier low-sugar brands.

**12.** a) Unimodal, symmetric　b) 2.5　　c) 3

**13.** a) Yes
  b) Although the ranges appear to be comparable for both groups (about 28%), the IQR is larger for the adult cereals, indicating that there's more variability in the sugar content of the middle 50% of adult cereals.

**14.** a) Biceps transfer
  b) No, one deltoid transfer was as good as at least 25% of the biceps transfers.
  c) Although the range in strength is approximately 2 units for both methods, the IQR is much smaller for the deltoid transfers, indicating more consistent results.

**15.** a)

  b) NE/MW states are tightly clustered near 5%. S/W states are bimodal with modes near 14 and 22. The S/W states have an outlier as well. Around all the modes, the distributions are fairly symmetric.

**16.** a) The distribution is strongly skewed to the right, so use the median and IQR.
  b) The IQR is 50, so the upper fence is the upper quartile + 1.5 IQRs; that is, 78 + 75 = 153. There appear to be 4 to 5 parks that should be considered as outliers with more than 153 camp sites.
  c)

  d) The distribution is unimodal with a strong skew to the right. There are several outliers past the 1.5 × IQR upper fence of 153 camp sites. The median number of camp sites is 43.5 sites. The mean is 62.8 sites. The mean is larger than the median because it has been influenced by the strong skew and the outliers.

**17.** a) They should be put on the same scale, from 0 to 20 days.
  b) Men have a mode at 1 day and then taper off from there. Women have a mode near 5 days, with a sharp drop afterward.
  c) A possible reason is childbirth.

**18.** a) Both are unimodal, skewed to the low end.
  b) A higher proportion of blacks die between 25 and 74 years old. A higher proportion of whites die at ages older than 75.
  c) Interval widths are not constant. Most bars are for 10-year intervals, but the first bars are only for ages 0–4, a 5-year span, and the last bars are for 85 and over.

**19. a)** Both girls have a median score of about 17 points per game, but Scyrine is much more consistent. Her IQR is about 2 points, while Alexandra's is over 10.

**b)** If the coach wants a consistent performer, she should take Scyrine. She'll almost certainly deliver somewhere between 15 and 20 points. But if she wants to take a chance and needs a "big game," she should take Alexandra. Alex scores over 24 points about a quarter of the time. (On the other hand, she scores under 11 points as often.)

**20. a)** Gas prices have been increasing, on average, over the 3-year period, and the spread has been increasing as well. The prices in 2002 were skewed to the left, with several low outliers. Since then, the distribution has been increasingly skewed to the right. There is a high outlier in 2004.

**b)** 2004 shows both the greatest range and the biggest IQR, so the prices varied a lot.

**21.** Women appear to marry about 3 years younger than men, but the two distributions are very similar in shape and spread.

**22.** Both fuel economy and its spread decrease from 4 to 6 to 8 cylinders (not enough data to compare 5-cylinder cars). The lower 75% of MPGs for the 8-cylinder cars corresponds roughly to the bottom 25% of MPGs for the 6-cylinder cars. All of the 8-cylinder cars get less mileage than all of the 4-cylinder cars.

**23.** (*Note:* Numerical details may vary.) In general, fuel economy is higher in cars than in either SUVs or vans. There are numerous outliers on both ends for cars and a few high outliers for SUVs. The top 50% of cars gets higher fuel economy than 75% of SUVs and nearly all vans. On average, SUVs and vans get about the same fuel economy, although the distribution for vans shows less spread. The range for vans is about 40 mpg, while for SUVs it is nearly 30 mpg.

**24.** (*Note:* Numerical details may vary.) On average, 2WD cars get better fuel economy that 4WD vehicles. The top 50% of 2WD cars have higher fuel economy than more than 3/4 of 4WD cars. Nearly 25% of 2WD cars get better fuel economy than any 4WD cars. There is more variation among 2WD cars than 4WD cars. The IQR for 2WD cars is about 6 mpg, while for 4WD cars it is only about 3 or 4 mpg.

**25. a)** Seneca      **b)** Seneca        **c)** Keuka

**d)** The Cayuga and Seneca wines have about the same average price; the boxplots show similar medians and similar IQRs, even though Seneca's range is larger. Keuka has consistently higher prices except for one low outlier, and a more consistent pricing as shown by the smaller IQR. Distributions for all three appear to be roughly symmetric around their centers.

**26. a)** April      **b)** February        **c)** August

**d)** The median ozone level in June is slightly higher than in January, but June's readings are much more consistent. June does show two outliers, one low and one high.

**e)** Strong seasonal pattern with low consistent ozone concentrations in later summer/early fall and high variable concentrations in early spring. The medians follow a cyclic pattern, rising from January to April, then falling to October and rising again from October to December.

**27. a)** Because the mean is larger than the median, we might suppose that the distribution is right skewed. An outlier or outliers might explain why the SD is so much larger than the IQR.

**b)** The differences in the statistics could be caused by skewness or by outliers on the high end.

**c)** The distribution of times in the men's 100-m swim in Sydney is unimodal, with most times between 48 and 53 seconds. There is a slight skew to the right, with three times between 58 and 63 and one very extreme outlier at about 113 seconds.

**28.** Since the mean or average is the balance point for the data, having 223 areas below the average and only 99 above the average indicates that the distribution of unemployment rates must be skewed to the right.

**29. a)** Class 3      **b)** Class 3

**c)** Class 3 because it is skewed. Median would be higher than the mean because it is skewed to the left.

**d)** Class 1      **e)** Class 1

**30. a)** Class 3. Highest median and almost 75% of class 3 scored at or above the medians of 1 and 2.

**b)** Fairly symmetric (except class 3). Quite spread out, ranging from about 30 to near 100.

**c)** The class A is 1, class B is 2, and class C is 3.

**31. a)** Probably slightly left skewed. The mean is slightly below the median, and the 25th percentile is farther from the median than the 75th percentile.

**b)** No, all data are within the fences.

**c)**

**d)** The 48 universities graduate, on average, about 68% of freshmen "on time," with percents ranging from 43% to 87%. The middle 50% of these universities graduate between 59% and 75% of their freshmen in 4 years.

**32. a)** Skewed to the right, since the mean is much larger than the median and the upper quartile is farther from the median than the lower quartile.

**b)** The IQR is about 36, so fences are below 0 and at 109. Since the range is 244 and the minimum is 6, the maximum is 250, which is certainly an outlier. Without knowing the data points, we are not sure of other outliers, but the standard deviation of 47.8 makes us suspect there are others.

**c)** We don't know if there are other outliers above the upper fence, but the boxplot may look something like this:

**d)** The vineyards range in size from 6 to 250 acres. The median size of the 36 vineyards is 33.5 acres, so half are larger and half are smaller. The middle 50% of the vineyards have sizes between 18.5 and 55 acres. The distribution of sizes is skewed to the right, with at least one outlier.

**33. a)** *Who:* Student volunteers
*What:* Memory test
*Where, when:* Not specified
*How:* Students took memory test 2 hours after drinking caffeine-free, half-dose caffeine, or high-caffeine soda.
*Why:* To see if caffeine makes you more alert and aids memory retention.

**b)** Drink: categorical; Test score: quantitative.

c)

d) The participants scored about the same with no caffeine and low caffeine. The medians for both were 21 points, with slightly more variation for the low-caffeine group. The high-caffeine group generally scored lower than the other two groups on all measures of the 5-number summary: min, lower quartile, median, upper quartile, and max.

34. a)

b) Median score by females, at 625 points, is 25 points higher than that by males. Female mean is higher by 12. The middle 50% of females scored between 530 and 680, while the middle 50% of males scored between 515 and 650. The males did have a larger range, from 310 to 800, the highest score for both genders. Both distributions are slightly skewed to the left.

35. a) About 36 mph
    b) $Q_1$ about 35 mph and $Q_3$ about 37 mph
    c) The range appears to be about 7 mph, from about 31 to 38 mph. The IQR is about 2 mph.
    d) We can't know exactly, but the boxplot may look something like this:

e) The median winning speed has been about 36 mph, with a max of about 38 and a min of about 31 mph. Half have run between about 35 and 37 mph, for an IQR of 2 mph.

36. Distribution is essentially symmetric, with median near 225. The IQR is about 75 points. Extremes are about 80 and 380.

37. a) Boys  b) Boys  c) Girls
    d) The boys appeared to have more skew, as their scores were less symmetric between quartiles. The girls' quartiles are the same distance from the median, although the left tail stretches a bit farther to the left.
    e) Girls. Their median and upper quartiles are larger. The lower quartile is slightly lower, but close.
    f) $[14(4.2) + 11(4.6)]/25 = 4.38$

38. a) The median and IQR, because the means are much larger than the median and the SDs are much larger than the IQR, indicating either right skewness and/or outliers.
    b) Since the median rainfall for seeded clouds is more than 4 time that for unseeded clouds, it appears that seeding clouds may be effective.

39. a) Boxplots are appropriate as well.

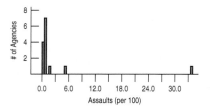

b) The distributions are unimodal but each has outliers. Rates of assaults tend to be slightly higher than those of injuries.
c) The Bureau for Indian Affairs is a high outlier in both assaults and injuries. The National Park Service is also an outlier, but not as extreme.

40.

Smoker's distribution has a lower median and is less spread out. There is an outlier in the smoker's group at 350. (Other answers are possible, too. Could possibly say that ex-smoker's distribution is more symmetric if histogram or stem-and-leaf provided.)

**41.**

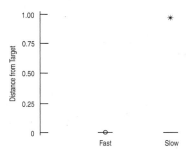

There appears to be an outlier! This point should be investigated. We'll proceed by redoing the plots with the outlier omitted:

It appears that slow speed provides much greater accuracy. But the outlier should be investigated. It is possible that slow speed can induce an infrequent very large distance.

**42.** No, boxplots are for quantitative data, and these are categorical, although coded as numbers. The numbers used for hair color and eye color are arbitrary, so the boxplot and any accompanying statistics for eye color make no sense.

**43.** a)

b) Mileage distribution for U.S. models is lower and less spread out. The median for U.S. models is around 18, compared to 28 for the others. The upper quartile of U.S. models is lower than the first quartile of others. There are two outliers in the U.S. Models distribution. (Other answers possible.)

**44.** a) (Other displays possible.)

b) The National League scores slightly fewer runs in general, but the distribution is more spread out. The median for both leagues is about 9.5, but the American League's is slightly higher. There is a high outlier in the National League at about 14 runs.

c) Yes, it looks like an outlier. It is nominated by the boxplot rule and is well separated from all the other parks.

**45.** a) Day 16 (but any estimate near 20 is okay).

b) Day 65 (but anything around 60 is okay).

c) Around day 50.

**46.** a)

b)

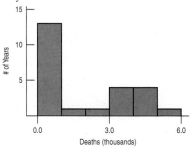

c) The histogram shows a bimodal distribution. The timeplot shows that drunk-driving deaths fell between 1980 and 1995, but after 1995, they have remained at about the same level.

**47.**

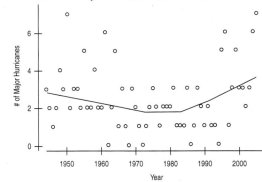

It appears that there was a lull in the number of hurricanes during the period from the mid-1960s to about 1990 and the number has increased fairly rapidly since. The number is now at least as high as it was at the beginning of the time period.

**48.** a)

b)

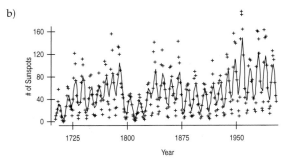

There appears to be a strong cycle of sunspot occurrence with a period of about 10 to 11 years.

49. a) Most of the data are found in the far left of this histogram. The distribution is very skewed to the right.
   b) Re-expressing the data by, for example, logs or square roots might help make the distribution more nearly symmetric.
50. a) The data are extremely skewed to the right. That makes it difficult to determine a center. Our perception of spread will be affected by the very long tail.
   b) Re-expressing the data by, for example, logs or square roots might help make the distribution more nearly symmetric.
51. a) The logarithm makes the histogram more symmetric. It is easy to see that the center is around 3.5 in log assets.
   b) That has a value of around 2,500 million dollars.
   c) That has a value of around 1,000 million dollars.
52. a) The numbers are manageable (each acre-foot is about 320,000 gallons).

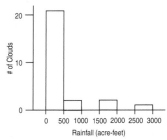

   b) The distribution is very skewed to the right.
   c)

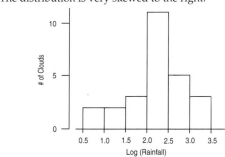

   d) $\log_{10}$ is the exponent of 10, which results in the original value. For example, $10^3 = 1000$, so $\log_{10}$ of 1000 is 3.
53. a) Fusion time and group.
   b) Fusion time is quantitative (units = seconds). Group is categorical.
   c) Both distributions are skewed to the right with high outliers. The boxplot indicates that visual information may reduce fusion time. The median for the Verbal/Visual group seems to be about the same as the lower quartile of the No/Verbal group.
54. The analysis would probably be improved by using the log-transformed data. The distributions are more symmetric, and it's easier to compare the groups. The outliers are eliminated.

# CHAPTER 6

1. a) 72 oz., 40 oz.   b) 4.5 lb, 2.5 lb
2. a) 264 sec, 138 sec   b) 240 sec, 138 sec
3. a) Skewed to the right; mean is higher than median.
   b) $350 and $950.
   c) Minimum $350. Mean $750. Median $550. Range $1200. IQR $600. Q1 $400. SD $400.
   d) Minimum $330. Mean $770. Median $550. Range $1320. IQR $660. Q1 $385. SD $440.
4. a) Range 3.30 pounds. IQR 0.95 pounds.
   b) Slightly skewed to the left because the mean is lower than the median and the first quartile is farther from the median than the third quartile.
   c) Mean 96 oz. SD 10.4 oz. Q1 89.6 oz. Q3 104.8 oz. Median 99.2 oz. IQR 15.2 oz. Range 52.8 oz.
   d) Mean 126 oz. SD 10.4 oz. Q1 119.6 oz. Q3 134.8 oz. Median 129.2 oz. IQR 15.2 oz. Range 52.8 oz.
   e) Median, IQR.
5. Lowest score = 910. Mean = 1230. SD = 120. Q3 = 1350. Median = 1270. IQR = 240.
6. Maximum temperature = 51.8°F. Range = 59.4°F. Mean = 33.8°F. SD = 12.6°F Median = 35.6°F. IQR = 28.8°F.
7. Your score was 2.2 standard deviations higher than the mean score in the class.
8. The boy's height is 1.88 standard deviations below the mean height of children his age.
9. $z = 1$   10. $z = 1.5$
11. 65   12. 140 or above
13. In January, a high of 55 is not quite 2 standard deviations above the mean, whereas in July a high of 55 is more than 2 standard deviations lower than the mean. So it's less likely to happen in July.
14. In French she scored 1.25 standard deviations higher than the mean. On the math exam she scored 1.50 standard deviations higher than the mean, so she did "better" on the math exam.
15. The z-scores, which account for the difference in the distributions of the two tests, are 1.5 and 0 for Derrick and 0.5 and 2 for Julie. Derrick's total is 1.5, which is less than Julie's 2.5.
16. The z-scores, which account for the difference in the distributions of the two tests, are 0 and 1 for Reginald, for a total of 1.0. For Sara, they are 2.0 and −0.33, for a total of 1.67. While her raw total is lower, her z-score total is higher.
17. a) Megan   b) Anna
18. a) To know something about their consistency and the chances they will last a certain amount of time.
   b) RockReady. Mean is larger and SD smaller.
   c) 16 hours is 2.5 SD higher than Dura Tunes's mean, and 2.67 SD higher than RockReady's mean. So, although neither battery has much chance of lasting 16 hours, Dura Tunes's chance is greater.
19. a) About 1.81 standard deviations below the mean
   b) 1000 ($z = 1.81$) is more unusual than 1250 ($z = 1.17$).
20. a) The z-score for 20 mph is $z = (20 - 23.84)/3.56 = -1.08$. It is 1.08 SD below the mean speed.
   b) The z-score for 34 is $z = (34 - 23.84)/3.56 = 2.85$. For 10 mph, it's $z = (10 - 23.84)/3.56 = -3.89$. So, 10 mph is more unusual.
21. a) Mean = $1152 - 1000 = 152$ pounds; SD is unchanged at 84 pounds.
   b) Mean = $0.40(1152) = $460.80$; SD = $0.40(84) = $33.60$.
22. a) The new mean is 3.84 mph. The standard deviation is unchanged.
   b) The new mean is $23.84(1.609) = 38.359$ kph. (The speed limit is 32.18 kph). The new standard deviation is 5.728 kph.

**23.** Min $= 0.40(980) - 20 = \$372$;
median $= 0.40(1140) - 20 = \$436$;
SD $= 0.40(84) = \$33.60$; IQR $= 0.40(102) = \$40.80$.

**24.** Mean $= 100 + 10(8) = \$180$; SD $= 10(2.4) = \$24$;
max $= 100 + 10(13) = \$230$; IQR $= 10(3.2) = \$32$

**25.** College professors can have between 0 and maybe 40 (or possibly 50) years' experience. A standard deviation of 1/2 year is impossible, because many professors would be 10 or 20 SDs away from the mean, whatever it is. An SD of 16 years would mean that 2 SDs on either side of the mean is plus or minus 32, for a range of 64 years. That's too high. So, the SD must be 6 years.

**26.** Probably 2000, but it could be 20,000 if they played to a few really large audiences (like sold-out stadiums).

**27.** a)

b) 18.6 to 31.0 mpg        c) 16%
d) 13.5%        e) less than 12.4 mpg

**28.** a)

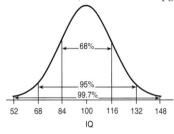

b) 68 to 132 IQ points        c) 16%
d) 13.5%        e) 2.5%

**29.** Any weight more than 2 standard deviations below the mean, or less than $1152 - 2(84) = 984$ pounds, is unusually low. We expect to see a steer below $1152 - 3(84) = 900$ pounds only rarely.

**30.** Any IQ more than 2 standard deviations above the mean, or $100 + 2(16) = 132$ points, is unusually high. We expect to find someone with an IQ over $100 + 3(16) = 148$ only rarely.

**31.** a) 16%        b) 3.8%
c) Because the Normal model doesn't fit well.
d) Distribution is skewed to the right.

**32.** a)

b) Chances are 84% that the strength is at least 750 pounds. That means 16% of the time it will be below. Seems like much too high a percentage.
c) 97.5%
d) In the extreme case, I would want a very small probability of failure, maybe less than 1 out of a million. For this I'd need to be sure that 800 was 6 SDs higher than my limit. So I might not use the rivets if I needed them to have shear strength more than 500 pounds.

**33.** a)

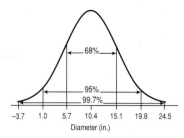

b) Between 1.0 and 19.8 inches        c) 2.5%
d) 34%        e) 16%

**34.** The histogram is unimodal and roughly symmetric, and the normal probability plot looks quite straight, so a normal model is appropriate.

**35.** Since the histogram is not unimodal and symmetric, it is not wise to have faith in numbers from the Normal model.

**36.** a) We know that 95% of the observations for a Normal model fall within 2 SDs of the mean. That corresponds to $23.84 - 2(3.56) = 16.72$ mph and $23.84 + 2(3.56) = 30.96$ mph.
b) The actual 97.5% and 2.5% tiles are 30.976 and 16.638, respectively. These are very close to the predicted values of 30.96 and 16.72 mph. The histogram is roughly unimodal and symmetric. It is very slightly right skewed and there is one outlier, but the Normal probability plot is quite straight. We should not be surprised that the approximation is good.

**37.** a) 2.5%
b) 2.5% of the receivers should gain less than $-333$ yards, but that's impossible, so the model doesn't fit well.
c) Data are strongly skewed to the right, not symmetric.

**38.** a) Median because the distribution is so skewed to the left.
b) IQR. Distribution is skewed.
c) 68%        d) More than 75%
e) Normal model is not appropriate. Data are strongly skewed.

**39.** a) 6.68%        b) 98.78%        c) 71.63%        d) 61.71%

**40.** a) 97.98%        b) 37.07%        c) 7.91%        d) 79.95%

**41.** a) 0.842        b) $-0.675$        c) $-1.881$        d) $-1.645$ to 1.645

**42.** a) $-1.175$        b) 0.524        c) 1.476        d) $-0.675$ to 0.675

**43.** a) 12.2%        b) 71.6%        c) 23.3%

**44.** a) 89.4%        b) 26.6%        c) 20.4%

**45.** a) 1259.7 lb        b) 1081.3 lb        c) 1108 lb to 1196 lb

**46.** a) 126.3        b) 91.6        c) 79.5 to 120.5

**47.** a) 1130.7 lb        b) 1347.4 lb        c) 113.3 lb

**48.** a) 83.4        b) 132.9        c) 21.6

**49.** a) 79.55        b) 18.50        c) 95.79        d) $-2.77$

**50.** a) 129.77        b) 0.05        c) 10.64        d) 615.77

**51.** a)

b) 30.85%        c) 17.00%        d) 32 points  e) 212.9 points

**52.** a) No, that's more than 3 SDs above the mean.
b) 21.2%        c) 67.3%
d) Quartiles at 30,314 and 33,686 miles, so 3372 miles
e) 27,623 miles

**53.** a) 11.1%        b) (35.9, 40.5) inches        c) 40.5 inches

**54.** a) Based on the Normal model, we expect 95% to be between 96.8 and 99.6°F
b) 28.4%        c) 97.6°F

**55.** The average Dutch man has a *z*-score of 2.31 in Athens. About 1% of Greek men are this tall or taller.

**56.** The man's *z*-score is 2.66; the woman's is 2.88, so she has the more extraordinarily large mouth. Only about 0.4% of men and about 0.2% of women have bigger mouths.

**57.** Mean 12.1 months, SD 1.3 months

**58.** Mean 3 lb, SD 1.3 lb

**59.** a) 5.3 grams    b) 6.4 grams
   c) Younger because SD is smaller.
   d) Mean 62.7 grams, SD 6.2 grams

**60.** a) 3.26 grams   b) 75.70 grams    c) 2.86 grams
   d) The new tomatoes are more consistent in their weights.

# PART I REVIEW

**1.** a)

   b) Median 49 cents, IQR 6 cents
   c) The distribution is unimodal and left skewed. The center is near 50 cents; values range from 42 cents to 53 cents.

**2.** a) It is (rounded to 1 decimal place), but there's no reason it should be unless the number of women receiving each type of care was roughly the same.
   b) Yes, but they do not prove that adequate prenatal care is important for pregnant women. The mortality rate is quite a bit lower for women with adequate care than for other women, but there may be a lurking variable.
   c) Intensive care is given for emergency conditions. The data do *not* suggest that the care is the *cause* of the higher mortality.

**3.** a) If enough sopranos have a height of 65 inches, this can happen.
   b) The distribution of heights for each voice part is roughly symmetric. The basses are slightly taller than the tenors. The sopranos and altos have about the same median height. Heights of basses and sopranos are more consistent than those of altos and tenors.

**4.** With only 3 cases, probably no display is appropriate.

**5.** a) It means their heights are also more variable.
   b) The *z*-score for women to qualify is 2.40, compared with 1.75 for men, so it is harder for women to qualify.

**6.** a) The distribution is unimodal and skewed to the right. The mode is near 100, and values range from 95 to 140.
   b) The mean will be larger than the median, since the distribution is right skewed.
   c) Create a boxplot with quartiles at 97 and 105.5, and median at 100. The IQR is 8.5, so the upper fence is at $(1.5 \times 8.5) + 105.5 = 118.25$. There are several outliers to the right. There are no outliers to the left because the minimum at 95 lies well within the left fence at $97 - (1.5 \times 8.5) = 84.25$.
   d) No, the Normal model is not appropriate for these data. They are unimodal but not symmetric.

**7.** a) *Who*—People who live near State University
   *What*—Age, attended college? Favorable opinion of State?
   *When*—Not stated
   *Where*—Region around State U.
   *Why*—To report to the university's directors
   *How*—Sampled and phoned 850 local residents
   b) Age—Quantitative (years); attended college?—categorical; favorable opinion?—categorical.

   c) The fact that the respondents know they are being interviewed by the university's staff may influence answers.

**8.** a)

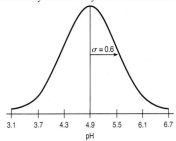

   b) 3.3%                    c) 6.7%
   d) pH 4.40          e) pH 5.89
   f) Quartiles at 4.50 and 5.30, so IQR is 0.80.

**9.** a) These are categorical data, so mean and standard deviation are meaningless.
   b) Not appropriate. Even if it fits well, the Normal model is meaningless for categorical data.

**10.** a) Stream name—categorical; substrate—categorical; pH—quantitative; temperature—quantitative (°C); BCI—quantitative (units missing).
   b) Bar chart or pie chart

**11.** a)

   b) The scores on Friday were higher by about 5 points. This is a drop of more than 10% off the average score and shows that students fared worse on Monday after preparing for the test on Friday. The spreads are about the same, but the scores on Monday are a bit skewed to the right.
   c)

   d) The changes (Friday–Monday) are unimodal and centered near 4 points, with a spread of about 5 (SD). They are fairly symmetric, but slightly skewed to the right. Only 3 students did better on Monday (had a negative difference).

**12.** No, you can't add these, since the groups are not disjoint.

**13.** a) Categorical
   b) Go fish. All you need to do is match the denomination. The denominations are not ordered. (Answers will vary.)
   c) Gin rummy. All cards are worth their value in points (face cards are 10 points). (Answers will vary.)

**14. a)**

(Bar chart: % of Accidents vs Miles from Home. Categories: less than 1, 1 to 5, 6 to 10, 11 to 15, 16 to 20, over 20)

b) We are given no information about how many miles are driven in each of these categories, so we have no idea how many accidents to *expect*. We also have no information about how many accidents were involved in compiling the data.

**15. a)** Annual mortality rate for males (quantitative) in deaths per 100,000 and water hardness (quantitative) in parts per million.

b) Calcium is skewed right, possibly bimodal. There looks to be a mode down near 12 ppm that is the center of a fairly tight symmetric distribution and another mode near 62.5 ppm that is the center of a much more spread out, symmetric (almost uniform) distribution. Mortality, however, appears unimodal and symmetric with the mode near 1500 deaths per 100,000.

**16. a)** Overall mean is $(34 \times 1631.59 + 27 \times 1388.85)/(34 + 27) = 1524.15$ deaths per 100,000.

b) Yes. The distribution for the Northern towns is higher than that for the South. Fully half of the towns in the South have mortality rates lower than the rates of *any* of the Northern towns. Some Northern towns have rates higher than the rates of all of the Southern towns. It seems clear that mortality is higher, in general, in the North.

**17. a)** They are on different scales.

b) January's values are lower and more spread out.

c) Roughly symmetric but slightly skewed to the left. There are more low outliers than high ones. Center is around 40 degrees with an IQR of around 7.5 degrees.

**18.** Bimodal with modes around 50 and 80 minutes. Fairly symmetric around each mode.

**19. a)** Bimodal with modes near 2 and 4.5 minutes. Fairly symmetric around each mode.

b) Because there are two modes, which probably correspond to two different groups of eruptions, an average might not make sense.

c) The intervals between eruptions are longer for long eruptions. There is very little overlap. More than 75% of the short eruptions had intervals less than about an hour (62.5 minutes), while more than 75% of the long eruptions had intervals longer than about 75 minutes. Perhaps the interval could even be used to predict whether the next eruption will be long or short.

**20.** The chance of an accident is not the same for different age groups. The distribution of ages for drivers involved in fatal crashes is not the same as that for other drivers. So, the two variables are not independent.

**21. a)**

(Histogram: # of Students vs Arm/Nose Ratio, horizontal axis 11 to 17)

The distribution is left skewed with a center of about 15. It has an outlier between 11 and 12.

b) Even though the distribution is somewhat skewed, the mean and median are close. The mean is 15.0 and the SD is 1.25.

c) Yes. 11.8 is already an outlier. 9.3 is more than 4.5 SDs below the mean. It is a very low outlier.

**22. a)** About 38%          b) 16%

c) Data are bimodal, and the Normal model is inappropriate.

**23.** If we look only at the overall statistics, it appears that the follow-up group is insured at a much lower rate than those not traced (11.1% of the time compared with 16.6%). But most of the follow-up group were black, who have a lower rate of being insured. When broken down by race, the follow-up group actually has a higher rate of being insured for both blacks and whites. So the overall statistic is misleading and is attributable to the difference in race makeup of the two groups.

**24. a)** 3, 24.5, 36, 50.5, 70

b) Because the IQR is so large, none are technically outliers, but the seasons with fewer than 20 home runs stand out as a separate group.

c)

(Boxplot: Home Runs vs Player, comparing McGwire and Ruth)

d) Without the injured seasons, McGwire and Ruth's home run production distributions look similar. (Ruth's seasons as a pitcher were not included as well.) Ruth's median is a little higher, and he was a little more consistent (less spread), but McGwire had the two highest season totals.

e)

```
        Stem and Leaf
            0 | 7
            5 | 6 | 0
           82 | 5 | 449
           92 | 4 | 1166679
McGwire  9932 | 3 | 45        Ruth
            2 | 2 | 25

        7|0 = 70 home runs
```

f) Now we can see how much more consistent Ruth was. Most of Ruth's seasons had home run totals in the 40s or 50s. McGwire's seasons are much more spread out (not even including the three at the bottom).

**25. a)**

(Normal curve: Reaction time (sec), with 68%, 95%, 99.7% ranges. Horizontal axis: 0.96, 1.14, 1.32, 1.50, 1.68, 1.86, 2.0)

b) According to the model, reaction times are symmetric with center at 1.5 seconds. About 95% of all reaction times are between 1.14 and 1.86 seconds.

c) 8.2%          d) 24.1%

e) Quartiles are 1.38 and 1.62 seconds, so the IQR is 0.24 seconds.

f) The slowest 1/3 of all drivers have reaction times of 1.58 seconds or more.

**26. a)** *Who*—62 people

*What*—Number of objects correctly memorized

*When*—Not stated

*Where*—Not stated

*Why*—To see if music affects memorization ability

*How*—Randomized experiment

b) Type of music (categorical) and number of items remembered (quantitative)

c) Because we do not have all the data, we can't know exactly how the boxplots look, but we do know that the minimums are all within the fences and that two groups have at least one outlier on the high side.

d) All three distributions are right skewed. Mozart and rap had very similar distributions. The scores for the None groups are, if anything, slightly higher than those for the other two groups. It is clear that groups listening to music did not score higher than those who heard none.

27. a)

b) Mean $100.25, SD $25.54.

c) The distribution is somewhat symmetric and unimodal, but the center is rather flat, almost uniform.

d) 64%. The Normal model seems to work reasonably well, since it predicts 68%.

28. a) 50.7%      b) 34.9% c) 13.3% d) 6.7%

29. a) 38 cars

b) Possibly because the distribution is skewed to the right.

c) Center—median is 148.5 cubic inches. Spread—IQR is 126 cubic inches.

d) No. It's bigger than average, but smaller than more than 25% of cars. The upper quartile is at 231 inches.

e) No. 1.5 IQR is 189, and 105 − 189 is negative, so there can't be any low outliers. 231 + 189 = 420. There aren't any cars with engines bigger than this, since the maximum has to be at most 105 (the lower quartile) + 275 (the range) = 380.

f) Because the distribution is skewed to the right, this is probably not a good approximation.

g) Mean, median, range, quartiles, IQR, and SD all get multiplied by 16.4.

30. a) Math/Sci—25.6%, Ag—41.7%, Humanities—19.3%, Other—13.5%

b) Math/Sci—30.1%, Ag—46.0%, Humanities—13.3%, Other—10.6%

c) Math/Sci—20.3%, Ag—39.1%, Humanities—24.6%, Other—15.9%

d) No; it appears that oldest children are more likely than second-born children to major in Math or Science (30% to 20%), while second-born children are more likely than first-born to major in the Humanities (25% to 13%)

31. a) *Who*—100 health food store customers
*What*—Have you taken a cold remedy?, and Effectiveness (scale 1 to 10)

*When*—Not stated
*Where*—Not stated
*Why*—Promotion of herbal medicine
*How*—In-person interviews

b) Have you taken a cold remedy?—categorical. Effectiveness—categorical or ordinal.

c) No. Customers are not necessarily representative, and the council had an interest in promoting the herbal remedy.

32. Chief executives have a mean salary less than the median, so the distribution is likely to be skewed to the left. General and operations managers have a mean salary larger than the median, so their distribution is likely to be skewed to the right.

33. a) 30.4%

b) If this were a random sample of all voters, yes.

c) 36.6%          d) 8.8%

e) 23.1%          f) 47.0%

34. a) Fairly symmetric, almost uniform except for the right tail.

b) 47 horses

c) IQR is 47, so fences are at 7.5 and 195.5. Since the range is only 90, we know there can't be any observations lower than 35 (upper quartile − range) or greater than 168 (lower quartile + range), so no.

d) Distribution is very roughly uniform, not unimodal, so the Normal modal might not be reasonable.

e) 22 of 38, or about 58%

f) Mean, median, and quartiles would increase by 10. SD, IQR, and range would not change.

35. a) Republican—16,535, Democrat—17,183, Other— 20,666; or Republican—30.4%, Democrat—31.6%, Other—38.0%

b)

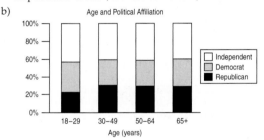

c) Among voters over 30, political affiliation appears to be largely unrelated to age. However there is some evidence that younger voters are more likely to be Independent and less likely to be Republican

d) Voters who identified themselves as "Other" seem to be generally younger than Democrats or Republicans.

36. a) The differences are 3% or more. This is too large for rounding. Perhaps some responded that they knew of her, but their opinion was neither favorable nor unfavorable. The poll should have included this option.

b) There are different people in each poll, so proportions will vary.

c)

d)

e)

f) The bar chart, when split by time period, shows the drop-off in favorable ratings fairly well. The timeplot is probably clearest (but note that the time periods are not evenly spaced). All three plots have something to say.

g) Her unfavorable ratings went up dramatically between June and July 2002.

37. a) *Who*—Years from 1994 to 2003
   *What*—Bicycle fatalities
   *When*—1994–2003
   *Where*—United States
   *Why*—To study bicycle helmet safety
   *How*—Bicycle Helmet Safety Institute Report

   b)

   | Stem | Leaf |
   |------|------|
   | 6    | 1    |
   | 6    | 68   |
   | 7    | 2    |
   | 7    | 5569 |
   | 8    | 12   |

   6/1 = 610 − 619 fatalities

   c)

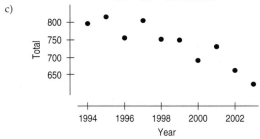

   d) The stem-and-leaf display shows the distribution is skewed to the left. It also provides some idea about the center and spread of the annual fatalities.

   e) The number of bicycle fatalities has decreased over the 10-year period.

   f) In the 10-year period from 1994 to 2003, reported bicycle fatalities decreased steadily from about 800 per year to around 620 a year.

38. a) −9, 1, 4, 9, 25

   b)

   c) Mean 4.72% of sales, SD 7.55% of sales

   d) Fairly symmetric and unimodal, centered around 4% of sales. 50% of the companies report % profit between 1% and 9%. There is one outlier at 25% of sales.

39. a) Mean 1.29 hours, SD 0.43 hours

   b) 1.4 hours

c) 0.89 hours (or 53.4 minutes)

d) Survey results vary, and the mean and the SD may have changed.

40. a) The homicide rate rose sharply from 1900 to 1930, then declined dramatically until the early 40s. It started increasing quickly in the early 60s to around 1980, where it remained fairly stable until 1990, when it started declining again.

   b) Executions rose sharply from 1900 to 1940, then fell as quickly, reaching near 0 in the decade 1970–1979. The last two decades have shown an increase.

   c) Not possible to reach cause-and-effect conclusion from two timeplots. There could be lurking variables.

# Chapter 7

1. a) Weight in ounces: explanatory; Weight in grams: response. (Could be other way around.) To predict the weight in grams based on ounces. Scatterplot: positive, straight, strong (perfectly linear relationship).

   b) Circumference: explanatory. Weight: response. To predict the weight based on the circumference. Scatterplot: positive, linear, moderately strong.

   c) Shoe size: explanatory; GPA: response. To try to predict GPA from shoe size. Scatterplot: no direction, no form, very weak.

   d) Miles driven: explanatory; Gallons remaining: response. To predict the gallons remaining in the tank based on the miles driven since filling up. Scatterplot: negative, straight, moderate.

2. a) Price: explanatory; Number sold: response. To predict the number sold based on the price. Scatterplot: negative, straight, moderate.

   b) Depth: explanatory; Water pressure: response. To predict water pressure based on depth. Scatterplot: positive, straight, strong.

   c) Visibility: explanatory; Depth: response. To predict depth based on visibility (although predicting visibility based on depth is also possible). Scatterplot: negative, straight(?), weak to moderate.

   d) Weight: explanatory; Reading score: response. To predict reading test scores based on weight. Scatterplot: positive, possibly straight, moderate.

3. a) Altitude: explanatory; Temperature: response. (Other way around possible as well.) To predict the temperature based on the altitude. Scatterplot: negative, possibly straight, weak to moderate.

   b) Ice cream cone sales: explanatory. Air-conditioner sales: response—although the other direction would work as well. To predict one from the other. Scatterplot: positive, straight, moderate.

   c) Age: explanatory; Grip strength: response. To predict the grip strength based on age. Scatterplot: curved down, moderate. Very young and elderly would have grip strength less than that of adults.

   d) Reaction time: explanatory; Blood alcohol level: response. To predict blood alcohol level from reaction time test. (Other way around is possible.) Scatterplot: positive, nonlinear, moderately strong.

4. a) Time: explanatory; Cost: response. To predict cost based on time. Scatterplot: positive, straight, strong.

   b) Time delay: explanatory; Distance: response. To predict the distance from the lightning based on the time delay of the thunder. Scatterplot: positive, straight, strong.

   c) Brightness: explanatory; Distance: response. To predict distance based on apparent brightness. Scatterplot: negative, curved, moderate.

   d) Weight of car: explanatory; Age of owner: response. To predict the age of the owner based on the weight of the car. (Or other way around.) Scatterplot: no direction, no shape, very weak.

**5.** a) None      b) 3 and 4      c) 2, 3, and 4
d) 1 and 2      e) 3 and possibly 1
**6.** a) 1      b) 4      c) 2 and 4      d) 3      e) 2 and 4
**7.** There seems to be a very weak—or possibly no—relation between brain size and performance IQ.
**8.** Nonlinear form. Moderately strong. The rate has not been constant; the rate of increase from the beginning to about 1950 is steeper than from 1950 to the present.
**9.** a)

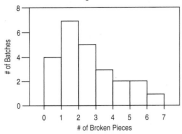

b) Unimodal, skewed to the right. The skew.
c) The positive, somewhat linear relation between batch number and broken pieces.
**10.** a)

b) Positive linear relation, so sales are increasing.
c) Unimodal, symmetric sales; average sales around $350.
**11.** a) 0.006      b) 0.777      c) −0.923      d) −0.487
**12.** a) −0.977      b) 0.736      c) 0.951      d) −0.021
**13.** There may be an association, but not a correlation unless the variables are quantitative. There could be a correlation between average number of hours of TV watched per week per person and number of crimes committed per year. Even if there is a relationship, it doesn't mean one causes the other.
**14.** There may be an association, but not a correlation; type of car is not a quantitative variable.
**15.** a) Yes. It shows a linear form and no outliers.
b) There is a strong, positive, linear association between drop and speed; the greater the coaster's initial drop, the higher the top speed.
**16.** a) No, no units for the Hamilton Depression Rating Scale are given. These variables are not truly quantitative.
b) Nothing—correlation isn't an appropriate statistic.
**17.** The scatterplot is not linear; correlation is not appropriate.
**18.** The scatterplot is not linear and it has two high outliers (LA and NY). Correlation is not appropriate for such a relationship.
**19.** The correlation may be near 0. We expect nighttime temperatures to be low in January, increase through spring and into the summer months, then decrease again in the fall and winter. The relationship is not linear.
**20.** The relation might be nonlinear, resulting in a correlation close to 0 even though the association is strong, or there might be an outlier.
**21.** The correlation coefficient won't change, because it's based on z-scores. The z-scores of the prediction errors are the same whether they are expressed in nautical miles or miles.
**22.** The correlation coefficient won't change, because it's based on z-scores. The z-scores of the prediction errors are not changed by adding or subtracting a constant.

**23.** a) Assuming the relation is linear, a correlation of −0.772 shows a strong relation in a negative direction.
b) Continent is a categorical variable. Correlation does not apply.
**24.** a) Correlation cannot be greater than 1. There is an error.
b) Assuming the relation is linear, the strong correlation shows a relation, but it does not show *causality*.
**25.** a) Actually, yes, taller children will tend to have higher reading scores, but this doesn't imply causation.
b) Older children are generally both taller and are better readers. Age is the lurking variable.
**26.** a) No. It just means that in countries where cell phone use is high, the life expectancy tends to be high as well.
b) General economic conditions of the country could affect both cell phone use and life expectancy. That's the lurking variable.
**27.** a) No. We don't know this from the correlation alone. There may be a nonlinear relationship or outliers.
b) No. We can't tell from the correlation what the form of the relationship is.
c) No. We don't know from the correlation coefficient.
d) Yes, the correlation doesn't depend on the units used to measure the variables.
**28.** a) We don't know this from the correlation alone. There may be a nonlinear relationship or outliers.
b) No. We can't tell from the correlation what the form of the relationship is.
c) No. We don't know this from the correlation coefficient.
d) No. The correlation doesn't depend on the units used to measure the variables.
**29.** This is categorical data even though it is represented by numbers. The correlation is meaningless.
**30.** The source of data is categorical. The correlation is meaningless.
**31.** a) The association is positive, moderately strong, and roughly straight, with several states whose HCI seems high for their median income and one state whose HCI appears low given its median income.
b) The correlation would still be 0.65.
c) The correlation wouldn't change.
d) DC would be a moderate outlier whose HCI is high for its median income. Including it would lower the correlation slightly.
e) No. We can only say that higher median incomes are associated with higher housing costs, but we don't know why. There may be other economic variables at work.
**32.** a) The association is negative, quite strong, and fairly straight; there are no outliers.
b) The correlation would still be −0.84.
c) The correlation wouldn't change.
d) That year would have a very high mortgage amount for an interest rate that high. That would tend to weaken the correlation (bring it closer to 0).
e) No. We can only say that lower interest rates are associated with larger mortgage amounts, but we don't know why. There may be other economic variables at work.
**33.** a) −0.649
b) The correlation will not change. Correlation does not change with change of units.
c) There is a moderately strong negative linear association between number of calories consumed and time at the table for toddlers. Longer times are associated with fewer calories consumed.
d) There appears to be a relation between time at the table and calories consumed, but there is no reason to believe increased time *causes* decreased calorie consumption. There may be a lurking variable.

**34.** a)

b) Positive, linear, very strong.

c) The new scale is able to predict the static weight fairly well, except possibly at the high end. It may be possible to predict the static weight from the new scale accurately enough to be useful. But the weight-in-motion measurements seem a bit too high.

d) 0.965.

e) The correlation would not change.

f) At the higher end of the weight-in-motion scale, there is one point where the weight in motion is much higher than the static weight. The line does not seem to go through the points where $x$ and $y$ are equal. The new scale may have to be recalibrated.

**35.** a)

b) Negative, linear, strong.

c) −0.869

d) There is a strong linear relation in a negative direction between horsepower and highway gas mileage. Lower fuel efficiency is associated with higher horsepower.

**36.** a)

b) 0.934

c) There is a strong linear relation in a positive direction between the percent of teens using marijuana and the percent of teens using other drugs.

d) There is no indication of causality. There could be lurking variables.

**37.**

(Plot could have explanatory and predictor variables swapped.) Correlation is 0.199. There does not appear to be a relation between sodium and fat content in burgers, especially without the low-fat, low-sodium item. The correlation of 0.199 shows a weak relationship, even with the outlier included.

**38.** Correlation is 0.961. There appears to be a strong linear relation in a positive direction. The correlation of 0.961 supports the conclusion of a strong relation. Even without the outlier at 410 calories and 19 grams of fat, the correlation is 0.837, still strong.

**39.** a) Yes, the scatterplot appears to be somewhat linear.

b) As the number of runs increases, the attendance also increases.

c) There is a positive association, but it does not *prove* that more fans will come if the number of runs increases. Association does not indicate causality.

**40.** a) There appears to be a moderately strong positive relationship between the number of wins and home attendance. The points show some significant scattering. The correlation of 0.697 is moderately strong.

b) Winning. The correlation is only slightly higher for wins vs. attendance (0.697) than for runs vs. attendance (0.667).

c) The correlation between runs and wins is 0.605.

**41.** A scatterplot shows a generally straight scattered pattern with no outliers. The correlation between *Drop* and *Duration* is 0.35, indicating that rides on coasters with greater initial drops generally last somewhat longer, but the association is weak.

**42.** a) −0.14

b) No, the low correlation occurs because the relation is not linear.

**43.** a)

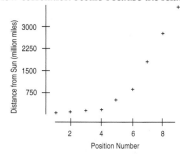

The relation between position and distance is nonlinear, with a positive direction. There is very little scatter from the trend.

b) The relation is not linear.

c)

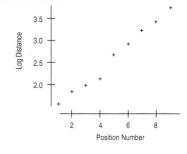

The relation between position number and log of distance appears to be roughly linear.

**44.** a) 0.828

b)

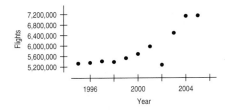

The trend is positive and curved. There is a low outlier at 2002.

c) The plot is not straight and has an outlier. Either violation would disqualify the correlation. It isn't unusual for growth in a business to be faster than linear. The outlier in 2002 is due to the drop in airline flights after the 9/11 attacks.

## CHAPTER 8

1. 281 milligrams
2. 30.07mpg
3. The potassium content is actually lower than the model predicts for a cereal with that much fiber.
4. The car gets better gas mileage than the model predicts for a car with that much horsepower.
5. The model predicts that cereals will have approximately 27 more milligrams of potassium for every additional gram of fiber.
6. The model estimates that cars lose an average of 0.84 miles per gallon for every additional 10 horsepower.
7. 81.5%
8. 75.5%
9. The true potassium contents of cereals vary from the predicted amounts with a standard deviation of 30.77 milligrams.
10. True fuel economy varies from the predicted amount with a standard deviation of 3.287 miles per gallon.
11.

|  | $x$ | $s_x$ | $\bar{y}$ | $s_y$ | $r$ | $\hat{y} = b_0 + b_1 x$ |
|---|---|---|---|---|---|---|
| a) | 10 | 2 | 20 | 3 | 0.5 | $\hat{y} = 12.5 + 0.75x$ |
| b) | 2 | 0.06 | 7.2 | 1.2 | −0.4 | $\hat{y} = 23.2 − 8x$ |
| c) | 12 | 6 | **152** | **30** | −0.8 | $\hat{y} = 200 − 4x$ |
| d) | 2.5 | 1.2 | 25 | 100 | **0.6** | $\hat{y} = −100 + 50x$ |

12.

|  | $x$ | $s_x$ | $\bar{y}$ | $s_y$ | $r$ | $\hat{y} = b_0 + b_1 x$ |
|---|---|---|---|---|---|---|
| a) | 30 | 4 | 18 | 6 | −0.2 | $\hat{y} = 27 − 0.3x$ |
| b) | 100 | 18 | 60 | 10 | 0.9 | $\hat{y} = 10 + 0.5x$ |
| c) | 4 | 0.8 | 50 | 15 | **0.8** | $\hat{y} = −10 + 15x$ |
| d) | 6 | **1.2** | 18 | 4 | −0.6 | $\hat{y} = 30 − 2x$ |

13. a) Model is appropriate.
b) Model is not appropriate. Relationship is nonlinear.
c) Model may not be appropriate. Spread is changing.
14. a) Model is not appropriate. Relationship is nonlinear.
b) Model may not be appropriate. Spread is changing.
c) Model is appropriate.
15. a) *Price* (in thousands of dollars) is $y$ and *Size* (in square feet) is $x$.
b) Slope is thousands of $ per square foot.
c) Positive. Larger homes should cost more.
16. a) *Duration* (in seconds) is $y$ and initial *Drop* (in feet) is $x$.
b) Slope is seconds per foot.
c) Positive. Bigger coasters probably provide longer rides.
17. 300 pounds/foot. If a "typical" car is 15 feet long, all of 3, 30, and 3000 would give ridiculous weights.
18. 1 ft/inch. If a typical circumference is around 20 inches, then other slopes give ridiculous heights.

19. A linear model on *Size* accounts for 71.4% of the variation in home *Price*.
20. A linear model on *Height* accounts for 12.4% of the variability in the *Duration* of the ride.
21. a) $R^2$ does not tell whether the model is appropriate, but measures the strength of the linear relationship. High $R^2$ could also be due to an outlier.
b) Predictions based on a regression line are for average values of $y$ for a given $x$. The actual wingspan will vary around the prediction.
22. a) $R^2$ measures the amount of variation accounted for. It does not imply that $x$ determines the values of $y$. Here, literacy rate *accounts for* 64% of the *observed* variation in life expectancy.
b) This interpretation is implying a causal relationship. Just because two variables are related does not mean one causes another. Here, one could say that an increase of 5% in literacy rate is associated with an average 2-year improvement in life expectancy.
23. a) 0.845
b) Price should be 0.845 SDs above the mean in price.
c) Price should be 1.690 SDs below the mean in price.
24. a) 0.352
b) Duration should be about 0.352 SDs below the mean duration.
c) Duration should be about 1.056 SDs above the mean duration.
25. a) Probably not. Your score is better than about 97.5% of people, assuming scores follow the Normal model. Your next score is likely to be closer to the mean.
b) The friend probably should retake the test. His score is better than only about 16% of people. His score is likely to be closer to the mean.
26. People on the cover are usually there for outstanding performances. Because they are so far from the mean, the performance in the next year is likely to be closer to the mean.
27. a) *Price* increases by about $0.061 × 1000, or $61.00, per square foot.
b) 230.82 thousand, or $230,820.
c) $115,020; $6000 is the residual.
28. a) On average, rides last about 0.242 seconds longer per foot of initial drop.
b) 139.433 seconds
c) That's 7.333 seconds shorter than the model predicts, a negative residual.
29. a) Probably. The residuals show some initially low points, but there is no clear curvature.
b) The linear model on *Tar* content accounts for 92.4% of the variability in *Nicotine*.
30. a) Yes, the relationship is not very strong, but it's reasonably straight.
b) The linear model on number of *Wins* accounts for 48.5% of the variation in *Attendance*.
c) The residuals spread out. There is more variation in *Attendance* as the number of wins increases.
d) The Yankees' attendance was about 13,000 fans more than we might expect given the number of wins.
31. a) $r = 0.961$
b) Nicotine should be 1.922 SDs below average.
c) Tar should be 0.961 SDs above average.
32. a) 0.697
b) Attendance should be 1.394 SDs above the average.
c) Number of games won should be 0.697 SDs below the average.
33. a) $\widehat{Nicotine} = 0.15403 + 0.065052\,Tar$
b) 0.414 mg
c) Nicotine content increases by 0.065 mg of nicotine per milligram of tar.
d) We'd expect a cigarette with no tar to have 0.154 mg of nicotine.
e) 0.1094 mg

**34.** a) $\widehat{Attendance} = -14364.5 + 538.915\ Wins$.
 b) 12,581 people.
 c) Every win adds an average 538.915 people in attendance.
 d) It means the team's average attendance is lower than the average for a team with as many wins.
 e) 12,222.56 attendees. This means that the Cardinals averaged over 12,000 more attendees than one would predict for a team with 83 wins.

**35.** a) Yes. The relationship is straight enough, with a few outliers. The spread increases a bit for states with large median incomes, but we can still fit a regression line.
 b) From summary statistics: $\widehat{HCI} = -156.50 + 0.0107\ MFI$; from original data: $\widehat{HCI} = -157.64 + 0.0107\ MFI$
 c) From summary statistics: predicted HCI = 324.93; from original data: 324.87.
 d) 223.09
 e) $\widehat{z_{HCI}} = 0.65 z_{MFI}$
 f) $\widehat{z_{MFI}} = 0.65 z_{HCI}$

**36.** a) Yes, the relationship is straight enough, both variables are quantitative, and the spread is roughly constant. There are no real outliers.
 b) $\widehat{MortAmt} = 220.88 - 7.768 IntRate$
 ($\widehat{MortAmt} = 220.89 - 7.775 IntRate$ from original data)
 c) $65.52 million ($65.39 from original data equation).
 d) Yes, 20% is outside the range of the original $x$-variable. It may not be appropriate.
 e) $\widehat{z_{Mort}} = -0.84 z_{Int}$
 f) $\widehat{z_{Int}} = -0.84 z_{Mort}$

**37.** a) $\widehat{Total} = 539.803 + 1.103 Age$
 b) Yes. Both variables are quantitative; the plot is straight (although flat); there are no apparent outliers; the plot does not appear to change spread throughout the range of $Age$.
 c) $559.65; $594.94
 d) 0.14%
 e) No. The plot is nearly flat. The model explains almost none of the variation in *Total Yearly Purchases*.

**38.** a) $\widehat{Total} = 28.73 + 0.0108 Income$
 b) Yes. Both variables are quantitative; the plot is straight enough; there are a few possible outliers, but none are extreme and there are 500 points; the plot does not appear to change spread throughout the range of *Income*.
 c) $244.76; $892.86
 d) 52.1%
 e) Yes, the model accounts for a good part of the variation in *Total Yearly Purchases*. The difference between the predicted amount of $208 and $922 is probably financially significant.

**39.** a) Moderately strong, fairly straight, and positive. Possibly some outliers (higher-than-expected math scores).
 b) The student with 500 verbal and 800 math.
 c) Positive, fairly strong linear relationship. 46.9% of variation in math scores is explained by verbal scores.
 d) $\widehat{Math} = 217.7 + 0.662 \times Verbal$.
 e) Every point of verbal score adds an average 0.662 points to the predicted math score.
 f) 548.5 points.
 g) 53.0 points.

**40.** a) $\widehat{GPA} = -1.262 + 0.00214\ SAT$.
 b) One could say that a person with a 0 SAT score would have a $-1.262$ GPA, but a score of 0 on the SAT is impossible, as is a negative GPA. So the $y$-intercept serves only to adjust the height of the line and is meaningless by itself.
 c) The expected GPA is higher by 0.21 points for every hundred combined SAT points scored.
 d) 3.23
 e) $SAT$ is probably only somewhat useful, since $R^2$ is only 0.221. There are many other factors that influence *GPA*.
 f) Positive. My GPA would be higher than expected for my *SAT* score.

**41.** a) 0.685
 b) $\widehat{Verbal} = 162.1 + 0.71 \times Math$.
 c) The observed verbal score is higher than predicted from the math score
 d) 516.7 points.
 e) 559.6 points
 f) Regression to the mean. Someone whose math score is below average is predicted to have a verbal score below average, but not as far (in SDs). So if we use *that* verbal score to predict math, they will be even closer to the mean in predicted math score than their observed math score. If we kept cycling back and forth, eventually we would predict the mean of each and stay there.

**42.** 1868.1 points

**43.** a) The relationship is straight enough, but not very strong.
 b) The amount of land damaged by wildfires has been increasing by about 0.138 million (= 138,000) acres per year.
 c) Yes, the intercept represents the model's starting point in 1982.
 d) The residuals are distributed around zero with a standard deviation of 1.857 million acres. Compared to the observed values, most of which are between 3 and 8 million acres, this amount of error in our model's predictions is quite large.
 e) 22.4% of the variation in the number of acres damaged by wildfires can be accounted for by the linear model on *Year*.

**44.** a) Wildfires have been getting bigger, especially in recent years. The year 2005 seems to have been a particularly bad one for large fires.
 b) These plots do not satisfy the Straight Enough Condition; there is a bend upward that grows especially strong after 1995. It is also likely that 2005 is an outlier, violating the Outlier Condition. Both variables are quantitative, so that condition is OK.

**45.** a)

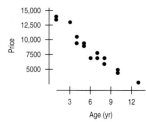

 b) Negative, linear, strong.
 c) Yes.
 d) $-0.972$
 e) *Age* accounts for 94.4% of the variation in *Advertised Price*.
 f) Other factors contribute—options, condition, mileage, etc.

**46.** a) Yes. Plot shows positive, linear, fairly strong relationship.
 b) Marijuana use accounts for 87.3% of variation in use of other drugs.
 c) $\widehat{Other\%} = -3.068 + 0.615\ Marijuana\%$.
 d) Each additional percent of teens using marijuana adds 0.615 percent to the percentage of teens using other drugs.
 e) The results do not *confirm* marijuana as a gateway drug. They do indicate an *association* between marijuana and other drug use.

**47.** a) $\widehat{Price} = 14,286 - 959 \times Years$.
 b) Every extra year of age decreases average value by $959.
 c) The average new Corolla costs $14,286.
 d) $7573
 e) Negative residual. Its price is below the predicted value for its age.
 f) $-$1195
 g) No. After age 14, the model predicts negative prices. The relationship is no longer linear.

**48.** a) 20.4 g
 b) $-10.4$ g. Veggie burgers have less fat than typical menu items have.

c) Answers will vary—should mention the predicted fat content, the observed fat content, and the residual.

**49.** a)

b) 92.3% of the variation in calories can be accounted for by the fat content.

c) $\widehat{Calories} = 211.0 + 11.06 \times Fat$.

d)

Residuals show no clear pattern, so the model seems appropriate.

e) Could say a fat-free burger still has 211.0 calories, but this is extrapolation (no data close to 0).

f) Every gram of fat adds 11.06 calories, on average.

g) 553.5 calories.

**50.** a) Yes.

b) Strong.

c) $\widehat{Calories} = 185.7 + 13.93 \times Fat$.

d) Every gram of fat adds 13.93 calories, on average.

e) A fat-free sandwich would have 185.7 calories, but this is extrapolation.

f) The sandwich has fewer calories than average for its grams of fat.

g) The chicken sandwich.

h) The calorie content of the fish sandwich is less than expected for burgers (498.4 calories) but much less than expected for chicken (547.9 calories). It seems more in line with burgers than chicken.

**51.** a) The regression was for predicting calories from fat, not the other way around.

b) $\widehat{Fat} = -15.0 + 0.083 \times Calories$.
Predict 34.8 grams of fat.

**52.** a) Linear, positive slope, and quite strong. There is, however, a slight curvature among lower costs of living. There appear to be three cities standing above the overall trend.

b) The cost of living in 2005 accounts for 71.6% of the variation in cost of living in 2006.

c) 12.7%

d) Moscow's cost of living is 12.7% higher than expected from the model.

**53.** a) 82.9 minutes.

b) The linear relationship is strong, but without seeing the data, we don't know if the model is appropriate.

c) Every extra minute of digital time adds 0.44 minutes of analog time, on average.

d) It lasts longer in analog mode than predicted for its number of digital minutes.

**54.** $\widehat{Sales} = -7.031 + 0.090 \times Year$.
2.512 million dollars.
The extrapolation proved to be inaccurate. Apparently the observed trend did not continue 5 more years.

**55.** a) 0.578

b) $CO_2$ levels account for 33.4% of the variation in mean temperature.

c) $\widehat{Mean\ Temperature} = 15.3066 + 0.004 \times CO_2$.

d) The predicted mean temperature has been increasing at an average rate of 0.004 degrees (C)/ppm of $CO_2$.

e) One *could* say that with no $CO_2$ in the atmosphere, there would be a temperature of 15.3066 degrees Celsius, but this is extrapolation to a nonsensical point.

f) No.

g) Predicted 16.7626 degrees C.

**56.** a)

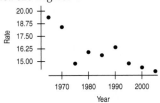

b) $\widehat{Birth\ Rate} = 25.345 - 0.11 \times Year$.

c)

There's a low outlier for 1975; we might want to investigate.

d) The *Birth Rate* has been decreasing by 0.11 births per 1000 women per *Year*, on average.

e) 16.807 live births per 1000 women.

f) Model predicts 1.807 live births per 1000 women; too high.

g) 13.28 live births per 1000 women. Caution: We are extrapolating.

h) 11.62 live births per 1000 women. Extrapolating this far is dangerous.

**57.** a) $\widehat{\%\ Body\ Fat} = -27.4 + 0.25 \times Weight$.

b) Residuals look randomly scattered around 0, so conditions are satisfied.

c) % *Body Fat* increases, on average, by 0.25 percent per pound of *Weight*.

d) Reliable is relative. $R^2$ is 48.5%, but residuals have a standard deviation of 7%, so variation around the line is large.

e) 0.9 percent.

**58.** $\widehat{\%\ Body\ Fat} = -62.6 + 2.22 \times Waist$.
$R^2$ is 78.7%, and the standard deviation of the residuals is smaller (4.5%), so this model should be better able to predict.

**59.** a) $\widehat{Highjump} = 2.681 - 0.00671 \times 800mTime$. High-jump height is lower, on average, by 0.00671 meters per second of 800-m race time.

b) 16.4%

c) Yes, the slope is negative. Faster runners tend to jump higher as well.

d) There is a slight tendency for less variation in high-jump height among the slower runners than among the faster runners.

e) Not especially. The residual standard deviation is 0.060 meters, which is not much smaller than the SD of all high jumps (0.066 meters). The model doesn't appear to do a very good job of predicting.

**60.** a) $\overline{LongJump}$ = 4.20053 + 1.10541$HighJump$. Every additional meter in the high jump is associated with an additional 1.1054 meters, on average, in the long jump.
   b) 12.6%
   c) Yes, the slope is positive.
   d) The residuals plot is fairly patternless.
   e) No. The residual standard deviation is 0.196 meters, not much smaller than the SD of all long jumps (0.206), and $R^2$ is only 12.6%.

**61.** a) As calcium levels increase, mortality rate decreases. Relationship is fairly strong, negative, and linear.
   b) $\overline{Mortality}$ = 1676.0 − 3.23 × $Calcium$.
   c) Mortality decreases 3.23 deaths per 100,000, on average, for each part per million of calcium. The intercept indicates a baseline mortality of 1676 deaths per 100,000 with no calcium, but this is extrapolation.
   d) Exeter has 348.6 fewer deaths per 100,000 than the model predicts.
   e) 1353 deaths per 100,000.
   f) Calcium concentration accounts for 43.0% of the variation in death rate per 100,000 people.

**62.** a) Yes—length is easier to judge from a picture than weight
   b) 0.914
   c) $\overline{Weight}$ = −393.0 + 5.9 × $Length$.
   d) Alligators weigh about 5.9 pounds per inch, on average.
   e) Fairly accurate. The $R^2$ value is 83.6%. The standard deviation of the residuals is 54.01 pounds. I would like to see a scatterplot and residual plots to assess the regression condition before having too much faith in this model.

**63.** The line $\hat{y}$ = 7.0 + 1.1$x$ minimizes the sum of squared vertical distances from the points to the line.

**64.** The line $\hat{y}$ = 1975 − 0.45$x$ minimizes the sum of squared vertical distances from the points to the line.

# CHAPTER 9

**1.** a) The trend appears to be somewhat linear up to about 1940, but from 1940 to about 1970 the trend appears to be nonlinear. From 1975 or so to the present, the trend appears to be linear.
   b) Relatively strong for certain periods.
   c) No, as a whole the graph is clearly nonlinear. Within certain periods (1975 to the present) the correlation is high.
   d) Overall, no. You could fit a linear model to the period from 1975 to 2003, but why? You don't need to interpolate, since every year is reported, and extrapolation seems dangerous.

**2.** a) The percent of men 18–24 who are smokers decreased dramatically between 1965 and 1990, but the trend has not been consistent since then.
   b) Stronger before 1990 than after.
   c) No. The relationship is not straight.

**3.** a) The relationship is not straight.
   b) It will be curved downward.
   c) No. The relationship will still be curved.

**4.** a) The relationship is not straight.
   b) It will be curved downward.

**5.** a) No. We need to see the scatterplot first to see if the conditions are satisfied, and models are always wrong.
   b) No, the linear model might not fit the data at all.

**6.** a) No, it just means that the model doesn't account for more than 13% of the variation of the response variable.
   b) She should look at $s$ to judge the accuracy of predictions. $R^2$ is not a direct measure of accuracy.

**7.** a) Millions of dollars per minute of run time.
   b) Costs for longer movies increase at the same rate.
   c) Regardless of run time, dramas cost less by about $20 million.

**8.** a) The slopes are about the same, so the costs increase at about the same rate as movies get longer.

b) Although the costs per minute are about the same, it costs about $20 million less to make an R-rated movie than a movie of the other rating types with the same running time.
   c) Omitting *King Kong* would make the slope for the PG-13 movies steeper. We'd conclude that the cost per minute of PG-13 movies was greater than the cost per minute of the other movies.

**9.** a) The use of Oakland airport has been growing at about 59,700 passengers/year, starting from about 282,000 in 1990.
   b) 71% of the variation in passengers is accounted for by this model.
   c) Errors in predictions based on this model have a standard deviation of 104,330 passengers.
   d) No, that would extrapolate too far from the years we've observed.
   e) The negative residual is September 2001. Air traffic was artificially low following the attacks on 9/11.

**10.** a) Tracking errors averaged about 292 nautical miles in 1970 and have decreased an average of 5.23 nautical miles per year since then.
   b) Residuals based on this model have a standard deviation of 42.87 nautical miles.
   c) The model predicts an error of only 88.1 nautical miles in 2009. However, the NHC has *already* achieved better than 125-nautical-mile accuracy, so it seems safe to assume that they can maintain that level of success even if the decline in prediction errors doesn't continue.
   d) A tracking error of 90 nautical miles would be achieved if the trend fit by the regression model were to persist, but that is an extrapolation beyond the data.
   e) We should be cautious in assuming that the improvements in prediction will continue at the same rate.

**11.** a) 1) High leverage, small residual.
      2) No, not influential for the slope.
      3) Correlation would decrease because outlier has large $z_x$ and $z_y$, increasing correlation.
      4) Slope wouldn't change much because the outlier is in line with other points.
   b) 1) High leverage, probably small residual.
      2) Yes, influential.
      3) Correlation would weaken and become less negative.
      4) Slope would increase toward 0, since outlier makes it negative.
   c) 1) Some leverage, large residual.
      2) Yes, somewhat influential.
      3) Correlation would increase, since scatter would decrease.
      4) Slope would increase slightly.
   d) 1) Little leverage, large residual.
      2) No, not influential.
      3) Correlation would become stronger and become more negative because scatter would decrease.
      4) Slope would change very little.

**12.** a) 1) High leverage, makes large residual a bit smaller.
      2) Yes, influential.
      3) Correlation would increase because scatter would decrease.
      4) Slope would increase because outlier pulls the line toward 0.
   b) 1) High leverage, small residual.
      2) Yes, influential.
      3) Correlation would become weaker because outlier has high $z_x$ and $z_y$ values, increasing correlation.
      4) Slope would decrease because outlier pulls the line from nearly flat to a positive slope.
   c) 1) Little leverage, large residual.
      2) No, not influential.
      3) Correlation would become stronger because scatter would decrease.
      4) About the same.

d) 1) High leverage, small residual.
   2) No, not influential.
   3) Correlation would become weaker and become less negative because outlier has large negative $z_x \times z_y$ value.
   4) Slope would stay about the same because outlier is consistent with slope determined by other points.

**13.** 1) e  2) d  3) c  4) b  5) a

**14.** 1) d  2) e  3) c  4) b  5) a

**15.** Perhaps high blood pressure causes high body fat, high body fat causes high blood pressure, or both could be caused by a lurking variable such as a genetic or lifestyle issue.

**16.** Perhaps playing computer games makes kids more violent, or more violent kids like to play computer games, or both behaviors could be influenced by a lurking variable such as the child's home life or a genetic predisposition to aggressiveness.

**17.** a) The graph shows that, on average, students progress at about one reading level per year. This graph shows averages for each grade. The linear trend has been enhanced by using averages.
b) Very close to 1.
c) The individual data points would show much more scatter, and the correlation would be lower.
d) A slope of 1 would indicate that for each 1-year grade level increase, the average reading level is increasing by 1 year.

**18.** The graph has a positive trend, showing that increased *SAT* score is associated with increased *GPA*. However, the graph is based on averages, not individual data. While *SAT* may be a fair predictor of *GPA* on average, there may also be lurking variables.

**19.** a) *Cost* decreases by $2.13 per degree of average daily *Temp*. So warmer temperatures indicate lower costs.
b) For an avg. monthly temperature of 0°F, the cost is predicted to be $133.
c) Too high; the residuals (observed − predicted) around 32°F are negative, showing that the model overestimates the costs.
d) $111.70
e) About $105.70
f) No, the residuals show a definite curved pattern. The data are probably not linear.
g) No, there would be no difference. The relationship does not depend on the units.

**20.** a) The slope indicates that *Fuel Efficiency* decreases by 0.1 mpg per mph of *Speed*; for every 10 mph of increase in speed, the fuel economy decreases by 1 mpg.
b) The intercept is the predicted fuel efficiency at 0 mph, which doesn't make any sense.
c) The residuals are negative, so the model is overestimating the mpg.
d) 27 mpg
e) 28.5 mpg
f) The association is strong, but not linear.
g) No, the residuals indicate a clear nonlinear relationship.

**21.** a) 0.88
b) Interest rates during this period grew at about 0.25% per year, starting from an interest rate of about 0.64%.
c) Substituting 50 in the model yields a predicted value of about 13%.
d) Not really. Extrapolating 20 years beyond the end of these data would be dangerous and unlikely to be accurate.

**22.** a) −0.8666
b) The *Age Difference* is decreasing by about 0.0166 years per *Year*.
c) About 1.61 years.
d) The latest data point is for the year 2003. Extrapolating to 2015 is risky because it depends on the assumption that the trend will continue in the same manner.

**23.** a) The two models fit comparably well, but they have very different slopes.
b) This model predicts the interest rate in 2000 to be 3.24%, much lower than the other model predicts.

c) We can trust the new predicted value because it is in the middle of the data used for the regression.
d) The best answer is "I can't predict that."

**24.** a) The data from the late 1800s to 1950 are high-leverage points. Since they follow generally the same linear trend as the 1975–1998 data, those data points increase the correlation and the $R^2$ value.
b) Probably. There is a slight bend, but it is difficult to tell whether it is enough to prevent using a linear model. We should proceed with caution.
c) The predicted *Age Difference* drops about 0.030 years per *Year*.
d) These data begin with $x = 75$. The $y$-intercept is the predicted difference in age at the year $x = 0$, quite an extrapolation.

**25.** a) Stronger. Both slope and correlation would increase.
b) Restricting the study to nonhuman animals would justify it.
c) Moderately strong.
d) For every year increase in life expectancy, the gestation period increases by about 15.5 days, on average.
e) About 270.5 days.

**26.** a) Only 1.3% of the variation in time is accounted for by the regression on year.
b) We can't say. The Outlier Condition is violated.
c) Probably not. This point doesn't have much leverage.

**27.** a) Removing hippos would make the association stronger, since hippos are more of a departure from the pattern.
b) Increase.
c) No, there must be a good reason for removing data points.
d) Yes, removing it lowered the slope from 15.5 to 11.6 days per year.

**28.** a) Errors of prediction should be smaller with the new model.
b) This regression accounts for only 4.1% of the variability in time, but it looks like swimmers are slowing down at the rate of about 6.2 minutes per year.

**29.** a) Answers may vary. Using the data for 1955–2000 results in a scatterplot that is relatively linear with some curvature. The residuals plot shows a definite trend, indicating that the data are not linear. If you used the line, for 2010 the predicted age is 26.07 years.
b) Not much, since the data are not truly linear and 2010 is 7 years from the last data point (extrapolating is risky).
c) No, that extrapolation of more than 50 years would be absurd. There's no reason to believe the trend from 1955 to 2000 will continue.

**30.** Answers may vary. There seem to be two periods. From 1980 to 1993 or so, there was a consistent increase of about 1% a year. A regression of those years gives:

$$\widehat{Percentage} = -1988.94 + 1.014\,Year$$

with an $R^2$ of 98.9%. The years from 1994 to 1998 are nearly flat. A model of those years yields:

$$\widehat{Percentage} = -87.28 + 0.060\,Year$$

with an $R^2$ of 17.3%.

How to use the data depends on the purpose of the study.

**31.**

a) Except for the outlier, Costa Rica, the data appear to have a linear form in a negative direction.

b) The outlier is Costa Rica, whose data appear to be wrong, with 25 births per woman. That's impossible.

c) With Costa Rica, $r = 0.168$ and $R$-squared = 2.8%, indicating that 2.8% of the variation in *Life Expectancy* is explained by the variation in *Births per Woman*. Without Costa Rica, $r = -0.796$ and $R$-squared = 63.3%, indicating that 63.3% of the variation in *Life Expectancy* is explained by the variation in *Births/Woman*.

d) With Costa Rica, $\widehat{Life\ Expectancy} = 72.6 + 0.15\ Births$; without Costa Rica, $\widehat{Life\ Expectancy} = 84.5 - 4.44\ Births$.

e) The model with Costa Rica is not appropriate. The residuals plot shows a distinct outlier, which is Costa Rica. Removing Costa Rica gives a better residuals plot, suggesting that the linear equation is more appropriate.

f) With Costa Rica, the slope is near 0, suggesting that the linear model is not very useful. The $y$-intercept suggests that with no births, the life expectancy is about 72.6 years. Without Costa Rica, the slope is –4.44, indicating that an average increase of one child per woman predicts a lower life expectancy of 4.44 years, on average. The $y$-intercept indicates that a country with a birth rate of zero would have a life expectancy of 84.5 years. This is extrapolation.

g) No, while there is an association, there is no reason to expect causality. Lurking variables may be involved.

**32.** a) The relationship is positive (increasing speed over time), with a moderate amount of scatter. There is a general linear trend, with several deviations. There were no races from 1915 to 1918 or from 1940 to 1946 because of world wars. After each, speeds didn't recover for several years. The unexpectedly low speed for 2006 may be due to the absence of several leading riders over suspicions of drug use.

b) $\widehat{Avgspeed} = -272.745 + 0.156\ Year$

c) No. The relationship is not straight enough in the early part of the 20th century to fit a regression line. The variables are quantitative, and there are no real outliers.

**33.** a) The scatterplot is clearly nonlinear; however, the last few years—say, from 1970 on—do appear to be linear.

b) Using the data from 1970 to 2006 gives $r = 0.997$ and $\widehat{CPI} = -9052.42 + 4.61\ Year$. Predicted CPI in 2016 = 241.34.

**34.** a) After an initial post-war increase, speeds leveled off in the 1960s. They began to climb again in the 1980s and have generally continued to do so. $\widehat{Avgspeed} = -205.8 + 0.123\ Year$

b) The slope says that average winning speed increases by about 0.123 kph per year.

c) Hinault's 1979 time has a residual of 2.79 kph. He raced much faster than the model would predict ($s_e = 1.34$ kph). Armstrong's 2005 speed of 41.65 kph has a residual of $-1.45$ kph. Hinault's performance was more remarkable for its era.

# CHAPTER 10

**1.** a) No re-expression needed.
  b) Re-express to straighten the relationship.
  c) Re-express to equalize spread.
**2.** a) Re-express to straighten the relationship.
  b) Re-express to equalize spread.
  c) No re-expression needed.
**3.** a) There's an annual pattern in when people fly, so the residuals cycle up and down.
  b) No, this kind of pattern can't be helped by re-expression.
**4.** a) The plot shows a wavy pattern, likely part of an annual cycle that repeats each year.
  b) Cyclic patterns like this cannot be straightened with a re-expression.
**5.** a) 2.8       b) 16.44       c) 7.84
  d) 0.36     e) 2.09

**6.** a) 1.44       b) 630.96       c) 2.33
  d) 0.77     e) 6.6
**7.** a) Fairly linear, negative, strong.
  b) Gas mileage decreases an average 7.652 mpg for each thousand pounds of weight.
  c) No. Residuals show a curved pattern.
**8.** a) The scatterplot shows upward curvature.
  b) Try plotting log (*GDP*) against *Crowdedness*.
**9.** a) Residuals are more randomly spread around 0, with some low outliers.
  b) $\widehat{Fuel\ Consumption} = 0.625 + 1.178 \times Weight$.
  c) For each additional 1000 pounds of *Weight*, an additional 1.178 gallons will be needed to drive 100 miles.
  d) 21.06 miles per gallon.
**10.** a) No. The student has gone too far. We now see marked downward curvature.
  b) A next step would be to try a "weaker" re-expression, like reciprocal square root or log (*GDP*).
**11.** No, an erratic relationship that goes down, up, and then down again cannot be linearized by re-expression.
**12.** No, a trend that goes up and down erratically cannot be linearized by re-expression.
**13.** a) Although more than 97% of the variation in GDP can be accounted for by this model, we should examine a scatterplot of the residuals to see if it's appropriate.
  b) No. The residuals show clear curvature.
**14.** About 31.59 dactyls.
**15.** Yes, the pattern in the residuals is much weaker.
**16.**

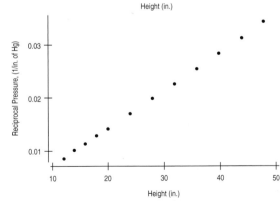

$1/Pressure$ is an exact relationship. $R^2$ is 100%.
$\widehat{reciprocal\ Pressure} = -0.000077 + 0.000713\ \widehat{Height}$

| Predictor | Coeff | SE Coeff | T | P |
|---|---|---|---|---|
| Intercept | $-0.00007670$ | 0.00007813 | $-0.98$ | 0.349 |
| Height | 0.00071307 | 0.00000260 | 274.30 | 0.000 |

$s = 0.0001057$    $R-Sq = 100.0\%$    $R-Sq(adj) = 100.0\%$

or $\widehat{\log (Pressure)} = 3.15 - 1.001 \log (Height)$

**17.** a)

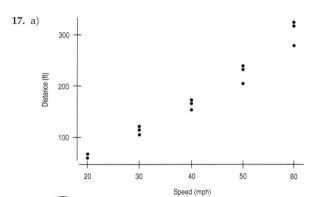

$\widehat{Distance} = -65.9 + 5.98\ Speed$.
But residuals have a curved shape, so linear model is not
appropriate.

b)

$\sqrt{Distance}$ linearizes the plot.
c) $Predicted\ \sqrt{Distance} = 3.30 + 0.235 \times Speed$.
d) 263.4 feet.
e) 390.2 feet.
f) Fairly confident, since $R^2 = 98.4\%$, and $s$ is small.

**18.** a)

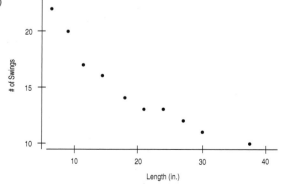

Relationship is curved, not straight.

b)

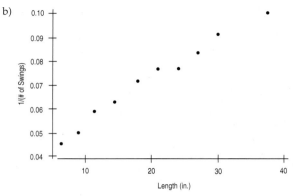

$1/Swings$ makes the plot more linear.
c) $\widehat{1/(Swings)} = 0.0367 + 0.00176 \times Length$.
   or $\widehat{\log(Swings)} = 1.721 - 0.453\log(Length)$
d) 22.9 swings.      e) 8.3 swings.
f) Fairly confident. These values are outside the data range, but
   not by a lot. Also, $R^2 = 98.1\%$.

**19.** a) The plot looks fairly straight. (It is okay to see a bend in the
   plot; there's one there.)

b) $\widehat{Salary} = -1913.88 + 0.965\ Year$

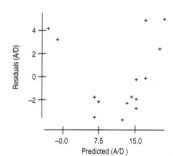

The residuals plot shows a strong bend.
c) $log(Salary)$ works well.
d) $\widehat{\log(Salary)} = -109.133 + 0.05516\ Year$

**20.** a)

Concave upward curve.

b)

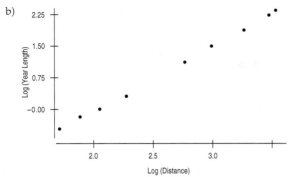

Taking the log of both variables linearizes the plot.
$\overline{\log(Length)} = -2.95 + 1.5\log(Distance)$.

c) Fits perfectly. $R^2 = 100\%$.

**21.** a)

Log(*Distance*) against position works pretty well.
$\overline{\log(Distance)} = 1.245 + 0.271 \times Position\ number$.

b) Pluto's residual is not especially larger in the log scale. However, a model without Pluto predicts the 9th planet should be 5741 million miles. Pluto, at "only" 3707 million miles, doesn't fit very well, giving support to the argument that Pluto doesn't behave like a planet.

**22.** $\overline{\log(Distance)} = 1.32 + 0.23 \times New\ Position$.
The linear relationship is very strong ($R^2 = 99.5\%$). The new position works better for modeling log(*Distance*), since the other model had $R^2 = 98.2\%$.

**23.** The predicted log(*Distance*) of Eris is 3.685, corresponding to a distance of 4841 million miles. That's short of the actual average distance of 6300 million miles.

**24.** Both models have high $R^2$, but the Exercise 20 model has $R^2 = 1$. That indicates that perhaps we have found a physical law. If we find another system with the same pattern, it would add evidence for Titius-Bode "law"; otherwise, we would discount the law.

**25.** a)

$\widehat{\sqrt{Bdft}} = -4 + diam$
The model is exact.

b) 36 board feet.

c) 1024 board feet.

**26.** a) $\widehat{Lift} = 164.97 + 2.56Class$

b)

Residuals show a curved pattern; need a different model.

c) Re-expressing *Class* by reciprocal works well. (Other models are possible.)
$\widehat{Lift} = 568.727 - 15243(1/Class)$; $R^2 = 99.4\%$

d) Less pattern in the residuals plot; higher $R^2$.

e) Asanidze's large negative residual indicates that he lifted less than expected.

**27.**

$\overline{\log Life} = 1.685 + 0.18497\log Decade$

**28.** a) $\widehat{Lift} = 573.257 - 15491.5(1/Class)$

b) This model predicts 391.0 kg for Asanidze.

c) He lifted 8.5 kg less than the model predicted.

**29.** The relationship cannot be made straight by the methods of this chapter.

**30.** a) $\overline{\dfrac{1}{ave\,Weight}} = 1.603 + 0.00112(Oranges)$

**31.** a) $\widehat{\sqrt{Left}} = 8.465 - 0.06926(Age)$

b) 52.10 years

c) No; the residuals plot still shows a pattern.

**32.** a) The linear model:
$\widehat{Diameter} = 1.97 + 0.463 \times Age$ gives $R^2 = 98\%$, but there is a clear pattern in the residuals. The pattern oscillates, so it cannot be made straight with the methods of this chapter.

b) Less strong, since averages are less variable than individuals.

**33.** a) $\overline{\log(Journals)} = 686.76 + 0.346(Year)$

b) 21497.04 journals.

c) Seems too high. Internet growth has exploded, but the model is unlikely to be very accurate.

**34.** Not successfully. Relationship curves up and down; is not linearizable by methods of this chapter.

**35.** a) The histogram is much more unimodal and symmetric after we take logs.

b) The plot is much straighter than the original, although it seems to have a bend in it around $HDI = 0.6$. There is more variation among the low-HDI countries.

c) The low-development countries seem to have a different slope than the more-developed countries.
d) The scatterplot appears to be straighter.

e) The correlation of $log(GDPPC)$ and $HDI$ for all 172 countries is 0.92. For the 141 high- and medium-developed countries it is 0.89, although that plot appears straighter.

**36.** a) The histogram of $sqrt(CellPhones)$ is much more unimodal and symmetric than that of *CellPhones*.
b) It is much straighter.

c) (Answers may vary.) The relationship is generally straight, but there are many outliers and countries with very high HDI do not necessarily have higher cell phone user rates than those with a slightly lower HDI. The relationship between cell phone rate and HDI for the extremely low HDI countries does not appear to be very strong.

## PART II REVIEW

**1.** % over 50, 0.69.
% under 20, −0.71.
% Graduating on time, −0.51.
% Full-time Faculty, 0.09

**2.** a) If no meals are eaten together, the *GPA* is 2.73.
b) For each increase of 1 meal, the *GPA* increases by 0.11.
c) 3.15
d) The predicted GPA was higher than the observed value.
e) There is no indication that there is a causal relation. There may be lurking variables.

**3.** a) There does not appear to be a linear relationship.
b) Nothing, there is no reason to believe that the results for the Finger Lakes region are representative of the vineyards of the world.
c) $\widehat{CasePrice} = 92.77 + 0.567 \times Years$.
d) Only 2.7 % of the variation in case price is accounted for by the ages of vineyards. Most of that is due to two outliers. We are better off using the mean price rather than this model.

**4.** a) No, no apparent relationship.
b) There is one very large leverage point.
c) Weaker. The cross point is extreme in the $x$ direction and low on the $y$-axis, causing the correlation to weaken (become closer to 0).
d) The slope of the line would increase.

**5.** a) $\widehat{TwinBirths} = -5119590 + 2618.25 \times Year$.
b) Each year, the number of twins born in a year increases, on average, by approximately 2618.25.
c) 143,092.5 births. The scatterplot appears to be somewhat linear, but there is some curvature in the pattern. There is no reason to believe that the increase will continue to be linear 5 years beyond the data.
d) The residuals plot shows a definite curved pattern, so the relation is not linear.

**6.** a) 0.914
b) $\widehat{DJIA} = -2294.01 + 341.095(Year - 1970)$.
c) Each year, the *DJIA* increased by about 341 points, on average.
d) The relationship does not appear to be linear, as the residuals have a definite pattern.

**7.** a) −0.520
b) Negative, not strong, somewhat linear, but with more variation as pH increases.
c) The BCI would also be average.
d) The predicted *BCI* will be 1.56 SDs of *BCI* below the mean *BCI*.

**8.** a) Number of motorboat registrations.
b) The association is fairly strong linear, and has a positive direction.
c) 0.946
d) 89.5% of the variation in manatees killed is explained by the variation in powerboat registrations.
e) No, there is no proof of causality.

**9.** a) $\widehat{Manatee\ Deaths} = -45.67 \times 0.1315\ Powerboat\ Registrations$ (in 1000s).
b) According to the model, for each increase of 10,000 motorboat registrations, the number of manatees killed increases by approximately 1.315.
c) If there were 0 motorboat registrations, the number of manatee deaths would be −45.67. This is obviously a silly extrapolation.
d) The predicted number is 82.41 deaths. The actual number of deaths was 79. The residual is 79 − 82.41 = −3.41. The model overestimated the number of deaths by 3.41.
e) Negative residuals would suggest that the actual number of deaths was lower than the predicted number.
f) Over time, the number of motorboat registrations has increased and the number of manatee kills has increased. The trend may continue. Extrapolation is risky, however, because the government may enact legislation to protect the manatee.

**10.** a) 73 points   b) 7 points   c) $r = 0.75$   d) 100 points
e) The regression equation is designed to predict final exam scores based on midterm exam scores. You would need to find the regression equation to predict midterm scores based on final exam scores.
f) −85 points
g) Increase. The point is unusual and has a high negative residual that would decrease the correlation; removing it would increase the correlation and the $R^2$ value.
h) Slope will increase.

**11. a)** $-0.984$   **b)** 96.9%   **c)** 32.95 mph   **d)** 1.66 mph
   **e)** Slope will increase.
   **f)** Correlation will weaken (become less negative).
   **g)** Correlation is the same, regardless of units.
**12. a)** 0.473
   **b)** A weak linear association in a positive direction.
   **c)** The actual score was higher than the predicted value for Monday.
   **d)** The predicted Monday score would be (0.473) SDs, or 2.37 points below the mean for Monday, or 34.9 points.
   **e)** Predicted Monday Score = $14.6 + 0.54 \times$ Friday Score.
   **f)** 36.0 points
**13. a)** Weight (but unable to verify linearity).
   **b)** As weight increases, mileage decreases.
   **c)** *Weight* accounts for 81.5% of the variation in *Fuel Efficiency*.
**14. a)** *Displacement* and *Weight* (but unable to verify linearity).
   **b)** No. Large engines (higher displacement) weigh more, so the engine itself may influence the weight somewhat. More likely, heavy cars are equipped with larger engines because their added weight needs a larger engine (higher displacement) to drive.
   **c)** The change in units will not affect the correlation.
   **d)** The predicted fuel economy will be 0.786 SDs below the mean fuel economy.
**15. a)** $\widehat{Horsepower} = 3.50 + 34.314 \times Weight$.
   **b)** Thousands. For the equation to have predicted values between 60 and 160, the X values would have to be in thousands of pounds.
   **c)** Yes. The residual plot does not show any pattern.
   **d)** 115.0 horsepower.
**16.** *Sex* and *Colorblindness* are both categorical variables, not quantitative. Correlation is meaningless for them, but we can say that the variables are associated.
**17. a)** The scatterplot shows a fairly strong linear relation in a positive direction. There seem to be two distinct clusters of data.
   **b)** $\widehat{Interval} = 33.967 \div 10.358 \times Duration$.
   **c)** The time between eruptions increases by about 10.4 minutes per minute of *Duration* on average.
   **d)** Since 77% of the variation in *Interval* is accounted for by *Duration* and the error standard deviation is 6.16 minutes, the prediction will be relatively accurate.
   **e)** 75.4 minutes.
   **f)** A residual is the observed value minus the predicted value. So the residual = $79 - 75.4 = 3.6$ minutes, indicating that the model underestimated the interval in this case.
**18. a)** Yes, the $R^2$ values indicate that 97.2% of the Indian crocodile length and 98% of the Australian crocodile length are explained by the head size.
   **b)** The slopes of the regression equations are similar, as are the $R^2$ values.
   **c)** The two models have different *y*-intercepts. It means that the Indian crocodile is smaller.
   **d)** Predicted body length for the Indian crocodile is 389.4 cm but is 458.2 cm for the Australian croc. The skeleton was probably from an Indian crocodile.
**19. a)** $r = 0.888$. Although $r$ is high, you must look at the scatterplot and verify that the relation is linear in form.
   **b)**

The association between diameter and age appears to be strong, somewhat linear, and positive.
   **c)** $\widehat{Age} = -0.97 + 2.21 \times Diameter$.
   **d)**

The residuals show a curved pattern (and two outliers).
   **e)** The residuals for five of the seven largest trees (15 in. or larger) are positive, indicating that the predicted values underestimate the age.
**20. a)** Yes.

   **b)** $\widehat{Age} = 7.24 + 0.11 \times Diameter^2$.

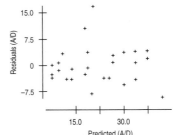

   **c)** The residuals appear to be more randomly scattered and have less of a pattern. But there are still some points with large residuals.
   **d)** 43.9 years old.
**21.** Most houses have areas between 1000 and 5000 square feet. Increasing 1000 square feet would result in either $1000(.008) = 8$ thousand dollars, $1000(.08) = 80$ thousand dollars, $1000(.8) = 800$ thousand dollars, or $1000(8) = 8000$ thousand dollars. Only $80,000 is reasonable, so the slope must be 0.08.
**22.**

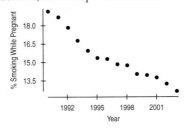

   **a)** The association is very strong, straight, and negative. However, there is some curvature to the scatterplot.
   **b)** $-0.972$
   **c)** Averaging increases the strength of the correlation, making it more negative.

d) $\overline{Percentage} = 9.46 - 0.4662 \times Year$. Each year, the average percent of women smoking while pregnant has decreased by about 0.47%.

23. a) The model predicts % smoking from year, not the other way around.
    b) $\overline{Year} = 2027.91 - 202.74 \times \% \, Smoking$.
    c) The smallest % smoking given is 12.7, and an extrapolation to $x = 0$ is probably too far from the given data. The prediction is not very reliable in spite of the strong correlation.

24. a) There is a very weak linear relationship between quality of service and tip size.
    b) $R^2 = 1.21\%$, indicating that the variation in quality of service accounts for only about 1% of the variation in tip percentages.

25. The relation shows a negative direction, with a somewhat linear form, but perhaps with some slight curvature. There are several model outliers.

26. a) Latitude, since the correlation $-0.848$ is stronger (but unable to verify linearity).
    b) The same.
    c) The same. Changes in units do not change the shape of the association nor correlation of the data.
    d) The predicted average January temperature would be 0.738 SDs below the mean average January temperature.

27. a) 71.9%
    b) As latitude increases, the January temperature decreases.
    c) $\overline{January \, Temperature} = 108.80 - 2.111 \times Latitude$.
    d) As the latitude increases by 1 degree, the average January temperature drops by about 2.11 degrees, on average.
    e) The $y$-intercept would indicate that the average January temperature is 108.8 when the latitude is 0. However, this is extrapolation and may not be meaningful.
    f) 24.4 degrees.
    g) The equation underestimates the average January temperature.

28. No. First, the $R^2$ indicates that only 4.6% of the variation in *Depression* is accounted for by *Internet Use*. That is a very low percentage. Even if it were higher, there may be lurking variables that explain the increase in both.

29. a) The scatterplot shows a strong, linear, positive association.
    b) There is an association, but it is likely that training and technique have increased over time and affected both jump performances.
    c) Neither; the change in units does not affect the correlation.
    d) The long-jumper would jump 0.925 SDs above the mean long jump, on average.

30. a) $\overline{High \, Jump} = -20.76 + 0.331 \times Long \, Jump$.
    b) As the long jump increases by 1 inch, the high jump increases by 0.331 inches, on average, according to the model.
    c) 95.09 inches.
    d) This equation is designed to predict high jump based on long jump. To predict the long jump, you would need the equation predicting long jump based on high jump.
    e) $\overline{Long \, Jump} = 99.26 + 2.5853 \times High \, Jump$. (99.055 + 2.588 *High Jump* with technology)

31. a) No relation; the correlation would probably be close to 0.
    b) The relation would have a positive direction and the correlation would be strong, assuming that students were studying French in each grade level. Otherwise, no correlation.
    c) No relation; correlation close to 0.
    d) The relation would have a positive direction and the correlation would be strong, since vocabulary would increase with each grade level.

32. a) There is a strong, fairly linear, positive trend for the data; as the year of birth increases, the preterm birth rate increases.
    b) The highest preterm birth rate is for mothers receiving adequate prenatal care utilization, and the lowest preterm birth rate is for mothers receiving inadequate prenatal care utilization. The slope is about the same for these relations. Mothers receiving intensive prenatal care utilization had more preterm births than mothers receiving inadequate prenatal care and fewer preterm births than mothers receiving adequate prenatal care; however, their rate of increase is higher.
    c) No, there is undoubtedly an underlying variable explaining these differences. Perhaps the level of prenatal care was determined by the complications the mothers experienced during the pregnancy.

33. $\overline{Calories} = 560.7 - 3.08 \times Time$.
    Each minute extra at the table results in 3.08 fewer calories being consumed, on average. Perhaps the hungry children eat fast and eat more.

34. a) $\overline{Gallons} = 12451.2 - 6.2 \times Year$.
    b) The model is designed to predict gallons based on the year. That question asks for a prediction of the year based on the gallons.
    c) $\overline{Year} = 2008.2 - 0.16 \times Gallons$ (in 1000s). Prediction is 2008.
    d) The prediction in the wrong direction is close because the relationship is so strong. The line that minimizes the $y$-residuals also does a pretty good job at minimizing the $x$-residuals.

35. There seems to be a strong, positive, linear relationship with one high-leverage point (Northern Ireland) that makes the overall $R^2$ quite low. Without that point, the $R^2$ increases to 61.5%. Of course, these data are averaged across thousands of households, so the correlation appears to be higher than it would be for individuals would be. Any conclusions about individuals would be suspect.

36. a) $\overline{Weight} = -1971.26 \mid 1.091 \times Year$.
    b) The scatterplot appears to have a linear trend in a positive direction; however, since the weights are averages, the linear trend would be stronger than for individual players.
    c) 214.75 pounds. Possibly, but it is a 10-year extrapolation from a range of only 20 years.
    d) 323.88 pounds. No, this is an extrapolation of 110 years, and the average weight seems absurd.
    e) 1306.11 pounds. Absolutely ridiculous to have an average weight of over 1000 pounds. The prediction is an extrapolation of 1010 years.

37. a) 3.842      b) 501.187      c) 4.0

38. a) $\overline{Weight} = -1121.66 + 0.673 \times Year$.
    b) 2032.
    c) No. That seems to be too much extrapolation for the model.

39. a) 30,818 pounds.
    b) 1302 pounds.
    c) 31,187.6 pounds.
    d) I would be concerned about using this relation if we needed accuracy closer than 1000 pounds or so, as the residuals are more than $\pm 1000$ pounds.
    e) Negative residuals will be more of a problem, as the predicted weight would overestimate the weight of the truck; trucking companies might be inclined to take the ticket to court.

40. a) Symmetric distributions of $x$ and $y$ may help ensure that the residuals around a line through the data will be more symmetric and normally distributed. The re-expressed data will not have extreme outliers as well.
    b) Yes. The scatterplot shows a linear trend in a positive direction. It has some moderate outliers in the $x$ direction. The residuals plot shows some moderate residuals in the negative direction and some curvature, but the model using re-expressed data is surely better than the model using the original data.
    c) $\overline{\log(Profit)} = -0.11 + 0.648 \times \log(Sales)$.
    d) $124.43 million.

41. The original data are nonlinear, with a significant curvature. Using reciprocal square root of diameter gave a scatterplot that is nearly linear:

$$\overline{1/\sqrt{Drain \, Time}} = 0.0024 + 0.219 \, Diameter.$$

**42.** The scatterplot of *Cost per Chip* vs. *Chips Produced* has a significant curvature. Taking the log of *Chips Produced* and the log of *Cost per Chip* provided a nearly linear scatterplot.

$$\overline{\log \text{Cost per Chip}} = 2.67 - 0.502 \times \log \text{Chips Produced}.$$

**43.** The predicted values are (12,774), (24,738), (36,702), (48,666).
The residuals are (12,26), (24, −58), (36, 38), (48, −6).
The squared residuals are (12,676), (24,3364), (36,1444), (48,36).
The "least squares" regression equation minimizes the sum of the squares of the residuals.

# CHAPTER 11

**1.** Yes. You cannot predict the outcome beforehand.

**2.** The outcomes cannot be predicted beforehand. Each of the individual outcomes, numbers 00 through 36, should be equally likely.

**3.** A machine pops up numbered balls. If it were truly random, the outcome could not be predicted and the outcomes would be equally likely. It is random only if the balls generate numbers in equal frequencies.

**4.** Answers may vary. **Rolling one die or two dice:** If the dice are fair, then each outcome, 1 through 6, should be equally likely.
**Spinning a spinner:** Each outcome should be equally likely, but the spinner might be more likely to land on one outcome than another due to friction or design.
**Shuffling cards and dealing a hand:** If the cards are shuffled adequately (7 times for riffle shuffling), the cards will be approximately equally likely.

**5.** Use two-digit numbers 00–99; let 00–02 = defect, 03–99 = no defect

**6.** Use random digits 0–9; let 0 = colorblind, 1–9 = no defect

**7.** a) 45, 10    b) 17, 22

**8.** 43, 9, 50, 13, 27

**9.** If the lottery is random, it doesn't matter which number you play; all are equally likely to win.

**10.** If the lottery is random, it doesn't matter which number you play; all are equally likely to win.

**11.** a) The outcomes are not equally likely; for example, tossing 5 heads does not have the same probability as tossing 0 or 9 heads, but the simulation assumes they are equally likely.
b) The even–odd assignment assumes that the player is equally likely to score or miss the shot. In reality, the likelihood of making the shot depends on the player's skill.
c) Suppose a hand has 4 aces. This might be represented by 1, 1, 1, 1, and any other number. The likelihood for the first ace in the hand is not the same as for the second or third or fourth. But with this simulation, the likelihood is the same for each.

**12.** a) The numbers would represent the sums, but the sums are not all equally likely. The simulation assumes they are equally likely.
b) The numbers of boys in a family of 5 children are not equally likely; for example, having a total of 5 boys is less likely than having 3 boys out of 5 children. The simulation assigns the same likelihood to each event.
c) The likelihoods for out, single, double, triple, and home run are not the same, but the simulation assumes they are.

**13.** The conclusion should indicate that the simulation *suggests* that the average length of the line would be 3.2 people. Future results might not match the simulated results exactly.

**14.** The simulation *suggests* that 24% of the people might contract the disease. The simulation does not represent what happened, but what might have happened.

**15.** a) The component is one voter voting. An outcome is a vote for our candidate or not. Use two random digits, giving 00–54 a vote for your candidate and 55–99 for the underdog.

b) A trial is 100 votes. Examine 100 two-digit random numbers, and count how many people voted for each candidate. Whoever gets the majority of votes wins that trial.
c) The response variable is whether the underdog wins or not.

**16.** a) The component is picking a single card. An outcome is the suit and denomination of the card. You could use the digits 01–52 for the 52 different cards, ignoring 00 and 53–99, or you could use a single digit 1, 2, 3, or 4 for the suit and then 01–13 for the denomination (ignoring 0, 5–9 for suits, and 00, 14–99 for denominations).
b) A trial is a single five-card hand. Use five sets of random numbers, ignoring repeated cards.
c) As response variable, we'll record whether the hand had two pairs, three of a kind, or neither.

**17.** Answers will vary, but average answer will be about 51.5%.

**18.** Answers will vary, but average answer will be about 5 boxes.

**19.** Answers will vary, but average answer will be about 26%.

**20.** Answers will vary, but few simulations will have any runs getting all 6 correct, leading us to conclude that the probability is very small. (The true probability is 0.00024.)

**21.** a) Answers will vary, but you should win about 10% of the time.
b) You should win at the same rate with any number.

**22.** Answers will vary, but you should win about 10% of the time.

**23.** Answers will vary, but you should win about 10% of the time.

**24.** Answers will vary, but you should win about 10% of the time.

**25.** Answers will vary, but average answer will be about 1.9 tests.

**26.** Answers will vary, but average answer will be about 18%.

**27.** Answers will vary, but average answer will be about 1.24 points.

**28.** Answers will vary, but average answer will be 6.8 people.

**29.** Do the simulation in two steps. First simulate the payoffs. Then count until $500 is reached. Answers will vary, but average should be near 10.2 customers.

**30.** Answers will vary, but average answer will be about $37.

**31.** Answers will vary, but average answer will be about 3 children.

**32.** Answers will vary, but average answer will be slightly less than 6 children.

**33.** Answers will vary, but average answer will be about 7.5 rolls.

**34.** Answers will vary, but average answer will be about 2.7 rolls.

**35.** No, it will happen about 40% of the time.

**36.** Answers will vary, but average answer will be about 39%.

**37.** Answers will vary, but average answer will be about 37.5%.

**38.** Answers will vary, but average answer will be about 37.5%.

**39.** Three women will be selected about 7.8% of the time.

**40.** Answers will vary, but if cell phone usage is only 12%, you should find four or more cell phone users among 10 drivers only about 2% of the time. Because that's what you saw while waiting for your bus, you'd suspect that the legislator's claim of 12% is probably too low.

**41.** Answers will vary, but average answer will be about 30 envelopes.

**42.** Answers will vary, but average answer will be about 38.5%.

# CHAPTER 12

**1.** a) No. It would be nearly impossible to get exactly 500 males and 500 females from every country by random chance.
b) A stratified sample, stratified by whether the respondent is male or female.

**2.** a) No. It would be nearly impossible to get exactly 50 from each class by random chance.
b) A stratified sample, stratified by the respondents' class.

**3.** a) Voluntary response.
b) We have no confidence at all in estimates from such studies.

**4.** a) A cluster sample, with teams being the clusters.
b) It is a reasonable solution to the problem of randomly sampling players because you can sample an entire team at once

relatively easily but couldn't efficiently draw a random sample of all players on the same day.

5. a) The population of interest is all adults in the United States aged 18 and older.
   b) The sampling frame is U.S. adults with landline telephones.
   c) Some members of the population (e.g, many college students) don't have landline phones, which could create a bias.
6. a) They are using a stratified design in which countries are strata, and a random sample is drawn in each stratum. They don't specify how the random samples are drawn.
   b) The difference in population size has no effect whatever on the precision of estimates from these surveys. Only the sample size matters.
7. a) Population—Human resources directors of Fortune 500 companies.
   b) Parameter—Proportion who don't feel surveys intruded on their work day.
   c) Sampling Frame—List of HR directors at Fortune 500 companies.
   d) Sample—23% who responded.
   e) Method—Questionnaire mailed to all (nonrandom).
   f) Bias—Nonresponse. Hard to generalize because who responds is related to the question itself.
8. a) Population—U.S. adults.
   b) Parameter—Proportion who feel marijuana should be legalized for medicinal purposes.
   c) Sampling Frame—None given; potentially all people with access to Web site.
   d) Sample—Those visiting the Web site who responded.
   e) Method—Voluntary response (no randomization employed).
   f) Bias—Voluntary response sample. Those who visit the Web site and respond may be predisposed to a particular answer.
9. a) Population—All U.S. adults.
   b) Parameter—Proportion who have used and benefited from alternative medicine.
   c) Sampling Frame—All Consumers Union subscribers.
   d) Sample—Those who responded (random).
   e) Method—Questionnaire to all (nonrandom).
   f) Bias—Nonresponse. Those who respond may have strong feelings one way or another.
10. a) Population—U.S. adults.
    b) Parameter—Proportion who believe in global warming.
    c) Sampling Frame—U.S. adults aged 18 and over.
    d) Sample—1007 randomly selected adults.
    e) Method—Not clear.
    f) Bias—Probably not biased. Conclusions could be generalized.
11. a) Population—Adults.
    b) Parameter—Proportion who think drinking and driving is a serious problem.
    c) Sampling Frame—Bar patrons.
    d) Sample—Every 10th person leaving the bar.
    e) Method—Systematic sampling.
    f) Bias—Those interviewed had just left a bar. They probably think drinking and driving is less of a problem than do adults in general.
12. a) Population—City voters.
    b) Parameter—Not clear; percentages of voters favoring various issues?
    c) Sampling Frame—All city residents.
    d) Sample—Cluster sample; one block from each district.
    e) Method—Convenience sample within each cluster.
    f) Bias—Parameter(s) of interest not clear. Sampling within clusters is not random and may bias results.
13. a) Population—Soil around a former waste dump.
    b) Parameter—Concentrations of toxic chemicals.
    c) Sampling Frame—Accessible soil around the dump.
    d) Sample—16 soil samples.

e) Method—Not clear.
f) Bias—Don't know if soil samples were randomly chosen. If not, may be biased toward more or less polluted soil.

14. a) Population—Cars.
    b) Parameter—Proportion with up-to-date registration, insurance, and safety inspections.
    c) Sampling Frame—All cars on that road.
    d) Sample—Those actually stopped by roadblock.
    e) Method—Cluster sample of location; census within cluster.
    f) Bias—Time of day and location may not be representative of all cars. Other than that, should be able to estimate proportion of all cars.
15. a) Population—Snack food bags.
    b) Parameter—Weight of bags, proportion passing inspection.
    c) Sampling Frame—All bags produced each day.
    d) Sample—Bags in 10 randomly selected cases, 1 bag from each case for inspection.
    e) Method—Multistage sampling.
    f) Bias—Should be unbiased.
16. a) Population—Dairy farms.
    b) Parameter—Proportion passing inspection.
    c) Sampling Frame—All dairy farms?
    d) Sample—Not clear. Perhaps a random sample of farms, and then milk within each farm?
    e) Method—Multistage sampling.
    f) Bias—Should be unbiased if farms and milk at each farm are randomly selected.
17. Bias. Only people watching the news will respond, and their preference may differ from that of other voters. The sampling method may systematically produce samples that don't represent the population of interest.
18. Sampling error. The description of the sampling method suggests that samples should be representative of the voting population. Nonetheless, random chance in selecting the individuals who were polled means that sample statistics will vary from the population parameter, perhaps by quite a bit.
19. a) Voluntary response. Only those who both see the ad *and* feel strongly enough will respond.
    b) Cluster sampling. One school may not be typical of all.
    c) Attempted census. Will have nonresponse bias.
    d) Stratified sampling with follow-up. Should be unbiased.
20. a) Voluntary response. Only those who see the show *and* feel strongly will call.
    b) Possibly more representative than part a, but only strongly motivated parents go to PTA meetings.
    c) Multistage sampling, with cluster sample within each school. Probably a good design if most of the parents in the class respond.
    d) Systematic sampling. Probably a reasonable design.
21. a) This is a multistage design, with a cluster sample at the first stage and a simple random sample for each cluster.
    b) If any of the three churches you pick at random is not representative of all churches, then you'll introduce sampling error by the choice of that church.
22. a) This is a multistage design, with one day picked at random as a cluster, then five boats picked as clusters within that day, and finally a census taken for each boat.
    b) If the day is not representative of all fishing days, that will introduce sampling error. If any of the five boats they pick at random is not representative of the types and amounts of fish taken by all boats, then that will introduce sampling error by the choice of that boat.
23. a) This is a systematic sample.
    b) It is likely to be representative of those waiting for the roller coaster. Indeed, it may do quite well if those at the front of the line respond differently (after their long wait) than those at the back of the line.

c) The sampling frame is patrons willing to wait for the roller coaster on that day at that time. It should be representative of the people in line, but not of all people at the amusement park.

24. They will get responses only from people who come to the park to use the playground. Parents who are dissatisfied with the playground may not come.

25. a) Answers will definitely differ. Question 1 will probably get many "No" answers, while Question 2 will get many "Yes" answers. This is wording bias.
   b) "Do you think standardized tests are appropriate for deciding whether a student should be promoted to the next grade?" (Other answers will vary.)

26. a) This is not a representative sample, but rather a voluntary response survey. Even a large sample size can't make it representative.
   b) The wording seems fair enough. It states the facts and gives voice to both sides of the issue.
   c) The sampling frame is, at best, those who visit this particular site, and even then depends on their volunteering to respond to the question.
   d) This is a true statement.

27. Only those who think it worth the wait are likely to be in line. Those who don't like roller coasters are unlikely to be in the sampling frame, so the poll won't get a fair picture of whether park patrons overall would favor still more roller coasters.

28. The first sentence points out problems the respondent may not have noticed, and might lead them to feel they should agree. The last phrase mentions higher fees, though, which could make people reject improvements to the playground.

29. a) Biased toward yes because of "pollute." "Should companies be responsible for any costs of environmental cleanup?"
   b) Biased toward no because of "old enough to serve in the military." "Do you think the drinking age should be lowered from 21?"

30. a) Seems unbiased.
   b) Biased toward yes because of "great tradition." Better to ask, "Do you favor continued funding for the space program?"

31. a) Not everyone has an equal chance. People with unlisted numbers, people without phones, and those at work cannot be reached.
   b) Generate random numbers and call at random times.
   c) Under the original plan, those families in which one person stays home are more likely to be included. Under the second plan, many more are included. People without phones are still excluded.
   d) It improves the chance of selected households being included.
   e) This takes care of phone numbers. Time of day may be an issue. People without phones are still excluded.

32. Cell phones are more likely to be used by higher income individuals. This will cause an undercoverage bias. As cell phones grow in use, this problem will be lessened.

33. a) Answers will vary.
   b) Your own arm length. Parameter is your own arm length; population is all possible measurements of it.
   c) Population is now the arm lengths of your friends. The average estimates the mean of these lengths.
   d) Probably not. Friends are likely to be of the same age and not very diverse or representative of the larger population.

34. a) Mean gas mileage for the last six fill-ups.
   b) Mean gas mileage for the vehicle.
   c) Recent driving conditions may not be typical.
   d) Mean gas mileage for all cars of this make and model.

35. a) Assign numbers 001 to 120 to each order. Use random numbers to select 10 transactions to examine.
   b) Sample proportionately within each type. (Do a stratified random sample.)

36. a) Most likely that all laborers are selected, no managers, and few foremen. Bias may be introduced because the company itself is conducting the survey.
   b) Assign a number from 001 to 439 to each employee. Use a random-number table or software to select the sample.
   c) Still heavily favors the laborers.
   d) Stratify by job type (proportionately to the members in each).
   e) Answers will vary. Assign numbers 01 to 14 to each person; use a random-number table or software to do the selection.

37. a) Select three cases at random; then select one jar randomly from each case.
   b) Use random numbers to choose 3 cases from numbers 61 through 80; then use random numbers between 1 and 12 to select the jar from each case.
   c) No. Multistage sampling.

38. What conclusions they may be able to make will depend on whether fish with discolored scales are equally likely to be caught as those without. It also depends on the level of compliance by fishermen. If fish are not equally likely to be caught, or fishermen are more disposed to bringing discolored fish, the results will be biased.

39. a) Depends on the Yellow Page listings used. If from regular (line) listings, this is fair if all doctors are listed. If from ads, probably not, as those doctors may not be typical.
   b) Not appropriate. This cluster sample will probably contain listings for only one or two business types.

40. a) Petition may bias people to say they support the playground. Also, many may not be home on Saturday afternoon.
   b) If the food at the largest cafeteria is representative, this should be OK. However, those who really don't like the food won't be eating there.

# CHAPTER 13

1. a) No. There are no manipulated factors. It is an observational study.
   b) There may be lurking variables that are associated with both parental income and performance on the SAT.

2. a) No, there are no manipulated factors. It is a retrospective study.
   b) No, there may be other lurking variables, such as age of the patient.

3. a) This is a retrospective observational study.
   b) That's appropriate because MS is a relatively rare disease.
   c) The subjects were U.S. military personnel, some of whom had developed MS.
   d) The variables were the vitamin D blood levels and whether or not the subject developed MS.

4. a) This is a stratified sample. The question was about population values (the proportions of men and women who look forward more to the commercials.) No treatment was applied, so it is not an experiment.
   b) Yes.

5. a) This was a randomized comparative, placebo-controlled experiment.
   b) Yes, such an experiment is the right way to determine whether black cohosh has an effect.
   c) 351 women aged 45 to 55 who reported at least two hot flashes a day.
   d) The treatments were black cohosh, a multiherb supplement, a multiherb supplement plus advice, estrogen, and a placebo.
   e) The response was the women's symptoms (presumably frequency of hot flashes.)

6. a) This is an experiment. The picture is the controlled factor. Randomization may have been used in deciding which days each picture appeared.
   b) The treatment was the picture behind the coffee station. The response was the average contribution.

c) The differences in money collected were larger than could be reasonably attributed to usual day-to-day variation.

7. a) Experiment.
   b) Bipolar disorder patients.
   c) Omega-3 fats from fish oil, two levels.
   d) 2 treatments.
   e) Improvement (fewer symptoms?).
   f) Design not specified.
   g) Blind (due to placebo), unknown if double-blind.
   h) Individuals with bipolar disease improve with high-dose omega-3 fats from fish oil.

8. a) Experiment.
   b) Men aged 60 to 75.
   c) Exercise (1 level).
   d) 1 treatment, 16-week, high-intensity resistance training twice a week.
   e) Strength levels pre- and postexercise program.
   f) Pre- and posttest–matched design.
   g) Not blinded.
   h) Applies only to men 60 to 75 who participate in similar exercise programs. However, since there is no random assignment, other factors might have explained the difference in strength.

9. a) Observational study.
   b) Prospective.
   c) Men and women with moderately high blood pressure and normal blood pressure, unknown selection process.
   d) Memory and reaction time.
   e) As there is no random assignment, there is no way to know that high blood pressure *caused* subjects to do worse on memory and reaction-time tests. A lurking variable may also be the cause.

10. a) Observational study.
    b) Prospective.
    c) Disabled women aged 65 and older with and without a vitamin $B_{12}$ deficiency, unknown selection process.
    d) Suffering severe depression.
    e) As there is no random assignment, there is no way to know that the deficiency caused the severe depression.

11. a) Observational study.
    b) Retrospective.
    c) Swedish men, unknown selection process.
    d) Risk of kidney cancer.
    e) As there is no random assignment, there is no way to know that the overweight or high blood pressure caused the higher risk for kidney cancer.

12. a) Experiment.
    b) 459 subjects.
    c) Diet with 3 levels.
    d) 3 treatments (3 groups—but only one diet and one control group were described).
    e) Systolic blood pressure.
    f) Completely randomized.
    g) Not blinded.
    h) Indicates that the DASH diet appears to lower systolic blood pressure.

13. a) Experiment.
    b) Postmenopausal women.
    c) Alcohol—2 levels; blocking variable—estrogen supplements (2 levels).
    d) 1 factor (alcohol) at 2 levels = 2 treatments.
    e) Increase in estrogen levels.
    f) Blocked.
    g) Not blind.
    h) Indicates that alcohol consumption *for those taking estrogen supplements* may increase estrogen levels.

14. a) Experiment.
    b) People suffering from insomnia.
    c) 2 factors: desserts and exercise (2 levels each).

d) 4 treatments.
e) Improvement in ability to sleep.
f) Completely randomized.
g) Not blind.
h) Insomniacs who exercise and refrain from desserts will experience improved ability to sleep.

15. a) Experiment.
    b) Locations in a garden.
    c) 1 factor: traps (2 levels).
    d) 2 treatments.
    e) Number of bugs in the trap.
    f) Blocked by location.
    g) Not blind.
    h) One type of trap is more effective than the other.

16. a) Observational study.
    b) Retrospective.
    c) Women exposed to dioxin from an industrial accident.
    d) Risk of breast cancer.
    e) As there is no random assignment, there is no way to know that the dioxin levels caused the increase in breast cancer; there may have been lurking variables that were not identified.

17. a) Observational study.
    b) Retrospective.
    c) Women in Finland, unknown selection process with data from church records.
    d) Women's lifespans.
    e) As there is no random assignment, there is no way to know that having sons or daughters shortens or lengthens the lifespan of mothers.

18. a) Observational study.
    b) Retrospective.
    c) Women; unknown selection process with information taken from work histories.
    d) Risk of breast cancer.
    e) As there is no random assignment, there is no way to know that working nights caused breast cancer; there may be confounding variables not identified in the study.

19. a) Observational study.
    b) Prospective.
    c) People with or without depression, unknown selection process.
    d) Frequency of crying in response to sad situations.
    e) There is no apparent difference in crying response (to sad movies) for depressed and nondepressed groups.

20. a) Experiment.
    b) People exposed to cold virus.
    c) 1 factor: herbal treatment (2 levels).
    d) 2 treatments.
    e) Severity of cold symptoms.
    f) No discussion of randomness.
    g) Blind, as subjects did not know if they received the herbal treatment or the placebo. Not clear if it was double-blind.
    h) There is no indication that the herbal treatment is effective.

21. a) Experiment.
    b) Rats.
    c) 1 factor: sleep deprivation; four levels.
    d) 4 treatments.
    e) Glycogen content in the brain.
    f) No discussion of randomness.
    g) Blinding is not discussed.
    h) The conclusion could be that rats deprived of sleep have significantly lower glycogen levels and may need sleep to restore that brain energy fuel. Extrapolating to humans would be very speculative.

22. a) Experiment.
    b) Racing greyhounds.
    c) 1 factor, diet with 3 levels.

d) 3 treatments.

e) Speed.

f) Random assignment to order of diets; matched design before and after diet.

g) No blinding.

h) Greyhounds who eat diets high in vitamin C run more slowly.

23. a) Experiment.

b) People experiencing migraines.

c) 2 factors (pain reliever and water temperature), 2 levels each.

d) 4 treatments.

e) Level of pain relief.

f) Completely randomized over 2 factors.

g) Blind, as subjects did not know if they received the pain medication or the placebo, but not blind, as the subjects will know if they are drinking regular or ice water.

h) It may indicate whether pain reliever alone or in combination with ice water gives pain relief, but patients are not blinded to ice water, so placebo effect may also be the cause of any relief seen caused by ice water.

24. a) Experiment.

b) Inactive dogs.

c) 1 factor: dog food (assuming amount of food to be determined by weight or size of dog) (2 levels).

d) 2 treatments.

e) Weight.

f) Blocked by size of breed.

g) Blinded, assuming dog owners do not know which food the dog is receiving.

h) Assuming the dog owners followed the prescribed feeding levels, there could be a conclusion as to whether or not the dog food helped maintain healthy weight.

25. a) Experiment.

b) Athletes with hamstring injuries.

c) 1 factor: type of exercise program (2 levels).

d) 2 treatments.

e) Time to return to sports.

f) Completely randomized.

g) No blinding—subjects must know what kind of exercise they do.

h) Can determine which of the two exercise programs is more effective.

26. a) Observational study.

b) Prospective.

c) General public; two random samples.

d) The purpose of the study was to identify variables on which there was a difference, so no response variable(s) could be identified at the start of the study.

e) Identify differences between people who can be reached by regular polling methods and those who cannot.

27. They need to compare omega-3 results to something. Perhaps bipolarity is seasonal and would have improved during the experiment anyway.

28. They need a basis for comparison. Perhaps insomnia is related to the amount of daylight, and that changed during the time the experiment was conducted.

29. a) Subjects' responses might be related to many other factors (diet, exercise, genetics, etc). Randomization should equalize the two groups with respect to unknown factors.

b) More subjects would minimize the impact of individual variability in the responses, but the experiment would become more costly and time consuming.

30. a) Subjects' responses might be related to many other factors (diet, medications, genetics, etc). Randomization should equalize the two groups with respect to unknown factors.

b) More subjects would minimize the impact of individual variability in the responses, but the experiment would become more costly and time consuming.

31. People who engage in regular exercise might respond differently to the omega-3 fats, and that additional variability could obscure the effectiveness of this treatment.

32. People who are overweight might respond differently to exercise, and that additional variability could obscure the effectiveness of this treatment.

33. Answers may vary. Use a random-number generator to randomly select 24 numbers from 01 to 24 without replication. Assign the first 8 numbers to the first group, the second 8 numbers to the second group, and the third 8 numbers to the third group.

34. Answers may vary. Use a random-number generator to randomly select 24 numbers from 01 to 24 without replication. Assign the first group of 4 numbers to the first treatment (no fertilizer, natural watering), the second group of 4 numbers to the second treatment (no fertilizer, daily water), the third group of 4 numbers to the third treatment (half fertilizer, natural watering), and so on to the sixth treatment.

35. a) First, they are using athletes who have a vested interest in the success of the shoe by virtue of their sponsorship. They should choose other athletes. Second, they should randomize the order of the runs, not run all the races with their shoes second. They should blind the athletes by disguising the shoes if possible, so they don't know which is which. The timers shouldn't know which athletes are running with which shoes, either. Finally, they should replicate several times, since times will vary under both shoe conditions.

b) Because of the problems in (a), the results they obtain may be biased in favor of their shoes. In addition, the results obtained for Olympic athletes may not be the same as for the general runner.

36. The "control" in this experiment is not the same for all swimmers. We don't know what "their old swimsuit" is. They should compare their new swimsuit to the same suit design. The order in which the swims are performed should be randomized. There may be a systematic effect from one swim to the next. Finally, there is no way to blind this test. The swimmers will know which kind of suit they have on, and this may bias their performance.

37. a) Allowing athletes to self-select treatments could confound the results. Other issues such as severity of injury, diet, age, etc., could also affect time to heal, and randomization should equalize the two treatment groups with respect to any such variables.

b) A control group could have revealed whether either exercise program was better (or worse) than just letting the injury heal.

c) Doctors who evaluated the athletes to approve their return to sports should not know which treatment the subject had engaged in.

d) It's hard to tell. The difference of 15 days seems large, but the standard deviations indicate that there was a great deal of variability in the times.

38. a) Self-selection could result in groups that were very different at the start of the experiment, making it impossible to attribute differences in the results to their diet.

b) This assured that the diets were followed and that all subjects in each group received comparable treatments.

c) The researchers can compare the change in blood pressure observed in the DASH group to the control group. They need to rule out the possibility that external variables (the season, news events, etc.) affected everyone's blood pressure.

d) We'd like to know the standard deviation of the changes, too. If it's very small, then 6.7 points would seem like a significant change.

39. a) The differences among the Mozart and quiet groups were more than would have been expected from ordinary sampling variation.

b)

c) The Mozart group seems to have the smallest median difference and thus the *least* improvement, but there does not appear to be a significant difference.

d) No, if anything, there is less improvement, but the difference does not seem significant compared with the usual variation.

40. Answers may vary. Suppose you select the next 12 batches of sake for the experiment. Divide the yeast into two parts. For each batch, play Mozart for half the yeast and no Mozart for the other half. When the sake is done, have trained sake testers (who don't know which experimental treatment was applied) taste samples from each group and rate the sake. Compare the ratings for the Mozart and the non-Mozart sake. Try to keep as many other variables as possible under control (type of yeast, size of batch, etc.)

41. a) Observational. Randomly select a group of children, ages 10 to 13, have them taste the cereal, and ask if they like the cereal.

b) Answers may vary. Get volunteers ages 10 to 13. Each volunteer will taste both cereals, randomizing the order in which they taste them. Compare the percentage of favorable ratings for each cereal.

c) Answers may vary. From the volunteers, identify the children who watch Frump and identify the children who do not watch Frump. Use a blocked design to reduce variation in cereal preference that may be associated with watching the Frump cartoon.

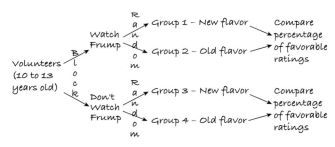

42. Use a retrospective observational study. For example, collect records from a random selection of police and emergency room logs for the past 3 years. Find the number of cases for the days when there is a full moon, when there is a waxing moon, when there is a waning moon, and when the moon is nearly dark. Compare the numbers for each group.

43. a) Observational, prospective study.

b) The supposed relation between health and wine consumption might be explained by the confounding variables of income and education.

c) None of these. While the variables have a relation, there is no causality indicated for the relation.

44. a) The difference in the depression rates for the two groups is greater than would be expected by natural sampling variation.

b) Observational study. There was no experimental treatment.

c) The difference could be explained by lurking variables. Perhaps swimmers are more affluent (can afford a membership at the Y or have access to a pool), or perhaps depressed people tend to swim less.

d) Answers may vary. Give the subjects a test to measure depression. Then randomly assign the 120 subjects to one of three groups: the control group (no exercise program), the anaerobic exercise group, and the aerobic exercise group. Monitor subjects' exercise (have them report to a particular gym or pool). At the end of 12 weeks, administer the depression test again. Compare the post-exercise and pre-exercise depression scores.

45. a) Arrange the 20 containers in 20 separate locations. Use a random-number generator to identify the 10 containers that should be filled with water.

b) Guessing, the dowser should be correct about 50% of the time. A record of 60% (12 out of 20) does not appear to be significantly different.

c) Answers may vary. You would need to see a high level of success—say, 90% to 100%, that is, 18 to 20 correct.

46. Answers may vary. Randomly select half of the patients who agree to the study to get large doses of vitamin E after surgery. Give the other half a similar-looking placebo pill. Monitor their progress, recording the time until they have reached an easily agreed upon level of healing. Have the evaluating doctor blinded to whether the patient received the placebo or not. Compare the number of days until recovery of the two groups.

47. Randomly assign half the reading teachers in the district to use each method. Students should be randomly assigned to teachers as well. Make sure to block both by school and grade (or control grade by using only one grade). Construct an appropriate reading test to be used at the end of the year, and compare scores.

48.

Answers may vary. This experiment has 1 factor (type of gasoline), at 2 levels (premium and regular), resulting in 2 treatments. The response variable is gas mileage. An experiment diagram for a matched design appears above. Have each of the volunteers use each kind of gas for a month. Randomly assign 10 of them to use regular first, the other 10 to use premium first. Ask them to keep driving logs (the number of miles driven and the gallons of gasoline) for each month. Compare the differences in the fuel economy for the two kinds of gasoline.

49. a) They mean that the difference is higher than they would expect from normal sampling variability.

b) An observational study.

c) No. Perhaps the differences are attributable to some confounding variable (e.g., people are more likely to engage in riskier behaviors on the weekend) rather than the day of admission.

d) Perhaps people have more serious accidents and traumas on weekends and are thus more likely to die as a result.

50. a) Answers may vary. Randomly assign the eight patients to either the current medication or the new medication. Have nurses assess the degree of shingles involvement for the patient. Ask patients to rate their pain levels. Administer the medications for a prescribed time. Have nurses reassess the degree of shingles involvement. Ask patients to rate their pain levels post medication. Compare the improvement levels for each group.

b) Let A = 1, B = 2 . . . H = 8.
Assign the first four randomly selected to the first group, the remainder to the second. So Group 1 is D, A, H, C, and Group 2 is B, E, F, G.

c) Assuming that the ointments look alike, it would be possible to blind the experiment for the subject and for the administrator of the treatment.

d) A block design with factors for gender and for ointment would be appropriate. Subjects would be randomly assigned to each treatment group in the blocked design.

51. Answers may vary. This experiment has 1 factor (pesticide), at 3 levels (pesticide A, pesticide B, no pesticide), resulting in 3 treatments. The response variable is the number of beetle larvae found on each plant. Randomly select a third of the plots to be sprayed with pesticide A, a third with pesticide B, and a third with no pesticide (since the researcher also wants to know whether the pesticides even work at all). To control the experiment, the plots of land should be as similar as possible with regard to amount of sunlight, water, proximity to other plants, etc. If not, plots with similar characteristics should be blocked together. If possible, use some inert substance as a placebo pesticide on the control group, and do not tell the counters of the beetle larvae which plants have been treated with pesticides. After a given period of time, count the number of beetle larvae on each plant and compare the results.

52. a) The students were not randomly assigned. Those who signed up for the prep course may be a special group whose scores would have improved anyway.
    b) Answers may vary. Find a group of volunteers who are willing to participate. Give all volunteers the SAT exam. Randomly assign the subjects to the review or no review group. Give the tutoring to the one group. After a reasonable time, retest both groups. Check to see that the tutored group had a significant improvement in scores when compared with the no-review group.
    c) After the volunteers have taken the first SAT exam, separate the volunteers into blocks of low, average, and high SAT exam score performance. Now assign half of each block to the review and half to the no-review groups. Give the tutoring. Now retest all groups. Compare the differences between treatments for each block.

53. Answers may vary. Find a group of volunteers. Each volunteer will be required to shut off the machine with his or her left hand and right hand. Randomly assign the left or right hand to be used first. Complete the first attempt for the whole group. Now repeat the experiment with the alternate hand. Check the differences in time for the left and right hands.

54. Answers may vary. There are two factors: temperature of the water and wash cycle. Since each factor has 2 levels, there are 4 treatment groups (hot-reg., cold-reg., hot-del., cold-del.). It would be nice to have 32 shirts, but equal numbers of shirts in each group is not necessary. Randomly assign shirts to each of the 4 treatment groups. Rate the level of cleaning for the grass-stained shirts. Compare the 4 groups and determine the best use of the product.

55. a) Jumping with or without a parachute.
    b) Volunteer skydivers (the dimwitted ones).
    c) A parachute that looks real but doesn't work.
    d) A good parachute and a placebo parachute.
    e) Whether parachutist survives the jump (or extent of injuries).
    f) All should jump from the same altitude in similar weather conditions and land on similar surfaces.
    g) Randomly assign people the parachutes.
    h) The skydivers (and the people involved in distributing the parachute packs) shouldn't know who got a working chute. And the people evaluating the subjects after the jumps should not be told who had a real parachute either!

# PART III REVIEW

1. Observational prospective study. Indications of behavior differences can be seen in the two groups. May show a link between premature birth and behavior, but there may be lurking variables involved.
2. Observational retrospective study. Can conclude there *may* be a link between tea drinking and survival after a heart attack. But lurking variables may also be involved.
3. Experiment, matched by gender and weight, randomization within blocks of two pups of same gender and weight. Factor is type of diet. Treatments are low-calorie diet and allowing the dog to eat all it wants. Response variable is length of life. Can conclude that, on average, dogs with a lower-calorie diet live longer.
4. Random sample. Population is all homes on the property tax list. Parameter is level of radon contamination. Procedure is probably a stratified random sample. May make inference about radon levels from sample to general population.
5. Observational prospective study. Indicates folate *may* help in reducing colon cancer for those with family histories of the disease.
6. Observational retrospective study. Indicates that during past 47 years first flowering has gotten earlier.
7. Sampling. Probably a simple random sample, although may be stratified by type of firework. Population is all fireworks produced each day. Parameter is proportion of duds. Can determine if the day's production is ready for sale.
8. Experiment, though there is no indication of a control group or differing treatments. Cosmetics *may* damage male reproductive systems in laboratory animals. Extrapolating to humans is risky.
9. Observational retrospective study. Living near strong electromagnetic fields may be associated with more leukemia than normal. Lurking variables, such as socioeconomic level, may be involved.
10. Observational retrospective study. Indicates no long-term risk of prostate cancer because of vasectomy.
11. Experiment. Blocked by sex of rat. Randomization is not specified. Factor is type of hormone given. Treatments are leptin and insulin. Response variable is lost weight. Can conclude that hormones can help suppress appetites in rats, and the type of hormone varies by gender.
12. Experiment. Factors are glaze type and temperature. Treatments are combinations of 4 glaze types and 3 temperatures. Response is age appearance of the pottery. Assuming an unbiased evaluator, can make a conclusion about best combination of glaze and temperature.
13. Experiment. Factor is gene therapy. Hamsters were randomized to treatments. Treatments were gene therapy or not. Response variable is heart muscle condition. Can conclude that gene therapy is beneficial (at least in hamsters).
14. Observational study (neither retrospective nor prospective). There seems to be a relationship between eye size and time of singing.
15. Sampling. Population is all oranges on the truck. Parameter is proportion of unsuitable oranges. Procedure is probably simple random sampling. Can conclude whether or not to accept the truckload.
16. Sampling. Population is all bottle-cap seals. Parameter is proportion with inadequate seals. Procedure is probably simple random sampling. Can conclude whether the bottling process is all right or needs to be adjusted.
17. Observational prospective study. Physically fit men may have a lower risk of death from cancer.
18. Experiment. Subjects blocked by calculus or not for analysis. Probably no randomization (students self-select into sections). Factor is software usage. Treatments are use of software or not. Response variable is final exam score. Can decide whether computer software is beneficial, and if so, is there a difference between the calculus and the noncalculus groups.

19. Answers will vary. This is a simulation problem. Using a random digits table or software, call 0–4 a loss, and 5–9 a win for the gambler on a game. Use blocks of 5 digits to simulate a week's pick.

20. a) Answers will vary. This is a simulation problem. Using a random-digits table or software, obtain 3 numbers between 01 and 20 for your pick, then 5 others between 01 and 20. Count how many matches.
    b) With more numbers to choose from, the odds of winning go down dramatically.

21. Answers will vary.

22. a) Experiment. Treatments were actively imposed, rats were randomized, there was control (rats with no radio wave exposure), and they used many rats.
    b) The differences in brain tumors were small enough that they could be explained by sampling variability.
    c) May cause bias of some sort, intended or not.

23. a) Experiment. Actively manipulated candy giving, diners were randomly assigned treatments, control group was those with no candy, lots of dining parties.
    b) It depends on when the decision was made. If early in the meal, the server may give better treatment to those who will receive candy—biasing the results.
    c) A difference in response so large it cannot be attributed to natural sampling variability.

24. a)

b) One factor (candy) with 4 levels (none, one, two, or one then another).
    c) 4.
    d) Tip percentage.
    e) Probably blinded (diners probably weren't aware they were in an experiment), but not double-blinded.
    f) If "randomization" is done early in the meal, she may treat some better than others.

25. a) Voluntary response. Only those who feel strongly will pay for the 900 phone call.
    b) "If it would help future generations live a longer, healthier life, would you be in favor of human cloning?"

26. a) Water (quality and temperature) and material can vary. Results may be influenced by these confounding variables.
    b) Unrealistic conditions. This won't say how SparkleKleen works in normal situations.
    c) Might work, but if all the swatches were stained at the same time, the stains on the later swatches will have more time to "set in," causing bias against SparkleKleen.
    
    Other variables (changes in water temperature or pressure) won't be randomized.
    d) No guarantee that conditions are comparable.

27. a) Simulation results will vary. Average will be around 5.8 points.
    b) Simulation results will vary. Average will also be around 5.8 points.
    c) Answers will vary.

28. a) 10.6% chance to break at 900 pounds or less.
    b) Simulation results will vary. Use groups of three digits to simulate each rivet. For every one that is less than "106," denote as a failed rivet. Count how many rivets you need until 3 failures are reached.

29. a) Yes.
    b) No. Residences without phones are excluded. Residences with more than one phone had a higher chance.
    c) No. People who respond to the survey may be of age but not registered voters.
    d) No. Households who answered the phone may be more likely to have someone at home when the phone call was generated. These may not be representative of all households.

30. a) A difference in response so large it cannot be attributed to natural sampling variability.
    b) More likely, younger looking individuals are more sexually active than older ones. We have no means of comparison (different levels of sexual activity in people of the same age, for example).

31. a) Does not prove it. There may be other confounding variables. Only way to prove this would be to do a controlled experiment.
    b) Alzheimer's usually shows up late in life. Perhaps smokers have died of other causes before Alzheimer's can be seen.
    c) An experiment would be unethical. One could design a prospective study in which groups of smokers and nonsmokers are followed for many years and the incidence of Alzheimer's is tracked.

32. a) Randomized block experiment.
    b) No—in an experiment we are looking for differences in response to treatments, not trying to generalize to all adults.
    c) A sugar pill may affect digestion, confounding the experiment.

33.

Numerous subjects will be randomly assigned to see shows with violent, sexual, or neutral content. They will see the same commercials. After the show, they will be interviewed for their recall of brand names in the commercials.

34. a) *Who*—900 Englishmen. *What*—reasons they go to a pub. *Why*—Kaliber alcohol-free beer wants to know. *When*—not stated. *Where*—England. *How*—survey (sampling method not specified).
    b) Englishmen.
    c) How those interviewed were chosen.
    d) Probably convenience samples of those in pubs.
    e) The study was financed by an alcohol-free beer.

35. a) May have been a simple random sample, but given the relative equality in age groups, may have been stratified.
    b) 35.1%.
    c) We don't know. Perhaps cell phones or unlisted numbers were excluded, and Democrats have more (or fewer) of those. Probably OK, though.
    d) Do party affiliations differ for different age groups?

36. a) Nonresponse bias by conservatives.
    b) U.S. adults.
    c) Results do not total 100%.
    d) Observed differences are of the same size one might expect from natural sampling variability.

37. The factor in the experiment will be type of bird control. I will have three treatments: scarecrow, netting, and no control. I will randomly assign several different areas in the vineyard to one of the treatments, taking care that there is sufficient separation that the possible effect of the scarecrow will not be confounded. At the end of the season, the response variable will be the proportion of bird-damaged grapes.

38. Since players vary in their ability to hit the ball, I will have each batter hit with both types of bats several times in a randomly chosen order. For each batter, calculate the average difference in distance, with metal or wood as the response variable.

**39. a)** We want all subjects treated as alike as possible. If there were no "placebo surgery," subjects would know this and perhaps behave differently.

**b)** The experiment was intended to see if there was a difference in the effectiveness of the two treatments. (If we wanted to generalize, we would need to assume that the results for these volunteers are the same as on all patients who might need this operation.)

**c)** "Statistically significant" means a difference in results so large it cannot be explained by natural sampling variability.

**40.** Results will vary.

(Use a random-number table or software to do the simulation. Numbers 1 to 11 will represent the "worst" team, 12 to 21 the second worst, 22 to 30 your third-place team, 31 to 66 the others. Obtain random numbers in the range, ignoring any duplications of the team that gets to pick first. Count the number of times the third-place team picks first or second out of the total number of trials.)

**41. a)** Use stratified sampling to select 2 first-class passengers and 12 from coach.

**b)** Number passengers alphabetically, 01 = Bergman to 20 = Testut. Read in blocks of two, ignoring any numbers more than 20. This gives 65, 43, 67, 11 (selects Fontana), 27, 04 (selects Castillo).

**c)** Number passengers alphabetically from 001 to 120. Use the random-number table to find three-digit numbers in this range until 12 have been selected.

**42.** Simulation results will vary. Theoretically, the chance is about 3%. (Select four numbers between 01 and 20 to represent the Middle Easterners. Count the number of times in several repetitions where both to be searched are among the selected four numbers.)

**43.** Simulation results will vary.

(Use integers 00 to 99 as a basis. Use integers 0 to 69 to represent a tee shot on the fairway. If on the fairway, use digits 00 to 79 to represent on the green. If off the fairway, use 00 to 39 to represent getting on the green. If not on the green, use digits 00 to 89 to represent landing on the green. For the first putt, use digits 00 to 19 to represent making the shot. For subsequent putts, use digits 00 to 89 to represent making the shot.)

**44. a)** Answers may vary. A component in this simulation is a shot. Use pairs of random digits 00 to 99 to represent a shot. The way in which this component is simulated depends on the type of shot. For the first shot, let pairs of digits 01 to 80 represent hitting the fairway, and let pairs of digits 81 to 99, and 00, represent not hitting the fairway. If the first simulated shot hits the fairway, let 01 to 80 represent landing on the green on the second shot, and let 81 to 99, and 00, represent not landing on the green on the second shot. If the first simulated shot does not hit the fairway, let 01 to 40 represent landing on the green on the second shot, and let 41 to 99, and 00, represent not landing on the green on the second shot. If the second simulated shot does not land on the green, let 01 to 90 represent landing on the green, and 91 to 99, and 00, represent not landing on the green. Keep simulating shots until the shot lands on the green. Once on the green, let 01 to 20 represent sinking the putt on the first putt, and let 21 to 99, and 00, represent not sinking the putt on the first putt. If second putts are required, continue simulating putts until a putt goes in, with 01 to 90 representing making the putt, and 91 to 99, and 00, representing not making the putt. A run consists of following the guidelines above until the final putt is made. The response variable is the number of shots required until the final putt is made. The simulated average score on the hole is the total number of shots required divided by the total number of runs. According to 20 runs of this simulation, a pretty good golfer can be expected to average about 3.7 strokes per hole. Your simulation results may vary.

**b)** Answers may vary. The simulation is set up identically to part a, with the exception of the second shot. Now, let 01 to

10 represent hitting the green, and let 11 to 99, and 00, represent not hitting the green. According to 20 runs of this simulation, a pretty good golfer can be expected to average about 5.3 strokes per hole. Your simulation results may vary.

**c)** Answers may vary.

# CHAPTER 14

**1. a)** S = {HH, HT, TH, TT}, equally likely.

**b)** S = {0, 1, 2, 3}, not equally likely.

**c)** S = {H, TH, TTH, TTT}, not equally likely.

**d)** S = {1, 2, 3, 4, 5, 6}, not equally likely.

**2. a)** S = {2, 3, 4, 5, 6, 7, 8, 9, 10, 11, 12}, not equally likely.

**b)** S = {BBB, BBG, BGB, BGG, GBB, GBG, GGB, GGG}, equally likely.

**c)** S = {0, 1, 2, 3, 4}, not equally likely.

**d)** S = {0, 1, 2, 3, 4, 5, 6, 7, 8, 9, 10}, not equally likely.

**3.** In this context "truly random" should mean that every number is equally likely to occur.

**4.** In circumstances "like this," rain occurs 25% of the time.

**5.** There is no "Law of Averages." She would be wrong to think that they are "due" for a harsh winter.

**6.** He's referring to the "Law of Averages," which doesn't exist. If rain in the fall and winter are independent of each other, a nice fall will have no bearing on winter rains.

**7.** There is no "Law of Averages." If at bats are independent, his chance for a hit does not change based on recent successes or failures.

**8. a)** There is no "Law of Averages." If crashes are independent, it makes no difference. If crashes were due to problems with the aircraft, another crash may be more likely; however, increased maintenance vigilance may *lessen* the chance of another crash.

**b)** A good safety record may be due to competence rather than luck. In any even, if events are independent, the probability of a crash has not changed.

**9. a)** There is some chance you would have to pay out much more than the $300.

**b)** Many customers pay for insurance. The small risk for any one customer is spread among all.

**10. a)** Almost all people make bets without winning the jackpot.

**b)** This creates publicity—more people may be attracted to play. (And, of course, it's not a loss. We assume that they take in more than they pay out.)

**11. a)** Legitimate.    **b)** Legitimate.

**c)** Not legitimate (sum more than 1).    **d)** Legitimate.

**e)** Not legitimate (can't have negatives or values more than 1).

**12. a)** Not legitimate (sum less than 1).

**b)** Not legitimate (sum greater than 1).    **c)** Legitimate.

**d)** Not legitimate (can't have negatives).    **e)** Legitimate.

**13.** A family may own both a car and an SUV. The events are not disjoint, so the Addition Rule does not apply.

**14.** A home may have both a garage and a pool. The events are not disjoint, so the Addition Rule does not apply.

**15.** When cars are traveling close together, their speeds are not independent, so the Multiplication Rule does not apply.

**16.** There may be a genetic factor making the handedness of siblings not independent, so the Multiplication Rule does not apply.

**17. a)** He has multiplied the two probabilities.

**b)** He assumes that being accepted at the colleges are independent events.

**c)** No. Colleges use similar criteria for acceptance, so the decisions are not independent.

**18. a)** He has added the three probabilities.

**b)** He is assuming that the events are disjoint.

**c)** No. Many students get into more than one of the three, so the events are not disjoint and the probabilities cannot simply be added together.

**19.** a) 0.72 b) 0.89 c) 0.28
**20.** a) 0.13 b) 0.45 c) 0.87
**21.** a) 0.5184 b) 0.0784 c) 0.4816
**22.** a) 0.3025 b) 0.2025 c) 0.2431
**23.** a) Repair needs for the two cars must be independent.
  b) Maybe not. An owner may treat the two cars similarly, taking good (or poor) care of both. This may decrease (or increase) the likelihood that each needs to be repaired.
**24.** a) The Calculus backgrounds of the students must be independent.
  b) Yes. The professor assigned students to the groups at random.
**25.** a) 342/1005 = 0.340.
  b) 30/1005 + 50/1005 = 80/1005 = 0.080.
**26.** a) 950/2020 = 0.47.
  b) 424/2020 + 566/2020 = 990/2020 = 0.49.
**27.** a) 0.195 b) 0.913
  c) Responses are independent.
  d) People were polled at random.
**28.** a) 0.044 b) 0.624 c) 0.332
  d) Responses are independent.
  e) People were polled at random.
**29.** a) 0.4712 b) 0.7112
  c) $(1 - 0.76) + 0.76(1 - 0.38)$ or $1 - (0.76)(0.38)$
**30.** a) 0.2888
  b) 0.400; more likely in 1997.
**31.** a) 1) 0.30 2) 0.30 3) 0.90 4) 0.0
  b) 1) 0.027 2) 0.128 3) 0.512 4) 0.271
**32.** a) 1) 0.04 2) 0.51 3) 0.55
  b) 1) 0.041 2) 0.849 3) 0.974 4) 0.373
**33.** a) Disjoint (can't be both red and orange).
  b) Independent (unless you're drawing from a small bag).
  c) No. Once you know that one of a pair of disjoint events has occurred, the other is impossible.
**34.** a) Disjoint.
  b) Independent (unless they are related).
  c) No. Once you know that one of a pair of disjoint events has occurred, the other is impossible.
**35.** a) 0.0046 b) 0.125 c) 0.296 d) 0.421 e) 0.995
**36.** a) 0.027 b) 0.125 c) 0.001 d) 0.729 e) 0.784
**37.** a) 0.027 b) 0.063 c) 0.973 d) 0.014
**38.** a) 0.0225 b) 0.092 c) 0.00008 d) 0.556
**39.** a) 0.024 b) 0.250 c) 0.543
**40.** a) 0.148 b) 0.600 c) 0.344
**41.** 0.078
**42.** 0.469
**43.** a) For any day with a valid three-digit date, the chance is 0.001, or 1 in 1000. For many dates in October through December, the probability is 0. (No three digits will make 10/15, for example.)
  b) There are 65 days when the chance to match is 0. (Oct. 10–31, Nov. 10–30, and Dec. 10–31.) The chance for no matches on the remaining 300 days is 0.741
  c) 0.259 d) 0.049
**44.** a) Yes. There are 42 cards left in the deck: 26 black and only 16 red.
  b) No. There is no "long run." You'll see the whole deck after 52 cards, and you know there will be 26 of each color then.

# CHAPTER 15

**1.** a) 0.68 b) 0.32 c) 0.04
**2.** a) 0.14 b) 0.23 c) 0.77
**3.** a) 0.31 b) 0.48 c) 0.31
**4.** a) 0.06 b) 0.50 c) 0.94
**5.** a) 0.2025 b) 0.6965 c) 0.2404 d) 0.0402
**6.** a) 0.193 b) 0.507 c) 0.067 d) 0.632
**7.** a) 0.50 b) 1.00 c) 0.077 d) 0.333
**8.** a) 0.333 b) 0.429 c) 0.667
**9.** a) 0.11 b) 0.27 c) 0.407 d) 0.344

**10.** a) 0.62 b) 0.867 c) 0.194 d) 0.66
**11.** a) 0.011 b) 0.222 c) 0.054 d) 0.337 e) 0.436
**12.** a) 0.103 b) 0.404 c) 0.209 d) 0.460 e) 0.559
**13.** 0.21
**14.** 0.08
**15.** a) 0.145 b) 0.118 c) 0.414 d) 0.217
**16.** a) 0.783 b) 0.013 c) 0.127 d) 0.586
**17.** a) 0.318 b) 0.955 c) 0.071 d) 0.009
**18.** a) 0.632 b) 0.140 c) 0.003 d) 0.624
**19.** a) 32% b) 0.135
  c) No, 7% of juniors have taken both.
  d) No, the probability that a junior has taken a computer course is 0.23. The probability that a junior has taken a computer course *given* he or she has taken a Statistics course is 0.135.
**20.** a) 0.25 b) 0.875
  c) No, 68% of all workers have health insurance. Of those with retirement plans, 87.5% have health insurance. These are not equal.
  d) No, 49% of the people have both.
**21.** a) 0.266
  b) No, 26.6% of homes with garages have pools; 21% of homes overall have pools.
  c) No, 17% of homes have both.
**22.** a) 0.444
  b) No, 4% of U.S. residents have been to both.
  c) No, 18% of U.S. residents have been to Canada; 44.4% of U.S. residents who have been to Mexico have been to Canada. If independent, these would be equal.
**23.** Yes, $P(\text{Ace}) = 1/13$. $P(\text{Ace}|\text{Spade}) = 1/13$.
**24.** Yes, 1/3 of the dogs are male and 1/3 of the cats are male.
**25.** a) 0.17
  b) No; 13% of the chickens had both contaminants.
  c) No; $P(C|S) = 0.87 \neq P(C)$. If a chicken is contaminated with salmonella, it's more likely also to have campylobacter.
**26.** a) Yes; a student can enroll in only one college.
  b) No. Nearly 42% of all students enrolled in the Agriculture college, but none of the Human Ecology students did.
  c) No. Almost 7% of these students were both firstborn and enrolled in Human Ecology.
  d) No. Over 19% of all students enrolled in Human Ecology, but only 13% of the firstborn students did.
**27.** No, 28.8% of men with OK blood pressure have high cholesterol, but 40.7% of those with high blood pressure do.
**28.** No, 86.7% of Republicans favor the death penalty, but only 33.3% of Democrats favor it.
**29.** a) 95.4%
  b) Probably. 95.4% of people with cell phones had landlines, and 95.6% of all people did.
**30.** a) 13.7%
  b) No. 39.3% of people over 30 snored, but only 36.8% of all people did.
**31.** No. Only 34% of men were Democrats, but over 41% of all voters were.
**32.** No. Although only 12.5% of all cars were of European origin, about 17% of students drive European cars.
**33.** a) No, the probability that the luggage arrives on time depends on whether the flight is on time. The probability is 95% if the flight is on time and only 65% if not.
  b) 0.695
**34.** a) Yes, the percentage who graduate depends on what kind of school they attend. The graduation rate is 75% for public school students and 90% for others.
  b) 79.5%
**35.** 0.975
**36.** 66.0%

**37.** a) No, the probability of missing work for day-shift employees is 0.01. It is 0.02 for night-shift employees. The probability depends on whether they work day or night shift.
b) 1.4%

**38.** a) Rates of the lung condition are different for smokers and nonsmokers, 57% and 13%, respectively. If independent, these would be the same.
b) 0.231

**39.** 57.1%

**40.** 0.567

**41.** a) 0.20   b) 0.272   c) 0.353   d) 0.033

**42.** a) 15%   b) 0.20
c) No. Advance-purchase customers are less likely to be no-shows (5% vs. 30% among regular-fare customers.)

**43.** 0.563

**44.** 0.467

**45.** Over 0.999

**46.** 0.814

# CHAPTER 16

**1.** a) 19   b) 4.2

**2.** a) 1.2   b) 280

**3.** a) $50   b) $50

**4.** $25

**5.** a)

| Amount won | $0 | $5 | $10 | $30 |
|---|---|---|---|---|
| P(Amount won) | $\frac{26}{52}$ | $\frac{13}{52}$ | $\frac{12}{52}$ | $\frac{1}{52}$ |

b) $4.13
c) $4 or less (answers may vary)

**6.** a)

| Amount won | $100 | $50 | $0 |
|---|---|---|---|
| P(Amount won) | $\frac{1}{6}$ | $\frac{5}{36}$ | $\frac{25}{36}$ |

b) $23.61
c) $23 or less (answers may vary).

**7.** a)

| Children | 1 | 2 | 3 |
|---|---|---|---|
| P(Children) | 0.5 | 0.25 | 0.25 |

b) 1.75 children   c) 0.87 boys

| Boys | 0 | 1 | 2 | 3 |
|---|---|---|---|---|
| P(Boys) | 0.5 | 0.25 | 0.125 | 0.125 |

**8.** a)

| Number of darts | 1 | 2 | 3 | 4 |
|---|---|---|---|---|
| P(Number of darts) | 0.10 | 0.09 | 0.081 | 0.729 |

| Amount won | $95 | $90 | $85 | $80 | -$20 |
|---|---|---|---|---|---|
| P(Amount won) | 0.10 | 0.09 | 0.081 | 0.073 | 0.656 |

b) 3.44 darts   c) $17.20

**9.** $27,000

**10.** $10,600

**11.** a) 7   b) 1.89

**12.** a) 0.75   b) 87.18

**13.** $5.44

**14.** $38.16

**15.** 0.83

**16.** $51.48

**17.** a) 1.7   b) 0.9

**18.** a) 2.25   b) 1.26

**19.** $\mu = 0.64, \sigma = 0.93$

**20.** a)

| Profit | $100 | -$9900 | -$2900 |
|---|---|---|---|
| P(Profit) | 0.9975 | 0.0005 | 0.002 |

b) $89.00   c) $260.54

**21.** a) $50   b) $100

**22.** a) Yes, the expected value is $300.
b) $100   c) $360.56

**23.** a) No. The probability of winning the second depends on the outcome of the first.
b) 0.42   c) 0.08
d)

| Games won | 0 | 1 | 2 |
|---|---|---|---|
| P(Games won) | 0.42 | 0.50 | 0.08 |

e) $\mu = 0.66, \sigma = 0.62$

**24.** a) No. The chance to get the second contract depends on whether your company got the first.
b) 0.16   c) 0.14
d)

| Contracts won | 0 | 1 | 2 |
|---|---|---|---|
| P(Contracts won) | 0.14 | 0.70 | 0.16 |

e) $\mu = 1.02, \sigma = 0.55$

**25.** a)

| Number good | 0 | 1 | 2 |
|---|---|---|---|
| P(Number good) | 0.067 | 0.467 | 0.467 |

b) 1.40   c) 0.61

**26.** a)

| Number males | 0 | 1 | 2 |
|---|---|---|---|
| P(Number males) | 0.143 | 0.571 | 0.286 |

b) 1.14   c) 0.64

**27.** a) $\mu = 30, \sigma = 6$   b) $\mu = 26, \sigma = 5$   c) $\mu = 30, \sigma = 5.39$
d) $\mu = -10, \sigma = 5.39$   e) $\mu = 20, \sigma = 2.83$

**28.** a) $\mu = 60, \sigma = 12$   b) $\mu = 6, \sigma = 1.50$
c) $\mu = 92, \sigma = 12.37$   d) $\mu = 68, \sigma = 12.37$
e) $\mu = 24, \sigma = 4.24$

**29.** a) $\mu = 240, \sigma = 12.80$   b) $\mu = 140, \sigma = 24$
c) $\mu = 720, \sigma = 34.18$   d) $\mu = 60, \sigma = 39.40$
e) $\mu = 600, \sigma = 22.63$

**30.** a) $\mu = 44, \sigma = 6$   b) $\mu = 240, \sigma = 36$
c) $\mu = 32, \sigma = 4.24$   d) $\mu = 20, \sigma = 19.21$
e) $\mu = 240, \sigma = 20.78$

**31.** a) 1.8   b) 0.87
c) Cartons are independent of each other.

**32.** a) 10   b) 2.68
c) Packets are independent of each other. OK if different types of seeds; if all the same type (and lot), assumption would probably not be valid.

**33.** $\mu = 13.6, \sigma = 2.55$ (assuming the hours are independent of each other).

**34.** $\mu = 11.25, \sigma = 2.82$

**35.** a) $\mu = 23.4, \sigma = 2.97$
b) We assume each truck gets tickets independently.

**36.** a) $\mu = \$3840, \sigma = \$591.54$
b) We assume pledges are independent among callers.

**37.** a) There will be many gains of $150 with a few large losses.
b) $\mu = \$300, \sigma = \$8485.28$
c) $\mu = \$1,500,000, \sigma = \$600,000$
d) Yes. $0 is 2.5 SDs below the mean for 10,000 policies.
e) Losses are independent of each other. A major catastrophe with many policies in an area would violate the assumption.

**38.** a) Gamblers lose a relatively small amount most of the time, but there are a few large payouts.
b) $\mu = \$0.40, \sigma = \$268.33$
c) $\mu = \$80.00, \sigma = \$3794.73$

d) If the machine is played only 1000 times a day, we can't guarantee that it will be profitable, since $80 is about 0.02 SDs above 0. But if the casino has many slot machines, the chances of being profitable will go up.

**39.** a) 1 oz    b) 0.5 oz    c) 0.023
   d) $\mu = 4$ oz, $\sigma = 0.5$ oz
   e) 0.159
   f) $\mu = 12.3$ oz, $\sigma = 0.54$ oz
**40.** a) $-\$20$    b) $46.10    c) 0.332
**41.** a) 12.2 oz    b) 0.51 oz    c) 0.058
**42.** a) $D =$ cost for a dog; $C =$ cost for a cat;
   total costs $= D_1 + D_2 + C$
   b) Normal, $\mu = \$320$, $\sigma = \$55$
   c) 0.073
**43.** a) $\mu = 200.57$ sec, $\sigma = 0.46$ sec
   b) No, $z = \dfrac{199.48 - 200.57}{0.461} = -2.36$. There is only 0.009
   probability of swimming that fast or faster.
**44.** a) $\mu = 37.6$ min, $\sigma = 3.7$ min
   b) No, 30 min is more than 2 SDs below the mean.
**45.** a) $A =$ price of a pound of apples; $P =$ price of a pound of potatoes; Profit $= 100A + 50P - 2$
   b) $63.00    c) $20.62
   d) Mean—no; SD—yes (independent sales prices).
**46.** a) $B =$ number basic; $D =$ number deluxe;
   Net $= 120B + 150D - 200$
   b) $928.00    c) $187.45
   d) Mean—no; SD—yes (sales are independent).
**47.** a) $\mu = 1920$, $\sigma = 48.99$; $P(T > 2000) = 0.051$
   b) $\mu = \$220$, $\sigma = 11.09$; No—$300 is more than 7 SD's above the mean.
   c) $P(D - \frac{1}{2}C > 0) \approx 0.26$
**48.** a) $\mu = 60$ lb, $\sigma = 0.346$ lb; $P(W > 60.5) \approx 0.074$
   b) $\mu = \$35$, $\sigma = \$0.187$
   c) $P(|D|) > 0.25 \approx 0.377$

# CHAPTER 17

**1.** a) No. More than two outcomes are possible.
   b) Yes, assuming the people are unrelated to each other.
   c) No. The chance of a heart changes as cards are dealt.
   d) No, 500 is more than 10% of 3000.
   e) If packages in a case are independent of each other, yes; otherwise, no.
**2.** a) Yes. Outcomes are {getting a 6} and {not getting a 6}.
   b) No. More than two outcomes are possible.
   c) If the dolls were manufactured independently of each other, yes.
   d) No. The chance of a Democrat (or Republican) changes depending on who has already been picked.
   e) Yes, assuming responses (and cheating) are independent among the students.
**3.** a) Use single random digits. Let $0, 1 =$ Tiger. Count the number of random numbers until a 0 or 1 occurs.
   c) Results will vary.
   d)

| $x$ | 1 | 2 | 3 | 4 | 5 | 6 | 7 | 8 | $\geq 9$ |
|---|---|---|---|---|---|---|---|---|---|
| $P(x)$ | 0.2 | 0.16 | 0.128 | 0.102 | 0.082 | 0.066 | 0.052 | 0.042 | 0.168 |

**4.** a) Use random digits 1–6, ignoring 0, 7–9. Count the number of random numbers until a 1 occurs.
   c) Results will vary.
   d)

| $x$ | 1 | 2 | 3 | 4 | 5 | 6 | 7 | 8 | $\geq 9$ |
|---|---|---|---|---|---|---|---|---|---|
| $P(x)$ | 0.167 | 0.139 | 0.116 | 0.096 | 0.080 | 0.067 | 0.056 | 0.047 | 0.232 |

**5.** a) Use single random digits. Let $0, 1 =$ Tiger. Examine random digits in groups of five, counting the number of 0's and 1's.
   c) Results will vary.
   d)

| $x$ | 0 | 1 | 2 | 3 | 4 | 5 |
|---|---|---|---|---|---|---|
| $P(x)$ | 0.33 | 0.41 | 0.20 | 0.05 | 0.01 | 0.0 |

**6.** a) Use pairs of random digits. Let 00–74 represent that a seatbelt is worn, 75–99 that it is not. Examine random digits in groups of five, counting the number of seatbelts.
   c) Results will vary.
   d)

| $x$ | 0 | 1 | 2 | 3 | 4 | 5 |
|---|---|---|---|---|---|---|
| $P(x)$ | 0.0 | 0.01 | 0.09 | 0.26 | 0.40 | 0.24 |

**7.** Departures from the same airport during a 2-hour interval may not be independent. All could be delayed by weather, for example.
**8.** What happens to pieces of luggage checked together and all traveling on the same flight probably aren't independent.
**9.** a) 0.0819    b) 0.0064    c) 0.992
**10.** a) 0.0184    b) 0.183
**11.** 5
**12.** 50
**13.** 20 calls
**14.** 100 donors
**15.** a) 25    b) 0.185    c) 0.217    d) 0.693
**16.** a) 12.5    b) 0.716    c) 0.0527    d) 0.528
**17.** a) 50    b) $E(X) = np = 100(0.5) = 50$.
**18.** a) 2    b) $E(X) = np = 2(2/38) = 2$.
**19.** a) 0.0745    b) 0.502    c) 0.211
   d) 0.0166    e) 0.0179    f) 0.9987
**20.** a) 0.032    b) 0.738    c) 0.00768
   d) 0.246    e) 0.901    f) 0.345
**21.** a) 0.65    b) 0.75    c) 7.69 picks
**22.** a) 4.8    b) 0.98    c) 1.25 shots
**23.** a) $\mu = 10.44$, $\sigma = 1.16$
   b) 0.812    c) 0.475    d) 0.00193    e) 0.998
**24.** a) $\mu = 8$, $\sigma = 1.26$
   b) 0.107    c) 0.624    d) 0.302    e) 0.967
**25.** $\mu = 20.28$, $\sigma = 4.22$
**26.** $\mu = 2.4$, $\sigma = 1.5$
**27.** a) 0.118    b) 0.324    c) 0.744    d) 0.580
**28.** a) 0.201    b) 0.453    c) 0.171    d) 0.989
**29.** a) $\mu = 56$, $\sigma = 4.10$
   b) Yes, $np = 56 \geq 10$, $nq = 24 \geq 10$, serves are independent.
   c) In a match with 80 serves, approximately 68% of the time she will have between 51.9 and 60.1 good serves, approximately 95% of the time she will have between 47.8 and 64.2 good serves, and approximately 99.7% of the time she will have between 43.7 and 68.3 good serves.
   d) Normal, approx.: 0.014; Binomial, exact: 0.016
**30.** a) $\mu = 160$, $\sigma = 5.66$
   b) Yes, $np = 160 \geq 10$, $nq = 40 \geq 10$.
   c) In matches with 200 arrows, about 68% of the time she will have between 154.34 and 165.66 bull's-eyes, about 95% of the time between 148.68 and 171.32 bull's-eyes, and about 99.7% of the time between 143.02 and 176.98 bull's-eyes.
   d) Yes, that's more than 3 SDs below the mean. Probability is less than 0.0015.
**31.** a) Assuming apples fall and become blemished independently of each other, Binom(300, 0.06) is appropriate. Since $np \geq 10$ and $nq \geq 10$, $N(18, 4.11)$ is also appropriate.
   b) Normal, approx.: 0.072; Binomial, exact: 0.085
   c) No, 50 is 7.8 SDs above the mean.
**32.** a) $\mu = 18.75$, $\sigma = 4.05$
   b) Yes, $np = 18.75 \geq 10$, $nq = 131.25 \geq 10$.
   c) No, 22 is only 0.8 SD above the mean; this is likely to happen by natural sampling variability.

**33.** Normal, approx.: 0.053; Binomial, exact: 0.061
**34.** Normal, approx.: 0.094; Binomial, exact: 0.116
**35.** The mean number of sales should be 24 with SD 4.60. Ten sales is more than 3.0 SDs below the mean. He was probably misled.
**36.** If the coin is fair, expect 125 heads, with SD 7.91; 140 is 1.9 SDs above the mean. From the Normal approximation, the chance of 140 or more heads is 2.9%. That's pretty unlikely to happen.
**37.** a) 0.0869    b) 0.0364
**38.** a) 0.7165    b) 0.0446
   c) The probabilities don't change, so this is neither a better nor a worse time.
**39.** a) 4 cases    b) 0.9817
**40.** a) 1/10    b) 0.0952
**41.** a) 5    b) 0.066    c) 0.107    d) $\mu = 24, \sigma = 2.19$
   e) Normal, approx.: 0.819; Binomial, exact: 0.848
**42.** a) 0.042    b) 0.107    c) 5    d) $\mu = 10, \sigma = 2.83$
   e) Normal, approx.: 0.025; Binomial, exact: 0.027
**43.** $\mu = 20, \sigma = 4$. I'd want *at least* 32 (3 SDs above the mean). (Answers will vary.)
**44.** $\mu = 25, \sigma = 3.54$. I'd want *at least* 36 (3 SDs above the mean). (Answers will vary.)
**45.** Probably not. There's a more than 9% chance that he could hit 4 shots in a row, so he can expect this to happen nearly once in every 10 sets of 4 shots he takes. That does not seem unusual.
**46.** No. If she were to shoot several flights of 6 arrows, an archer of her ability could be expected to get all bull's-eyes about 26% of the time. That's not an unusual result.
**47.** Yes. We'd expect him to make 22 shots, with a standard deviation of 3.15 shots. 32 shots is more than 3 standard deviations above the expected value, an unusually high rate of success.
**48.** No. We'd expect her to hit the bull's-eye with 40 of the 50 arrows, with a standard deviation of 2.83 bull's-eyes. She got 45, less than 2 standard deviations above the mean. Good shooting, but probably not unusual for her.

## PART IV REVIEW

**1.** a) 0.34    b) 0.27    c) 0.069
   d) No, 2% of cars have both types of defects.
   e) Of all cars with cosmetic defects, 6.9% have functional defects. Overall, 7.0% of cars have functional defects. The probabilities here are estimates, so these are probably close enough to say the defects are independent.
**2.** a) i) 0.60    ii) 0.90    iii) 0.615    iv) 0.80
   b) No. Fewer than half of the managers are female, but 60% of all workers are female.
**3.** a) $C$ = Price to China; $F$ = Price to France; Total = $3C + 5F$
   b) $\mu = \$5500, \sigma = \$672.68$
   c) $\mu = \$500, \sigma = \$180.28$
   d) Means—no. Standard deviations—yes; ticket prices must be independent of each other for different countries, but all tickets to the same country are at the same price.
**4.** $np = 100 \geq 10$ and $nq = 9900 \geq 10$, so Success/Failure Condition is verified. Also, we assume that cases are independent. $\mu = 100$, $\sigma = 9.95$. Over 200 would be more than 10 SDs above the mean. Probability is essentially 0.
**5.** a) $\mu = -\$0.20, \sigma = \$1.89$
   b) $\mu = -\$0.40, \sigma = \$2.67$
**6.** a) 3%
   b) No; 62% of those who can do it with their right hand can do it with their left, but 83.3% of those who can't do it with their right hand can do it with their left.
   c) No; 51% can use both hands.
**7.** a) 0.106    b) 0.651    c) 0.442
**8.** Expected (extra) cost of the cheaper policy with the deductible is $2.50, much less than the $12 for the no-deductible surcharge, so on average, she will save money by going with the deductible.

But she should consider standard deviation as well ($35.27). Value of the car shouldn't influence the decision.
**9.** a) 0.590    b) 0.328    c) 0.00856
**10.** a) $\mu = 6.775, \sigma = 2.60$
   b) No, since $np = 6.78 < 10$.
**11.** a) $\mu = 15.2, \sigma = 3.70$
   b) Yes, $np \geq 10$ and $nq \geq 10$
   c) Normal, approx.: 0.080; Binomial, exact: 0.097
**12.** a)

| Spaces | 5 | 10 | 20 |
|---|---|---|---|
| P(Spaces) | 0.5 | 0.25 | 0.25 |

   b) $\mu = 10, \sigma = 6.12$
   c)

| Spaces | 0 | 1 | 2 | 3 | 4 |
|---|---|---|---|---|---|
| P(Spaces) | 1/3 | 1/6 | 1/6 | 1/6 | 1/6 |

   d) $\mu = 1.67, \sigma = 1.49$
   e) $\mu = 11.67, \sigma = 6.30$
**13.** a) 0.0173    b) 0.591
   c) Left: 960; right: 120; both: 120
   d) $\mu = 120, \sigma = 10.39$
   e) About 68% chance of between 109 and 130; about 95% between 99 and 141; about 99.7% between 89 and 151.
**14.** $\mu = 8.33, \sigma = 6.30$
**15.** a) Men's heights are more variable than women's.
   b) Men
   c) $M$ = Man's height; $W$ = Woman's height; $M - W$ is how much taller the man is.
   d) 5.1"    e) 3.75"    f) 0.913
   g) If independent, it should be about 91.3%. We are told 92%. This difference seems small and may be due to natural sampling variability.
**16.** a) 0.389    b) 0.284    c) 0.793    d) 0.896
**17.** a) The chance is $1.6 \times 10^{-7}$.
   b) 0.952    c) 0.063
**18.** a) No, this does not confirm the advice. If you follow the advice, it seems that the chances of its going up are 0.75.
   b) It actually has risen in 73% of all years. Not much difference from their strategy.
**19.** $-\$2080.00$
**20.** a) 0.240    b) 0.050    c) 0.383
**21.** a) 0.717    b) 0.588
**22.** a) 36    b) 5.02
   c) Because both $np = 36 \geq 10$ and $nq = 84 \geq 10$.
   d) There is a 68% chance between 30.98 and 41.02 (31 and 41 students); 95% chance between 25.96 and 46.04 (26 and 46 students); 99.7% chance between 20.94 and 51.06 (21 and 51 students).
**23.** a) $\mu = 100, \sigma = 8$
   b) $\mu = 1000, \sigma = 60$
   c) $\mu = 100, \sigma = 8.54$
   d) $\mu = -50, \sigma = 10$
   e) $\mu = 100, \sigma = 11.31$
**24.** Assuming policies are independent, we add the profit variances. The resulting standard deviation of total profit is less than the sum of the SDs of individual profits. This means the profit for the large company will be less variable than the total of profits for the smaller companies.
**25.** a) Many do both, so the two categories can total more than 100%.
   b) No. They can't be disjoint. If they were, the total would be 100% or less.
   c) No. Probabilities are different for boys and girls.
   d) 0.0524
**26.** a) $\mu = \$27.00, \sigma = \$9.90$
   b) Spending on different days is independent. This might not be

reasonable, since a student may be more likely to spend less on a day after he had spent a lot.

c) $\mu = \$94.50, \sigma = \$18.52$

d) No. \$50 is 2.4 SDs below the mean. We assumed independence of costs each day.

**27.** a) 21 days

b) 1649.73 som

c) 3300 som extra. About 157-som "cushion" each day.

**28.** a) 4 lb   b) 3.20 lb   c) 0.894

**29.** No, you'd expect 541.2 homeowners, with an SD of 13.56. 523 is 1.34 SDs below the mean; not unusual.

**30.** $\mu = \$2.54, \sigma = \$0.94$

**31.** a) 0.018   b) 0.300   c) 0.26

**32.** a) 0.0156   b) 0.0039

c) Answer b would become 0.0026.

**33.** a) 6   b) 15   c) 0.402

**34.** a) 3

b) $X$ = current score; expect to lose $X/6$ points.

c) 18

d) Roll until you score 18 points, then stop.

**35.** a) 34%   b) 35%   c) 31.4%

d) 31.4% of classes that used calculators used computer assignments, while in classes that didn't use calculators, 30.6% used computer assignments. These are close enough to think the choice is probably independent.

**36.** a) 0.5929   b) 0.407   c) 0.053   d) 0.0025

**37.** a) A Poisson model   b) 0.1 failures   c) 0.090   d) 0.095

**38.** a) A Poisson model   b) 4.8 episodes   c) 0.008   d) 0.706

**39.** a) 1/11   b) 7/22   c) 5/11   d) 0   e) 19/66

**40.** a) $\mu = 18, \sigma = 3$

b) 6

c) No, $\sigma$ is now 5.

d) 10 or more

e) What appears "surprising" in the short run becomes expected in a large number of trials.

**41.** a) Expected number of stars with planets.

b) Expected number of planets with intelligent life.

c) Probability of a planet with a suitable environment having intelligent life.

d) $f_l$: If a planet has a suitable environment, the probability that life develops.

$f_i$: If a planet develops life, the probability that the life evolves intelligence.

$f_c$: If a planet has intelligent life, the probability that it develops radio communication.

**42.** a) 0.017   b) 0.824

**43.** 0.991

**44.** a) 0.01   b) 0.0098   c) 0.366   d) First

e) The chance of winning is 0.01 anywhere in line, so position does not matter.

# CHAPTER 18

**1.** All the histograms are centered near 0.05. As $n$ gets larger, the histograms approach the Normal shape, and the variability in the sample proportions decreases.

**2.** All the histograms are centered near 0.85. As $n$ gets larger, the histograms approach the Normal shape, and the variability in the sample proportions decreases.

**3.** a)

| $n$ | Observed mean | Theoretical mean | Observed st. dev. | Theoretical st. dev. |
|---|---|---|---|---|
| 20 | 0.0497 | 0.05 | 0.0479 | 0.0487 |
| 50 | 0.0516 | 0.05 | 0.0309 | 0.0308 |
| 100 | 0.0497 | 0.05 | 0.0215 | 0.0218 |
| 200 | 0.0501 | 0.05 | 0.0152 | 0.0154 |

b) They are all quite close to what we expect from the theory.

c) The histogram is unimodal and symmetric for $n = 200$.

d) The success/failure condition says that $np$ and $nq$ should both be at least 10, which is not satisfied until $n = 200$ for $p = 0.05$. The theory predicted my choice.

**4.** a)

| $n$ | Observed mean | Theoretical mean | Observed st. dev. | Theoretical st. dev. |
|---|---|---|---|---|
| 20 | 0.8481 | 0.85 | 0.0803 | 0.0799 |
| 50 | 0.8507 | 0.85 | 0.0509 | 0.0505 |
| 75 | 0.8481 | 0.85 | 0.0406 | 0.0412 |
| 100 | 0.8488 | 0.85 | 0.0354 | 0.0357 |

b) They are all quite close to what we expect from the theory.

c) The histogram is unimodal and symmetric for $n = 75$.

d) The success/failure condition says that $np$ and $nq$ should both be at least 10, which, for $p = 0.85$ and $q = 0.15$, would be satisfied at a sample size of about 67. So my choice of $n = 75$ is reasonable.

**5.** a) Symmetric, because probability of heads and tails is equal.

b) 0.5   c) 0.125   d) $np = 8 < 10$

**6.** a) Probability skewed right.

b) No. $np = 5 < 10$   c) 0.10   d) 0.042

**7.** a) About 68% should have proportions between 0.4 and 0.6, about 95% between 0.3 and 0.7, and about 99.7% between 0.2 and 0.8.

b) $np = 12.5, nq = 12.5$; both are $\geq 10$.

c)

$np = nq = 32$; both are $\geq 10$.

d) Becomes narrower (less spread around 0.5).

**8.** a) $np = 20, np = 180$; both are $\geq 10$.

b) About 68% will be between 7.9% and 12.1%, about 95% will be between 5.8% and 14.2%, and about 99.7% should be between 3.7% and 16.3%.

c) Same center, less spread.

**9.** This is a fairly unusual result: about 2.26 SDs below the mean. The probability of that is about 0.012. So, in a class of 100 this is certainly a reasonable possibility.

**10.** No. It's only 1.49 SDs above the mean.

**11.** a)

b) Both $np = 56$ and $nq = 24 \geq 10$. Drivers *may* be independent of each other, but if flow of traffic is very fast, they may not be. Or weather conditions may affect all drivers. In these cases they may get more or fewer speeders than they expect.

**12.** There is a 68% chance that between 20.2% and 32.6% are smokers, 95% chance between 14% and 38.8%, and 99.7% chance between 7.8% and 45%. The 50 adults would have to be a random sample whose choice to smoke is independent of the others in the sample. The Success/Failure Condition is satisfied, $np = 13.2$, and $nq = 36.8$. Both are $\geq 10$.

13. a) Assume that these children are typical of the population. They represent fewer than 10% of all children. We expect 20.4 nearsighted and 149.6 not; both are at least 10.

   b)

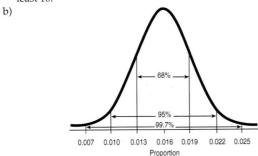

   c) Probably between 12 and 29.

14. a) Assume that this bank's mortgages are typical of the population. They represent fewer than 10% of all mortgages. We expect 27.7 foreclosures and 1703.3 "failures"; both are at least 10.

   b)

   c) Probably between 17 and 38.

15. a) $\mu = 7\%$, $\sigma = 1.8\%$
   b) Assume that clients pay independently of each other, that we have a random sample of all possible clients, and that these represent less than 10% of all possible clients. $np = 14$ and $nq = 186$ are both at least 10.
   c) 0.048

16. a) Normal, $\mu = 30\%$, $\sigma = 4.6\%$; SRS, $np = 30$, $nq = 70$.
   b) 0.234

17.

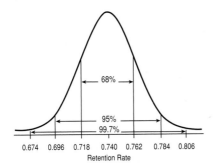

These are not random samples, and not all colleges may be typical (representative). $np = 296$, $nq = 104$ are large enough.

18.

Conditions are met: It's a random sample, with $np = 88$ and $nq = 112$.

19. Yes; if their students were typical, a retention rate of $522/603 = 86.6\%$ would be over 7 standard deviations above the expected rate of 74%.

20. Probably not; his sample proportion of 39.3% is less than 1.5 standard deviations below the national result of 44%.

21. 0.212. Reasonable that those polled are independent of each other and represent less than 10% of all potential voters. We assume the sample was selected at random. Success/Failure Condition met: $np = 208$, $nq = 192$. Both $\geq 10$.

22. 0.081. Assume the seeds are a random sample, germinate independently of each other, and represent less than 10% of all seeds of this type. Since the seeds are in the same pack, they may not be independent of each other, or be a random sample. Success/Failure Condition met: $np = 147.2$, $nq = 12.8$. Both $\geq 10$.

23. 0.088 using $N(0.08, 0.022)$ model.

24. 0.960 using $N(0.04, 0.007)$ model.

25. Answers will vary. Using $\mu + 3\sigma$ for "very sure," the restaurant should have 89 nonsmoking seats. Assumes customers at any time are independent of each other, a random sample, and represent less than 10% of all potential customers. $np = 72$, $nq = 48$, so Normal model is reasonable ($\mu = 0.60$, $\sigma = 0.045$).

26. Answers will vary. Using $\mu + 2\sigma$ for "pretty sure," he should plan on having at least 47 steak specials ($\mu = 0.20$, $\sigma = 0.030$).

27. a) Normal, center at $\mu$, standard deviation $\sigma/\sqrt{n}$.
   b) Standard deviation will be smaller. Center will remain the same.

28. a) Skewed left, center at $\mu$, standard deviation $\sigma/\sqrt{n}$.
   b) Becomes more Normal, center at $\mu$, standard deviation $\sigma/\sqrt{n}$.
   c) Becomes more like the population—skewed to the left.

29. a) The histogram is unimodal and slightly skewed to the right, centered at 36 inches with a standard deviation near 4 inches.
   b) All the histograms are centered near 36 inches. As $n$ gets larger, the histograms approach the Normal shape and the variability in the sample means decreases. The histograms are fairly normal by the time the sample reaches size 5.

30. a) The histogram is unimodal, but strongly skewed to the right with several large outliers.
   b) All the histograms are centered near 10,000 ($1000). As $n$ gets larger, the variability in sample means decreases and histograms approach a Normal shape; however, they are still visibly skewed, with the possible exception of the last one at $n = 200$.
   c) The rule of thumb doesn't seem to account for highly skewed distributions.

**31.** a)

| $n$ | Observed mean | Theoretical mean | Observed st. dev. | Theoretical st. dev. |
|---|---|---|---|---|
| 2 | 36.314 | 36.33 | 2.855 | 2.842 |
| 5 | 36.314 | 36.33 | 1.805 | 1.797 |
| 10 | 36.341 | 36.33 | 1.276 | 1.271 |
| 20 | 36.339 | 36.33 | 0.895 | 0.899 |

b) They are all very close to what we would expect.
c) For samples as small as 5, the sampling distribution of sample means is unimodal and very symmetric.
d) The distribution of the original data is nearly unimodal and symmetric, so it doesn't take a very large sample size for the distribution of sample means to be approximately Normal.

**32.** a)

| $n$ | Observed mean | Theoretical mean | Observed st. dev. | Theoretical st. dev. |
|---|---|---|---|---|
| 30 | 10,251.73 | 10,307.31 | 3359.64 | 3279.88 |
| 50 | 10,343.93 | 10,307.31 | 2483.84 | 2540.58 |
| 100 | 10,329.94 | 10,307.31 | 1779.18 | 1796.46 |
| 200 | 10,340.37 | 10,307.31 | 1260.79 | 1270.29 |

b) They are all reasonably close to what we would expect.
c) All the sampling distributions are still quite skewed, with the possible exception of the sampling distribution for $n = 200$, which is still somewhat skewed.
d) The distribution of the data is strongly skewed, so it will take a very large sample size before the sampling distribution of the mean is approximately normal.

**33.**

Mean GPA

Normal, $\mu = 3.4$, $\sigma = 0.07$. We assume that the students are randomly assigned to the seminars and represent less than 10% of all possible students, and that individual's GPAs are independent of one another.

**34.**

Mean Value ($1000)

**35.** a) The mean of 100 coins varies less from sample to sample than the individual coins.
b) $SD(\bar{y}) = \dfrac{\sigma}{\sqrt{n}} = \dfrac{0.09}{\sqrt{100}} = 0.009$

**36.** The standard deviation of the sampling distribution model for the mean is $\dfrac{\sigma}{\sqrt{n}}$. So cities in which the average is based on a

smaller number of drivers will have greater variation in their averages and will be more likely to both safest and least safe.

**37.** a) 21.1%
b) 276.8 days or more
c) $N(266, 2.07)$
d) 0.002

**38.** a) 13.7%
b) 31.9″
c) $N(35.4, 2.1)$
d) 0.005

**39.** a) There are more premature births than very long pregnancies. Modern practice of medicine stops pregnancies at about 2 weeks past normal due date.
b) Parts (a) and (b)—yes—we can't use Normal model if it's very skewed. Part (c)—no—CLT guarantees a Normal model for this large sample size.

**40.** a) Some people work far longer than the mean +2 or 3 SDs.
b) The CLT says $\bar{y}$ is approximately Normal for large sample sizes, but not for samples of size 1 (individuals).

**41.** a) $\mu = \$2.00$, $\sigma = \$3.61$
b) $\mu = \$4.00$, $\sigma = \$5.10$
c) 0.191. Model is $N(80, 22.83)$.

**42.** a)

| Amount won | 40 | 0 | −10 |
|---|---|---|---|
| P(amount won) | 1/6 | 5/36 | 25/36 |

b) $\mu = -\$0.28$, $\sigma = \$18.33$
c) $\mu = -\$1.40$, $\sigma = \$40.99$
d) 0.56

**43.** a) $\mu = 2.859$, $\sigma = 1.324$
b) No. The score distribution in the sample should resemble that in the population, somewhat uniform for scores 1–4 and about half as many 5's.
c) Approximately $N\left(2.859, \dfrac{1.324}{\sqrt{40}}\right)$.

**44.** a) $\mu = \$137.50$, $\sigma = \$148.56$
b) No. These 50 members will probably make donations typical of the current member population, and that's skewed to the right.
c) Approximately $N\left(137.5, \dfrac{148.56}{\sqrt{50}}\right)$.

**45.** About 20%, based on $N(2.859, 0.167)$.

**46.** Nearly 99%, based on $N(137.5, 16.61)$.

**47.** a) $N(2.9, 0.045)$
b) 0.0131
c) 2.97 gm/mi

**48.** a) 0.0478
b) 0.863
c) 0.0019
d) Essentially 0

**49.** a) Can't use a Normal model to estimate probabilities. The distribution is skewed right—not Normal.
b) 4 is probably not a large enough sample to say the average follows the Normal model.
c) No. This is 3.16 SDs above the mean.

**50.** a) Can't use a Normal model to estimate probabilities. The distribution is skewed right—not Normal.
b) Probably not. 10 is not a large sample. It depends on the amount of skewness of the distribution.
c) No. With 50 customers, $\bar{y}$ is $N(32, 2.83)$. The probability is 0.0023.

**51.** a) 0.0003. Model is $N(384, 34.15)$.
b) $427.77 or more

**52.** a) 0.482. Model is $N(9984, 353.27)$.
b) $9531.27 or less

**53.** a) 0.734
   b) 0.652. Model is $N(10, 12.81)$.
   c) 0.193. Model is $N(120, 5.774)$.
   d) 0.751. Model is $N(10, 7.394)$.

**54.** a) 0.309
   b) 0.696. Model is $N(4, 7.810)$.
   c) 0.037. Model is $N(43, 1.118)$.
   d) 0.325. Model is $N(4, 2.202)$.

# CHAPTER 19

**1.** He believes the true proportion is within 4% of his estimate, with some (probably 95%) degree of confidence.

**2.** He believes the true proportion is within 3% of his estimate, with some (probably 95%) degree of confidence.

**3.** a) Population—all cars; sample—those actually stopped at the checkpoint; $p$—proportion of all cars with safety problems; $\hat{p}$—proportion actually seen with safety problems (10.4%); if sample (a cluster sample) is representative, then the methods of this chapter will apply.
   b) Population—general public; sample—those who logged onto the Web site; $p$—population proportion of those who favor prayer in school; $\hat{p}$—proportion of those who voted in the poll who favored prayer in school (81.1%); can't use methods of this chapter—sample is biased and nonrandom.
   c) Population—parents at the school; sample—those who returned the questionnaire; $p$—proportion of all parents who favor uniforms; $\hat{p}$—proportion of respondents who favor uniforms (60%); have to use caution with methods of this chapter, since nonresponse may bias results.
   d) Population—students at the college; sample—the 1632 students who entered that year; $p$—proportion of all students who will graduate on time; $\hat{p}$—proportion of that year's students who graduate on time (85.0%); can use methods of this chapter if that year's students (a cluster sample) are viewed as a representative sample of all possible students at the school.

**4.** a) Population—people who recently bought new cars; sample—167 people surveyed; $p$—proportion of all new car buyers who are dissatisfied with the salesperson; $\hat{p}$—proportion of those surveyed who are unsatisfied (3%); can't use methods of this chapter because only 5 people were dissatisfied.
   b) Population—college students; sample—2883 students who were asked about cell phones; $p$—proportion of college students with cell phones; $\hat{p}$—proportion of those asked who have cell phones (8.4%); use methods of this chapter with caution—students entering the football stadium may not reflect all students.
   c) Population—potato plants in the United States; sample—240 plants checked; $p$—proportion of all plants in the field with blight; $\hat{p}$—proportion of the 240 plants checked with blight (2.9%); can't use methods of this chapter—fewer than 10 "successes."
   d) Population—employees at the company; sample—all employees that year; $p$—proportion of all employees who will have an injury on the job in a year; $\hat{p}$—proportion of that year's employees with an injury (3.9%); can use methods of this chapter if that year's employees are viewed as a random sample of all possible employees.

**5.** a) Not correct. This implies certainty.
   b) Not correct. Different samples will give different results. Many fewer than 95% will have 88% on-time orders.
   c) Not correct. The interval is about the population proportion, not the sample proportion in different samples.
   d) Not correct. In this sample, we *know* 88% arrived on time.
   e) Not correct. The interval is about the parameter, not about the days.

**6.** a) Not correct. The interval is about the proportion of heads, not individual coins.
   b) Not correct. We know in this sample that 56% of the spins were heads.
   c) Correct.
   d) Not correct. The interval is about the proportion of heads, not about individual spins.
   e) Not correct. The interval is about the proportion of heads, not about the percentage of euros.

**7.** a) False    b) True    c) True    d) False

**8.** a) True    b) True    c) True    d) True

**9.** On the basis of this sample, we are 90% confident that the proportion of Japanese cars is between 29.9% and 47.0%.

**10.** On the basis of this sample, we are 95% confident that the proportion of paroles granted by the Nebraska Board of Parole is between 56.1% and 62.5%.

**11.** a) (0.798, 0.862)
   b) We're 95% confident that between 80% and 86% of all broiler chicken sold in U.S. food stores is infected with *Campylobacter*.
   c) The size of the population is irrelevant. If *Consumer Reports* had a random sample, 95% of intervals generated by studies like this will capture the true contamination level.

**12.** a) It's not clear how the sample was chosen, but coming from many stores in 23 states, it may be representative of all broiler chicken sold. And it's important that the researchers kept the chicken samples separated. The sample was far less than 10% of the population. There were 79 successes and 446 failures, both at least 10.
   b) (0.12, 0.18)
   c) We're 95% confident that between 12% and 18% of all broiler chicken sold in U.S. food stores is infected with *Salmonella*.

**13.** a) 0.025
   b) We're 90% confident that this poll's estimate is within $\pm 2.5\%$ of the true proportion of people who are baseball fans.
   c) Larger. To be more certain, we must be less precise.
   d) 0.039
   e) less confidence
   f) No evidence of change; given the margin of error, 0.37 is a plausible value for 2007 as well.

**14.** a) 1.9% (0.019)
   b) The pollsters are 95% confident that the true proportion of adults who approve of attempts to clone humans is within 1.9% of the estimated 11%.
   c) Smaller. Less confidence allows a narrower interval.
   d) 1.6%
   e) Larger

**15.** a) (0.0465, 0.0491). The assumptions and conditions for constructing a confidence interval are satisfied.
   b) The confidence interval gives the set of plausible values (with 95% confidence). Since 0.05 is outside the interval, that seems to be a bit too optimistic.

**16.** a) (0.0223, 0.0250). The assumptions and conditions for constructing a confidence interval are satisfied.
   b) Since 0.02 is below the confidence interval, it isn't one of the plausible values.

**17.** a) (12.7%, 18.6%)
   b) We are 95% confident, based on this sample, that the proportion of all auto accidents that involve teenage drivers is between 12.7% and 18.6%.
   c) About 95% of all random samples will produce confidence intervals that contain the true population proportion.
   d) Contradicts. The interval is completely below 20%.

**18.** a) (10.6%, 14.0%)
   b) We are 90% confident, based on this sample, that the proportion of people contacted who may buy something is between 10.6% and 14.0%.

c) About 90% of all random samples will produce confidence intervals that contain the true population proportion.
d) Do the mass mailing. The interval is considerably above 5%.
19. Probably nothing. Those who bothered to fill out the survey may be a biased sample.
20. Nothing. Those who showed up for the meeting are probably a biased group. In addition, a show-of-hands vote may influence people, making the votes nonindependent.
21. a) (49.7%, 58.3%)
    b) No
22. a) 19.1%
    b) Maybe. The proportion is significantly lower than 30%, but this is just one estimate.
    c) (11.7%, 26.4%)
    d) Yes, 30% is above the interval.
23. a) Response bias (wording)
    b) (54%, 60%)
    c) Smaller—the sample size was larger.
24. a) The class's interval will be larger, since its sample size is smaller.
    b) Newspaper: (50.2%, 55.8%) class: (49.4%, 58.6%).
    c) Students because 50% is in their interval.
25. a) (18.2%, 21.8%)
    b) We are 98% confident, based on the sample, that between 18.2% and 21.8% of English children are deficient in vitamin D.
    c) About 98% of all random samples will produce a confidence interval that contains the true proportion.
26. a) (18.8%, 28.5%)
    b) We are 90% confident, based on this sample, that between 18.8% and 28.5% of women under 40 who are helped at this clinic will become pregnant and give birth.
    c) About 90% of all random samples will produce intervals that contain the true proportion.
    d) No, 25% is in the interval.
27. a) The students' birth orders are likely to be independent. The sample was random and consisted of less than 10% of the population of students. There were 20 successes and 206 failures.
    b) (5.1%, 12.6%)
    c) We're 95% confident that between 5.1% and 12.6% of all college students are "only" children.
    d) If we were to select repeated samples like this we'd expect about 95% of the confidence intervals we created to contain the true proportion of all college students who are "only" children.
28. a) It's a random sample; both 74% and 26% of 1644 are greater than 10.
    b) (71.5%, 76.5%)
    c) We're 98% confident that between 71.5% and 76.5% of college freshman return to college their sophomore years.
    d) If we were to select repeated samples like this we'd expect about 98% of the confidence intervals we created to contain the true proportion of all college freshmen who return to be sophomores.
29. This was a random sample of less than 10% of adults; there were $1008(0.08) = 81$ successes and 927 failures, both at least 10. We're 95% confident that between 6.3% and 9.7% of adult consumers are uncomfortable with their abilities to make their monthly payments during the next three months.
30. a) The larger sample of private college students will produce a narrower confidence interval.
    b) (68.0%, 75.8%)
    c) No. Based on the confidence interval, the overall public college retention rate could in fact be higher than 75%.
31. a) Wider. The sample size is probably about one-fourth of the sample size for all adults, so we'd expect the confidence interval to be about twice as wide.
    b) Smaller. The second poll used a slightly larger sample size.

32. a) The parameter is the proportion of digital songs that are legal. The population is the population of all songs held in digital music libraries (by students?). The sample size is 117,079 (not 168).
    b) The songs and whether or not they were paid for are likely to be independent. We have a random sample, but this is a cluster sample—we have information on 168 "clusters" of songs in the 168 music libraries we asked about. It is these that were sampled at random. The 10% and Success/Failure Conditions are met.
    c) $0.231 \pm 0.00241$
    d) The CI says we can be 95% confident that the true proportion of legal songs in student digital music libraries is between 0.229 and 0.233, but the very large sample size has made this interval unreasonably narrow. It is hard to believe that such a narrow interval really captures the parameter we want. Our methods assume we have simple random samples; the cluster sampling done here adds to our uncertainty.
33. a) (15.5%, 26.3%)   b) 612
    c) Sample may not be random or representative. Deer that may legally be hunted may not be representative of all sexes and ages.
34. a) 828 women
    b) This large a sample might be larger than 10% of the population.
35. a) 141   b) 318   c) 564
36. a) 542, assuming $p = 0.50$.
    b) 1503
    c) Would need 13,526 employers.
37. 1801
38. 1037
39. 384 total, using $p = 0.15$.
40. 581
41. 90%
42. a) 50% is in the interval.
    b) 98%

# CHAPTER 20

1. a) $H_0: p = 0.30$; $H_A: p < 0.30$
   b) $H_0: p = 0.50$; $H_A: p \neq 0.50$
   c) $H_0: p = 0.20$; $H_A: p > 0.20$
2. a) $H_0: p = 0.40$; $H_A: p \neq 0.40$
   b) $H_0: p = 0.20$; $H_A: p < 0.20$
   c) $H_0: p = 0.60$; $H_A: p > 0.60$
3. Statement d is correct.
4. Statement d is correct.
5. No, we can say only that there is a 27% chance of seeing the observed effectiveness just from natural sampling variation. There is no *evidence* that the new formula is more effective, but we can't conclude that they are equally effective.
6. There's no evidence of a change. Even if there's been no real change in public opinion, there's a 37% chance we'd see this much difference—or more—from one sample to another.
7. The ads may be working. If there had been no real change in name recognition, there'd be only about a 3% chance the percentage of voters who heard of this candidate would be at least this much higher in a different sample.
8. Yes. If there is no difference, there is only a 1.7% chance of seeing such a high sample proportion just from natural sampling variation.
9. a) No. There's a 25% chance of losing twice in a row. That's not unusual.
   b) 0.125
   c) No, we expect that to happen 1 time in 8.
   d) Maybe 5? The chance of 5 losses in a row is only 1 in 32, which seems unusual.

**10.** a) 0.091

b) Perhaps. If so, we'd get 3 vanillas in a row about 9% of the time.

c) No. The probability of getting 4 vanillas in a row is only about 3%; that's unlikely to have happened by chance.

**11.** 1) Use $p$, not $\hat{p}$, in hypotheses.

2) The question was about failing to meet the goal, so $H_A$ should be $p < 0.96$.

3) Did not check $0.04(200) = 8$. Since $nq < 10$, the Success/ Failure Condition is violated. Didn't check 10% Condition.

4) $188/200 = 0.94$; $SD(\hat{p}) = \sqrt{\dfrac{(0.96)(0.04)}{200}} = 0.014$

5) $z$ is incorrect; should be $z = \dfrac{0.94 - 0.96}{0.014} = -1.43$.

6) $P = P(z < -1.43) = 0.076$

7) There is only weak evidence that the new instructions do not work.

**12.** 1) Use $p$ in hypotheses, not $\hat{p}$.

2) The question asks, "*not accurate*," so $H_A$ should be two sided: $p \neq 0.9$.

3) The correct conditions are SRS, $750 < 10\%$ of county population $(0.9)(750) \geq 10$, and $(0.10)(750) \geq 10$.

4) $\hat{p} = 657/750 = 0.876$; $SD(\hat{p}) = \sqrt{\dfrac{(0.9)(0.1)}{750}} = 0.011$

5) $z$ is incorrect; should be $z = \dfrac{0.876 - 0.9}{0.011} = -2.18$.

6) $P = 2P(z < -2.18) = 0.029$

7) There is only a 2.9% chance of observing a $\hat{p}$ as far from 0.90 by sampling variation, so we believe that the proportion of adults who drink milk here is different from the claimed 90%.

**13.** a) $H_0: p = 0.30$; $H_A: p > 0.30$

b) Possibly an SRS; we don't know if the sample is less than 10% of his customers, but it could be viewed as less than 10% of all possible customers; $(0.3)(80) \geq 10$ and $(0.7)(80) \geq 10$. Wells are independent only if customers don't have farms on the same underground springs.

c) $z = 0.73$; P-value $= 0.232$

d) If his dowsing is no different from standard methods, there is more than a 23% chance of seeing results as good as those of the dowser's, or better, by natural sampling variation.

e) These data provide no evidence that the dowser's chance of finding water is any better than normal drilling.

**14.** a) $H_0: p = 0.05$; $H_A: p > 0.05$

b) SRS (not clear from information provided), $< 10\%$ of all children, $(0.05)(384) \geq 10$, and $(0.95)(384) \geq 10$.

c) $z = 6.28$, $P = 2 \times 10^{-10}$

d) If the abnormality rate has not increased, the chance of observing at least 46 children with abnormalities in a sample of 384 is $2 \times 10^{-10}$ (almost 0).

e) Reject $H_0$. These data show that the rate of abnormalities is now more than 5%.

f) We do not know that chemicals cause abnormalities, only that the rate is higher now than in the past.

**15.** a) $H_0: p_{2000} = 0.34$; $H_A: p_{2000} \neq 0.34$

b) Students were randomly sampled and should be independent. 34% and 66% of 8302 are greater than 10. 8302 students is less than 10% of the entire student population of the United States.

c) $P = 0.058$

d) With such a small P-value, I reject $H_0$. There has been a statistically significant change in the proportion of students who have no absences.

e) No. A difference this small, although statistically significant, is not meaningful. We might look at new data in a couple of years.

**16.** a) $H_0: p_{2000} = 0.31$; $H_A: p_{2000} \neq 0.31$

b) Students are randomly sampled and should be independent; 31% and 69% of 8368 are both at least 10. 8368 students is less

than 10% of the entire student population of the United States.

c) $P = 0.048$

d) With a P-value so low, I reject $H_0$. There is a statistically significant difference in the proportion of mothers with a college education.

e) A difference this small, although statistically significant, may not be meaningful.

**17.** a) $H_0: p = 0.05$ vs. $H_A: p < 0.05$

b) We assume the whole mailing list has over 1,000,000 names. This is a random sample, and we expect 5000 successes and 95,000 failures.

c) $z = -3.178$; P-value $= 0.00074$, so we reject $H_0$; there is strong evidence that the donation rate would be below 5%.

**18.** a) $H_0: p = 0.02$ vs. $H_A: p \neq 0.02$

b) We assume the company has over 500,000 cardholders. This is a random sample, and we expect 1000 successes and 49,000 failures.

c) $z = 5.878$; the P-value is less than 0.0001, so we reject $H_0$, concluding that there is strong evidence that the success rate will be more than 2%.

**19.** a) Based on these data, we are 95% confident that the proportion of adults in 2004 who had never smoked cigarettes is between 51.3% and 57.9%.

b) $H_0: p = 0.44$; $H_A: p \neq 0.44$. Since 44% is not in the confidence interval, we reject $H_0$ and conclude that the proportion of adults in 2004 who had never smoked was more than in the 1960s.

**20.** a) Based on these data, we are 95% confident that the proportion of dissatisfied customers is between 1.1% and 4.6%.

b) $H_0: p = 0.05$; $H_A: p < 0.05$. Since 5% is above the 95% confidence interval, we will reject $H_0$ at $\alpha = 0.025$ and conclude that the proportion of dissatisfied customers is less than 5%, so the company has met its goal.

**21.** a) $H_0: p = 0.63$, $H_A: p > 0.63$

b) The sample is representative. $240 < 10\%$ of all law school applicants. We expect $240(0.63) = 151.2$ to be admitted and $240(0.37) = 88.8$ not to be, both at least 10. $z = 1.58$; P-value $= 0.057$.

c) Although the evidence is weak, there is some indication that the program may be successful. Candidates should decide whether they can afford the time and expense.

**22.** a) $H_0: p = 0.46$; $H_A: p < 0.46$

b) Assume the sample is representative of all applicants from this college. $180 < 10\%$ of all medical school applicants. We expect $180(0.46) = 82.8$ to be admitted and $180(0.54) = 97.2$ not to be, both at least 10. $z = -0.87$; P-value $= 0.19$.

c) The high P-value says this isn't an unusual result; it may be just year-to-year variation, as the president says.

**23.** $H_0: p = 0.20$; $H_A: p > 0.20$. SRS (not clear from information provided); 22 is more than 10% of the population of 150; $(0.20)(22) < 10$. Do not proceed with a test.

**24.** $H_0: p = 0.02$; $H_A: p > 0.02$. SRS; less than 10% of all washers and dryers made by the company; $(0.02)(60) < 10$. Do not proceed with a test.

**25.** $H_0: p = 0.03$; $p \neq 0.03$. $\hat{p} = 0.015$. One mother having twins will not affect another, so observations are independent; not an SRS; sample is less than 10% of all births. However, the mothers at this hospital may not be representative of all teenagers; $(0.03)(469) = 14.07 \geq 10$; $(0.97)(469) \geq 10$. $z = -1.91$; P-value $= 0.0556$. With a P-value this low, reject $H_0$. These data show some evidence that the rate of twins born to teenage girls at this hospital is less than the national rate of 3%. It is not clear whether this can be generalized to all teenagers.

**26.** $H_0: p = 0.50$; $H_A: p > 0.50$. Results of one game should not affect another, so games are independent; data are all results for one season, which should be representative of all seasons; sample is less than 10% of all games; $(0.50)(240) \geq 10$; $(0.50)(240) \geq 10$.

$z = 2.07$; P-value = 0.02. With a P-value this low, reject $H_0$. These data show strong evidence that the home team does have an advantage; they win more than 50% of games at home.

27. $H_0: p = 0.25$; $H_A: p > 0.25$. SRS; sample is less than 10% of all potential subscribers; $(0.25)(500) \geq 10$; $(0.75)(500) \geq 10$. $z = 1.24$; P-value = 0.1076. The P-value is high, so do not reject $H_0$. These data do not show that more than 25% of current readers would subscribe; the company should not go ahead with the WebZine on the basis of these data.

28. $H_0: p = 0.92$; $H_A: p < 0.92$. Seeds in a single packet may not be independent of each other. This is a cluster sample of all seeds in the packet. We may view this cluster as representative of all year-old seeds, in which case the sample is less than 10% of all seeds; $(0.92)(200) \geq 10$; $(0.08)(200) \geq 10$. $z = -3.39$; P-value = 0.0004. Because the P-value is very low, we reject $H_0$. There is strong evidence that these seeds have lost viability; their germination rate is less than 92%.

29. $H_0: p = 0.40$; $H_A: p < 0.40$. Data are for all executives in this company and may not be able to be generalized to all companies; $(0.40)(43) \geq 10$; $(0.60)(43) \geq 10$. $z = -1.31$; P-value = 0.0955. Because the P-value is high, we fail to reject $H_0$. These data do not show that the proportion of women executives is less than the 40% of women in the company in general.

30. $H_0: p = 0.19$; $H_A: p < 0.19$. $\hat{p} = 0.125$. $z = -1.41$; P-value = 0.0793. Because the P-value is high, we fail to reject $H_0$. These data do not show convincing evidence that Hispanics are represented in the jury pool at less than their 19% proportion in the population in general, but the data do indicate that the percentage is below what was expected.

31. $H_0: p = 0.103$; $H_A: p > 0.103$. $\hat{p} = 0.118$; $z = 2.06$; P-value = 0.02. Because the P-value is low, we reject $H_0$. These data provide evidence that the dropout rate has increased.

32. $H_0: p = 0.15$; $H_A: p > 0.15$. $\hat{p} = 0.25$; $z = 2.80$; P-value = 0.0026. The 95% confidence interval is $(0.165, 0.335)$. We must assume that the trees sampled are an SRS of the trees in the area and are less than 10% of all trees in the forest. The results are generalizable only to the Hopkins forest (or nearby if the forest is viewed as representative). Because the P-value is so low, we reject $H_0$. There is strong evidence that the proportion of trees damaged by acid rain in the Hopkins forest is higher than the 15% average for the Northeast.

33. $H_0: p = 0.90$; $H_A: p < 0.90$. $\hat{p} = 0.844$; $z = -2.05$; P-value = 0.0201. Because the P-value is so low, we reject $H_0$. There is strong evidence that the actual rate at which passengers with lost luggage are reunited with it within 24 hours is less than the 90% claimed by the airline.

34. $H_0: p = 0.40$; $H_A: p > 0.40$. $\hat{p} = 0.431$; $z = 1.29$; P-value = 0.0977. Because the P-value is high, we fail to reject $H_0$. These data do not show that at least 40% of the public recognizes the brand; I would not recommend they continue to advertise during Super Bowls on the basis of these data.

35. a) Yes; assuming this sample to be a typical group of people, $P = 0.0008$. This cancer rate is very unusual.
    b) No, this group of people may be atypical for reasons that have nothing to do with the radiation.

36. No; the P-value of 0.47 indicates that her school's results could be explained by random variation (sampling error).

## CHAPTER 21

1. a) Two sided. Let $p$ be the percentage of students who prefer Diet Pepsi. $H_0: p = 0.5$ vs. $H_A: p \neq 0.5$
   b) One sided. Let $p$ be the percentage of teenagers who prefer the new formulation. $H_0: p = 0.5$ vs. $H_A: p > 0.5$
   c) One sided. Let $p$ be the percentage of people who intend to vote for the override. $H_0: p = 2/3$ vs. $H_A: p > 2/3$
   d) Two sided. Let $p$ be the percentage of days that the market goes up. $H_0: p = 0.5$ vs. $H_A: p \neq 0.5$

2. a) Two sided. Let $p$ be the percentage of students who prefer plastic. $H_0: p = 0.5$ vs. $H_A: p \neq 0.5$
   b) Two sided. Let $p$ be the percentage of juniors applying for study abroad. $H_0: p = 0.1$ vs. $H_A: p \neq 0.1$
   c) One sided. Let $p$ be the percentage of people who experience relief. $H_0: p = 0.22$ vs. $H_A: p > 0.22$
   d) One sided. Let $p$ be the percentage of hard drives that pass the test the first time. $H_0: p = 0.6$ vs. $H_A: p > 0.6$

3. If there is no difference in effectiveness, the chance of seeing an observed difference this large or larger is 4.7% by natural sampling variation.

4. If harsher penalties and ad campaigns have made no difference in seat-belt use, there is a 17% chance of seeing an observed difference this large or larger by natural sampling variation.

5. $\alpha = 0.10$: Yes. The P-value is less than 0.05, so it's less than 0.10. But to reject $H_0$ at $\alpha = 0.01$, the P-value must be below 0.01, which isn't necessarily the case.

6. At $\alpha = 0.10$, they reach the same decision only if the P-value is $> 0.10$. We know only that it's $> 0.05$. But we know that it's $> 0.01$, so at $\alpha = 0.01$, they reach the same decision.

7. a) There is only a 1.1% chance of seeing a sample proportion as low as 89.4% vaccinated by natural sampling variation if 90% have really been vaccinated.
   b) We conclude that $p$ is below 0.9, but a 95% confidence interval would show that the true proportion is between $(0.889, 0.899)$. Most likely, a decrease from 90% to 89.9% would not be considered important. On the other hand, with 1,000,000 children a year vaccinated, even 0.1% represents about 1000 kids—so this may very well be important.

8. a) There is only a 2.3% chance of seeing a sample proportion of 15.1% of students not attaining grade level by natural sampling variation if 15.9% is the true population value.
   b) Under old methods, 1352 students would not be expected to read at grade level. With the new program, 1284 did not. This is only a decrease of 68 students. It would depend on the costs of switching to the new program.

9. a) $(1.9\%, 4.1\%)$
   b) Because 5% is not in the interval, there is strong evidence that fewer than 5% of all men use work as their primary measure of success.
   c) $\alpha = 0.01$; it's a lower-tail test based on a 98% confidence interval.

10. a) $(0.498, 0.622)$; we are 95% confident that the true proportion of heads is between 49.8% and 62.2%.
    b) No; 0.50 is within the confidence interval, so it's a plausible value for the proportion of heads.
    c) $\alpha = 0.05$; it's a two-tailed test based on a 95% confidence interval.

11. a) $(0.274, 0.327)$
    b) Since 0.27 is not in the confidence interval, we reject the hypothesis that $p = 0.27$.

12. a) $(19.0\%, 25.1\%)$
    b) Since the confidence interval extends well below 25%, we can't be sure that over 25% of men are stay-at-home dads. The company should not buy the ads.
    c) Yes, 25% is in the interval. It's a plausible value, but we can never prove that the null hypothesis is true.

13. a) Type II error
    b) Type I error
    c) By making it easier to get the loan, the bank has reduced the alpha level.
    d) The risk of a Type I error is decreased and the risk of a Type II error is increased.

14. a) Type II error
    b) Type I error
    c) Lower alpha: It takes more evidence to classify the e-mail as spam.
    d) The risk of a Type I error is decreased and the risk of a Type II error is increased.

15. a) Power is the probability that the bank denies a loan that would not have been repaid.
    b) Raise the cutoff score.
    c) A larger number of trustworthy people would be denied credit, and the bank would miss the opportunity to collect interest on those loans.

16. a) Power is the probability the filter spots spam.
    b) Lower the cutoff score.
    c) More real messages would end up in the junk mailbox.

17. a) The null is that the level of home ownership remains the same. The alternative is that it rises.
    b) The city concludes that home ownership is on the rise, but in fact the tax breaks don't help.
    c) The city abandons the tax breaks, but they were helping.
    d) A Type I error causes the city to forego tax revenue, while a Type II error withdraws help from those who might have otherwise been able to buy a home.
    e) The power of the test is the city's ability to detect an actual increase in home ownership.

18. a) The null hypothesis is that a person is healthy (there is no parameter here). The alternative is that the person has Alzheimer's disease.
    b) A Type I error is a false positive—deciding a person has Alzheimer's disease when he or she doesn't.
    c) A Type II error is a false negative—failing to diagnose Alzheimer's disease when the person has it.
    d) A Type I error would require more testing, resulting in time and money lost. A Type II error would mean that the person did not receive the treatment he or she needed. A Type II error is much worse.
    e) The power is $1 - P(\text{Type II error}) = 1 - 0.08 = 0.92$.

19. a) It is decided that the shop is not meeting standards when it is.
    b) The shop is certified as meeting standards when it is not.
    c) Type I
    d) Type II

20. a) Deciding there has been an increase in defective items when there has not.
    b) Deciding the number of defectives is small when it has increased.
    c) Probably Type II, depending on the costs of shutting the line down. Generally, because of warranty costs and lost customer loyalty, defects that are caught in the factory are much cheaper to fix than defects found after items are sold.
    d) Type II

21. a) The probability of detecting a shop that is not meeting standards.
    b) 40 cars. Larger $n$.
    c) 10%. More chance to reject $H_0$.
    d) A lot. Larger differences are easier to detect.

22. a) The probability of deciding there are too many defectives when this is true.
    b) Advantage: More power. Disadvantage: More work testing.
    c) Advantage: Smaller Type I error chance. Disadvantage: Less power.
    d) Increases because the effect size increases.

23. a) One-tailed. The company wouldn't be sued if "too many" minorities were hired.
    b) Deciding the company is discriminating when it is not.
    c) Deciding the company is not discriminating when it is.
    d) The probability of correctly detecting discrimination when it exists.
    e) Increases power.
    f) Lower, since $n$ is smaller.

24. a) One-tailed because we are interested only in whether they are more visible. If the new design is less visible, we don't care how much less visible it is.
    b) Deciding that the signs are more visible when they are not.

    c) Failing to decide that new signs are more visible when they are.
    d) Ability (probability) to detect that a more visible sign works.
    e) It will decrease power, because you'll need more evidence to reject $H_0$.
    f) It will decrease power because it will make the SD larger.

25. a) One-tailed. Software is supposed to decrease the dropout rate.
    b) $H_0: p = 0.13$; $H_A: p < 0.13$
    c) He buys the software when it doesn't help students.
    d) He doesn't buy the software when it does help students.
    e) The probability of correctly deciding the software is helpful.

26. a) $H_0: p = 0.20$; $H_A: p > 0.20$
    b) The company wants more "proof" the ad is effective before deciding it is.
    c) The probability of correctly deciding that more than 20% have heard the ad and recognize the product when it's true.
    d) 10%. More chance to reject $H_0$.
    e) Lower. Larger $n$ has more power and smaller Type II error probability.

27. a) $z = -3.21$, $p = 0.0007$. The change is statistically significant. A 95% confidence interval is (2.3%, 8.5%). This is clearly lower than 13%. If the cost of the software justifies it, the professor should consider buying the software.
    b) The chance of observing 11 or fewer dropouts in a class of 203 is only 0.07% if the dropout rate is really 13%.

28. a) $z = 1.33$, $p = 0.0923$. The company should not renew the contract.
    b) There is a 9.23% chance of having 133 or more of 600 people in a random sample remember the ad if in fact 20% of people do.

29. a) $H_A: p = 0.30$, where $p$ is the probability of heads
    b) Reject the null hypothesis if the coin comes up tails—otherwise fail to reject.
    c) P(tails given the null hypothesis) $= 0.1 = \alpha$
    d) P(tails given the alternative hypothesis) $=$ power $= 0.70$
    e) Spin the coin more than once and base the decision on the sample proportion of heads.

30. a) The null hypothesis is that the drive is good ($p = 0.96$). The alternative is that it is bad; ($p = 0.35$), where $p$ is the probability of passing the test.
    b) Reject the null hypothesis if the computer fails the test—otherwise fail to reject.
    c) P(fails test given the null hypothesis) $= 0.04 = \alpha$
    d) P(fails test given the alternative hypothesis) $=$ power $= 0.65$

31. a) 0.0464   b) Type I   c) 37.6%
    d) Increase the number of shots. Or keep the number of shots at 10, but increase alpha by declaring that 8, 9, or 10 will be deemed as having improved.

32. a) 0.0464   b) Type I   c) 0.6242
    d) Increase the number of pieces tested, or keep the number of pieces tested at 10, but increase the number of "acceptable broken pieces" from 1 to 2.

33. Laborers only.

34. Single-family home only.

35. a) (21.8%, 30.2%)
    b) No, 20% is below the low end of the interval.

36. The 95% CI is 55% ± 3%, or from 52% to 58%. This interval does not include 61%, so at the corresponding $\alpha$ level of 5%, reject the null hypothesis that the true level is still 61%.

# CHAPTER 22

1. It's very unlikely that samples would show an observed difference this large if in fact there is no real difference in the proportions of boys and girls who have used online social networks.

2. If in fact there is no difference in the proportion of the population who get science news from the Internet and from TV, then it's not unusual to observe a difference of 1% by sampling.

3. The responses are not from two independent groups, but are from the same individuals.

4. The 790 parents are a subset of the 935 parents, so the two groups are not independent. That violates the independence assumption.

5. a) Stratified
   b) 6% higher among males
   c) 4%
   d)

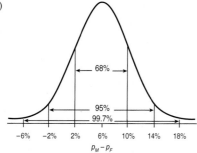

   e) Yes; a poll result showing little difference is only 1–2 standard deviations below the expected outcome.

6. a) Stratified
   b) 2% higher among owners of Japanese cars
   c) 2.8%
   d)

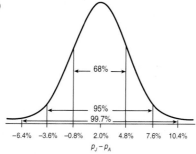

   e) Yes; a poll result showing greater satisfaction among owners of American cars (a negative difference) is less than one standard deviation below the expected outcome.

7. a) Yes. Random sample; less than 10% of the population; samples are independent; more than 10 successes and failures in each sample.
   b) (0.055, 0.140)
   c) We are 95% confident, based on these samples, that the proportion of American women age 65 and older who suffer from arthritis is between 5.5% and 14.0% more than the proportion of American men of the same age who suffer from arthritis.
   d) Yes; the entire interval lies above 0.

8. a) Yes. Random sample; less than 10% of the population; samples are independent; more than 10 successes and failures in each sample.
   b) (0.024, 0.040)
   c) We are 95% confident, based on these samples, that the proportion of 24-year-old American women who have graduated from high school is between 2.4% and 4.0% more than that of 24-year-old American men.
   d) Yes; the entire interval lies above 0.

9. a) 0.035
   b) (0.356, 0.495)
   c) We are 95% confident, based on these data, that the proportion of pets with a malignant lymphoma in homes where herbicides are used is between 35.6% and 49.5% higher than the proportion of pets with lymphoma in homes where no pesticides are used.

10. a) 0.068
    b) (0.116, 0.384)
    c) We are 95% confident, based on these data, that the proportion of patients who show improvement in carpal tunnel syndrome with surgery is between 11.6% and 38.4% more than the proportion who show improvement with wrist splints.

11. a) Experiment. Men were randomly assigned to have surgery or not.
    b) (0.006, 0.080)
    c) Since the entire interval lies above 0, there is evidence that surgery may be effective in preventing death from prostate cancer.

12. a) (0.007, 0.076)
    b) $H_0: p_1 - p_2 = 0$; $H_A: p_1 - p_2 \neq 0$. Since 0 is not in the interval, this survey provides evidence of a race-based difference in smoking percentages.
    c) $\alpha = 0.10$

13. a) Differences have a larger standard error than single samples.
    b) No. The confidence interval 2% ± 4% includes 0.

14. a) 45%
    b) Greater. Differences have standard errors larger than single samples.

15. a) Yes, subjects were randomly divided into independent groups, and more than 10 successes and failures were observed in each group.
    b) (4.7%, 8.9%)
    c) Yes, we're 95% confident that the rate of infection is 5–9 percentage points lower. That's a meaningful reduction, considering the 20% infection rate among the unvaccinated kids.

16. a) Yes, subjects were randomly divided into independent groups, and more than 10 successes and failures were observed in each group.
    b) (−20%, 17%)
    c) No, because 0 is in the confidence interval. There's no evidence of any difference between Prozac and the placebo.

17. a) $H_0: p_V - p_{NV} = 0$, $H_A: p_V - p_{NV} < 0$
    b) Because 0 is not in the confidence interval, reject the null. There's evidence that the vaccine reduces the rate of ear infections.
    c) Type I
    d) Babies would be given ineffective vaccinations.

18. a) $H_0: p_{prozac} - p_{placebo} = 0$, $H_A: p_{prozac} - p_{placebo} > 0$
    b) Because 0 is in the confidence interval, fail to reject the null. The data provide no evidence that Prozac is an effective treatment for anorexia.
    c) Type II
    d) We'd overlook a potentially helpful treatment.

19. a) Prospective study
    b) $H_0: p_1 - p_2 = 0$; $H_A: p_1 - p_2 \neq 0$ where $p_1$ is the proportion of students whose parents disapproved of smoking who became smokers and $p_2$ is the proportion of students whose parents are lenient about smoking who became smokers.
    c) Yes. We assume the students were randomly selected; they are less than 10% of the population; samples are independent; at least 10 successes and failures in each sample.
    d) $z = -1.17$, P-value = 0.2422. These samples do not show evidence that parental attitudes influence teens' decisions to smoke.
    e) If there is no difference in the proportions, there is about a 24% chance of seeing the observed difference or larger by natural sampling variation.
    f) Type II

20. a) Prospective study
    b) $H_0: p_1 - p_2 = 0$; $H_A: p_1 - p_2 < 0$, where $p_1$ is the proportion of people without depression who died within the 4 years and $p_2$ is the proportion of depressed people who died within the same period.

c) Yes. We assume the patients were representative; they are less than 10% of the population; samples are independent; at least 10 successes and failures in each sample.

d) $z = -2.22$, P-value $= 0.0131$. With a P-value this low, we reject $H_0$. This study indicates that the death rate for patients with heart disease who die within 4 years is less in non-depressed patients than in depressed patients.

e) If there is no difference in the proportions, we will see an observed difference this large or larger only about 1.3% of the time by natural sampling variation.

f) Type I

**21.** a) $(-0.065, 0.221)$

b) We are 95% confident that the proportion of teens whose parents disapprove of smoking who will eventually smoke is between 6.5% less and 22.1% more than for teens with parents who are lenient about smoking.

c) 95% of all random samples will produce intervals that contain the true difference.

**22.** a) $(0.004, 0.209)$

b) We are 95% confident, based on these data, that the proportion of heart disease patients who die within 4 years is between 0.4% and 20.9% higher for depressed patients than for nondepressed patients.

c) 95% of all random samples will produce intervals that contain the true value.

**23.** a) $H_0: p_1 - p_2 = 0$; $H_A: p_1 - p_2 \neq 0$. $z = 3.56$, P-value $= 0.0004$. With a P-value this low, we reject $H_0$. There is a significant difference in the clinic's effectiveness. Younger mothers have a higher birth rate than older mothers. Note that the Success/Failure Condition is met based on the pooled estimate of $p$.

b) We are 95% confident, based on these data, that the proportion of successful live births at the clinic is between 10.0% and 27.8% higher for mothers under 38 than in those 38 and older. However, the Success/Failure Condition is not met for the older women, since # Successes < 10. We should be cautious in trusting the confidence interval.

**24.** a) $H_0: p_1 - p_2 = 0$; $H_A: p_1 - p_2 > 0$. $z = 2.56$, P-value $= 0.005$ (with technology, $z = 2.71$, P-value $= 0.003$). With a P-value this low we reject $H_0$. This study shows a significantly higher rate of low-weight babies born to mothers exposed to high levels of air pollution during pregnancy.

b) We are 90% confident that the proportion of low-birth weight babies will be between 0.8% and 7.6% higher for mothers exposed to high levels of air pollution than those who were not.

**25.** $H_0: p_1 - p_2 = 0$; $H_A: p_1 - p_2 > 0$. $z = 1.18$, P-value $= 0.118$. With a P-value this high, we fail to reject $H_0$. These data do not show evidence of a decrease in the voter support for the candidate.

**26.** a) $H_0: p_1 - p_2 = 0$; $H_A: p_1 - p_2 \neq 0$. $z = 2.16$, P-value $= 0.031$. With a P-value this low, we reject $H_0$. This is moderately strong evidence that men and women have different outlooks.

b) We are 95% confident that between 1.7% and 16.3% more men than women expect to have enough money in retirement.

**27.** a) $H_0: p_1 - p_2 = 0$; $H_A: p_1 - p_2 \neq 0$. $z = -0.39$, P-value $= 0.6951$. With a P-value this high, we fail to reject $H_0$. There is no evidence of racial differences in the likelihood of multiple births, based on these data.

b) Type II

**28.** a) $H_0: p_1 - p_2 = 0$; $H_A: p_1 - p_2 > 0$. $z = 0.78$, P-value $= 0.2166$. With a P-value this high, we fail to reject $H_0$. There is no evidence, based on this information, that men are more likely than women to make online purchases of books.

b) Type II

**29.** a) $H_0: p_1 - p_2 = 0$; $H_A: p_1 - p_2 > 0$. $z = 2.17$, P-value $= 0.0148$. With a P-value this low, we reject $H_0$. These data do suggest that mammograms may reduce breast cancer deaths.

b) Type I

**30.** a) $H_0: p_1 - p_2 = 0$; $H_A: p_1 - p_2 > 0$. $z = 0.24$, P-value $= 0.4068$. With a P-value this high, we fail to reject $H_0$. These data do not suggest that mammograms are effective in reducing breast cancer deaths.

b) Type II

**31.** a) We are 95% confident, based on this study, that between 67.0% and 83.0% of patients with joint pain will find medication A effective.

b) We are 95% confident, based on this study, that between 51.9% and 70.3% of patients with joint pain will find medication B effective.

c) Yes, they overlap. This might indicate no difference in the effectiveness of the medications, although this is not a proper test.

d) We are 95% confident that the proportion of patients with joint pain who will find medication A effective is between 1.7% and 26.1% higher than the proportion who will find medication B effective.

e) No. There is a difference in the effectiveness of the medications.

f) To estimate the variability in the difference of proportions, we must add variances. The two one-sample intervals do not. The two-sample method is the correct approach.

**32.** a) We are 95% confident, based on the data, that between 47.5% and 56.5% of male voters will vote for the candidate.

b) We are 95% confident, based on the data, that between 40.7% and 49.3% of female voters will vote for the candidate.

c) Yes, they overlap. There appears to be no discernible gender gap, but this is not the proper approach.

d) We are 95% confident, based on the data, that the proportion of men who will vote for the candidate is between 0.8% and 13.2% higher than the proportion of female voters who will vote for him.

e) No. There is a gender gap.

f) To estimate the variability in the difference of proportions, we must add variances. The two one-sample intervals do not. The two-sample method is the correct approach.

**33.** A 95% confidence interval is $(-1.6\%, 5.6\%)$; 0%—or no bounce—is a plausible value. They should have said that there was no evidence of a bounce from their poll, however, since they can't prove there was none at all.

**34.** a) The conditions are satisfied. We are 95% confident that the true difference in the proportion of black men staying at home as parents and the proportion of Hispanic men doing the same is between $-3.4\%$ and 5.8%.

b) The margin of error is larger because the sample sizes are so much smaller. This question focused only on black and Latino respondents.

**35.** The conditions are satisfied to test $H_0: p_{\text{young}} = p_{\text{old}}$ against $H_A: p_{\text{young}} > p_{\text{old}}$. The one-sided P-value is 0.0619, so we may reject the null hypothesis. Although the evidence is not strong, *Time* may be justified in saying that younger men are more comfortable discussing personal problems.

**36.** The conditions are satisfied to test $H_0: p_{2004} = p_{2002}$ against $H_A: p_{2004} > p_{2002}$. With a one-sided P-value of 0.0001, these results are unlikely to have occurred by chance. We reject the null hypothesis and conclude that the increase is real.

**37.** We assume these innings are typical of results we anticipate in future games, and test a two-sided hypothesis that the Giants are equally likely to score whether the other team pitches to Bonds or walks him. The P-value of 0.075 provides some evidence that the Giants will score in a higher percentage of innings if Bonds is intentionally walked.

**38.** The conditions are met to test the hypothesis that public and private colleges have the same retention rates. The two-sided P-value is 0.1996, too high to reject the null. We don't have evidence of an overall difference.

**39.** Yes. With a low P-value of 0.003, reject the null hypothesis of no difference. There's evidence of an increase in the proportion of parents checking the Web sites visited by their teens.

**40.** No. Based on a high P-value of 0.11, fail to reject the hypothesis that there's no age-based difference in computer gaming among teenage boys.

**41.** Yes. With a low P-value of 0.0013, reject the null hypothesis of no difference. There is strong evidence to suggest that the percentages are different for the two groups: People from urban areas are more likely to agree with the statement than those from rural areas.

**42.** Yes. Reject the null hypothesis of equal proportions based on a low P-value < 0.0001. There is very strong evidence to suggest that people over 35 are more likely to avoid fast foods than those under 35.

# Part V Review

**1.** $H_0$: There is no difference in cancer rates, $p_1 - p_2 = 0$. $H_A$: The cancer rate in those who use the herb is higher, $p_1 - p_2 > 0$.

**2.** a) Yes, $0.08 \times 325 = 26$, so we expect more than 10 successes and more than 10 failures.
   b) $\mu = 0.08$, $\sigma = 0.015$
   c)

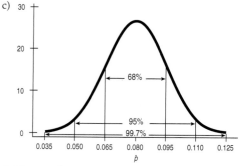

   d) There is about a 68% chance of observing between 6.5% and 9.5% of colorblind males in a class of this size and a 95% chance of having between 5% and 11% colorblind males. Almost all classes of this size will have a percentage between 3.5% and 12.5% colorblind males.

**3.** a) 10.29
   b) Not really. The z-score is $-1.11$. Not any evidence to suggest that the proportion for Monday is low.
   c) Yes. The z-score is 2.26 with a P-value of 0.024 (two-sided).
   d) Some births are scheduled for the convenience of the doctor and/or the mother.

**4.** a) No. There is always natural sampling variation.
   b) 47.6% and 53.8% (using 1.96 SDs)
   c) We expect only 4 "successes", so we can't use a normal model.
   d) Less. Proportions farther from 0.5 have smaller standard deviations.

**5.** a) $H_0$: $p_1 = 0.40$; $H_A$: $p_1 < 0.40$
   b) Random sample; less than 10% of all California gas stations, $0.4(27) = 10.8$, $0.6(27) = 16.2$. Assumptions and conditions are met.
   c) $z = -1.49$, P-value = 0.0677
   d) With a P-value this high, we fail to reject $H_0$. These data do not provide evidence that the proportion of leaking gas tanks is less than 40% (or that the new program is effective in decreasing the proportion).
   e) Yes, Type II.
   f) Increase $\alpha$, increase the sample size.
   g) Increasing $\alpha$—increases power, lowers chance of Type II error, but increases chance of Type I error.
   Increasing sample size—increases power, costs more time and money.

**6.** a) An experiment.
   b) $H_0$: There is no difference, $p_1 - p_2 = 0$.
   $H_A$: Patients with carbolic acid are more likely to live, $p_1 - p_2 > 0$.
   $z = 2.91$, P-value = 0.0018; with a P-value so low, we reject $H_0$. These data show that carbolic acid is effective in increasing the chances of surviving an amputation.
   c) We are not told whether the patients were randomized to the treatments. We are not told whether the experiment was double-blinded or even blinded at all. This could have biased the results toward a more favorable outcome.

**7.** a) The researcher believes that the true proportion of "A's" is within 10% of the estimated 54%, namely, between 44% and 64%.
   b) Small sample
   c) No, 63% is contained in the interval.

**8.** 0.647
   $\bar{y} \approx N(3.5, 0.538)$. Rolls are independent.

**9.** a) Pew believes that the true proportion is within 3% of the 33% from the sample; that is, between 30% and 36%.
   b) Larger, since it's a smaller sample.
   c) We are 95% confident that the proportion of active traders who rely on the Internet for investment information is between 38.7% and 51.3%, based on this sample.
   d) Larger, since it's a smaller sample.

**10.** a) 42.7% to 51.1%
   b) Since the interval extends above 50%, it is possible that the death penalty does have majority support.
   c) About 3382 people

**11.** a) Bimodal!
   b) $\mu$, the population mean. Sample size does not matter.
   c) $\sigma/\sqrt{n}$; sample size does matter.
   d) It becomes closer to a Normal model and narrower as the sample size increases.

**12.** a) Individuals were probably independent of one another, they are less than 10% of all African-American women, and there were clearly at least 10 successes and 10 failures. Is the sample a random sample from the population of African-American women?
   b) 39.5% to 44.5%
   c) We are 95% confident, based on this study, that between 39.5% and 44.5% of African-American women have a vitamin D deficiency.
   d) 95% of all such random samples will produce intervals that contain the true proportion.

**13.** a) $\mu = 0.80$, $\sigma = 0.028$
   b) Yes. $0.8(200) = 160$, $0.2(200) = 40$. Both $\geq 10$.
   c)

   d) 0.039

**14.** a) $(-4.5\%, 6.5\%)$
   b) No. The interval for the difference includes 0.

**15.** $H_0$: There is no difference, $p_1 - p_2 = 0$. $H_A$: Early births have increased, $p_1 - p_2 < 0$. $z = -0.729$, P-value $= 0.2329$. Because the P-value is so high, we do not reject $H_0$. These data do not show an increase in the incidence of early birth of twins.

**16.** a) We are 95% confident that the increase in the proportion of women who may develop side effects from magnesium sulfide is between 18.1% and 20.8%.

b) $H_0$: There is no difference, $p_1 - p_2 = 0$. $H_A$: Treatment prevents eclampsia, $p_1 - p_2 < 0$. $z = -4.84$, P-value $= 6.4 \times 10^{-7}$. Because the P-value is so low, we reject $H_0$. This study shows evidence that treatment with magnesium sulfide is effective in preventing eclampsia.

**17.** a) $H_0$: There is no difference, $p_1 - p_2 < 0$. $H_A$: Treatment prevents deaths from eclampsia, $p_1 - p_2 < 0$.

b) Samples are random and independent; less than 10% of all pregnancies (or eclampsia cases); more than 10 successes and failures in each group.

c) 0.8008

d) There is insufficient evidence to conclude that magnesium sulfide is effective in preventing eclampsia deaths.

e) Type II

f) Increase the sample size, increase $\alpha$.

g) Increasing sample size: decreases variation in the sampling distribution, is costly. Increasing $\alpha$: Increases likelihood of rejecting $H_0$, increases chance of Type I error.

**18.** a) 33.7%

b) 0.073

c)

Total Weight

**19.** a) It is not clear what the pollster asked. Otherwise they did fine.

b) Stratified sampling.

c) 4%    d) 95%

e) Smaller sample size.

f) Wording and order of questions (response bias).

**20.** About 1800

**21.** a) $H_0$: There is no difference, $p = 0.143$. $H_A$: The fatal accident rate is lower in girls, $p < 0.143$. $z = -1.67$, P-value $= 0.0479$. Because the P-value is low, we reject $H_0$. These data give some evidence that the fatal accident rate is lower for girls than for teens in general.

b) If the proportion is really 14.3%, we will see the observed proportion (11.3%) or lower 4.8% of the time by sampling variation.

**22.** a) $H_0$: There is no difference, $p_1 - p_2 = 0$. $H_A$: There is a difference, $p_1 - p_2 \neq 0$.

b) There is a difference in the proportion of students with perfect pitch; more Asians are likely to have it.

c) If there is no difference, the observed 25% difference will be seen by sampling variation less than about 1 time in 10,000.

d) The data do not "prove" anything about genetic differences *causing* differences in perfect pitch—merely that Asian students are more likely to have it.

**23.** a) One would expect many small fish, with a few large ones.

b) We don't know the exact distribution, but we know it's not Normal.

c) Probably not. With a skewed distribution, a sample size of five is not a large enough sample to say the mean is approximately Normal.

d) 0.961

**24.** a) Random sample; less than 10% of all high-school students; many more than 10 successes and 10 failures. 90% confidence interval for proportion who cheat: 72.9% to 75.1%.

b) Based on this information, we are 90% confident that the proportion of all high-school students who have cheated at least once on a test is between 72.9% and 75.1%.

c) 90% of all such random samples will produce confidence intervals that contain the true proportion of students who cheat.

d) Wider. More confidence means a larger margin of error.

**25.** a) Yes. $0.8(60) = 48$, $0.2(60) = 12$. Both are $\geq 10$.

b) 0.834

c) Higher. Bigger sample means smaller standard deviation for $\hat{p}$.

d) Answers will vary. A sample size of 500 makes the probability 0.997.

**26.** a) $H_0$: Progress is on track, $p = 0.20$. $H_A$: Progress is off track, $p > 0.20$.

b) Random samples; less than 10% of all high-school students; many more than 10 failures and successes.

c) 0.0008

d) If the proportion were 20%, the probability of seeing a value as high as (or higher than) 23% in a random sample this large is about 0.0008.

e) By 2006, the rate of cigarette smoking in high-school students was higher than the target of 20%.

f) Type I

**27.** a) 54.4 to 62.5%

b) Based on this study, with 95% confidence the proportion of Crohn's disease patients who will respond favorable to infliximab is between 54.4% and 62.5%.

c) 95% of all such random samples will produce confidence intervals that contain the true proportion of patients who respond favorably.

**28.** No. The probability of 30% or more is very small: $6.1 \times 10^{-5}$.

**29.** At least 423, assuming that $p$ is near 50%.

**30.** a) An experiment

b) A one-sided test, since they are interested only in a decrease in percentage needing repairs.

c) Deciding the additive reduces the number of repairs needed when there really is no difference.

d) Deciding the additive makes no difference when it really does reduce the number of repairs needed.

e) Type II

f) Given that the two groups received roughly the same use and care, yes. They can't necessarily claim it will work for all cars, only cars similar to their fleet.

**31.** a) Random sample (?); certainly less than 10% of all preemies and normal babies; more than 10 failures and successes in each group. 1.7% to 16.3% greater for normal-birth weight children.

b) Since 0 is not in the interval, there is evidence that preemies have a lower high school graduation rate than children of normal birth weight.

c) Type I, since we rejected the null hypothesis.

**32.** a) We are 95% confident that between 11.6% and 16.4% of Texas children wear helmets when biking, roller skating, or skateboarding, based on these data.

b) The data might not be a random sample.

c) About 408, using the previous 14% as $\hat{p}$.

**33.** a) $H_0$: The computer is undamaged. $H_A$: The computer is damaged.

b) 20% of good PCs will be classified as damaged (bad), while all damaged PCs will be detected (good).

c) 3 or more.

d) 20%

e) By switching to two or more as the rejection criterion, 7% of the good PCs will be misclassified, but only 10% of the bad ones will, increasing the power from 20% to 90%.

**34.** a) Increase

b) Decrease

**35.** The null hypothesis is that Bush's disapproval proportion is 66%—the Nixon benchmark. The one-tailed test has a z-value of −2.00, so the P-value is 0.0228. It looks like Bush's May 2007 ratings were better than the Nixon benchmark low.

**36.** The null hypothesis is that the percentage of students who attain a GPA of at least 3.5 remained 20% in 2000. The sample proportion of 25% is more than four standard deviations above the hypothesized rate, strong evidence the results are not due to chance. This may be an indication of grade inflation.

**37.** a) The company is interested only in confirming that the athlete is well known.

b) Type I: the company concludes that the athlete is well known, but that's not true. It offers an endorsement contract to someone who lacks name recognition. Type II: the company overlooks a well-known athlete, missing the opportunity to sign a potentially effective spokesperson.

c) Type I would be more likely, Type II less likely.

**38.** a) Although 27% of the people polled could identify her, her name recognition rate in the whole population could be less than the required 25%.

b) Type II.

c) Higher.

**39.** I am 95% confident that the proportion of U.S. adults who favor nuclear energy is between 7 and 19 percentage points higher than the proportion who would accept a nuclear plant near their area.

**40.** We're 95% confident that between 46% and 60% of anorexia patients will drop out of treatment programs. However, this wasn't a random sample of all patients; they were assigned a treatment rather than choosing one on their own, and they may have had different experiences if they were not part of an experiment.

# CHAPTER 23

**1.** a) 1.74  b) 2.37  c) 0.0524  d) 0.0889

**2.** a) 2.36  b) 2.62  c) 0.9829  d) 0.0381

**3.** Shape becomes closer to Normal; center does not change; spread becomes narrower.

**4.** The critical value becomes smaller, approaching 1.96.

**5.** a) The confidence interval is for the population mean, not the individual cows in the study.

b) The confidence interval is not for individual cows.

c) We *know* the average gain in this study was 56 pounds!

d) The average weight gain of all cows does not vary. It's what we're trying to estimate.

e) No. There is not a 95% chance for another sample to have an average weight gain between 45 and 67 pounds. There is a 95% chance that another sample will have its average weight gain within two standard errors of the true mean.

**6.** a) Nine out of 10 intervals will contain the true mean salary; different samples will produce different intervals.

b) This is correct.

c) The interval is for the population mean, not individual teachers.

d) The interval is for the mean, not individual teachers.

e) The interval addresses only Nevada teachers, not the entire country.

**7.** a) No. A confidence interval is not about individuals in the population.

b) No. It's not about individuals in the sample, either.

c) No. We know the mean cost for students in the sample was $1196.

d) No. A confidence interval is not about other sample means.

e) Yes. A confidence interval estimates a population parameter.

**8.** a) No. The confidence interval is not about the years in the sample.

b) No. The confidence interval does not predict what will happen in any one year.

c) No. The confidence interval was not based on a sample of days.

d) Yes. The confidence interval estimates the true mean.

e) No. We know that the mean annual snowfall for the last century was 23".

**9.** a) Based on this sample, we can say, with 95% confidence, that the mean pulse rate of adults is between 70.9 and 74.5 beats per minute.

b) 1.8 beats per minute

c) Larger

**10.** a) Based on this sample, we can say, with 95% confidence, that the mean age at which babies begin to crawl is between 29.2 and 31.8 weeks.

b) 1.3  c) Smaller

**11.** The assumptions and conditions for a *t*-interval are not met. The distribution is highly skewed to the right and there is a large outlier.

**12.** The assumptions and conditions for a *t*-interval are not met. There is one cardholder who spent over $3,000,000 on his card. This made the standard deviation, and hence the SE, huge, resulting in a *t*-interval too wide to be useful.

**13.** a) Yes. Randomly selected group; less than 10% of the population; the histogram is not unimodal and symmetric, but it is not highly skewed and there are no outliers, so with a sample size of 52, the CLT says $\bar{y}$ is approximately Normal.

b) (98.06, 98.51) degrees F

c) We are 98% confident, based on the data, that the average body temperature for an adult is between 98.06°F and 98.51°F.

d) 98% of all such random samples will produce intervals containing the true mean temperature.

e) These data suggest that the true normal temperature is somewhat less than 98.6° F.

**14.** a) The data are a representative sample of less than 10% of all days; $n = 44$ is a large sample.

b) ($122.20, $129.80)

c) We are 90% confident the mean daily income for the parking garage is between $122.20 and $129.80, based on this sample.

d) 90% of all such samples will produce intervals that contain the true mean daily fee.

e) No. The interval is below $130.

**15.** a) Narrower. A smaller margin of error, so less confident.

b) Advantage: more chance of including the true value. Disadvantage: wider interval.

c) Narrower; due to the larger sample, the SE will be smaller.

d) About 252

**16.** a) More chance the interval contains the true mean.

b) The interval would be wider.

c) More data would result in a narrower interval at same confidence level.

d) About 99

**17.** a) (298.5, 321.5)

b) Normal population, random sample. These seem reasonable here—but we would need to check the Nearly Normal Condition.

c) With 95% confidence, the mean sodium content in these "reduced sodium" hot dogs is between 298.5 mg and 321.5 mg, based on this sample.

**18.** a) (709.90, 802.54)

b) With 95% confidence, based on these data, the speed of light is between 299,709.9 and 299,802.5 km/sec.

c) Normal model for the distribution, independent measurements. These seem reasonable here, but it would be nice to see if the Nearly Normal Condition held for the data.

**19.** a) Yes. Larger sample, smaller SE.

b) 4.1 mg sodium

c) With 95% confidence, the mean sodium content of all hot dogs is between 309.7 mg and 326.3 mg, based on this sample.

d) $0.7(465) = 325.5$. Since the confidence interval extends above this, it is possible these should not be labeled as "reduced sodium."

**20.** a) 7.9 km/sec

b) Should be narrower. Different mean will change the center of the interval. Larger sample size and smaller standard deviation will reduce the SE. Since the $t$-critical value is also smaller, the margin of error will be smaller.

c) New interval: (836.72, 868.08) km/sec. This experiment is worse than the first, which included 710.5. This interval is considerably above that value. There may have been a bias in this experiment's measurements.

**21.** a) Given no time trend, the monthly on-time departure rates should be independent. Though not a random sample, these months should be representative, and they're fewer than 10% of all months. The histogram looks unimodal, but slightly left-skewed; not a concern with this large sample.

b) $80.57 < \mu$(OT Departure%) $< 81.80$

c) We can be 90% confident that the interval from 80.57% to 81.80% holds the true mean monthly percentage of on-time flight departures.

**22.** a) Given no time trend, the monthly late-arrival rates should be independent. Though not a random sample, these months should be representative, and they're fewer than 10% of all months. The histogram looks unimodal and symmetric.

b) $19.19 < \mu$(Late Arrival%) $< 21.0$

c) We can be 99% confident that the interval from 19.19% to 21.0% holds the true mean monthly percentage of late flight arrivals.

**23.** The 95% confidence interval lies entirely above the 0.08 ppm limit, evidence that mirex contamination is too high and consistent with rejecting the null. We used an upper-tail test, so the P-value should therefore be smaller than $\frac{1}{2}(1 - 0.95) = 0.025$, and it was.

**24.** The 90% confidence interval contains the 30 mph speed limit, so we can't assert that the mean speed is too high—consistent with not rejecting the null. We used an upper-tail test, so the P-value should therefore be more than $\frac{1}{2}(1 - 0.90) = 0.05$, and it was.

**25.** If in fact the mean cholesterol of pizza eaters does not indicate a health risk, then only 7 of every 100 samples would have mean cholesterol levels as high (or higher) as observed in this sample.

**26.** If in fact this ball meets the velocity standard, then 34% of samples tested would have mean speeds at least as high as was recorded in this sample.

**27.** a) Upper-tail. We want to show it will hold 500 pounds (or more) easily.

b) They will decide the stands are safe when they're not.

c) They will decide the stands are unsafe when they are in fact safe.

**28.** a) Two-sided. If they're too big, they won't fit through the vein. If they're too small, they probably won't work well.

b) The catheters are rejected when in fact the diameters are fine, and the manufacturing process is needlessly stopped.

c) Catheters that do not meet specifications are allowed to be produced and sold.

**29.** a) Decrease $\alpha$. This means a smaller chance of declaring the stands safe if they are not.

b) The probability of correctly detecting that the stands are capable of holding more than 500 pounds.

c) Decrease the standard deviation—probably costly. Increase the sample size—takes more time for testing and is costly. Increase $\alpha$—more Type I errors. Increase the "design load" to be well above 500 pounds—again, costly.

**30.** a) Increase

b) The probability of correctly detecting deviations from 2 mm in diameter.

c) Increase

d) Increase the sample size or increase $\alpha$.

**31.** a) $H_0$: $\mu = 23.3$; $H_A$: $\mu > 23.3$

b) We have a random sample of the population. Population may not be normally distributed, as it would be easier to have a few much older men at their first marriage than some very young men. However, with a sample size of 40, $\bar{y}$ should be approximately Normal. We should check the histogram for severity of skewness and possible outliers.

c) $(\bar{y} - 23.3)/(s/\sqrt{40}) \sim t_{39}$

d) 0.1447

e) If the average age at first marriage is still 23.3 years, there is a 14.5% chance of getting a sample mean of 24.2 years or older simply from natural sampling variation.

f) We lack evidence that the average age at first marriage has increased from the mean of 23.3 years.

**32.** a) $H_0$: $\mu = 26$; $H_A$: $\mu < 26$

b) We have a representative sample, fewer than 10% of all trips, and a large enough sample that skewness should not be a problem.

c) $(\bar{y} - 26)/(4.83/\sqrt{50}) \sim t_{49}$

d) 0.0789

e) If the average fuel economy is 26 mpg, the chance of obtaining a sample mean of 25.02 or less by natural sampling variation is 8%.

f) Since $0.05 < P < 0.10$, there is some evidence that the company may not be achieving the fuel economy goal.

**33.** a) Probably a representative sample; the Nearly Normal Condition seems reasonable from a Normal probability plot. The histogram is nearly uniform, with no outliers or skewness.

b) $\bar{y} = 28.78$, $s = 0.40$

c) (28.36, 29.21) grams

d) Based on this sample, we are 95% confident the average weight of the content of Ruffles bags is between 28.36 and 29.21 grams.

e) The company is erring on the safe side, as it appears that, on average, it is putting in slightly more chips than stated.

**34.** a) Probably a representative sample; the Nearly Normal Condition seems reasonable from a Normal probability plot. The data are fairly symmetric with no apparent outliers.

b) $\bar{y} = 28.98$, $s = 0.36$

c) (28.61, 29.36) grams

d) With 95% confidence, the average weight of the content of Doritos bags is between 28.61 and 29.36 grams, based on this sample.

e) The company is erring on the safe side, as it appears that, on average, it is putting in slightly more chips than stated.

**35.** a) Type I; he mistakenly rejected the null hypothesis that $p = 0.10$ (or worse).

b) Yes. These are a random sample of bags and the Nearly Normal Condition is met; $t = -2.51$ with 7 df for a one-sided P-value of 0.0203.

**36.** a) He would have made a Type II error.

b) No. We'll consider these races a representative sample, and the Nearly Normal Condition is met; $t = -0.7646$ with 7 df for a one-sided P-value of 0.2347.

**37.** No. Based on this large random sample, $t = -1.45$; P-value = 0.1495. Because the P-value is high, we fail to reject $H_0$. These data do not provide evidence to support the claim that the average weight of all cars is not 3000 pounds. We retain the null hypothesis that the mean is 3000 pounds.

**38.** Yes. Based on this large random sample, $t = -4.42$, P-value = $3.27 \times 10^{-5}$. Because the P-value is low, we reject $H_0$. These data strongly suggest that the mean range of these phones is less than 150 feet.

**39.** a) Random sample; the Nearly Normal Condition seems reasonable from a Normal probability plot. The histogram is roughly unimodal and symmetric with no outliers.

b) (1187.9, 1288.4) chips

c) Based on this sample, the mean number of chips in an 18-ounce bag is between 1187.9 and 1288.4, with 95% confidence. The *mean* number of chips is clearly greater than 1000. However, if the claim is about individual bags, then it's not necessarily true. If the mean is 1188 and the SD deviation is near 94, then 2.5% of the bags will have fewer than 1000 chips, using the Normal model. If in fact the mean is 1288, the proportion below 1000 will be less than 0.1%, but the claim is still false.

**40.** a) Random sample. Nearly Normal Condition is reasonable by examining a Normal probability plot. The histogram is roughly unimodal (although somewhat uniform) and symmetric with no outliers.

b) (132.0, 183.7) calories

c) Based on this sample, the mean number of calories in a serving of vanilla yogurt is between 132 and 183.7, with 95% confidence. We conclude that the diet guide's claim of 120 calories is too low.

**41.** a) The Normal probability plot is relatively straight, with one outlier at 93.8 sec. Without the outlier, the conditions seem to be met. The histogram is roughly unimodal and symmetric with no other outliers.

b) $t = -2.63$, P-value $= 0.0160$. With the outlier included, we might conclude that the mean completion time for the maze is not 60 seconds; in fact, it is less.

c) $t = -4.46$, P-value $= 0.0003$. Because the P-value is so small, we reject $H_0$. Without the outlier, we see strong evidence that the average completion time for the maze is less than 60 seconds. The outlier here did not change the conclusion.

d) The maze does not meet the "one-minute average" requirement. Both tests rejected a null hypothesis of a mean of 60 seconds.

**42.** The data value of 102 feet is an outlier. When this is removed, the Normal probability plot is relatively straight. The Nearly Normal Condition seems satisfied. With the outlier removed, the histogram is roughly unimodal and symmetric with no other outliers. $H_0: \mu = 125$; $H_A: \mu > 125$ feet. With the outlier eliminated, $\bar{y} = 128.89$, $t = 3.29$, P-value $= 0.01$. With a P-value this low, we reject $H_0$. There is strong evidence to suggest that the tires will not bring the car to a complete stop within 125 feet. On the basis of these data, the company should not adopt the new tread pattern. Only 2 out of the 10 data values were less than the desired 125 feet, and 1 of these was an outlier.

**43.** a) $287.3 < \mu(\text{Drive Distance}) < 289.9$

b) These data are not a random sample of golfers. The top professionals are (unfortunately) not representative and were not selected at random. We might consider the 2006 data to represent the population of all professional golfers, past, present, and future.

c) The data are means for each golfer, so they are less variable than if we looked at all the separate drives.

**44.** a) The timeplot shows no pattern, so it seems that the measurements are independent. Although this is not a random sample, an entire year is measured, so it is likely that we have representative values. We certainly have fewer than 10% of all possible wind readings. Both the histogram and normal probability plot indicate near normality.

b) Testing $H_0: \mu = 8$ mph vs. $H_A: \mu > 8$ mph with 1113 df gives $t = 0.1663$ for a P-value of about 0.44. Even though the observed mean wind speed is over 8 mph, I can't be confident that the true annual mean wind speed exceeds 8 mph. I would not recommend building a turbine at this site.

## CHAPTER 24

**1.** Yes. The high P-value means that we lack evidence of a difference, so 0 is a possible value for $\mu_{Meat} - \mu_{Beef}$.

**2.** Yes. The high P-value means that we lack evidence of a difference, so 0 is a possible value for $\mu_{Meat} - \mu_{Beef}$.

**3.** a) Plausible values of $\mu_{Meat} - \mu_{Beef}$ are all negative, so the mean fat content is probably higher for beef hot dogs.

b) The difference is significant.

c) 10%

**4.** a) Plausible values of $\mu_{Top} - \mu_{Front}$ are all negative, so the mean cycle time is probably higher for front-loading machines.

b) The difference is significant.

c) 2%

**5.** a) False. The confidence interval is about means, not about individual hot dogs.

b) False. The confidence interval is about means, not about individual hot dogs.

c) True.

d) False. CI's based on other samples will also try to estimate the true difference in population means; there's no reason to expect other samples to conform to this result.

e) True.

**6.** a) False. The confidence interval is about means, not about individual machines.

b) False. The confidence interval is about means, not about individual machines.

c) False. CI's based on other samples will also try to estimate the true difference in population means; there's no reason to expect other samples to conform to this result.

d) True.    e) True.

**7.** a) 2.927

b) Larger

c) Based on this sample, we are 95% confident that students who learn Math using the CPMP method will score, on average, between 5.57 and 11.43 points better on a test solving applied Algebra problems with a calculator than students who learn by traditional methods.

d) Yes; 0 is not in the interval.

**8.** a) Based on this sample, we are 90% confident that people who receive either no or only verbal information about the image in a stereogram will take between 0.55 and 5.47 seconds longer, on average, to report they saw the image than people who receive both verbal and visual information.

b) Yes, since 0 is not in the interval.

c) 2.46

d) 90% of all random samples will produce intervals that contain the true value of the mean difference between the times for these two groups.

e) Wider. More confidence means less precision.

f) Possibly. The wider interval may contain 0.

**9.** a) $H_0: \mu_C - \mu_T = 0$ vs. $H_A: \mu_C - \mu_T \neq 0$

b) Yes. Groups are independent, though we don't know if students were randomly assigned to the programs. Sample sizes are large, so CLT applies.

c) If the means for the two programs are really equal, there is less than a 1 in 10,000 chance of seeing a difference as large as or larger than the observed difference just from natural sampling variation.

d) On average, students who learn with the CPMP method do significantly worse on Algebra tests that do not allow them to use calculators than students who learn by traditional methods.

**10.** $H_0: \mu_C - \mu_T = 0$; $H_A: \mu_C - \mu_T \neq 0$. $t = 1.406$, df $= 590.05$, P-value $= 0.1602$. Because of the large P-value, we fail to reject $H_0$.

Based on these samples, there is no evidence of a difference in mean scores on a test of word problems, whether students learned with CPMP or traditional methods.

**11.** a) (1.36, 4.64)

b) No; 5 minutes is beyond the high end of the interval.

**12.** a) The mean rates are roughly equal, but females are more variable.

b) Yes; boxplots look symmetric.

c) $(-3.025, 3.275)$

d) Yes, 0 is in the interval.

**13.** These were random samples, both less than 10% of properties sold. Prices of houses should be independent, and random sampling makes the two groups independent. The boxplots make the price distributions appear to be reasonably symmetric, and with the large sample sizes the few outliers don't affect the means much. Based on this sample, we're 95% confident that, in New York, having a waterfront is worth, on average, about $59,115 to $140,904 more in sale price.

**14.** Both types of houses were selected randomly, with each sample less than 10% of all such houses. Prices of houses should be independent, and random sampling makes the two groups independent. The boxplots make the price distributions appear to be reasonably symmetric, and with the large sample sizes the few outliers don't affect the means much. Based on this sample, we're 95% confident that, in New York, a house with new construction will sell for, on average, between $39,891 and $92,450 more than one without new construction.

**15.**

Random sample—questionable, but probably representative, independent samples, less than 10% of all cereals; boxplot shows no outliers—not exactly symmetric, but these are reasonable sample sizes. Based on these samples, with 95% confidence, children's cereals average between 32.49% and 40.80% more sugar content than adult's cereals.

**16.** a) Random sample (we assume), independent samples, boxplots look symmetric.

b) (1.88, 6.66) mm

c) These data provide evidence that mean maximum skull breadth in Egyptians in 200 B.C.E. was between 1.88 and 6.66 mm larger than that in 4000 B.C.E.

**17.** $H_0: \mu_N - \mu_C = 0$ vs. $H_A: \mu_N - \mu_C > 0$; $t = 2.076$; P-value = 0.0228; df = 33.4. Because of the small P-value, we reject $H_0$. These data do suggest that new activities are better. The mean reading comprehension score for the group with new activities is significantly (at $\alpha = 0.05$) higher than the mean score for the control group.

**18.** a) $H_0: \mu_L - \mu_S = 0$ vs. $H_A: \mu_L - \mu_S \neq 0$

b) Don't know if the streams were a random sample or whether they are less than 10% of all Adirondack streams. Boxplots show outliers and shale may be skewed (median is equal to Q1 or Q3), but samples are large.

c) Based on these data, it appears that water flowing over limestone is less acidic, on average, than water flowing over shale.

**19.**

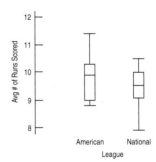

There are several concerns here. First, we don't have a random sample. We have to assume that the actual number of hurricanes in a given year is a random sample of the hurricanes that might occur under similar weather conditions. Also, the data for 1944–1969 are not symmetric and have four outliers. The outliers will tend to make the average for the period 1944–1969 larger. These data are not appropriate for inference. The boxplots provide little evidence of a change in the mean number of hurricanes in the two periods.

**20.** a) If there is no difference between ginkgo and the placebo, there is a 93.74% chance of seeing a difference as large as or larger than that observed, just from natural sampling variation.

b) There is no evidence based on this study that ginkgo biloba improves memory, as the difference in mean memory score was not significant and, in fact, lower.

c) Type II

**21.** a)

Both are reasonably symmetric, except for the outlier in the National League.

b) Based on these data, the average number of runs in an American League stadium is between 9.36 and 10.23, with 95% confidence.

c) No. The boxplot indicates it isn't an outlier.

d) We want to work directly with the average difference. The two separate confidence intervals do not answer questions about the difference. The difference has a different standard deviation, found by adding variances.

**22.** a) Males: (18.67, 20.11) pegs; females: (16.95, 18.87) pegs.

b) It suggests that there is no evidence of a difference, but the method is incorrect.

c) (0.29, 2.67) pegs

d) There is evidence of a difference: Males do better, on average, by between 0.29 and 2.67 pegs.

e) Two–sample inference

f) If we examine the gap between the means using two separate confidence intervals, we are essentially adding the margins of error, which are based on standard deviations. To be correct, we must instead add variances. That's exactly what happens when we create the confidence interval for the difference in means—the proper approach.

23. a) $(-0.18, 0.89)$

b) Based on these data, with 95% confidence, American League stadiums average between 0.18 fewer runs and 0.89 more runs per game than National League stadiums.

c) No; 0 is in the interval.

24. a) $H_0: \mu_N - \mu_S = 0$ vs. $H_A: \mu_N - \mu_S \neq 0$. $t = 6.47$, df $= 53.49$, P-value $= 3.2 \times 10^{-8}$. Because the P-value is low, we reject $H_0$. On the basis of these data, there is clear evidence that mortality rates are different. The mean rate in the north is significantly higher.

b) It will raise $\bar{y}$ for the north, but from looking at the boxplots and the fact that the mean and median are nearly the same, it probably will not change the conclusion of the test.

25. These are not two independent samples. These are before and after scores for the same individuals.

26. These are before and after scores for the same individuals, not independent samples.

27. a) These data do not provide evidence of a difference in ad recall between shows with sexual content and violent content.

b) $H_0: \mu_S - \mu_N = 0$ vs. $H_A: \mu_S - \mu_N \neq 0$. $t = -6.08$, df $= 213.99$, P-value $= 5.5 \times 10^{-9}$. Because the P-value is low, we reject $H_0$. These data suggest that ad recall between shows with sexual and neutral content is different; those who saw shows with neutral content had higher average recall.

28. a) With 95% confidence, those who watch shows with violent content remembered an average of between 1.6 and 0.6 fewer brand names than those who saw shows with neutral content.

b) If they want viewers to remember their brand, advise that they consider advertising in shows with neutral content in preference to those with violent content. Of course, costs of the ad should be considered.

29. a) $H_0: \mu_V - \mu_N = 0$ vs. $H_A: \mu_V - \mu_N \neq 0$. $t = -7.21$, df $= 201.96$, P-value $= 1.1 \times 10^{-11}$. Because of the very small P-value, we reject $H_0$. There is a significant difference in mean ad recall between shows with violent content and neutral content; viewers of shows with neutral content remember more brand names, on average.

b) With 95% confidence, the average number of brand names remembered 24 hours later is between 1.45 and 2.41 higher for viewers of neutral content shows than for viewers of sexual content shows, based on these data.

30. a) He would conclude that recall is higher 24 hours later.

b) The samples are not independent. They are the same people asked at two different periods.

c) The first inquiry might influence people.

d) Use two different groups for each type of show. Interview one group immediately, the other 24 hours later.

31. $H_0: \mu_{big} - \mu_{small} = 0$ vs. $H_A: \mu_{big} - \mu_{small} \neq 0$; bowl size was assigned randomly; amount scooped by individuals and by the two groups should be independent. With 34 df, $t = 2.104$ and P-value $= 0.0428$. The low P-value leads us to reject the null hypothesis and conclude that there is a difference in the average amount of ice cream that people scoop when given a bigger bowl.

32. $H_0: \mu_{tumbler} - \mu_{highball} = 0$ vs. $H_A: \mu_{tumbler} - \mu_{highball} \neq 0$; glass size was assigned randomly; amount poured by individuals and by the two groups should be independent. With 194 df, $t = 7.71$; P-value $< 0.001$. The low P-value leads us to reject

the null hypothesis and conclude that there is a difference in the amount of liquid that people pour, on average, when given a small wide tumbler as opposed to a tall narrow highball glass.

33. a) The 95% confidence interval for the difference is $(0.61, 5.39)$. 0 is not in the interval, so scores in 1996 were significantly higher. (Or the $t$, with more than 7500 df, is 2.459 for a P-value of 0.0070.)

b) Since both samples were very large, there shouldn't be a difference in how certain you are, assuming conditions are met.

34. a) The observed differences are too large to attribute to chance or natural sampling variation.

b) Type I

c) No. There may be many other factors.

35. a) We can be 95% confident that the interval 74.8 ± 178.05 minutes includes the true difference in mean crossing times between men and women. Because the interval includes zero, we cannot be confident that there is any difference at all.

b) Independence Assumption: There is no reason to believe that the swims are not independent or that the two groups are not independent of each other.

Randomization Condition: The swimmers are not a random sample from any identifiable population, but they may be representative of swimmers who tackle challenges such as this.

Nearly Normal Condition: the boxplots show no outliers. The histograms are unimodal; the histogram for men is somewhat skewed to the right.

36. a) The 95% confidence interval of $-21.5 \pm 165.83$ minutes contains 0. There is no significant difference in mean crossing times.

b) It is reasonable to assume that the same swimmer crossing the lake on two different occasions might perform similarly, so these are not all independent events. That could reduce the variability within each of the groups, reducing the standard error.

37. Independent Groups Assumption: The runners are different women, so the groups are independent. The Randomization Condition is satisfied since the runners are selected at random for these heats.

Nearly Normal Condition: The boxplots show an outlier, but we will proceed and then redo the analysis with the outlier deleted. When we include the outlier, $t = 0.035$ with a two-sided P-value of 0.97. With the outlier deleted, $t = -1.14$, with P $= 0.2837$. Either P-value is so large that we fail to reject the null hypothesis of equal means and conclude that there is no evidence of a difference in the mean times for runners in unseeded heats.

38. Independent Groups Assumption: The swimmers in the two heats are different women, so the groups are independent. The Nearly Normal Condition is satisfied. The Randomization Condition is not strictly satisfied since the swimmers are not selected at random, but if we can consider these heats to be representative of seeded heats, we may be able to generalize the results. With

$t = 7.19$ and a P-value less than 0.001, we reject the null hypothesis of equal means. There is strong evidence to suggest that seeded swimming heats have different mean times.

39. With $t = -4.57$ and a very low P-value of 0.0013, we reject the null hypothesis of equal mean velocities. There is strong evidence that golf balls hit off Stinger tees will have a higher mean initial velocity.

40. With $t = -9.70$ and a P-value less than 0.0001, we reject the null hypothesis of equal mean distances. There is strong evidence that the mean distance traveled will be greater for golf balls hit off Stinger tees. We can be 95% confident that they'll travel an average of between 10.7 and 17.0 yards farther.

41. The 90% confidence interval for the difference in mean number of months to publication between *Applied Statistics* and *The American Statistician* is (8.43, 11.57) months. We assume that the articles are a random sample of the kinds of articles typically submitted to these two journals and that they represent fewer than 10% of all articles that could have been submitted. Both samples are large.

42. a) $H_0: \mu_M - \mu_R = 0$ vs. $H_A: \mu_M - \mu_R > 0$. $t = -0.70$, df = 45.88, P-value = 0.7563. Because the P-value is so large, we do not reject $H_0$. These data provide no evidence that listening to Mozart while studying is better than listening to rap.

    b) With 90% confidence, the average difference in score is between 0.189 and 5.351 objects more for those who listen to no music while studying, based on these samples.

43. a) $H_0: \mu_R - \mu_N = 0$ vs. $H_A: \mu_R - \mu_N < 0$. $t = -1.36$, df = 20.00, P-value = 0.0945. Because the P-value is large, we fail to reject $H_0$. These data show no evidence of a difference in mean number of objects recalled between listening to rap or no music at all.

    b) Didn't conclude any difference.

44.

$H_0: \mu_S - \mu_R = 0$ vs. $H_A: \mu_S - \mu_R \neq 0$.
$t = 1.641$, df = 21.60, P-value = 0.115.
Since $P > 0.05$, fail to reject $H_0$. There is no evidence of a difference in mean cuckoo egg length between robin and sparrow foster parents.
$H_0: \mu_S - \mu_W = 0$ vs. $H_A: \mu_S - \mu_W \neq 0$.
$t = 0.549$, df = 26.86, P-value = 0.587.

Since $P > 0.05$, fail to reject $H_0$. There is no evidence of a difference in mean cuckoo egg length between sparrow and wagtail foster parents.

$H_0: \mu_R - \mu_W = 0$ vs. $H_A: \mu_R - \mu_W \neq 0$.
$t = -1.012$, df = 23.60, P-value = 0.322.

Since $P > 0.05$, fail to reject $H_0$. There is no evidence of a difference in mean cuckoo egg length between robin and wagtail foster parents.

In general, we should be wary of doing three *t*-tests on the same data. Our Type I error rate is not the same for doing three tests as it is for doing one test. However, because none of the tests showed significant differences, this is less of a concern here.

# CHAPTER 25

1. a) Randomly assign 50 hens to each of the two kinds of feed. Compare production at the end of the month.

    b) Give all 100 hens the new feed for 2 weeks and the old food for 2 weeks, randomly selecting which feed the hens get first. Analyze the differences in production for all 100 hens.

    c) Matched pairs. Because hens vary in egg production, the matched-pairs design will control for that.

2. a) Randomly assign half the volunteers to do the puzzles in a quiet room and half to do them with MTV on. Compare times.

    b) Randomly assign half the volunteers to do a puzzle in a quiet room and half to do a puzzle with MTV on. Then have each do a puzzle under the other condition. Look at the differences in completion times.

    c) Matched pairs. People vary in their ability to do crossword puzzles.

3. a) Show the same people ads with and without sexual images, and record how many products they remember in each group. Randomly decide which ads a person sees first. Examine the differences for each person.

    b) Randomly divide volunteers into two groups. Show one group ads with sexual images and the other group ads without. Compare how many products each group remembers.

4. a) Select a random sample of freshmen. Weigh them when college starts in the fall and again when they leave for home in the spring. Examine the difference in weights.

    b) Weigh a random sample of freshmen as they enter college in the fall to determine their average weight. Repeat with a new sample of students at the end of the spring semester. Compare the mean weights of the two groups.

5. a) Matched pairs—same cities in different periods.

    b) There is a significant difference (P-value = 0.0244) in the labor force participation rate for women in these cities; women's participation increased between 1968 and 1972.

6. a) Two-sample. Clouds are independent of one another.

    b) Based on these data, there is some evidence of a difference (P-value = 0.0538) in the amount of rain between seeded and unseeded clouds.

7. a) The paired *t*-test is appropriate since we have pairs of Fridays in 5 different months. Data from adjacent Fridays within a month may be more similar than data from randomly chosen Fridays.

    b) We conclude that there is evidence (P-value 0.0212) that the mean number of cars found on the M25 motorway on Friday the 13th is less than on the previous Friday.

    c) We don't know if these Friday pairs were selected at random. Obviously, if these are the Fridays with the largest differences, this will affect our conclusion. The Nearly Normal Condition appears to be met by the differences, but the sample size is small.

8. a) The paired *t*-test is appropriate since we have pairs of Fridays in 6 different months. Data from adjacent Fridays within a month may be more similar than data from randomly chosen Fridays.

    b) We conclude that there is evidence (P-value 0.0211) that the mean number of admissions to hospitals found on Friday the 13th is more than on the previous Friday.

c) We don't know if these Friday pairs were selected at random. Obviously, if these are the Fridays with the largest differences, this will affect our conclusion. The Nearly Normal Condition appears to be met by the differences, but the sample size is small.

9. Adding variances requires that the variables be independent. These price quotes are for the same cars, so they are paired. Drivers quoted high insurance premiums by the local company will be likely to get a high rate from the online company, too.

10. Adding variances requires that the variables be independent. The wind speeds were recorded at nearby sites, so they are likely to be both high or both low at the same time.

11. a) The histogram—we care about differences in price.
    b) Insurance cost is based on risk, so drivers are likely to see similar quotes from each company, making the differences relatively smaller.
    c) The price quotes are paired; they were for a random sample of fewer than 10% of the agent's customers; the histogram of differences looks approximately Normal.

12. a) The outliers are particularly windy days, but they were windy at both sites, making the difference in wind speeds less unusual.
    b) The histogram and summaries of the differences are more appropriate because these are paired observations and all we care about is which site was more windy.
    c) The wind measurements at the same times at two nearby sites are paired. We should be concerned that there might be a lack of independence from one time to the next, but the times were 6 hours apart and the *differences* in speeds are likely to be independent. Although the sample is not random, we can regard a sample this large as generally representative of wind speeds at these sites. The histogram of differences is unimodal, symmetric, and bell-shaped.

13. $H_0$: $\mu(Local - Online) = 0$ vs. $H_A$: $\mu(Local - Online) > 0$; with 9 df, $t = 0.83$. With a high P-value of 0.215, we don't reject the null hypothesis. These data don't provide evidence that online premiums are lower, on average.

14. $H_0$: $\mu(2 - 4) = 0$ vs. $H_A$: $\mu(2 - 4) \neq 0$; $t = 2.667$ with 1114 df. The P-value of 0.008 is very low, so we reject the null. There's strong evidence that the average wind speed is higher at site 2.

15. a) Even if the individual times show a trend of improving speed over time, the differences may well be independent of each other. They are subject to random year-to-year fluctuations, and we may believe these data to be representative of similar races. We don't have any information with which to check the Nearly Normal Condition.
    b) With 95% confidence, we can say the mean time difference is between −15.49 minutes (men are faster) and +11.25 minutes (women are faster).
    c) The interval contains 0, so we would not reject the hypothesis of no mean difference at $\alpha = 0.05$. We can't discern a difference between the female wheelchair times and the male running times.

16. a) Even if the individual times show a trend of improving speed over time, the differences may well be independent of each other. They are subject to random year-to-year fluctuations, and we may believe these data to be representative of similar races. After removing the three initial years, the remaining part of the histogram is a bit skewed (and possibly bimodal), but we can probably use paired-$t$ methods with caution.
    b) With 95% confidence, it appears that female wheelchair marathoners average between 4.61 and 19.74 minutes faster than male runners.
    c) This interval does not include zero. A paired $t$-test would reject the null hypothesis of no difference at $\alpha = 0.05$. From the CI, we can see that there is strong evidence that female wheelchair racers are faster than male runners.

17. a) Same cows before and after injection; the cows should be representative of others of their breed; cows are independent of

each other; fewer than 10% of all cows; don't know about nearly Normal differences.
    b) (12.66, 15.34)
    c) Based on this sample, with 95% confidence, the average increase in milk production for Ayrshire cows given BST is between 12.66 and 15.34 pounds per day.
    d) $0.25(47) = 11.75$. The average increase is much more than this, so we would recommend he go to the extra expense.

18. $H_0$: $\mu_A - \mu_J = 0$ vs. $H_A$: $\mu_A - \mu_J \neq 0$. $t = 5.29$, df = 109.55, P-value = $6.4 \times 10^{-7}$. Because $P < 0.01$, reject $H_0$. These data provide strong evidence that the average increase for the two kinds of cows is different; Ayrshire cows have a greater increase in milk production with BST. We need to assume these two groups of cows are representative of their breeds.

19.

Data are paired for each city; cities are independent of each other; boxplot shows the temperature differences are symmetric, with no outliers. This is probably not a random sample, so we might be wary of inferring that this difference applies to all European cities. Based on these data, we are 90% confident that the average temperature in European cities in July is between 32.3°F and 41.3°F higher than in January.

20. We are 90% confident that the average women's winning marathon time is between 16.25 and 17.45 minutes higher than the men's based on this sample.

21. Based on these data, we are 90% confident that boys, on average, can do between 1.6 and 13.0 more push-ups than girls (independent samples—not paired).

22. a) (4.8, 15.2) minutes
    b) (4.9, 20.4) minutes
    c) Margin of error for raw data will be higher.

23. a) Paired sample test. Data are before/after for the same workers; workers randomly selected; assume fewer than 10% of all this company's workers; boxplot of differences shows them to be symmetric, with no outliers.

    b) $H_0$: $\mu_D = 0$ vs. $H_A$: $\mu_D > 0$. $t = 3.60$, P-value = 0.0029. Because $P < 0.01$, reject $H_0$. These data show that average job satisfaction has increased after implementation of the exercise program.

24. $H_0$: $\mu_D = 0$ vs. $H_A$: $\mu_D > 0$. $t = 1.75$, P-value = 0.0699. Because $P > 0.05$, we fail to reject $H_0$. These data do not provide enough evidence to conclude that the summer school program is worthwhile, at $\alpha = 0.05$.

25. a) $H_0$: $\mu_D = 0$ vs. $H_A$: $\mu_D > 0$
    b) 0.0025
    c) If there is no gain of additional hours of sleep with the herb, the chance of seeing a mean difference as large as or larger than the one observed is about one-quarter percent.

d) The data provide evidence that the herb is helpful in gaining additional sleep.

e) Type I

26. a) $H_0: \mu_D = 0$ vs. $H_A: \mu_D > 0$. $t = 4.47$, P-value = 0.0008. Because of the very small P-value, we reject $H_0$. These data provide strong evidence that cars get significantly better mileage, on average, with premium than with regular gasoline.

b) (1.18, 2.82) miles per gallon

c) Premium gasoline costs more than regular.

d) $t = 1.25$, P-value is 0.1144. Would have decided no difference. The variation in the cars' performances is larger than the differences.

27. $H_0: \mu_D = 0$ vs. $H_A: \mu_D \neq 0$. Data are paired by brand; brands are independent of each other; fewer than 10% of all yogurts (questionable); boxplot of differences shows an outlier (100) for Great Value:

With the outlier included, the mean difference (Strawberry – Vanilla) is 12.5 calories with a $t$-stat of 1.332, with 11 df, for a P-value of 0.2098. Deleting the outlier, the difference is even smaller, 4.55 calories with a $t$-stat of only 0.833 and a P-value of 0.4241. With P-values so large, we do not reject $H_0$. We conclude that the data do not provide evidence of a difference in mean calories.

28. a) $H_0: \mu_D = 0$ vs. $H_A: \mu_D \neq 0$. $t = -1.21$, P-value = 0.2466. Since $P > 0.05$, fail to reject $H_0$. There is no evidence that the mean score will change after using caffeine.

b) $H_0: \mu_D = 0$ vs. $H_A: \mu_D \neq 0$. $t = 2.27$, P-value = 0.0397. Since $P < 0.05$, reject $H_0$. There is evidence that the mean score will increase when no caffeine is used.

c) No. Might be variation due to the people in the two groups that produced a Type I error. (Answers will vary.)

29. a) Not a simple random sample, but most likely representative; stops most likely independent of each other; boxplot is symmetric with no outliers.

Based on these data, with 95% confidence, the average braking distance for these tires on dry pavement is between 133.6 and 145.2 feet.

b) Not simple random samples, but most likely representative; stops most likely independent of each other; less than 10% of all possible wet stops; Normal probability plots are relatively straight.

Based on these data, with 95% confidence, the average increase in distance for these tires on wet pavement is between 51.4 and 74.6 feet

30. a) $H_0: \mu_{NC} - \mu_C = 0$ vs. $H_A: \mu_{NC} - \mu_C \neq 0$; $\mu_{NC}$ is the mean for nonconfined inmates, $\mu_C$ is the mean for inmates confined to solitary.

b) Groups are independent of each other, not paired; random assignment to groups, less than 10% of all inmates, boxplot shows no outliers in either group.

c) Two-sample $t$-test statistic: 3.357, P-value = 0.0038.

d) Because the P-value is so small, we reject $H_0$. Solitary confinement makes a difference in mean alpha-wave frequencies; it seems those subjected to confinement have lower frequencies.

31. a) Cars were probably not a simple random sample, but may be representative in terms of stopping distance; boxplot does not show outliers, but does indicate right skewness. A 95% confidence interval for the mean stopping distance on dry pavement is (131.8, 145.6) feet.

b) Data are paired by car; cars were probably not randomly chosen, but representative; boxplot shows an outlier (car 4) with a difference of 12. With deletion of that car, a Normal probability plot of the differences is relatively straight.

Having deleted an outlier difference of 12 feet, we estimate with 95% confidence that the average braking distance is between 47.2 and 62.8 feet more on wet pavement than on dry, based on this sample. (With the outlier, the confidence interval is 38.8 to 62.6 feet.)

32. a) Paired Data Assumption: Data are paired by college. Randomization Condition: This was a random sample of public colleges and universities. 10% Condition: these are fewer than 10% of all public colleges and universities.

Normal Population Assumption: U.C. Irvine seems to be an outlier; we shoud remove it.

b) Having deleted the observation for U.C.-Irvine, whose difference of $9300 was an outlier, we are 90% confident, based on the remaining data, that nonresidents pay, on average, between $2615.31 and $3918.02 more than residents.

c) Assertion is reasonable; $3500 is in the confidence interval.

33. Using a $t$-test for paired differences, $t = -0.86$ and two-tailed $P = 0.396$. With a P-value so high, we fail to reject the null

hypothesis of no mean difference. There is no evidence that sexual images in ads affects people's ability to remember the product being advertised.

**34.** If this group is representative of all students, we can be 95% confident that freshmen gain a mean of between 1.40 and 2.43 pounds during their first 12 weeks at college. That's strong evidence of a weight gain, but it's unlikely that it amounts to 15 pounds for the whole first year.

**35.** a) 60% is 30 strikes; $H_0: \mu = 30$ vs. $H_A: \mu > 30$. $t = 6.07$, P-value $= 3.92 \times 10^{-6}$. With a very small P-value, we reject $H_0$. There is very strong evidence that players can throw more than 60% strikes after training, based on this sample.
  b) $H_0: \mu_D = 0$ vs. $H_A: \mu_D > 0$. $t = 0.135$, P-value $= 0.4472$. With such a high P-value, we do not reject $H_0$. These data provide no evidence that the program has improved pitching in these Little League players.

**36.** $H_0: \mu_D = 0$ vs. $H_A: \mu_D > 0$. $t = -1.74$, P-value $= 0.956$. These data show no evidence that more people were without health insurance during the recession of 2000–2001 than in 1999–2000. In fact, the mean for 2000–2001 was lower than the mean for 1999–2000. (Using the sign test, we find that there were 25 states where the percentage decreased, 21 where it increased, and 5 where it stayed the same. The $z$-score is 0.5898 for a one-sided P-value of 0.7223. The data show no evidence that the percentage increased. Same conclusions as for the $t$-test.)

**37.** We are told this is an SRS, and certainly 99 is fewer than 10% of all cardholders. These are three months' spending for the same cardholders, so the months are paired. One cardholder's spending should not affect another's. The histogram of differences shows a unimodal and roughly symmetric distribution. $\bar{d} = \$280.74$, $s_d = \$990.049$.

Based on this sample, we can say with 95% confidence that cardholders, on average, charge between $83.32 and $478.16 less in January than December.

**38.** a) We are told this is an SRS, and certainly 99 is fewer than 10% of all cardholders. These are three months' spending for the same cardholders, so the months are paired. One cardholder's spending should not affect another's. The histogram of differences shows a unimodal and roughly symmetric distribution. $\bar{d} = \$127.31$, $s_d = \$766.039$; with 98df, $t = 1.658$. With a P-value of 0.1005, we are unable to reject the null hypothesis of no difference in mean charges between January and February.
  b) The CI shows that, with 95% confidence, cardholders charge, on average, between $280.06 more and $25.44 less in February than in January. The interval contains 0, consistent with our failure to reject $H_0$.

# PART VI REVIEW

**1.** a) $H_0: \mu_{Jan} - \mu_{Jul} = 0$; $H_A: \mu_{Jan} - \mu_{Jul} \neq 0$. $t = -1.94$, df $= 43.68$, P-value $= 0.0590$. Since $P < 0.10$, reject the null. These data show a significant difference in mean age to crawl between January and July babies.
  b) $H_0: \mu_{Apr} - \mu_{Oct} = 0$; $H_A: \mu_{Apr} - \mu_{Oct} \neq 0$. $t = -0.92$; df $= 59.40$; P-value $= 0.3610$. Since $P > 0.10$, do not reject the null; these data do not show a significant difference between April and October with regard to the mean age at which crawling begins.
  c) These results are not consistent with the claim.

**2.** $H_0: \mu_D = 0$; $H_A: \mu_D > 0$. $t = 1.36$; df $= 20$; P-value $= 0.0949$. Because the P-value is high, we do not reject $H_0$. These data do not show that floral scent improved the average maze completion time between scented and unscented.

**3.** $H_0: p = 0.26$; $H_A: p \neq 0.26$. $z = 0.946$; P-value $= 0.3443$. Because the P-value is high, we do not reject $H_0$. These data do

not show that the Denver-area rate is different from the national rate in the proportion of businesses with women owners.

**4.** a) Based on these data, we are 95% confident the average savings in Canada for prescription drugs is between $77.57 and $174.43.
  b) Based on these data, we are 95% confident that the average savings in Canada for prescription drugs is between 40.1% and 64.2%.
  c) Using percents makes the histogram more unimodal and symmetric.
  d) Probably would change. The pharmacy may have listed only the 12 drugs with the "best" savings.

**5.** Based on these data, we are 95% confident that the mean difference in aluminum oxide content is between $-3.37$ and 1.65. The means in aluminum oxide content of the pottery made at the two sites could reasonably be the same.

**6.** Based on these data, we are 95% confident that the proportion of streams in the Adirondacks with shale substrates is between 32.8% and 47.4%.

**7.** a) $H_0: p_{ALS} - p_{Other} = 0$; $H_A: p_{ALS} - p_{Other} > 0$. $z = 2.52$; P-value $= 0.0058$. With such a low P-value, we reject $H_0$. This is strong evidence that there is a higher proportion of varsity athletes among ALS patients than those with other disorders.
  b) Observational retrospective study. To make the inference, one must assume the patients studied are representative.

**8.** Paired samples; boxplots show no strong skewness or outliers. One might wonder how the individuals in the study were selected. We are 95% confident that average percentage of 15-year-old males who have been drunk is between 4.5% and 11.4% more than 15-year-old females for these countries. We cannot infer that these percentages are true for other countries.

**9.** $H_0: \mu = 7.41$; $H_A: \mu \neq 7.41$. $t = 2.18$; df $= 111$; P-value $= 0.0313$. With such a low P-value, we reject $H_0$. Assuming that Missouri babies fairly represent the United States, these data show that American babies are different from Australian babies in birth weight; American babies are heavier, on average.

**10.** a) 88.6%   b) 82.2%
  c) The petition would be certified when there are not enough valid signatures.
  d) A correct petition is not certified.
  e) $H_0: p = 0.822$; $H_A: p > 0.822$. $z = 7.48$; P-value $= 3.64 \times 10^{-14}$ With such a low P-value, we reject $H_0$. This sample provides sufficient evidence for certification of the petition.
  f) Increase sample size.

**11.** a) If there is no difference in the average fish sizes, the chance of seeing an observed difference this large just by natural sampling variation is 0.1%.
  b) If cost justified, feed them a natural diet.
  c) Type I

**12.** We have two independent samples, but we don't know how these vehicles were chosen. Even if we consider them representative, the samples are small, and the data for SUVs are skewed to the right. These data are not appropriate for inferences.

**13.** a) Assuming the conditions are met, from these data we are 95% confident that patients with cardiac disease average between 3.39 and 5.01 years older than those without cardiac disease.
  b) Older patients are at greater risk from a variety of other health issues, and perhaps more depressed.

**14.** a) We are 95% confident that the proportion of smokers is between 3.67% and 12.93% more in patients with heart disease than in those without heart disease, based on this information.
  b) Yes. The interval lies completely above 0.
  c) Could be a confounding variable. The smokers are at even greater risk for heart attack.

**15.** a) Stratified sample survey.

b) We are 95% confident that boys are between 7.0% and 17.0% more likely to play computer games than girls, based on the survey.

c) Yes. The entire interval lies above 0.

**16.** a) Based on the data, we are 95% confident that the difference in recruiting is between $-4.2\%$ and 8.2%.

b) No. The interval contains 0 and negative values—it may actually be the case that the new strategy lowers acceptance rates.

**17.** Based on the data, we are 95% confident that the mean difference in words misunderstood is between $-3.76$ and 3.10. Because 0 is in the confidence interval, we would conclude that the two tapes are not equivalent.

**18.** $H_0: p_{VT} - p_{NH} = 0$; $H_A: p_{VT} - p_{NH} \neq 0$. $z = -0.59$; P-value $= 0.5563$. With such a high P-value, we do not reject $H_0$. These data show no evidence of a difference in the rates of cesarean deliveries between Vermont and New Hampshire.

**19.** a)

M − W Difference

The countries that appear to be outliers are Spain, Italy, and Portugal. They are all Mediterranean countries.

b) $H_0: \mu_D = 0$; $H_A: \mu_D > 0$.
$t = 5.56$; df $= 10$; P-value $= 0.0001$. With such a low P-value, we reject $H_0$. These data show that European men are more likely than women to read newspapers.

**20.** $H_0: \mu = \$10$; $H_A: \mu > \$10$. $t = 0.66$; df $= 13$. P-value $= 0.26$. With such a high P-value, we do not reject $H_0$. These data do not provide evidence that he is likely to overspend his budget of \$10 per day.

**21.** Based on the survey, we are 95% confident that the proportion of American adults who would agree with the statement is between 57.0% and 63.0%.

**22.** $H_0: \mu_{Cert} - \mu_{UC} = 0$; $H_A: \mu_{Cert} - \mu_{UC} > 0$. $t = 1.57$; df $= 86$; P-value $= 0.0598$. The P-value is low enough to reject $H_0$. These data provide evidence that students of certified teachers achieve higher mean reading scores than students of uncertified teachers.

**23.** Data are matched pairs (before and after for the same rooms); less than 10% of all rooms in a large hotel; uncertain how these rooms were selected (are they representative?). Histogram shows that differences are roughly unimodal and symmetric, with no outliers. A 95% confidence interval for the difference, before − after, is (0.58, 2.65) counts. Since the entire interval is above 0, these data show that the new air-conditioning system was effective in reducing average bacteria counts.

**24.** There is a significant difference in Math performance; students of certified teachers do better. There is a significant difference in language performance at $\alpha = 0.05$ between students of certified teachers and those of uncertified teachers.

**25.** a) We are 95% confident that between 19.77% and 38.66% of children with bipolar symptoms will be helped with medication and psychotherapy, based on this study.

b) 221 children

**26.** a) $H_0: \mu_D = 0$; $H_A: \mu_D \neq 0$. $t = 0.381$; df $= 19$; P-value $= 0.7078$. With a high P-value, we do not reject $H_0$. There is no evidence that the tests differ in mean difficulty.

b) $H_0: \mu_D = 0$; $H_A: \mu_D \neq 0$. The boxplot of the differences shows three outliers, but they are symmetric. A paired $t$-test with them included shows $t = -0.2531$ with 16 df and a P-value of 0.8029, showing no evidence of a difference in mean scores. With the three outliers removed, the $t$-test shows $t = -1.1793$ with 16 df and a P-value of 0.2555—still no evidence of a

difference in means. We conclude the testing environment does not affect mean score.

**27.** a) From this histogram, about 115 loaves or more. (Not Normal.) This assumes the last 100 days are typical.

b) Large sample size; CLT says $\bar{y}$ will be approximately Normal.

c) From the data, we are 95% confident that the bakery will sell between 101.2 and 104.8 loaves of bread on an average day.

d) 25

e) Yes, 100 loaves per day is too low—the entire confidence interval is above that.

**28.** a)

Petal Length

b) *Versicolor* generally has longer petals than *virginica*.

c) (10.14, 14.46)

d) We are 95% confident, based on the information given, that the average petal length for *versicolor* irises is between 10.14 and 14.46 mm longer than that of *virginica* irises.

e) Yes. The entire interval is above 0.

**29.** a) $H_0: p_{High} - p_{Low} = 0$; $H_A: p_{High} - p_{Low} \neq 0$. $z = -3.57$; P-value $= 0.0004$. Because the P-value is so low, we reject $H_0$. These data show the IRS risk is different in the two groups; people who consume dairy products often have a lower risk, on average.

b) Doesn't prove it; this is not an experiment.

**30.** a) $H_0: p = 0.16$; $H_A: p > 0.16$. $z = 4.42$; P-value $= 5 \times 10^{-6}$. Because the P-value is so low, we reject $H_0$. These data show that the proportion of tickets given to blacks on this section of the New Jersey Turnpike is unusually high.

b) Doesn't prove it; there may be other factors.

c) Answers will vary. Possibly what proportion of drivers on this highway is black?

**31.** Based on these data, we are 95% confident that seeded clouds will produce an average of between $-4.76$ and 559.56 more acre-feet of rain than unseeded clouds. Since the interval contains negative values, it may be that seeding is unproductive.

**32.** a) $H_0: \mu = 35.4$; $H_A: \mu < 35.4$

b) There is one high value, but it is technically not an outlier. Otherwise the histogram appears roughly unimodal and symmetric (only 6 values).

c) $t = 0.726$; P-value $= 0.7497$. With such a large P-value, we do not reject $H_0$. The data do not show that the average weight is less than claimed.

d) $t = -0.53$; P-value $= 0.3107$. Without the high outlier, the data still do not show that the average weight is significantly less than claimed.

e) The stated weight seems legitimate based on these 6 bags.

**33.** a) Randomizing order of the tasks helps avoid bias and memory effects. Randomizing the cards helps avoid bias as well.

b) $H_0: \mu_D = 0$; $H_A: \mu_D > 0$

c)

Boxplot of the differences looks symmetric with no outliers.
d) $t = -1.70$; P-value = 0.0999; do not reject $H_0$, because P > 0.05.
e) The data do not provide evidence that the color or written word dominates.

34. a) $373.50
   b) They are 95% confident that the average loss in a home burglary is between $1644 and $2391, based on their sample.
   c) 95% of all random samples will produce confidence intervals that contain the true mean loss.

35. a) Different samples give different means; this is a fairly small sample. The difference may be due to natural sampling variation.
   b) $H_0: \mu = 100$; $H_A: \mu < 100$
   c) Batteries selected are a SRS (representative); fewer than 10% of the company's batteries; lifetimes are approximately Normal.
   d) $t = -1.0$; P-value = 0.1666; do not reject $H_0$. This sample does not show that the average life of the batteries is significantly less than 100 hours.
   e) Type II.

36. a) Based on these data, we are 90% confident that the average hamster litter will have between 7.11 and 8.33 babies.
   b) Larger—to be more confident, we need a wider interval.
   c) About 27 (based on $t_{24}^*$).

# CHAPTER 26

1. a) Chi-square test of independence. We have one sample and two variables. We want to see if the variable *Account Type* is independent of the variable *Trade Type*.
   b) Other test. The variable *Account Size* is quantitative, not counts.
   c) Chi-square test of homogeneity. We want to see if the distribution of one variable, *Courses*, is the same for two groups (resident and nonresident students).

2. a) Chi-square goodness-of-fit test. We want to see if the distribution of defects is uniform over the work days.
   b) Other test. *Cholesterol Level* is a quantitative variable, not counts.
   c) Chi-square test of independence. We have data on two variables, *Political Leaning* and *Major*, for one group of students.

3. a) 10
   b) Goodness-of-fit
   c) $H_0$: The die is fair (all faces have $p = 1/6$).
      $H_A$: The die is not fair.
   d) Count data; rolls are random and independent; expected frequencies are all bigger than 5.
   e) 5
   f) $\chi^2 = 5.600$, P-value = 0.3471
   g) Because the P-value is high, do not reject $H_0$. The data show no evidence that the die is unfair.

4. a) Yellow and red: 21.2; orange, blue, and green: 10.6; brown; 31.8
   b) Goodness-of-fit
   c) $H_0$: The distribution is as specified by the company.
      $H_A$: The distribution is not as specified.
   d) Count data; bag may not be a random sample, but most likely representative; expected counts are all bigger than 5.
   e) 5

f) $\chi^2 = 9.315$, P-value = 0.0972
g) Because the P-value is high, do not reject $H_0$. These data do not provide evidence that the distribution is other than specified.

5. a) Weights are quantitative, not counts.
   b) Count the number of each kind of nut, assuming the company's percentages are based on counts rather than weights.

6. Data are averages, not counts.

7. $H_0$: The police force represents the population (29.2% white, 28.2% black, etc.). $H_A$: The police force is not representative of the population. $\chi^2 = 16516.88$, df = 4, P-value = 0.0000. Because the P-value is so low, we reject $H_0$. These data show that the police force is not representative of the population. In particular, there are too many white officers in relationship to their membership in the community.

8. $H_0$: Murders among women have the same distribution of weapons as all murders (63.4% guns, etc.). $H_A$: Murders among women have a different distribution of weapons than all murders. $\chi^2 = 389.54$, df = 3, P-value < 0.0001. Because the P-value is so low, we reject $H_0$. Women's murders do not have the same distribution of weapons as all murders nationwide. Women are much less likely to be killed by other weapons and more likely to be killed by personal attack.

9. a) $\chi^2 = 5.671$, df = 3, P-value = 0.1288. With a P-value this high, we fail to reject $H_0$. Yes, these data are consistent with those predicted by genetic theory.
   b) $\chi^2 = 11.342$, df = 3, P-value = 0.0100. Because of the low P-value, we reject $H_0$. These data provide evidence that the distribution is not as specified by genetic theory.
   c) With small samples, many more data sets will be consistent with the null hypothesis. With larger samples, small discrepancies will show evidence against the null hypothesis.

10. $H_0$: Digits are all equally likely (all occur with frequency 1/10). $H_A$: Digits are not all equally likely. $\chi^2 = 5.509$, df = 9, P-value = 0.7879. Because the P-value is large, we do not reject $H_0$. These data provide no evidence that the digits in pi are not all equally likely.

11. a) 96/16 = 6
    b) Goodness of Fit
    c) $H_0$: The number of large hurricanes remains constant over decades.
       $H_A$: The number of large hurricanes has changed.
    d) 15
    e) P-value = 0.63
    f) The very high P-value means these data offer no evidence that the numbers of large hurricanes has changed.
    g) The final period is only 6 years rather than 10 and already 7 large hurricanes have been observed. Perhaps this decade will have an unusually large number of such hurricanes.

12. a) Goodness of Fit
    b) 655/49 = 13.367
    c) $H_0$: All numbers are equally likely;
       $H_A$: Some numbers are more likely than others.
    d) 48     e) 0.93
    f) The very high P-value means these data offer no evidence that some lottery numbers are more likely to come up than others.

13. a) Independence
    b) $H_0$: Breastfeeding success is independent of having an epidural.
       $H_A$: There's an association between breastfeeding success and having an epidural.

14. a) Homogeneity
    b) $H_0$: The same proportion of articles used statistics in the three time periods surveyed. $H_A$: The proportion of articles using statistics changed over time.

15. a) 1     b) 159.34

c) Breastfeeding behavior should be independent for these babies. They are fewer than 10% of all babies; we assume they are representative. We have counts, and all the expected counts are at least 5.

**16.** a) 2    b) 21.85

c) These are counted data. One article shouldn't affect another (except perhaps for the rare article based on a previous one in an earlier year cohort included in this study). We can regard the selected years as representative of those nearby, and the authors (judging by their title) seem to want to regard these articles as representative of those appearing in other similar-quality medical journals, so they're fewer than 10% of all articles. All expected counts are at least 5.

**17.** a) 5.90    b) P-value < 0.005

c) The P-value is very low, so reject the null. There's evidence of an association between having an epidural and subsequent success in breastfeeding.

**18.** a) 2.82    b) P-value < 0.001

c) The P-value is very low, so reject the null. There's evidence that the percentage of medical journal articles that include statistics has changed over time.

**19.** a) $\dfrac{(190 - 159.34)}{\sqrt{159.34}} = 2.43$

b) It appears that babies whose mothers had epidurals during childbirth are much less likely to be breastfeeding 6 months later.

**20.** a) $\dfrac{(14 - 21.85)}{\sqrt{21.85}} = -1.68$

b) The residuals for No stats are decreasing and those for Stats are increasing over time, indicating that, over time, fewer articles are appearing without statistics.

**21.** These factors would not be mutually exclusive. There would be yes or no responses for every baby for each.

**22.** The methods would not have been mutually exclusive. Articles might use more than one statistical method.

**23.** a) 40.2%    b) 8.1%

c) 62.2%    d) 285.48

e) $H_0$: Survival was independent of status on the ship. $H_A$: Survival depended on the status.

f) 3

g) We reject the null hypothesis. Survival depended on status. We can see that first-class passengers were more likely to survive than passengers of any other class.

**24.** a) 15.0%    b) 13.0%    c) 730.4

d) Independence

e) $H_0$: *Rank* is independent of *Sex*. $H_A$: *Rank* and *Sex* are not independent.

f) Count data; not a random sample, but all NYPD officers; expected counts all greater than 5.

g) 5

h) $\chi^2 = 290.131$, P-value < 0.0001

i) Because the P-value is so low, we reject $H_0$. *Sex* and *Rank* in the NYPD are not independent.

j) Standardized residuals are

|  | Male | Female |
|---|---|---|
| **Officer** | −2.3434 | 5.5747 |
| **Detective** | −1.1759 | 2.7973 |
| **Sergeant** | 3.8429 | −9.1421 |
| **Lieutenant** | 3.5824 | −8.5223 |
| **Captain** | 2.4617 | −5.8563 |
| **Higher ranks** | 1.7412 | −4.1423 |

Women are overrepresented at the lower ranks and underrepresented at every rank from sergeant up.

**25.** a) Independence.

b) $H_0$: *College* is independent of *Birth Order*. $H_A$: There is an association between *Birth Order* and *College*.

c) Counted Data Condition—these are counts of students; Randomization Condition—a class is not a random sample, but there's little reason to think this particular group of students isn't representative; Expected Cell Frequency Condition—the expected frequencies are low for both the Social Science and Professional Colleges, for third and fourth or higher birth orders (check residuals later).

d) 9

e) With a P-value this low, we reject the null hypothesis. There is some evidence of an association between *Birth Order* and *College*.

f) Unfortunately, 3 of the 4 largest standardized residuals are in cells with expected counts less than 5. We should be very wary of drawing conclusions from this chi-square test.

**26.** a) Independence.

b) $H_0$: *Political Position* is independent of *Binge Drinking*. $H_A$: There is an association between *Political Position* and *Binge Drinking*.

c) Counted Data Condition—these are counts of students; Randomization Condition—a class is not a random sample, but there's little reason to think this particular group of students isn't representative; Expected Cell Frequency Condition—the expected frequencies are all at least 5.

d) 8

e) With a P-value this large, we fail to reject the null hypothesis. There's no evidence of an association between *Binge Drinking* and *Political Opinion*.

f) A larger sample probably could attain statistical significance. Chi-square tests can be made significant with a sufficiently large sample.

**27.** a) Experiment—actively imposed treatments (different drinks)

b) Homogeneity

c) $H_0$: The rate of urinary tract infection is the same for all three groups. $H_A$: The rate of urinary tract infection is different among the groups.

d) Count data; random assignment to treatments; all expected frequencies larger than 5.

e) 2

f) $\chi^2 = 7.776$, P-value = 0.020.

g) With a P-value this low, we reject $H_0$. These data provide reasonably strong evidence that there is a difference in urinary tract infection rates between cranberry juice drinkers, lactobacillus drinkers, and the control group.

h) The standardized residuals are

|  | Cranberry | Lactobacillus | Control |
|---|---|---|---|
| **Infection** | −1.87276 | 1.19176 | 0.68100 |
| **No Infection** | 1.24550 | −0.79259 | −0.45291 |

From the standardized residuals (and the sign of the residuals), it appears those who drank cranberry juice were less likely to develop urinary tract infections; those who drank lactobacillus were more likely to have infections.

**28.** a) Homogeneity

b) $H_0$: The distribution of *Car Origin* is the same for students and staff. $H_A$: The distribution of *Car Origin* is different for students and staff.

c) Count data; random survey of cars in lots (probably can't generalize to other universities); expected frequencies greater than 5.

d) $\chi^2 = 7.828$, df $= 2$, P-value $= 0.020$.

e) With a P-value this low, we reject $H_0$. The distribution of car origins differs between students and staff. Examination of the residuals shows that students are more likely than staff to drive European cars and less likely than staff to drive American cars.

29. a) Independence

b) $H_0$: *Political Affiliation* is independent of *Sex*.

$H_A$: There is a relationship between *Political Affiliation* and *Sex*.

c) Counted data; probably a random sample, but can't extend results to other states; all expected frequencies greater than 5.

d) $\chi^2 = 4.851$, df $= 2$, P-value $= 0.0884$.

e) Because of the high P-value, we do not reject $H_0$. These data do not provide evidence of a relationship between *Political Affiliation* and *Sex*.

30. a) Prospective study; individuals were selected and then subsequently followed.

b) Independence

c) $\chi^2 = 3.677$, df $= 3$, P-value $= 0.2985$. Because of the high P-value, we do not reject $H_0$. These data do not provide evidence of a relationship between the amount of fish in the diet and prostate cancer. (Data are for totals and cancer, not non-cancer and cancer.)

d) No. There may be many other factors involved.

31. $H_0$: *Political Affiliation* is independent of *Region*. $H_A$: There is a relationship between *Political Affiliation* and *Region*. $\chi^2 = 13.849$, df $= 4$, P-value $= 0.0078$. With a P-value this low, we reject $H_0$. *Political Affiliation* and *Region* are related. Examination of the residuals shows that those in the West are more likely to be Democrat than Republican; those in the Northeast are more likely to be Republican than Democrat.

32. a) Survey

b) Homogeneity

c) $\chi^2 = 4.030$, df $= 4$, P-value $= 0.4019$. Because the P-value is so high, we fail to reject $H_0$. These data do not show evidence of a change in attitudes about the ideal family between 1991 and 2001.

33. a) Homogeneity

b) $H_0$: The grade distribution is the same for both professors.

$H_A$: The grade distributions are different.

c)

|   | Dr. Alpha | Dr. Beta |
|---|-----------|----------|
| A | 6.667 | 5.333 |
| B | 12.778 | 10.222 |
| C | 12.222 | 9.778 |
| D | 6.111 | 4.889 |
| F | 2.222 | 1.778 |

Three cells have expected frequencies less than 5.

34. a) Homogeneity

b) $H_0$: The crime distribution is the same for both phases of the moon.

$H_A$: The crime distributions are different for the different moon phases.

c) Expected counts.

|   | Full moon | Not full |
|---|-----------|----------|
| **Violent** | 2.558 | 2.442 |
| **Property** | 19.442 | 18.558 |
| **Drugs/alcohol** | 23.535 | 22.465 |
| **Domestic abuse** | 12.791 | 12.209 |
| **Other offenses** | 7.674 | 7.326 |

Two cells have expected counts less than 5.

35. a)

|   | Dr. Alpha | Dr. Beta |
|---|-----------|----------|
| **A** | 6.667 | 5.333 |
| **B** | 12.778 | 10.222 |
| **C** | 12.222 | 9.778 |
| **Below C** | 8.333 | 6.667 |

All expected frequencies are now larger than 5.

b) Decreased from 4 to 3.

c) $\chi^2 = 9.306$, P-value $= 0.0255$. Because the P-value is so low, we reject $H_0$. The grade distributions for the two professors are different. Dr. Alpha gives fewer A's and more grades below C than Dr. Beta.

36. a) Combine Violent and Domestic abuse into one category (or Violent and Other).

b) $\chi^2 = 2.877$, df $= 3$, P-value $= 0.4109$. Because the P-value is so high, we do not reject $H_0$. These data do not provide any evidence of a difference in type of illegal activity in different moon phases.

37. a) Answers will vary. Stacked bar charts or pie charts would work well.

b) Chi-square test of independence. One person's response should not influence another's. We have counts, an SRS of less than 10% of the population, and all expected cell frequencies are much larger than 5. With 8 df, $\chi^2 = 190.96$. Because the P-value $< 0.001$, reject the null. There is strong evidence to suggest that responses are not independent of age.

38. a) Answers will vary. Stacked bar charts or pie charts would work well.

b) Chi-square test of homogeneity. One person's response should not influence another's. We have counts, SRS's of less than 10% of each population, and all expected cell frequencies are much larger than 5. With 16 df, $\chi^2 = 470.88$. Because the P-value $< 0.001$, reject the null. This test provides strong evidence to suggest that the distributions of responses vary over the five countries. France seems especially different in the number of people who Agree with the question—having a much lower percentage than the other four countries.

39. $\chi^2 = 14.058$, df $= 1$, P-value $= 0.0002$. With a P-value this low, we reject $H_0$. There is evidence of racial steering. Blacks are much less likely to rent in Section A than Section B.

40. $\chi^2 = 453.476$, df $= 1$, P-value $< 0.0001$. With a P-value this low, we reject $H_0$. Survival was related to gender. Females were much more likely than males to survive (72.98% to 21.20%).

41. a) $z = 3.74936$, $z^2 = 14.058$.

b) P-value $(z) = 0.0002$ (same as in Exercise 25).

42. a) $z = 21.29498$.

b) $z^2 = 453.476$.

c) Both P-values are near 0.

43. $\chi^2 = 2815.968$, df $= 9$, P-value $< 0.0001$. Because the P-value is so low, we reject $H_0$. There are definite differences in education levels attained by the groups. The largest component indicates that Hispanics are more likely not to have high-school diplomas. The next-largest residual indicates that fewer whites than expected do not have a high-school diploma.

44. $\chi^2 = 5.89$, df $= 3$, P $= 0.117$. Because the P-value is $>0.05$, these data show no evidence of an association between the mother's age group and the outcome of the pregnancy.

45. $\chi^2 = 0.870$, df $= 2$, P-value $= 0.6471$. Because the P-value is so large, we do not reject $H_0$. These data show no evidence of a difference in higher education opportunities between blacks and Hispanics.

46. $\chi^2 = 178.453$, df $= 12$, P-value $< 0.0001$, Because the P-value is so low, we reject $H_0$. There is a difference is education level among the different age groups. The largest component indicates those 35 to 44 were less likely to have only a high-school

diploma. The second-largest indicates the same age group is more likely than other age groups to have at least four years of college.

**47.** A goodness-of-fit test with 2 df yields $\chi^2 = 12.26$, with P = 0.002. Compared to the top 500 universities, the top 100 seem to be more heavily concentrated in the Americas and sparser in the Asia, Africa, and Pacific regions.

**48.** A test of independence with 8 df yields $\chi^2 = 30.68$, with P = 0.0002. Among the world's top 500 universities, institutions in the Americas are more likely to be ranked higher and those in the Asia, Africa, and Pacific regions tend to be ranked lower.

## CHAPTER 27

**1.** a) $\widehat{Error} = 453.22 - 8.37\ YearSince1970$; according to the model, the error made in predicting a hurricane's path was about 453 nautical miles, on average, in 1970. It has been declining at a rate of about 8.37 nautical miles per year.

b) $H_0: \beta_1 = 0$; there has been no change in prediction accuracy. $H_A: \beta_1 \neq 0$; there has been a change in prediction accuracy.

c) With a P-value < 0.001, I reject the null hypothesis and conclude that prediction accuracies have in fact been changing during this period.

d) 58.5% of the variation in hurricane prediction accuracy is accounted for by this linear model on time.

**2.** a) $\widehat{\%Other} = -3.068 + 0.615\ \%\ Marijuana.$ The percentage of ninth graders in these countries who have used other drugs is estimated to have increased 0.615% for each 1% increase in the percentage of ninth graders who have used marijuana.

b) $H_0$: There is no (linear) relationship between marijuana use and use of other drugs, $\beta_1 = 0$. $H_A$: There is a relationship, $\beta_1 \neq 0$.

c) $t = 7.85$, P-value = 0.0001. With such a low P-value, we reject $H_0$. Percentage of teens using other drugs is positively related to percentage using marijuana.

d) Percentage using marijuana accounts for 87.3% of the variation in other drug usage for ninth graders in these countries.

e) The use of other drugs is associated with marijuana use, but there is no proof of causality. There may be lurking variables.

**3.** a) $\widehat{Budget} = -31.387 + 0.714\ RunTime.$ The model suggests that movies cost about $714,000 per minute to make.

b) A negative starting value makes no sense, but the P-value of 0.07 indicates that we can't discern a difference between our estimated value and zero. The statement that a movie of zero length should cost $0 makes sense.

c) Amounts by which movie costs differ from predictions made by this model vary, with a standard deviation of about $33 million.

d) 0.154 $m/min

e) If we constructed other models based on different samples of movies, we'd expect the slopes of the regression lines to vary, with a standard deviation of about $154,000 per minute.

**4.** a) $\widehat{Price} = -0.312 + 94.5\ Size.$ The model suggests that Saratoga houses cost about $94.5 per square foot.

b) The P-value for the intercept is 0.50. That means that we cannot discern a difference between the intercept value and zero. A value of $0 for a house of zero size makes sense.

c) Amounts by which house prices differ from predictions made by this model vary, with a standard deviation of about $54,000.

d) $2.393/sq. ft.

e) If we constructed other models based on different samples of houses, we'd expect the slopes of the regression lines to vary, with a standard deviation of about $2.39 per square foot.

**5.** a) The scatterplot looks straight enough, the residuals look random and nearly normal, and the residuals don't display any clear change in variability.

b) I'm 95% confident that the cost of making longer movies increases at a rate of between 0.41 and 1.02 million dollars per minute.

**6.** a) The scatterplot looks straight enough, the residuals look random and nearly normal, and the residuals don't display any clear change in variability.

b) I'm 95% confident that Saratoga housing costs increase at a rate of between $89.8 and $99.2 per square foot.

**7.** a) $H_0: \beta_1 = 0$; there's no association between calories and sodium content in all-beef hot dogs. $H_A: \beta_1 \neq 0$: there is an association.

b) Based on the low P-value (0.0018), I reject the null. There is evidence of an association between the number of calories in all-beef hot dogs and their sodium contents.

**8.** a) $H_0$: There is no linear relationship between *Age* and *Cholesterol Level*, $\beta_1 = 0$. $H_A$: Cholesterol levels change with age, $\beta_1 \neq 0$

b) $t = 3.00$, P-value = 0.0056. Because the P-value is so small, we reject $H_0$. These data show a significant positive relationship between *Age* and *Cholesterol Level*.

**9.** a) Among all-beef hot dogs with the same number of calories, the sodium content varies, with a standard deviation of about 60 mg.

b) 0.561 mg/cal

c) If we tested many other samples of all-beef hot dogs, the slopes of the resulting regression lines would be expected to vary, with a standard deviation of about 0.56 mg of sodium per calorie.

**10.** a) Among adults of the same age, cholesterol levels vary with a standard deviation of about 46 points.

b) 0.2574 pts/yr

c) If we tested many other samples of adults, the slopes of the resulting regression lines would be expected to vary with a standard deviation of 0.26 cholesterol points per year of age.

**11.** I'm 95% confident that for every additional calorie, all-beef hot dogs have, on average, between 1.03 and 3.57 mg more sodium.

**12.** I'm 95% confident that, on average, adult cholesterol levels increase between 0.27 and 1.28 points per year of age.

**13.** a) $H_0$: Difference in age at first marriage has not been changing, $\beta_1 = 0$. $H_A$: Difference in age at first marriage has been changing, $\beta_1 \neq 0$.

b) Residual plot shows no obvious pattern; histogram is not particularly Normal, but shows no obvious skewness or outliers.

c) $t = -7.04$, P-value < 0.0001. With such a low P-value, we reject $H_0$. These data show evidence that difference in age at first marriage is decreasing.

**14.** a)

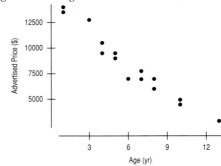

b) Yes, the plot seems linear.

c) $\widehat{Advertised\ Price} = 14286 - 959 \times Age$

d)

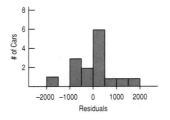

The residual plot shows some possible curvature. Inference may not be valid here, but we will proceed (with caution).

15. Based on these data, we are 95% confident that the average difference in age at first marriage is decreasing at a rate between 0.039 and 0.021 years per year.

16. Based on these data, we are 95% confident that a used car's *Price* decreases between $819.50 and $1099 per year.

17. a) $H_0$: *Fuel Economy* and *Weight* are not (linearly) related, $\beta_1 = 0$. $H_A$: *Fuel Economy* changes with *Weight*, $\beta_1 \neq 0$. P-value $< 0.0001$, indicating strong evidence of an association.
    b) Yes, the conditions seem satisfied. Histogram of residuals is unimodal and symmetric; residual plot looks OK, but some "thickening" of the plot with increasing values.
    c) $t = -12.2$, P-value $< 0.0001$. These data show evidence that *Fuel Economy* decreases with the *Weight* of the car.

18. a) The scatterplot suggests a positive linear relationship. $H_0$: There is no (linear) relationship between *SAT Verbal* and *SAT Math* scores, $\beta_1 = 0$. $H_A$: There is a relationship, $\beta_1 \neq 0$.
    b) Assumptions seem reasonable, since conditions are satisfied. Residual plot shows no patterns (one outlier); histogram is unimodal and roughly symmetric.
    c) $t = 11.9$; P-value $< 0.0001$. These data show evidence of a positive relationship between *SAT Verbal* and *SAT Math* scores.

19. a) $(-9.57, -6.86)$ mpg per 1000 pounds.
    b) Based on these data, we are 95% confident that *Fuel Efficiency* decreases between 6.86 and 9.57 miles per gallon, on average, for each additional 1000 pounds of *Weight*.

20. a) $(0.581, 0.769)$
    b) Based on the sample, we are 90% confident that average *SAT Math* scores increase between 0.58 and 0.769 points for each additional point scored on the *SAT Verbal* test.

21. a) Based on this regression, we are 95% confident that 2500-pound cars will average between 27.44 and 28.97 miles per gallon.
    b) Based on the regression, a 3450-pound car will get between 16.00 and 24.81 miles per gallon, with 95% confidence.

22. a) Based on the regression, we are 90% confident that the mean Math score for students with a Verbal score of 500 is between 534.0 and 560.18.
    b) Based on the regression, we are 90% confident that the Math score for the valedictorian will be between 569 and 800 (SAT scores cannot be higher than 800).

23. a) Yes. $t = 2.73$, P-value $= 0.0079$. With a P-value so low, we reject $H_0$. There is a positive relationship between *Calories* and *Sodium* content.

b) No. $R^2 = 9\%$ and $s$ appears to be large, although without seeing the data, it is a bit hard to tell.

24. a) $H_0$: No linear relationship between *Brain Size* and *IQ*, $\beta_1 = 0$. $H_A$: There is evidence of a relationship, $\beta_1 \neq 0$. $t = 1.12$; this will not be significant.
    b) With $R^2 = 6.5\%$, the relationship is very weak. There seem to be three students with large brains who also scored high. Without them, there seems to be no association at all.

25. Plot of *Calories* against *Fiber* does not look linear; this is borne out in the residuals plot, which also shows increasing variance as predicted values get large. The histogram of residuals is right skewed.

26. Scatterplot of *Temperature* against *Latitude* shows curvature (downward). Histogram of residuals is right skewed; residual plot shows decreasing variance as predicted values increase.

27. a) $H_0$: No (linear) relationship between *BCI* and *pH*, $\beta_1 = 0$. $H_A$: There is a relationship, $\beta_1 \neq 0$.
    b) $t = -7.73$ with 161 df; P-value $< 0.0001$
    c) There is a negative relationship; *BCI* decreases as *pH* increases at an average of 197.7 *BCI* units per increase of 1 *pH*.

28. a) $\widehat{Temp} = 15.31 + 0.004 \times CO_2$
    b) Yes; $t = 4.44$, P-value $= 8.5 \times 10^{-5}$
    c) The standard deviation of the residuals is $0.0809°C$, so we don't expect the model to predict to an accuracy greater than about $\pm 0.16°C$.

29. a) $H_0$: No linear relationship between *Population* and *Ozone*, $\beta_1 = 0$. $H_A$: *Ozone* increases with *Population*, $\beta_1 > 0$. $t = 3.48$, P-value $= 0.0018$. With a P-value so low, we reject $H_0$. These data show evidence that *Ozone* does increase with *Population*.
    b) Yes, *Population* accounts for 84% of the variability in *Ozone* level, and $s$ is just over 5 parts per million.

30. a) $H_0$: No linear relationship between *Sales* and *Profit*, $\beta_1 = 0$. $H_A$: There is a relationship, $\beta_1 \neq 0$. $t = 12.33$; P-value $\sim 0$. There is a relationship between *Sales* and *Profit*.
    b) Somewhat. *Sales* accounts for 66% of the variability in *Profits*; although $s$ is nearly a half million dollars, the mean *Profit* for these companies is over $200 million.

31. a) Based on this regression, each additional million residents corresponds to an increase in average ozone level of between 3.29 and 10.01 ppm, with 90% confidence.
    b) Based on the regression, the mean *Ozone* level for cities with 600,000 people is between 18.47 and 27.29 ppm, with 90% confidence.

32. a) Based on this regression, average *Profits* increase between 0.078 and 0.107 million dollars ($78,000 and $107,000) for every million dollars in sales, with 95% confidence.
    b) Based on the regression, the profit for Eli Lilly, Inc., should be between –281.1 and 1592.8 million dollars (–$281,100,000 and $1,592,800,000), with 95% confidence. This interval is so wide that it's really useless.

33. a) 33 batteries.
    b) The scatterplot of the data is roughly linear with lots of scatter; plot of residuals vs. predicted values shows no overt patterns; Normal probability plot of residuals is reasonably straight.
    c) $H_0$: No linear relationship between *Cost* and *Cranking Amps*, $\beta_1 = 0$. $H_A$: *Cranking Amps* increase with cost, $\beta_1 > 0$. $t = 3.23$; P-value $= \frac{1}{2}(0.0029) = 0.00145$. With a P-value so low, we reject $H_0$. These data provide evidence that more expensive batteries do have more cranking amps.
    d) No. $R^2 = 25.2\%$ and $s = 116$ amps. Considering that the range of amperage is only about 400 amps, an $s$ of 116 is not very useful.
    e) $\widehat{Cranking\ amps} = 384.59 + 4.15 \times Cost$.
    f) $(1.97, 6.32)$ cold cranking amps per dollar.

g) *Cranking amps* increase, on average, between 1.97 and 6.32 per dollar of battery *Cost* increase, with 90% confidence.

**34.**

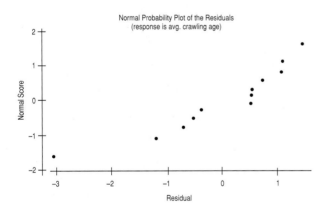

Residuals vs. the fitted values
(response is avg. crawling age)

Normal Probability Plot of the Residuals
(response is avg. crawling age)

a) Weaker. Individuals are more variable than averages.
b) The residuals plot shows a large negative outlier; the Normal probability plot is not very straight, but the sample size is small. We will proceed with the inference with caution. $H_0$: No linear relationship between *6-Month Temperature* and *Crawling Age*, $\beta_1 = 0$. $H_A$: Linear relationship between *6-Month Temperature* and *Crawling Age*, $\beta_1 \neq 0$. $t$ with 10 df is $-3.10$, with P-value 0.0113. With a P-value so low, we reject $H_0$. There does seem to be a negative relationship between temperature and crawling age.
c) $(-0.134, -0.022)$ weeks per °F.

**35.**

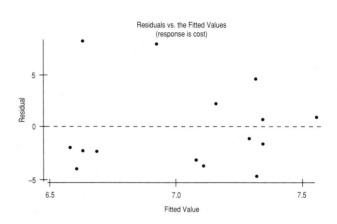

Residuals vs. the Fitted Values
(response is cost)

Normal Probability Plot of the Residuals
(response is cost)

Data plot does not show any indication of a linear relationship. There may be a curved relationship. Normal probability plot of the residuals is not linear (residuals not Normal). Inference for linear regression is not valid here.

**36.**

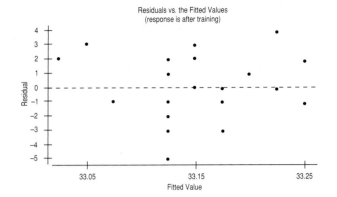

Residuals vs. the Fitted Values
(response is after training)

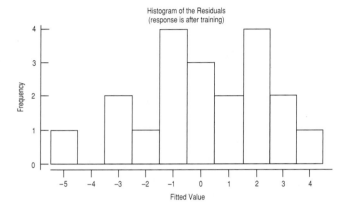

Histogram of the Residuals
(response is after training)

Data plot does not show a linear relationship. Histogram of residuals is reasonable.

$H_0$: No linear relationship between *Initial Ability* and *Effectiveness*, $\beta_1 = 0$. $H_A$: There is a linear relationship, $\beta_1 \neq 0$.
$t = 0.11$;
P-value = 0.912. Because P is high, we do not reject $H_0$. This regression shows no evidence of a relationship between *Initial Ability* and *Effectiveness* of the video.

**37.** a) $H_0$: No linear relationship between *Waist* size and *%Body Fat*, $\beta_1 = 0$. $H_A$: *%Body Fat* changes with *Waist* size, $\beta_1 \neq 0$.
$t = 8.14$; P-value < 0.0001. *%Body Fat* seems to increase with *Waist* size.
b) With 95% confidence, mean *%Body Fat* for people with 40-inch waists is between 23.58 and 29.02, based on this regression.

**38.** a) (0.145, 0.355) % per pound.
b) Based on the regression, average *%Body Fat* increases between 0.145% and 0.355% for each pound of weight.
c) With 95% confidence, a person weighing 165 pounds will have between 0% (−1.61%) and 29.32% body fat, based on this regression.

**39.** a) The regression model is $\widehat{Midterm2} = 12.005 + 0.721\ Midterm1$ with output:

| | Estimate | Std Error | t-ratio | P-value |
|---|---|---|---|---|
| Intercept | 12.00543 | 15.9553 | 0.752442 | 0.454633 |
| Slope | 0.72099 | 0.183716 | 3.924477 | 0.000221 |
| **RSquare** | 0.198982 | | | |
| **s** | 16.78107 | | | |
| **n** | 64 | | | |

b) The scatterplot shows a weak, somewhat linear, positive relationship. There are several outlying points, but removing them only makes the relationship slightly stronger. There is no obvious pattern in the residual plot. The regression model

appears appropriate. The small P-value for the slope shows that the slope is statistically distinguishable from 0 even though the $R^2$ value of 0.199 suggests that the overall relationship is weak.
c) No. The $R^2$ value is only 0.199 and the value of *s* of 16.8 points indicates that she would not be able to predict performance on *Midterm2* very accurately.

**40.** a) The regression model is $\widehat{MT\ total} = 46.062 + 1.580\ Homework$ with output:

| | Estimate | Std Error | t-ratio | P-value |
|---|---|---|---|---|
| Intercept | 46.0619317 | 14.4608874 | 3.18527698 | 0.00226414 |
| Slope | 1.5800598 | 0.197715 | 7.99160308 | 4.0922e-11 |
| **RSquare** | 0.507412 | | | |
| **s** | 18.30433 | | | |
| **n** | 64 | | | |

b) The scatterplot shows a strong, mostly linear, positive relationship between midterm total and homework scores. There is a model outlier and a high influence point, but the model is not significantly changed by deleting both points. There is no obvious pattern in the residual plot. The regression model appears appropriate. The small P-value for the slope shows that the slope is statistically distinguishable from 0.
c) The $R^2$ value of 0.507 suggests that the overall relationship is fairly strong. However, this does not mean that midterm total is accurately predicted from homework scores. The error standard deviation of 18.30 points indicates that a prediction of midterm total could easily be off by 20 to 30 points or more. If this is a significant number of points for deciding grades, then homework score alone will not suffice.

**41.** a) We want to know whether the times to swim across Lake Ontario have changed over time. We know the time of each swim in minutes and the year of the swim. $H_0$: $\beta_1 = 0$ (no linear relationship); $H_A$: $\beta_1 \neq 0$.
b) The Straight Enough Condition fails because there is an outlier.
c) We cannot continue this analysis.
d) With the outlier removed, the relationship looks straight enough. Swims are separate, but some swimmers performed the feat more than once, so swims may not be entirely independent. There is no thickening of the plot. The normal probability plot of the residuals looks straight. The conditions appear to be met.
e) The analysis shows that swim *Times* have been increasing at about 14.9 minutes per *Year*. The P-value of 0.0158 is small enough to reject the null hypothesis, so this looks like a real increase.
f) The SE depends on three things: the standard deviation of the residuals around the line, $s_e$, the standard deviation of $x$, and the number of data values. Only the first of these was changed substantially by removing the outlier. Indeed, we can see that $s_e$ was 447.3 with the outlier present and only 277.2 when it was removed. This accounts for most of the change in the SE and therefore in the P-value. Because the outlier was at a value of $x$ near the middle of the $x$ range, it didn't affect the slope very much.

**42.** a) We'd like to know if there is a linear association between *Price* and *Fuel Efficiency* in cars. We have data on 2004 model-year cars giving their highway mpg and retail price. $H_0$: $\beta_1 = 0$ (no linear relationship); $H_A$: $\beta_1 \neq 0$.
b) The scatterplot fails the Straight Enough Condition. It shows a bend and it has an outlier. There is also some spreading from right to left, which would violate the Plot Thickens Condition. We cannot continue the analysis.
c) The conditions are not met; the regression equation should not be interpreted.

**43.** a) Data plot looks linear; no overt pattern in residuals; histogram of residuals roughly symmetric and unimodal.

b) $H_0$: No linear relationship between *Education* and *Mortality*, $\beta_1 = 0$. $H_A$: $\beta_1 \neq 0$. $t = -6.24$; P-value $< 0.001$. There is evidence that cities in which the mean education level is higher also tend to have a lower mortality rate.

c) No. Data are on cities, not individuals. Also, these are observational data. We cannot predict causal consequences from them.

d) $(-65.95, -33.89)$ deaths per 100,000 people.

e) *Mortality* decreases, on average, between 33.89 and 65.95 deaths per 100,000 for each year of average *Education,* based on the regression.

f) Based on the regression, the average *Mortality* for cities with an average of 12 years of *Education* will be between 874.239 and 914.196 deaths per 100,000 people.

**44.** a) Data plot looks linear; no obvious pattern in residuals; Normal plot of residuals is roughly linear.

b) $H_0$: No linear relationship between *Square Footage* and *Assessed Value*, $\beta_1 = 0$. $H_A$: Larger houses have higher assessed values, $\beta_1 > 0$. $t = 2.77$; P-value $= 0.0068$. With the very low P-value, we reject $H_0$. There is evidence that larger houses do have higher assessed values.

c) 32.5%

d) I am 90% confident that average *Assessed Value* increases between $4.58 and $19.22 for each square foot.

e) No. These are observational data, not an experiment. We cannot conclude anything about the consequences of changes. Also, the data are for one city and may not apply to other locations.

f) No. A 95% confidence interval for the assessed value of his 2100-square-foot house is from $45,619 to $78,572.

**45.** a) $\widehat{Jan} = 120.73 + 0.6995 \times Dec.$ (We are told this is an SRS. One cardholders' spending should not affect another's. These are quantitative data with no apparent bend in the scatterplot. The residual plot shows some increased spread for larger values of January charges. A histogram of residuals is unimodal and slightly skewed to the right with several high outliers.)

b) $1519.73

c) ($1330.24, $1709.24)

d) ($290.76, $669.76)

e) The residuals show increasing spread, so the confidence intervals may not be valid. I would be skeptical of interpreting them too literally.

**46.** a) $\widehat{Feb} = 164.37 + 0.7236 \times Jan.$ (We are told this is an SRS. One cardholders' spending should not affect another's. These are quantitative data with no apparent bend in the scatterplot. The residual plot shows some increased spread for larger values of January charges. A histogram of residuals is unimodal and slightly skewed to the right with several high outliers.)

b) $1611.57

c) ($1451.59, $1771.56)

d) ($228.44, $548.41)

e) The residuals show increasing spread, so the confidence intervals may not be valid. I would be skeptical of interpreting them too literally.

## PART VII REVIEW

**1.** $H_0$: The proportions are as specified by the ratio 1:3:3:9; $H_A$: The proportions are not as stated. $\chi^2 = 5.01$; df $= 3$; P-value $= 0.1711$. Since P $> 0.05$, we fail to reject $H_0$. These data do not provide evidence to indicate that the proportions are other than 1:3:3:9.

**2.** a) 59 products

b) 84.5%

c) (2.21, 2.78) dollars per minute

d) Based on this regression, average price increases between $2.21 and $2.78 for each minute of polishing time, with 95% confidence.

**3.** a) $H_0$: *Mortality* and *calcium concentration* in water are not linearly related, $\beta_1 = 0$; $H_A$: They are linearly related, $\beta_1 \neq 0$.

b) $t = -6.73$; P-value $< 0.0001$. There is a significant negative relationship between calcium in drinking water and mortality.

c) $(-4.19, -2.27)$ deaths per 100,000 for each ppm calcium.

d) Based on the regression, we are 95% confident that mortality (deaths per 100,000) decreases, on average, between 2.27 and 4.19 for each part per million of calcium in drinking water.

**4.** a) Based on these data, with 95% confidence 5-year yields are between 3.15 and 5.93% higher than 3-year yields, on average (paired data).

b) Yes (at least for this data set). The regression line is $\widehat{5\text{-}year} = 6.93 + 0.719\ \widehat{3\text{-}year}$. $H_0$: $\beta_1 = 0$ against $H_A$: $\beta_1 \neq 0$ has $t = 4.27$; P-value $= 0.0009$. Since P is so small, we reject $H_0$. There is evidence of an association. (But we don't know that this was an SRS or even a representative sample of large cap funds.)

**5.** 404 checks

**6.** a) (36.21, 60.51) feet.

b) Yes, 40 is in the interval.

c) Wider; we'd need to have a wider interval to be more confident.

d) Roughly 4 times as big—44 flights.

**7.** $H_0$: *Income* and *Party* are independent. $H_A$: *Income* and *Party* are not independent. $\chi^2 = 17.19$; P-value $= 0.0018$. With such a small P-value, we reject $H_0$. These data show evidence that income level and party are not independent. Examination of components shows Democrats are most likely to have low incomes; Independents are most likely to have middle incomes, and Republicans are most likely to have high incomes.

**8.** a) 38

b) Data plot looks linear; residuals plot shows random scatter; histogram of residuals approximately Normal.

c) (0.131, 0.177) foals per adult.

d) Based on this regression, we have 95% confidence that for every adult horse, an average of between 0.131 and 0.177 foals will be born.

e) A herd with 80 adult horses will have between 2.27 and 19.21 foals, with 90% confidence.

**9.** $H_0$: $p_L - p_R = 0$; $H_A$: $p_L - p_R \neq 0$. $z = 1.38$; P-value $= 0.1683$. Since P $> 0.05$, we do not reject $H_0$. These data do not provide evidence of a difference in musical abilities between right- and left-handed people.

**10.** a) Combining boys and girls, $\chi^2 = 42.80$; P-value $< 0.0001$. Reject $H_0$. These data show evidence that the distribution of scores at this school is significantly different from national results.

b) Pooling those with scores of 2 or 1, $\chi^2 = 5.59$, P-value $= 0.1336$. There is no significant difference in the distribution of scores for boys and girls.

**11.** a) $H_0$: $\mu_D = 0$; $H_A$: $\mu_D \neq 0$.
Boxplot of the differences indicates a strong outlier (1958). With the outlier kept in, the *t*-stat is 0, with a P-value of 1.00 (two sided). There is no evidence of a difference (on average) of actual and that predicted by Gallup. With the outlier taken out, the *t*-stat is still only $-0.8525$ with a P-value of 0.4106, so the conclusion is the same.

b) $H_0$: There is no (linear) relationship between predicted and actual number of Democratic seats won ($\beta_1 = 0$). $H_A$: There is a relationship ($\beta_1 \neq 0$). The relationship is very strong, with an $R^2$ of 97.7%. The *t*-stat is 22.56. Even with only 12 df, this is clearly significant (P-value $< 0.0001$). There is an outlying residual (1958), but without it, the regression is even stronger.

**12.** $\chi^2 = 6.14$; P-value $= 0.1887$. Since P $> 0.05$, we do not reject $H_0$. These data do not provide evidence of an association between duration of pregnancy and level of care.

**13.** $\chi^2 = 0.69$; P-value $= 0.9526$. Since P $> 0.05$, we do not reject $H_0$. These data provide no evidence to show that the way the hospital deals with twin pregnancies has changed.

**14.** $H_0: p_P - p_N = 0$; $H_A: p_P - p_N > 0$. $z = 1.96$; P-value = 0.0249. With such a small P-value, we reject $H_0$. These data provide moderately strong evidence to suggest that preemies are more likely than babies of normal weight to be of "subnormal height" as adults.

**15.** a) Based on these data, the average annual rainfall in LA is between 11.65 and 17.39 inches, with 90% confidence.
b) About 46 years
c) No. The regression equation is $\widehat{Rain} = -51.684 + 0.033 \times Year$. $R^2 = 0.1\%$. The $t$-stat for the slope is 0.12 with a P-value of 0.9029.

**16.** a) Independence—individuals classified on two variables.
b) $H_0$: No relationship between *Age* and *Party*; $H_A$: There is a relationship. $\chi^2 = 16.66$; P-value = 0.0106. With such a small P-value, we reject $H_0$. These data indicate a relationship between *Age* and *Party*.
c) There is a relationship between age and party: The "largest" standardized residual is for Republicans 18 to 29 ($-2.07$). The next-largest is for Independents in the same age group (1.79). These data indicate that young people are much more likely to be Independents than Republicans. We also see that the oldest group is more likely to be Democrat (1.57).

**17.** a) This is a linear regression that is meaningless—the data are categorical.
b) This is a two-way table that is appropriate. $H_0$: *Eye* and *Hair* color are independent. $H_A$: *Eye* and *Hair* color are not independent. However, four cells have expected counts less than 5, so the $\chi^2$ analysis is not valid unless cells are merged. However, with a $\chi^2$ value of 223.6 with 16 df and a P-value $< 0.0001$, the results are not likely to change if we merge appropriate eye colors.

**18.** a) $H_0$: There is no (linear) relationship between *Depression* and *Internet usage*. $\beta_1 = 0$. $H_A$: There is a linear relationship. $\beta_1 \neq 0$. $t = 2.76$; P-value = 0.0064. With such a small P-value, we reject $H_0$. These data provide strong evidence of a relationship between Internet use and depression.
b) The study says nothing about causality. Many other factors may be involved.
c) $H_0: \mu_D = 0$; $H_A: \mu_D \neq 0$. $t = -2.73$; P-value = 0.014. With such a small P-value, we reject $H_0$. These data indicate that mean depression level actually got better (decreased) during the study.

**19.** a) $H_0: p_Y - p_O = 0$; $H_A: p_Y - p_O \neq 0$. $z = 3.56$; P-value = 0.0004. With such a small P-value, we reject $H_0$. We conclude there is evidence of a difference in effectiveness; it appears the methods are not as good for older women.
b) $\chi^2 = 12.70$; P-value = 0.0004. Same conclusion.
c) The P-values are the same; $z^2 = (3.563944)^2 = 12.70 = \chi^2$.

**20.** $\chi^2 = 40.715$; P-value $< 0.0001$. These data do indicate an association between education and family planning. More educated women have fewer unplanned pregnancies.

**21.** a) Positive direction, generally linear trend; moderate scatter.
b) $H_0$: There is no linear relationship between *Interval* and *Duration*. $\beta_1 = 0$. $H_A$: There is a linear relationship, $\beta_1 \neq 0$.
c) Yes; histogram is unimodal and roughly symmetric; residuals plot shows random scatter.
d) $t = 27.1$; P-value $\leq 0.001$. With such a small P-value, we reject $H_0$. There is a significant positive linear relationship between duration and time to next eruption of Old Faithful.
e) Based on this regression, the average time to next eruption after a 2-minute eruption is between 53.24 and 56.12 minutes, with 95% confidence.
f) Based on this regression, we will have to wait between 63.23 and 87.57 minutes after a 4-minute eruption, with 95% confidence.

**22.** a) $H_0: \beta_1 = 0$; $H_A: \beta_1 \neq 0$. $t = 4.16$, P-value $< 0.0001$. These data show evidence of a positive relationship between number of meals eaten together and grades.
b) No. $R^2$ is small and $s = 0.66$ points. So we could predict only to within 1.32 grade points at best.

c) No. The slope is clearly not 0, but that doesn't mean the relationship is strong or the predictions are useful.

**23.** a) $t = 1.42$, P-value = 0.1574. Since $P > 0.05$, we do not reject $H_0$. The two groups did not differ in ability at the start of the study.
b) $t = 15.11$; P-value $< 0.0001$. The group taught using the accelerated Math program showed a significant improvement.
c) $t = 9.24$; P-value $< 0.0001$. The control group showed a significant improvement in test scores.
d) $t = 5.78$; P-value $< 0.0001$. The Accelerated Math group had significantly higher gains than the control group.

**24.** $H_0: p = 0.512$; $H_A: p < 0.512$. $z = -3.35$; P-value = 0.0004. With such a small P-value, we reject $H_0$. These data provide evidence that exposure to dioxin reduces the rate of male births.

**25.** a) The regression—he wanted to know about association.
b) There is a moderate relationship between cottage cheese and ice cream sales; for every million pounds of cottage cheese, 1.19 million pounds of ice cream are sold, on average.
c) Testing if the mean difference is 0 (matched $t$-test). Regression won't answer this question.
d) The company sells more cottage cheese than ice cream, on average.
e) part (a)—linear relationship; residuals have a Normal distribution; residuals are independent with equal variation about the line. (c)—Observations are independent; differences are approximately Normal; less than 10% of all possible months' data.
f) About 71.32 million pounds.
g) (0.09, 2.29)
h) From this regression, every million pounds of cottage cheese sold is associated with an increase in ice cream sales of between 0.09 and 2.29 million pounds.

**26.** $\chi^2 = 14.96$; P-value = 0.0006. With such a small P-value, we reject $H_0$. These data provide evidence that continued treatment with inflixamab is of value.

**27.** Based on these data, the average weight loss for the clinic is between 8.24 and 10.06 pounds, with 95% confidence. The clinic's claim is plausible.

**28.** a) Yes. Data plot is linear; residuals plot shows random scatter; histogram of residuals is roughly normal.
b) Yes; $t = 5.19$; P-value $\leq 0.0001$.
c) Weaker. Individuals are more variable than averages.
d) Based on this regression, every extra year of median education in a city is associated with an increase of between $1500.48 and $3389.10 in median income.
e) Based on the regression, median income for cities where residents spent an average of 11 years in school is between $32,198.81 and $33,526.67, with 90% confidence.

**29.** $\chi^2 = 8.23$; P-value = 0.0414. There is evidence of an association between *cracker type* and *bloating*. Standardized residuals for the gum cracker are $-1.32$ and 1.58. Prospects for marketing this cracker are not good.

**30.** a) $H_0: \mu_1 - \mu_2 = 0$; $H_A: \mu_1 - \mu_2 > 0$. $t = 0.98$; P-value = 0.1864. Since $P > 0.05$, we do not reject $H_0$. Weeklong study scores were not significantly higher.
b) $H_0: p_1 - p_2 = 0$; $H_A: p_1 - p_2 \neq 0$. $z = -3.10$, P-value = 0.0019. With such a small P-value, we reject $H_0$. There is evidence of a difference in proportion for passing on Friday; it appears that cramming may be more effective.
c) $H_0: \mu_D = 0$; $H_A: \mu_D > 0$. $t = 5.17$, P-value $< 0.0001$. These data show evidence that learning does not last for 3 days because mean score declined.
d) Based on these data, the average number of words forgotten by crammers is between 3.03 and 7.05, with 95% confidence.
e) Yes. Regression equation is $\widehat{Monday} = 14.6 + 0.536 \times Friday$. $t = 2.57$; P-value = 0.0170

Page 2 ©AP/Wideworld **Page 3** ©United Features Syndicate **Page 7** ©Dorling Kindersley **Page 8** ©AP/Wideworld **Page 10** ©Photoyear (RF) **Page 14** ©Eric Gaillard/Reuters/Corbis **Page 20** ©PhotoFest **Page 21** ©The Florence Nightingale Museum **Page 25** ©AP/Wideworld **Page 31** ©Stone/Getty Images **Page 48** ©Getty Images **Page 54** ©Corbis Sygma **Page 55** ©MGM/PhotoFest **Page 60** ©Digital Vision **Page 88** ©PhotoDisc **Page 97** Courtesy of Beth Anderson **Page 114** ©Francois-Xavier Marit/AFP/Getty Images **Page 121** ©Jeff Haynes/ AFP/Getty Images **Page 123** ©Pete Saloutos/Corbis **Page 166** Courtesy of National Oceanic and Atmospheric Administration **Page 169** ©Corbis **Page 181** ©AP Wideworld Photos **Page 194** ©Landov Photo **Page 199** ©Digital Vision **Page 202** ©Bettmann/Corbis **Page 227** Courtesy of the authors **Page 230** ©Universal Press Syndicate **Page 232 (Ralph Nader)** ©Getty Images **Page 232 (Pat Buchanan)** ©AP/Wideworld Photo **Page 236** ©PhotoDisc **Page 244** ©PhotoDisc **Page 252** ©Getty Images **Page 289** ©PhotoDisc **Page 290** ©United Feature Syndicate, Inc. **Page 291 (Tiger Woods)** ©Getty Images **Page 291 (Serena Williams)** ©Reuters/Corbis **Page 291 (David Beckham)** ©Getty Sports **Page 303** ©Digital Vision **Page 304 (George Gallup)** ©AP Wideworld Photos **Page 312** ©FoodPix/Jupiter Images **Page 315** ©Universal Press Syndicate **Page 317** ©Creators Syndicate **Page 329** Courtesy of Beth Anderson **Page 330** ©iStockphoto **Page 333** ©United Feature Syndicate, Inc. **Page 335** ©Dorling Kindersley **Page 334** ©Digital Vision **Page 341** By permission of John L. Hart FLP and Creators Syndicate, Inc. **Page 343** ©iStockphoto **Page 345** ©Shutterstock **Page 364** ©Shutterstock **Page 368** ©PhotoEdit **Page 369** ©PhotoDisc Red **Page 383** ©Getty News & Sport **Page 384 (colored glass)** ©Corbis Royalty Free **Page 384 (dollar bills)** Courtesy of the US Department of Treasury **Page 401** ©St. Andrew's University History of Mathematics Archive **Page 402** ©St. Andrew's University History of Mathematics Archive **Page 409** ©Digital Vision **Page 419** ©University of Texas **Page 421** ©PhotoDisc **Page 432 (conveyor belt of jacks)** ©Stephen Mallon/Imagebank/Getty Images **Page 432 (Tiger Woods)** ©Getty Images **Page 433 (Bernoulli)** ©St. Andrew's University History of Mathematics Archive **Page 433 (Calvin and Hobbes)** ©Universal Press Syndicate **Page 439** ©PhotoDisc **Page 441** ©The Kobal Collection **Page 443** ©Hulton-Deutsch Collection/Corbis **Page 455** Courtesy of Richard De Veaux **Page 458** ©Columbia/Photofest **Page 460** ©St. Andrew's University MacTutor Archive **Page 486** ©PhotoDisc **Page 491** ©Universal Press Syndicate **Page 508** ©Adam Woolfitt/Corbis **Page 531** ©Getty Royalty Free **Page 538** ©University of York Department of Mathematics **Page 542** Courtesy of the Massachusetts Governor's Highway Safety Bureau **Page 557** ©Digital Vision **Page 558** ©The Kobal Collection **Page 564** ©PhotoDisc **Page 586** ©Digital Vision **Page 589** ©University of York Department of Mathematics **Page 616** ©Corbis Royalty Free **Page 629** ©PhotoDisc, Corbis Royalty Free and Beth Anderson **Page 630** ©PhotoDisc **Page 642** Courtesy of Beth Anderson **Page 650** ©Getty Editorial **Page 669** ©Dorling Kindersley **Page 686** ©Royalty-Free/Corbis **Page 694** ©PhotoDisc **Page 696** ©PhotoDisc **Page 701** ©PhotoDisc **Page 720** ©Stone/Getty Images **Page 724** ©PhotoDisc **Page 733** ©Nenana Ice Classic **Page 28-1 (on DVD)** ©PhotoDisc **Page 28-20 (on DVD)** ©St. Andrew's University MacTutor Archive **Page 29-1 (on DVD)** ©PhotoDisc

# Index

*Note:* Page numbers in **boldface** indicate chapter-level topics; FE indicates For Example references.

# Tables and Selected Formulas

| Row | | | | | TABLE OF RANDOM DIGITS | | | | | |
|---|---|---|---|---|---|---|---|---|---|---|
| 1 | 96299 | 07196 | 98642 | 20639 | 23185 | 56282 | 69929 | 14125 | 38872 | 94168 |
| 2 | 71622 | 35940 | 81807 | 59225 | 18192 | 08710 | 80777 | 84395 | 69563 | 86280 |
| 3 | 03272 | 41230 | 81739 | 74797 | 70406 | 18564 | 69273 | 72532 | 78340 | 36699 |
| 4 | 46376 | 58596 | 14365 | 63685 | 56555 | 42974 | 72944 | 96463 | 63533 | 24152 |
| 5 | 47352 | 42853 | 42903 | 97504 | 56655 | 70355 | 88606 | 61406 | 38757 | 70657 |
| 6 | 20064 | 04266 | 74017 | 79319 | 70170 | 96572 | 08523 | 56025 | 89077 | 57678 |
| 7 | 73184 | 95907 | 05179 | 51002 | 83374 | 52297 | 07769 | 99792 | 78365 | 93487 |
| 8 | 72753 | 36216 | 07230 | 35793 | 71907 | 65571 | 66784 | 25548 | 91861 | 15725 |
| 9 | 03939 | 30763 | 06138 | 80062 | 02537 | 23561 | 93136 | 61260 | 77935 | 93159 |
| 10 | 75998 | 37203 | 07959 | 38264 | 78120 | 77525 | 86481 | 54986 | 33042 | 70648 |
| 11 | 94435 | 97441 | 90998 | 25104 | 49761 | 14967 | 70724 | 67030 | 53887 | 81293 |
| 12 | 04362 | 40989 | 69167 | 38894 | 00172 | 02999 | 97377 | 33305 | 60782 | 29810 |
| 13 | 89059 | 43528 | 10547 | 40115 | 82234 | 86902 | 04121 | 83889 | 76208 | 31076 |
| 14 | 87736 | 04666 | 75145 | 49175 | 76754 | 07884 | 92564 | 80793 | 22573 | 67902 |
| 15 | 76488 | 88899 | 15860 | 07370 | 13431 | 84041 | 69202 | 18912 | 83173 | 11983 |
| 16 | 36460 | 53772 | 66634 | 25045 | 79007 | 78518 | 73580 | 14191 | 50353 | 32064 |
| 17 | 13205 | 69237 | 21820 | 20952 | 16635 | 58867 | 97650 | 82983 | 64865 | 93298 |
| 18 | 51242 | 12215 | 90739 | 36812 | 00436 | 31609 | 80333 | 96606 | 30430 | 31803 |
| 19 | 67819 | 00354 | 91439 | 91073 | 49258 | 15992 | 41277 | 75111 | 67496 | 68430 |
| 20 | 09875 | 08990 | 27656 | 15871 | 23637 | 00952 | 97818 | 64234 | 50199 | 05715 |
| 21 | 18192 | 95308 | 72975 | 01191 | 29958 | 09275 | 89141 | 19558 | 50524 | 32041 |
| 22 | 02763 | 33701 | 66188 | 50226 | 35813 | 72951 | 11638 | 01876 | 93664 | 37001 |
| 23 | 13349 | 46328 | 01856 | 29935 | 80563 | 03742 | 49470 | 67749 | 08578 | 21956 |
| 24 | 69238 | 92878 | 80067 | 80807 | 45096 | 22936 | 64325 | 19265 | 37755 | 69794 |
| 25 | 92207 | 63527 | 59398 | 29818 | 24789 | 94309 | 88380 | 57000 | 50171 | 17891 |
| 26 | 66679 | 99100 | 37072 | 30593 | 29665 | 84286 | 44458 | 60180 | 81451 | 58273 |
| 27 | 31087 | 42430 | 60322 | 34765 | 15757 | 53300 | 97392 | 98035 | 05228 | 68970 |
| 28 | 84432 | 04916 | 52949 | 78533 | 31666 | 62350 | 20584 | 56367 | 19701 | 60584 |
| 29 | 72042 | 12287 | 21081 | 48426 | 44321 | 58765 | 41760 | 43304 | 13399 | 02043 |
| 30 | 94534 | 73559 | 82135 | 70260 | 87936 | 85162 | 11937 | 18263 | 54138 | 69564 |
| 31 | 63971 | 97198 | 40974 | 45301 | 60177 | 35604 | 21580 | 68107 | 25184 | 42810 |
| 32 | 11227 | 58474 | 17272 | 37619 | 69517 | 62964 | 67962 | 34510 | 12607 | 52255 |
| 33 | 28541 | 02029 | 08068 | 96656 | 17795 | 21484 | 57722 | 76511 | 27849 | 61738 |
| 34 | 11282 | 43632 | 49531 | 78981 | 81980 | 08530 | 08629 | 32279 | 29478 | 50228 |
| 35 | 42907 | 15137 | 21918 | 13248 | 39129 | 49559 | 94540 | 24070 | 88151 | 36782 |
| 36 | 47119 | 76651 | 21732 | 32364 | 58545 | 50277 | 57558 | 30390 | 18771 | 72703 |
| 37 | 11232 | 99884 | 05087 | 76839 | 65142 | 19994 | 91397 | 29350 | 83852 | 04905 |
| 38 | 64725 | 06719 | 86262 | 53356 | 57999 | 50193 | 79936 | 97230 | 52073 | 94467 |
| 39 | 77007 | 26962 | 55466 | 12521 | 48125 | 12280 | 54985 | 26239 | 76044 | 54398 |
| 40 | 18375 | 19310 | 59796 | 89832 | 59417 | 18553 | 17238 | 05474 | 33259 | 50595 |

| Table Z | | Second decimal place in $z$ | | | | | | | | | |
|---|---|---|---|---|---|---|---|---|---|---|---|
| Areas under the standard Normal curve | 0.09 | 0.08 | 0.07 | 0.06 | 0.05 | 0.04 | 0.03 | 0.02 | 0.01 | 0.00 | $z$ |
| | | | | | | | | | | 0.0000[†] | −3.9 |
| | 0.0001 | 0.0001 | 0.0001 | 0.0001 | 0.0001 | 0.0001 | 0.0001 | 0.0001 | 0.0001 | 0.0001 | −3.8 |
| | 0.0001 | 0.0001 | 0.0001 | 0.0001 | 0.0001 | 0.0001 | 0.0001 | 0.0001 | 0.0001 | 0.0001 | −3.7 |
| | 0.0001 | 0.0001 | 0.0001 | 0.0001 | 0.0001 | 0.0001 | 0.0001 | 0.0001 | 0.0002 | 0.0002 | −3.6 |
| | 0.0002 | 0.0002 | 0.0002 | 0.0002 | 0.0002 | 0.0002 | 0.0002 | 0.0002 | 0.0002 | 0.0002 | −3.5 |
| | 0.0002 | 0.0003 | 0.0003 | 0.0003 | 0.0003 | 0.0003 | 0.0003 | 0.0003 | 0.0003 | 0.0003 | −3.4 |
| | 0.0003 | 0.0004 | 0.0004 | 0.0004 | 0.0004 | 0.0004 | 0.0004 | 0.0005 | 0.0005 | 0.0005 | −3.3 |
| | 0.0005 | 0.0005 | 0.0005 | 0.0006 | 0.0006 | 0.0006 | 0.0006 | 0.0006 | 0.0007 | 0.0007 | −3.2 |
| | 0.0007 | 0.0007 | 0.0008 | 0.0008 | 0.0008 | 0.0008 | 0.0009 | 0.0009 | 0.0009 | 0.0010 | −3.1 |
| | 0.0010 | 0.0010 | 0.0011 | 0.0011 | 0.0011 | 0.0012 | 0.0012 | 0.0013 | 0.0013 | 0.0013 | −3.0 |
| | 0.0014 | 0.0014 | 0.0015 | 0.0015 | 0.0016 | 0.0016 | 0.0017 | 0.0018 | 0.0018 | 0.0019 | −2.9 |
| | 0.0019 | 0.0020 | 0.0021 | 0.0021 | 0.0022 | 0.0023 | 0.0023 | 0.0024 | 0.0025 | 0.0026 | −2.8 |
| | 0.0026 | 0.0027 | 0.0028 | 0.0029 | 0.0030 | 0.0031 | 0.0032 | 0.0033 | 0.0034 | 0.0035 | −2.7 |
| | 0.0036 | 0.0037 | 0.0038 | 0.0039 | 0.0040 | 0.0041 | 0.0043 | 0.0044 | 0.0045 | 0.0047 | −2.6 |
| | 0.0048 | 0.0049 | 0.0051 | 0.0052 | 0.0054 | 0.0055 | 0.0057 | 0.0059 | 0.0060 | 0.0062 | −2.5 |
| | 0.0064 | 0.0066 | 0.0068 | 0.0069 | 0.0071 | 0.0073 | 0.0075 | 0.0078 | 0.0080 | 0.0082 | −2.4 |
| | 0.0084 | 0.0087 | 0.0089 | 0.0091 | 0.0094 | 0.0096 | 0.0099 | 0.0102 | 0.0104 | 0.0107 | −2.3 |
| | 0.0110 | 0.0113 | 0.0116 | 0.0119 | 0.0122 | 0.0125 | 0.0129 | 0.0132 | 0.0136 | 0.0139 | −2.2 |
| | 0.0143 | 0.0146 | 0.0150 | 0.0154 | 0.0158 | 0.0162 | 0.0166 | 0.0170 | 0.0174 | 0.0179 | −2.1 |
| | 0.0183 | 0.0188 | 0.0192 | 0.0197 | 0.0202 | 0.0207 | 0.0212 | 0.0217 | 0.0222 | 0.0228 | −2.0 |
| | 0.0233 | 0.0239 | 0.0244 | 0.0250 | 0.0256 | 0.0262 | 0.0268 | 0.0274 | 0.0281 | 0.0287 | −1.9 |
| | 0.0294 | 0.0301 | 0.0307 | 0.0314 | 0.0322 | 0.0329 | 0.0336 | 0.0344 | 0.0351 | 0.0359 | −1.8 |
| | 0.0367 | 0.0375 | 0.0384 | 0.0392 | 0.0401 | 0.0409 | 0.0418 | 0.0427 | 0.0436 | 0.0446 | −1.7 |
| | 0.0455 | 0.0465 | 0.0475 | 0.0485 | 0.0495 | 0.0505 | 0.0516 | 0.0526 | 0.0537 | 0.0548 | −1.6 |
| | 0.0559 | 0.0571 | 0.0582 | 0.0594 | 0.0606 | 0.0618 | 0.0630 | 0.0643 | 0.0655 | 0.0668 | −1.5 |
| | 0.0681 | 0.0694 | 0.0708 | 0.0721 | 0.0735 | 0.0749 | 0.0764 | 0.0778 | 0.0793 | 0.0808 | −1.4 |
| | 0.0823 | 0.0838 | 0.0853 | 0.0869 | 0.0885 | 0.0901 | 0.0918 | 0.0934 | 0.0951 | 0.0968 | −1.3 |
| | 0.0985 | 0.1003 | 0.1020 | 0.1038 | 0.1056 | 0.1075 | 0.1093 | 0.1112 | 0.1131 | 0.1151 | −1.2 |
| | 0.1170 | 0.1190 | 0.1210 | 0.1230 | 0.1251 | 0.1271 | 0.1292 | 0.1314 | 0.1335 | 0.1357 | −1.1 |
| | 0.1379 | 0.1401 | 0.1423 | 0.1446 | 0.1469 | 0.1492 | 0.1515 | 0.1539 | 0.1562 | 0.1587 | −1.0 |
| | 0.1611 | 0.1635 | 0.1660 | 0.1685 | 0.1711 | 0.1736 | 0.1762 | 0.1788 | 0.1814 | 0.1841 | −0.9 |
| | 0.1867 | 0.1894 | 0.1922 | 0.1949 | 0.1977 | 0.2005 | 0.2033 | 0.2061 | 0.2090 | 0.2119 | −0.8 |
| | 0.2148 | 0.2177 | 0.2206 | 0.2236 | 0.2266 | 0.2296 | 0.2327 | 0.2358 | 0.2389 | 0.2420 | −0.7 |
| | 0.2451 | 0.2483 | 0.2514 | 0.2546 | 0.2578 | 0.2611 | 0.2643 | 0.2676 | 0.2709 | 0.2743 | −0.6 |
| | 0.2776 | 0.2810 | 0.2843 | 0.2877 | 0.2912 | 0.2946 | 0.2981 | 0.3015 | 0.3050 | 0.3085 | −0.5 |
| | 0.3121 | 0.3156 | 0.3192 | 0.3228 | 0.3264 | 0.3300 | 0.3336 | 0.3372 | 0.3409 | 0.3446 | −0.4 |
| | 0.3483 | 0.3520 | 0.3557 | 0.3594 | 0.3632 | 0.3669 | 0.3707 | 0.3745 | 0.3783 | 0.3821 | −0.3 |
| | 0.3859 | 0.3897 | 0.3936 | 0.3974 | 0.4013 | 0.4052 | 0.4090 | 0.4129 | 0.4168 | 0.4207 | −0.2 |
| | 0.4247 | 0.4286 | 0.4325 | 0.4364 | 0.4404 | 0.4443 | 0.4483 | 0.4522 | 0.4562 | 0.4602 | −0.1 |
| | 0.4641 | 0.4681 | 0.4721 | 0.4761 | 0.4801 | 0.4840 | 0.4880 | 0.4920 | 0.4960 | 0.5000 | −0.0 |

[†]For $z \le -3.90$, the areas are 0.0000 to four decimal places.

**Table Z (cont.)**

Areas under the standard Normal curve

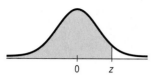

| | Second decimal place in $z$ | | | | | | | | | |
|---|---|---|---|---|---|---|---|---|---|---|
| $z$ | 0.00 | 0.01 | 0.02 | 0.03 | 0.04 | 0.05 | 0.06 | 0.07 | 0.08 | 0.09 |
| 0.0 | 0.5000 | 0.5040 | 0.5080 | 0.5120 | 0.5160 | 0.5199 | 0.5239 | 0.5279 | 0.5319 | 0.5359 |
| 0.1 | 0.5398 | 0.5438 | 0.5478 | 0.5517 | 0.5557 | 0.5596 | 0.5636 | 0.5675 | 0.5714 | 0.5753 |
| 0.2 | 0.5793 | 0.5832 | 0.5871 | 0.5910 | 0.5948 | 0.5987 | 0.6026 | 0.6064 | 0.6103 | 0.6141 |
| 0.3 | 0.6179 | 0.6217 | 0.6255 | 0.6293 | 0.6331 | 0.6368 | 0.6406 | 0.6443 | 0.6480 | 0.6517 |
| 0.4 | 0.6554 | 0.6591 | 0.6628 | 0.6664 | 0.6700 | 0.6736 | 0.6772 | 0.6808 | 0.6844 | 0.6879 |
| 0.5 | 0.6915 | 0.6950 | 0.6985 | 0.7019 | 0.7054 | 0.7088 | 0.7123 | 0.7157 | 0.7190 | 0.7224 |
| 0.6 | 0.7257 | 0.7291 | 0.7324 | 0.7357 | 0.7389 | 0.7422 | 0.7454 | 0.7486 | 0.7517 | 0.7549 |
| 0.7 | 0.7580 | 0.7611 | 0.7642 | 0.7673 | 0.7704 | 0.7734 | 0.7764 | 0.7794 | 0.7823 | 0.7852 |
| 0.8 | 0.7881 | 0.7910 | 0.7939 | 0.7967 | 0.7995 | 0.8023 | 0.8051 | 0.8078 | 0.8106 | 0.8133 |
| 0.9 | 0.8159 | 0.8186 | 0.8212 | 0.8238 | 0.8264 | 0.8289 | 0.8315 | 0.8340 | 0.8365 | 0.8389 |
| 1.0 | 0.8413 | 0.8438 | 0.8461 | 0.8485 | 0.8508 | 0.8531 | 0.8554 | 0.8577 | 0.8599 | 0.8621 |
| 1.1 | 0.8643 | 0.8665 | 0.8686 | 0.8708 | 0.8729 | 0.8749 | 0.8770 | 0.8790 | 0.8810 | 0.8830 |
| 1.2 | 0.8849 | 0.8869 | 0.8888 | 0.8907 | 0.8925 | 0.8944 | 0.8962 | 0.8980 | 0.8997 | 0.9015 |
| 1.3 | 0.9032 | 0.9049 | 0.9066 | 0.9082 | 0.9099 | 0.9115 | 0.9131 | 0.9147 | 0.9162 | 0.9177 |
| 1.4 | 0.9192 | 0.9207 | 0.9222 | 0.9236 | 0.9251 | 0.9265 | 0.9279 | 0.9292 | 0.9306 | 0.9319 |
| 1.5 | 0.9332 | 0.9345 | 0.9357 | 0.9370 | 0.9382 | 0.9394 | 0.9406 | 0.9418 | 0.9429 | 0.9441 |
| 1.6 | 0.9452 | 0.9463 | 0.9474 | 0.9484 | 0.9495 | 0.9505 | 0.9515 | 0.9525 | 0.9535 | 0.9545 |
| 1.7 | 0.9554 | 0.9564 | 0.9573 | 0.9582 | 0.9591 | 0.9599 | 0.9608 | 0.9616 | 0.9625 | 0.9633 |
| 1.8 | 0.9641 | 0.9649 | 0.9656 | 0.9664 | 0.9671 | 0.9678 | 0.9686 | 0.9693 | 0.9699 | 0.9706 |
| 1.9 | 0.9713 | 0.9719 | 0.9726 | 0.9732 | 0.9738 | 0.9744 | 0.9750 | 0.9756 | 0.9761 | 0.9767 |
| 2.0 | 0.9772 | 0.9778 | 0.9783 | 0.9788 | 0.9793 | 0.9798 | 0.9803 | 0.9808 | 0.9812 | 0.9817 |
| 2.1 | 0.9821 | 0.9826 | 0.9830 | 0.9834 | 0.9838 | 0.9842 | 0.9846 | 0.9850 | 0.9854 | 0.9857 |
| 2.2 | 0.9861 | 0.9864 | 0.9868 | 0.9871 | 0.9875 | 0.9878 | 0.9881 | 0.9884 | 0.9887 | 0.9890 |
| 2.3 | 0.9893 | 0.9896 | 0.9898 | 0.9901 | 0.9904 | 0.9906 | 0.9909 | 0.9911 | 0.9913 | 0.9916 |
| 2.4 | 0.9918 | 0.9920 | 0.9922 | 0.9925 | 0.9927 | 0.9929 | 0.9931 | 0.9932 | 0.9934 | 0.9936 |
| 2.5 | 0.9938 | 0.9940 | 0.9941 | 0.9943 | 0.9945 | 0.9946 | 0.9948 | 0.9949 | 0.9951 | 0.9952 |
| 2.6 | 0.9953 | 0.9955 | 0.9956 | 0.9957 | 0.9959 | 0.9960 | 0.9961 | 0.9962 | 0.9963 | 0.9964 |
| 2.7 | 0.9965 | 0.9966 | 0.9967 | 0.9968 | 0.9969 | 0.9970 | 0.9971 | 0.9972 | 0.9973 | 0.9974 |
| 2.8 | 0.9974 | 0.9975 | 0.9976 | 0.9977 | 0.9977 | 0.9978 | 0.9979 | 0.9979 | 0.9980 | 0.9981 |
| 2.9 | 0.9981 | 0.9982 | 0.9982 | 0.9983 | 0.9984 | 0.9984 | 0.9985 | 0.9985 | 0.9986 | 0.9986 |
| 3.0 | 0.9987 | 0.9987 | 0.9987 | 0.9988 | 0.9988 | 0.9989 | 0.9989 | 0.9989 | 0.9990 | 0.9990 |
| 3.1 | 0.9990 | 0.9991 | 0.9991 | 0.9991 | 0.9992 | 0.9992 | 0.9992 | 0.9992 | 0.9993 | 0.9993 |
| 3.2 | 0.9993 | 0.9993 | 0.9994 | 0.9994 | 0.9994 | 0.9994 | 0.9994 | 0.9995 | 0.9995 | 0.9995 |
| 3.3 | 0.9995 | 0.9995 | 0.9995 | 0.9996 | 0.9996 | 0.9996 | 0.9996 | 0.9996 | 0.9996 | 0.9997 |
| 3.4 | 0.9997 | 0.9997 | 0.9997 | 0.9997 | 0.9997 | 0.9997 | 0.9997 | 0.9997 | 0.9997 | 0.9998 |
| 3.5 | 0.9998 | 0.9998 | 0.9998 | 0.9998 | 0.9998 | 0.9998 | 0.9998 | 0.9998 | 0.9998 | 0.9998 |
| 3.6 | 0.9998 | 0.9998 | 0.9999 | 0.9999 | 0.9999 | 0.9999 | 0.9999 | 0.9999 | 0.9999 | 0.9999 |
| 3.7 | 0.9999 | 0.9999 | 0.9999 | 0.9999 | 0.9999 | 0.9999 | 0.9999 | 0.9999 | 0.9999 | 0.9999 |
| 3.8 | 0.9999 | 0.9999 | 0.9999 | 0.9999 | 0.9999 | 0.9999 | 0.9999 | 0.9999 | 0.9999 | 0.9999 |
| 3.9 | 1.0000[†] | | | | | | | | | |

[†]For $z \geq 3.90$, the areas are 1.0000 to four decimal places.

| Two-tail probability | 0.20 | 0.10 | 0.05 | 0.02 | 0.01 | |
| One-tail probability | 0.10 | 0.05 | 0.025 | 0.01 | 0.005 | |
| **Table T** df | | | | | | df |
| Values of $t_\alpha$   1 | 3.078 | 6.314 | 12.706 | 31.821 | 63.657 | 1 |
| 2 | 1.886 | 2.920 | 4.303 | 6.965 | 9.925 | 2 |
| 3 | 1.638 | 2.353 | 3.182 | 4.541 | 5.841 | 3 |
| 4 | 1.533 | 2.132 | 2.776 | 3.747 | 4.604 | 4 |
| 5 | 1.476 | 2.015 | 2.571 | 3.365 | 4.032 | 5 |
| 6 | 1.440 | 1.943 | 2.447 | 3.143 | 3.707 | 6 |
| 7 | 1.415 | 1.895 | 2.365 | 2.998 | 3.499 | 7 |
| 8 | 1.397 | 1.860 | 2.306 | 2.896 | 3.355 | 8 |
| 9 | 1.383 | 1.833 | 2.262 | 2.821 | 3.250 | 9 |
| 10 | 1.372 | 1.812 | 2.228 | 2.764 | 3.169 | 10 |
| 11 | 1.363 | 1.796 | 2.201 | 2.718 | 3.106 | 11 |
| 12 | 1.356 | 1.782 | 2.179 | 2.681 | 3.055 | 12 |
| 13 | 1.350 | 1.771 | 2.160 | 2.650 | 3.012 | 13 |
| 14 | 1.345 | 1.761 | 2.145 | 2.624 | 2.977 | 14 |
| 15 | 1.341 | 1.753 | 2.131 | 2.602 | 2.947 | 15 |
| 16 | 1.337 | 1.746 | 2.120 | 2.583 | 2.921 | 16 |
| 17 | 1.333 | 1.740 | 2.110 | 2.567 | 2.898 | 17 |
| 18 | 1.330 | 1.734 | 2.101 | 2.552 | 2.878 | 18 |
| 19 | 1.328 | 1.729 | 2.093 | 2.539 | 2.861 | 19 |
| 20 | 1.325 | 1.725 | 2.086 | 2.528 | 2.845 | 20 |
| 21 | 1.323 | 1.721 | 2.080 | 2.518 | 2.831 | 21 |
| 22 | 1.321 | 1.717 | 2.074 | 2.508 | 2.819 | 22 |
| 23 | 1.319 | 1.714 | 2.069 | 2.500 | 2.807 | 23 |
| 24 | 1.318 | 1.711 | 2.064 | 2.492 | 2.797 | 24 |
| 25 | 1.316 | 1.708 | 2.060 | 2.485 | 2.787 | 25 |
| 26 | 1.315 | 1.706 | 2.056 | 2.479 | 2.779 | 26 |
| 27 | 1.314 | 1.703 | 2.052 | 2.473 | 2.771 | 27 |
| 28 | 1.313 | 1.701 | 2.048 | 2.467 | 2.763 | 28 |
| 29 | 1.311 | 1.699 | 2.045 | 2.462 | 2.756 | 29 |
| 30 | 1.310 | 1.697 | 2.042 | 2.457 | 2.750 | 30 |
| 32 | 1.309 | 1.694 | 2.037 | 2.449 | 2.738 | 32 |
| 35 | 1.306 | 1.690 | 2.030 | 2.438 | 2.725 | 35 |
| 40 | 1.303 | 1.684 | 2.021 | 2.423 | 2.704 | 40 |
| 45 | 1.301 | 1.679 | 2.014 | 2.412 | 2.690 | 45 |
| 50 | 1.299 | 1.676 | 2.009 | 2.403 | 2.678 | 50 |
| 60 | 1.296 | 1.671 | 2.000 | 2.390 | 2.660 | 60 |
| 75 | 1.293 | 1.665 | 1.992 | 2.377 | 2.643 | 75 |
| 100 | 1.290 | 1.660 | 1.984 | 2.364 | 2.626 | 100 |
| 120 | 1.289 | 1.658 | 1.980 | 2.358 | 2.617 | 120 |
| 140 | 1.288 | 1.656 | 1.977 | 2.353 | 2.611 | 140 |
| 180 | 1.286 | 1.653 | 1.973 | 2.347 | 2.603 | 180 |
| 250 | 1.285 | 1.651 | 1.969 | 2.341 | 2.596 | 250 |
| 400 | 1.284 | 1.649 | 1.966 | 2.336 | 2.588 | 400 |
| 1000 | 1.282 | 1.646 | 1.962 | 2.330 | 2.581 | 1000 |
| $\infty$ | 1.282 | 1.645 | 1.960 | 2.326 | 2.576 | $\infty$ |
| **Confidence levels** | 80% | 90% | 95% | 98% | 99% | |

Two tails

One tail

| Right-tail probability | | 0.10 | 0.05 | 0.025 | 0.01 | 0.005 |
|---|---|---|---|---|---|---|
| **Table X** | df | | | | | |
| Values of $\chi_\alpha^2$ | 1 | 2.706 | 3.841 | 5.024 | 6.635 | 7.879 |
| | 2 | 4.605 | 5.991 | 7.378 | 9.210 | 10.597 |
| | 3 | 6.251 | 7.815 | 9.348 | 11.345 | 12.838 |
| | 4 | 7.779 | 9.488 | 11.143 | 13.277 | 14.860 |
| | 5 | 9.236 | 11.070 | 12.833 | 15.086 | 16.750 |
| | 6 | 10.645 | 12.592 | 14.449 | 16.812 | 18.548 |
| | 7 | 12.017 | 14.067 | 16.013 | 18.475 | 20.278 |
| | 8 | 13.362 | 15.507 | 17.535 | 20.090 | 21.955 |
| | 9 | 14.684 | 16.919 | 19.023 | 21.666 | 23.589 |
| | 10 | 15.987 | 18.307 | 20.483 | 23.209 | 25.188 |
| | 11 | 17.275 | 19.675 | 21.920 | 24.725 | 26.757 |
| | 12 | 18.549 | 21.026 | 23.337 | 26.217 | 28.300 |
| | 13 | 19.812 | 22.362 | 24.736 | 27.688 | 29.819 |
| | 14 | 21.064 | 23.685 | 26.119 | 29.141 | 31.319 |
| | 15 | 22.307 | 24.996 | 27.488 | 30.578 | 32.801 |
| | 16 | 23.542 | 26.296 | 28.845 | 32.000 | 34.267 |
| | 17 | 24.769 | 27.587 | 30.191 | 33.409 | 35.718 |
| | 18 | 25.989 | 28.869 | 31.526 | 34.805 | 37.156 |
| | 19 | 27.204 | 30.143 | 32.852 | 36.191 | 38.582 |
| | 20 | 28.412 | 31.410 | 34.170 | 37.566 | 39.997 |
| | 21 | 29.615 | 32.671 | 35.479 | 38.932 | 41.401 |
| | 22 | 30.813 | 33.924 | 36.781 | 40.290 | 42.796 |
| | 23 | 32.007 | 35.172 | 38.076 | 41.638 | 44.181 |
| | 24 | 33.196 | 36.415 | 39.364 | 42.980 | 45.559 |
| | 25 | 34.382 | 37.653 | 40.647 | 44.314 | 46.928 |
| | 26 | 35.563 | 38.885 | 41.923 | 45.642 | 48.290 |
| | 27 | 36.741 | 40.113 | 43.195 | 46.963 | 49.645 |
| | 28 | 37.916 | 41.337 | 44.461 | 48.278 | 50.994 |
| | 29 | 39.087 | 42.557 | 45.722 | 59.588 | 52.336 |
| | 30 | 40.256 | 43.773 | 46.979 | 50.892 | 53.672 |
| | 40 | 51.805 | 55.759 | 59.342 | 63.691 | 66.767 |
| | 50 | 63.167 | 67.505 | 71.420 | 76.154 | 79.490 |
| | 60 | 74.397 | 79.082 | 83.298 | 88.381 | 91.955 |
| | 70 | 85.527 | 90.531 | 95.023 | 100.424 | 104.213 |
| | 80 | 96.578 | 101.879 | 106.628 | 112.328 | 116.320 |
| | 90 | 107.565 | 113.145 | 118.135 | 124.115 | 128.296 |
| | 100 | 118.499 | 124.343 | 129.563 | 135.811 | 140.177 |

# Selected Formulas

$Range = Max - Min$

$IQR = Q3 - Q1$

Outlier Rule-of-Thumb: $y < Q1 - 1.5 \times IQR$ or $y > Q3 + 1.5 \times IQR$

$$\bar{y} = \frac{\sum y}{n}$$

$$s = \sqrt{\frac{\sum (y - \bar{y})^2}{n - 1}}$$

$$z = \frac{y - \mu}{\sigma} \text{ (model based)}$$

$$z = \frac{y - \bar{y}}{s} \text{ (data based)}$$

$$r = \frac{\sum z_x z_y}{n - 1}$$

$$\hat{y} = b_0 + b_1 x \qquad \text{where } b_1 = r\frac{s_y}{s_x} \text{ and } b_0 = \bar{y} - b_1\bar{x}$$

$$P(\mathbf{A}) = 1 - P(\mathbf{A}^C)$$

$$P(\mathbf{A} \text{ or } \mathbf{B}) = P(\mathbf{A}) + P(\mathbf{B}) - P(\mathbf{A} \text{ and } \mathbf{B})$$

$$P(\mathbf{A} \text{ and } \mathbf{B}) = P(\mathbf{A}) \times P(\mathbf{B}|\mathbf{A})$$

$$P(\mathbf{B}|\mathbf{A}) = \frac{P(\mathbf{A} \text{ and } \mathbf{B})}{P(\mathbf{A})}$$

If $\mathbf{A}$ and $\mathbf{B}$ are independent, $P(\mathbf{B}|\mathbf{A}) = P(\mathbf{B})$

$E(X) = \mu = \sum x \cdot P(x)$ $\qquad Var(X) = \sigma^2 = \sum(x - \mu)^2 P(x)$

$E(X \pm c) = E(X) \pm c$ $\qquad Var(X \pm c) = Var(X)$

$E(aX) = aE(X)$ $\qquad Var(aX) = a^2 Var(X)$

$E(X \pm Y) = E(X) \pm E(Y)$ $\qquad Var(X \pm Y) = Var(X) + Var(Y)$

$\qquad\qquad\qquad\qquad\qquad\qquad$ if $X$ and $Y$ are independent

Geometric: $\qquad P(x) = q^{x-1}p \qquad\qquad \mu = \frac{1}{p} \qquad \sigma = \sqrt{\frac{q}{p^2}}$

Binomial: $\qquad P(x) = {}_nC_x p^x q^{n-x} \qquad \mu = np \qquad \sigma = \sqrt{npq}$

$$\hat{p} = \frac{x}{n} \qquad \mu(\hat{p}) = p \qquad SD(\hat{p}) = \sqrt{\frac{pq}{n}}$$

Sampling distribution of $\bar{y}$:

(CLT) As $n$ grows, the sampling distribution approaches the Normal model with

$$\mu(\bar{y}) = \mu_y \qquad SD(\bar{y}) = \frac{\sigma}{\sqrt{n}}$$

## INFERENCE:

Confidence interval for parameter = **statistic ± critical value × SE(statistic)**

Test statistic $= \dfrac{statistic - parameter}{SD(statistic)}$

| Parameter | Statistic | SD(statistic) | SE(statistic) |
|---|---|---|---|
| $p$ | $\hat{p}$ | $\sqrt{\dfrac{pq}{n}}$ | $\sqrt{\dfrac{\hat{p}\hat{q}}{n}}$ |
| $p_1 - p_2$ | $\hat{p}_1 - \hat{p}_2$ | $\sqrt{\dfrac{p_1 q_1}{n_1} + \dfrac{p_2 q_2}{n_2}}$ | $\sqrt{\dfrac{\hat{p}_1 \hat{q}_1}{n_1} + \dfrac{\hat{p}_2 \hat{q}_2}{n_2}}$ |
| $\mu$ | $\bar{y}$ | $\dfrac{\sigma}{\sqrt{n}}$ | $\dfrac{s}{\sqrt{n}}$ |
| $\mu_1 - \mu_2$ | $\bar{y}_1 - \bar{y}_2$ | $\sqrt{\dfrac{\sigma_1^2}{n_1} + \dfrac{\sigma_2^2}{n_2}}$ | $\sqrt{\dfrac{s_1^2}{n_1} + \dfrac{s_2^2}{n_2}}$ |
| $\mu_d$ | $\bar{d}$ | $\dfrac{\sigma_d}{\sqrt{n}}$ | $\dfrac{s_d}{\sqrt{n}}$ |
| $\sigma_\varepsilon$ | $s_e = \sqrt{\dfrac{\Sigma(y - \hat{y})^2}{n - 2}}$ | | |
| $\beta_1$ | $b_1$ | | $\dfrac{s_e}{s_x\sqrt{n - 1}}$ |
| $\mu_\nu$ | $\hat{y}_\nu$ | | $\sqrt{SE^2(b_1) \cdot (x_\nu - \bar{x})^2 + \dfrac{s_e^2}{n}}$ |
| $y_\nu$ | $\hat{y}_\nu$ | | $\sqrt{SE^2(b_1) \cdot (x_\nu - \bar{x})^2 + \dfrac{s_e^2}{n} + s_e^2}$ |

Pooling: For testing difference between proportions: $\hat{p}_{pooled} = \dfrac{y_1 + y_2}{n_1 + n_2}$

For testing difference between means: $s_p = \sqrt{\dfrac{(n_1 - 1)s_1^2 + (n_2 - 1)s_2^2}{n_1 + n_2 - 2}}$

Substitute these pooled estimates in the respective SE formulas for both groups when assumptions and conditions are met.

Chi-square: $\chi^2 = \sum \dfrac{(Obs - Exp)^2}{Exp}$

## Proportions (z)

- **One sample**
  1. Individuals are independent.
  2. Sample is sufficiently large.

  1. SRS and $n < 10\%$ of the population.
  2. Successes and failures each $\geq 10$.

- **Two Groups**
  1. Groups are independent.
  2. Data in each group are independent.

  3. Both samples are sufficiently large.

  1. (Think about how the data were collected.)
  2. Both are SRSs and $n < 10\%$ of populations OR random allocation.
  3. Successes and failures each $\geq 10$ for both groups.

## Means (t)

- **One Sample** (df $= n - 1$)
  1. Individuals are independent.
  2. Population has a Normal model.

  1. SRS and $n < 10\%$ of the population.
  2. Histogram is unimodal and symmetric.*

- **Matched pairs** (df $= n - 1$)
  1. Data are matched.
  2. Individuals are independent.
  3. Population of differences is Normal.

  1. (Think about the design.)
  2. SRS and $n < 10\%$ OR random allocation.
  3. Histogram of differences is unimodal and symmetric.*

- **Two independent samples** (df from technology)
  1. Groups are independent.
  2. Data in each group are independent.
  3. Both populations are Normal.

  1. (Think about the design.)
  2. SRSs and $n < 10\%$ OR random allocation.
  3. Both histograms are unimodal and symmetric.*

## Distributions/Association ($\chi^2$)

- **Goodness of fit** (df $=$ # of cells $- 1$; one variable, one sample compared with population model)
  1. Data are counts.
  2. Data in sample are independent.
  3. Sample is sufficiently large.

  1. (Are they?)
  2. SRS and $n < 10\%$ of the population.
  3. All expected counts $\geq 5$.

- **Homogeneity** [df $= (r - 1)(c - 1)$; many groups compared on one variable]
  1. Data are counts.
  2. Data in groups are independent.
  3. Groups are sufficiently large.

  1. (Are they?)
  2. SRSs and $n < 10\%$ OR random allocation.
  3. All expected counts $\geq 5$.

- **Independence** [df $= (r - 1)(c - 1)$; sample from one population classified on two variables]
  1. Data are counts.
  2. Data are independent.
  3. Sample is sufficiently large.

  1. (Are they?)
  2. SRSs and $n < 10\%$ of the population.
  3. All expected counts $\geq 5$.

## Regression (t, df $= n - 2$)

- **Association of each quantitative variable** ($\beta = 0$?)
  1. Form of relationship is linear.
  2. Errors are independent.
  3. Variability of errors is constant.
  4. Errors have a Normal model.

  1. Scatterplot looks approximately linear.
  2. No apparent pattern in residuals plot.
  3. Residuals plot has consistent spread.
  4. Histogram of residuals is approximately unimodal and symmetric, or Normal probability plot reasonably straight.*

---

(*less critical as $n$ increases)